Special Publications Series Editor: A. A. Levinson
Department of Geology and Geophysics
The University of Calgary
Calgary, Alberta T2N 1N4 Canada

Stable Isotope Geochemis

A Tribute to Samuel Epst

# Stable Isotope Geochemistry: A Tribute to Samuel Epstein

Hugh P. Taylor, Jr., James R. O'Neil and Isaac R. Kaplan
Editors

*Division of Geological and Planetary Sciences*
*California Institute of Technology, Pasadena, California 91125, U.S.A.*

and

*Department of Geological Sciences*
*The University of Michigan, Ann Arbor, Michigan 48109, U.S.A.*

and

*Department of Earth and Space Sciences*
*University of California, Los Angeles, California 90024, U.S.A.*

Special Publication No. 3

THE GEOCHEMICAL SOCIETY

Library of Congress Catalogue Number 91-76040

ISBN 0–941809–02–1

Printed in The United States of America
by Lancaster Press, Inc.

# TABLE OF CONTENTS

Table of Contents          vii

## Part G. Extraterrestrial Geochemistry

Samuel Epstein, the William E. Leonhard Professor of Geology, California Institute of Technology.

Stable Isotope Geochemistry: A Tribute to Samuel Epstein
© The Geochemical Society, Special Publication No. 3, 1991
Editors: H. P. Taylor, Jr., J. R. O'Neil and I. R. Kaplan

# Preface

*Stable Isotope Geochemistry: A Tribute to Samuel Epstein* is a collection of 39 papers written by 75 of Sam Epstein's former students, postdoctoral fellows, colleagues, and friends. These contributors travelled from all over the world, gathering together with many other participants in Pasadena, California in December, 1989, to join in a scientific symposium organized to honor this eminent geochemist on the occasion of his 70th birthday. Much of the material in the present volume was presented orally at the Epstein Symposium, which was held over a two-day period in the Division of Geological and Planetary Sciences at the California Institute of Technology, where Samuel Epstein has taught and carried out pioneering research in stable isotope geochemistry for the past 38 years. Participants at the symposium are linked to Professor Epstein in many ways, with some associations going back 40 or 50 years. Many universities and research laboratories were represented, but there were particularly strong contingents from Canada, Israel, Caltech, and the University of Chicago, four places very dear to Sam's heart. The birthday celebration and symposium culminated in a banquet attended by 245 of his friends and relatives, and in the succeeding months the present volume was put together by all the contributors as a tangible expression of the genuine affection and respect that we all have for Samuel Epstein.

Sam is a world-renowned pioneer in the field of stable isotope geochemistry. His career in isotope chemistry began in association with Harry Thode and Harold Urey just after World War II, and it was very interesting for the younger generation of geochemists at the symposium to hear Harry Thode reminisce about his experiences with Sam during these early years. One of Sam's first major scientific contributions was his work with Harold Urey on the development of the carbonate isotopic paleotemperature scale, a discovery which had a truly monumental impact on the earth sciences. The analytical and mass spectrometric techniques described in these early papers are literally the foundation stones upon which all future developments in light stable isotope geochemistry are based. Sam continued to make seminal contributions on a broad range of scientific problems over the next four decades. Throughout his career he has demonstrated remarkable insight into the application of stable isotope measurements to the earth and biological sciences, seeking out the expertise he needed, and selecting talented young scientists to work with him on the myriad challenging aspects of this powerful discipline.

The breadth of Sam's scientific interests are very well represented by the subjects covered in the papers in this volume, in that the pioneering research that forms the basis for many of these studies was done by Sam himself. The subjects cover experimental and theoretical studies of stable isotope fractionation, development of new analytical techniques, numerous hydrological investigations including various aspects of water/rock interactions and the sources and flow paths of crustal fluids, studies of ore deposits, archaeological and environmental applications, igneous and metamorphic petrology, and several areas in which Professor Epstein is continuing to work at the present time, including the history of ancient oceans, paleoclimatology, and isotope exchange reactions in meteorites and the early solar system. Note that three of the papers by a few of Sam's oldest and dearest friends deal mainly with the radiogenic isotopes of lead (but these are in fact "stable isotopes" as well, and in any case we very much wished to have these contributions included). Note also that Sam is a co-author on two papers in the present volume, continued proof of a continuing and marvelously active scientific career (in spite of his recent "retirement" to Emeritus Professor). It is fair to say that essentially all modern researchers in the field of stable isotope geochemistry have in some way been touched or guided by Professor Epstein, either by personal contact or through his writings; this statement certainly applies to the three editors of this volume, as well as to all of the other participants in the Epstein Symposium. We all warmly salute Samuel Epstein as he enters the sixth decade of his brilliant and creative scientific career!

HUGH P. TAYLOR, JR.
JAMES R. O'NEIL
ISAAC R. KAPLAN
October, 1991

Group photo of speakers and session chairmen at the Epstein Symposium, December 1989. LEFT TO RIGHT, TOP ROW: J. R. Gat, S. M. Wickham, A. J. Gow, I. R. Kaplan, C. J. Yapp, D. W. Beaty, F. Robert, H. P. Taylor, Jr., R. T. Gregory, D. B. Wenner, S. M. F. Sheppard, Y. Kolodny, S. J. Lambert, T. K. Kyser, B. E. Taylor, M. J. DeNiro, A. H. Truesdell, J. R. O'Neil, and J. R. Goldsmith. MIDDLE ROW: H. A. Lowenstam, H. G. Thode, R. N. Clayton, M. Magaritz, E. M. Stolper, H. P. Schwarcz, C. Emiliani, S. Epstein, M. H. Thiemens, D. S. Stakes, S. M. Savin, B. Turi, M. Javoy, F. Albarede, and I. Friedman. BOTTOM ROW: L. P. Knauth, J. A. Karhu, L. S. Land, R. E. Criss, K. K. Turekian, Y. N. Shieh, R. V. Krishnamurthy, J. R. Lawrence, H. O. Ajie, S. M. Miller, K. K. Liu, and J. I. Stone.

x

# Acknowledgements

Very generous financial support for the preparation of this volume was provided by the Division of Geological and Planetary Sciences, California Institute of Technology. We particularly want to thank the two Division Chairmen, G. J. Wasserburg and David Stevenson, for giving us adequate personnel and resources to prepare this volume and to put together the Epstein Symposium and associated activities in December 1989. We were thereby able to defray some of the travel expenses of the overseas participants at the symposium. Much of the success of this entire enterprise is due to the dedication of Meg Garstang, who handled all the administrative details connected with the symposium and with the banquet at the Athenaeum, and to Mary Mellon, who helped enormously in the preparation of the actual volume itself. We also want to thank Candi Taylor who put on a well-attended cocktail party at her home on the final evening of the symposium. The central administration of the California Institute of Technology provided a great deal of support for this project, and we particularly want to thank Theodore Hurwitz, formerly Vice President for Institute Relations, and Thomas E. Everhart, the President of Caltech, for their help and encouragement. In addition many geochemistry graduate students from Caltech contributed in several ways to the overall success of the symposium. In all these interactions, it became more and more clear to us how much Sam Epstein is loved and respected by all of his colleagues, students and associates.

At the banquet in the Athenaeum, Sam was presented with a photograph album for which he later selected a large number of pictures taken during the symposium. Some of the photographs are distributed through this volume, together with several other photographs that illustrate various stages of his career. This is perhaps an unusual feature to see in a volume of scientific papers, but we believe that they provide an added dimension and reflect the warm, human attributes of this man. Sam also was presented a plaque on which were mounted several symbols of his scientific career, including a meteorite, a chert nodule, a belemnite, a foraminifera model, and a piece of bristlecone pine. We want to thank Clair Patterson of Caltech, and Bruce Runnegar and Rainer Berger of U.C.L.A. for their help in preparing this plaque.

It is necessary to say something about the make-up of the present volume and the selection of contributors, which had to be limited because of various constraints imposed by the size of the volume and the two-day time period allotted for the symposium. Most of the speakers at the symposium gathered for the group photograph shown on the opposite page, although a few stragglers missed it for one reason or another. Most of these participants then came through with completed manuscripts and 39 papers are published in this volume. Almost all of these authors have been closely associated with Samuel Epstein over the years, including 17 who got their Ph.D. degrees at Caltech, 16 former post-doctoral fellows in geochemistry at Caltech, and 8 present or former colleagues of Sam's at Caltech or the University of Chicago. Most of the other authors of the papers can also be considered to be "scientific grandsons/daughters" or "scientific great-grandsons/daughters" of Sam, so all of the papers in this volume show a close scientific linkage to Samuel Epstein. In addition to contributions from his former students, however, we particularly wanted to emphasize Sam's scientific and cultural heritage in Canada and Israel, and isotope geochemists from those countries were given priority invitations. We apologize to all of the other workers in the field of isotope geochemistry who were not invited to give papers at the Epstein Symposium, and we hope they understand the constraints under which we operated. We want to thank all of the participants in the symposium for helping to review the manuscripts in this volume, and we apologize to some of the authors who met all of the original deadlines but then had to wait almost two years to see their papers published.

We want to thank The Geochemical Society for its overwhelming support, from the initiation of this project until its completion. Prof. Douglas Brookins handled the initial editorial matters on behalf of The Geochemical Society and after Doug's untimely death earlier this year, Professor A. A. Levinson graciously came to our aid and assumed those responsibilities. We shall be forever grateful to Al Levinson for sharing with us his considerable editorial expertise and for his enthusiastic and unselfish dedication to the success of this project.

Photographs at the Epstein Symposium Banquet at the Athenaeum, Caltech. CLOCKWISE FROM THE UPPER LEFT: (a) Jim O'Neil making a presentation to Sam, with Sam's sister, Dora Leb, of Winnipeg, Canada, in the foreground. (b) The Epstein family table. LEFT TO RIGHT, STANDING: Ian Kaplan, Dora Leb, Sam Epstein, Diane Epstein, Albert Epstein, Helen Kaplan. SEATED: Reuben Epstein, his daughter Chloe, his wife Jody, and his son Eric. Aaron, Reuben's eldest son, was seated at another table. (c) Thomas Everhart, President of Caltech, congratulating Sam Epstein and Hugh Taylor on the success of the Epstein Symposium. (d) Ian Kaplan presenting Sam Epstein a plaque commemorating a career in isotope geochemistry, 1942–1990, with mounted examples from his research on meteorites, tree rings, carbonate paleotemperatures, and cherts.

Stable Isotope Geochemistry: A Tribute to Samuel Epstein
© The Geochemical Society, Special Publication No. 3, 1991
Editors: H. P. Taylor, Jr., J. R. O'Neil and I. R. Kaplan

# SAMUEL EPSTEIN
## Scientist, Teacher and Friend

SAMUEL EPSTEIN was born near Kobryn, Poland (now Belarus) in 1919. His father was a businessman who was also born in Poland (then Czarist Russia), but who moved to New York City around the turn of the century. Sam's father had to return to Russia in 1904 to present himself for the required military service, and there (in 1907) he met and married the woman who would become Sam's mother. After many adventures and difficulties associated with living in the midst of battlegrounds during and after World War I, during which time Sam's two sisters Dora and Bella were born, the family settled on the small farm where Sam was born. They lived in the "Pale of the Settlement," as members of a large Jewish community in eastern Europe, and it is an interesting fact that Sam grew up within 100 km of the future birthplaces of Yehoshua Kolodny (Pinsk) and Ian Kaplan (Bananowicze). Both Yehoshua and Ian also grew up to become isotope geochemists and both later worked at Caltech with Sam as postdoctoral fellows; both are also contributors to this volume.

In September, 1927, Sam and his family moved to Winnipeg, Manitoba, thereby escaping the tragic fate of all his relatives who remained behind when the Holocaust descended on Poland twelve years later. In Canada, Sam grew up with an interest in mathematics and science, and after graduating from high school in 1937, he attended the University of Manitoba where he received a B.Sc. in geology and chemistry in 1941 and a M.Sc. in chemistry in 1942. In 1944 he received his Ph.D. in chemistry at McGill University where he worked on the kinetics of reactions involving the high explosive RDX. Sam then joined the Canadian Atomic Energy Project in Montreal where he worked on rare-gas fission products, and it was also in Montreal that Sam met Diane Vool, who later became his wife on September 22, 1946. There, Sam met the future Day Medalist Harry Thode, who invited him to come to McMaster University in Hamilton, Ontario. Thode later became President of McMaster University. The two became close friends for life, and Thode played a key role in Sam's career, orienting his interests toward isotope chemistry and recommending him to Nobel Laureate Harold Urey as an ideal research fellow to work on the oxygen isotope paleotemperature project Urey was then initiating at the University of Chicago.

In his classic paper "The Thermodynamic Properties of Isotopic Substances" published in 1946, Urey had calculated the temperature coefficient of the oxygen isotope exchange reaction between $CaCO_3$ and $H_2O$ and had proposed that the oxygen isotope compositions of marine carbonates might provide us with information on the temperatures of ancient oceans, if the recognized and rather formidable analytical problems could be resolved. Urey was fascinated with the mass extinction of the dinosaurs at the end of the Cretaceous, and he thought that if a sharp temperature change was the cause of this extinction then perhaps an isotope geothermometer might be able to see such an effect. Seizing this wonderful opportunity to work with a famous scientist on a truly fascinating scientific problem, Sam and his bride Diane moved to Chicago in 1947, renting a tiny apartment above Professor Urey's garage. For the young newlyweds, this continuing proximity to the forceful and dynamic Harold Urey made life "interesting" to say the least.

Sam frequently recounts his experiences in the often-unheated garage apartment, such as when Harold Urey would stand at the back door to his house and summon Sam to the door of his apartment on those occasions when Urey had some thought which he wanted to try out on Sam. Frequently late at night, often in the sub-zero temperature of Chicago winters, the two men would stand shouting scientific ideas across the width of a patio and driveway!

Sam dove into the carbonate paleotemperature project with immense drive and dedication. Within a year, he and his talented research team made the appropriate modifications to the Nier isotope mass spectrometer, such that the oxygen isotope ratios of calcium carbonate could be determined reproducibly to within 0.1 per mil, exceeding the precision Urey had calculated to be necessary for a viable oxygen isotope paleotemperature scale. At this important time, Diane and Sam Epstein had a problem with their visas, and they were forced to return to Canada. However, Sam had by this time become so essential to the project that Urey personally visited the Immigration Bureau and, using his scientific prestige and his uniquely forceful manner he persuaded the authorities to allow Sam to return to the United States, which they did in the Spring of 1949. By this time John McCrea and Charles

McKinney had left the project and Urey's interests had largely turned to his next major project, namely the origin of the solar system. So, with the help of Heinz Lowenstam and Toshiko Mayeda, Sam again took up the reins and together the three of them resolved most of the remaining difficult problems connected with the chemistry of extracting $CO_2$ from the biogenic skeletal carbonate shells and the refining of the carbonate paleotemperature scale. During this period Sam also started several other research projects, including the first survey of the oxygen isotope compositions of natural waters.

In June 1952, Harrison Brown moved from the University of Chicago to Caltech and invited Sam Epstein, Clair Patterson and Charles McKinney to join him. Together with Lee Silver, then a graduate student in geology, this group formed the nucleus of what would become one of the most innovative and productive isotope geochemistry operations in the world. The University of Chicago exodus to Caltech was concluded when Heinz Lowenstam and Jerry Wasserburg also migrated in 1953 and 1955, respectively. Sam and Diane became citizens of the U.S.A. in 1953, raised two sons, Reuben and Albert, and are now the proud grandparents of three.

In addition to his flesh and blood family there is another family comprising dozens of former students, postdoctoral fellows, and visiting scientists with whom Samuel Epstein has developed strong personal relationships. The first group of Sam's scientific disciples gives testimony to the breadth of his research interests, which is one of the hallmarks of his career in science. For example, while most of the other graduate students in the chemistry department at Caltech were vying with each other to work in Linus Pauling's large group, the future Goldschmidt Medalist Bob Clayton decided he wanted to do something unique and different, so he went over to investigate what "those new geochemists" were doing. In the midst of all the construction activity on the new mass spectrometers, Bob spoke to Harrison Brown, who told him that he should talk to Clair Patterson about "the strontium problem" and to Sam Epstein about "the oxygen problem." Bob wasn't aware that these two elements were particularly problematical, but he indeed did speak to both men, and he quickly became intrigued by the research project outlined by Sam. They decided to look further (than Sol Silverman had) into the oxygen isotope variations of coexisting minerals in high temperature rocks, laying the groundwork for what later developed into a major sub-discipline in geochemistry. Sam's next student was Rod Park, then a graduate student in the Division of Biology at Caltech, and who later

became Vice-Chancellor of the University of California at Berkeley. Park and Epstein performed the pioneering experiments on the fractionation of carbon isotopes in plants. They were able to show that the fixation of carbon resulted in a very large kinetic isotope fractionation, and that the total photosynthetic pathway should result in a $^{13}C$ depletion of about 27 per mil compared to the initial $CO_2$. Sam's third Ph.D. student was Hugh Taylor, who had worked with Sam as an undergraduate student in geology at Caltech at the time the new laboratories were being set up. After going away for a year, Hugh returned to Caltech specifically to work with Sam on the problem of oxygen isotope variations in coexisting minerals of igneous rocks. Thus each of Sam's first three students came from different scientific disciplines, a good early indication of the remarkable interdisciplinary nature of most of Sam's research, and an early measure of Sam's enormous scientific breadth.

Over the succeeding years at Caltech, Samuel Epstein was never afraid to explore a variety of uncharted scientific terrains. In fact, he welcomed the prospect of applying the newly developed techniques and principles of stable isotope fractionation to almost every aspect of natural science, as demonstrated by the following (incomplete) list of some of his achievements. Most of the students and research fellows that have worked with Sam have gone on to eminent careers of their own, which is a testimony to the pervasive influence that Sam has had on the field of isotope geochemistry.

With Heinz Lowenstam and Cesare Emiliani, Sam continued to refine the carbonate paleotemperature method and to understand the temperature-shell growth relations of $CaCO_3$-secreting organisms. With Sol Silverman he investigated the origin of petroleum and organic matter in sedimentary rocks. With Al Engel and Bob Clayton, and later with Don Garlick, he was the first to apply these isotopic techniques to aqueous fluid-rock interactions and the origin of hydrothermal ore deposits. With Bob Sharp he made pioneering studies of D/H and $^{18}O/^{16}O$ records in the Malaspina, Saskatchewan and Blue glaciers, and in Antarctic snow, firn, and ice. With Don Graf and Egon Degens he carried out the first major isotopic studies of the origin of dolomites and cherts, and of the preservation of the $^{18}O/^{16}O$ record in ancient sedimentary rocks. With Hugh Taylor, he carried out $^{18}O/^{16}O$ studies of all of the tektite fields of the world, helping to confirm their terrestrial impact origin. With Jim O'Neil, who was Bob Clayton's first Ph.D. student at Chicago, and who then continued his career as a post-doctoral fellow at Caltech, Sam pioneered the most widely used method for direct isotopic analysis of milligram quantities of water. With J. Hoefs he did the first oxygen isotope studies of migmatites and orbicular igneous rocks. With Sam Savin he did the first systematic survey of D/H and $^{18}O/^{16}O$ in clay minerals and sedimentary rocks, and with Don Garlick he did the first major study of coexisting minerals in metamorphic rocks. With Hugh Taylor, Mike Duke, Helmut Reuter, and Lee Silver, Sam was the first to systematically measure $^{18}O/^{16}O$ ratios of the minerals in meteorites, showing that an oxygen isotope classification of meteorites could be set up indicating how these materials are genetically related. Later, with the discovery of $^{18}O$-$^{17}O$-$^{16}O$ variations in meteorites, this classification was beautifully refined by Bob Clayton and Tosh Mayeda into one of the most widely accepted ways of classifying meteorite groups. With Bruce Smith, Sam continued his pioneering work on carbon isotope applications to botany, monitoring the isotopic effects of the change from lipids to carbohydrates, and showing that the higher plants are divided into two major groups with different $^{13}C/^{12}C$ ratios. With Lynton Land he continued his studies of the processes of dolomization. With Simon Sheppard he was the first to characterize D/H and $^{18}O/^{16}O$ ratios of minerals brought up from the Earth's upper mantle in kimberlites.

Beginning in the late 1960's, like many other scientists around the world, Sam Epstein and Hugh Taylor started to prepare their laboratories for analysis of the soon-to-be returned lunar samples. Their role was the measurement of the isotope ratios of carbon, oxygen, hydrogen, and silicon, and they developed a number of new techniques to accomplish this. They showed that the hydrogen in the lunar soil was essentially deuterium-free, and thus totally derived from solar wind, and they were also the first to discover the enormous $^{18}O$ and $^{30}Si$ enrichments in the grain surfaces of the lunar soil, a result they attributed to micrometeorite and particle bombardment. Much of Sam's research in the 1970's continued to be focused on the returned lunar samples, but he also worked on other projects. With Tony Gow he continued his studies of ice cores from the Antarctic ice sheet. With Tetsuro Suzuoki he developed the hydrogen isotope geothermometric equations for exchange between hornblendes, micas, chlorites, and water. With Paul Knauth and Yehoshua Kolodny he instituted a systematic study of D/H and $^{18}O/^{16}O$ on cherts. With Steve Lambert he studied the hydrothermal systems at The Geysers in California and the Valles caldera in New Mexico. With Crayton Yapp and later with R. V. Krishnamurthy he developed techniques for

determining the D/H ratios of the non-exchangeable hydrogen in cellulose of plants, using these techniques to monitor past climatic changes recorded in tree rings. With Mike DeNiro he developed techniques for looking at stable isotope variations in paleodiets of humans and animals. With Francois Robert, Richard Becker, Jon Yang, and John Stone, he started an effort that continues to this day of looking at hydrogen, carbon, silicon, and nitrogen isotope variations in different fractions of unequilibrated meteorites, including the carbonaceous chondrites. In these studies Sam and his coworkers discovered some truly gigantic isotope fractionation effects, some of which can be traced back to a time prior to the formation of the solar system. This work has evolved into a succession of studies that are actively continuing at present (*e.g.* see the paper in this volume by STONE *et al.,* 1991). Finally, with the arrival at Caltech of an energetic young colleague in igneous petrology, Ed Stolper, Sam started to do experiments on oxygen isotope exchange of volatiles and silicates at high temperature (*e.g.* see STOLPER and EPSTEIN, 1991, this volume) and also on the hydrogen isotope fractionations between coexisting vapor and the different species of $H_2O$ dissolved in silicate melts. A whole new younger generation of graduate students and research fellows at Caltech (*e.g.* Phil Ihinger, Laurie Watson, Pat Dobson, Jen Blank, and Sally Newman) are working with Ed Stolper and with Sam on these important problems, which show much future promise. The Stolper-Epstein cooperative efforts are expected to continue to flourish during the decade of the 1990's.

Most of the former students and associates of Samuel Epstein listed above, together with many others not mentioned, gathered at Caltech in December 1989 to celebrate Sam's 70th birthday. The Epstein Symposium was a wonderful, warm tribute to the human qualities of this man, held in a lecture hall festooned with large poster-size photographs of Sam at various stages in his career. The participants in the symposium all recalled the history of their association with Sam and Diane. At various times, we had all suffered with him on those days when his ulcer was acting up, or had happily witnessed him abandon smoking, or had enjoyed lunching with him at the Athenaeum where he would voice strong opinions on science, world politics and baseball before negotiating with the waiter for a piece of Camembert of *just* the right degree of ripeness. We remembered how we were charmed by his sincere affection for children, anyone's children, and by the warmth and respect with which he had treated all of us over the years. Countless times he also told us how grateful he was to his wife Diane, and how important she has been to him and to his scientific career. Their warm, successful partnership is now in its 45th year.

Sam has left indelible marks on the members of his scientific family, particularly through his intuitive feel for seemingly intractable, but very important problems which he has a knack for solving with a little clever laboratory work, a refusal to become bogged down in extraneous and unimportant details, and an understanding of the intrinsic accuracy required for a given measurement to be decisive. There were several scientists around in the 1950's and 1960's who recognized the power of stable isotope measurements, but it was Sam more than anyone else who had the insight and the drive to carry it off in so many diverse fields, including paleothermometry, high-temperature geothermometry, origins of natural waters, paleoclimatology, glacier research, biological processes including plant and animal physiology, ore deposits, oceanography, meteorology, weathering and soil formation, and studies of the origin of igneous, metamorphic, and sedimentary rocks, meteorites, lunar rocks, and tektites.

Samuel Epstein has been widely recognized for his monumental scientific achievements. He was the recipient of the Geochemical Society's Goldschmidt Medal in 1977, and the Geological Society of America's Day Medal in 1976. In 1976, Sam was elected to both the National Academy of Sciences and the American Academy of Arts and Sciences. In 1980, he received the honorary degree LL.D from his old alma mater, the University of Manitoba. Sam was President of the Geochemical Society in 1978–1979. From 1984 until his retirement in June 1990, Sam held the position of William E. Leonhard Professor of Geology at Caltech. He is presently "retired" as the Leonhard Professor Emeritus, but he still continues to work full time in the laboratory every day, just as productively as ever.

# Part A.
# Experimental and Theoretical Isotopic Fractionation Studies

Diane and Sam Epstein at the Symposium Banquet in the Athenaeum, standing next to a poster autographed by and containing personal congratulations from all of the participants. The photograph on the poster was taken by Harmon Craig in Chicago in the summer of 1951 when Reuben Epstein was three years old.

Stable Isotope Geochemistry: A Tribute to Samuel Epstein
© The Geochemical Society, Special Publication No. 3, 1991
Editors: H. P. Taylor, Jr., J. R. O'Neil and I. R. Kaplan

# Oxygen isotopic thermometer calibrations

ROBERT N. CLAYTON

Enrico Fermi Institute, Department of Chemistry and Department of the Geophysical Sciences,
University of Chicago, Chicago, IL 60637, U.S.A.

and

SUSAN W. KIEFFER

Department of Geology, Arizona State University, Tempe, AZ 85287, U.S.A.

**Abstract**—The equilibrium oxygen isotopic fractionation between mineral $A$ and mineral $B$ can be expressed as the algebraic difference between two functions $f_A$ and $f_B$, which are the logarithms of the reduced isotopic partition function ratios for the two minerals. A combination of laboratory experiment and statistical thermodynamic calculation is used to give these functions over a wide temperature range. For several major rock-forming minerals, the following polynomial expressions are good approximations for temperatures greater than 400 K:

$$\text{calcite} \quad f_{Ca} = 11.781x - 0.420x^2 + 0.0158x^3$$

$$\text{quartz} \quad f_{Qz} = 12.116x - 0.370x^2 + 0.0123x^3$$

$$\text{albite} \quad f_{Ab} = 11.134x - 0.326x^2 + 0.0104x^3$$

$$\text{anorthite} \quad f_{An} = 9.993x - 0.271x^2 + 0.0082x^3$$

$$\text{diopside} \quad f_{Di} = 9.237x - 0.199x^2 + 0.0053x^3$$

$$\text{forsterite} \quad f_{Fo} = 8.326x - 0.142x^2 + 0.0032x^3$$

$$\text{magnetite} \quad f_{Mt} = 5.674x - 0.038x^2 + 0.0003x^3$$

where $x = 10^6 T^{-2}$ ($T$ in kelvins).

## INTRODUCTION

OXYGEN ISOTOPIC FRACTIONATIONS among the major rock-forming minerals are useful for geologic thermometry and for modeling fluid-rock exchange processes. These applications require knowledge of the equilibrium fractionation factors for many mineral pairs over a broad range of temperatures. The fractionation factors are expressed most succinctly as differences between reduced partition function ratios for each mineral pair (UREY, 1947). The reduced partition function ratio is equivalent to the equilibrium constant for exchange of one isotopic atom between a mineral and an oxygen atom gas, *e.g.* for quartz

$$\tfrac{1}{2}Si^{16}O_{2(s)} + {}^{18}O_{(g)} \leftrightarrow \tfrac{1}{2}Si^{18}O_{2(s)} + {}^{16}O_{(g)}$$

$$K = \frac{({}^{18}O/{}^{16}O)_{SiO_2}}{({}^{18}O/{}^{16}O)_O} = \frac{(Q'/Q)_{SiO_2}}{(Q'/Q)_O}, \quad (1)$$

where $Q$ and $Q'$ are reduced partition functions for quartz, and the prime denotes the $^{18}O$-substituted mineral. Thus, the quantities $\ln(Q'/Q)$ are proportional to the Gibbs Free Energy, and differences in

the values for any two phases at the same temperature give the equilibrium constant for isotopic exchange between those two phases:

$$A + B' \leftrightarrow A' + B$$

$$\ln K_{AB} = \ln(Q'/Q)_A - \ln(Q'/Q)_B. \quad (2)$$

Values of $Q'/Q$ can be determined by laboratory exchange experiments (*e.g.* CLAYTON *et al.*, 1989) or by statistical mechanical calculations (*e.g.* KIEFFER, 1982). Each method has advantages and disadvantages. The experimental method can produce results of high accuracy but only over limited ranges of temperature. The experiments are time-consuming, so that accumulation of results for a large number of minerals is slow. The calculations have no inherent temperature limitations, and can be applied to any phase for which adequate spectroscopic and mechanical data are available. However, they are limited in accuracy as a consequence of the approximations needed to carry out the calculations and the limited accuracy of the spectroscopic data. The purpose of this paper is to effect a combination of these two methods so as to achieve the advantages

3

of both. This is done by applying a small "adjustment factor" to the calculated partition function ratios so as to bring them into agreement with experiment. The modified partition function ratios can then be used to extrapolate to temperatures beyond the experimentally accessible range. It is found that simple polynomial expressions are adequate to express partition function ratios at all temperatures above 400 K.

The mineral calcite plays a key role in this approach. Over 90% of the isotopic partition function ratio for calcite arises from the internal vibrational modes of the carbonate ion, for which frequencies and isotopic frequency shifts are well known (KIEFFER, 1982; CHACKO et al., 1991). For these modes, the carbonate ion can be treated almost as if it were gaseous, thus greatly enhancing the accuracy of the result. The remaining contributions to the partition function ratio, coming from the lattice vibrations of the crystal, have been estimated using two completely different sets of approximations (KIEFFER, 1982; CHACKO et al., 1991), and agreement between the calculations is excellent. Thus, the calculated partition function ratios for oxygen in calcite are probably better known than those for oxygen in any other mineral.

Furthermore, experimental measurements have been made of oxygen isotopic fractionation between calcite and gaseous carbon dioxide (CHACKO et al., 1991). Since the isotopic partition function ratios for $CO_2$ gas are very accurately known, the experiments provide an independent check on the accuracy of the calculated partition function ratios for calcite. The agreement is excellent for high-temperature exchange experiments (400–800°C), as well as for experiments at 0 and 25°C (CHACKO et al., 1991).

Calcite can thus provide the link between accurate *theoretical* calculations for $CO_2$, and accurate *experimental* measurements of isotopic exchange between calcite and silicates (CLAYTON et al., 1989; CHIBA et al., 1989). Such calcite-silicate experiments have been done for quartz, albite, anorthite, diopside, and forsterite at temperatures in the range 600–1300°C. Calcite-magnetite fractionations have also been measured from 800 to 1200°C (CHIBA et al., 1989).

## COMPARISON OF THEORY AND EXPERIMENT

The isotopic partition function ratios of KIEFFER (1982) form the basis of this paper. However, because these were computed from a combination of Einstein and Debye functions representing different frequency ranges of the crystal vibrations, the resulting data are not in a convenient analytical form. Ratios have been computed at intervals of 5 K from 325 to 1200 K, and at intervals of 500 K from 1500 to 4000 K. These were shown graphically by KIEFFER (1982). UREY (1947) and BIGELEISEN and MAYER (1947) showed that ln $(Q'/Q)$ is asymptotically proportional to $1/T^2$ at high temperatures. This suggests that a polynomial in $1/T^2$ might be a good approximation to the curves over some temperature range. We have found empirically that a cubic function in $1/T^2$ fits the calculated results within ±0.02 per mil for all temperatures from 400 K to infinity. Extension of the temperature range down to 300 K results in a much poorer fit: residuals increase by a factor of five. The constant term in all the cubic fits was found to be less than 0.01 and has been set equal to zero for convenience. A cubic function in $1/T$ fits almost as well as the $1/T^2$ function for most of the temperature range above 400 K but, as is expected, fits poorly at the highest temperatures.

The polynomial curve for each silicate mineral can then be combined with that for calcite to give a calculated calcite-silicate fractionation curve. This can be compared directly with the corresponding calcite-silicate experimental data. The results for calcite-anorthite and calcite-forsterite are shown in Figs. 1 and 2. In both cases, the experimental data conform to the calculated curves within the analytical uncertainty (which is rather large for anorthite). It is evident that a straight line through the origin would fit the data equally well, but the curvature of the plots shows that extrapolation of such a straight line to lower temperature would result in serious error.

Similar graphs for calcite-albite and calcite-diopside are shown in Figs. 3 and 4. The calculated calcite-albite curve lies about 0.1 per mil below the experimental points, and the calcite-diopside curve lies about 0.1 per mil above the experimental points. These small differences are well within the uncertainties which result from the necessary approximations of the calculations. A modified curve was obtained in each case by applying a multiplicative factor to the calculated partition function ratios for albite and diopside. The factors used were 0.994 and 1.008, respectively. That is, adjustments of less than 1% are needed to bring calculation and experiment into agreement. The rationale for a multiplicative correction comes from the fact that the isotopic fractionation is approximately proportional to terms of the form $\omega \cdot \Delta\omega$ (BIGELEISEN and MAYER, 1947), so that an error of 1% in the assignment of the vibrational frequency, $\omega$, or its iso-

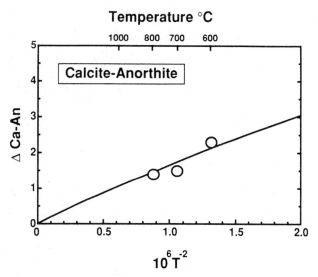

FIG. 1. Oxygen isotopic fractionation between calcite and anorthite. Experimental data points are from CLAYTON *et al.* (1989); theoretical curve is from KIEFFER (1982).

topic shift, $\Delta\omega$, results in a 1% error in the contribution of that vibrational mode to the partition function ratio.

The results for calcite-quartz were less satisfactory (Fig. 5). Two calculated curves are shown, one by KIEFFER (1982) and one recalculated from the vibrational frequencies determined by the lattice-dynamic treatment of KAWABE (1978). The Kawabe curve is a much better fit to the experimental data, and an excellent fit is achieved by use of an "adjustment factor" of 1.004.

Magnetite is an important mineral for oxygen isotope geochemistry, because it is usually the most

$^{18}$O-poor mineral in a rock and, thus, in combination with quartz or feldspar, gives the most sensitive geothermometer. Magnetite was not included in the calculations of KIEFFER (1982) because its opacity prevents adequate spectroscopic determination of its vibrational spectrum. An estimate of the magnetite partition function ratio was made by BECKER (1971), who used a combination of low-temperature heat capacity data for the acoustic modes and a single Einstein frequency to represent the unknown vibrational frequencies. The value of that frequency was chosen to fit the experimental magnetite-water fractionations of O'NEIL and

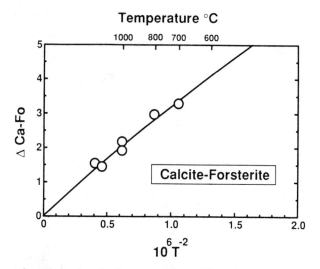

FIG. 2. Oxygen isotopic fractionation between calcite and forsterite. Experimental data points are from CHIBA *et al.* (1989); theoretical curve is from KIEFFER (1982).

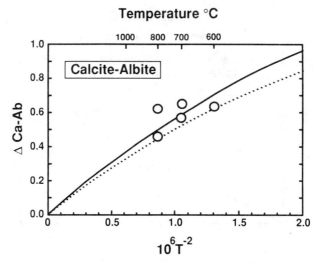

FIG. 3. Oxygen isotopic fractionation between calcite and albite. Experimental data points are from CLAYTON *et al.* (1989); theoretical curve (dashed line) is from KIEFFER (1982). Solid line is obtained by multiplying the Kieffer calculations for albite by 0.994 in order to fit the experimental data. Note expanded scale.

CLAYTON (1964) at 700 and 800°C. We have followed the same spirit in making a new estimate of the magnetite partition function ratio. The acoustic modes were represented by a Debye temperature of 585 K (as in BECKER, 1971) with an isotopic shift factor of 0.983123 (square root of the ratio of formula weights). The remaining degrees of freedom were represented by a set of identical Einstein functions with $\omega_{16} = 447$ cm$^{-1}$, and an isotopic shift factor of 0.964144, determined from the product rule (BECKER, 1971; KIEFFER, 1982). The frequency of 447 cm$^{-1}$ was chosen to fit the calcite-magnetite experimental data of CHIBA *et al.* (1989). The resulting calcite-magnetite curve is shown in Fig. 6. The polynomial approximation of the magnetite partition function ratio is

$$f = 5.674x - 0.038x^2 + 0.0003x^3, \qquad (3)$$

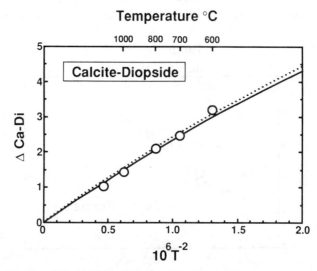

FIG. 4. Oxygen isotopic fractionation between calcite and diopside. Experimental data points are from CHIBA *et al.* (1989); theoretical curve (dashed line) is from KIEFFER (1982). Solid line is obtained by multiplying the Kieffer calculations for diopside by 1.008 in order to fit the experimental data.

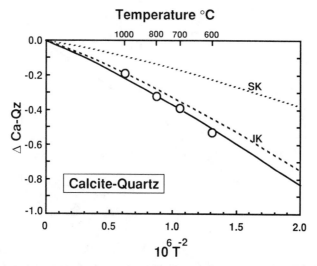

FIG. 5. Oxygen isotopic fractionation between calcite and quartz. Experimental data points are from CLAYTON *et al.* (1989); theoretical curves are from KIEFFER (1982) (dotted line SK) and recalculated from the data of KAWABE (1978) (dashed line IK). Solid line is obtained by multiplying the Kawabe recalculations for quartz by 1.004 in order to fit the experimental data. Note expanded scale.

where $x = 10^6 T^{-2}$. This function is almost a straight line on a $T^{-2}$ plot, as is expected for a phase with no high-frequency ($>1000$ cm$^{-1}$) vibrations. The same property is seen in other oxides (KIEFFER, 1982).

The magnetite partition function ratios given here are 11% smaller than those of BECKER (1971) at all temperatures. This difference is due *entirely* to the different choice of experimental data used for curve fitting and is independent of minor details in the modeling. For purposes of isotopic thermometry, the result is to increase silicate-magnetite temperatures somewhat: the effect on quartz-magnetite temperatures is an increase of about 40°C over a wide temperature range.

The polynomial functions for the seven minerals considered here are given in Table 1. Previous fits to the same experimental data, valid only at high temperatures, were provided by simple one-parameter equations of the form

$$\Delta_{ij} = A_{ij} \times 10^6 T^{-2} \qquad (4)$$

(CLAYTON *et al.*, 1989; CHIBA *et al.*, 1989), where $\Delta_{ij}$ is the fractionation between mineral $i$ and mineral $j$. Thus, the fractionation at $T = 1000$ K is simply $A$. The present results can be compared with the previous ones by evaluating the polynomials at $T = 1000$ K, as is done in Table 2. The results are almost identical, as is expected, since 1000 K is in the middle of the experimental temperature range

to which both sets of curves are tied. The advantage of the polynomial curves is that they allow extrapolation to temperatures hundreds of degrees below the experimental range.

Graphs of the polynomial functions for the reduced partition function ratios of individual minerals over an extended temperature range are shown in Fig. 7. The nearly linear portions of these graphs at temperatures $> 600°$C are determined by fitting the experimental data, whereas the curvatures at lower temperatures are determined by the statistical-mechanical calculations.

## ERROR ESTIMATES

Uncertainties in the coefficients for the equations in Table 1 arise from several sources: analytical error in the experimental measurements, approximations in the assignment of vibrational frequencies and their isotopic shifts, neglect of anharmonicity effects, and the use of polynomial approximations. Errors in the experimental calcite-mineral fractionations have been estimated by CHIBA *et al.* (1989), based on the internal scatter of the data and the accuracy of isotopic measurements. They found little variation in the error from one system to another, with an average uncertainty in the coefficient $A$, in Eq. (4), of $\pm 0.10$ (1$\sigma$ standard error). The error in $A$ is independent of the magnitude of $A$. In terms of the polynomial expressions used here, the coefficient $A$ is determined by the *difference* in the curves for the

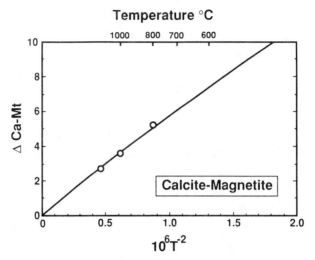

FIG. 6. Oxygen isotopic fractionation between calcite and magnetite. Experimental data points are from CHIBA et al. (1989). Curve is an empirical fit to the data based on a simple combination of Debye and Einstein functions for magnetite (see text).

two minerals involved, so that the absolute uncertainty in $A$ can be partitioned between the two curves. Thus, the dominant term for calcite, $11.781 \times 10^6 T^{-2}$, has an uncertainty of about 0.07 at $T = 1000$ K, i.e. about 0.6%. Absolute uncertainties in the coefficient of $x$ should be similar for other minerals, so that relative uncertainties range from 0.6% for quartz, calcite, and albite, to 1.2% for magnetite.

Errors introduced by the statistical mechanical calculations are significant only to the extent that they are not removed by tying the calculations to the experimental data. For example, an error of 5% in the assignment of a vibration frequency in quartz which is on the order of 500 cm$^{-1}$ leads to an error of about 0.3% in the partition function ratio. However, this fractional error is virtually constant over all temperatures considered, and hence its effect is removed by the experimental normalization used. The same is not true for a higher-frequency vibration (>1000 cm$^{-1}$), where a similar 5% error can

produce an error of 1.1% at 1000 K and 0.9% at 400 K. If the calculation is normalized to experimental data at 1000 K, the extrapolated partition function will be in error by 0.13 per mil at 400 K, an uncertainty which is still small compared to the errors in the experimental data used for normalization.

Effects of vibrational anharmonicity are necessarily neglected for solids since sufficiently accurate vibrational data are unavailable. Calculations with

Table 1. Partition function ratios for individual minerals*

| Calcite | $f = 11.781x - 0.420x^2 + 0.0158x^3$ |
|---|---|
| Quartz | $f = 12.116x - 0.370x^2 + 0.0123x^3$ |
| Albite | $f = 11.134x - 0.326x^2 + 0.0104x^3$ |
| Anorthite | $f = 9.993x - 0.271x^2 + 0.0082x^3$ |
| Diopside | $f = 9.237x - 0.199x^2 + 0.0053x^3$ |
| Forsterite | $f = 8.326x - 0.142x^2 + 0.0032x^3$ |
| Magnetite | $f = 5.674x - 0.038x^2 + 0.0003x^3$ |

\* $f$ = reduced partition function ratio, as $1000 \ln (Q'/Q)$. $x = 10^6 T^{-2}$.

Table 2. Comparison of polynomial and linear fits for mineral pairs at 1000 K*

|    | Qz | Ab | An | Di | Fo | Mt |
|----|----|----|----|----|----|----|
| Ca | −0.38 | 0.56 | 1.65 | 2.33 | 3.19 | 5.74 |
|    | −0.38 | 0.56 | 1.61 | 2.37 | 3.29 | 5.91 |
| Qz |    | 0.94 | 2.03 | 2.72 | 3.57 | 6.12 |
|    |    | 0.94 | 1.99 | 2.75 | 3.67 | 6.29 |
| Ab |    |    | 1.09 | 1.78 | 2.63 | 5.18 |
|    |    |    | 1.05 | 1.81 | 2.73 | 5.35 |
| An |    |    |    | 0.69 | 1.54 | 4.09 |
|    |    |    |    | 0.76 | 1.68 | 4.30 |
| Di |    |    |    |    | 0.86 | 3.41 |
|    |    |    |    |    | 0.92 | 3.54 |
| Fo |    |    |    |    |    | 2.55 |
|    |    |    |    |    |    | 2.62 |

\* For each entry, a positive value indicates $^{18}$O enrichment in the phase on the left. The upper entry is the fractionation at 1000 K based on the equations of Table 1; the lower entry is the value of $A$ in the equations

$$\Delta = A \times 10^6 T^{-2}$$

of CHIBA et al. (1989).

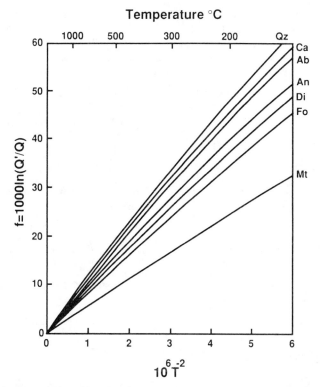

FIG. 7. Isotopic reduced partition function curves for the seven minerals discussed here. Mineral-pair isotopic fractionations are obtained by subtraction of one curve from another.

and without anharmonic corrections have been done for carbon dioxide, and show that the anharmonic correction is an almost constant fraction of the total partition function ratio at all temperatures, and its effect is thus removed in the experimental normalization used here.

Finally, the polynomial approximations have been found to fit the calculated partition functions of KIEFFER (1982) to better than ±0.02 per mil for all temperatures above 400 K, and thus add no significant uncertainty to the analysis.

Of all the sources of error considered, that associated with the laboratory measurement of fractionation factors is much larger than the others. The final results are thus limited by the accuracy of the experiments. However, in assessing the accuracy of a particular isotopic thermometer, the functional dependence of $\Delta$ on $T$ must be taken into account. For example, for the quartz-magnetite mineral pair, an uncertainty of 1.3% in the coefficients of the calibration equation produces an error in a temperature estimate of 7 K at 1000 K and 3 K at 400 K. These numbers can be compared with the effects of analytical uncertainty in the *rock data* to which the thermometer may be applied: an error

in the quartz-magnetite fractionation of 0.2 per mil gives an error in the temperature estimate of 17 K at 1000 K and 2 K at 400 K.

## CONCLUSIONS

Oxygen isotopic fractionations among several major rock-forming minerals can be calculated from a set of polynomial expressions which are good approximations to the reduced partition function ratios for individual minerals for all temperatures above 400 K. These equations are excellent fits to the equilibrium fractionation factors measured in laboratory exchange experiments and permit extrapolation of those data to higher and lower temperatures, thus covering almost all the temperature range for which such isotopic partition function ratios are needed.

Other minerals may be added to this scheme as calculations and laboratory experiments become available. KIEFFER's (1982) calculations include muscovite, clinoenstatite, pyrope, grossular, andradite, zircon, and rutile, for which calcite exchange experiments can be carried out. It should be noted that, in principle, only one well-determined experimental point is sufficient to "calibrate" each theoretical curve. It is particularly desirable to include the garnet minerals because of their importance in metamorphic rocks.

*Acknowledgements*—This research was supported by National Science Foundation grant EAR 89 20584.

## REFERENCES

BECKER R. H. (1971) Carbon and oxygen isotope ratios in iron-formation and associated rocks from the Hamersley Range of Western Australia and their implications. Ph.D. thesis, University of Chicago.

BIGELEISEN J. and MAYER M. G. (1947) Calculation of equilibrium constants for isotopic exchange reactions. *J. Chem. Phys.* **13,** 261–267.

CHACKO T., MAYEDA T. K., CLAYTON R. N. and GOLDSMITH J. R. (1991) Oxygen and carbon isotope fractionations between $CO_2$ and calcite. *Geochim. Cosmochim. Acta* (in press).

CHIBA H., CHACKO T., CLAYTON R. N. and GOLDSMITH J. R. (1989) Oxygen isotope fractionations involving diopside, forsterite, magnetite, and calcite: Application to geothermometry. *Geochim. Cosmochim. Acta* **53,** 2985–2995.

CLAYTON R. N., GOLDSMITH J. R. and MAYEDA T. K. (1989) Oxygen isotope fractionation in quartz, albite, anorthite and calcite. *Geochim. Cosmochim. Acta* **53,** 725–733.

KAWABE I. (1978) Calculation of oxygen isotope fractionation in quartz-water system with special reference to low temperature fractionation. *Geochim. Cosmochim. Acta* **42,** 613–621.

KIEFFER S. W. (1982) Thermodynamics and lattice vibrations of minerals: 5. Applications to phase equilibria, isotopic fractionation, and high-pressure thermodynamic properties. *Rev. Geophys. Space Phys.* **20,** 827–849.

O'NEIL J. R. and CLAYTON R. N. (1964) Oxygen isotope thermometry. In *Isotopic and Cosmic Chemistry* (eds. H. CRAIG, S. L. MILLER and G. J. WASSERBURG), pp. 157–168. Amsterdam: North-Holland.

UREY H. C. (1947) The thermodynamic properties of isotopic substances. *J. Chem. Soc. (London),* 562–581.

Stable Isotope Geochemistry: A Tribute to Samuel Epstein
© The Geochemical Society, Special Publication No. 3, 1991
Editors: H. P. Taylor, Jr., J. R. O'Neil and I. R. Kaplan

# Temperature dependence of isotopic fractionation factors

ROBERT E. CRISS

Department of Geology, University of California, Davis, CA 95616, U.S.A.

**Abstract**—The temperature dependences of the partition function ratios of gaseous molecules at low and high temperatures, originally investigated by UREY (1947) and BIGELEISEN and MAYER (1947), are derived and clarified. For diatomic molecules at low temperatures, the logarithm of the partition function ratio becomes

$$\ln\left[\frac{Q_2}{Q_1}\right] \cong \frac{U_1 - U_2}{2} + \ln\left[\frac{\sigma_1\nu_2}{\sigma_2\nu_1}\right]$$

where $U$ represent values of $h\nu/kT$, $\nu$ represent the molecular vibrational frequencies, and $\sigma$ are the symmetry numbers. This expression is linear in $1/T$, as it is of the form $y = m/T + $ const., where $m$ is proportional to the difference between the zero point energies of the ordinary (1) and isotopically substituted (2) molecules. At high temperatures the partition function ratio may be expanded in a power series; for example, for diatomic molecules:

$$\ln\left[\frac{Q_2}{Q_1}\right] = \ln\left[\frac{\sigma_1}{\sigma_2}\right] - \frac{U_2^2 - U_1^2}{24} + \frac{U_2^4 - U_1^4}{2880} - \frac{U_2^6 - U_1^6}{181440} + \cdots$$

The well-known $1/T^2$ dependence arises from the second term ($U^2/24$), which becomes increasingly important relative to the higher-order terms as temperature increases. Extension of these results to polyatomic molecules and to isotopic fractionation factors is straightforward.

## INTRODUCTION

IT IS WELL KNOWN that the isotopic fractionation factor between two substances $A$ and $B$, $\alpha_{AB}$, is a function of absolute temperature ($T$) but generally not a function of pressure. Several useful introductory discussions (*e.g.*, O'NEIL, 1986; HOEFS, 1987) state that $\ln(\alpha_{AB})$ varies as $1/T$ at low temperatures and as $1/T^2$ at higher temperatures, ultimately approaching zero fractionation ($\alpha = 1$) at infinite temperature. Such discussions invariably refer to the seminal papers by UREY (1947) and BIGELEISEN and MAYER (1947) on isotopic fractionation, but when the latter are consulted for a detailed explanation of these functional dependences, one is apt to be left unsatisfied. UREY (1947), for example, merely states that his equations for the partition function ratios can be "easily expanded" at high temperatures to give his single term demonstrating the $U^2/24$ dependence. BIGELEISEN and MAYER (1947), on the other hand, make numerous approximations to represent the ratios in terms of their function "$G$," which they then graphically analyze to determine the temperature dependence.

The following derivations were undertaken in order that I might provide a more satisfactory explanation for the temperature dependences of isotopic fractionation factors for a class. Through a subsequent literature search I learned that many of these results had been previously published (BIGELEISEN, 1958; STERN *et al.*, 1968), albeit in papers that are little referenced by the geochemical community. For some years I have wondered why simplification of the partition function ratios (eqns. 3a,b, below) using the well-known approximation $e^U \approx 1 + U$, which would be expected to be very accurate at extremely high temperatures (small $U$), does not lead to the $U^2/24$ dependence derived by UREY. Similarly, one may immediately verify that this approximation does not reduce BIGELEISEN and MAYER's "$G$" function, represented by the sum $\frac{1}{2} - 1/U + 1/(e^U - 1)$, to its high temperature value of $U/12$. The proper derivation in either case requires that great care be taken to account for all product terms to sufficiently high order, which in turn requires that no less than *four* terms of the exponential expansion for $e^U$ are used, together with sufficient terms in binomial expansions that are subsequently needed to invert the resulting denominators. Moreover, one would be very hard pressed to use such methods to calculate the succeeding term of a power series representing the partition function ratio, even though this term is of interest because it represents the bulk of the deviation of this ratio from the simple $U^2/24$ dependence. Also, the BIGELEISEN and MAYER approximation does not give the proper $y$-intercept for the $\ln K$ vs $1/T$ relation in the low temperature case.

In short, the above points number among several that to my knowledge have not been clearly discussed in the literature. It is hoped that the simple derivations and discussions presented here will enlighten geochemists about the straightforward basis for the temperature dependence of isotopic fractionation factors for gaseous molecules, and remind them of some important but nearly forgotten papers.

## BASIC EQUATIONS

A generalized equation may be written to express isotopic exchange between two substances $A$ and $B$, where the subscripts 1 and 2 indicate that the molecules, respectively, only contain either the light or the heavy isotope:

$$aA_1 + bB_2 = aA_2 + bB_1. \tag{1}$$

The equilibrium constant $K$ for such reactions may be written in terms of the simplified partition functions ($Q$'s) of UREY (1947), where each $Q$ represents the equilibrium constant between the compound of interest and its separated atoms, *i.e.*

$$K = \left(\frac{Q_{2A}}{Q_{1A}}\right)^a \Bigg/ \left(\frac{Q_{2B}}{Q_{1B}}\right)^b. \tag{2}$$

Here

$$\frac{Q_2}{Q_1} = \frac{\sigma_1}{\sigma_2} \frac{U_2}{U_1} \frac{e^{-U_2/2}}{1 - e^{-U_2}} \frac{1 - e^{-U_1}}{e^{-U_1/2}} \tag{3a}$$

for diatomic molecules, and

$$\frac{Q_2}{Q_1} = \frac{\sigma_1}{\sigma_2} \prod_{i=1}^{3n-6} \frac{U_{2i}}{U_{1i}} \frac{e^{-U_{2i}/2}}{1 - e^{-U_{2i}}} \frac{1 - e^{-U_{1i}}}{e^{-U_{1i}/2}} \tag{3b}$$

for nonlinear polyatomic molecules. The expression for linear polyatomic molecules is the same as the latter, except that there are only $3n - 5$ vibrational modes instead of $3n - 6$. In the above, the $\sigma$ denote the symmetry numbers, that is, the number of indistinguishable ways of orienting the molecule in space (*e.g.*, $\sigma = 12$ for the tetrahedral molecule $CH_4$). In addition, the $U_i$ represent the quantities $h\nu_i/kT$, where $h$ is Planck's constant, $k$ is Boltzmann's constant, $T$ is temperature in Kelvins, and the $\nu_i$ are the vibrational frequencies of the molecules.

The equilibrium constant ($K$) is related to the isotopic fractionation factor ($\alpha$) by the expression (*e.g.*, FERRONSKY and POLYAKOV, 1982)

$$\alpha = \left(\frac{K}{K_\infty}\right)^{1/ab} \tag{4a}$$

where the product $ab$ is equal to the number of atoms exchanged in the isotopic exchange reaction. Here $K_\infty$ represents the limiting equilibrium constant at very high temperature, which is related only

to the stoichiometric coefficients of the exchange equation and to the symmetry numbers of the molecules:

$$K_\infty = \frac{(\sigma_{1A}/\sigma_{2A})^a}{(\sigma_{1B}/\sigma_{2B})^b}. \tag{4b}$$

Note that the symmetry numbers cancel in the expression for $\alpha$ (Eqn. 4a), because the same factors are present in the expressions for both $K$ and $K_\infty$. Isotopic fractionation is a purely quantum mechanical effect and does not depend on classical factors such as symmetry numbers (BIGELEISEN and MAYER, 1947; STERN et al., 1968).

The above equations, and the assumptions upon which they are based, have been extensively discussed in the literature, so no additional description will be given here. For present purposes these equations will be taken as given, and attention will be confined to examination of their functional behavior in the cases where the $U_i$ are either large (low temperature and/or high frequency) or small (high temperature and/or low frequency). These conditions are referred to below simply as the "low-temperature" and "high-temperature" cases, respectively.

## LOW-TEMPERATURE CASE

At low temperatures (large $U$), it is evident that the $(1 - e^{-U})$ factors all approach unity. Accordingly, the basic equations (3a,b) for the simplified partition function ratios reduce to

$$\frac{Q_2}{Q_1} \cong \frac{\sigma_1}{\sigma_2} \frac{U_2}{U_1} e^{(U_1 - U_2)/2} \tag{5a}$$

for diatomic molecules and to

$$\frac{Q_2}{Q_1} \cong \frac{\sigma_1}{\sigma_2} \prod_{i=1}^{3n-6} \frac{U_{2i}}{U_{1i}} e^{(U_{1i} - U_{2i})/2} \tag{5b}$$

for nonlinear polyatomic molecules. The logarithm of these ratios may then be written as

$$\ln\left[\frac{Q_2}{Q_1}\right] \cong \frac{U_1 - U_2}{2} + \ln\left[\frac{\sigma_1\nu_2}{\sigma_2\nu_1}\right] \tag{6a}$$

for diatomic gases and

$$\ln\left[\frac{Q_2}{Q_1}\right] \cong \sum_{i=1}^{3n-6} \frac{U_{1i} - U_{2i}}{2} + \sum_{i=1}^{3n-6} \left[\ln\frac{\sigma_1\nu_{2i}}{\sigma_2\nu_{1i}}\right] \tag{6b}$$

for nonlinear polyatomic molecules, respectively. This equation is similar to one given, but not derived or justified, by STERN et al. (1968). Note that Eqns. (6a,b) are linear in $1/T$, being of the form $y = m/T + \text{const.}$, where the slope $m$ is the difference between the zero point energies ($h\nu_i/2$) of the ordinary and isotopically substituted molecules divided by Boltzmann's constant. The identical slope is predicted by the $G\Delta U$ formulation of BIGELEISEN and MAYER (1947), although it does not predict the correct $y$-intercept in the low-temperature case. The dependence of $\ln (Q_2/Q_1)$ on the zero-point energy difference arises because, at low temperatures, the lowest possible vibrational energy states are populated by the molecules.

## HIGH-TEMPERATURE SERIES

Considering that the $Q_2/Q_1$ ratios (Eqns. 3a,b) have so many product terms that are exponential in nature, and that the equilibrium constants and isotopic fractionation factors depend on quotients of these factors raised to stoichiometric powers, it is surprising that in their original papers neither UREY (1947) nor BIGELEISEN and MAYER (1947) took the logarithm of the basic equations before attempting to expand them in series. Equations (3a,b) directly become

$$\ln\left[\frac{Q_2}{Q_1}\right] = \ln\left[\frac{\sigma_1}{\sigma_2}\right] + \ln\left[\frac{U_2}{U_1}\right]$$

$$+ \frac{U_1 - U_2}{2} + \ln\left[\frac{1 - e^{-U_1}}{1 - e^{-U_2}}\right] \quad (7a)$$

for diatomic molecules and

$$\ln\left[\frac{Q_2}{Q_1}\right] = \ln\left[\frac{\sigma_1}{\sigma_2}\right] + \ln\prod_{i=1}^{3n-6}\left[\frac{U_{2i}}{U_{1i}}\right]$$

$$+ \sum_{i=1}^{3n-6}\frac{U_{1i} - U_{2i}}{2} + \ln\prod_{i=1}^{3n-6}\left[\frac{1 - e^{-U_{1i}}}{1 - e^{-U_{2i}}}\right] \quad (7b)$$

for nonlinear polyatomic molecules.

Equations (7a,b) can be simplified if the $\ln [1 - e^{-U_i}]$ terms are expanded in a series. This can be accomplished by first expanding $e^{-U_i}$ in the well-known exponential series and factoring out $U_i$, e.g.

$$\ln [1 - e^{-U_1}]$$

$$= \ln\left[U_1\left\{1 - \frac{U_1}{2} + \frac{U_1^2}{6} - \frac{U_1^3}{24} + \ldots\right\}\right] \quad (8a)$$

or:

$$\ln [1 - e^{-U_1}] = \ln [U_1]$$

$$+ \ln\left[1 - \frac{U_1}{2} + \frac{U_1^2}{6} - \frac{U_1^3}{24} + \ldots\right]. \quad (8b)$$

Now, expanding the right-hand term in a Taylor (Maclaurin) series about $U_i = 0$ gives for high temperatures

$$\ln [1 - e^{-U_1}] = \ln [U_1] - \frac{U_1}{2} + \frac{U_1^2}{24}$$

$$- \frac{U_1^4}{2880} + \frac{U_1^6}{181440} - \frac{U_1^8}{9676800} + \ldots \quad (8c)$$

The computations become extremely laborious beyond the first few terms, and in practice this series was generated by the computer program "Mathematica" (WOLFRAM, 1988). Equation (8c) implies that

$$\ln\left[\frac{1 - e^{-U_1}}{1 - e^{-U_2}}\right] = \ln\left[\frac{U_1}{U_2}\right] - \left(\frac{U_1 - U_2}{2}\right)$$

$$+ \left(\frac{U_1^2 - U_2^2}{24}\right) - \left(\frac{U_1^4 - U_2^4}{2880}\right)$$

$$+ \left(\frac{U_1^6 - U_2^6}{181440}\right) - \left(\frac{U_1^8 - U_2^8}{9676800}\right) + \ldots \quad (8d)$$

Now using expansion (8d), Eqn. (7a) for diatomic gases becomes

$$\ln\left[\frac{Q_2}{Q_1}\right] = \ln\left[\frac{\sigma_1}{\sigma_2}\right] + \ln\left[\frac{U_2}{U_1}\right] + \frac{U_1 - U_2}{2}$$

$$+ \left\{\ln\left[\frac{U_1}{U_2}\right] - \frac{U_1 - U_2}{2} + \frac{U_1^2 - U_2^2}{24} - \frac{U_1^4 - U_2^4}{2880}\right.$$

$$\left. + \frac{U_1^6 - U_2^6}{181440} - \frac{U_1^8 - U_2^8}{9676800} + \ldots\right\}. \quad (9)$$

Cancellation of like terms gives, for diatomic gases,

$$\ln\left[\frac{Q_2}{Q_1}\right] = \ln\left[\frac{\sigma_1}{\sigma_2}\right] + \frac{U_1^2 - U_2^2}{24} - \frac{U_1^4 - U_2^4}{2880}$$

$$+ \frac{U_1^6 - U_2^6}{181440} - \frac{U_1^8 - U_2^8}{9676800} + \ldots \quad (10a)$$

Similarly, Eqn. (7b), for polyatomic molecules, becomes

$$\ln\left[\frac{Q_2}{Q_1}\right] = \ln\left[\frac{\sigma_1}{\sigma_2}\right]$$

$$+ \sum_{i=1}^{3n-6}\left\{\frac{U_{1i}^2 - U_{2i}^2}{24} - \frac{U_{1i}^4 - U_{2i}^4}{2880}\right.$$

$$\left. + \frac{U_{1i}^6 - U_{2i}^6}{181440} - \frac{U_{1i}^8 - U_{2i}^8}{9676800} + \ldots\right\}. \quad (10b)$$

The $U^2/24$ dependence of $\ln [Q_2/Q_1]$ is evident from the second term of the series in Eqns. (10a,b) because the higher order terms become insignificant in comparison. Note that, as $T \rightarrow \infty$, Eqns. (10a,b) reduce to

$$\frac{Q_2}{Q_1} = \frac{\sigma_1}{\sigma_2}. \tag{11}$$

The latter result, which along with Eqn. (2) leads directly to the classical value given by Eqn. (4b), can also be obtained by applying l'Hopital's rule to Eqn. (3a), again as $T \to \infty$.

In terms of illustrating the high-temperature variation of the fundamental Eqns. (3a,b), these Taylor series representations have several advantages. First, the higher order terms are explicit in Eqns. (10a,b). Also, the expansion of $\ln \{Q_2/Q_1\}$ in series, rather than of $Q_2/Q_1$, is advantageous because the equilibrium constant and the isotopic fractionation factors depend on quotients of the $Q$ ratios raised to various powers. This dependence can in the logarithmic representation be exactly taken into account by simple addition of like terms. In contrast, to derive $K$ or $\alpha$ from the approximations given by UREY (1947) or BIGELEISEN and MAYER (1947), one must apply the rather poor approximation $\ln (1 + x) \approx x$ to the $Q_2/Q_1$ ratio for each molecule. It is therefore unfortunate that BIGELEISEN (1958), who long ago derived Eqn. (10) by a somewhat different method, published his result in a proceedings volume that is not available in most libraries. BIGELEISEN (1958) was also able to show that the numerical coefficients of the series (Eqns. (10a,b) are related to the Bernoulli numbers $B_n$ (see GRADSHTEYN and RYZHIK, 1980, pp. xxix and 1079–1080). In the present notation, the coefficients are given by $B_n/\{n(n!)\}$, where $n$ is the exponent of $U$ for the term of interest.

## TEMPERATURE DEPENDENCE OF ISOTOPIC FRACTIONATION FACTORS

It is straightforward to relate Eqns. (6a,b) and (10a,b) to the logarithm of the fractionation factors for isotopic exchange reactions, because Eqn. (4a) may be written as

$$\ln \alpha = \frac{1}{b} \ln \left[\frac{\sigma_2 Q_2}{\sigma_1 Q_1}\right]_A - \frac{1}{a} \ln \left[\frac{\sigma_2 Q_2}{\sigma_1 Q_1}\right]_B. \tag{12}$$

Making appropriate substitutions (from Eqn. 6a) for the $Q_2/Q_1$ ratios of the diatomic molecules $A$ and $B$ at low temperatures gives an expression that is linear in $1/T$:

$$\ln \alpha \cong \frac{a(U_{1A} - U_{2A}) - b(U_{1B} - U_{2B})}{2ab}$$

$$+ \ln \left[\left(\frac{\nu_{2A}}{\nu_{1A}}\right)^{1/b}\left(\frac{\nu_{1B}}{\nu_{2B}}\right)^{1/a}\right]. \tag{13}$$

Proceeding similarly (i.e., by combining Eqns. 10a

and 12, but ignoring high-order terms) for reactions involving diatomic molecules at elevated temperatures gives an expression linear in $1/T^2$ with an intercept of zero:

$$\ln \alpha \cong \frac{a(U_{1A}^2 - U_{2A}^2) - b(U_{1B}^2 - U_{2B}^2)}{24ab}. \tag{14}$$

In addition to representing these well-known temperature proportionalities, Eqns. (13) and (14) explicitly indicate the theoretical values for the slopes and y-intercepts of the fractionation lines in the low- and high-temperature cases. These two equations apply only to isotopic exchange between diatomic molecules; equations for exchange reactions involving polyatomic molecules are similar in form but contain sum and product terms. A linear, zero intercept relation between $\ln \alpha$ and $1/T^2$ also appears to have useful application to the empirical description of oxygen isotopic equilibria among nonhydrous silicates or oxides, in effect because the values of $U$ are generally small for these substances at geologically relevant temperatures (BOTTINGA and JAVOY, 1975).

It needs to be pointed out, however, that Eqns. (13) and (14) cannot predict many of the complex behaviors that may be exhibited in gaseous equilibria, and which are accounted for by Eqns. (3a,b). For example, Eqn. (14) does not predict any crossovers, inflection points, or maxima or minima in fractionation equations. Equation (13) predicts a single crossover, albeit one that may lie outside its range of validity (see below). An interesting discussion and examples of such effects are given by STERN et al. (1968).

Equations of the form $\ln \alpha = C_1 + C_2/T + C_3/T^2$, where the $C$'s are empirical constants, are commonly used to describe laboratory determinations of certain fractionation factors that, over temperature ranges of interest, do not appear to strictly follow either the $1/T$ and $1/T^2$ limiting dependences (e.g., MAJOUBE, 1971). JONES (1958) argues theoretically that equations of this form (with $C_1 = 0$) are useful in the description of the vapor pressure ratios of isotopic solids. In an attempt to establish the theoretical validity of this latter type of equation for isotopic equilibria among gaseous molecules, the partition function ratios (Eqn. 3) were expanded in terms of asymptotic series in powers of $1/T$. All terms in odd powers of $1/T$ cancelled, so that an expression of the above form was not obtained. The result in fact reaffirmed Eqns. (10a,b) by yet another independent method, but did not provide any additional justification for the type of power series mentioned above.

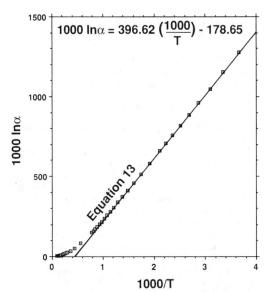

FIG. 1. Graph showing the variation of 1000 ln α with inverse temperature, for deuterium exchange between hydrogen gas and hydrogen fluoride. The individual points (squares) were calculated by combining Eqns. (2, 3a, and 4), whereas the straight line represents the low-temperature correlation represented by the indicated formula, which was determined from Eqn. (13). As temperature increases, the deviation increases between this straight line and the calculated points, and a crossover would erroneously be predicted from the linear approximation at 2220 K (*i.e.*, $1000/T \approx 0.45$).

Of course, the range of Eqn. (14) can be extended by inclusion of additional terms, for example

$$\ln \alpha \cong \frac{a(U_{1A}^2 - U_{2A}^2) - b(U_{1B}^2 + U_{2B}^2)}{24ab}$$

$$+ \frac{a(U_{1A}^4 - U_{2A}^4) - b(U_{1B}^4 - U_{2B}^4)}{2880ab} + \dots \quad (15)$$

Unfortunately, convergence is lost before the $1/T$ dependence is reached.

### EXAMPLE CALCULATION

For purposes of illustration, it is useful to compare the predictions of the high- and low-temperature approximations given above with the more exact values for the fractionation factors that, given the availability of computers, are easily calculated with Eqns. (3a,b). As an elementary example, consider the exchange of deuterium between hydrogen gas and hydrogen fluoride, represented by the exchange reaction

$$HD + HF = H_2 + DF. \quad (16)$$

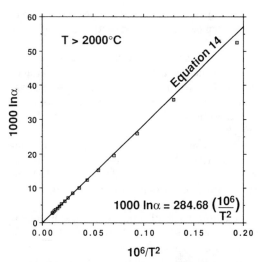

FIG. 2. Graph showing the variation of 1000 ln α with the square of the inverse temperature, for deuterium exchange between hydrogen gas and hydrogen fluoride. At extremely high temperatures, Eqn. (14), the straight line represented by the indicated formula, agrees very well with individual points (squares) calculated with Eqns. (2, 3a, and 4), but the agreement deteriorates below 3000 K. Note that the isotopic fractionation effect vanishes at extremely high temperatures, even though the equilibrium constant for the exchange reaction (Eqn. 16) approaches ½.

The number of atoms exchanged in the reaction ($ab$) equals 1 and the symmetry numbers ($\sigma$'s) for the HD, HF, and DF molecules are all equal to unity, whereas that for $H_2$ is equal to 2. The equilibrium constant and the isotopic fractionation factor accordingly differ by the factor $K_\infty = 1/2$ (Eqn. 4a,b). RICHET *et al.* (1977) list the following values for the wavenumbers (cm$^{-1}$) of the pertinent diatomic molecules: $\omega_{DF} = 2998.192$; $\omega_{HF} = 4138.32$; $\omega_{HD} = 3812.293$; $\omega_{H_2} = 4401.118$. These values may be converted to frequencies (sec$^{-1}$) simply by multiplying by the speed of light. RICHET *et al.* (1977) also calculated that $K_{(0°C)} = 1.77141$ and $K_{(1000°C)} = 0.58021$ for the above reaction. These values compare well with the values of 1.78641 and 0.58164 that one can easily calculate with Eqns. (2) and (3a), given above. The small discrepancy arises from the inclusion of corrections for anharmonicity by RICHET *et al.* (1977); such corrections are in fact well known to be significant for hydrogen isotopes.

The smooth variation of 1000 ln α with temperature for these gases, as calculated with Eqns. (2, 3a, and 4), is shown by the individual points on Figs. 1 and 2. At temperatures below 1000 K, ln α varies inversely with temperature, as expressed by the straight line (Eqn. 13) having a slope of 396.62

K and a $y$-intercept of $-178.65$. At progressively higher temperatures, the deviation increases between this line and the fractionations calculated with Eqns. (2, 3a, and 4). Were this straight line, representing the low-temperature behavior, extrapolated to high temperatures beyond its range of validity, a "crossover" (reversal in the sign of ln $\alpha$) would erroneously be predicted at about 2220 K (Fig. 1).

At high temperatures ($>3000$ K), ln $\alpha$ varies linearly with $1/T^2$ for these gases (Fig. 2). The numerical value for the slope ($284.68$ K$^2$) of the high-temperature correlation may be calculated from Eqn. (14), and it is evident that the $y$-intercept, representing the limiting fractionation at high temperature, is zero (*i.e.* $\alpha = 1$). Note on Fig. 2 that at progressively lower temperatures, the deviation increases between the points calculated with Eqns. (2, 3a, and 4) and the high-temperature line given by Eqn. (14).

## CONCLUSIONS

For isotopic exchange reactions between gases at low and very high temperatures, the logarithms of the isotopic fractionation factors may be expressed as straightforward linear relations of inverse temperature or inverse temperature squared, respectively. The slopes and intercepts of these equations are explicitly related to the vibrational frequencies of the molecules and the stoichiometric coefficients of the exchange reaction, but (unlike $K$) are independent of the symmetry numbers. Extrapolation of these limiting equations beyond their range of applicability leads to erroneous predictions. No theoretical justification was found for the inclusion of both $1/T$ and $1/T^2$ terms in the same fractionation equation for isotopic equilibria among gaseous molecules.

*Acknowledgements*—I thank S. Epstein and S. M. Savin for valuable discussions and lectures on isotopic fractionation. A. M. Hofmeister made several important mathematical suggestions, including the use of the asymptotic series. J. H. Jones, P. Richet, and J. R. O'Neil provided useful critical comments, and C. J. Yapp pointed out a serious error in the original manuscript. This research was supported by NSF Grant EAR 89-15788.

## REFERENCES

BIGELEISEN J. (1958) The significance of the product and sum rules to isotope fractionation processes. In *Proc. Intl. Symp. Isotope Separation* (eds. J. KISTEMAKER, J. BIGELEISEN and A. O. C. NIER), pp. 121–157. Amsterdam, 1957.

BIGELEISEN J. and MAYER M. G. (1947) Calculation of equilibrium constants for isotopic exchange reactions. *J. Chem. Phys.* **15**(3), 261–267.

BOTTINGA Y. and JAVOY M. (1975) Oxygen isotope partitioning among the minerals in igneous and metamorphic rocks. *Rev. Geophys. Space Phys.* **13**, 401–418.

FERRONSKY V. I. and POLYAKOV V. A. (1982) *Environmental Isotopes in the Hydrosphere.* J. Wiley & Sons.

GRADSHTEYN I. S. and RYZHIK I. M. (1980) *Table of Integrals, Series, and Products.* Academic Press.

HOEFS J. (1987) *Stable Isotope Geochemistry*, 3rd edn. Springer-Verlag.

JONES T. F. (1958) Vapor pressures of some isotopic substances. In *Proc. Intl. Symp. Isotope Separation.* (eds. J. KISTEMAKER, J. BIGELEISEN and A. O. C. NIER), pp. 74–102. Amsterdam, 1957.

MAJOUBE M. (1971) Fractionnement en oxygène 18 et en deutérium entre l'eau et sa vapeur. *J. Chim. Phys.* **68**, 1425–1436.

O'NEIL J. R. (1986) Theoretical and experimental aspects of isotopic fractionation. In *Stable Isotopes in High Temperature Geological Processes* (eds. J. W. VALLEY, H. P. TAYLOR JR. and J. R. O'NEIL); *Rev. Mineral.* **16**, pp. 1–40.

RICHET P., BOTTINGA Y. and JAVOY M. (1977) A review of hydrogen, carbon, nitrogen, oxygen, sulphur, and chlorine stable isotope fractionation among gaseous molecules. *Ann. Rev. Earth Planet. Sci.* **1977**(5), 65–110.

STERN M. J., SPINDEL W. and MONSE E. U. (1968) Temperature dependence of isotope effects. *J. Chem. Phys.* **48**, 2908–2919.

UREY H. C. (1947) The thermodynamic properties of isotopic substances. *J. Chem. Soc. (London)*, 562–581.

WOLFRAM S. (1988) *Mathematica.* Addison-Wesley.

Stable Isotope Geochemistry: A Tribute to Samuel Epstein
© The Geochemical Society, Special Publication No. 3, 1991
Editors: H. P. Taylor, Jr., J. R. O'Neil and I. R. Kaplan

# Oxygen isotope fractionation studies of solute-water interactions

JAMES R. O'NEIL and ALFRED H. TRUESDELL

Department of Geological Sciences, University of Michigan, Ann Arbor, MI 48109-1063, U.S.A.
U.S. Geological Survey, 345 Middlefield Road, Menlo Park, CA 94025, U.S.A.

**Abstract**—Equilibrium oxygen isotope fractionations were measured between $CO_2$ and concentrated aqueous solutions and compared to those between $CO_2$ and pure $H_2O$ at 0, 25, and 38.5°C. Inferences from these data are that (1) the direction and relative magnitudes of the measured fractionations at any temperature are well correlated with the structure-making and structure-breaking capacity of the solute, (2) concentrated aqueous solutions of structure-making salts assume at least two thermodynamically distinct structural states that depend on critical concentrations of di- and trivalent cationic charge equivalents, (3) the same structural state of solutions of structure-breaking salts can be attained with organic solutes, (4) $Mg^{2+}$ and $Al^{3+}$ ions are completely solvated in their respective sulfate ion-pairs, and (5) after a critical concentration of about 50 volume % dioxane, additional dioxane breaks hydrogen bonds between water molecules causing the liquid water in the solution to have isotopic properties more like those of water vapor. The simple $CO_2$-equilibration technique has provided insights into important aspects of aqueous chemistry in the past and continues to hold great promise for future investigations of fundamental interactions between solutes and water.

## INTRODUCTION

THE STUDIES reported in this paper are a direct outgrowth of the work of TAUBE (1954) who first applied the $CO_2$-equilibration technique to the study of aqueous solutions. The technique consists of equilibrating the oxygen isotopes of $CO_2$ with pure water and with aqueous solutions at constant temperature. Taube found that the $^{18}O/^{16}O$ ratio of $CO_2$ equilibrated with pure water at 25°C decreased upon the addition of $MgCl_2$, $AlCl_3$, HCl, and LiCl; remained essentially unchanged for NaCl, NaI, and $NaClO_4$; and increased when $CaCl_2$ was added to the water. The changes in $^{18}O/^{16}O$ ratio are roughly linear with the molality of the solute (our data are shown in Fig. 1) and this is normally taken to indicate a constant coordination number of the cation for water in the first hydration sphere with no effect attributed to hydration of the anion. Taube attributed such isotopic effects to differences between the isotopic properties of water in the hydration sheath of the cation and the remaining "bulk" water. These oxygen isotope fractionations are described in terms of the vibrational frequencies (and frequency shifts on isotopic substitution) associated with the bonding in the two types of water and consequently bear on fundamental thermodynamic properties of water and aqueous solutions.

Using this oxygen isotope technique, SOFER and GAT (1972, 1975) studied a series of solutions of geochemical interest. They called attention to the difference between the activity of $H_2^{18}O$ (the quantity actually measured by this technique) and the concentration of $H_2^{18}O$ and also pointed out the importance of correcting for salt effects when analyzing natural brines for their $^{18}O$ content by the $CO_2$-equilibration method. The questions of variation in oxygen isotope activity of aqueous solutions with temperature and the importance of making corrections to natural and experimental data has been examined several times (TRUESDELL, 1974; KENDALL et al., 1983; KASAHAYA, 1986; COLE and WESOLOWSKI, 1989; LIGANG et al., 1989) but these issues remain effectively unresolved. O'NEIL and ADAMI (1969) used the $CO_2$-equilibration technique to measure the oxygen isotope partition function ratios of liquid water at frequent intervals from 2 to 85°C and discussed the temperature dependence of this property in relation to its compatibility with theories of the structure of water. The results of their study provide a reference for the solution data taken at the relatively low temperatures employed in the present work.

The topics covered in this report include: (1) the temperature dependence of the fractionation of oxygen isotopes between concentrated aqueous solutions and pure water, (2) the variation of water structure with the nature and concentration of added solutes, (3) the correlation of oxygen isotope effects with the structure-making and structure-breaking properties of various solutes, with separation of the effects into those caused by cations and anions, (4) the nature of sulfate ion pairs of $Mg^{+2}$ and $Al^{+3}$ and the 1:1 fluoride complex of $Al^{+3}$, and (5) the nature of the interactions between water and organic solutes.

## EXPERIMENTAL PROCEDURES

The $CO_2$-equilibration technique used is a modification of the technique first described by COHN and UREY (1938)

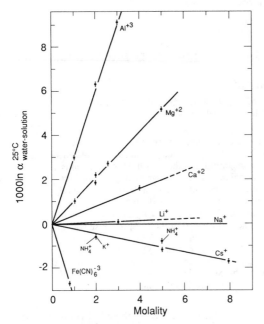

FIG. 1. Oxygen isotope per mil fractionations between pure water and solutions of various ions. Positive values are associated with structure-making electrolytes and negative values with structure-breaking electrolytes and organic solutes (see text).

and employed by EPSTEIN and MAYEDA (1953) in their seminal publication on the variations in the $^{18}O$ contents of natural waters. Approximately 150 $\mu$moles of dried $CO_2$ were transferred to vessels containing 5 ml of degassed water or solution. These large amounts of $CO_2$ and $H_2O$ were used in order to be able to take several aliquots of $CO_2$ during the equilibration as a check on rates of isotopic exchange and to use the same preparations for runs at different temperatures. The vessels were placed in a constant temperature bath regulated to ±0.1°C and shaken several times a day. Isotopic equilibration was assumed to be complete when the isotopic composition of the $CO_2$ ceased to change with time (normally 1–2 days depending on the degree of shaking and the nature and concentration of the solution). For the very viscous and acidic $AlCl_3$ solutions, isotopic equilibrium was demonstrated in this work by approaching the equilibrium value from opposite sides of the equilibrium distribution. An aliquot of the $CO_2$ was removed at the equilibration temperature and its $\delta^{18}O$ value measured on an isotope ratio mass spectrometer. This value is the relative difference, in parts per thousand (per mil), between the $^{18}O/^{16}O$ ratio of the sample and that of the working standard of the mass spectrometer and can be determined with a precision of better than ±0.1 per mil.

Many of the salts used in these studies are hygroscopic and extensive precautions were taken to avoid contamination by extraneous water. Commercial anhydrous salts were heated on a vacuum line to remove traces of water and then weighed into the equilibration vessel in a dry box. In some cases, hydrated salts were weighed into the equilibration vessels and dehydrated by vacuum distillation at 100°C. Water of known isotopic composition was then distilled into the vessel on the vacuum line. After equilibration, conventional chemical analyses were made of the solutions as a check on concentration. In the case of $AlCl_3$, chemical analyses of the solutions indicated that hydrolysis and loss of HCl during the dehydration of the salt was negligible. No solution that was chemically analyzed differed by more than 0.1–0.2 in molality from that expected from the weights of salt and water used in the preparation. Equilibrations were made on three separate 1.0 molal solutions of $AlCl_3$ as a check on the reproducibility of the method as the $AlCl_3$ solutions proved to be the most intractable in the laboratory. The results given in Table 1 indicate that the reproducibility of the method for this solution, and by inference for all the other solutions, is typically about 0.1 per mil or better.

## MODELS OF ION HYDRATION AND ORIGIN OF ISOTOPIC EFFECTS

FRANK and WEN (1957) proposed that water associated with ions in solution exists in several forms. In the inner hydration sheaths of ions of high ionic potential ($F^-$, polyvalent cations, alkali cations other than $Rb^+$ and $Cs^+$), water is dense, immobilized and structured with its dipoles oriented radially to the ion. Water in the outer hydration sheaths of cations and probably all water associated with anions (other than $F^-$) and large, singly-charged cations is unstructured and mobile though still more dense than normal water. For cations, this unstructured water results from the discontinuity between the structure of normal water and the structure of inner-sphere, tightly-bound water. In anions it results from disruption due to the physical presence of the ion.

This model can be successfully applied to the isotopic effects of salts through an equation that relates the concentration of ions, their hydration number, and the fractionation factor between bulk water and water of hydration (TAUBE, 1954). This equation is here extended to include water in the several distinct hydration spheres postulated by Frank and Wen. The derivation of the equation is not exact because the $^{18}O/^{16}O$ ratio is taken as the mole fraction of $^{18}O$. For ordinary water, however, these quantities differ by very little. The extended equation is

$$10^3 \ln \alpha = \frac{\sum m_i \sum n_{ij}(K_{ij} - 1)}{55.51}$$

where $m_i$ is the molality of the ion, $n_{ij}$ is the number of water molecules in the $j$th hydration shell of each $i$th ion, and $K_{ij}$ is the oxygen isotope fractionation factor between water in the $j$th hydration shell of the $i$th ion and bulk water defined as

$$K_{ij} = \frac{(^{18}O/^{16}O)_{ij \text{ hydrate water}}}{(^{18}O/^{16}O)_{\text{bulk water}}}.$$

Using this equation the total isotopic effect can in theory be divided into the individual effects due to the inner and outer hydration spheres, to the cation, and to the hydration sphere of the anion.

Before attempting to correlate the observed isotopic effects with properties of aqueous solutions, it is useful to consider the possible origins of these effects. Taube chose to explain them in terms of a separation of the available water into at least two different species: water bound in coordination spheres of the solutes and remaining "bulk" water—the latter behaving isotopically like pure water. That is, when the three oxygen-containing species in the system ($CO_2$, bound water, and bulk water) are all in oxygen isotope equilibrium, and when the bound water concentrates $^{18}O$ relative to the bulk water, the $CO_2$ becomes isotopically lighter on addition of the solute to pure water. Another point of view considers the effects to be a consequence of the different fractionation factors between $CO_2$ and the various solutions treated as homogeneous substances. That is, if the solute alters the water structure, the resultant changes in the vibrational frequencies of the water will change the $CO_2$-$H_2O$ fractionation factor with a corresponding change in the isotopic composition of the $CO_2$.

The second hypothesis above is not readily amenable to quantitative treatment but is an important consideration in this paper. It is instructive, however, to point out that there is a problem in relating the absolute magnitude of the isotopic effects observed to thermodynamic properties of the solution. There is little doubt that ions in aqueous solutions are solvated and that the bonds between water molecules and the solute ions are different from the bonds between water molecules themselves. So, indeed, there are different species of $H_2O$ in an aqueous solution and each species has its unique isotopic properties. O'NEIL and ADAMI (1969) demonstrated that thermodynamic differences between the various molecular varieties of $H_2O$ should be detectable by the isotopic fractionation technique. Bulk water in a concentrated solution, then, should have isotopic properties that are different from those of pure water. Thus, the lack of knowledge of the fractionation factors between $CO_2$ and bulk waters places constraints on the application of the $CO_2$-equilibration technique to quantitative thermodynamic problems of aqueous solutions. The observed isotopic effects undoubtedly arise from *both* a separation of the water into two or more $H_2O$ species *and* to changes in the structure of water upon the addition of solute. Experiments to delineate these effects were performed and are discussed below.

## RESULTS

The per mil fractionations between pure water and the solutions at various concentrations and temperatures are given in Tables 1, 2, and 3. The lack of data in certain columns arises from either a failed experiment (typically a leaky stopcock during the equilibration) or simply that the experiment was made only at 25°C. The fractionation factor between pure water and the solution, $\alpha$($H_2O$-soln), is given by the following expression:

$$\alpha(H_2O\text{-soln}) = \frac{(^{18}O/^{16}O)_{water}}{(^{18}O/^{16}O)_{soln}}$$

$$= \frac{1000 + \delta(CO_2\text{-}H_2O)}{1000 + \delta(CO_2\text{-soln})}$$

where $\delta$($CO_2$-$H_2O$) means the $\delta^{18}O$ value of $CO_2$ which was equilibrated with pure water. Water of the same isotopic composition was used in all the experiments. Values of $10^3 \ln\alpha$ rather than of $\alpha$ are tabulated because of the greater simplicity of the numbers and because the logarithmic function has theoretical significance (UREY, 1947; BIGELEISEN and MAYER, 1947). It is this function which is normally used in relating the variation of $\alpha$ with temperature. In Table 1, the first entry at 0°C means that at 0°C, $CO_2$ in isotopic equilibrium with pure water is enriched in $^{18}O$ by 1.25 per mil relative to $CO_2$ in equilibrium with a 1.0 molal solution of $MgSO_4$. A negative value means that $CO_2$ in equi-

Table 1. Experimental determinations of the per mil fractionations, $10^3 \ln \alpha$, between pure water and solutions of structure-making electrolytes at different temperatures

| Solution | 0.0°C | 25.0°C | 38.5°C |
|---|---|---|---|
| 6.0 m NaCl | — | 0.00 | |
| 1.0 m LiCl | — | 0.10 | — |
| 1.0 m MgSO$_4$ | 1.25 | 1.05 | 0.79 |
| 2.0 m MgSO$_4$ | 2.42 | 1.82 | 1.70 |
| 2.0 m MgCl$_2$ | 2.22 | 1.80 | 1.63 |
| 3.0 m MgCl$_2$ | 3.60 | 3.00 | 2.80 |
| 3.5 m MgCl$_2$ | 4.30 | 3.65 | 3.32 |
| 4.0 m MgCl$_2$ | 6.30 | 4.50 | 3.70 |
| 5.0 m MgCl$_2$ | 7.35 | 5.20 | 4.35 |
| 1.0 m AlCl$_3$ | | 3.55 | 3.00 | 2.85 |
| 1.0 m AlCl$_3$ | | 3.65 | 3.04 | 2.78 |
| 1.0 m AlCl$_3$ | | 3.60 | 2.98 | 2.70 |
| 2.0 m AlCl$_3$ | | 7.05 | 6.30 | 5.85 |
| 1.0 m Al$_2$(SO$_4$)$_3$ | — | 6.19 | 5.66 |
| 3.0 m AlCl$_3$ | 11.25 | 9.05 | 8.05 |
| 1.0 m AlCl$_3$ + 1 m NaF | — | 2.46 | — |
| 4.0 m CaCl$_2$ | 1.91 | 1.63 | — |
| 4.0 m CdCl$_2$ | — | 1.10 | — |

Table 2. Experimental determinations of the per mil fractionations, $10^3 \ln \alpha$, between pure water and solutions of structure-breaking electrolytes at different temperatures

| Solution | 0.0°C | 25.0°C | 38.5°C |
|---|---|---|---|
| 2.0 m KCl | — | −0.56 | — |
| 6.0 m NaI | −1.10 | −0.77 | −0.60 |
| 11.7 m NaI | −1.11 | −0.83 | −0.62 |
| 2.0 m NH$_4$Cl | — | −0.50 | — |
| 5.0 m NH$_4$Cl | — | −0.77 | — |
| 6.0 m NH$_4$I | — | −0.78 | — |
| 5.0 m CsCl | −1.41 | −1.13 | −1.22 |
| 8.0 m CsCl | −1.97 | −1.62 | — |
| 0.8 m Na$_3$Fe(CN)$_6$ | — | −2.83 | −0.64 |

librium with pure water is depleted in $^{18}O$ by that amount relative to $CO_2$ in equilibrium with the solution. As discussed above, this technique is extremely reproducible and for that reason the fractionations are reported to the nearest ±0.01 per mil although a figure of ±0.05 is more realistic. Errors in solution preparation or hydrolysis reactions for certain solutes will introduce additional errors outside the small analytical error of isotopic measurement and explain some of the scatter observed.

The measured fractionations range from −3.71 for a concentrated solution of dioxane to 11.25 for a 3.0 molal solution of AlCl$_3$, so the effects of added solutes to the isotopic properties of water are indeed very large and meaningful.

## STRUCTURE-MAKING AND STRUCTURE-BREAKING SOLUTES

It is readily apparent from the data in Tables 1 and 2 that electrolytes normally considered structure makers (e.g., Mg$^{+2}$, Al$^{+3}$) yield positive values of $10^3 \ln \alpha$ and that the structure breakers (e.g., Cs$^+$) yield negative values. FRANK and WEN (1957) were the first to discuss the structure-making and structure-breaking effects of electrolytes on water, and others have since couched these discussions in other terms, like "flickering clusters." We choose not to use terms germane to only one theory of the structure of water and solutions but merely to use the operational definition implied above: structure makers yield positive isotopic fractionations and structure breakers yield negative isotopic fractionations. This definition is not arbitrary because the isotopic fractionation between ice and liquid water is positive (O'NEIL, 1968) and the fractionation between vapor and liquid is negative (MAJOUB, 1971). That is, any solute that results in a positive value of $10^3 \ln \alpha$ is one that causes the solution to be more structured or ice-like.

Equilibrations were made with alkali chloride solutions and the results indicate the following structure-breaking order: Cs$^+$ > K$^+$ > Na$^+$ > Li$^+$ with Li$^+$ just at the experimentally detectable limit (0.1 per mil) of being a structure maker. Inasmuch as the net isotopic effect caused by both cations and anions is measured, it is probable that Li$^+$ is a *bona fide* structure maker by isotopic criteria, and runs made with sodium salts indicate that I$^-$ is a greater structure breaker than Cl$^-$. Another sequence examined in this work is the following group of structure makers: Al$^{+3}$ > Mg$^{+2}$ > Ca$^{+2}$ (Table 1). Cs$^+$, NH$_4^+$ salts, urea, and dioxane all yield negative isotopic fractionations (Table 2) and are thus classified as structure breakers. The results of other techniques are in agreement with these classifications and sequences in some cases and not in others. No attempt will be made to compare results considering the vast literature on this subject.

### Structure makers

Several experiments were made in an attempt to assess the relative importance of ionic size, mass, and electronic configuration of cations to their structure-making properties. In general, ions with large ionic potentials are the greatest structure makers. There is little doubt that the development of hydration sheathes around small, highly charged positive ions is chiefly responsible for the increased order observed in their solutions. The vibrational frequencies of water bonded to cations are different from those of water bonded to other water molecules and thus an isotopic fractionation between bound and bulk water is expected. In the case of Al$^{+3}$ solutions, the isotopic fractionation between bound and bulk water is 25.6 per mil at 25°C. This value is calculated from the measured 3.1 per mil fractionation between pure water and 1.0 molal AlCl$_3$ solution, and assuming a coordination number of 6 for Al$^{+3}$, complete dissociation, and equal values for the fractionation factors between CO$_2$-bulk water and CO$_2$-pure water. This fractionation of 25.6 per mil is on the order of those measured between crystalline silicates and water and between solid carbonates and water (e.g., FRIEDMAN and O'NEIL, 1977). On this basis the fractionations between bound and bulk waters measured in these experiments seem too large, although this cannot be rigorously proved. In accordance with the model used, 32% of the water in a 3.0 molal solution of AlCl$_3$ is bonded to Al$^{+3}$ in the first coordination sphere. Given this high percentage of bound water, the remaining bulk water should not have the properties of pure water. At higher concentrations this problem becomes acute. In the 5 molal $MgCl_2$ solution studied, 54% of the water is bound water. The assumption that the fractionation factor between $CO_2$ and bulk water is identical to that between $CO_2$ and pure water is clearly weak in these cases of very concentrated solutions. Nonetheless, it is safe to say that for those solutions with a positive value of $10^3 \ln \alpha$, the bound water is indeed enriched in $^{18}O$ relative to the bulk water. This is tantamount to saying that the cation-$H_2O$ bonds are stronger than the $H_2O$-$H_2O$ bonds in these solutions.

In light of the above discussion, it is interesting to compare the results of equilibrations of $CO_2$ with solutions of $CdCl_2$ and of $CaCl_2$. It was mentioned above that $Ca^{+2}$ is a structure maker on isotopic grounds, a 1.0 molal solution yielding $10^3 \ln \alpha$ equal to +0.40. $Cd^{+2}$ is almost identical in ionic radius to $Ca^{+2}$ and therefore any difference in the isotopic behavior of these two solutions must be attributed to differences in mass and/or electronic configuration of the ions. The value of $10^3 \ln \alpha$ for a 1.0 molal solution of $CdCl_2$ is +0.25. Assuming equal coordination numbers for the two cations and similar isotopic properties for the bulk waters, the data are interpreted to reflect an enrichment of $^{18}O$ in the water sheath of $Ca^{+2}$ relative to $Cd^{+2}$. The effect is principally one of mass, the higher vibrational frequencies (of the bonds between cation and water) and tendency to concentrate $^{18}O$ being correlated with the lighter $Ca^{+2}$ ion (e.g., O'NEIL, 1986). A similar correlation was observed in the case of oxygen isotope fractionation between $H_2O$ and the carbonates $CaCO_3$ and $CdCO_3$ (O'NEIL et al., 1969).

*Structure breakers*

A size comparison can also be made for structure breakers using, for example, salts of $NH_4^+$ and $K^+$ whose ionic radii are very similar. With the notable exception of $Fe(CN)_6^{-3}$, however, *all ionic structure breakers investigated yield approximately the same negative value of $10^3 \ln \alpha$*. For these solutions one might say that the cation-$H_2O$ bonds are weaker than the $H_2O$-$H_2O$ bonds, but if this were the nature of the isotopic effect, there should be a variety of fractionations for the various solutions. From the similarity of the results, we suggest that the addition of these structure-breaking cations results in a uniform alteration of the water structure with a concomitant change in the $CO_2$-$H_2O$ fractionation factor. Implied here is little or no isotopic fractionation between bound and free water.

NaCl is an unique salt in its failure to cause an appreciable isotopic effect. On comparing the results of TAUBE (1954), SOFER and GAT (1972), and this

work, it is clear that at low temperatures $Na^+$ is nearly equal and opposite in its properties to $Cl^-$ even at very high concentrations. If anything, $Na^+$ acts as a mild structure breaker. $NH_4Cl$, on the other hand, acts as a distinct structure breaker. Inasmuch as the $Cl^-$ ion is common to both NaCl and $NH_4Cl$, it is reasonable to assume that $NH_4^+$ is the dominant structure breaker. Similarly NaI is a distinct structure breaker and $I^-$ is reasonably assumed to be the cause. If each structure breaker altered the water structure in an unique way, then combinations of structure breakers, for example, the salt $NH_4I$, should produce an isotopic effect greater than that of either ion alone or as much as the sum of the effects of each ion. From Table 2 it is seen that 5.0 molal $NH_4Cl$, 6.0 molal NaI, and 6.0 molal $NH_4I$ yield values of $10^3 \ln \alpha$ of $-0.77$, $-0.83$, and $-0.78$, respectively, which are identical within the limits of analytical error. This is further evidence that the average-size, structure-breaking ion, *regardless of sign*, alters the structural state of the water in an unique and common way.

The importance of ionic size in disrupting water structure can be tested by using an extremely large ion. Unfortunately, most salts of the large ions used in other studies are not soluble enough to produce a measurable isotopic effect. The salt $Na_3Fe(CN)_6$ was chosen because of its fairly high solubility (0.8 molal at 25°C). The equilibration vessel was covered with aluminum foil to prevent any photochemical reactions that might occur during the equilibration time. The measured isotopic fractionation of $-2.8$ per mil is as large a negative fractionation on a 1.0 molal basis as is found for $Al^{+3}$ in the other direction (Fig. 1). This ion is particularly susceptible to a variety of chemical reactions in solution so that the magnitude of this isotopic effect should be viewed with reservation. Cyanide hydrolysis was proved to be insignificant by analyzing the $^{13}C/^{12}C$ ratio of the $CO_2$. This ratio did not change during the equilibration. The result was reproducible and it is tentatively concluded that the size of anionic structure breakers can be extremely important in determining the nature of water-structure alteration.

Considering the similarity of the isotopic fractionations among solutions of structure breakers that are not too different in size and the unusual result for the very large ferricyanide ion, it may be that there is a critical size of the ion above which a profound alteration in water structure is necessary in order to provide accommodation sites for the large ion. The change of over 2.0 permil in the value of $10^3 \ln \alpha$ on going from $Cs^+$ or $I^-$ to $Fe(CN)_6^{-3}$ is indeed a very large isotopic effect and cannot be explained by differences in the "relatively weak" bonding between anions and water. Rather it must have something to do with a fundamental change in the structure of the water.

*Non-electrolytes*

The influence of non-electrolytes on the isotopic properties of water was investigated by equilibrating $CO_2$ with a solution of urea and with a series of dioxane-water mixtures. The measured fractionations for all these experiments are given in Table 3 and shown graphically in Fig. 3. Similar experiments with a different approach and somewhat different goals were conducted with pyridine by BETTS *et al.* (1977) and with urea by KAKIUCHI and MATSUO (1985). The fractionations for the one (5.0 molal) solution of urea analyzed and the relatively dilute dioxane solutions are all about −0.55 per mil. This is a value similar to those of the solutions of structure-breaking electrolytes except for those of highly concentrated solutions of CsCl and the solution of $Na_3Fe(CN)_6$ which are significantly larger. The important implication is that water may be assuming the same structural state for all these solutions regardless of whether ionic species are present. Apparently, for each non-electrolyte there is a critical concentration above which water assumes a different and more disordered structural state.

If the dioxane does nothing more than break hydrogen bonds to accommodate itself into the water structure, it would tend to make the water behave isotopically more like water vapor. This is indeed the direction of the change (Fig. 2). With increasing dioxane/water ratio, however, a limiting fractionation of about 4.0 per mil is reached. Liquid water is enriched in $^{18}O$ by 9.0 per mil relative to water vapor at 25°C (MAJOUB, 1971). This difference of five per mil presumably reflects the restrictions placed on the motions of the separated water molecules in this condensed state.

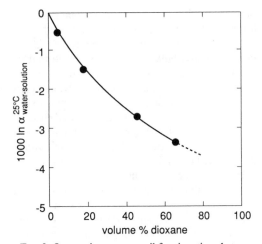

FIG. 2. Oxygen isotope per mil fractionations between pure water and solutions of dioxane. With increasing dioxane content more hydrogen bonds in water are broken and the water becomes isotopically more like water vapor.

Equilibrations were carried out with solutions of 0.01 mole of $MgCl_2$ or $MgSO_4$ in 10 ml of 50–50 mixtures of dioxane and water. The preliminary results presented in Table 3 are from a series of experiments designed to elucidate the effect of changes in dielectric constant of the solvent on the solute-solvent interactions. Changing the dielectric constant of the solution by temperature alone presents certain technical difficulties and, in addition, the sensitivity of the technique is lowered at high temperatures because isotopic fractionations decrease with increasing temperature. The addition of dioxane to water permits the equilibrations to be done at low temperatures in solutions of reduced dielectric constant. The data are most easily interpreted by separating the interaction of the magnesium salt and water from that of dioxane and water. The isotopic effects for $MgSO_4$ and $MgCl_2$ solutions at 25°C are close to being the sum of the ion-water effect and the dioxane-water effect. At 38.5°C, however, the fractionation is nearly identical to that of the 50–50 dioxane-water mixture alone. It is tentatively concluded that under these conditions of temperature and dielectric constant, the $Mg^{+2}$-$H_2O$ interactions are drastically reduced or eliminated.

## ION-PAIRING IN CONCENTRATED SULFATE SOLUTIONS

The largest isotopic effects observed in the earlier and present work are for the magnesium and aluminum chloride solutions. Of interest, then is the magnitude of the effects when magnesium and aluminum ions are extensively associated as in their

Table 3. Experimental determinations of the per mil fractionations, $10^3 \ln \alpha$, between pure water and solutions of organic solutes at different temperatures

| Solution | 0.0°C | 25.0°C | 38.5°C |
|---|---|---|---|
| 5.0 m urea | — | −0.56 | — |
| 20% dioxane | −0.35 | −0.49 | — |
| 30% dioxane | −0.50 | −0.58 | — |
| 50% dioxane | −1.19 | −1.48 | −1.75 |
| 80% dioxane | −3.07 | −2.66 | −2.59 |
| 90% dioxane | −3.71 | −3.39 | −3.11 |
| 0.01 mole $MgSO_4$ in 10 ml 50–50 mixture | — | 0.77 | — |
| 0.01 mole $MgCl_2$ in 10 ml 50–50 mixture | — | 0.86 | −1.90 |

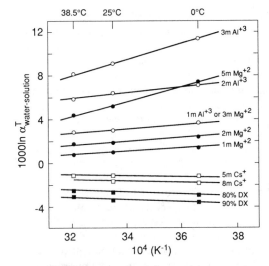

FIG. 3. Temperature dependence of the per mil fractionations between pure water and various solutions. Note the similarity in slopes of structure makers and structure breakers and that the curves for 1 m $Al^{+3}$ and 3 m $Mg^{+2}$ are identical. At certain critical concentrations of $Al^{+3}$ and $Mg^{+2}$, the slope of the curves change, signalling a transition to another structural state of the solution.

concentrated sulfate solutions. The dissociation constants for $MgSO_4^0$ and $Al(SO_4)^+$ at 25°C are $10^{-2.3}$ and $10^{-3.2}$, respectively. That is, the predominant solute species at the concentrations studied are the ion-pairs. It was expected that the formation of stable ion-pairs would decrease the magnitude and extent of the cation-water interaction such that the measured isotopic effect would approach that characteristic of pure water. As seen in Table 1, however, the fractionation factors are about the same for the $MgCl_2$ and $MgSO_4$ solutions and for the $AlCl_3$ and $Al_2(SO_4)_3$ solutions. On a 1.0 molal cation basis, at 25°C, the values of $10^3 \ln \alpha$ are approximately 3.0 for the aluminum solutions and 1.0 for the magnesium solutions. These data show unambiguously that the cations are solvated in the sulfate ion-pairs to the same extent that they are solvated in the unassociated chloride solutions. In addition, the presence of $SO_4^{-2}$ in the vicinity of the solvated $Mg^{+2}$ or $Al^{+3}$ ions does not appear to alter the isotopic behavior of the aqueous solutions. This is a very surprising result.

The common characterization of magnesium and aluminum sulfate ion-pairs as "outer-sphere" complexes is of some concern in light of current usage of aqueous complex ions as kinetic entities. FRENKEL *et al.* (1967) concluded from NMR experiments with $MnSO_4$ solutions that the predominant species at high concentrations is the contact ion-pair, the $SO_4^{-2}$ ion acting as a bidentate ligand. But it is clear

from the isotopic measurements that at least one water molecule separates the $Mg^{+2}$ and $Al^{+3}$ ions from $SO_4^{-2}$. This conclusion is in agreement with the findings of ATKINSON and PETRUCCI (1966) who deduced from ultrasonic absorption experiments that ten Angstroms, or the distance of two water molecules, separates the $Mg^{+2}$ and $SO_4^{-2}$ ions in the ion-pair. In addition, HESTER and PLANE (1964) reported Raman spectral evidence for the existence of bonds between magnesium and water-oxygen in concentrated $MgSO_4$ solutions. According to the results of ultrasonic absorption experiments, there are at least three ion-pair species present in a 2:2 electrolyte (ATKINSON and KOR, 1965). These species differ in their degree of solvation and are in equilibrium. The isotopic effects measured in these systems are the averages of the effects due to all species present. In the case of the concentrated sulfate solutions examined here, the isotopic data indicate that the predominant magnesium and aluminum species are those that are extensively hydrated.

## TEMPERATURE DEPENDENCE OF $10^3 \ln \alpha$(WATER-SOLUTION)

$CO_2$ equilibrations were carried out at 0, 25, and 38.5°C and values of $10^3 \ln \alpha$(water-soln) are plotted against $1/T$ in Fig. 3. At low temperatures, a straight-line relation between $10^3 \ln \alpha$ and $1/T$ is justified by theoretical arguments of UREY (1947) and BIGELEISEN and MAYER (1947). There are several points of interest in Fig. 3:

(1) The isotopic properties of water and the solutions vary smoothly from 0 to 40°C, in contrast to reports of profound and abrupt changes (kinks) in thermodynamic properties of water over this same range.

(2) The slopes of related families of straight lines (fractionation curves) are identical indicating that the $^{18}O$ *fractionation between hydration water and bulk water is temperature independent.*

(3) At a critical concentration which varies for each salt (between 3.5 and 4.0 m for $MgCl_2$), the slope of the lines changes to a steeper one that is constant for very concentrated solutions of magnesium and aluminum chloride.

(4) The fractionation curves for 1 m $AlCl_3$ and 3 m $MgCl_2$ are identical.

(5) The slopes of the fractionation curves of structure breakers are negative and equal, regardless of whether the solute is an electrolyte ($Cs^+$) or nonelectrolyte (dioxane).

The lack of a measurable temperature dependence for the fractionation factors between the pos-

tulated bound and unbound waters is a most unexpected and important result. While $d\alpha/dT$ may
indeed be zero for these fractionations, it would not
be in keeping with the isotopic behavior of other
substances. As mentioned above, fractionation factors between hydration water and bulk water, calculated assuming a separation of available water
into these two types and a coordination number of
six, are relatively large and very different for the
various cations (25.6 per mil for $Al^{+3}$ versus 8.3 per
mil for $Mg^{+2}$ at 25°C). In comparison to other $^{18}O$
fractionations this large, temperature coefficients of
around 0.1–0.2 per mil/degree might be expected
for the fractionations between the various hydration
waters and bulk water, corresponding to changes of
4–8 per mil over the 40° range of temperature studied. Such changes would be reflected by different
slopes of the fractionation curves for each solute
and easily detected by the techniques used. It is
strongly suggested from these results that the conventional interpretation of isotopic effects associated
with solute additions to water is either too simplistic
or incorrect.

The solutions behave isotopically as if the addition of a solute does nothing more than change the
isotopic properties of the water in the solution as a
whole. If the solute were to alter the structure of
water (by breaking a specific number of hydrogen
bonds, changing the relative positions and bonding
characteristics of discrete clusters of water molecules, or whatever), the overall changes in the vibrational frequencies of the water would be reflected
by changes in $\alpha(CO_2\text{-}H_2O)$. With this interpretation,
concentrated aqueous solutions are viewed as ex-
isting in a number of thermodynamically distinct
states (two for structure makers and at least one for
structure breakers, by isotopic criteria).

There is abundant spectroscopic evidence that
cations, particularly those of high ionic potential,
are solvated in aqueous solution. In fact one of our
experiments (Table 1) supports the traditional view
that $Al^{+3}$ is strongly bonded to six water molecules
in its first coordination sphere: the $10^3\ln\alpha$ value of
2.46 for a solution that is 1.0 m in both NaF and
$AlCl_3$ is $\frac{5}{6}$ the value of 3.00 measured for $AlCl_3$
alone demonstrating that the strong $F^-$ ligand has
taken up the position of one of the six water molecules in the first hydration sphere of $Al^{+3}$. The evidence for strong bonding between cations and water
molecules must be reconciled with the lack of temperature dependence of the fractionation factor between bound and bulk water.

The fractionation curves for 1 m $AlCl_3$ and 3 m
$MgCl_2$ are indistinguishable, and there is an abrupt
change in slope that occurs at some critical con-

centration for solutions of both $MgCl_2$ and $AlCl_3$.
These results suggest that it is a property of the solution, probably involving critical concentrations
of cationic charge equivalents, and not the chemical
nature of the cations, that is dominant in controlling
the isotopic effects. At some critical concentration
of solute, the structure of bulk water may change
in some significant way that would be reflected in
$\alpha(CO_2\text{-}H_2O)$. Consider the properties of bulk water
in a 3 m solution of $AlCl_3$ where 32% of the water
is bound in the first coordination sphere of $Al^{+3}$.
Unbound waters in such concentrated solutions
cannot have the properties of pure water.

Oxygen isotope effects attendant on addition of
solutes to water are best explained as a combination
of the effects of partitioning of $^{18}O$ between bound
and bulk water and the establishment of discrete
structural states of aqueous solutions that have
unique isotopic properties. Kinetics may be playing
a role in these observations. That is, during the times
of the experiments, isotopic equilibrium may be
established between $CO_2$ and bulk water but not
between hydration waters and bulk waters. If, however, the rates of isotopic exchange between bound
and free waters are indeed fast, the structural
changes dominate the observed isotope effects and
we are overestimating the magnitude of the incorporation of $^{18}O$ in hydration sheathes.

## CONCLUSIONS

The oxygen isotope $CO_2$-equilibration technique
has been used in this and previous studies in an
attempt to elucidate details of solute-water interactions. The conventional interpretation of the
equilibrium partitioning of oxygen isotopes between
hydration water and bulk water to explain the often
large isotopic effects attendant on addition of solutes
to water is shown to be inadequate. Such partitioning should and probably does occur, but there is
strong isotopic evidence in the data reported here
that solutions can assume thermodynamically distinct structural forms with characteristic oxygen
isotope properties. In most cases this structural effect
supersedes the isotopic distinction between bulk
water and hydration water. For structure-making
electrolytes, different structural states were identified
by a change in the temperature coefficient of the
oxygen isotope fractionation between pure water
and the solution. The abruptness of the change at
what appears to be a critical concentration of charge
equivalents signals a first order transition. In the
case of structure-breaking solutes, solutions of both
relatively low concentrations of certain electrolytes
and non-electrolytes have similar oxygen isotope

properties (roughly the same value of $10^3 \ln \alpha$ at $T$ and the same temperature coefficient of $\alpha$). This implies a common structural state of disordered water. At higher concentrations of some structure breakers, the matter becomes more complex.

The concepts of solvation numbers and contact ion-pairs have been brought into question numerous times over the years. Our data on the 1:1 Al-F complex ion support the traditional view that six molecules of water are strongly bonded to aluminum ion in the first coordination sphere. Our data on the sulfate ion pairs of magnesium and aluminum, however, do not support the idea of contact ion pairs. There is little or no difference in the isotopic effects of adding chlorides (highly dissociated) or sulfates (highly associated) to water demonstrating that the cations in both environments are solvated to about the same extent. This simple technique so useful to the isotope geochemist is very well suited to the investigation of these and other details of solute-water interactions.

*Acknowledgements*—The authors thank Lanford Adami for his help in the laboratory. Financial support for this research was provided partially by NSF Grant EAR-9005717.

## REFERENCES

ATKINSON G. and KOR S. K. (1967) The kinetics of ion association in manganese sulfate solutions. II. Thermodynamics of stepwise association in water. *J. Phys. Chem.* **71**, 673–677.

ATKINSON G. and PETRUCCI S. (1966) Ion association of magnesium sulfate in water at 25°. *J. Phys. Chem.* **70**, 3122–3128.

BETTS R. H., BRON J., BUCHANNON W. D. and WU K.-Y. D. (1977) Oxygen isotope effects in the liquid water-pyridine system as a probe of intermolecular forces. *Canadian J. Chem.* **55**, 2966–2970.

BIGELEISEN J. and MAYER M. G. (1947) Calculation of equilibrium constants for isotopic exchange reactions. *J. Chem. Phys.* **15**, 261–267.

BOPP P., HEINZINGER K. and VOGEL P. C. (1974) Calculations of the oxygen isotope fractionation between hydration water of cations and free water. *Z. Naturforsch.* **29a**, 1608–1613.

BOPP P., HEINZINGER K. and KLEMM A. (1977) Oxygen isotope fractionation and the structure of aqueous alkali halide solutions. *Z. Naturforsch.* **32a**, 1419–1425.

COHN M. and UREY H. C. (1938) Oxygen exchange reactions of organic compounds and water. *J. Amer. Chem. Soc.* **60**, 679–682.

COLE D. R. and WESOLOWSKI D. J. (1989) Influence of NaCl aqueous solutions on isotopic equilibria and rates of exchange in mineral-fluid systems. *Trans. Geotherm. Res. Council* **13**, 227–234.

EPSTEIN S. and MAYEDA T. K. (1953) Variation of $^{18}O$ content of waters from natural sources. *Geochim. Cosmochim. Acta* **4**, 213–224.

FRANK H. S. and WEN W.-Y. (1957) Ion-solvent interaction, Structural aspects of ion-solvent interaction in aqueous solutions: A suggested picture of water structure. *Disc. Faraday. Soc.* **24**, 133–140.

FRENKEL L. S., STENGLE T. R. and LANGFORD C. H. (1967) $MnSO_4$ association and sulphate chelation: A solvent NMR study. *J. Inorg. Nucl. Chem.* **29**, 243–245.

FRIEDMAN I. and O'NEIL J. R. (1977) Compilation of stable isotope fractionation factors of geochemical interest. In *Data of Geochemistry, Chapter KK* (ed. M. FLEISCHER); *U.S. Geol. Surv. Prof. Paper, 440-K*.

HESTER R. E. and PLANE R. A. (1964) Raman spectrometric study of complex formation in aqueous solutions of calcium nitrate. *J. Chem. Phys.* **40**, 411–414.

KAKIUCHI M. and MATSUO S. (1985) Fractionation of hydrogen and oxygen isotopes between hydrated and free water molecules in aqueous urea solution. *J. Phys. Chem.* **89**, 4627–4632.

KASAHAYA K. (1986) Chap. II. D/H and $^{18}O/^{16}O$ fractionations in NaCl solution-vapor systems at elevated temperatures. Ph.D. thesis, Tokyo Institute of Technology.

KENDALL C., CHOU I.-M. and COPLEN T. P. (1983) Salt effect on oxygen isotope equilibria. *Trans. Am. Geophys. Union* **64**, 334–335.

LIGANG Z., JINGXIU L., HUANBO Z. and ZHENSHENG C. (1989) Oxygen isotope fractionation in the quartz-water-salt system. *Econ. Geol.* **84**, 16433–1650.

MAJOUB M. (1971) Fractionnement en oxygene 18 et en deuterium entre l'eau et sa vapeur. *J. Chim. Phys.* **68**, 1423–1436.

O'NEIL J. R. (1968) Hydrogen and oxygen isotope fractionation between ice and water. *J. Phys. Chem.* **72**, 3683–3684.

O'NEIL J. R. (1986) Theoretical and experimental aspects of isotopic fractionation. In *Stable Isotopes in High Temperature Geological Processes* (eds. J. W. VALLEY, H. P. TAYLOR, JR. and J. R. O'NEIL); *Rev. Mineral.* **16**, pp. 1–40.

O'NEIL J. R. and ADAMI L. H. (1969) The oxygen isotope partition function ratio of water and the structure of liquid water. *J. Phys. Chem.* **73**, 1553–1558.

O'NEIL J. R., CLAYTON R. N. and MAYEDA T. K. (1969) Oxygen isotope fractionation in divalent metal carbonates. *J. Chem. Phys.* **51**, 5547–5558.

SOFER Z. and GAT J. R. (1972) Activities and concentrations of oxygen-18 in concentrated aqueous salt solutions: Analytical and geophysical implications. *Earth Planet. Sci. Lett.* **15**, 232–238.

SOFER Z. and GAT J. R. (1975) The isotope composition of evaporating brines: Effect of the isotopic activity ratio in saline solutions. *Earth Planet. Sci. Lett.* **26**, 179–186.

TAUBE H. (1954) Use of oxygen isotope effects in the study of hydration of ions. *J. Chem. Phys.* **58**, 523–528.

TRUESDELL A. H. (1974) Oxygen isotope activities and concentrations in aqueous salt solutions at elevated temperatures: Consequences for isotope geochemistry. *Earth Planet. Sci. Lett.* **23**, 387–396.

UREY H. C. (1947) The thermodynamic properties of isotopic substances. *J. Chem. Soc. (London)* 562–581.

Stable Isotope Geochemistry: A Tribute to Samuel Epstein
© The Geochemical Society, Special Publication No. 3, 1991
Editors: H. P. Taylor, Jr., J. R. O'Neil and I. R. Kaplan

# Oxygen diffusion in leucite: Structural controls

KARLIS MUEHLENBACHS and CATHY CONNOLLY

Department of Geology, University of Alberta, Edmonton, Alberta, Canada T6G 2E3

**Abstract**—Oxygen self-diffusion coefficients were measured in natural crystals of leucite by gas/solid isotope exchange. The diffusion rates can be expressed (from 1000 to 1300°C) by the Arrhenius relation

$$D = (1.3 \pm {}^3_1) \times 10^{-11} \exp[(-14 \pm 3)/RT].$$

The activation energy of diffusion in leucite, 14 kcal/mole, is the lowest yet reported for oxygen diffusion in an anhydrous silicate. Because of the low activation energy, oxygen mobility persists to lower temperatures in leucite than in other silicates. The isotopic disequilibrium between coexisting leucite and pyroxene observed in volcanic rocks results from post-solidus oxygen exchange in leucite.

Oxygen diffusion in leucite and a wide variety of other minerals follows the "compensation law" which states that the pre-exponential factor of the Arrhenius equation is proportional to the activation energy. Furthermore, these two diffusion parameters are both proportional to anion porosity of the minerals indicating that anhydrous self-diffusion of oxygen proceeds by a common interstitial mechanism. The correlations of anion porosity to the pre-exponential factor and activation energy can be converted to a numerical expression predicting oxygen diffusion in any mineral as a function of temperature and anion porosity.

Hydrous oxygen diffusion rates are known to be much faster than equivalent anhydrous rates. The explanation may be that the species carrying oxygen during hydrous diffusion is significantly smaller than the mobile species for anhydrous diffusion.

## INTRODUCTION

OXYGEN DIFFUSION PROCESSES are of considerable geochemical interest. The intrinsic mobility of oxygen atoms in minerals determines how successfully the isotopic record can be preserved in geological samples. Some situations where diffusion of oxygen may thwart simple geological interpretations are isotopic paleothermometry of Mesozoic and older carbonate fossils, geothermometry of high-grade metamorphic rocks, and isotopic anomalies in meteorites. However, information on geological processes (cooling rates, metasomatism, etc.) may be gleaned from the $\delta^{18}O$ values of coexisting minerals that are out of isotopic equilibrium if one knew the actual rates of oxygen movement in the various components as function of temperature.

Experimental measurements of diffusion rates are difficult and usually not very precise. Furthermore, the results depend on extrinsic variables such as water pressure (YUND and ANDERSON, 1978; FARVER and YUND, 1991), presence of hydrogen (ELPHICK and GRAHAM, 1988), or defect density in the minerals. Despite simple experimental designs, more than one mechanism of oxygen movement may be operating, thus confusing interpretation of the results. Theoretical insights into the controls on oxygen mobility in silicates would greatly simplify the extraction of information from the geochemical data base.

Oxygen is the largest and usually the most abundant ion in rock-forming minerals; thus, mineral structure likely controls oxygen diffusivity. DOWTY (1980) suggested that, generally, anion porosity (one minus volume of anions divided by volume of unit cell), electrostatic site energy, and size of ions all affect the mobility of ions in minerals. His model is relatively successful but he could not directly relate published oxygen diffusion rates in minerals with their anion porosity. CONNOLLY and MUEHLENBACHS (1988) showed that anion porosity was proportional to the activation energy of oxygen diffusion.

In this paper we present measurements of oxygen diffusion rates in leucite. Leucite was chosen for study because leucite phenocrysts are often out of isotopic equilibrium with their volcanic host (TAYLOR et al., 1984), suggesting rapid oxygen diffusion. Furthermore, leucite has a high anion porosity and would, according to the model of CONNOLLY and MUEHLENBACHS (1988), have a proportionately low activation energy of oxygen diffusion. We also examine published anhydrous diffusion rates in other silicate minerals and suggest a simple relationship that predicts oxygen diffusion coefficients based solely on anion porosity. This relationship will be compared to a similar one proposed by FORTIER and GILETTI (1989) for hydrous oxygen diffusion.

## EXPERIMENTAL PROCEDURE

### Starting materials

Natural leucite ($KAlSi_2O_6$) was obtained from amygdules from the Civita Castellana basalt, Italy. Leucite was extracted from the vesicles, and ultrasonically cleaned to remove any altered surface layers adhering to the grains. Leucite crystals were hand picked from the concentrate under a binocular microscope. The purified leucite was carefully checked by XRD for the common alteration minerals of analcime, orthoclase, and nepheline. The leucite was further examined by electron microprobe to test if any alteration had occurred that might not be detected by XRD. Sulfide minerals were identified and removed using heavy liquids. Pure leucite was ground and sieved, using laser etched sieves, to a uniform size fraction (10 to 20 $\mu$m); further uniformity was achieved by using selective settling. Photographs were taken of the starting materials and final products using scanning electron microscopy.

Gas for the exchange experiments was high purity, dry, $CO_2$ gas obtained commercially. The isotopic composition of the gas was monitored closely during the experiments and did not change.

*Diffusion experiments*

The method of MUEHLENBACHS and KUSHIRO (1974) was used to determine oxygen diffusion in leucite. Leucite ($\delta^{18}O = +8.94$) was suspended in a Pt basket within a gas-tight, vertical tube furnace. Air was purged from the system by flushing with $CO_2$ gas ($\delta^{18}O = +30.36$); this same gas was used subsequently for the high temperature isotopic exchange experiments. Diffusion constants calculated from exchange with either $CO_2$ or $O_2$ are identical within experimental error (MUEHLENBACHS and KUSHIRO, 1974; CANIL and MUEHLENBACHS, 1987). The temperature (1000 to 1400°C) in the furnace was monitored with a Pt-$Pt_{87}Rh_{13}$ thermocouple; the uncertainty in temperature was ±3°C. The advantage of the above method is that the isotopic composition of the gas does not change and therefore, only the changes in isotopic composition of the mineral need to be determined to calculate the diffusion coefficient.

Diffusion coefficients were calculated from the partial exchange experiments using the following diffusion equation (JOST, 1960):

$$\frac{\delta^{18}O_f - \delta^{18}O_e}{\delta^{18}O_i - \delta^{18}O_e} = \frac{6}{\pi^2} \sum_\nu \frac{1}{\nu^2} \exp\left[\frac{-\nu^2\pi^2}{r_0^2}Dt\right] \quad (1)$$

where $D$ is the diffusion coefficient ($cm^2$/s); $t$ is time (sec); $r_0$ is the sample radius (cm); $\delta^{18}O_f$ is the isotopic composition of the exchanged sample; $\delta^{18}O_i$ is the isotopic composition of the starting material; and $\delta^{18}O_e$ is the isotopic composition of material at isotopic equilibrium with the flowing gas. The equilibrium fractionation between $CO_2$ gas and leucite was taken to be 2.3 per mil as in previous studies (HAYASHI and MUEHLENBACHS, 1986; CONNOLLY and MUEHLENBACHS, 1988). Equation (1) converges depending on the degree of exchange; a minimum of 50 terms was used for each calculation. Equation (1) assumes spherical symmetry of the mineral grains and no limiting surface reactions such as grain boundary or surface diffusion. Evidence that these conditions are met is that similar diffusion coefficients are obtained at the same temperature regardless of run time.

$\delta^{18}O$ analyses of the minerals were done using the $BrF_5$ method (CLAYTON and MAYEDA, 1963) and the isotopic ratios were determined by gas source mass spectrometry. Replicate analyses had a reproducibility of better than ±0.1 per mil. Results are reported in the usual δ-notation relative to the SMOW standard.

## RESULTS

The results of the exchange experiments and the calculated oxygen diffusion coefficients for leucite are presented in Table 1. Exchange experiments ranged in temperature from 1000 to 1400°C at 100 degree intervals for durations of from 2 to 90 hours. At least three run durations were made at each temperature. The percentage of oxygen exchanged in the leucite samples ranged from 7 to almost 70%, and no systematic variation in calculated diffusion coefficient with exchange time was noted.

The calculated oxygen diffusion coefficients are plotted against $1/T$ (K) on an Arrhenius diagram in Fig. 1. Inspection of the figure shows that oxygen diffusion rates in leucite are relatively insensitive to temperature from 1000 to 1300°C, implying a very low activation energy. The diffusion data at 1400°C seem fast in comparison with the trend established by the lower temperature runs. However, SEM observations of leucite products from the 1400°C experiments show them to be substantially sintered to rounded, shapes that violate the conditions for the diffusion Eqn. (1) and thus invalidating the calculated log D values. In the subsequent discussion the 1400°C runs will be ignored.

The 1000 to 1300°C data fit a simple linear Arrhenius diffusion relation:

$$D = D_0 e^{-E_{act}/RT}$$

where $D$ ($cm^2$/sec) is the diffusion coefficient, $D_0$ is the pre-exponential factor (Arrhenius frequency factor), $E_{act}$ is the activation energy (in kcal) of diffusion, $R$ is the gas constant, and $T$ is absolute temperature. The data for leucite (1000–1300°C) yield the following equation:

$$D = (1.3 \pm {}^3_1) \times 10^{-11} \exp[(-14 \pm 3)/RT]. \quad (2)$$

The activation energy of oxygen diffusion in leucite is 14 ± 3 kcal/mole, the lowest yet observed in any silicate.

## DISCUSSION

*Application to volcanic rocks*

Oxygen diffusion rates in leucite are compared to those in nepheline, melilite, and diopside on an Arrhenius plot in Fig. 2. Oxygen diffuses slower in leucite than in melilite or nepheline, although all have low activation energies. Oxygen diffusion rates in diopside, although comparable to those in leucite at high temperatures, decrease rapidly with temperature due to a high activation energy. This implies that in rocks, oxygen exchangeability in leucite

Table 1. Experimental conditions and results for oxygen diffusion in leucite crystals

| Temperature (°C) | Time (h) | $\delta^{18}O_f$ | Exchange* % | log $D$ (cm²/s) |
|---|---|---|---|---|
| 1000 | 2 | 10.55 | 7.9 | −13.29 |
| 1000 | 4 | 10.98 | 9.8 | −13.41 |
| 1000 | 8 | 11.86 | 14.0 | −13.39 |
| 1000 | 32 | 12.82 | 15.5 | −13.35 |
| | | | | −13.36 ± 0.05 |
| 1100 | 8 | 11.57 | 12.6 | −13.48 |
| 1100 | 16 | 14.97 | 29.9 | −12.99 |
| 1100 | 32 | 15.90 | 34.5 | −13.15 |
| 1100 | 90 | 18.29 | 44.8 | −13.33 |
| | | | | −13.24 ± 0.21 |
| 1200 | 2 | 11.61 | 12.5 | −12.89 |
| 1200 | 16 | 15.93 | 34.4 | −12.85 |
| 1200 | 32 | 16.17 | 35.8 | −13.11 |
| 1200 | 68 | 20.14 | 55.5 | −12.99 |
| | | | | −12.94 ± 0.12 |
| 1300 | 4 | 12.77 | 18.3 | −12.84 |
| 1300 | 8 | 12.81 | 18.5 | −13.13 |
| 1300 | 16 | 15.81 | 33.8 | −12.86 |
| | | | | −12.94 ± 0.16 |
| 1400 | 2 | 13.18 | 20.9 | −12.42 |
| 1400 | 8 | 15.59 | 31.8 | −12.62 |
| 1400 | 16 | 20.49 | 56.9 | −12.33 |
| 1400 | 32 | 22.62 | 67.4 | −12.43 |
| | | | | −12.45 ± 0.12 |

* Starting leucite = 8.94 per mil; Exchange $CO_2$ gas, 30.36‰ (SMOW).

(or nepheline and melilite) may persist to low temperatures, whereas diffusion rates in diopside become vanishingly small at similar temperatures. The diffusion data can explain the oxygen isotope disequilibrium observed between leucite and pyroxene in the lavas from New South Wales, Australia (TAYLOR *et al.*, 1984). Small phenocrysts of leucite can exchange with air or water at temperatures as low as 500°C in a matter of decades while the $\delta^{18}O$ of pyroxene crystals would remain unaffected. However, diffusion rates in leucite are slow enough that larger size crystals would take thousands of years to exchange oxygen with an external fluid at sub-solidus temperatures.

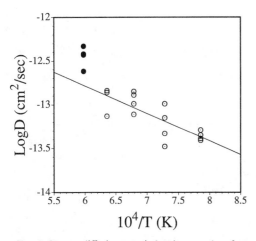

FIG. 1. Oxygen diffusion rates in leucite crystals as function of temperature—1400°C data not included in the regression line (see text).

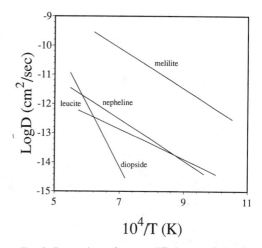

FIG. 2. Comparison of oxygen diffusion rates in leucite, melilite (HAYASHI and MUEHLENBACHS, 1986), nepheline, and diopside (CONNOLLY and MUEHLENBACHS, 1988).

*Structural controls on diffusion*

Oxygen mobility varies enormously in minerals. Not only do the diffusion coefficients of minerals vary by many orders of magnitude at any one temperature, but their temperature sensitivity, as reflected in the $E_{act}$, can vary by nearly a factor of ten. Table 2 lists anhydrous oxygen diffusion data, compiled from the literature, obtained from gas/mineral exchange experiments analogous to those of this study. Cursory inspection of Table 2 reveals that the minerals with low activation energies for oxygen diffusion, including leucite (14 kcal/mol), nepheline (25 kcal/mol) and melilite (31 kcal/mol) are all characterized by loosely packed, open structures. In contrast, the minerals with high activation energies; diopside (96 kcal/mol), forsterite (70–99 kcal/mol), spinel (100 kcal/mol), and sapphire (148 kcal/mol) are all characterized by densely packed lattices. It is possible that in minerals with low activation energies, the open structures allow the passage of mobile species capable of exchanging with the lattice oxygen, such as in $SiO_2$ glass (SCHAEFFER and MUEHLENBACHS, 1978). The greater oxygen mobility in melilite compared to leucite may be a result of the sheet-like structures in the former,

which allow continuous passage of the diffusing species in contrast to the non-intersecting channels in the latter (DEER *et al.,* 1966).

WINCHELL (1969) suggested that diffusion in silicates obeys the "compensation law" which states that, in the Arrhenius expression, the preexponential term is proportional to the activation energy. COLE and OHMOTO (1986) gave a detailed compilation of diffusion parameters in a wide variety of mineral types and reaction conditions and showed that separate compensation laws held for oxygen diffusion in silicates, sulfates, and carbonates. Figure 3 demonstrates that for anhydrous oxygen diffusion the "compensation law" is indeed observed. The high degree of correlation ($R = 0.80$) between $\ln D_0$ and $E_{act}$ shown in Fig. 3 is surprising because the "compensation law" should hold only if similar mechanisms of oxygen diffusion are operative in these diverse minerals. The strong correlation is even more remarkable if one considers that the data come from different laboratories, using drastically different analytical methods on both natural and synthetic samples. The inference to be drawn is that oxygen diffuses in these minerals by predominantly one type of mechanism involving the same carrier species. Note that GERARD and

Table 2. Diffusion parameters for anhydrous oxygen diffusion in silicate minerals

| Mineral | Anion porosity (%) | $\ln D_0$ | $E_{act}$ kcal/mole | Ref. |
|---------|-------------------|-----------|---------------------|------|
| Leucite (lu) | 58.0 | −25.10 | 14 | (1) |
| Nepheline (ne) | 54.1 | −18.95 | 25.0 | (2) |
| Melilite (50) (mel) | 51.4 | −11.66 | 33.5 | (3) |
| Melilite (75) (mel) | 51.8 | −11.84 | 31.9 | (3) |
| Anorthite (an) | 49.7 | −11.51 | 56.3 | (4) |
| Forsterite (fo) | 42.0 | −3.56 | 99.3 | (5) |
| Forsterite (fo) | 42.0 | −12.98 | 70 | (6) |
| Diopside (di) | 42.4 | +1.84 | 96.7 | (2) |
| Quartz (q) | 46.5 | −15.02 | 53 | (4) |
| $SiO_2$ glass ($SiO_2$) | 53.5 | −23.85 | 19.7 | (7) |
| Mg-Spinel (sp) | 36.2 | −0.12 | 105 | (8) |
| Mg-Spinel (sp) | 36.2 | −4.55 | 99.1 | (9) |
| MgO (MgO) | 43.5 | −8.57 | 88.3 | (10) |
| $\alpha Fe_2O_3$ ($Fe_2O_3$) | 37.1 | +6.45 | 99.7 | (10) |
| Sapphire (saph) | 25.5 | +5.60 | 146.8 | (11) |
| Perovskite (pr) | 43.3 | +1.61 | 74.8 | (12) |

(1) This work.
(2) CONNOLLY and MUEHLENBACHS (1988).
(3) HAYASHI and MUEHLENBACH (1986).
(4) ELPHICK *et al.* (1988).
(5) ANDO *et al.* (1981).
(6) JAOUL *et al.* (1983).
(7) SCHAEFFER and MUEHLENBACHS (1978).
(8) ANDO and OISHI (1974).
(9) REDDY and COOPER (1981).
(10) REDDY and COOPER (1983).
(11) REDDY and COOPER (1982).
(12) Revised from GAUTASON and MUEHLENBACHS (1991).

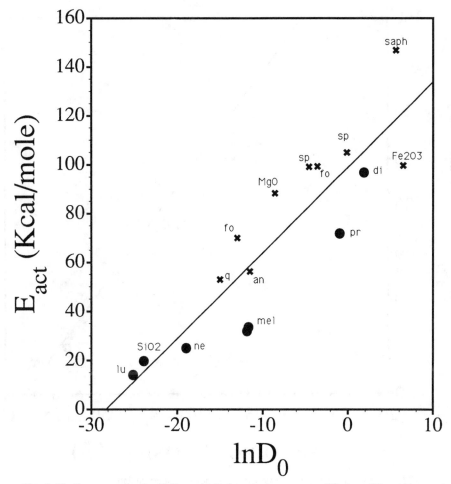

FIG. 3. The "compensation law." $E_{act}$ vs. ln $D_0$ for anhydrous oxygen diffusion. Abbreviations and references given in Table 2 ($R = 0.80$).

JAOUL (1989) and RYERSON *et al.* (1989) concluded that oxygen diffused by an interstitial mechanism in San Carlos olivine. GERARD and JAOUL (1989) further suggest that the requisite interstitial defects can be produced by incorporation of gaseous oxygen into the olivine.

Anion porosities for each mineral are also given in Table 2. In a study of ionic diffusion in minerals, DOWTY (1980) suggested that anion porosity, electrostatic site energy, and the size of the diffusing ion are all factors in determining the diffusion rate. CONNOLLY and MUEHLENBACHS (1988) suggested that anion porosity correlates directly with the activation energy of oxygen diffusion. Figure 4 is a plot of those parameters taken from Table 2. A high degree of correlation ($R = 0.93$) is found between anion porosity and measured activation energies of oxygen diffusion in a wide variety of silicates and oxides ranging from leucite to sapphire. Closer examination of Fig. 4 reveals that the slope of the overall trend of anion porosity against $E_{act}$ may be biased by the oxides: sapphire, spinel, and $\alpha Fe_2O_3$. Thus, the line drawn in Fig. 4 is based on regressing only the oxygen diffusion data measured by us ($R = 0.95$).

If, as is implied by the above arguments, anion porosity is proportional to $E_{act}$, then anion porosity should also be proportional to ln $D_0$ if the "compensation law" holds true. Figure 5 is a plot of ln $D_0$ vs. anion porosity. Again, a good correlation ($R = 0.73$) between anion porosity and ln $D_0$ for oxygen diffusion is observed in very diverse minerals. As in Fig. 4, the line on Fig. 5 is based on fitting our data alone ($R = 0.92$). From the above arguments, anhydrous oxygen diffusion rates in minerals appear to be controlled dominantly by the void space in the crystal.

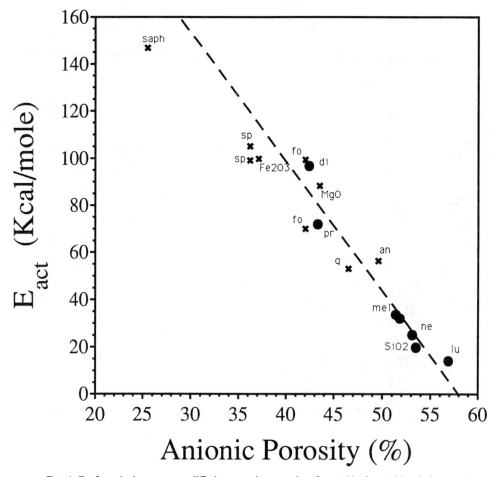

FIG. 4. $E_{act}$ for anhydrous oxygen diffusion vs. anion porosity of crystal lattices. Abbreviations and references given in Table 2 ($R = 0.95$, our data only).

The relations between anion porosity and $E_{act}$ (Fig. 4) or ln $D_0$ (Fig. 5) can be substituted directly into an Arrhenius equation to yield a numerical relation predicting the anhydrous oxygen mobility in any mineral at any temperature from its anion porosity ($P$, given as percent) alone:

$$D = \exp\left\{81.2 - 1.87 \times P - \left(\frac{318 - 5.49 \times P}{RT}\right)10^3\right\}. \quad (3)$$

The validity of Eqn. (3) is difficult to assess independently because Eqn. (3) is derived from most of the published measurements of anhydrous, gas/solid diffusion studies. However, MUEHLENBACHS and CHACKO (1991) showed that the rate of oxygen exchange between aragonite and sanidine above 50 kbars slows down substantially in proportion to the compressibility of sanidine, indirectly substantiating the logic behind Eqn. (3).

*Comparison with hydrous diffusion*

Equation (3) is similar to the relation proposed by FORTIER and GILETTI (1989) that predicts hydrous oxygen diffusion rates from ionic porosity. Both relations are based on the Arrhenius equation but the coefficients are significantly different. The apparent discrepancy in the coefficients is to be expected because, as many authors have commented (DOWTY, 1980; ELPHICK *et al.*, 1988; FARVER and YUND, 1991), hydrous and anhydrous oxygen diffusion experiments yield fundamentally different results, implying a crucial role for "water" during oxygen transport in silicates.

FARVER's (1989) hydrothermal oxygen diffusion rates in diopside (ln $D_0 = -13.4$; $E_{act} = 54$ kcal) fit

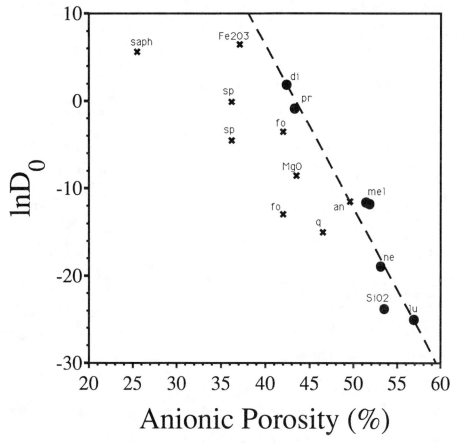

FIG. 5. ln $D_0$ for anhydrous oxygen diffusion vs. anion porosity of crystal lattices. Abbreviations and references in Table 2 ($R = 0.92$, our data only).

the "compensation law" (Fig. 3) but do not fall along the trends relating anhydrous diffusion parameters to porosity (Figs. 4 and 5). As is observed in many other minerals, oxygen diffusion in diopside is much faster under hydrothermal conditions than under 1 atmosphere anhydrous conditions. If both anhydrous and hydrous diffusion rates are controlled by porosity or vacant space within the diopside and the crystal does not expand with water pressure, then it must be concluded that the mobile "wet species" in oxygen diffusion is smaller than the oxygen carrier in dry systems. The apparent changes in porosity to reconcile wet diffusion rates to dry ones in diopside is substantial. Results from the wet and dry experiments are compatible if the space available for hydrous diffusion in diopside were 50% instead of the true 42.4%. We suggest that the correct interpretation is that the diffusing species in the wet experiments is correspondingly smaller ($\sim$1/6) than for anhydrous oxygen diffusion.

## CONCLUSIONS

Oxygen self-diffusion coefficients for leucite from 1000 to 1300°C fit an Arrhenius relation of the form

$$D = (1.3 \pm \tfrac{3}{1}) \times 10^{-11} \exp[(-14 \pm 3)/RT].$$

The activation energy for anhydrous oxygen self-diffusion in leucite is the lowest ever reported for an anhydrous silicate mineral. Significant oxygen mobility persists to sub-solidus temperatures in leucite crystals explaining the observed isotopic disequilibrium between leucite and pyroxene that has been observed in some volcanic rocks.

The activation energy of diffusion in a wide variety of silicates and oxides is proportional to the pre-exponential factor, implying one dominant mechanism of diffusion. Both the $E_{act}$ and ln $D_0$ are proportional to anion porosity of the lattices, suggesting that diffusion occurs through the movement of some species through the interstices of the crystal. The leucite data, and previously published data, can be generalized to give numerical values of oxygen diffusion coefficients in minerals as functions of temperature and anion porosity ($P$ in %):

$$D = \exp\left\{81.2 - 1.87 \times P - \left(\frac{318 - 5.49 \times P}{RT}\right)10^3\right\}.$$

The above relation applies only to anhydrous diffusion. Hydrothermal diffusion rates are described by a different equation (FORTIER and GILETTI, 1989) but one of the same form. These differing rate laws for "wet versus dry" diffusion can be reconciled if the diffusing species in the hydrothermal experiments were much smaller than the diffusing species in the anhydrous experiments.

*Acknowledgements*—I would like to thank Sam Epstein for proving that novel insights into geochemical problems can be generated by conventional isotopic techniques (that Sam helped develop in the first place). His grandfatherly wisdom and interest over the past 20 years has been appreciated.

Mr. B. Murowchick and Mrs. E. Toth are thanked for donating the leucite bearing lavas and help with the analyses, respectively. T. Chacko is thanked for a timely review. The work was funded by the Canadian NSERC.

## REFERENCES

ANDO K. and OISHI Y. (1974) Self-diffusion coefficients of oxygen ion in single crystals of $MgO \cdot nAl_2O_3$ spinels. *J. Chem. Phys.* **61**, 625–629.

ANDO K., KUROKAWA H. and OISHI Y. (1981) Self-diffusion coefficient of oxygen in single-crystal forsterite. *Com. Amer. Ceram. Soc.* **64**, C30.

CANIL D. and MUEHLENBACHS K. (1987) Self-diffusion of oxygen in an Fe-rich basal melt. *Geol. Soc. Amer. Abstr. Prog.* **19**, 610.

CLAYTON R. N. and MAYEDA T. K. (1963) The use of bromine pentafluoride in the extraction of oxygen from oxides and silicates for isotopic analysis. *Geochim. Cosmochim. Acta* **27**, 42–52.

COLE D. R. and OHMOTO H. (1986) Kinetics of isotope exchange at elevated temperatures and pressures. In *Stable Isotopes in High Temperature Geologic Processes* (eds. J. W. VALLEY, H. P. TAYLOR, JR. and J. R. O'NEIL), *Reviews in Mineralogy 16*, pp. 41–87. Mineralogical Society of America.

CONNOLLY C. and MUEHLENBACHS K. (1988) Contrasting oxygen diffusion in nepheline, diopside and other silicates and their relevance to isotopic systematics in meteorites. *Geochim. Cosmochim. Acta* **52**, 1585–1591.

DEER W. A., HOWIE R. A. and ZUSSMAN J. (1966) *An Introduction to the Rock-Forming Minerals.* J. Wiley & Sons, New York.

DOWTY E. (1980) Crystal-chemical factors affecting the mobility of ions in minerals. *Amer. Mineral.* **65**, 174–182.

ELPHICK S. C. and GRAHAM C. M. (1988) The effect of hydrogen on oxygen diffusion in quartz: evidence for fast proton transients. *Nature* **335**, 243–245.

ELPHICK S. C., GRAHAM C. M. and DENNIS P. F. (1988) An ion microprobe study of anhydrous oxygen diffusion in anorthite: A comparison with hydrothermal data and some geological implications. *Contrib. Mineral. Petrol.* **100**, 490–495.

FARVER J. R. (1989) Oxygen self-diffusion in diopside with application to cooling rate determinations. *Earth Planet. Sci. Lett.* **92**, 386–396.

FARVER J. R. and YUND R. A. (1991) Oxygen diffusion in quartz: Dependence on temperature and water fugacity. *Chem. Geol.* **90**, 55–70.

FORTIER S. M. and GILETTI B. J. (1989) An empirical model for predicting diffusion coefficients in silicate minerals. *Science* **245**, 1481–1484.

GAUTASON B. and MUEHLENBACHS K. (1991) Rapid oxygen diffusion in $CaTiO_3$ perovskite. *Geol. Assoc. Canada Prog. Abstr.* **16**, A43.

GERARD O. and JAOUL O. (1989) Oxygen diffusion in San Carlos olivine. *J. Geophys. Res.* **94**, 4119–4128.

HAYASHI T. and MUEHLENBACHS K. (1986) Rapid oxygen diffusion in melilite and its relevance to meteorites. *Geochim. Cosmochim. Acta* **50**, 585–591.

JAOUL O., HOULIER B. and ABEL F. (1983) Study of $^{18}O$ diffusion in magnesium orthosilicate by nuclear microanalysis. *J. Geophys. Res.* **88**, 613–624.

JOST W. (1960) *Diffusion in Solids, Liquids, and Glasses.* Academic Press, New York.

MUEHLENBACHS K. and CHACKO T. (1991) The effect of very high pressure (35–85 Kbar) on oxygen isotope exchange rates between potassium feldspar and calcium carbonate. *Geol. Assoc. Canada Progr. Abstr.* **16**, A86.

MUEHLENBACHS K. and KUSHIRO I. (1974) Oxygen isotope exchange and equilibration of silicates with $CO_2$ and $O_2$. *Carnegie Inst. Wash. Yearbk.* **73**, 232–236.

REDDY K. P. R. and COOPER A. R. (1981) Oxygen diffusion in magnesium aluminate spinel. *J. Amer. Ceram. Soc.* **64**, 368–371.

REDDY K. P. R. and COOPER A. R. (1982) Oxygen diffusion in sapphire. *J. Amer. Ceram. Soc.* **65**, 634–638.

REDDY K. P. R. and COOPER A. R. (1983) Oxygen diffusion in MgO and $\alpha$-$Fe_2O_3$. *J. Amer. Ceram. Soc.* **66**, 664–666.

RYERSON F. J., DURHAM W. B., CHERNIAK D. J. and LANFORD W. A. (1989) Oxygen diffusion in olivine: Effect of oxygen fugacity and implications for creep. *J. Geophys. Res.* **94**, 4105–4118.

SCHAEFFER H. A. and MUEHLENBACHS K. (1978) Correlations between oxygen transport phenomena in noncrystalline silica. *J. Mat. Sci.* **13**, 1146–114.

TAYLOR H. P., JR., TURI B. and CUNDARI A. (1984) $^{18}O/^{16}O$ and chemical relationships in K-rich volcanic rocks from Australia, East Africa, Antarctica, and San Venanzo-Cupaello, Italy. *Earth Planet. Sci. Lett.* **69**, 263–276.

VOLTAGGIO M. (1985) Estimation of diffusion constants by observations of isokinetic effects test for radiogenic argon and strontium. *Geochim. Cosmochim. Acta* **49**, 2117–2122.

WINCHELL P. (1969) The compensation law for diffusion in silicates. *High Temp. Sci.* **1**, 200–215.

YUND R. A. and ANDERSON T. F. (1978) Oxygen isotope exchange between feldspar and fluid as a function of fluid pressure. *Geochim. Cosmochim. Acta* **42**, 235–239.

Stable Isotope Geochemistry: A Tribute to Samuel Epstein
© The Geochemical Society, Special Publication No. 3, 1991
Editors: H. P. Taylor, Jr., J. R. O'Neil and I. R. Kaplan

# An experimental study of oxygen isotope partitioning between silica glass and $CO_2$ vapor

EDWARD STOLPER and SAMUEL EPSTEIN

Division of Geological and Planetary Sciences, California Institute of Technology, Pasadena, CA 91125, U.S.A.

**Abstract**—The fractionation of oxygen isotopes between $CO_2$ vapor and silica glass was determined at a total pressure of ~0.5 bars at temperatures of 550–950°C. Experiments were conducted by equilibrating a small amount of $CO_2$ gas with a large amount of silica glass of known isotopic composition. Because most of the oxygen in the system is in the glass, its oxygen isotope ratio changes negligibly over the course of the experiment, and the fractionation factor ($\alpha$) can be determined by measurement of the isotopic composition of $CO_2$ in the vapor at the end of the experiment. Results are independent of the grain size of the silica glass and of time in long duration runs; these are among the criteria used to conclude that isotopic equilibrium was achieved.

The $\delta^{18}O$ value of $CO_2$ vapor is higher than that of coexisting silica glass at equilibrium. The fractionation factor decreases from $1.0042 \pm 0.0002$ at 550°C to $1.0022 \pm 0.0002$ at 950°C. $\text{Ln}(\alpha)$ is linear with $1/T$ over the temperature range we investigated, corresponding to a standard state enthalpy change for the isotopic exchange reaction of approximately $-10$ cal/mole. The reduced partition function ratio for silica glass is well described by multiplying that of crystalline quartz by 1.035. Comparison of our results with data in the literature on crystalline quartz suggests that silica glass is enriched in $^{18}O$ relative to quartz with which it is in isotopic equilibrium by 0.3–0.6 per mil over the temperature range we have investigated. This appears to confirm previous suggestions that oxygen isotopic fractionations between crystalline and amorphous materials of the same composition and similar short-range structures are small. In contrast to the $CO_2$-silica glass fractionation factor, the logarithm of the crystalline quartz-silica glass fractionation factor is expected to be roughly proportional to $1/T^2$ over the temperature range of this study.

Experiments were also conducted to determine the kinetics of oxygen isotopic exchange between $CO_2$ vapor and silica glass. The activation energy for apparent self-diffusion of oxygen in the glass is similar to those for diffusion of Ar and molecular $CO_2$, $O_2$, and $H_2O$ in silica-rich glasses. This suggests that isotopic exchange in our experiments occurs by diffusion of $CO_2$ molecules into the glass followed by exchange with the oxygen atoms of the glass structure and that the rate limiting step is the diffusion of the $CO_2$ molecules, not their reaction with the glass network.

## INTRODUCTION

FRACTIONATION FACTORS FOR oxygen isotopes provide essential constraints on interpretations of their distributions in natural systems and for understanding the principles underlying their behavior. There have been over the years many efforts to determine vapor-mineral and mineral-mineral fractionation factors (see review by O'NEIL, 1986), and recent studies suggest that in some of the most critical of these systems, workers may be converging on the correct values (*e.g.*, CLAYTON *et al.*, 1989; CHIBA *et al.*, 1989; CHACKO *et al.*, 1991). However, few measurements have been made of fractionation factors involving silicate melts or glasses, even though knowledge of such fractionation factors is necessary for understanding the behavior of oxygen isotopes during igneous processes.

Studies of oxygen isotope fractionations between coexisting crystals and naturally occurring glass (or groundmass, usually assumed to be representative of a melt phase) have shown that for some minerals, mineral-melt fractionations can be on the order of a few per mil at magmatic temperatures and that melt composition and crystal chemistry exert strong controls on fractionation factors (*e.g.*, GARLICK, 1966; TAYLOR, 1968; ANDERSON *et al.*, 1971; MATSUHISA, 1979). However, little experimental work has been done that is relevant to the fractionation of oxygen isotopes between silicate glasses or melts and other phases. MUEHLENBACHS and KUSHIRO (1974) measured oxygen isotope fractionations between 1 atm of $CO_2$ (or $O_2$) vapor and basaltic melt, plagioclase, and enstatite at 1250–1500°C. MUEHLENBACHS and SCHAEFFER (1977) estimated from these results that at 1150–1430°C, oxygen gas has about a two per mil higher $^{18}O/^{16}O$ ratio than coexisting silica glass. MATSUHISA *et al.* (1979) reported a single determination for hydrous albitic melt and water at 825°C, 3 kbar (0.0 per mil) and estimated that oxygen isotope fractionation between crystalline albite and hydrous albitic melt under these conditions may be as small as 0.2 per mil. CONNOLLY and MUEHLENBACHS (1988) state that melilite, "basalt," and "silicate glass" all have 2.33 per mil lower $^{18}O/^{16}O$ ratios than coexisting $CO_2$ gas.

In this paper, we report the results of experiments to determine the fractionation of oxygen isotopes between $CO_2$ vapor and silica glass at 550–950°C, $P \sim 0.5$ bar. Although these results are not directly applicable to mineral-melt fractionation factors in complex igneous systems, in combination with available data on $CO_2$-quartz fractionations they provide data relevant to fractionations among crystalline and amorphous silicates. They also can be used to evaluate the hypothesis that oxygen isotope fractionations between minerals and melts of the same composition are small (GARLICK, 1966; MATSUHISA et al., 1979) and to predict the likely dependence of mineral-melt fractionation factors on temperature.

## EXPERIMENTAL TECHNIQUES

The design of our experiments was similar in principle to that employed by O'NEIL and EPSTEIN (1966) in their study of the partitioning of oxygen and carbon isotopes among calcite, dolomite, and $CO_2$ vapor and by LIU and EPSTEIN (1984) in their study of the partitioning of hydrogen isotopes between kaolinite and water vapor. In each experiment, a small amount of $CO_2$ gas (typically a few tens of micromoles) of known isotopic composition was sealed in a tube along with a large amount of silica glass (up to several grams) of known isotopic composition, and held at elevated temperature and allowed to exchange oxygen isotopes. Once equilibrium is achieved in such experiments, the fractionation factor can be determined simply by measuring the isotopic composition of the $CO_2$ because the oxygen isotope ratio of the silica glass (which contains most of the oxygen in the system) changes negligibly over the course of the experiment. By using fine-grained glass as the starting material, the success of the experiment does not require complete exchange between the gas and the entire silicate sample; i.e., by maximizing the surface area to volume ratio of the silicate, it is possible for the number of oxygen atoms sufficiently deep within the glass so as to be representative of the bulk glass yet still near enough to the surface to be readily exchanged to far exceed the number of oxygens in the vapor phase.

In addition to such experiments designed to determine the equilibrium fractionation factor, we conducted a series of experiments in which $CO_2$ gas of known isotopic composition was sealed in empty silica and Vycor glass tubes and allowed to exchange for varying times in order to set constraints on the kinetics of oxygen isotope exchange between $CO_2$ gas and silica-rich glass.

### Starting materials

Experiments were conducted on three different batches of silica glass. Most experiments were conducted on samples taken from a batch of silica glass wool (referred to as Qtz Wool 1) with an average thread diameter of about 10 $\mu$m. A smaller number of experiments was conducted on a second batch of quartz wool with a similar average thread diameter (referred to as Qtz Wool 3; manufactured by Heraeus Amersil, Inc.). The third batch of glass was prepared from chunks of General Electric #214 fused quartz (referred to as GE214) by crushing in a stainless steel mortar followed by dry sieving with nylon screens. Most experiments on this material were conducted on a <400 mesh (<37 $\mu$m) fraction, but several experiments were conducted on 325–400 mesh (37–44 $\mu$m) and 200–325

(44–74 $\mu$m) size fractions. The $\delta^{18}O_{SMOW}$ values of the three batches of glass are +14.1 (Qtz Wool 1), +16.8 (Qtz Wool 3), and +11.2 (GE214). Techniques for isotopic analysis of these glasses and precision of the analyses are discussed below.

One of three sources of $CO_2$ gas was used in each experiment: a tank of liquid $CO_2$ ($\delta^{18}O_{SMOW} \approx -1$); $CO_2$ prepared from commercial $CaCO_3$ powder ($\delta^{18}O_{SMOW} \approx +20$); or $CO_2$ prepared from a conch shell (Strombus gigas; $\delta^{18}O_{SMOW} \approx +42$). Techniques for isotopic analysis of the gases and precision of the analyses are discussed below.

### Experiments

Silica glass wool or powder (0.3–2.2 g) was placed in a fused quartz (General Electric #214; $\delta^{18}O_{SMOW} = +11.2$; <5 ppm by weight $OH^-$) or Vycor glass (Corning Code No. 7913; 96% $SiO_2$; $\delta^{18}O_{SMOW} = +20.7$) tube with an OD of 9 mm and an ID of 7 mm. Tubes were typically $\sim$15 cm long. After heating in air for 20–30 minutes at 850°C to oxidize any organic contaminants in the samples and tubes, the loaded tubes were attached to a vacuum line and 30–75 $\mu$moles of $CO_2$ were frozen into the tube along with the glass sample, after which the tube was sealed with a torch. Tubes were loaded into the hotspots of home-built, wire-wound horizontal furnaces and held at 550, 650, 750, 850, or 950°C (monitored with Type K or S thermocouples located at the hotspot) for 1–428 days. Hotspot temperatures were controlled by Eurotherm temperature controllers (model 808) and typically varied by less than 1°C. Temperature gradients were such that the temperature varied by at most 15°C over the length of each sample tube, and typically less than 5°C over the segment of the tube containing the silica glass sample. Many experiments could be run simultaneously in each furnace; transient temperature fluctuations up to several tens of degrees and lasting several minutes were experienced when cold samples were introduced into an already hot furnace. For several experiments, samples were first held at one temperature for sufficient time (based on other experiments) to closely approach equilibrium, then placed in a furnace at a higher or lower temperature and allowed to approach equilibrium at the second temperature. For a few experiments, the run products and/or tubes from previous experiments were reused in later experiments, and in others about 0.6 $\mu$moles of $H_2O$ was loaded into the tube along with the sample and the $CO_2$.

Analysis of Qtz Wool 1 material after a 850°C, 30 minute preheating in air gave a value within 1$\sigma$ of the mean value (see below), indicating that our procedure for removing organics does not significantly influence the bulk isotopic composition of the starting material, although some exchange between oxygen near the surfaces of the threads and air undoubtedly occurred. Based on our determination of the self-diffusion coefficient for oxygen in silica glass (see below), the depth of penetration of oxygen exchange during the preheating would be about 0.03 $\mu$m.

Several experiments were conducted by sealing 37–132 $\mu$moles of the $CO_2$ prepared from the conch shell inside GE214 fused quartz or Vycor glass tubes (preheated at 850°C in air for 30 minutes) without any silicate sample, and then holding these tubes at 550–850°C for 1 hour to 153 days to examine the kinetics of exchange between the glass tube and $CO_2$.

### Analytical techniques

After removal from the furnace and cooling in air, each tube was cracked on an extraction line; the $CO_2$ was collected, its quantity measured manometrically, and its $\delta^{18}O$ and $\delta^{13}C$ analyzed on a mass spectrometer. Starting materials and several run products were examined by scanning electron microscopy; no changes were detected. X-ray diffraction measurements on run products showed no evidence of crystallization of the glasses over the course of the experiments.

To evaluate the precision of our mass spectrometric analyses of $CO_2$, we prepared a large batch of $CO_2$ from the conch shell and sealed $\sim$100–150 $\mu$moles into each of about 50 pyrex tubes. The gas from one or more of these tubes was analyzed in most of the sessions on the mass spectrometer during which the gases extracted from our experiments were analyzed. Based on 13 such analyses obtained over more than a year, the precision of the $\delta^{18}O$ values we report for $CO_2$ gas is 0.14 per mil ($1\sigma$).

Oxygen was extracted from the starting materials by reaction with either $BrF_5$ or $F_2$ and then reacted with graphite to produce $CO_2$ that was then analyzed mass spectrometrically. Precisions of the isotopic analyses of the starting materials include contributions both from uncertainties in the mass spectrometry and from uncertainties introduced during the extraction procedure. Multiple analyses of the starting materials suggest a procedural contribution to the uncertainty in our silicate $\delta^{18}O$ values of about 0.1 per mil ($1\sigma$). Accuracy of the oxygen isotope analyses is difficult to assess and, except for systematic inaccuracies introduced during the extraction procedure, is of little consequence to us since we are primarily interested in differences between measurements. However, Professor R. Clayton and T. Mayeda of the University of Chicago analyzed samples of the Qtz Wool 1 and GE214 glass for us and obtained $\delta^{18}O_{SMOW}$ values of +13.8 and +10.9 compared to our values of +14.1 and +11.2. Previous comparisons have also shown that $\delta^{18}O$ values obtained at Caltech are characteristically higher than those reported by the Chicago group by about 0.3 per mil (H. P. TAYLOR, pers. comm.).

## RESULTS

### Silica glass exchange experiments.

Results of all experiments on silica glass are listed in Tables 1–3 and representative results on Qtz Wool 1 and GE214 are shown graphically versus run duration in Figs. 1 and 2. Our best estimates of the fractionation factors for each sample at each temperature are listed in Table 4 and shown versus $10^6/T$ (K)$^2$ in Fig. 3. At each temperature, the fractionation factors determined for the three starting materials are essentially identical. For the quartz wool samples at 550–850°C, these values are averages of all results obtained at durations long enough so that results similar within error were obtained. For the quartz wool samples at 950°C, only samples run in silica glass tubes were included in the averages, although for the Qtz Wool 3 experiments, when samples and tubes were reused from previous experiments, results were similar whether silica or Vycor tubes were used. For the GE214 experiments, only the results of experiments on the <37 $\mu$m size fraction were included in the averages,

and then only if the run duration was sufficiently long that the results appeared independent of run duration.

In the context of our study, a "reversal" is a pair of experiments in which the $\delta^{18}O$ of the gases from two experiments run at the same temperature approached the equilibrium value from a starting value heavier than the equilibrium value in one experiment and from a value lighter than the equilibrium value in the other. Reversals are available over most of the temperature range for all three starting materials. In some experiments, the direction from which the equilibrium gas composition was approached was controlled by pre-equilibrating the gas and the silica glass rather than by loading a starting gas with a particular $\delta^{18}O$ value. For example, experiment #15B (Table 1) was first equilibrated with glass wool for 31 days at 650°C, during which time the $\delta^{18}O_{SMOW}$ of the gas *decreased* from the starting value of +20 to a value of +18.0 (based on the results of #15C, run simultaneously under identical conditions); after removal from the 650°C furnace, the sealed tube was then placed in the 550°C furnace for 76 days, during which time the $\delta^{18}O_{SMOW}$ of the $CO_2$ gas *increased* to a final value of +18.7. Four experiments of this sort were conducted, giving values at 550, 650, 750, and 850°C. In every case, including runs such as #15C in which the final $\delta^{18}O$ value was overshot in the pre-equilibration stage, the results of these experiments were indistinguishable from the values we report as the equilibrium values based on long duration runs held only at a single temperature.

Long duration runs on the 37–44 $\mu$m size fraction of the GE214 starting material at temperatures $\geq$ 650°C yield results indistinguishable from reversed results of shorter experiments conducted on the <37 $\mu$m size fraction (Fig. 2). Lengthy experiments on this size fraction at 550°C approach to within 0.4 per mil of the results on finer size fractions at shorter times. Similarly, reversal experiments on the 44–74 $\mu$m size fraction reproduce results on finer size fractions in experiments of sufficiently long duration (*e.g.*, runs #23R and #23V at 850°C; Fig. 2). Results at the lower temperatures on the 37–44 $\mu$m size fraction are in most cases also consistent with the results on finer grained samples, but some experiments appear to have incompletely exchanged (*e.g.*, runs #23S and #23T at 550 and 650°C). All experiments at 950°C on the GE214 starting material yield gas anomalously rich in $^{18}O$; this could reflect a transient because all of these experiments were of short duration, or perhaps incipient crystallization of the glass, although X-ray and optical evidence do not support this latter suggestion.

Table 1. Qtz wool 1 experimental conditions and results

| Sample[a] | $T$ (°C)[b] | Duration (days)[b] | Tube[c] | μmoles $CO_2$ (initial)[d] | Yield (%)[d] | $\delta^{13}C_{PDB}$ (‰, initial) | $\delta^{13}C_{PDB}$ (‰, final) | $\delta^{18}O_{SMOW}$ (‰, initial) | $\delta^{18}O_{SMOW}$ (‰, final) | wt (g)[e] | $SiO_2/CO_2$[f] |
|---|---|---|---|---|---|---|---|---|---|---|---|
| #6B | 550 | 71.9 | q | 57.3 | 101.0 | −13.0 | −13.0 | 20.0 | 17.7 | 0.61 | 176 |
| #6D | 550 | 12.9 | q | 50.9 | 105.1 | −30.1 | −30.0 | 20.0 | 16.2 | 0.59 | 192 |
| #6F | 550 | 30.2 | q | 47.7 | 107.8 | −0.4 | −0.6 | 41.9 | 18.7 | 0.55 | 191 |
| #15B | 650/550 | 30.8/76.2 | q | 44.4 | 97.5 | −12.9 | −12.8 | 20.1 | 18.7 | 1.03 | 386 |
| #15E | 550 | 94.8 | q | 42.3 | 99.1 | −30.1 | −29.8 | 0.0 | 18.2 | 0.99 | 390 |
| #15I | 550 | 91.0 | q | 40.1 | 99.3 | −12.8 | −12.9 | 19.8 | 18.7 | 1.02 | 422 |
| #16A | 550 | 66.8 | v | 37.3 | 98.7 | −12.9 | −13.0 | 20.1 | 18.5 | 1.03 | 460 |
| #16G | 550 | 152.8 | v | 40.0 | 96.5 | −12.9 | −12.6 | 20.1 | 18.7 | 0.92 | 383 |
| #22B | 550 | 231.9 | v | 39.8 | 103.3 | −12.8 | −12.9 | 20.1 | 18.5 | 0.96 | 400 |
| | | | | 35.4 | | | | | 18.6 | | |
| #22D | 550 | 231.9 | q | | 98.6 | −12.8 | −12.8 | 20.1 | 18.2 | 1.04 | 488 |
| | | | | | | | −12.9 | | 18.1 | | |
| | | | | | | | | | 18.0 | | |
| #6A | 650 | 12.9 | q | 65.3 | 102.8 | −13.0 | −13.0 | 20.0 | 17.1 | 0.52 | 133 |
| #6C | 650 | 12.9 | q | 58.8 | 102.7 | −30.1 | −29.9 | 0.0 | 16.9 | 0.66 | 187 |
| #6E | 650 | 10.9 | q | 47.7 | 109.6 | −0.4 | −0.5 | 41.9 | 17.9 | 0.59 | 206 |
| #15C | 650 | 30.8 | q | 45.3 | 102.2 | −12.9 | −12.8 | 20.1 | 18.1 | 1.02 | 375 |
| | | | | | | | −12.8 | | 18.1 | | |
| #15G | 750/650 | 30.8/29.0 | q | 44.5 | 98.2 | −30.1 | −30.0 | 0.0 | 18.0 | 1.01 | 378 |
| #15K | 650 | 43.8 | q | 46.3 | 97.8 | −29.8 | −29.5 | −0.2 | 18.1 | 0.98 | 352 |
| #16E | 650 | 30.8 | v | 44.4 | 105.9 | −12.9 | −12.9 | 20.1 | 18.0 | 1.01 | 379 |
| #16F | 650 | 66.7 | v | 43.1 | 97.2 | −12.9 | −12.9 | 20.1 | 17.9 | 0.97 | 375 |
| #22A | 650 | 231.9 | v | 35.4 | 99.7 | −12.8 | −12.8 | 20.1 | 17.5 | 1.06 | 497 |
| | | | | | | | | | 17.6 | | |
| | | | | | | | | | 17.6 | | |
| | | | | | | | | | 17.5 | | |
| #22C | 650 | 231.9 | q | 35.4 | 96.0 | −12.8 | −12.8 | 20.1 | 18.5 | 1.04 | 488 |
| | | | | | | | | | 18.0 | | |
| | | | | | | | | | 18.0 | | |
| #22E | 650 | 2.0 | q | 52.0 | 96.9 | −12.8 | −12.8 | 20.1 | 17.8 | 0.52 | 167 |
| #22F | 650 | 4.7 | q | 52.0 | 100.2 | −12.8 | −12.8 | 20.1 | 17.5 | 0.49 | 158 |
| #22G | 650 | 6.7 | q | 51.9 | 96.9 | −12.8 | −12.9 | 20.1 | 17.6 | 0.55 | 176 |
| #22H | 650 | 8.7 | q | 51.9 | 99.4 | −12.8 | −12.8 | 20.1 | 17.9 | 0.49 | 159 |
| #22I | 650 | 10.9 | q | 51.5 | 99.6 | −12.8 | −12.8 | 20.1 | 17.9 | 0.50 | 162 |
| #22J | 650 | 15.7 | q | 51.1 | 100.4 | −12.8 | −12.8 | 20.1 | 17.9 | 0.50 | 161 |
| #22K | 650 | 20.9 | q | 51.1 | 100.4 | −12.8 | −12.9 | 20.1 | 18.0 | 0.50 | 164 |
| #22L | 650 | 30.0 | q | 50.2 | 100.4 | −12.8 | −12.7 | 20.1 | 17.8 | 0.49 | 163 |
| #22M | 650 | 66.7 | q | 50.2 | 98.6 | −12.8 | −12.8 | 20.1 | 17.8 | 0.53 | 176 |
| #22N | 650 | 120.9 | q | 50.2 | 96.8 | −12.8 | −12.6 | 20.1 | 17.9 | 0.49 | 162 |
| #3C[g] | 750 | 12.1 | q | 55.0 | 102.2 | −0.5 | −0.6 | 42.2 | 17.1 | 0.53 | 160 |
| #3D[g] | 750 | 12.1 | q | 29.0 | 92.1 | −0.5 | −1.2 | 42.2 | 17.2 | 0.69 | 393 |
| #3E[g] | 750 | 12.1 | v | 25.9 | 106.2 | −0.5 | −1.2 | 42.2 | 17.3 | 0.55 | 355 |

Table 1. (Continued)

| Sample[a] | $T$ (°C)[b] | Duration (days)[b] | Tube[c] | $\mu$moles $CO_2$ (initial)[d] | Yield (%)[d] | $\delta^{13}C_{PDB}$ (‰, initial) | $\delta^{13}C_{PDB}$ (‰, final) | $\delta^{18}O_{SMOW}$ (‰, initial) | $\delta^{18}O_{SMOW}$ (‰, final) | wt (g)[e] | $SiO_2/CO_2$[f] |
|---|---|---|---|---|---|---|---|---|---|---|---|
| #4C | 750 | 10.8 | q | 44.9 | 104.7 | −0.3 | −0.4 | 41.8 | 17.7 | 0.65 | 241 |
| #4D | 750 | 12.1 | q | 40.2 | 101.2 | −30.1 | −29.9 | −2.3 | 17.5 | 0.73 | 302 |
| #4E | 750 | 22.8 | q | 33.9 | 100.0 | −30.1 | −29.8 | −2.3 | 17.4 | 0.52 | 255 |
| #4F | 750 | 25.8 | q | 75.3 | 102.8 | −0.3 | −0.5 | 41.8 | 17.7 | 0.32 | 71 |
| #4H | 750 | 22.8 | q | 30.7 | 99.0 | −0.3 | −1.1 | 41.8 | 17.8 | 0.86 | 466 |
| #15D | 650/750 | 30.8/29.0 | q | 47.1 | 98.5 | −12.9 | −12.9 | 20.1 | 17.1 | 1.07 | 378 |
| #15F | 750 | 30.8 | q | 47.0 | 98.3 | −30.1 | −30.0 | 0.0 | 16.9 | 0.94 | 333 |
| #15J | 750 | 43.8 | q | 41.9 | 99.8 | −12.8 | −13.0 | 19.8 | 17.7 | 1.02 | 406 |
| #16B | 750 | 30.8 | v | 50.6 | 101.8 | −12.9 | −12.7 | 20.1 | 17.2 | 0.99 | 326 |
| #16C | 750 | 66.8 | v | 48.8 | 104.1 | −12.9 | −13.6 | 20.1 | 17.3 | 1.02 | 348 |
| #3A | 850 | 9.0 | q | 40.0 | 120.3 | −0.5 | −0.9 | 42.2 | 16.6 | 0.62 | 258 |
| #3B | 850 | 9.0 | q | 21.2 | 108.0 | −0.5 | −0.5 | 42.2 | 16.6 | 0.37 | 287 |
| #3F | 850 | 9.0 | v | 32.2 | 103.1 | −0.5 | −0.6 | 42.2 | 16.7 | 0.47 | 243 |
| #4A | 850 | 8.9 | q | 41.8 | 104.3 | −0.3 | −0.4 | 41.8 | 17.4 | 0.77 | 307 |
| #4B | 850 | 38.9 | q | 44.9 | 102.4 | −0.3 | −0.5 | 41.8 | 17.2 | 0.56 | 208 |
| #4G | 850 | 10.2 | q | 37.0 | 100.5 | −30.1 | −29.8 | −2.3 | 16.6 | 0.65 | 292 |
| #4I | 850 | 20.8 | q | 48.1 | 101.0 | −0.3 | −0.4 | 41.8 | 17.1 | 0.73 | 253 |
| #4J | 850 | 20.8 | q | 33.9 | 102.4 | −30.1 | −29.8 | −2.3 | 16.8 | 0.81 | 398 |
| #15A | 850 | 30.8 | q | 42.6 | 98.4 | −12.9 | −12.7 | 20.1 | 16.9 | 0.76 | 297 |
| | | | | | | | −12.8 | | 17.0 | | |
| #15H | 750/850 | 30.8/29.0 | q | 47.9 | 96.5 | −30.1 | −29.9 | 0.0 | 16.8 | 1.05 | 365 |
| #16D | 850 | 30.8 | v | 45.7 | 104.6 | −12.9 | −12.8 | 20.1 | 17.2 | 0.89 | 324 |
| #16H | 850 | 66.8 | v | 40.9 | 98.0 | −12.9 | −12.9 | 20.1 | 16.7 | 0.95 | 387 |
| #20A | 950 | 8.0 | q | 64.8 | 96.9 | −29.9 | −29.8 | −0.5 | 16.6 | 0.99 | 254 |
| #20I | 950 | 8.0 | q | 65.6 | 98.2 | −13.0 | −13.0 | 20.0 | 16.3 | 1.12 | 283 |
| #25C | 950 | 67.0 | qrt(20A) | 42.5 | 100.2 | −30.0 | | −0.3 | 16.0 | 0.99 | 387 |
| #25M | 950 | 67.0 | qrt(20I) | 40.6 | 102.7 | −12.6 | −12.9 | 20.6 | 16.2 | 1.12 | 457 |
| #20E | 950 | 8.0 | v | 63.9 | 100.9 | −29.9 | | −0.5 | 17.0 | 1.02 | 267 |
| #20M | 950 | 8.0 | v | 64.7 | 99.5 | −13.0 | | 20.0 | 17.0 | 1.01 | 260 |
| #25H | 950 | 67.0 | vrt(20E) | 41.6 | 101.4 | −30.0 | −30.1 | −0.3 | 17.1 | 1.02 | 410 |
| #25R | 950 | 67.0 | vrt(20M) | 39.3 | 101.8 | −12.6 | −12.9 | 20.6 | 17.0 | 1.01 | 429 |

Notes for Tables 1–3:

[a] Sample numbers in italics indicate runs the results of which were included in the averages listed in Table 4. Unlabeled rows correspond to repeat analyses of the gas extracted from the sample indicated by the last labelled row above.

[b] Samples that were first held at one temperature for a given duration and then transferred to a second temperature for a second duration are indicated in these columns as $x/y$, where $x$ is the initial temperature or run duration and $y$ is the second temperature or run duration.

[c] v = Vycor tube; q = GE214 quartz glass tube. qr and vr indicate experiments in which the silicate sample and the quartz glass and Vycor tubes from a previous experiment were reused with a fresh aliquot of $CO_2$; the number in parentheses corresponds to the experiment in which the tube and sample were previously used. When a number is given in parentheses but there is no "r" designation, it signifies that the sample from the experiment indicated in parentheses was reloaded along with a new batch of $CO_2$ into a new tube and rerun.

[d] Measured number of micromoles of $CO_2$ loaded into the capsule at the start of the experiment and the measured yield of $CO_2$ extracted at the close of the experiment in percent of the initial, as loaded, value.

[e] Mass of silica glass loaded into the capsule.

[f] Ratio of moles of silica glass to $CO_2$ loaded into the capsule.

[g] Samples contain ~0.6 micromoles of $H_2O$ in addition to $CO_2$.

[h] Grain size based on nominal sizes of nylon sieves used to divide the sample into size fractions. The size fraction that passed through a 400 mesh sieve is designated <37 $\mu$m.

Table 2. Qtz wool 3 experimental conditions and results

| Sample[a] | T (°C) | Duration (days) | Tube[c] | μmoles CO$_2$ (initial)[d] | Yield (%)[d] | δ$^{13}$C$_{PDB}$ (‰, initial) | δ$^{13}$C$_{PDB}$ (‰, final) | δ$^{18}$O$_{SMOW}$ (‰, initial) | δ$^{18}$O$_{SMOW}$ (‰, final) | wt (g)[e] | SiO$_2$/CO$_2$[f] |
|---|---|---|---|---|---|---|---|---|---|---|---|
| #25A | 750 | 66.2 | qr (24A) | 40.7 | 100.7 | −30.0 | −30.0 | −0.3 | 19.5 | 1.38 | 563 |
| #25F | 750 | 66.2 | vr (24D) | 42.5 | 98.1 | −30.0 | | −0.3 | 20.1 | 1.74 | 683 |
| #25K | 750 | 66.2 | qr (24G) | 37.9 | 105.5 | −12.6 | | 20.6 | 19.5 | 1.23 | 542 |
| #25P | 750 | 66.2 | vr (24J) | 39.9 | 100.3 | −12.6 | | 20.6 | 19.6 | 1.68 | 701 |
| #25D | 750 | 66.2 | q | 41.7 | 103.1 | −30.0 | | −0.3 | 19.9 | 1.52 | 605 |
| #25J | 750 | 66.2 | v | 41.3 | 101.0 | −30.0 | | −0.3 | 20.1 | 1.96 | 788 |
| #25N | 750 | 66.2 | q | 40.7 | 102.5 | −12.6 | | 20.6 | 20.4 | 2.09 | 855 |
| #25S | 750 | 66.2 | v | 39.1 | 102.6 | −12.6 | | 20.6 | 21.1 | 2.05 | 874 |
| #24A | 950 | 84.0 | q | 41.9 | 99.5 | −30.1 | −29.8 | −0.4 | 19.0 | 1.38 | 547 |
| #24B | 950 | 32.8 | q | 41.0 | 102.4 | −30.1 | −29.8 | −0.4 | 20.1 | 1.74 | 707 |
| #24C | 950 | 66.3 | q | 42.3 | 100.5 | −30.1 | −29.9 | −0.4 | 19.6 | 1.63 | 640 |
| #24D | 950 | 84.0 | v | 42.3 | 98.6 | −30.1 | −29.7 | −0.4 | 19.2 | 1.74 | 686 |
| #24E | 950 | 32.8 | v | 41.4 | 102.7 | −30.1 | −29.9 | −0.4 | 19.9 | 1.16 | 466 |
| #24F | 950 | 66.3 | v | 42.3 | 101.2 | −30.1 | −30.0 | −0.4 | 21.4 | 1.71 | 672 |
| #24G | 950 | 84.0 | q | 43.2 | 98.4 | −12.9 | −12.9 | 20.1 | 19.2 | 1.23 | 476 |
| #24H | 950 | 32.8 | q | 43.2 | 100.5 | −12.9 | −13.2 | 20.1 | 19.6 | 1.28 | 494 |
| #24I | 950 | 66.3 | q | 43.2 | 102.5 | −12.9 | −13.3 | 20.1 | 19.3 / 19.4 | 1.46 | 564 |
| #24J | 950 | 84.0 | v | 43.2 | 101.6 | −12.9 | −13.6 | 20.1 | 19.2 | 1.68 | 648 |
| #24K | 950 | 32.8 | v | 42.4 | 106.4 | −12.9 | −13.3 | 20.1 | 21.2 | 1.72 | 677 |
| #24L | 950 | 66.3 | v | 41.5 | 105.3 | −12.9 | −13.4 | 20.1 | 21.3 | 1.82 | 729 |
| #25E | 950 | 67.0 | q | 41.7 | 104.3 | −30.0 | | −0.3 | 18.9 | 1.96 | 782 |
| #25I | 950 | 67.0 | v | 41.6 | 101.4 | −30.0 | | −0.3 | 19.3 | 2.06 | 823 |
| #25O | 950 | 67.0 | q | 40.6 | 103.0 | −12.6 | | 20.6 | 19.7 | 1.99 | 814 |
| #25G | 950 | 67.0 | vr (24E) | 42.5 | 102.4 | −30.0 | | −0.3 | 18.8 / 18.7 | 1.16 | 454 |
| #25L | 950 | 67.0 | qr (24L) | 41.1 | 101.5 | −12.6 | | 20.6 | 18.9 / 18.9 | 1.28 | 519 |
| #25B | 950 | 67.0 | qr (24B) | 41.7 | 102.4 | −30.0 | | −0.3 | 18.9 | 1.74 | 695 |
| #25Q | 950 | 67.0 | vr (24K) | 39.6 | 101.0 | −12.6 | | 20.6 | 19.0 | 1.72 | 725 |

Notes: See Table 1.

Table 3. GE214 glass powder experimental conditions and results

| Sample[a] | T (°C) | Duration (days) | Tube[c] | μmoles CO$_2$ (initial)[d] | Yield (%)[d] | δ$^{13}$C$_{PDB}$ (‰, initial) | δ$^{13}$C$_{PDB}$ (‰, final) | δ$^{18}$O$_{SMOW}$ (‰, initial) | δ$^{18}$O$_{SMOW}$ (‰, final) | Size fraction (μm)[h] | wt (g)[e] | Silicate/CO$_2$[f] |
|---|---|---|---|---|---|---|---|---|---|---|---|---|
| #17D | 550 | 152.8 | q | 38.9 | 102.8 | −12.9 | −12.5 | 20.1 | 15.8 | <37 | 1.00 | 429 |
| #18D | 550 | 428.0 | v | 38.9 | 100.0 | −12.9 | −12.7 | 20.1 | 15.2 | 37–44 | 1.00 | 430 |
| | | | | | | | | | 15.0 | | | |
| #18H | 550 | 152.8 | v | 43.5 | 103.9 | −12.9 | −12.8 | 20.1 | 15.4 | <37 | 1.01 | 385 |
| #23S | 550 | 231.9 | q | 42.6 | 93.0 | −27.5 | −29.0 | −1.8 | 14.6 | 44–74 | 1.01 | 393 |
| #7A | 650 | 2.3 | q | 46.5 | 106.9 | −12.9 | −13.3 | 20.0 | 14.8 | <37 | 1.83 | 656 |
| #7D | 650 | 2.3 | q | 46.4 | 104.3 | −0.4 | −1.0 | 42.0 | 14.8 | <37 | 1.89 | 679 |
| #17C | 650 | 113.9 | q | 40.3 | 103.0 | −12.9 | −12.6 | 20.1 | 15.1 | <37 | 1.01 | 417 |
| #17G | 650 | 113.9 | q | 49.9 | 99.0 | −30.1 | −29.5 | 0.0 | 15.0 | <37 | 1.01 | 336 |
| #18C | 650 | 427.9 | v | 41.9 | 97.9 | −12.9 | −11.8 | 20.1 | 15.1 | 37–44 | 1.00 | 398 |
| | | | | | | | −12.0 | | 15.0 | | | |
| | | | | | | | −12.0 | | 15.0 | | | |
| | | | | | | | −12.4 | | 15.4 | | | |
| #18G | 650 | 113.9 | v | 41.9 | 103.3 | −12.9 | −12.5 | 20.1 | 15.0 | <37 | 1.00 | 398 |
| #23P | 650 | 231.9 | q | 46.8 | 87.6 | −12.7 | −11.3 | 20.1 | 14.9 | 44–74 | 1.01 | 358 |
| #23T | 650 | 231.9 | q | 44.3 | 90.5 | −27.5 | −29.0 | −1.8 | 14.4 | 44–74 | 1.01 | 378 |
| | | | | | | | | | 14.4 | | | |
| | | | | | | | | | 14.5 | | | |
| #7B | 750 | 1.3 | q | 40.1 | 100.0 | −12.9 | −12.9 | 20.0 | 15.5 | <37 | 2.23 | 924 |
| #7E | 750 | 1.3 | q | 44.9 | 93.1 | −0.4 | −0.6 | 42.0 | 15.3 | <37 | 1.68 | 624 |
| #17B | 750 | 66.8 | q | 43.5 | 96.6 | −12.9 | −12.4 | 20.1 | 14.5 | <37 | 1.01 | 386 |
| #17F | 750 | 66.8 | q | 49.8 | 98.2 | −30.1 | −29.5 | 0.0 | 14.4 | <37 | 1.00 | 335 |
| #18B | 750 | 114.0 | v | 45.1 | 100.0 | −12.9 | −12.9 | 20.1 | 14.8 | 37–44 | 1.00 | 370 |
| #18F | 750 | 66.8 | v | 40.3 | 99.5 | −12.9 | −12.8 | 20.1 | 14.6 | <37 | 1.00 | 414 |
| #23Q | 750 | 231.9 | q | 45.0 | 97.8 | −12.7 | −12.7 | 20.1 | 15.4 | 44–74 | 1.01 | 372 |
| #23U | 750 | 231.9 | q | 43.4 | 87.8 | −27.5 | −28.5 | −1.8 | 14.3 | 44–74 | 1.00 | 385 |
| #7C | 850 | 2.3 | q | 35.4 | 93.2 | −12.9 | −12.4 | 20.0 | 16.0 | <37 | 2.01 | 944 |
| #17A | 850 | 30.8 | q | 46.6 | 91.6 | −12.9 | −12.1 | 20.1 | 14.1 | <37 | 1.00 | 358 |
| #17E | 850 | 30.8 | q | 38.9 | 96.1 | −30.1 | −29.1 | 0.0 | 14.2 | <37 | 1.00 | 429 |
| #18A | 850 | 110.8 | v | 48.3 | 104.6 | −12.9 | −13.0 | 20.1 | 14.1 | 37–44 | 1.00 | 345 |
| #18E | 850 | 30.8 | v | 43.5 | 102.1 | −12.9 | −12.7 | 20.1 | 14.2 | <37 | 1.00 | 383 |
| #23R | 850 | 232.1 | q | 45.0 | 85.1 | −12.7 | −11.6 | 20.1 | 14.1 | 44–74 | 1.01 | 373 |
| #23V | 850 | 232.1 | q | 44.3 | 81.9 | −27.5 | −28.5 | −1.8 | 14.0 | 44–74 | 1.01 | 378 |
| #20B | 950 | 8.0 | q | 65.6 | 83.5 | −29.9 | −29.0 | −0.5 | 14.5 | <37 | 1.00 | 254 |
| #20F | 950 | 8.0 | v (7A) | 65.7 | 93.9 | −29.9 | −29.7 | −0.5 | 14.2 | <37 | 1.04 | 263 |
| #20J | 950 | 8.0 | q | 63.8 | 88.7 | −13.0 | −12.0 | 20.0 | 14.9 | <37 | 1.00 | 261 |
| #20N | 950 | 8.0 | v (7B) | 61.9 | 95.6 | −13.0 | −12.8 | 20.0 | 14.4 | <37 | 1.12 | 300 |

Notes: See Table 1.

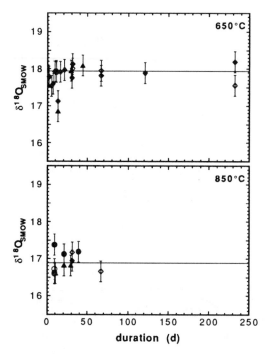

FIG. 1. Summary of $CO_2$ $\delta^{18}O_{SMOW}$ values for Qtz Wool 1 silica glass experiments as a function of run duration at 650 and 850°C. Error bars are $\pm 2\sigma$ for our gas analyses on our mass spectrometer (see text). Horizontal lines are averages of long duration runs (listed in Table 1 in italics); these average values are listed in Table 4 and are the values used in determining fractionation factors. Open symbols indicate experiments conducted in Vycor tubes; closed symbols indicate experiments conducted in GE214 silica glass tubes. Circles indicate experiments with a starting $\delta^{18}O_{SMOW}$ value for the $CO_2$ of +42; diamonds indicate a starting $\delta^{18}O_{SMOW}$ value for the $CO_2$ of +20; triangles indicate a starting $\delta^{18}O_{SMOW}$ value for the $CO_2$ of $\approx 0$.

At 550 and 650°C, short duration runs (<30 days at 650°C; 70 days at 550°C) give erratic results; these may be influenced by surface fractionations (and the effects on the surfaces of the preheating step in air at 850°C) or kinetic isotope effects (see below), but results of longer experiments at these temperatures are not correlated with run duration provided runs on the same silicate size fractions are compared. Similarly, except for a few 1–2 day experiments on the GE214 powder at 750 and 850°C, results at these temperatures are not correlated with run duration over the range of run durations examined.

It is well known that water pressure enhances the apparent self-diffusion of oxygen in silica glass (PFEFFER and OHRING, 1982) and in silicate minerals and glasses generally (see review in ZHANG *et al.*, 1991b). Thus, a few experiments in which the vapor phase contained a small amount (~0.6

$\mu$moles) of $H_2O$ in addition to $CO_2$ were conducted on the Qtz Wool 1 starting material at 750°C. The final $\delta^{18}O$ values of $CO_2$ in the experiments that had both water and $CO_2$ turned out to be indistinguishable from those of samples run for comparable times but with $CO_2$ alone, and from experiments run with $CO_2$ alone but for much longer durations. This offers strong support for our conclusion that the long duration runs closely approached equilibrium.

$CO_2$ yields (*i.e.*, a comparison of the amount of gas initially loaded with the amount collected at the end of the experiment) are nearly all 100 ± 5% (Tables 1–3). The only significant exceptions are some of the experiments on GE214, which have yields as low as 82%. We think this is due to formation of CO by reaction of $CO_2$ with the minor amounts of stainless steel that contaminated this sample during crushing. This is consistent with the larger amounts (up to a few $\mu$moles) of non-condensable (at liquid nitrogen temperatures) gas we detected in these experiments. Nevertheless, the final $\delta^{18}O$ values of $CO_2$ in these experiments are indistinguishable from those of experiments with yields near 100%. We

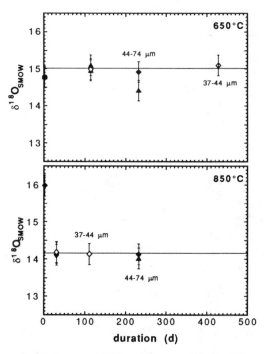

FIG. 2. Summary of $CO_2$ gas $\delta^{18}O_{SMOW}$ values for GE214 silica glass experiments as a function of run duration at 650 and 850°C. Error bars are $\pm 2\sigma$ for our gas analyses on our mass spectrometer (see text). Horizontal lines are averages of long duration runs (listed in Table 3 in italics) on <37 $\mu$m powder; these average values are listed in Table 4 and are the values used in determining fractionation factors. Symbols as in Fig. 1.

note that except for these samples, the concentration of non-condensable gaseous species was negligible. We often checked for water in the gas collected at the close of the experiments, and this was also usually negligible.

Results of similar experiments in silica and Vycor glass tubes at all temperatures below 950°C are usually nearly indistinguishable. The fact that there are no systematic differences between these experiments (despite the fact that the Vycor tubes are about 10 per mil heavier than the GE214 silica tubes and have self-diffusion coefficients $\approx$ 2 orders of magnitude higher; see Table 5) demonstrates that interaction of the vapor with the container does not have a significant influence on the results. However, at 950°C, results of experiments in Vycor tubes are erratic, with $\delta^{18}O$ values often much higher than expected based on lower temperature experiments run in Vycor tubes and on results of experiments run simultaneously in silica tubes. We take this as indicating that the results in Vycor at temperatures above 850°C are not reliable, probably due to extensive interaction between the $CO_2$ and the Vycor tube at these temperatures.

In short duration experiments and at low temperatures, there is evidence for complexity in the exchange process, as anticipated by WILLIAMS (1965) and MUEHLENBACHS and SCHAEFFER (1977). For example, gas exposed to the <37 $\mu$m size fraction of the GE214 glass in runs of 1–2 days duration at 650–850°C experienced anomalous amounts of exchange and in some cases even converged from initially heavy and light $\delta^{18}O$ values to spurious, short-term "reversed" values. These observations could be evidence of surface-correlated

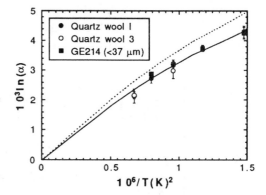

FIG. 3. Summary of $CO_2$-silica glass fractionation factors from this study. Errors are ±two standard errors on the equilibrium gas compositions and do not include uncertainties in the silicate analyses (see Table 4). The solid curve is calculated based on the reduced partition function ratios given for $CO_2$ in CHACKO et al. (1991) and 1.035 times the crystalline quartz-1 reduced partition function ratio given by CLAYTON et al. (1989). The dashed curve is the calculated $CO_2$-crystalline quartz fractionation factor based on these reduced partition function ratios.

fractionations (perhaps influenced by the 850°C preheating step) and/or kinetic isotope effects (e.g., such as would be observed if there were several distinguishable oxygen sites in the glass with different fractionation factors and with different exchange rates). Similarly, in short duration experiments at 550 and 650°C on Qtz Wool 1 with starting gas heavier than the equilibrium value (based on long duration runs), the final gas is frequently lighter than the equilibrium value (see Fig. 1); i.e., they appear to "overshoot" the equilibrium value. With

Table 4. Summary of experimental results on $CO_2$-silica glass fractionation

| Sample | $T$ (°C) | $\delta^{18}O_{SMOW}$ (‰) (final gas) | $\delta^{18}O_{SMOW}$ (‰) (silicate) | 1000 ln ($\alpha$) (vapor/glass) |
|---|---|---|---|---|
| Qtz Wool 1 | 550 | 18.49 (0.20)[a] | 14.12 (0.06)[a] | 4.30 (0.21)[b] |
| | 650 | 17.94 (0.10) | | 3.76 (0.12) |
| | 750 | 17.37 (0.16) | | 3.20 (0.17) |
| | 850 | 16.89 (0.16) | | 2.73 (0.17) |
| | 950 | 16.29 (0.24) | | 2.14 (0.25) |
| Qtz Wool 3 | 750 | 19.86 (0.26) | 16.82 (0.16) | 2.99 (0.30) |
| | 950 | 19.02 (0.12) | | 2.16 (0.20) |
| GE214 | 550 | 15.56 (0.20) | 11.24 (0.11) | 4.26 (0.23) |
| | 650 | 15.02 (0.09) | | 3.73 (0.14) |
| | 750 | 14.49 (0.09) | | 3.21 (0.14) |
| | 850 | 14.16 (0.05) | | 2.88 (0.12) |

[a] Numbers in parentheses are $2\sigma$ of the mean of the analyses used to compute the average of gas analyses from all successful experiments or silicate extractions, except for GE214 at 550°C where there were only two successful experiments. The reported error in this case is one-half of the difference in $\delta^{18}O$ between the two results.

[b] Numbers in parentheses are $2\sigma$ errors based on propagation of the errors on the gas and silicate analyses reported in the two previous columns.

E. Stolper and S. Epstein

Table 5. Diffusion experiments: experimental conditions and results

| Sample | $T$ (°C) | Duration (days) | Tube[a] | μmoles $CO_2$ (initial)[b] | Yield (%)[b] | $\delta^{13}C_{PDB}$ (‰, initial) | $\delta^{13}C_{PDB}$ (‰, final) | $\delta^{18}O_{SMOW}$ (‰, initial) | $\delta^{18}O_{SMOW}$ (‰, final) | Tube length (cm)[c] | $\log_{10}(D)$ (cm²/s)[d] |
|---|---|---|---|---|---|---|---|---|---|---|---|
| #10O | 550 | 0.2 | q | 44.8 | 95.1 | −0.5 | −0.5 | 41.8 | 40.0 | 15.7 | −15.5 (0.2) |
| #12K | 550 | 2.0 | q | 56.7 | 96.8 | −0.4 | −0.4 | 42.0 | 39.6 | 14.6 | −16.0 (0.2) |
| #12C | 550 | 4.0 | q | 45.3 | 100.4 | −0.4 | −0.4 | 42.0 | 37.8 | 16.6 | −16.1 (0.1) |
| #12D | 550 | 8.0 | q | 45.3 | 98.5 | −0.4 | −0.4 | 42.0 | 37.1 | 15.2 | −16.2 (0.1) |
| #12E | 550 | 16.0 | q | 44.4 | 100.5 | −0.4 | −0.5 | 42.0 | 34.5 | 16.3 | −16.1 (0.1) |
| #12A | 550 | 32.0 | q | 61.1 | 100.3 | −0.4 | −0.4 | 42.0 | 34.8 | 16.3 | −16.1 (0.1) |
| #12B | 550 | 64.0 | q | 62.0 | 97.6 | −0.4 | −0.6 | 42.0 | 34.9 | 16.8 | −16.5 (0.1) |
| #14F | 550 | 66.8 | q | 173.4 | 96.7 | −1.2 | −1.1 | 40.5 | 36.4 | 15.4 | −16.1 (0.1) |
| #14G | 550 | 152.8 | q | 163.5 | 97.4 | −1.2 | −1.0 | 40.5 | 35.3 | 14.3 | −16.1 (0.1) |
| #12L | 650 | 1.0 | q | 41.9 | 97.6 | −0.4 | −0.5 | 42.0 | 37.3 | 15.2 | −15.4 (0.1) |
| #12J | 650 | 2.0 | q | 40.9 | 98.0 | −0.4 | −0.4 | 42.0 | 36.5 | 15.6 | −15.6 (0.1) |
| #12I | 650 | 4.0 | q | 40.9 | 100.0 | −0.4 | −0.7 | 42.0 | 35.2 | 15.7 | −15.6 (0.1) |
| #12F | 650 | 8.0 | q | 44.4 | 96.4 | −0.4 | −0.4 | 42.0 | 33.4 | 16.7 | −15.7 (0.1) |
| #12H | 650 | 16.0 | q | 40.9 | 95.6 | −0.4 | −0.4 | 42.0 | 34.2 | 16.4 | −16.1 (0.1) |
| #12G | 650 | 32.0 | q | 39.2 | 95.7 | −0.4 | −0.3 | 42.0 | 30.4 | 17.2 | −16.0 (0.1) |
| #14D | 650 | 66.8 | q | 180.3 | 99.8 | −1.2 | −1.2 | 40.5 | 34.0 | 15.3 | −15.5 (0.1) |
| #14E | 650 | 152.8 | q | 177.4 | 99.2 | −1.2 | −1.1 | 40.5 | 33.6 | 14.4 | −15.8 (0.1) |
| #14J | 650 | 66.8 | q | 43.0 | 95.3 | −1.2 | −1.2 | 40.5 | 28.7 | 14.6 | −16.0 (0.1) |
| #10J | 750 | 0.04 | q | 47.8 | 97.5 | −0.5 | −0.4 | 41.8 | 40.2 | 16.6 | −15.0 (0.3) |
| #10I | 750 | 0.08 | q | 48.3 | 98.1 | −0.5 | −0.3 | 41.8 | 38.6 | 15.6 | −14.6 (0.1) |
| #10H | 750 | 0.17 | q | 48.7 | 96.7 | −0.5 | −0.4 | 41.8 | 38.6 | 15.7 | −14.9 (0.1) |
| #10G | 750 | 0.3 | q | 49.6 | 95.8 | −0.5 | −0.2 | 41.8 | 36.6 | 16.1 | −14.7 (0.1) |
| #10K | 750 | 0.7 | q | 47.0 | 98.1 | −0.5 | −0.2 | 41.8 | 36.1 | 15.5 | −14.9 (0.1) |
| #10F | 750 | 1.3 | q | 50.5 | 97.4 | −0.5 | −0.4 | 41.8 | 36.3 | 15.4 | −15.2 (0.1) |
| #10L | 750 | 2.7 | q | 46.1 | 98.0 | −0.5 | −0.5 | 41.8 | 33.9 | 14.6 | −15.2 (0.1) |
| #5C | 750 | 1.1 | q | 120.4 | 101.2 | −0.4 | −0.5 | 41.9 | 37.6 | 15[f] | −14.6 (0.1) |

Table 5. (Continued)

| Sample | $T$ (°C) | Tube[a] | Duration (days) | $\mu$moles $CO_2$ (initial)[b] | Yield (%)[b] | $\delta^{13}C_{PDB}$ (‰, initial) | $\delta^{13}C_{PDB}$ (‰, final) | $\delta^{18}O_{SMOW}$ (‰, initial) | $\delta^{18}O_{SMOW}$ (‰, final) | Tube length (cm)[c] | $\log_{10}(D)$ (cm²/s)[d] |
|---|---|---|---|---|---|---|---|---|---|---|---|
| #5B | 750 | q | 2.1 | 125.4 | 100.9 | −0.4 | −0.4 | 41.9 | 36.1 | 15[f] | −14.5 (0.1) |
| #5A | 750 | q | 5.7 | 132.0 | 100.6 | −0.4 | −0.5 | 41.9 | 36.8 | 15[f] | −15.1 (0.1) |
| #5D | 750 | q | 16.8 | 115.6 | 102.5 | −0.4 | −0.4 | 41.9 | 32.4 | 15[f] | −14.9 (0.1) |
| #5E | 750 | q | 38.0 | 104.2 | 104.0 | −0.4 | −0.5 | 41.9 | 28.5 | 15[f] | −14.9 (0.1) |
| #14B | 750 | q | 66.8 | 196.3 | 98.7 | −1.2 | −1.2 | 40.5 | 32.8 | 14.1 | −15.2 (0.1) |
| #14C | 750 | q | 152.8 | 189.8 | 97.6 | −1.2 | −1.3 | 40.5 | 31.1 | 15.3 | −15.5 (0.1) |
| #14K | 750 | v | 1.0 | 67.6 | 97.2 | −1.2 | −1.3 | 40.5 | 34.6 | 16.3 | −14.3 (0.1)[e] |
| #14L | 750 | v | 2.0 | 53.4 | 99.4 | −1.2 | −1.3 | 40.5 | 30.1 | 17.2 | −13.9 (0.1)[e] |
| #14M | 750 | v | 4.1 | 51.4 | 101.0 | −1.2 | −1.3 | 40.5 | 26.4 | 17.8 | −13.3 (0.1)[e] |
| #14N | 750 | v | 8.1 | 55.9 | 99.8 | −1.2 | −1.3 | 40.5 | 24.7 | 16.9 | —[e] |
| #14H | 750 | v | 30.8 | 203.1 | 99.1 | −1.2 | −1.2 | 40.5 | 27.7 | 15.6 | −13.3 (0.1)[e] |
| #14I | 750 | v | 66.8 | 209.5 | 99.2 | −1.2 | −1.3 | 40.5 | 23.1 | 16.4 | —[e] |
| #10A | 850 | q | 0.04 | 54.5 | 100.7 | −0.5 | −0.5 | 41.8 | 39.4 | 15.7 | −14.5 (0.2) |
| #10B | 850 | q | 0.08 | 53.7 | 99.8 | −0.5 | −0.4 | 41.8 | 38.5 | 16.4 | −14.5 (0.1) |
| #10C | 850 | q | 0.17 | 53.2 | 98.1 | −0.5 | −0.5 | 41.8 | 37.8 | 16.1 | −14.6 (0.1) |
| #10D | 850 | q | 0.3 | 51.4 | 99.2 | −0.5 | −0.5 | 41.8 | 37.2 | 15.3 | −14.8 (0.1) |
| #10M | 850 | q | 0.7 | 45.7 | 98.0 | −0.5 | −0.4 | 41.8 | 34.7 | 15.5 | −14.7 (0.1) |
| #10E | 850 | q | 1.3 | 51.4 | 98.4 | −0.5 | −0.3 | 41.8 | 34.1 | 15.1 | −14.8 (0.1) |
| #10N | 850 | q | 2.7 | 45.6 | 97.4 | −0.5 | −0.4 | 41.8 | 30.6 | 16.7 | −14.9 (0.1) |
| #4L | 850 | q | 10.2 | 41.8 | 97.4 | −0.3 | −0.4 | 41.8 | 24.5 | 15[f] | −14.7 (0.1) |
| #4K | 850 | q | 20.8 | 37.0 | 93.8 | −0.3 | −0.6 | 41.8 | 23.8 | 15[f] | −15.1 (0.1) |
| #14A | 850 | q | 66.8 | 205.9 | 98.2 | −1.2 | −1.1 | 40.5 | 30.1 | 15.1 | −14.9 (0.1) |

[a] v = Vycor tube; q = GE214 quartz glass tube.

[b] Measured number of $\mu$moles of $CO_2$ loaded into the capsule at the start of the experiment and the measured yield of $CO_2$ extracted at the close of the experiment in percent of the initial, as loaded, value.

[c] Length of tube. Inside diameter of all tubes was 0.7 cm.

[d] Diffusion coefficient calculated as described in the text. Errors propagated assuming uncertainties in $\delta^{18}O_{SMOW}$ (final) of 0.3, in run duration of 0.01 days, in gas content of 1 $\mu$mole, in tube length of 1 cm, and in tube inner radius of 0.01 cm.

[e] The calculation of diffusion coefficients for experiments run in Vycor tubes assumed a fractionation factor equal to that determined for silica glass (i.e., $\Delta \approx 3.25$ per mil). For one experiment (14N), the $\delta^{18}O_{SMOW}$ of the $CO_2$ at the end of the experiment was so close to the value expected at equilibrium with the Vycor tube that a meaningful D could not be calculated. In the case of experiment 14I, the final $\delta^{18}O_{SMOW}$ of the gas actually was within 3.25 per mil of the bulk Vycor tube, so no D was calculated in this case.

[f] Tube length not measured. Value of 15 cm assumed based on similarity to all other experiments.

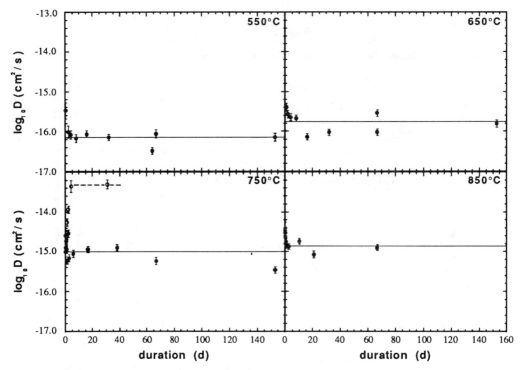

FIG. 4. Apparent self-diffusion coefficients for oxygen in silica (closed symbols) and Vycor (open symbols) glass as a function of run duration at temperatures of 550–850°C based on the experiments and calculations described in the text (data listed in Table 5). The solid horizontal lines show the average values for silica glass at each temperature based on runs of >0.5 days duration; runs of shorter duration were excluded to minimize the possible influence of surface exchange kinetics on the results. The dashed horizontal line at 750°C shows the approximate long duration value for Vycor glass.

increasing run duration, the final gas value increases slowly with time to a near constant value. Similar effects are also suggested by some of our diffusion experiments (discussed below) and were observed by LIU and EPSTEIN (1984) in hydrogen isotope exchange experiments between water vapor and kaolinite. Although we do not fully understand these phenomena, we have tried to avoid their influence by (1) basing our evaluations of equilibrium fractionation factors on the results of experiments run for long enough times that the results do not appear to be time dependent, thereby ensuring that substantial exchange occurred between the gas and oxygen deep within the silicate material (see discussion of diffusion experiments below); and (2) verifying our results using different starting materials and size fractions.

### Kinetics of oxygen isotope exchange

The results of experiments in which only $CO_2$ gas was loaded into glass tubes are listed in Table 5. In order to extract quantitative information from these data, we assumed that the inner surface of the glass tube and the vapor were in local equilibrium (with fractionation factors as given in Table 4) and that simple interdiffusion of $^{18}O$ and $^{16}O$ occurs within the glass. The time dependence of the isotopic composition of the inner surface of the tube was then approximated by a polynomial. This led to a series solution to the diffusion equation, from which the self-diffusion coefficient for oxygen, $D$, was obtained for each experiment. $D$ values are listed in Table 5 and shown in Fig. 4 as a function of run duration for each temperature.

Despite some scatter in the results, calculated $D$ values for the silica glass tubes (which at 750°C are $\approx 2$ orders of magnitude lower than calculated $D$ values for the Vycor glass tubes) are essentially independent of time and of the amount of gas loaded into the tube, confirming the appropriateness of treating the exchange as a diffusive phenomenon. We do not have an explanation for the scatter in calculated $D$ values at each temperature; it could reflect slightly different geometries for each sample (*i.e.*, the effects of the sealed ends of the tubes are not considered in our treatment), the influence at short times and in the lower temperature experiments of surface exchange phenomena with different kinetics (possibly affected by partial equilibration of the inner surface of the tube with air during the preheating step), or irregularities in the inner surface of the tubes (*e.g.*, microcracks).

Figure 5 compares the temperature dependence of the self-diffusion coefficient for oxygen in silica glass based on our $CO_2$ exchange experiments with previous determinations, all of which were based on isotope exchange between glass and $O_2$ gas (HAUL and DÜMBGEN, 1962; SUCOV, 1963; WILLIAMS, 1965; MUEHLENBACHS and SCHAEFFER, 1977). Our results are consistent with the two most recent of these determinations; because these were based on high temperature experiments in which the effects of surface phenomena could definitively be ruled out, the similarity between their results and those from our long duration experiments conducted at lower temperature supports our conclusion that such phenomena play at most a minor role in our most lengthy experiments. In addition, WILLIAMS (1965) obtained similar results whether diffusion experiments were conducted on fine silica fibers or silica tubes; this is consistent with our finding that grain size and sample preparation techniques are not major factors in the results of long duration isotope exchange experiments.

## DISCUSSION

### Evaluation of pitfalls

The most serious potential pitfall of our experiments is the possibility that the fractionation measured is between vapor and a surface layer rather than between vapor and bulk sample. Several observations and lines of reasoning suggest that this was not a major factor in most of our experiments.

Using our self-diffusion coefficients for oxygen in silica glass (Fig. 5), we calculate that for experiments lasting longer than about 18 days at 850°C, 6 weeks at 750°C, and 14 months at 550°C, the depth of penetration of oxygen exchange into silica glass is greater than about 1 μm. This is well into the bulk of the sample and indicates that the fractionation factors obtained from experiments of this duration are not likely to be influenced by surface effects. Experiments of at least these durations were conducted at each temperature, and inspection of the results (*e.g.*, Figs. 1 and 2) reveals that approximately constant $\delta^{18}O$ values for the gas, whether approached from heavier or lighter initial values, were achieved in runs of similar duration. In determining the "best" fractionation factors for each temperature, no runs in which calculated depths of

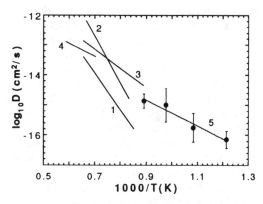

FIG. 5. Summary of data on the apparent oxygen self-diffusion coefficient in silica glass from this study and from the literature. Values from this study are averages of results of all runs of >0.5 days duration; error bars are ±2σ based on the distribution of analyses used to calculate these average values. The line through our data is given by

$$\log_{10} D \ (cm^2/s) = -11.0(1.4) - 4.3(1.3) \times 10^3/T \ (K)$$

and corresponds to an activation energy of ≈20 kcal/mole. Numbers on lines refer to: 1—HAUL and DÜMBGEN (1962); 2—SUCOV (1963); 3—WILLIAMS (1965); 4—MUEHLENBACHS and SCHAEFFER (1977); 5—this work.

penetration of exchange are less than 0.36 μm were used. For the GE214 experiments, the convergence of the results of experiments on several different size fractions to similar final $\delta^{18}O$ values at temperatures of ≥650°C also supports our conclusion that surface fractionations did not significantly influence our long duration results. Also consistent with this conclusion are the results of experiments covering a wide range of $CO_2$/silica glass ratios; in particular, indistinguishable results were obtained in 23–26 day experiments at 750°C whether the ratio of oxygen in glass wool to that in the vapor was 71 (run #4F) rather than the more typical value of about 300–500. We emphasize, however, as discussed above, that in short duration runs, there *is* evidence of the influence of surface phenomena in our experiments, including early rapid reaction, overshooting of the equilibrium values in short duration runs starting with gases with high initial $\delta^{18}O$ values (*e.g.*, experiments #22F and #22G at 650°C), and false convergences at anomalously light values (*e.g.*, experiments #7A and #7D at 650°C). Using our $D$ values, we calculate depths of penetration of at most a few tenths of a micron under the conditions of the experiments that show such effects.

Note that even if exchange extends well into the sample, but the amount of vapor is too large or its initial isotopic composition is too far away from the value in equilibrium with the silicate, then the vapor may "see" a silicate in the exchanged layer with an isotopic composition significantly different from the bulk silicate, leading to an incorrect fractionation factor if this effect were not taken into account. Although this effect is apparent in very few runs, in experiments on the coarsest size fractions of the GE214 material there is evidence of such incomplete convergence, with gas with an initial composition close to the equilibrium value more closely approaching the equilibrium value than gas with an initial value far from the equilibrium value (*e.g.,* compare #23P and #23T at 650°C). We minimized the potential impact of this problem on our results by choosing initial gas compositions close to the final value, by maximizing the silicate/vapor ratio, by decreasing grain size (in the GE214 experiments), by increasing run duration, or by some combination of these factors. The convergence of results from initially heavy and initially light $CO_2$ to final $\delta^{18}O$ values that are identical within error in long duration runs indicates that this effect of incomplete equilibration was not a problem in those runs most critical to us in evaluating fractionation factors. The lack of a dependence of the results on the ratio of the mass of $CO_2$ in an experiment to the mass of silica glass (*e.g.,* compare the results of #4F and #4H) also supports our contention that this effect was not significant in most of our experiments.

A second possible problem could be that interaction of the $CO_2$ vapor with the glass container may compete with exchange between vapor and the fine-grained sample, thus leading to spurious results. If this were a problem, we would expect the results of experiments conducted in Vycor tubes to be systematically heavier than those conducted in silica tubes, because the Vycor tubes are about 10 per mil heavier than the silica tubes (and heavier than the $\delta^{18}O$ gas values in equilibrium with the silica glass samples in all cases) and the apparent oxygen self-diffusion coefficient in Vycor is $\approx 2$ orders of magnitude greater than in silica glass (Fig. 4). Except at 950°C, experiments conducted in Vycor and silica glass tubes yield indistinguishable results. It is especially significant that in GE214 experiments conducted in silica tubes, the tube and the powdered sample were both GE214 glass with the same $\delta^{18}O$ value; these experiments could not have been disturbed by equilibration with the tube, yet experiments in Vycor tubes and GE214 tubes yield indistinguishable results except at 950°C. In hindsight, the fact that the influence of the tubes is generally negligible is not surprising based on the D values determined for oxygen self-diffusion in silica glass. For example, in an experiment on one gram of silica glass wool with a thread diameter of 10 microns in which the diffusion front has penetrated $\leq 1 \ \mu m$, the ratio of the number of oxygens exchanged in the glass wool to that exchanged in the enclosing glass tube would be about 50. At ratios this high, the effects of such interactions with the tube would generally be negligible. In extensions of the work reported here, we are using Pt tubes rather than glass to avoid entirely the possible influence of exchange with the container, but since this approach is significantly more expensive than using glass, we may return to our present methods for conditions at which interactions with glass containers can be shown to have negligible influence on the results.

## Mechanism of isotopic exchange

The activation energy for self-diffusion given by our results (20 ± 3 kcal/mole) and the two most recent previous studies of oxygen isotope exchange between silica glass and $O_2$ vapor (20–29 kcal/mole; WILLIAMS, 1965; MUEHLENBACHS and SCHAEFFER, 1977) is low compared to that of oxygen self-diffusion in jadeite melt (assumed to be a nearly fully polymerized network of aluminosilicate tetrahedra as in silica glass) based on melt diffusion couples in which a vapor phase was not present ($\sim 60$ kcal/mole; SHIMIZU and KUSHIRO, 1984) and compared to Si-O bond energies ($\sim 100$ kcal/mole; DOREMUS, 1973). Our activation energy is, however, similar to those for $O_2$ permeation (22 kcal/mole; NORTON, 1961), $O_2$ diffusion (27–31 kcal/mole; BARRER, 1951; NORTON, 1961) and Ar diffusion (24–28 kcal/mole; PERKINS and BEGEAL, 1971; CARROLL and STOLPER, 1991) in silica glass. It is also similar to those for Ar (34 kcal/mole; CARROLL, 1991), molecular $CO_2$ (34 kcal/mole; BLANK *et al.,* 1991) and molecular $H_2O$ (25 kcal/mole; ZHANG *et al.,* 1991a) in rhyolitic glass. This suggests to us that the exchange we observe is due to diffusion of molecular $CO_2$ into the glass, followed by exchange with the network of silicate tetrahedra, rather than actual self-diffusion of oxygen by exchange between oxygen sites of the network of silicate tetrahedra of which the glass is constructed. Based on similar reasoning, WILLIAMS (1965) and MUEHLENBACHS and SCHAEFFER (1977) concluded that $O_2$ mobility in the glass dominated the kinetics of isotope exchange between $O_2$ gas and fused silica.

ZHANG *et al.* (1991b) discuss in detail the relation between the apparent self-diffusion coefficient of oxygen and the diffusivity of a carrier in cases such as this in which the flux of oxygen is due to diffusion of the $CO_2$ carrier. One characteristic of such a diffusive process is that the apparent self-diffusion coefficient is equal to the product of the diffusivity of the carrier species and its concentration (provided that there is only one carrier species; note that the activation energy of apparent self-diffusion based on exchange with a vapor will in general be even lower than that for diffusion of the carrier species, because it will include a contribution from the temperature dependence of the solubility of the carrier species). Thus, the diffusion coefficient for $O_2$ in silica glass based on permeation experiments is several orders of magnitude greater than the apparent self-diffusion coefficient based on isotopic exchange experiments (WILLIAMS, 1965), because the solubility of $O_2$ in silica glass under the conditions of the exchange experiments is very low. We therefore predict that if oxygen exchange is controlled by diffusion of $CO_2$ molecules into the glass as we have concluded, then the apparent self-diffusion coefficient of oxygen will vary approximately linearly with the fugacity of $CO_2$ in the experiments. From a practical standpoint, this suggests that enhancement of sluggish isotope exchange reactions could be achieved by conducting experiments at elevated fluid pressures, an effect observed by CHACKO et al. (1991) in exchange experiments between $CO_2$ and calcite at pressures up to 13 kbar. This effect was quantified by WILLIAMS (1965) who documented a proportionality between the self-diffusion coefficient of oxygen and $pO_2$ in exchange experiments between $O_2$ vapor and silica glass.

The fact that in silica glass the activation energies of diffusion of rare gases and neutral molecular species and the activation energy for self-diffusion of oxygen in exchange experiments with $CO_2$ gas are similar suggests, based on the discussion of ZHANG et al. (1991b), that the diffusion of $CO_2$ molecules is slow relative to the exchange reaction(s) between these molecules and oxygen sites in the glass. Otherwise, the apparent activation energy for self-diffusion should be higher than 20–30 kcal/mole due to a significant contribution from the activation energy for the exchange reaction, which we expect to be on the order of 100 kcal/mole since it requires the breaking of Si-O bonds. It may be that at sufficiently low temperatures, the exchange reaction becomes the rate limiting step as a consequence of its higher activation energy; this would be observable as an increase in slope of the Arrhenius plot for apparent oxygen self-diffusion. If oxygen exchange between $CO_2$ gas and silicate glass is rate limited by the diffusion of neutral $CO_2$ molecules, available results on diffusion of rare gases suggest that exchange may be even more rapid in more complex felsic glass compositions such as rhyolite, albite, and orthoclase, in which argon diffuses more rapidly at the temperatures of interest than it does in silica glass (CARROLL, 1991; CARROLL and STOLPER, 1991).

*Temperature dependence of fractionation*

The temperature dependence of isotopic fractionation factors between vapor and condensed phases can be complex (see O'NEIL, 1986), but the logarithm of the fractionation factor is expected to be approximately proportional to $1/T^2$ at high temperatures. Although our data can be described by such a relation at 650–950°C, our 550°C data points clearly deviate from such a linear trend and the overall trend of the data is slightly concave downwards toward the $10^6/T^2$ axis in Fig. 3.

Given values for the reduced partition function ratio for oxygen in $CO_2$ vapor (BOTTINGA, 1968; CHACKO et al., 1991), our data can be used to calculate reduced partition function ratios for oxygen in silica glass. These calculated values are compared in Fig. 6 with the reduced partition function ratios for $CO_2$ vapor, quartz, and albite. Our data (which are basically linear in $1/T^2$) are well described by multiplying the reduced partition function ratio for crystalline quartz (CLAYTON et al., 1989) by 1.035. The solid curves in Figs. 3 and 6 are based on such a reduced partition function ratio for silica glass.

In Fig. 7, we have replotted the data shown in Fig. 3 with $1/T$ as the abscissa. In this representation, the data are linear and the variation in $1000\ln(\alpha)$ calculated from the reduced partition function ratios is indistinguishable from a straight line. The slope of the tangent to a curve defining an exchange reaction plotted in these coordinates is equal to $-\Delta H^0/R$, where $\Delta H^0$ is the standard state enthalpy

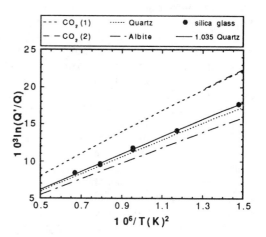

FIG. 6. Reduced partition function ratios versus $10^6/T(K)^2$. Curves for $CO_2$ are "$CO_2$ (1)" from CHACKO et al. (1991) and "$CO_2$ (2)" from BOTTINGA (1968). Curves for crystalline albite and quartz are from CLAYTON et al. (1989). Data points for silica glass (error bars are smaller than symbols) are from this study and were obtained by subtracting $1000\ln(\alpha)$ (Table 4) from the $CO_2$ reduced partition function ratio.

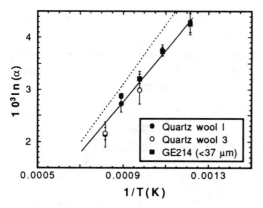

Quartz wool I
Quartz wool 3
GE214 (<37 μm)

FIG. 7. Natural logarithm of the fractionation factor between $CO_2$ vapor and silica glass versus $1/T(K)$. Error bars as in Fig. 3. The solid curve (which is essentially a straight line in this temperature range) is calculated based on the reduced partition function ratios given for $CO_2$ in CHACKO et al. (1991) and 1.035 times the crystalline quartz-1 reduced partition function ratio given in CLAYTON et al. (1989). The dashed curve is the calculated $CO_2$-crystalline quartz fractionation factor based on these reduced partition function ratios.

change of the isotopic exchange reaction. The slope of the data shown in Fig. 7 corresponds to $\Delta H^0 \approx -10$ cal/mole.

*Comparison to $CO_2$-quartz fractionation factors*

Figure 3 shows, in addition to the $CO_2$-silica glass fractionation factor from our study, the calculated $CO_2$-quartz fractionation factor based on the reduced partition function ratio for crystalline quartz (CLAYTON et al., 1989). The difference between the quartz and silica glass fractionations against $CO_2$ vapor suggests that silica glass is heavier than coexisting quartz by 0.3–0.6 per mil over the temperature range of this study. This difference is probably not resolvable at the present time given the uncertainties in our silicate and $CO_2$ gas analyses and those of CLAYTON et al. (1989) and CHACKO et al. (1991) on which the quartz-$CO_2$ fractionation is based. However, at the level of several tenths of a per mil, these results appear to confirm previous suggestions (GARLICK, 1966; MATSUHISA et al., 1979) that oxygen isotope fractionations between crystalline and amorphous materials of the same composition and similar short-range structures are small.

Note that neither the quartz-$CO_2$ nor the silica glass-$CO_2$ fractionation factors are proportional to $1/T^2$ over the temperature range of these experiments (Fig. 3). However, the fractionation factor for oxygen isotopes between these two condensed phases does closely approximate this simple rela-

tion. This reflects the fact that the reduced partition function ratios for both of the condensed phases are roughly proportional to $1/T^2$ over this temperature range, but that of $CO_2$ is not (Fig. 6).

## SUMMARY

(1) The fractionation of oxygen isotopes between $CO_2$ vapor and silica glass was determined at a total pressure of ~0.5 bars at temperatures of 550–950°C. The $^{18}O/^{16}O$ ratio of $CO_2$ vapor is higher than that of coexisting silica glass. The fractionation factor decreases from 1.0042 ± 0.0002 at 550°C to 1.0022 ± 0.0002 at 950°C.

(2) Ln($\alpha$) is linear with $1/T$ over the temperature range we investigated, corresponding to a standard state enthalpy change for the isotopic exchange reaction of approximately $-10$ cal/mole. The reduced partition function ratio for silica glass implied by our results is well described by 1.035 times that proposed for crystalline quartz by CLAYTON et al. (1989).

(3) Comparison of our results with data in the literature for quartz suggests that silica glass is enriched in $^{18}O$ relative to quartz with which it is in isotopic equilibrium by 0.3–0.6 per mil over the temperature range we have investigated. This small difference is probably not resolvable at present given the uncertainties but does confirm previous suggestions (GARLICK, 1966; MATSUHISA et al., 1979) that oxygen isotope fractionations between crystalline and amorphous materials of the same composition and similar short-range structures are small. In contrast to the vapor-glass fractionation factor, the logarithm of the crystalline quartz-silica glass fractionation factor is expected to be roughly proportional to $1/T^2$ over the temperature range of this study.

(4) Experiments were conducted to determine the kinetics of oxygen isotopic exchange between $CO_2$ vapor and silica glass. The activation energy for the apparent self-diffusion of oxygen in silica glass is similar to those for diffusion of Ar and molecular $CO_2$, $O_2$, and $H_2O$ in network glasses. This suggests that isotopic exchange in our experiments occurs by diffusion of $CO_2$ molecules into the glass followed by exchange with the oxygen atoms of the glass structure, and that the rate limiting step is the diffusion of the $CO_2$ molecules, not their reaction with the glass network. If so, oxygen isotopic exchange rates should be significantly enhanced in $CO_2$-glass experiments at elevated pressures.

(5) The success of our experiments suggests that the technique we used of equilibrating small amounts of vapor with large amounts of fine-grained solid, followed by analysis of the vapor, may be of

wide utility in determining isotopic fractionation factors, provided that, as we have done for silica glass, care is taken to distinguish bulk from surface fractionations and to demonstrate a close approach to equilibrium. This technique should be particularly useful for determining fractionation factors involving other framework glasses (*e.g.*, albite, orthoclase, etc.) that are known to have higher diffusivities of noble gases than does silica glass and for minerals with open structures into which water and carbon dioxide can readily diffuse.

*Acknowledgements*—We thank Ms. E. Dent for assistance with sample preparation and analysis, Dr. P. Dobson and Ms. J. Blank for assistance with some of the experiments, and Dr. S. Newman for help in sample characterization. We also thank Professor A. Matthews for invaluable advice and comments on this work, Professor Youxue Zhang for assistance in reducing the diffusion data, Professor R. Clayton and Ms. T. Mayeda for analyzing several of our starting materials, and Dr. J. Beckett, Professor J. R. O'Neil, and Professor H. P. Taylor for careful reviews. This work was supported by DOE Grant DE-FG03-85ER13445. Caltech Division of Geological and Planetary Sciences Contribution 5044.

# REFERENCES

ANDERSON A. T., JR., CLAYTON R. N. and MAYEDA T. K. (1971) Oxygen isotope thermometry of mafic igneous rocks. *J. Geol.* **79**, 715–729.

BARRER R. M. (1951) *Diffusion In and Through Solids.* Cambridge University Press.

BLANK J. G., STOLPER E. M. and ZHANG Y. (1991) Diffusion of $CO_2$ in rhyolitic melt. *Eos* **72**, 312.

BOTTINGA Y. (1968) Calculation of fractionation factors for carbon and oxygen isotopic exchange in the system calcite-carbon dioxide-water. *J. Phys. Chem.* **72**, 800–808.

CARROLL M. R. (1991) Diffusion of Ar in rhyolite, orthoclase and albite composition glasses. *Earth Planet. Sci. Lett.* **103**, 156–168.

CARROLL M. R. and STOLPER E. (1991) Argon solubility and diffusion in silica glass: Implications for the solution behavior of molecular gases. *Geochim. Cosmochim. Acta* **55**, 211–225.

CHACKO T., MAYEDA T. K., CLAYTON R. N. and GOLDSMITH J. R. (1991) Oxygen and carbon isotope fractionations between $CO_2$ and calcite. *Geochim. Cosmochim. Acta* **55**, 2867–2882.

CHIBA H., CHACKO T., CLAYTON R. N. and GOLDSMITH J. R. (1989) Oxygen isotope fractionations involving diopside, forsterite, magnetite, and calcite: Application to geothermometry. *Geochim. Cosmochim. Acta* **53**, 2985–2995.

CLAYTON R. N., GOLDSMITH J. R. and MAYEDA T. K. (1989) Oxygen isotope fractionation in quartz, albite, anorthite, and calcite. *Geochim. Cosmochim. Acta* **53**, 725–733.

CONNOLLY C. and MUEHLENBACHS K. (1988) Contrasting oxygen diffusion in nepheline, diopside and other silicates and their relevance to isotopic systematics in meteorites. *Geochim. Cosmochim. Acta* **52**, 1585–1591.

DOREMUS R. H. (1973) *Glass Science.* J. Wiley & Sons.

GARLICK G. D. (1966) Oxygen isotope fractionation in igneous rocks. *Earth Planet. Sci. Lett.* **1**, 361–368.

HAUL R. and DÜMBGEN G. (1962) Untersuchung der Sauerstoffbeweglichkeit in Titandioxyd, Quarz und Quarzglas mit Hilfe des heterogenen Isotopenaustausches. *Z. Elektrochemie* **66**, 636–641.

LIU K. K. and EPSTEIN S. (1984) The hydrogen isotope fractionation between kaolinite and water. *Isotope Geosci.* **2**, 335–350.

MATSUHISA Y. (1979) Oxygen isotopic compositions of volcanic rocks from the East Japan island arcs and their bearing on petrogenesis. *J. Volcanol. Geotherm. Res.* **5**, 271–296.

MATSUHISA Y., GOLDSMITH J. R. and CLAYTON R. N. (1979) Oxygen isotope fractionation in the system quartz-albite-anorthite-water. *Geochim. Cosmochim. Acta* **43**, 1131–1140.

MUEHLENBACHS K. and KUSHIRO I. (1974) Oxygen isotope exchange and equilibrium of silicates with $CO_2$ or $O_2$. *Carnegie Inst. Wash. Yearb.* **73**, 232–236.

MUEHLENBACHS K. and SCHAEFFER H. A. (1977) Oxygen diffusion in vitreous silica—Utilization of natural oxygen abundances. *Canadian Mineral.* **15**, 179–184.

NORTON F. J. (1961) Permeation of gaseous oxygen through vitreous silica. *Nature* **191**, 701.

O'NEIL J. R. (1986) Theoretical and experimental aspects of isotopic fractionation. In *Stable Isotopes in High Temperature Geological Processes* (eds. J. H. VALLEY, H. P. TAYLOR, and J. R. O'NEIL); *Rev. Mineral.* **16**, pp. 1–40. Mineralogical Society of America.

O'NEIL J. R. and EPSTEIN S. (1966) Oxygen isotope fractionation in the system dolomite-calcite-carbon dioxide. *Science* **152**, 198–201.

PERKINS W. G. and BEGEAL D. R. (1971) Diffusion and permeation of He, Ne, Ar, Kr, and $D_2$ through silicon oxide thin films. *J. Chem. Phys.* **54**, 1683–1694.

PFEFFER R. and OHRING M. (1982) Network oxygen exchange during water diffusion in $SiO_2$. *J. Appl. Phys.* **52**, 777–784.

SHIMIZU N. and KUSHIRO I. (1984) Diffusivity of oxygen in jadeite and diopside melts at high pressures. *Geochim. Cosmochim. Acta* **48**, 1295–1303.

SUCOV E. W. (1963) Diffusion of oxygen in vitreous silica. *J. Amer. Ceram. Soc.* **46**, 14–20.

TAYLOR H. P., JR. (1968) The oxygen isotope geochemistry of igneous rocks. *Contrib. Mineral. Petrol.* **19**, 1–71.

WILLIAMS E. L. (1965) Diffusion of oxygen in fused silica. *J. Amer. Ceram. Soc.* **48**, 190–194.

ZHANG Y., STOLPER E. and WASSERBURG G. J. (1991a) Diffusion of water in rhyolitic glasses. *Geochim. Cosmochim. Acta* **55**, 441–456.

ZHANG Y., STOLPER E. and WASSERBURG G. J. (1991b) Diffusion of a multi-species component and its role in oxygen and water transport in silicates. *Earth Planet. Sci. Lett.* **103**, 228–240.

Stable Isotope Geochemistry: A Tribute to Samuel Epstein
© The Geochemical Society, Special Publication No. 3, 1991
Editors: H. P. Taylor, Jr., J. R. O'Neil and I. R. Kaplan

# D/H analysis of minerals by ion probe

E. DELOULE, C. FRANCE-LANORD and F. ALBARÈDE

Centre de Recherches Pétrographiques et Géochimiques, et Ecole Nationale Supérieure de Géologie,
BP 20, 54501 Vandoeuvre Cedex, France

**Abstract**—D/H ratios with a precision of ±10 per mil have been measured by ion microprobe on 13 amphiboles, 7 biotites, and 3 muscovites of different chemical compositions previously analyzed for major elements by electron probe and for D/H ratios by standard mass spectrometry. Amphiboles have Fe/(Fe + Mg) ratios of 0.06 to 1 (actinolite, edenite, pargasite, richterite, kaersutite, arfvedsonite). The instrumental D/H fractionation factor $\alpha_{ins}$, taken as D/H$_{SIMS}$ divided by D/H$_{MS}$, ranges from 0.47 to 0.61. Such a variation greatly exceeds the reproducibility of the measurements on each sample and must result from a matrix effect. Calibration of the fractionation as a function of chemical composition allows the D/H ratio of hydrous minerals to be measured *in situ* by ion microprobe. A strong correlation between $\alpha_{ins}$ and the total electronegativity of the surrounding octahedral cations is observed for both amphiboles and micas, and indicates that fractionation depends essentially on the strength of the OH bond. The relation between D/H fractionation and ion energy is opposite to that commonly observed and invalidates the bond-breaking model for H$^+$ sputtering. Fitting the hydrogen energy spectrum with different distribution laws supports a model in which repeated absorption of near-infrared photons initially captured by the surrounding elements increases the OH stretching energy until a H$^+$ is emitted.

## INTRODUCTION

THE FIRST ATTEMPTS to use the ion probe for D/H ratio measurements by HINTON *et al.* (1983) and ZINNER *et al.* (1983) were made on meteoritic samples and strastospheric dust for which isotopic variations ($\delta D = -500$ to $+4500$) could be expected to exceed greatly the large and variable instrumental fractionations reported by the authors (>100 per mil). The present work describes an analytical procedure for *in situ* measurement of hydrogen isotope compositions by ion probe applicable to terrestrial hydrous minerals, principally amphiboles but also micas. It is useful to be able to measure the $\delta D$ value of individual minerals from, for example, mantle xenoliths, mixed mineral populations associated with superimposed alteration, or hydrothermal processes, or to characterize D/H zoning. As the $\delta D$ values of most terrestrial samples lie in the range $-200$ to $+20$, a precision of ±10 per mil provides significant results. The present study is devoted primarily to the understanding of the chemical factors which determine instrumental D/H fractionations in amphiboles. Some biotites and muscovites were also analyzed in order to assess the effects of crystallographic parameters.

## ANALYTICAL PROCEDURE

Crystals are mounted in epoxy, polished, gold coated, and stored in an oven at 70°C in order to minimize water adsorption. Poor reproducibility is achieved for muscovite and this is ascribed to strong crystal orientation effects. Therefore, an aliquot of the muscovite is gently powdered in an agate mortar and pressed as a flat pellet, 5 mm in diameter, before mounting as above.

A negative primary oxygen beam, with intensity ranging from 2 to 5 mA, is focused to produce a 10 $\mu$m wide beam and scanned over 25 $\mu$m. The secondary beam, permanently realigned with the principal axis by a dynamic transfer optical device, is centered in a 60 $\mu$m image field aperture. This is small enough to obtain high resolving power and wide enough to transmit the whole beam, including its spatial aberration due to the use of the widest contrast aperture. Mass resolution is set at 1300 in order to separate D$^+$ from H$_2^+$ ions. Magnet control was modified for better resolution by narrowing the field range from 300 to 50 amu. Positive secondary ions of hydrogen and deuterium are collected as single atomic ions. H, H$_2$, and D are measured by peak switching, the H$_2$ peak being included to improve the magnet settings on D. The flat peak top comprises five magnet DAC units within a few per mil of the maximum intensity (Fig. 1). As the drift of the magnetic field over an hour exceeds the peak width, the three central DAC channels are counted. Every five minutes, the position of the H peak center is updated, and the field adjustment is estimated for D and H$_2$ from the drift of the magnetic field on H. When counting statistics become precise enough, *i.e.* after about an hour, an intrinsic adjustment is made.

No energy filtering is applied and the energy slit is kept wide open. The electron multiplier is used in the counting mode. For H, the counting rates range from 30,000 to 100,000 cps. Counting times of 3, 2, and 15 seconds are used for H, H$_2$, and D, respectively, and waiting time is 1.5 seconds. Successive measurement cycles are accumulated for 90 to 120 minutes on the same sample position until good counting statistics are achieved on D ($\approx 5$ per mil).

Moisture from evaporation of absorbed water in the ion probe favors formation of hydrides. The D/H ratio of moisture is very low, and so the presence of moisture increases the H$_2$/H ratio and decreases the D/H ratio (Fig. 2). Special care is taken to remove moisture by baking the sample and ion probe at 120°C, and using a liquid nitrogen trap. When the H$_2$/H ratio is reduced to lower than $10^{-3}$, there is no contribution of the low D/H moisture component (Fig. 3). Analyses are carried out only

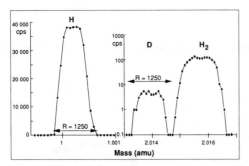

FIG. 1. High resolution mass spectrum of H, D, and $H_2$ ions. Primary beam intensity of 5 nA, beam size of 15 $\mu$m, image field aperture 60 $\mu$m, energy slit wide open, full magnetic field range 50 amu.

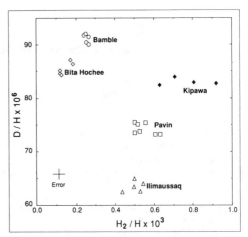

FIG. 3. D/H and $H_2$/H ratios of different amphiboles upon overnight baking of the sample and ion probe with cold trap in use.

under the conditions where the $H_2$/H ratio is less than 8 × $10^{-4}$. This value is probably characteristic of $H_2$ production during the analysis of water-bearin minerals in a water-free environment.

The size of the sputtered area is about 30 × 30 $\mu$m and the hole is up to 6 $\mu$m deep. It corresponds to about 10 nanograms of amphibole and 20 picomoles of hydrogen. A conventional analysis by mass spectrometry may involve tens to hundreds of micromoles. Calculation of the useful hydrogen yield for SIMS isotopic measurement suggests a value of about $10^{-4}$. The long-term reproducibility of measurements on the same mineral is better than 10 per mil (Fig. 4).

Major elements were analyzed with similar primary beam adjustments, no energy offset, and the energy slit open at ±20 V. H, Li, F, Na, Mg, Al, Si, K, Ca, Ti, Cr, Mn, and Fe beams were measured. As $O^+$ and $Cl^+$ abundances were found to be very low, their measurement was discontinued. Mass resolution was set at a high value (4500) to overcome isobaric interferences, essentially hydrides and oxides. The Ca and Cr peaks were corrected

for respective Ti and Fe contributions. For each element having at least two isotopes, possible interferences were monitored by measuring one major and one minor isotope of the same element concurrently and checking the isotopic ratios against accepted values. Oxide and hydride molecular compounds and the doubly-charged ions were found to represent less than a few per cent of their corresponding atomic singly-charged ion: for instance, a typical value of a few $10^{-4}$ was measured for the $H_2$/H ratio. Counting rates were kept under 500,000 cps and dead time was corrected. Achievement of reproducible analytical conditions was given a very high priority.

## RESULTS

The standard minerals consist of single crystals, 13 amphiboles, 7 biotites, and 3 powdered muscovites, for which chemical compositions and $\delta$D were determined by electron probe and conventional mass spectrometry, respectively (Table 1). Standard amphibole minerals were selected in order to cover a broad range of Fe and Mg content, with Fe/(Fe + Mg) ratios of 0.06 to 1 (actinolite, edenite,

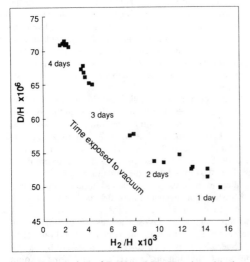

FIG. 2. Evolution of D/H and $H_2$/H ratios with time spent in the evacuated ion probe for the amphibole sample Etoile. Sample and ion-probe not baked, no cold trap.

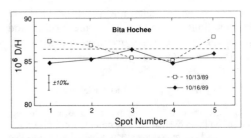

FIG. 4. Long-term reproducibility of D/H measurements. Analyzed area: 30 × 30 $\mu$m; measurement duration: 1.5 hours. Analyzed spots spaced by 125 $\mu$m. Horizontal lines represent the mean value for five analyses.

pargasite, richterite, kaersutite, and arfvedsonite). On each sample, the D/H ratio was measured on 10 to 20 points distributed over different minerals from the same sample. The instrumental D/H fractionation factor $\alpha_{ins}$ corresponds to the ratio of D/H measured by SIMS to the absolute D/H determined from measured $\delta$D values and absolute D/H ratio for SMOW (HAGEMANN et al., 1970). $\alpha_{ins}$ is highly variable between 0.47 to 0.61 (Table 1). Such a variation exceeds the reproducibility of the measurements on each sample and is therefore likely to result from a matrix effect.

Quite frequently, instrumental isotopic fractionation in non-metallic solids decreases linearly with the reciprocal of emission velocity $v_i$ calculated as $(2E/M)^{1/2}$ where $E$ and $M$ are the ion energy and mass, respectively (SLODZIAN et al., 1980). The curve representing the measured distribution of energy or energy spectrum of hydrogen is reported in Fig. 5. Two difficulties arise in obtaining such a curve. First, since the energy slit cannot be narrowed indefinitely without a dramatic loss in sensitivity, the measured intensity represents an average over a finite energy interval. This biases somewhat the results for regions with sharp gradients. Secondly, positioning of the energy window relative to the optical of the probe and charge build-up on the sample surface make the absolute position of zero energy uncertain. However, since only ions with positive energy may be extracted from the surface, it will be assumed that the zero energy level coincides with the well-defined onset of the signal as energy increases. Noticeably, $\alpha_{ins}$ for amphibole is positively correlated with $v_i^{-1}$, with a decrease of D emissivity relative to H for increasing emission velocity (Fig. 6).

In order to assess possible relations between instrumental mass fractionation and elemental emissivity in amphiboles, beam intensities were also measured for major elements. Matrix effects on instrumental D/H fractionation were calibrated empirically as a function of the beam intensity of major chemical species and the regression coefficients calculated with a standard commercial package. Elements which did not contribute significantly to the quality of the fit (i.e. those which have no effect on the probable error) were progressively dropped out in order to make the regression as overconstrained as possible. The best fit was obtained for the following equation:

$$\alpha_{ins} = 0.56975 + 0.00604 I_{Si} - 0.00056 I_{Ca}$$
$$- 0.01799 I_{Ti} - 0.16976 I_{Mn} \quad (1)$$

where $I_j$ refers to the beam intensity of the element $j$ corrected for isotopic abundances and normalized to a unit sum over all measured elements. The probable error of the fit is 0.00376, which amounts to an average uncertainty of less than 7 per mil (Fig. 7). Si and Mn induce the strongest shifts of $\alpha_{ins}$, while the effects of Ca and Ti are fairly small (Fig. 8). It is rather surprising to find that Mn produces a more significant shift than, for instance, Fe, which is ten times more concentrated. The reason is largely fortuitous. Fe and Mn being well-correlated and both measured accurately, the present procedure which selects only independent parameters produces more precise results with only one of them; for the present set of samples, this happens to be Mn.

Understanding the empirical relation (1) requires the assessment of hydrogen emissivity with respect to the emissivity of other elements. The elemental ionization yields relative to Si (RIY) for an element $j$ is calculated from

$$RIY_j = \frac{I_j/C_j}{I_{Si}/C_{Si}} \quad (2)$$

where $C$ refers to the concentration of the elements $j$ and Si measured by electron probe. Average $RIY_j$ values vary from 0.06 for H to ca. 44 for K. For all measured elements the $RIY_j$ value varies by an order of magnitude among the different amphiboles (Table 2). From previous studies (ANDERSEN and HINTHORNE, 1973), it is known that $RIY_j$ is inversely correlated with the first ionization potential (Fig. 9). As for $\alpha_{ins}$, $RIY_j$ values were handled as a linear combination of the beam intensity of the major elements and the significant coefficients calculated by linear regression. A good fit is obtained for each element, implying that amphibole composition can be calculated from measured secondary beam intensities.

It has been shown by SHIMIZU (1986) that ion emissivity in silicates increases with Si content. In amphiboles this is true only for Na, K, and Ca which have a large ionic radius. For other elements, the $RIY_j$ values decrease when the silica content increases. Cross-effects of elements other than Si are complex; in general, Ca enhances, and Mg and Mn decrease the emissivity of most elements except H. H seems to be controlled by a markedly different sputtering mechanism, its very low emissivity being enhanced by Al and depressed by Ca and Ti. Metal hydride formation could selectively depress $H^+$ emissivity. Therefore, the beam intensity has been measured for the hydride species of all the major elements, both in positive and negative secondary ions. The H distributions among H-bearing species are reported in Fig. 10. Metal hydride intensities are always less than 1% relative to the metal inten-

Table 1. Structural formula, δD values and D/H instrumental

| Sample | Type | Si | Al_tetr | Al_oct | Fe^II | Fe^III | Mg | Mn |
|--------|------|----|---------|--------|-------|--------|----|----|
| *Amphibole* | | | | | | | | |
| PavinA | Mg Kaers. | 5.64 | 2.36 | 0.14 | 1.17 | 0.12 | 2.94 | 0.01 |
| MtEmma | Pargasite | 6.01 | 1.95 | 0.47 | 0.88 | 0.33 | 3.14 | 0.01 |
| Kipawa | Mg Hast. | 6.75 | 1.25 | 0.22 | 1.33 | 0.27 | 3.13 | 0.03 |
| LacKip | Richterite | 8.00 | 0.01 | 0.08 | 1.08 | 0.00 | 3.75 | 0.05 |
| BitaHochee | Mg Kaers. | 6.07 | 1.93 | 0.23 | 1.28 | 0.12 | 2.90 | 0.01 |
| Bamble | Mg Hast. | 7.38 | 0.62 | 0.12 | 0.84 | 0.17 | 3.87 | 0.01 |
| PavinB | Mg Kaers | 5.79 | 2.21 | 0.23 | 1.23 | 0.02 | 2.88 | 0.01 |
| IlimaussaqB | Fe Richt. | 7.98 | 0.02 | 0.34 | 4.26 | 0.00 | 0.09 | 0.05 |
| AlpesFA | Pargasite | 5.87 | 2.13 | 0.71 | 0.95 | 0.43 | 2.85 | 0.02 |
| Australia DV | Richerite | 7.66 | 0.07 | 0.00 | 0.29 | 0.00 | 4.63 | 0.01 |
| Mickland | Mg Hast. | 7.53 | 0.45 | 0.14 | 0.81 | 0.14 | 3.92 | 0.01 |
| AlpesUR | Gedrite | 7.57 | 0.43 | 0.26 | 0.71 | 0.17 | 3.89 | 0.04 |
| Seljas | Tremolite | 7.99 | 0.01 | 0.00 | 0.92 | 0.00 | 4.21 | 0.01 |
| Etoile | Mg Kaers. | 5.84 | 2.13 | 0.38 | 1.00 | 0.18 | 2.95 | 0.01 |
| IlimaussaqA | Mg Arfv. | 8.13 | 0.00 | 0.16 | 3.85 | 0.58 | 0.00 | 0.09 |
| *Biotite* | | | | | | | | |
| BE 114 | | 5.42 | 2.58 | 0.60 | 1.45 | 0.30 | 3.26 | 0.01 |
| M 114 | | 5.46 | 2.54 | 0.75 | 1.74 | 0.30 | 2.75 | 0.01 |
| NA 28 | | 5.45 | 2.55 | 0.89 | 2.30 | 0.07 | 2.21 | 0.01 |
| D 14 | | 5.45 | 2.55 | 0.98 | 3.05 | 0.00 | 1.18 | 0.02 |
| D 65 | | 5.48 | 2.52 | 1.08 | 2.39 | 0.42 | 0.96 | 0.04 |
| U 315 | | 5.42 | 2.58 | 1.12 | 2.86 | 0.42 | 0.64 | 0.09 |
| X 77 | | 5.46 | 2.54 | 1.44 | 2.48 | 0.44 | 0.55 | 0.09 |
| *Muscovite* | | | | | | | | |
| D 14 | | 6.16 | 1.84 | 3.62 | 0.27 | — | 0.16 | 0.00 |
| DK 127 | | 6.25 | 1.75 | 3.65 | 0.34 | — | 0.09 | 0.01 |
| NL 506 | | 6.16 | 1.84 | 3.66 | 0.26 | — | 0.14 | 0.00 |

Chemical compositions measured by electron microprobe except for Li measured by atomic absorbtion and $H_2$ measured manometrically after quantitative extraction. Structural formulas of amphibole are calculated according to PAPIKE *et al.* (1974). m/c: mean mass/charge ratio for the octahedrally coordinated cations (SUZUOKI and EPSTEIN, 1976). TEN: total electronegativity of the M(1,3) site. δD measured by mass spectrometry (*e.g.* FRANCE-LANORD *et al.* 1988). $\alpha_{ins}$: instrumental fractionation as $(D/H_{IMS})/(D/H_{MS})$. Data for micas are from FRANCE-LANORD (1987) and FRANCE-LANORD *et al.* (1988) and for IlimaussaqB amphibole from SHEPPARD (1986).

sities. In the positive secondary beam, $H^+$ is largely dominant, the main hydrides (Mg, Ca, Si, Al, in this order) being less than ten per cent of the total. Conversely, the dominant negative secondary species are $OH^-$ and $H^-$, with an $OH^-/H^-$ ratio of about five. Due to the very low emissivity of the metals as negative ions, the negative hydrides ($CaH^-$, $MgH^-$, $SiH^-$) are less abundant than their positive counterparts.

## DISCUSSION

### Instrumental fractionation

Most published data on isotopic effects in ionization process concern pure metals (*e.g.* SHIMIZU and HART, 1982a,b; SOEDERVALL *et al.,* 1988) or simple salts and oxides (*e.g.* SLODZIAN *et al.,* 1980; LORIN *et al.,* 1982; CHAUSSIDON and DEMANGE, 1988; GNASER and HUTCHEON, 1988). As hydrogen is a minor element, even in hydrous minerals, hydrogen-hydrogen effects are expected to be insig-

nificant compared to those of hydrogen-silicate. The lighter isotopes are preferentially extracted, and this effect is more pronounced for light elements because of their larger relative mass difference. Mass fractionation has been suggested to depend on (i) the mass ratio of the isotopes, (ii) the strength of the chemical bond between the analyzed ion and its matrix, (iii) the work function of the surface, and (iv) the energy of the secondary ions. Due to the large relative mass difference between D and H, a large mass fractionation in sputtering and ionization was anticipated.

The bond breaking model (SLODZIAN *et al.,* 1980), widely accepted for ionic solids, predicts that fractionation depends on ion emission velocity. The isotopic fractionation $\alpha_{ins}$ is the relative difference of the ionization probability of isotope $i$ and $j$, and can be expressed as

$$F_{ji} = \alpha_{ins} - 1 = \frac{P_j}{P_i} - 1 \# - \frac{M_0 v_0}{v_i} \quad (3)$$

fractionation of the standard amphiboles and biotites.

| Ti | Cr | Ca | Na | K | Li | F | Cl | OH | m/c | TEN | δD | $\alpha_{ins}$ |
|---|---|---|---|---|---|---|---|---|---|---|---|---|
| 0.66 | 0.001 | 1.92 | 0.66 | 0.23 | — | 0.067 | 0.022 | 0.98 | 15.82 | 4.051 | −48 | 0.543 |
| 0.32 | 0.011 | 1.70 | 0.73 | 0.29 | — | 0.032 | 0.011 | 1.40 | 14.81 | 4.019 | −50 | 0.576 |
| 0.09 | 0.006 | 1.75 | 0.72 | 0.20 | 0.029 | 0.344 | 0.151 | 1.45 | 16.41 | 4.051 | −88 | 0.563 |
| 0.02 | 0.001 | 0.84 | 1.85 | 0.43 | — | 1.310 | 0.002 | 0.57 | 15.68 | 3.878 | −112 | 0.573 |
| 0.49 | 0.002 | 1.73 | 0.71 | 0.37 | — | 0.023 | 0.016 | 1.27 | 16.11 | 4.051 | −52 | 0.542 |
| 0.04 | 0.002 | 1.83 | 0.45 | 0.05 | 0.002 | 0.043 | 0.031 | 1.99 | 14.83 | 3.794 | −61 | 0.591 |
| 0.64 | 0.001 | 1.91 | 0.63 | 0.23 | — | 0.038 | 0.015 | 0.97 | 15.89 | 4.050 | −48 | 0.543 |
| 0.08 | 0.000 | 0.38 | 2.96 | 0.18 | — | 0.152 | 0.004 | 1.05 | 26.04 | 4.861 | −190 | 0.480 |
| 0.04 | 0.000 | 1.99 | 0.84 | 0.08 | 0.005 | 0.004 | 0.004 | 4.17 | 15.32 | 3.911 | −100 | 0.556 |
| 0.34 | 0.000 | 1.03 | 0.91 | 0.99 | — | 1.505 | 0.003 | 0.21 | 12.22 | 3.730 | −149 | 0.597 |
| 0.04 | 0.002 | 1.82 | 0.38 | 0.04 | 0.001 | 0.022 | 0.014 | 1.98 | 14.72 | 3.900 | −60 | |
| 0.01 | 0.054 | 1.73 | 0.19 | 0.01 | 0.005 | 0.008 | 0.006 | 2.34 | 14.21 | 3.843 | −52 | 0.591 |
| 0.00 | 0.001 | 1.85 | 0.03 | 0.00 | — | 0.004 | 0.010 | 2.09 | 14.64 | 3.784 | −64 | 0.607 |
| 0.56 | 0.002 | 1.67 | 0.77 | 0.28 | 0.001 | 0.019 | 0.017 | 0.83 | 15.18 | 4.054 | −112 | 0.568 |
| 0.07 | 0.000 | 0.06 | 2.32 | 0.68 | 0.606 | 0.085 | 0.003 | 2.38 | 25.91 | 4.945 | −142 | 0.469 |
| | | | | | | | | | | | | |
| 0.19 | — | 0.00 | 0.20 | 1.50 | — | — | — | 2 | 16.11 | 4.163 | −68 | 0.566 |
| 0.20 | — | 0.00 | 0.03 | 1.57 | — | — | — | 2 | 16.87 | 4.263 | −87 | 0.546 |
| 0.23 | — | 0.00 | 0.16 | 1.57 | — | — | — | 2 | 18.11 | 4.356 | −81 | 0.517 |
| 0.31 | — | 0.00 | 0.04 | 1.83 | — | — | — | 2 | 20.32 | 4.765 | −188 | 0.493 |
| 0.25 | — | 0.00 | 0.00 | 1.68 | 0.550 | — | — | 2 | 18.25 | 4.470 | −99 | 0.504 |
| 0.21 | — | 0.00 | 0.05 | 1.88 | — | — | — | 2 | 20.69 | 4.711 | −162 | 0.507 |
| 0.24 | — | 0.00 | 0.03 | 1.68 | — | — | — | 2 | 19.54 | 4.703 | −99 | 0.513 |
| | | | | | | | | | | | | |
| 0.05 | — | 0.00 | 0.14 | 1.80 | — | 0.003 | 0.000 | 2 | 9.86 | 2.996 | −184 | 0.636 |
| 0.01 | — | 0.00 | 0.12 | 1.79 | — | 0.235 | 0.000 | 2 | 10.63 | 3.012 | −84 | 0.637 |
| 0.02 | — | 0.00 | 0.57 | 1.39 | — | 0.045 | 0.000 | 2 | 10.33 | 3.000 | −57 | 0.644 |

where $P_i$ is the ionization probability of atom $i$, $v_i$ its emission velocity, $v_0$ a constant for a given matrix, and $M_0 = (M_j/M_i)^{1/2} - 1$, $M_j$ and $M_i$ being the atomic mass. This relation has received further support from later studies of SLODZIAN (1982), SROUBEK (1988), GNASER and HUTCHEON (1988), GOLDBERG et al., (1988), and SOEDERVALL et al., (1988). Although the average $RIY_j$ of each element is indeed roughly inversely related to the first ionization potential (Fig. 9), which is an essential feature of this model (YU, 1988), the dependence of D/H fractionation in amphibole with emission velocity is opposite to what the bond breaking model predicts (Fig. 6). A low yield for hydrogen relative to those of most other cations could be taken as supporting a model of self-ionization of excited atoms (YU, 1988), which is known to describe adequately light atom sputtering (SROUBEK, 1988). However, the equation proposed by YU (1988) for transition probability predicts that isotopic fractionation is independent of emission velocity, which makes this model unacceptable.

Few other cases of inverse relationships between mass fractionation and emission velocity have been observed; they seem to be restricted to metals (SHIMIZU and HART, 1982a,b). Interatomic forces in metals, however, cannot be compared to those in silicates.

Even though conventional models fail to predict the positive correlation of fractionation with $v^{-1}$, several arguments support control of the hydrogen yield by its bonding energy with the surrounding atoms. SUZUOKI and EPSTEIN (1976) showed that, at a given temperature, D/H fractionation between OH-bearing minerals and water is strongly correlated with the mean atomic mass/charge (m/c) ratio of the octahedrally coordinated cations. $\alpha_{ins}$ values are reported in Fig. 11 for amphiboles, biotites, and muscovites against the m/c ratio. The linear array calculated for these three minerals has a probable error of 0.011. Although this empirical correlation is difficult to account for quantitatively in terms of a simple physical model, consistent variations for

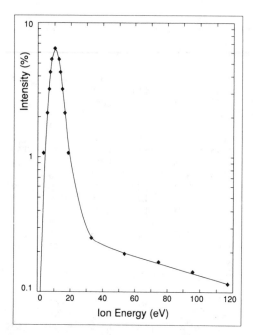

FIG. 5. Full diamonds: measured energy spectrum of hydrogen ions with energy slit open at $\pm 2.5$ V. Charge buildup makes absolute energy offset uncertain by $\pm 2$ V. The curve represents the energy distribution fitted through Eqns. (6) and (7).

widely different structures supports control of D/H fractionation by the configuration and/or bonding energy of the OH-sites.

The good correlation of $\alpha_{ins}$ with the product of the mean electronegativity (MEN) by the number $N_\diamondsuit$ of octahedral cations surrounding OH shown in Fig. 12 allows a better formulation involving the energy of the oxygen-hydrogen bond. HAWTHORNE (1981) reviewed the infrared data relevant to the variation of the O-H bond strength in amphibole with the nature of surrounding octahedral cations, the fundamental O-H stretching band shifting from 3675 cm$^{-1}$ for a magnesian-cummingtonite end member to 3615 cm$^{-1}$ for a ferro-actinolite end member. In addition, MEN is also known to be extremely well correlated with the frequency shift of the infrared absorption lines, and therefore with the O-H bond energy. The same dependence of the O-H bond shift on the nature of the octahedral cations and its correlation with their MEN are observed for micas (VELDE, 1983; ROSSMAN, 1984). The frequency shifts are 96 cm$^{-1}$ per MEN unit in trioctahedral micas, 170 cm$^{-1}$ for dioctahedral micas (VELDE, 1983), and 100 cm$^{-1}$ for amphiboles (HAWTHORNE, 1981). Amphibole data suggest that the shift of the OH bond strength due to each octahedral cation is reasonably additive. Hence, a convenient measure of the relative bond strength

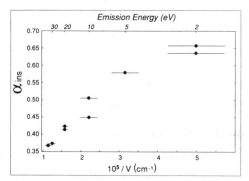

FIG. 6. D/H instrumental fractionation ($\alpha_{ins}$) vs. emission velocity ($1/v$) for hydrogen sputtered from the amphibole sample Lac Kip. The energy slit width is open at $\pm 5$ V.

will be the sum of the contribution of each neighbor which we take as the product of $N_\diamondsuit$ by MEN, with $N_\diamondsuit$ set to two for muscovite and three for biotite and amphibole. Figure 12 is a strong indication that for the three different hydrous minerals, the structural environment, which ultimately controls the strength of the O-H bond, is the predominant control of the D/H fractionation.

Nevertheless, it is known that non-octahedral cations also affect O-H stretching. Na and K in the

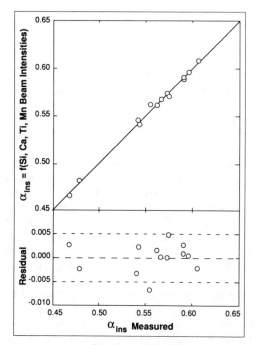

FIG. 7. Comparison of the values calculated from Si, Ca, Ti, and Mn beam intensities through Eqn. (1) (top) and residual errors (bottom) with the measured $\alpha_{ins}$ values.

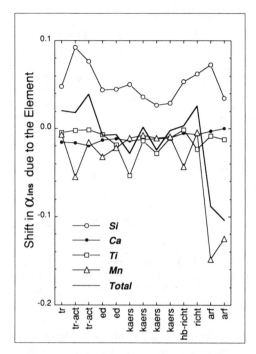

FIG. 8. Contribution of Si, Ca, Ti, and Mn beam intensities to the variation of the D/H instrumental fractionation factor $\alpha_{ins}$, as calculated from Eqn. (1), on each of the standard amphiboles.

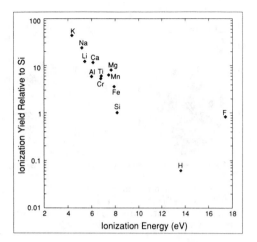

FIG. 9. Mean values of element ionization yield relative to Si ($RIY_j$) as a function of the first ionization energy for the major element measured in amphiboles.

"A" sites of amphiboles raises the frequency by about 60 cm$^{-1}$ in the richterite-tremolite series (ROWBOTHAM and FARMER, 1973), by 30–40 cm$^{-1}$ for hastingsite and pargasite (SEMET, 1973), by 24 cm$^{-1}$ in riebeckite (STRENS, 1974), and GRAHAM et al. (1984) suggested that these cations could affect D-H fractionation between water and amphiboles. Ca in the M(4) positions also increases the stretch-

ing frequency by about 2 cm$^{-1}$ (HAWTHORNE, 1981). Because of these complex effects, the relation displayed in Fig. 12 is no more than a good first-order physical model valid for different hydrous phases. For practical purposes, an empirical calibration of the D/H fractionation with amphibole composition can be expected to provide better results.

As hydrogen isotope fractionation is related to mineral structure, most of the hydrogen ionization should occur below the layer disturbed by the sputtering process (= mixing layer) without later recombination. Unfortunately, the thickness of this mixing layer, which is known to be some 10 nm in the case of semi-conductors and metals at 10 kV (HOFMANN, 1982; ARMOUR et al., 1988), is unknown for silicates.

Table 2. Ionization yield relative to Si for standard amphiboles.

| | H/Si | F/Si | Na/Si | Mg/Si | Al/Si | K/Si | Ca/Si | Ti/Si | Cr/Si | Mn/Si | Fe/Si | $^{28}$Si cps |
|---|---|---|---|---|---|---|---|---|---|---|---|---|
| PavinA | 0.016 | 0.10 | 13.01 | 5.51 | 4.58 | 14.59 | 8.88 | 3.07 | 5.09 | 3.79 | 2.9 | 27000 |
| MtEmma | 0.026 | 0.40 | 24.40 | 7.84 | 6.43 | 33.09 | 13.06 | 2.53 | 5.44 | 6.76 | 3.25 | 34500 |
| Kipawa | 0.012 | 0.37 | 24.76 | 7.39 | 6.33 | 33.57 | 12.52 | 4.07 | 5.01 | 5.80 | 3.71 | 200660 |
| LacKip | 0.031 | 0.15 | 17.61 | 6.09 | 4.75 | 28.29 | 10.20 | 4.72 | 1.33 | 4.88 | 3.08 | 107000 |
| BitaHochee | 0.066 | 1.68 | 37.93 | 10.32 | 7.95 | 50.89 | 16.58 | 4.42 | 9.16 | 8.12 | 4.87 | 31890 |
| Bamble | 0.033 | 0.68 | 32.19 | 8.51 | 6.28 | 47.40 | 14.62 | 5.71 | 13.48 | 4.94 | 4.27 | 43370 |
| PavinB | 0.087 | 1.57 | 50.25 | 12.12 | 9.22 | 73.55 | 19.91 | 4.86 | 8.19 | 9.39 | 5.56 | 38575 |
| IlimaussaqB | 0.115 | 0.52 | 29.32 | 15.49 | 10.63 | 104.5 | 8.74 | 3.97 | — | 11.46 | 4.69 | 44720 |
| AlpesFA | — | — | 19.54 | 6.82 | 3.14 | 82.71 | 8.14 | 20.37 | — | 4.70 | 2.78 | 92290 |
| AustrDV | 0.051 | 0.12 | 13.64 | 5.47 | 4.30 | 17.98 | 8.98 | 2.89 | — | 3.68 | 2.77 | 159050 |
| Mickland | 0.010 | 0.35 | 12.71 | 5.14 | 4.29 | 16.91 | 8.51 | 4.58 | 7.73 | 3.21 | 2.68 | 185500 |
| AlpesUR | 0.009 | 0.47 | 9.21 | 5.26 | 2.91 | 15.67 | 8.59 | 7.21 | 0.95 | 4.01 | 2.65 | 243500 |
| Seljas | 0.110 | 2.79 | — | 6.89 | 3.69 | — | 11.36 | — | 0.92 | 4.25 | 3.14 | 61460 |
| Etoile | 0.205 | 1.99 | 34.86 | 9.44 | 7.47 | 45.77 | 14.60 | 1.29 | 1.62 | 7.33 | 4.07 | 46500 |
| IlimaussaqA | 0.086 | 0.33 | 33.45 | 18.13 | 5.14 | 47.38 | 10.59 | 14.08 | — | 11.87 | 3.19 | 39300 |
| Average | 0.061 | 0.823 | 23.33 | 8.69 | 5.81 | 43.738 | 11.72 | 5.985 | 5.36 | 6.28 | 3.58 | |

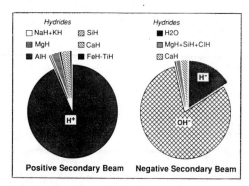

FIG. 10. Hydrogen allotment to atomic H, hydrides, and hydroxide in the secondary positive and negative ion beams. Same measurements conditions as for isotopic analyses, except for a mass resolution of 4500.

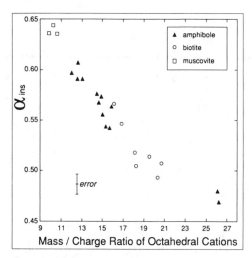

FIG. 11. D/H isotopic fractionation $\alpha_{ins}$ vs. the mean mass to charge ratio of the octahedral cations (m/c) for amphibole, biotite, and muscovite.

*Hydrogen energy distribution*

Understanding the mechanisms of hydrogen emission hinges around a discussion of the energy spectrum (Fig. 5). It can be shown that commonly accepted theoretical distributions of energy are inappropriate. Let us call $f^H(E)$ the fraction of ions with secondary energy $E$ in the range $E$ to $E + dE$. To a constant of normalization, $f^H(E)$ is equal to the counts per second measured at $E$ provided the energy window is small (5 volts). The linear collision cascade of GRIES and RUEDENAUER (1975) predicts a dependence of $f^H(E)$ with $E$ given by

$$f^H(E) \propto \frac{E}{(E + U_s)^3} \qquad (4)$$

where $U_s$ is the surface binding energy. This equation implies a linear relation between $\dfrac{E}{f^H(E)}$ and $(E + U_s)^{1/3}$, which is not observed. The bond breaking model of SLODZIAN *et al.* (1980) would predict a different relation:

$$f^H(E) \propto \exp\left(-\frac{k}{\sqrt{E}}\right) \qquad (5)$$

which can be tested by searching linear arrays in a plot $\text{Log}^2 [f^H(E)]$ vs. $1/E$, but is again not observed.

Inspection of the curve (Fig. 5) suggests that it is made up of two distinct sections, a sharp peak, $f_1^H(E)$, centered at $\approx 12$ eV and a gently decreasing segment, $f_2^H(E)$, above 40 eV, hinting at the superposition of distinct physical processes such as $f^H(E)$ is the sum of $f_1^H(E)$ and $f_2^H(E)$. The $f_2^H(E)$ vs. $E$ relation at high energy is nearly perfectly exponential and can be fitted by

$$f_2^H(E) = 3.2\ 10^{-3} \exp(-0.0089 \pm 6E). \qquad (6)$$

Once this exponential contribution is removed from the energy spectrum, the remainder $f_1^H(E)$ was fitted with different acceptable functions such as exponential, polynomial, or power laws, but the outcome was uniformly poor. In contrast, excellent results were obtained for a fit by a gamma distribution:

$$f_1^H(E) = 2.0\ 10^{-5} E^{7.2 \pm 3} \exp(-0.86 \pm 3E). \qquad (7)$$

The first constants in $f_1^H(E)$ and $f_2^H(E)$ have been normalized in such a way that their sum is normalized over $[0, +\infty]$.

Deuterium is not abundant enough for its energy

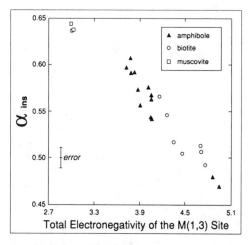

FIG. 12. D/H isotopic fractionation $\alpha_{ins}$ vs. the total electronegativity ($N_\diamond \times$ MEN, see text) of ions in the M(1,3) octahedral site for amphibole, biotite, and muscovite.

spectrum to be measured accurately. However, the D/H fractionation measured at different values of $E$ (Fig. 6) can be fitted to a power law:

$$\alpha_{ins} = c' E^{-0.203}. \qquad (8)$$

No data are available at high energy; hence, the energy spectrum will be modelled as a simple low energy peak. Applying Eqn. (8) to the H energy spectrum in the low energy range gives upon normalization

$$f^D(E) = 2.5 \ 10^{-5} E^{6.1 \pm 3} \exp(-0.76 \pm 4E). \quad (9)$$

The exponential form of the high energy distribution of Eqn. (6) is suggestive of a Boltzman-type energy distribution. The constant in the exponential term is $0.0089^{-1} = 112$ eV and is high enough to correspond to energy transferred during electronic excitation in the collision cascade (inelastic collision).

As far as the lower energy peak is concerned, it is well known that gamma functions such as those of Eqns. (7) and (9) are simply related to exponential distributions (*e.g.* LLOYD, 1980, p. 202): let $E$ be a random variable distributed exponentially as $\lambda \exp(-\lambda E)$ with $\lambda^{-1}$ representing the expected value of $E$, then the sum of m variables with the same $\lambda$ value is distributed as a gamma density function:

$$f(E) = \frac{\lambda^n}{\Gamma(n)} E^{n-1} \exp(-\lambda E). \qquad (10)$$

As suggested by the relation between the yield and the bond energy, it is likely that this process has an activation threshold. The fairly good fit of the peak shape in the energy spectrum with gamma distributions suggests an additive process of energy transfer leading to ion emission. From Eqns. (7) and (9), $n_H$ and $n_D$ are, respectively, 8.16 and 7.10. Hence, for hydrogen, one could conceive ion emission after $\approx 8$ transfers of energy "quantum" $\lambda^{-1}$ of 1.16 eV above the energy required for bond rupture, whereas $\approx 7$ transfers of 1.32 eV would be necessary for deuterium. This is indeed consistent with bond energies usually being stronger for deuterium than for hydrogen (HERZBERG, 1970; KERR and TROTMAN-DICKENSON, 1977). Interestingly, the average energy of emitted ions, given by $n\lambda^{-1}$, is nearly identical for hydrogen and deuterium (9.5 and 9.4 eV, respectively). The energy "quanta" $\lambda^{-1}$ corresponds to wavenumbers of 9,300–10,700 cm$^{-1}$ (near-infrared), values which fall in a range typical of photon absorption by transition elements ($Fe^{2+}$, $Fe^{3+}$, $Mn^{2+}$, $Cr^{3+}$, $\cdots$) in a distorted octahedral site (*e.g.* HAWTHORNE, 1981). OH-bond energy would therefore increase up to ion ejection as the surrounding transition element atoms absorbs the electromagnetic radiation known (BENNINGHOVEN *et al.*, 1987, p. 180) to be produced by ion bombardment.

## CONCLUSIONS

The instrumental D/H fractionation during SIMS analysis is strongly correlated with the octahedrally coordinated cation for amphiboles and micas. Relations between $\alpha_{ins}$ and m/c ratio or MEN support its control by the H bond energy with the surrounding atoms. Using an empirical calibration of the D/H fractionation with amphibole composition, $\delta D$ can be measured on a mineral smaller than 50 $\mu$m with a precision of $\pm 10$ per mil.

Notwithstanding the relation between D/H fractionation and H bond energy, its variation with emission velocity is opposite to that which is predicted by the bond breaking model. Examination of the H and D energy spectra suggests that most $H^+$ is emitted upon repeated absorption of near-infrared photons.

*Acknowledgements*—We thank M. Chaussidon and S. M. F. Sheppard for thoughtful discussions. The manuscript benefited from a helpful review by Richard Hinton. Ion microprobe maintenance and improvement were made possible through the expertise of P. Allé and J.-C. Demange. We thank C. Alibert, B. Azambre, A.-M. Boullier, A. Ploquin, S. M. F. Sheppard, J.-M. Stussi, U. Robert, D. Velde, B. Villemant for sample donation, and J. M. Claude for help in electron microprobe analyses. Financial support by grant DBT 89 3827 from the Institut National des Sciences de l'Univers is gratefully acknowledged. This is CRPG-CNRS contribution no. 878 and CNRS-INSU (DBT thème fluide et cinétique) contribution no. 330.

## REFERENCES

ANDERSEN C. A. and HINTHORNE J. R. (1973) Thermodynamic approach to the quantitative interpretation of sputtered ion mass spectra. *Anal. Chem.* **45**, 1421–1438.

ARMOUR D. G., WADSWORTH M., BADHEKA R., VAN DEN BERG J., BLACKMORE G., COURTNEY S., WHITEHOUSE C. R., CLARK E. A., SYKES D. E. and COLLINS R. (1988) Fundamental processes which affect the depth resolution obtainable in sputter depth profiling. In *SIMS VI Proceedings* (eds. A. BENNINGHOVEN, A. M. HUBER and H. M. WERNER), pp. 399–408. Wiley.

BENNINGHOVEN A., RÜDENAUER F. G. and WERNER H. W. (1987) *Secondary Ion Mass Spectrometry, Basic Concepts, Instrumental Aspects, Applications and Trends.* Wiley.

CHAUSSIDON M. and DEMANGE J.-C. (1988) Instrumental mass fractionation in ion microprobe studies of sulphur isotopic ratios. In *SIMS VI Proceedings* (eds. A. BENNINGHOVEN, A. M. HUBER and H. M. WERNER), pp. 937–940. Wiley.

FRANCE-LANORD C. (1987) Chevauchement, métamorphisme et magmatisme en Himalaya du Népal central. Etude isotopique H, C, O. Thesis, INPL, Nancy, France.

FRANCE-LANORD C., SHEPPARD S. M. F. and LE FORT P. (1988) Hydrogen and oxygen isotope variations in the High Himalaya peraluminous Manaslu leucogranite: evidence for heterogeneous sedimentary source. *Geochim. Cosmochim. Acta* **52**, 513–526.

GNASER H. and HUTCHEON I. D. (1988) The velocity dependence of isotope effects in secondary ion emission. In *SIMS VI Proceedings* (eds. A. BENNINGHOVEN, A. M. HUBER and H. M. WERNER), pp. 29–32. Wiley.

GOLDBERG E. C., FERRON J. and PASSEGGI M. C. G. (1988) Effects of the ion velocity changes on the ionization probability in secondary ion emission. In *SIMS VI Proceedings* (eds. A. BENNINGHOVEN, A. M. HUBER and H. M. WERNER), pp. 75–78. Wiley.

GRAHAM C. M., HARMON R. S. and SHEPPARD S. M. F. (1984) Experimental hydrogen isotope studies: hydrogen isotope exchange between amphibole and water. *Amer. Mineral.* **69**, 128–138.

GRIES N. H. and RUEDENAUER F. G. (1975) A quantitative model for the interpretation of secondary ion mass spectra of dilute alloys. *Intl. J. Mass Spectrum. Ion Phys.* **18**, 111–127.

HAGEMANN R., NIEF G. and ROTH E. (1970) Absolute isotopic scale for deuterium analysis of natural waters. Absolute D/H ratio for SMOW. *Tellus* **22**, 712–715.

HAWTHORNE F. C. (1981) Amphibole spectroscopy, vibrational spectroscopy, the hydroxyl stretching region. In *Amphiboles and Other Hydrous Pyriboles—Mineralogy* (ed. D. R. VEBLEN); *Reviews in Mineralogy 9a*, pp. 103–140. Mineralogical Society of America.

HAWTHORNE F. C. (1983) Quantitative characterization of site-occupancies in minerals. *Amer. Mineral.* **68**, 287–306.

HERZBERG G. (1970) The dissociation energy of the hydrogen molecule. *J. Mol. Spectrosc.* **33**, 147–168.

HINTON R. W., LONG J. V. P., FALLICK A. E. and PILLINGER C. T. (1983) Ion probe measurements of D/H ratios in meteorites. *Lunar Planet. Sci.* **XIV**, 313–314.

HOFMANN S. (1982) Disturbing effects in sputter profiling. In *SIMS III Proceedings* (eds. A. BENNINGHOVEN et al.), pp. 186–200. Springer.

KERR J. A. and TROTMAN-DICKENSON A. F. (1977) Strengths of chemical bonds. In *Handbook of Chemistry and Physics* (ed. R. C. WEAST), pp. F219–F229. CRC Press.

LLOYD E. (1980) Handbook of Applicable Mathematics, Vol. II: Probability (ed. W. Lederman). Wiley London, 450 p.

LORIN J. C., HAVETTE A. and SLODZIAN G. (1982) Isotope effects in secondary ion emission. In *SIMS III Proceedings* (eds. A. BENNINGHOVEN et al.), pp. 140–150. Springer.

PAPIKE J. J., CAMERON K. L. and BALDWIN K. (1974) Amphiboles and pyroxenes: characterization of other than quadrilateral components and estimates of ferric iron from microprobe data (abstr.). *Geol. Soc. Amer. Abstr. Prog.* **6**, 1053–1054.

ROSSMAN G. R. (1984) Spectroscopy of micas, infrared spectra. In *Micas* (ed. S. W. BAILEY); *Reviews in Mineralogy 13*, pp. 145–177. Mineralogical Society of America.

ROWBOTHAM G. and FARMER V. C. (1973) The effect of "A" site occupancy upon hydroxyl stretching frequency in clinoamphiboles. *Contr. Mineral. Petrol.* **38**, 147–149.

SEMET M. P. (1973) A crystal-chemical study of synthetic magnesiohastingsite. *Amer. Mineral.* **58**, 480–494.

SHEPPARD S. M. F. (1986) Igneous rocks: III. Isotopic case studies of magmatism in Africa, Eurasia, and oceanic islands. In *Stable Isotopes in High Temperature Geological Processes* (eds. J. W. VALLEY, H. P. TAYLOR and J. R. O'NEIL); *Reviews in Mineralogy 16*, pp. 319–372. Mineralogical Society of America.

SHIMIZU N. (1986) Silicon-induced enhancement in secondary ion emission from silicates. *Intl. J. Mass. Spectrom. Ion Proc.* **69**, 325–338.

SHIMIZU N. and HART S. R. (1982a) Isotope fractionation in secondary ion mass spectrometry. *J. Appl. Phys.* **53**, 1303–1311.

SHIMIZU N. and HART S. R. (1982b) Applications of the ion microprobe to geochemistry and cosmochemistry. *Ann. Rev. Earth Planet. Sci.* **10**, 483–526.

SLODZIAN G. (1982) Dependence of ionisation yields upon elemental composition; isotopic variations. In *SIMS III Proceedings* (ed. A. BENNINGHOVEN et al.), pp. 115–123. Springer.

SLODZIAN G., LORIN J. C. and HAVETTE A. (1980) Isotopic effect on the ionization probabilities in secondary ion emission. *J. Phys.* **23**, 555–558.

SOEDERVALL U., ENGSTROEM E. U., ODELIUS H. and LODDING A. (1988) Isotope mass effects in secondary ion emission. In *SIMS VI Proceedings* (eds. A. BENNINGHOVEN, A. M. HUBER and H. M. WERNER), pp. 83–88. Wiley.

SROUBEK Z. (1988) Formation of secondary ions. In: *SIMS VI Proceedings* (eds. A. BENNINGHOVEN, A. M. HUBER and H. M. WERNER), pp. 25–28. Wiley.

STRENS R. G. J. (1974) The common chain, ribbon, and ring silicates. In *The Infrared Spectra of Minerals*, pp. 305–330. Mineralogical Society, London.

SUZUOKI T. and EPSTEIN S. (1976) Hydrogen isotope fractionation between OH-bearing minerals and water. *Geochim. Cosmochim. Acta* **40**, 1229–1240.

VELDE B. (1983) Infrared OH-stretch bands in potassic micas, talcs and saponites; influence of electronic configuration and site of charge compensation. *Amer. Mineral.* **68**, 1169–1173.

YU M. L. (1988) A bond-breaking model for the sputtering of secondary ions and excited atoms. In *SIMS VI Proceedings* (eds. A. BENNINGHOVEN, A. M. HUBER and H. M. WERNER), pp. 83–88. Wiley.

ZINNER E., MCKEEGAN R. M. and WALKER R. M. (1983) Laboratory measurements of D/H ratios in interplanetary dust. *Nature* **305**, 119–121.

# Part B.
# The Hydrosphere and
# Ancient Oceans

A gathering of some of Sam's former colleagues from the period 1947–1952 at the University of Chicago. LEFT TO RIGHT: Harmon Craig, Cesare Emiliani, Tosh Mayeda, Irving Friedman, Clair Patterson, Diane and Sam Epstein, Sol Silverman, Stanley Miller, and Julian Goldsmith.

Stable Isotope Geochemistry: A Tribute to Samuel Epstein
© The Geochemical Society, Special Publication No. 3, 1991
Editors: H. P. Taylor, Jr., J. R. O'Neil and I. R. Kaplan

# Oxygen isotope history of seawater revisited: Timescales for boundary event changes in the oxygen isotope composition of seawater

R. T. GREGORY

Department of Geological Sciences, Southern Methodist University, Dallas, Texas 75275, U.S.A.

**Abstract**—Oxygen isotopic data from hydrothermally altered oceanic pillow lavas suggest that the $\delta^{18}O$ value of seawater has not changed very much over geologic time. However, several studies on sedimentary rocks attribute 3–6 per mil changes in the $\delta^{18}O$ values of carbonate rocks to changes in the $\delta^{18}O$ of the coexisting seawater. These changes appear to occur over very short time intervals (<20 Ma), and therefore it is important to examine the characteristic times associated with processes that can affect the isotopic composition of seawater. Material-balance equations describing the secular change in the $\delta^{18}O$ of seawater resulting from isotopic exchange between the lithosphere and the hydrosphere have solutions that give the steady-state value of seawater as: $\sum k_i(\delta_i^0 - \Delta_i)/\sum k_i$, where the $\Delta_i$ are the bulk fractionation factors between the various rock reservoirs (i) and water, the $\delta_i^0$ are the initial $\delta^{18}O$ values of the various rock reservoirs, the $k_i$ are the rate constants in units of 1/time, and $\sum k_i$ is the total rate. For a global ridge system, typical of present-day Earth, with a spreading rate of 3 km$^2$/yr and a 4 km depth of seawater penetration, the k value for exchange between the oceanic crustal reservoir and seawater is $\approx 0.008$/Ma with a mean lifetime (1/k) of 125 Ma. Similarly, a continental weathering rate of 2.5 km$^3$/yr yields a rate constant for the seawater cycle of 0.002/Ma with a mean lifetime of 420 Ma. Even for high estimates of continental weathering rates ($\approx 7$ km$^3$/ yr), the mean life for the weathering process is still 150 Ma, which is longer than the mean lifetime of the ridge crest cycle. By these mechanisms, a 6 per mil change in the $\delta^{18}O$ value of seawater requires 60–150 km$^3$/yr of continental weathering, which would occur over $\approx 15$ Ma at the expense of processing up to a third of the continental crust! Clearly, if such changes in the $^{18}O$ composition of the oceans do in fact occur, they should be reflected in dramatic and easily identifiable changes in the tectonic regime of the Earth, and no such changes are documented in the rock record. From this analysis of the time constants involved in the global cycles, it would seem that apparent boundary event changes in the $\delta^{18}O$ values of carbonates must be attributable to other mechanisms.

## INTRODUCTION

NEW $\delta^{18}O$ DATA on the Darb Zubaydah ophiolite, Saudi Arabia, and the Yilgarn and the Pilbara blocks, Western Australia, complement earlier data sets (*e.g.*, MUEHLENBACHS, 1986; GREGORY and TAYLOR, 1981; BEATY and TAYLOR, 1982; KERRICH, 1987; SMITH *et al.*, 1984; HOFFMAN *et al.*, 1986) that show that there is little or no variation over geologic time in the range of $\delta^{18}O$ values of the upper crustal products of seafloor hydrothermal alteration (Fig. 1). In the Pilbara block, over 100 analyses of samples from a pillow lava section covering over 600 km$^2$ display a range of $\delta^{18}O$ values nearly the same as that for Cenozoic and Mesozoic oceanic pillow lava sections. The simplest interpretation of the data shown in Fig. 1 is that the isotopic composition of seawater has not changed much through geologic time.

Conflicting ideas regarding the secular change in the isotopic composition of seawater come from the studies of sedimentary carbonates, cherts, and phosphates (*e.g.*, DEGENS and EPSTEIN, 1962; VEIZER *et al.*, 1986; POPP *et al.*, 1986; LOHMANN and WALKER, 1989; BURDETT *et al.*, 1990; KNAUTH and EPSTEIN, 1976; LUZ *et al.*, 1984). In these studies, there is a clear conflict in the interpretation of the cause of a general lowering of the $\delta^{18}O$ values of sedimentary materials back through geologic time. One group of researchers invariably interprets the change in terms of changes in the isotopic composition of seawater; a second group interprets the change in isotopic composition in terms of higher surface temperatures (warmer paleoclimates); and a third group interprets the change in terms of a later-stage, secondary alteration of the original isotopic compositions of the rocks. The first two interpretations require that the secular change in oxygen isotopes of sedimentary rocks is a primary feature which has not been affected by diagenesis or metamorphism.

Paleoclimatic constraints derived from models of atmospheric evolution argue for the stability of temperature distributions on the ancient Earth (*e.g.*, KASTING, 1989). Numerical simulations of atmospheric circulation predict only a $\approx 5°C$ change between global mean temperatures of glacial and nonglacial epochs (*e.g.*, BARRON and WASHINGTON, 1984). Also, because the types of continental shelf marine sediments that have been subjected to stable isotopic studies formed over a restricted range of latitude, large changes in apparent paleotemperature are unlikely (unless the climatic models are in serious error).

R. T. Gregory

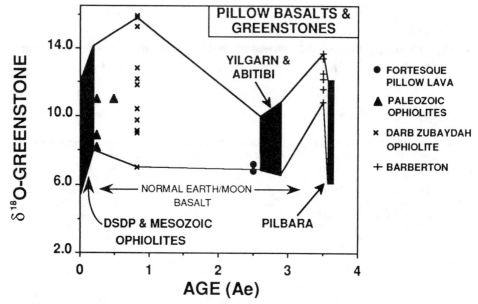

FIG. 1. The $\delta^{18}O$ values of pillow basalts and greenstones are shown as a function of age in Ga. These data suggest that the range of $\delta^{18}O$ values of metabasalts altered on the seafloor has not changed throughout geologic time. The $^{18}O$-enriched character of greenstones of any age is difficult to reconcile with oceans that were depleted in $^{18}O$ in the past. The areas shown in black represent rock localities and types where there are many analyses. The DSDP & Mesozoic ophiolite field represents the data summarized by MUEHLENBACHS (1986); the Yilgarn & Abitibi (Australia and Canada, respectively) field is from the work of BEATY and TAYLOR (1982), KERRICH (1987), and unpublished data; the Pilbara (Australia) field represents the range of over 100 new data points. The triangles, ×'s, dots, and crosses represent limited data from greenstones of all ages. The Paleozoic samples are from the Bay of Islands complex and the Canyon Mountain ophiolite, North America (GREGORY and TAYLOR, 1981), the ×'s from the Darb Zubaydah ophiolite complex, Arabia (GREGORY and QUICK, 1990); the dots from the Fortescue Group, Australia, and the crosses from the Barberton greenstone belt (SMITH *et al.*, 1984; HOFFMAN *et al.*, 1986).

In view of interpretations which attribute 3–6 per mil changes in the $\delta^{18}O$ values of carbonate rocks to changes in the $\delta^{18}O$ of coexisting seawater, as well as the interpretations that these changes occur over very short time intervals (*e.g.*, VEIZER *et al.*, 1986; LOHMANN and WALKER, 1989), it is important to examine the characteristic times associated with processes that affect the $\delta^{18}O$ value of seawater. Recent work toward the development of isotopic chronostratigraphies, in which oxygen isotope data are represented side by side with carbon, sulfur, and strontium isotopic data, must recognize the major differences in the behaviour of these systems. It is clear that secular trends in the carbon and sulfur isotopic composition of sedimentary materials are related to the interplay on short time scales between oxidized and reduced species that results from the exchange between the biosphere and the reservoirs of these elements in the atmosphere, hydrosphere, and lithosphere (*e.g.*, HOLSER *et al.*, 1988; BERNER, 1989).

HOLLAND (1984) reviews the isotopic composition of Sr and O in seawater and concludes that both isotopic systems are mainly controlled by a competition between seafloor processes and continental weathering. This phenomenon is by now reasonably well understood (*e.g.*, MUEHLENBACHS and CLAYTON, 1976; HOLLAND, 1984; PALMER and EDMOND, 1989). It is interesting to note that the Sr isotopic composition of Phanerozoic seawater changes by only 4 per mil with Sr present at ≈8 ppm (*e.g.*, PETERMAN *et al.*, 1970; VEIZER *et al.*, 1986), a minor perturbation compared with the rapid 6 per mil change in the $\delta^{18}O$ value of seawater (89 wt.% oxygen) required by interpretations of the sedimentary oxygen record. For oxygen isotopes, because seawater is predominantly oxygen, the mass of the ocean must have a large damping effect on possible changes in the oxygen isotopic composition of seawater. The purpose of this paper is to investigate the stability of the $\delta^{18}O$ value of seawater in relation to the various plausible perturbations away from steady state.

## MASS BALANCE RELATIONSHIPS

The general material balance equation describing the change in the $\delta^{18}O$ of seawater as a function of time resulting from isotopic exchange between the lithosphere and the hydrosphere is given by

$$d\delta W/dt = -\sum k_i(\delta W + \Delta_i - \delta_i^0) \qquad (1)$$

where $\delta W$ is the instantaneous $\delta^{18}O$ value of seawater, the $\Delta_i$ are the bulk fractionation factors between the various rock reservoirs (i) and water, the $\delta_i^0$ are the initial $\delta^{18}O$ values of the various rock reservoirs, and the $k_i$ are the rate constants in units of $1/time$. Equation (1) is similar to the types of material-balance equations put forward in GREGORY and TAYLOR (1981), CRISS et al. (1987) and GREGORY et al. (1989). The main difference is that the rate constants are rock cycling rates normalized to the mass of the oceans.

Equation (1) can be solved analytically as long as the $k_i$, the $\Delta_i$ and the $\delta_i^0$ are held constant by separating variables and integrating from $\delta W_0$ and $t = 0$ to $\delta W$ and $t$ to obtain

$$\delta W = (\delta W_0 - \delta W_{\text{steady state}})$$
$$\times \exp - (\sum k_i t) + \delta W_{\text{steady state}}. \qquad (2)$$

From the definition of the $\Delta_i$, $\delta_i^0 - \Delta_i$ is the value seawater would obtain if steady state was achieved with the ith reservoir. Thus, the steady state $\delta$ value of seawater is given by

$$\delta W_{\text{steady state}} \equiv [\sum k_i(\delta_i^0 - \Delta_i)]/\sum k_i. \qquad (3)$$

If seawater exchanged with a single massive crustal reservoir, the steady-state $\delta$ value of the oceans would simply be the initial composition of the crustal reservoir minus the bulk fractionation factor ($\Delta$) of the interaction. If the formation of sediments by weathering of pristine igneous rocks with $\delta^{18}O = +8$ occurs at a bulk $\Delta^{18}O$ of $+20$, the steady-state $\delta^{18}O$ value of seawater would be $-12$. Similarly, if the $\delta^{18}O$ of seawater is dominated by the ridge-crest interaction with the oceanic crust ($\delta^{18}O \approx +6$ per mil) at a bulk $\Delta^{18}O$ of approximately $+6$ in the style dictated by the present-day plate tectonic regime, the steady-state $\delta$ value of seawater would be roughly zero. Crudely over geologic time seawater should vary between these extremes, unless one process dominates (e.g., MUEHLENBACHS and CLAYTON, 1976; GREGORY and TAYLOR, 1981). From Eqn. (3), the process with the largest k value is proportionally the most important control on the isotopic composition of seawater.

In the following discussion of the ridge crest-seawater interaction, the low- and high-temperature interactions are not treated separately but as parts of the same process. This is a departure from the approach used by MUEHLENBACHS (1986) and HOLLAND (1984) where the low- and high-temperature ridge interactions are treated as separate processes. In the present treatment, one bulk fractionation factor applies to the whole ridge system, and thus the rates of exchange of oxygen isotopes can be more directly related back to plate tectonic processes. The major problem with treating the ridge-crest interaction as a single process revolves around the uncertainty in the choice of the bulk fractionation factor, $\Delta$. Because this factor, $\Delta$, is ultimately related to the average temperature of isotopic exchange in the oceanic crust, its value is tied to the mechanics of the accretion of new oceanic crust and to the contrast between the temperature of mid-ocean ridge magmas and surface oceans. GREGORY and TAYLOR (1981) argued that as long as a plate tectonic regime obtains (i.e., global spreading rates greater than $\approx 1$ km$^2$/yr), the value of the bulk fractionation factor would be close to $+6$.

Assuming that Cretaceous seawater was close to its steady-state oxygen isotopic composition during a time of rapid seafloor spreading, the material balance for the $^{18}O$ distribution in the altered Cretaceous oceanic crust achieves special significance. When the isotopic composition of seawater approaches a steady-state relationship with a single dominant reservoir, the average value of this rock reservoir should not change as a result of subsequent interaction. This means that the amount of $^{18}O$ enrichment will balance the amount of $^{18}O$ depletion in the altered oceanic crust (e.g., MUEHLENBACHS and CLAYTON, 1976). If the oxygen isotope balance in a section of oceanic crust is real, then it implies that seawater was indeed at its steady-state isotopic composition and that the ridge-crest interaction dominates the system. However, if another reservoir exchanges at a fast enough rate to make a proportionally significant contribution to the isotopic composition of seawater, then the oxygen isotope profile of the oceanic crust *should not* balance.

Alternatively, if the mechanism of ocean-crust formation changes as a function of spreading rate, some changes in the bulk fractionation factor might occur as the average temperature of exchange changes. Thus, it might be possible for some oceanic ridge segments to exhibit a local oxygen isotope imbalance, while others forming at spreading rates closer to the global average would be in oxygen isotopic balance. Because it is difficult to differentiate between the effect of another important exchange reservoir from possible fluctuations that might occur as a result of the accretion of the oceanic crust, it is particularly important to constrain the exchange rates for oxygen isotopes between seawater and the various crustal reservoirs. Obviously, these rates would have to be consistent with rates of tectonic processes.

In Fig. 2, the behavior of oxygen isotopes is shown to be strikingly different than that of Sr isotopes for profiles of the composite Ibra section of the Cretaceous Samail ophiolite (GREGORY and TAYLOR, 1981; LANPHERE *et al.*, 1981; MCCULLOCH *et al.*, 1981). The oxygen isotope profile exhibits rocks which are both depleted and enriched in $^{18}O$ relative to their primary igneous $\delta^{18}O$ values. Because the integrated average bulk $\delta^{18}O$ value of the altered oceanic crust is close to the initial $\delta^{18}O$ value, there was little or no flux of $^{18}O$ in or out of the oceans. This balance for oxygen isotopes obtains even though there is abundant evidence for fluid flow throughout the oceanic crust. From the profile of $^{87}Sr/^{86}Sr$, it is clear that the Sr isotopic system was not close to a condition of steady-state. Because of the major differences in the behavior of these two isotopic systems, by casting the rates of exchange in terms of volumetric rates, we can discern whether the behavior of the two dissimilar systems is qualitatively correct and compatible with observation.

## RATES

### Ridge crest-seawater interaction

Following GREGORY and TAYLOR (1981), the rate constant, k, for seawater exchange with the oceanic crust would be $[\phi/(\phi + 1)]Rc/W$, where $R$ is the global spreading rate in km$^2$/yr, $\phi$ is the actual water/rock ratio for the rocks exchanged at the ridge, $W$ is the mass of the oceans (in oxygen units), and $c$ is a constant that takes into account the depth of alteration (in terms of oxygen isotopes) and the oxygen content of the oceanic crust. The mean life of the process is simply $1/k$. For a global ridge system with a spreading rate of 3 km$^2$/yr, $\phi = 2$, and a 4 km depth of seawater penetration, the rate constant is 0.008/Ma for the ocean crust-seawater interaction, and the mean lifetime is 125 million years.

Note that the term $\phi/(\phi + 1)$ takes into account the actual water/rock ratio (in oxygen units) in the ridge system, and this is related to the integrated fluid flux. Because of the near balance between $^{18}O$ depleted and enriched rocks in the altered oceanic crust (MUEHLENBACHS and CLAYTON, 1976; GREGORY and TAYLOR, 1981), it is difficult to estimate the water/rock ratio for the overall ridge system from oxygen isotope data. This, by itself, is a

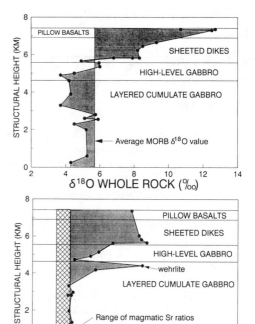

FIG. 2. A comparison of oxygen and strontium isotope profiles through the Cretaceous oceanic crust is shown using the Ibra section of the Samail ophiolite. This figure clearly illustrates the major difference in the behavior of Sr and O isotopes in the altered oceanic crust. In each diagram, the primary isotopic composition is shown as a vertical line, $\delta^{18}O = 5.7$, or as a field for $^{87}Sr/^{86}Sr$. The shaded areas represent the deviations from the primary magmatic composition. It is clear that the hydrothermal alteration resulted in a net transfer of $^{87}Sr$ into the crust. Excluding the wehrlite samples which have almost no Sr, the average $^{87}Sr/^{86}Sr$ of the altered Samail crust is approximately 0.7036, enriched relative to a primary value of less than 0.703. In contrast, the inferred bulk $\delta^{18}O$ of the altered section is approximately the same as the original primary magmatic value of the rocks; i.e., the shaded areas representing enriched and depleted rocks are nearly equal. This means that there was no net transfer of $^{18}O$ in or out of seawater as a result of the hydrothermal interaction. The data are from GREGORY and TAYLOR (1981), LANPHERE *et al.* (1981) and MCCULLOCH *et al.* (1981).

statement that the oxygen isotopic composition of seawater is close to a steady-state value and that the bulk fractionation for the ridge crest-seawater interaction is close to +6. When the difference between the oxygen isotope composition of seawater and pristine oceanic crust is close to the value of the bulk fractionation factor, the water/rock ratio calculated from oxygen isotopes becomes indeterminate.

Strontium isotopes display a different behavior (*e.g.*, Fig. 2), and thus can be used to infer the actual water/rock ratio of the ridge. In a recent summary of estimates for the ridge-crest water flux based on thermal and chemical constraints, PALMER and EDMOND (1989) concluded that the ridge-system water flux is in the vicinity of 0.9 to 1.3 × 10^14 kg/ yr. For a 3 km²/yr global spreading rate, this flux would translate into an integrated water/rock ratio of 3.6 to 5.2 in oxygen units. These numbers are similar to an independent estimate from the Sr-isotope work on the Ibra section of the Samail ophiolite.

This latter calculation can be done by integrating the profiles for $^{87}Sr/^{86}Sr$ and Sr content as a function of depth in the Samail ophiolite to get averages for these parameters. Then the water/rock ratio can be calculated in the normal way (*e.g.,* MCCULLOCH *et al.,* 1981). Using the data on the Ibra section from LANPHERE *et al.* (1981) and MCCULLOCH *et al.* (1981), the water/rock ratio for the Samail ridge system is estimated to be about 4–6 in oxygen units. This estimate, derived from material-balance considerations, suggests that the term $\phi/(\phi + 1)$ is probably greater than 0.8. Note that if the water/ rock ratio is very large, $\phi/(\phi + 1)$ approaches one, and the rate constant reflects the fastest rate that seawater can approach steady state through the ridge-crest interaction. In all of the calculations below, a conservative value of $\phi$ equal to 2 ($\phi/(\phi + 1)$ = 0.67) has been used. Thus, uncertainties about the magnitude of the fluid flux will not affect the results.

The variability of global spreading rates over geologic time is related to heat generation in the mantle. Plate velocities follow the mean velocity of mantle convection, which is related to the square root of the Rayleigh number (TURCOTTE and SCHUBERT, 1982). The Rayleigh number in turn is proportional to heat generation in the mantle. Considering that heat generation due to radioactive decay has approximately halved over the last three billion years (TURCOTTE and SCHUBERT, 1982; LEE, in YODER, 1976), global spreading rates in the past were probably at least as high as at present.

The constant $c$ reflects the depth of penetration of seawater into the oceanic crust. From the evidence of veining in the layered gabbro section of the Samail ophiolite, and from isotopic studies (HOPSON *et al.,* 1981; GREGORY and TAYLOR, 1981; LANPHERE *et al.,* 1981; MCCULLOCH *et al.,* 1981), seawater penetrates the entire cooling oceanic crust. However, the mineralogic and isotopic effects are less pronounced with depth, and thus a conservative value of 4 km has been used as the average depth of penetration.

## Continental weathering-seawater interaction

The exchange of oxygen isotopes between the continental crust and seawater is a result of the chemical weathering of the continents. Because the equilibrium oxygen isotope fractionations between minerals and water increase as temperature decreases, the weathering of low-$^{18}O$ rocks formed at high temperature results in a net $^{18}O$-depletion of the hydrosphere. If the original oceans were outgassed and equilibrated at high temperatures with the mantle, then there has been an approximately 8 per mil depletion of the $\delta^{18}O$ of the oceans to their present-day value. If this was accomplished largely by weathering igneous rocks with $\delta^{18}O$ values close to +6, then it is possible to estimate the average weathering rate provided that the bulk $\delta^{18}O$ value of sedimentary and metamorphic rocks is known. The weathering rate (Table 1) credited to MUEHLENBACHS and CLAYTON (1976) is an example of this type of calculation and as such gives a characteristic time for the seawater cycle on the order of the age of the Earth. Because of the potential for recycling sediments in subduction zones or in metamorphic terranes, the slow rate inferred from this type of analysis would be a lower limit.

Other estimates of chemical weathering rates can be inferred from the elemental fluxes carried by rivers into the oceans and from the rates of deposition of pelagic sediments. An additional constraint comes from estimates of continental growth rates. Weathering rates must not exceed the apparent continental growth rate; otherwise the continental mass would not appear to be growing with time. ARMSTRONG (1981), in his analysis of the evidence for continental crustal recycling, reports that the amount of sediment that must be recycled to justify a steady-state continental crustal volume is 1–3 km³/yr. This range, according to ARMSTRONG's (1981) analysis, is similar to the deposition rate of pelagic sediments and to the rate of crustal accretion on the continents. By balancing the rates of accretion of new continental crust with the subduction of pelagic sediments, ARMSTRONG (1981) concludes that a steady-state model for the evolution of the continental crust is permitted by the data. This suggests that chemical weathering rates cannot exceed the long-term averages for crustal growth rates without seriously disturbing the age distribution of the continental crust. Thus, there is an additional constraint on chemical weathering rates deduced from measurement of elemental fluxes carried by rivers, provided the fluxes can be converted into volumetric rates (km³/yr).

In order to change the contribution from conti-

R. T. Gregory

Table 1. Weathering rates and time constants

| Reference | Weathering rate km³/yr | Method* | $1/k$† Ma | $\tau_{continents}$‡ Ga |
|---|---|---|---|---|
| HOLLAND (1984) | 7.4 | 1 | 140 | 1.0 |
| BERNER et al. (1983) | 5.1 | 2 | 200 | 1.1 |
| WALKER and LOHMANN (1989) | 3.5 | 3 | 300 | 2.1 |
| GILLULY (1964) | 2.5 | 4 | 420 | 3.0 |
| DREVER et al. (1988) | 1.9 | 5 | 550 | 4.0 |
| CLARKE (1924) | 1.0 | 6 | 1040 | 7.5 |
| GILLULY (1955) | 0.2 | 7 | 5200 | 38 |
| MUEHLENBACHS and CLAYTON (1976) | 0.2 | 1 | 5200 | 38 |

* Methods: (1) Oxygen isotope flux due to weathering. For HOLLAND (1984) this number is tied to HOLEMAN's (1968) estimate for the weathering rates from river fluxes. In the case of MUEHLENBACHS and CLAYTON (1976), this is based upon the $^{18}O$ flux necessary to produce the observed sedimentary mass over geologic time. (2) Calcium balance. (3) Magnesium balance. (4) Speculative dissolved river load necessary to make denudation rates agree with tectonic arguments. (5) Silicon balance. (6) River flux analysis. (7) Volume of pelagic sediments.

† The mass of oxygen of the ocean divided by the weathering rate in moles of oxygen. This is the time it would take a perturbation in the $\delta^{18}O$ value of seawater to decay to $1/e$ ($e$ is Euler's constant) of the initial value if weathering was the only process controlling the isotopic composition of seawater.

‡ Note that characteristic times for the continental crust are simply the approximate present day volume of the continental crust divided by the volumetric weathering rate.

nental weathering into a rate constant ($k$ value), the dissolved river load or the denudation rate is converted into the number of cubic kilometers of crust dissolved or eroded; this result is then normalized for the oxygen content of rocks. Thus, for a rate of 2.5 km³/yr, the $k$ value for continental weathering would be 0.0024/Ma with a mean lifetime of 420 million years. Estimates for continental weathering (Table 1) vary from a low value of 0.2 km³/yr (GILLULY, 1955; MUEHLENBACHS and CLAYTON, 1976) to a high value of >7 km³/yr (HOLEMAN, 1968; HOLLAND, 1984).

For a constant continental crustal volume of 7.5 $\times 10^9$ km³ and a weathering rate of 3 km³/yr, the inferred mean age of the continents by dimensional analysis would be 2,500 million years. Long-term weathering rates cannot be much faster than 3 km³/ yr, because then the continents would be younger than what is observed. Because continental growth rates (GEBAUER and WILLIAMS, 1990) are probably less than 3 km³/yr, it is not plausible to assume that weathering rates have been much higher than this over geologic time. Global weathering rates that are much higher than inferred continental growth rates will result in an age distribution inconsistent with what is observed. To get the characteristic times for the continental crust shown in Table 1, the entire volume of the present-day continental crust was used. For smaller volumes of continental crust, the constraint on weathering rates becomes even more prohibitive.

The mean lifetime for the multiple reservoir system is $1/\sum k_i$, and is shorter than the values for any

single reservoir plus seawater. Using the values of 0.008 and 0.0024 (Ma⁻¹), the combined oceanic crust and continental weathering cycles give a mean lifetime of 96 Ma compared with 125 Ma for the oceanic crust cycle by itself. Given that these response times are ultimately controlled by tectonic processes driven by mantle convection, it is unlikely that long-term average rates would change by much more than a factor of two over Earth history. Nevertheless, it is important to understand the effect of variable rates of continental weathering and seafloor spreading rates on the steady-state $\delta^{18}O$ value of seawater and on the response time of the system.

## IMPACT OF CHANGING THE RATES

Because the response times of the cycles are short ($\approx 100$ Ma) compared to the age of the Earth, all of the transient terms in Eqn. (2) can be neglected. Differentiation of Eqn. (3) with respect to one of the $k$ values results in an equation which relates the change in the $\delta$ value of seawater to the change in any one of the rate constants. For a two-rock reservoir system, integration of the resultant equation between initial and final states yields the following relationship:

$$\delta W^f - \delta W^0 = (\Delta_1 - \delta_1^0 - \Delta_2 + \delta_2^0)$$
$$\times k_2[1/(k_1^f + k_2) - 1/(k_1^0 + k_2)] \quad (4)$$

where the superscript f and 0 refer to the final and initial values. The first factor on the right-hand side of the equation represents the difference in the target steady-state $\delta$ values for the two reservoirs. A value of 8 per mil for the factor $(\Delta_1 - \delta_1^0 - \Delta_2 + \delta_2^0)$ and a change in the ratio of $k_1/k_2$ (*e.g.*, ratio of continental weathering to the mid-ocean ridge exchange rates) from 1/9 to 50/9 results in a decrease in the steady-state $\delta$ value of seawater of 6 per mil. If the initial ratio of the continental weathering contribution to the ocean ridge contribution was obtained at a global continental weathering rate of 3 km$^3$/yr, this 6 per mil change in the $\delta^{18}O$ of seawater would require 150 km$^3$/yr of continental weathering! If such weathering rates could be sustained for 15 million years, the $\delta^{18}O$ value of the oceans could change by close to 6 per mil, but only at the expense of processing about a third of the continental crust!

Alternatively, seafloor spreading could be shut off to achieve the change in the ratio of the rates. This comes at the expense of the response time, which becomes more than twenty times longer than the observed rate of the presumed seawater $\delta^{18}O$ transition (<20 Ma) observed at the Devonian-Carboniferous boundary (LOHMANN and WALKER, 1989).

In Fig. 3, the impact of changing the continental weathering rate has been enhanced by maximizing the value of the first factor on the right side of Eqn. (4). This is accomplished by setting the $\delta$ values of both rock reservoirs equal to +6 per mil. The value of the first factor changes from 8 to 14 per mil. To achieve a 6 per mil change in the $\delta^{18}O$ value of seawater still requires a twenty-fold increase in weathering rates (from 3 to 60 km$^3$/yr). Such an increase could not be sustained for any length of time without leaving some trace in the rock record.

In Fig. 4, the effect of increasing the global spreading rate is shown for an Earth that initially starts out with the continental and ridge oxygen fluxes equal. Once again the impact of changing the rates has been maximized by setting the two initial rock reservoir $\delta^{18}O$ values to +6. The calculation shows that approximately a ten-fold increase in spreading rates is required to generate a 6 per mil change in the $\delta^{18}O$ value of seawater. This scenario would only work if some other process besides the ridge-crest interaction contributed significantly to the steady-state value of seawater (Eqn. 3). The constraints on the cooling of the Earth and the age distribution of the continents would suggest that it would be improbable that a ten-fold increase in spreading rates could be sustained on top of the background rate that must be maintained to dissipate the internal heat of the Earth.

The calculations represented by Figs. 3 and 4 give minimum estimates for the magnitude of the changes in the rate parameters required to produce

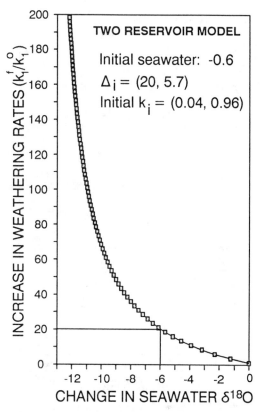

FIG. 3. The increase in weathering rates (final value divided by the initial value) necessary to change the $\delta^{18}O$ value of seawater from an initial value of −0.6 to −12 is illustrated. The bulk fractionation factor associated with continental weathering is assumed to be approximately +20, whereas the oceanic crust-seawater interaction is assigned a fractionation factor of 5.7. In order to maximize the change in the $\delta^{18}O$ value of seawater, the initial rock reservoir $\delta^{18}O$ values have been arbitrarily set to +6 for the calculations in Figs. 3 and 4. In this example, a 6 per mil change in oxygen isotopic composition of seawater comes at the expense of a 20-fold increase in weathering rates. Clearly, such an increase in weathering rates would be unsustainable for any length of time without grossly changing the age distribution of the continental crust. The values of 0.04 and 0.96 represent the initial normalized rates for the two competing processes.

6 per mil changes in the $\delta^{18}O$ value of seawater. Because the average $\delta^{18}O$ value of the continental crust is certainly [18]O-enriched relative to the mantle and the oceanic crust, changes of only 3 per mil in the $\delta^{18}O$ value of seawater are probably more realistic. Even these more modest changes occur at the expense of very large increases in weathering rates or spreading rates. For example, a 100-fold increase in weathering rates from ≈1 km$^3$/yr only changes seawater $\delta^{18}O$ from −0.3 to −3.3 in a calculation where average continental crustal rocks

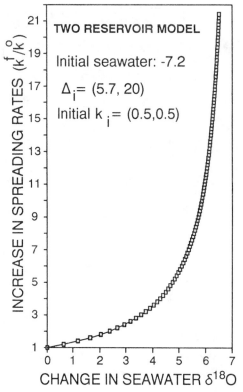

FIG. 4. The calculated curve shows the increase in global spreading rates required to change the oxygen isotopic composition of seawater by 6 per mil. In this calculation, the initial contribution from the continental weathering flux is assumed to be equal to the flux from the seawater-oceanic crustal interaction. The 6 per mil change requires a ten-fold increase in seafloor spreading rates, which is at odds with thermal models of the Earth. Also, if the oceanic crust-seawater interaction was already dominating the steady-state isotopic composition of seawater, the increase in spreading rates would not have any effect on the isotopic composition of seawater unless the bulk fractionation of the seawater-ocean crust interaction was sensitive to spreading rates. As this fractionation factor is more likely to be controlled by the contrast between the surface temperature of the Earth and the liquidus temperature of mid-ocean ridge basalts, it is not obvious that such a hypothesis could account for a spreading rate dependence of the $\Delta$ value between the seawater and the oceanic crust.

have $\delta^{18}O = +16$ and the rate constant for the ridge-crest interaction is a more robust 0.016/Ma.

In order to constrain the oxygen isotope cycle for seawater, rate constants have been used which do not intrinsically depend on the oxygen isotope parameters. By scaling the problem to the rates reported in terms of surface area or volume per unit time, the rates can be checked independently against the age distribution of the continents and ocean basins. Realistic changes in the rate constants do

not produce the changes required by any objective interpretation of the sedimentary oxygen isotope record.

Strontium isotopes can be used as an independent check on the validity of the rate constants inferred from the volumetric constraints. For example, for a 3 km³/yr continental weathering rate that affects average continental crust with a Sr content of 370 ppm (JACOBSEN and WASSERBURG, 1979), and a mass of Sr in the ocean equivalent to $1.1 \times 10^{16}$ kg, the rate constant is 0.278/Ma and the mean life is $\approx 3.5$ Ma. In contrast, if the Sr content of oceanic crust is approximately 150 ppm (LANPHERE et al., 1981), the spreading rate is 3 km²/yr, and the depth of penetration of seawater for Sr isotopes is about 2 km at a $\phi = 2$ (mass units), then the rate constant for the ridge crest–seawater interaction is 0.16 and the mean life is $\approx 6$ Ma. This would indicate that the flux from the continental crust would dominate over the ridge-crest flux, about 64:36. If the river flux into the ocean has $^{87}Sr/^{86}Sr \approx 0.712$ (PALMER and EDMOND, 1989) and the oceanic crust is about 0.703, the present-day isotopic composition of seawater comes out to approximately 0.709, similar to the observed value (PALMER and EDMOND, 1989).

For the following reasons, the Sr isotope composition of seawater *should change* as a function of time: (1) the time constants are short, millions of years compared to 100 Ma time constants for oxygen isotopes; (2) the heterogeneity of continental crustal rocks can change the target isotopic composition of seawater, and the system can respond fast enough to reflect the changes; and (3) the ridge crest–seawater interaction has a time constant sufficiently close to the time constant for the continental weathering flux that changes in spreading rates could make a difference.

In contrast, the time constants for oxygen isotope exchange are too long to permit rapid excursions in the $\delta^{18}O$ value of seawater. In addition, as shown above, reasonable estimates of the rate constants indicate that the ridge-crest interaction is dominant. The homogeneity of the oxygen isotope composition of magmas erupted at mid-ocean ridges will militate against secular changes in seawater $\delta^{18}O$ values. Nevertheless, the parameter that may have the greatest potential for perturbing the oxygen isotopic composition of seawater may be the isotopic composition of the rocks involved in the rock cycle. Namely, is the heterogeneity of the oxygen isotope composition of the continental crust sufficient to overcome the restrictions imposed by the rate constants?

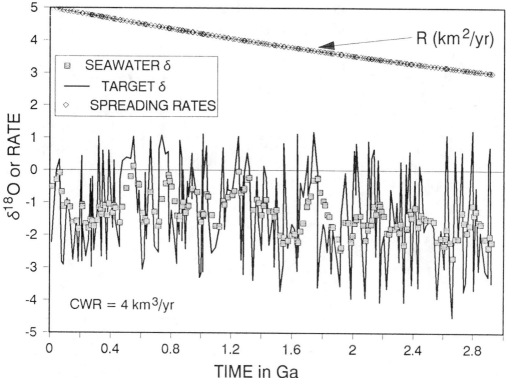

FIG. 5. A 3 Ga simulation of the $^{18}O$ evolution of seawater for a seafloor-spreading dominated regime where: (1) the global spreading declines at rate dictated by the decline of radioactive heat production in the mantle, (2) the continental weathering rate is fixed at an average value of 4 km$^3$/yr and which is allowed to fluctuate by ±25%, and (3) the range in the $\delta^{18}O$ values of continental rocks is allowed to vary by $\approx 20$ per mil in a random fashion. The changing isotopic composition of the rocks involved in the weathering cycle is a perturbation on the system, and the parameters are fixed for random intervals not longer than 25 Ma (a time consistent with changes in plate motions). The solid thin line represents the target steady-state $\delta^{18}O$ value of seawater and the squares represent the actual value seawater achieves at the end of a time interval. In the simulation, the isotopic composition of seawater is constant to within ±1 per mil, and the most rapid change in the $\delta^{18}O$ value of seawater is $\approx 1$ per mil/100 Ma.

## IMPACT OF CHANGING THE ISOTOPIC COMPOSITION OF EXPOSED CONTINENTAL CRUST

Inspection of the steady-state term (Eqn. 3) indicates that changing the bulk $\delta^{18}O$ of the rocks participating in the weathering cycle may be an effective mechanism for changing the steady-state $\delta$ value of seawater through a long-term global cycle, because the isotopic composition of basalt is fixed by the mantle reservoir and the $\Delta$'s for the ocean crust-seawater cycle are not likely to change very much (GREGORY and TAYLOR, 1981). The change in the steady state $\delta$ value of seawater is proportional to the change in the bulk composition of the rocks involved in the cycle, weighted according to the rate constant of the process. Because continental crustal

rocks do have a very large range in $\delta^{18}O$ values, >25 per mil, changes in the average $\delta^{18}O$ value of the continental crust participating in the weathering cycle could have a significant impact on the "target" steady-state value of seawater.

In Figs. 5 and 6, two simulations have been performed which illustrate the impact of changing the average $\delta^{18}O$ value of continental crustal rocks involved in the weathering cycle. Figure 5 illustrates a simulated 3 Ga isotopic history of seawater where: (1) global seafloor spreading rates (in km$^2$/yr) decline according to the decay of radioactive elements in the Earth's mantle; (2) the continental weathering rate averages a robust 4 km$^3$/yr over the entire simulation (it is allowed to randomly fluctuate within 1 km$^3$/yr of that value); and (3) the average $\delta^{18}O$

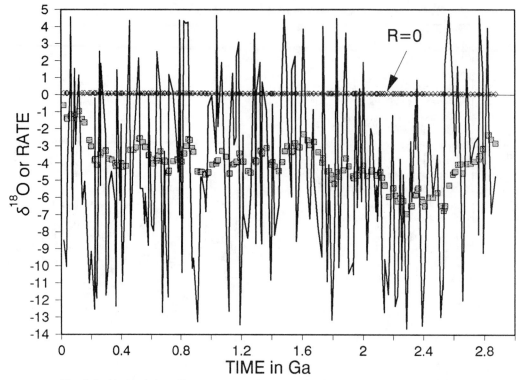

FIG. 6. In this simulation, all parameters are the same as in Fig. 5, with the exception of the global spreading rate which is now set to zero. Even though the target isotopic composition of seawater swings through extreme changes reflecting the oxygen isotope heterogeneity of the continental crust, the isotopic composition of seawater remains relatively constant over billion year intervals, and the 4 per mil excursions occur over 0.5 Ga intervals. No short time scale ($\approx$20 Ma) 3–6 per mil changes occur, because the rate constants are too slow.

value of continental crustal rocks is allowed to randomly fluctuate over a $\approx$20 per mil range in random time steps less than 25 Ma in duration. The effect of the latter is to perturb the system towards a new target steady-state value. The target steady-state values are shown by the sharply fluctuating solid curve, and the actual $\delta^{18}O$ value of seawater at the end of a time step is shown by the squares. In simulations with seafloor spreading, seawater settles in at an isotopic composition close to $-1$ $\pm 1$, and no change in the oxygen isotopic composition of seawater occurs at a rate faster than about 1 per mil/100 Ma.

In Fig. 6, the effect of totally shutting-down seafloor spreading is shown with all other parameters the same as in Fig. 5. The target steady-state $\delta^{18}O$ value of seawater fluctuates over a wide range (four times greater than in Fig. 5) because buffering effect of the ridge is now eliminated. In spite of the more dramatic changes in the target steady-state $\delta$ values, the average $\delta^{18}O$ value of seawater declines slightly but still does not vary all that much. The lack of a

precipitous decline in the $\delta^{18}O$ value of seawater is a consequence of the fact that the simulation allows the weathering of sediments which formed in the presence of seawater with $\delta^{18}O \approx 0$. The time constants are now much longer, so that the large changes in the target values are more than compensated by the slower response time; thus, the isotopic composition of seawater still does not change at the rates required by some interpretations of the sedimentary record.

This latter type of regime (the zero seafloor spreading case) would occur only when global seafloor spreading rates decline to and remain at levels well below their present levels of 3–4 km$^2$/yr, again at the expense of response time of the global cycle which becomes much longer by several hundred million years. As long as continental weathering affects rocks of all types and ages which have $^{18}O/$ $^{16}O$ ratios covering the full diversity of $\delta^{18}O$, the time dependent variation in the $\delta^{18}O$ of seawater *should be much less* than the time dependent variation of the target "steady-state" $\delta^{18}O$ of seawater.

## CONCLUSIONS

If the $\delta^{18}O$ value of seawater does change substantially on short time scales as a result of changing the proportions of the fluxes related to ridge-crest and continental weathering effects, then such changes require dramatic changes in the tectonic regime of the Earth. In the search for the interpretation of the secular variation in the $\delta^{18}O$ values of sedimentary rocks, we must recognize that the rate constants for changing the global oxygen isotope composition of the oceans appear much too slow to account for the apparent timescales of the changes observed in sedimentary rocks. Even if the latter timescales were correct, the magnitude of the tectonic changes required to shift the steady-state isotopic composition of seawater to the extremes suggested by some literal interpretations of the sedimentary data are too large to be reconciled with constraints imposed by the age distributions of the continents or the ocean crust.

At present, continental glaciation and deglaciation are the only known mechanisms that seem to operate on short enough time scales to produce rapid changes in the $\delta^{18}O$ of seawater. The oxygen isotopic changes associated with cycles of glaciation are of insufficient magnitude to explain the changes in the oxygen isotope composition of seawater that some workers have inferred from the Paleozoic sedimentary record. In the absence of other plausible explanations, the significance of the secular oxygen isotope record would appear to lie in some local (up to continent scale) environmental parameters or, alternatively, some problem with the time constants for the preservation of surface oxygen isotope signatures.

*Acknowledgements*—This work was supported by a grant from the Australian Research Council to the author at Monash University, Melbourne, Victoria. Ian Richards and Jenny Mikucki assisted in the laboratory. Reviews by Bob Criss, Hugh Taylor, Chuck Douthitt and Patrick Brady improved earlier versions of the manuscript.

## REFERENCES

ARMSTRONG R. L. (1981) Radiogenic isotopes: the case for crustal recycling on a near-steady-state no-continental-growth Earth. *Phil. Trans. Reg. Soc. London* **A301**, 443–472.

BARRON E. J. and WASHINGTON W. M. (1984) The role of geographic variables in paleoclimates: results from Cretaceous climate model sensitivity studies. *J. Geophys. Res.* **89**, 1267–1279.

BEATY D. W. and TAYLOR H. P., JR. (1982) Some petrologic and oxygen isotopic relationships in the Amulet mine, Noranda, Quebec, and their bearing on the origin of Archean massive sulfide deposits. *Econ. Geol.* **77**, 95–108.

BERNER R. A. (1989) Biogeochemical cycles of carbon and sulfur and their effect on atmospheric oxygen over Phanerozoic time. *Paleogeogr. Paleoclimat. Paleoecol. (Global Planet. Change Sec.)* **75**, 97–122.

BERNER R. A., LASAGA A. C. and GARRELS R. M. (1983) The carbonate-silicate cycle and its effect on atmospheric carbon dioxide over the past 100 million years. *Amer. J. Sci.* **283**, 641–683.

BURDETT J. W., GROTZINGER J. P. and ARTHUR M. A. (1990) Did major changes in the isotopic composition of Proterozoic seawater occur? *Geology* **18**, 227–230.

CLARKE F. W. (1924) *The Data of Geochemistry,* 5th edn; *U.S. Geol. Surv. Bull. 770.*

CRISS R. E., GREGORY R. T. and TAYLOR H. P., JR. (1987) Kinetic theory of oxygen isotopic exchange between minerals and water. *Geochim. Cosmochim. Acta* **51**, 1099–1108.

DEGENS E. T. and EPSTEIN S. (1962) Relationship between $^{18}O/^{16}O$ ratios in coexisting carbonates, cherts, and diatomites. *Bull. Amer. Assoc. Petrol. Geol.* **46**, 534–542.

DREVER J. I., LI Y.-H. and MAYNARD J. B. (1988) Geochemical cycles: the continental crust and oceans. In *Chemical Cycles in the Evolution of the Earth* (eds. C. B. GREGOR, R. M. GARRELS, F. T. MACKENZIE and J. B. MAYNARD), pp. 17–54, Wiley Interscience, New York.

GEBAUER D. and WILLIAMS I. S. (1990) Crust and mantle evolution of the European Hercynides. *Geol. Soc. Australia Abstr.* **27**, 38.

GILLULY J. (1955) Geologic contrasts between continents and ocean basins. In *Crust of the Earth* (ed., A. POLDERVART); *Geol. Soc. Amer. Spec. Paper 62,* pp. 7–13.

GILLULY J. (1964) Atlantic sediments, erosion rates, and the evolution of the continental shelf, some speculations. *Geol. Soc. Amer. Bull.* **75**, 483–492.

GREGORY R. T. and QUICK J. E. (1990) Seafloor hydrothermal alteration of a Proterozoic island arc: the Darb Zubaydah ophiolite complex, Saudi Arabia. *Symp. Ophiolite Genesis Evol. Oceanic Lithosphere.* Ministry Petrol. Mineral. Sultanate Oman G5:7.

GREGORY R. T. and TAYLOR H. P., JR. (1981) An oxygen isotope profile in a section of Cretaceous oceanic crust, Samail ophiolite, Oman: evidence for $\delta^{18}O$ buffering of the oceans by deep (>5 km) seawater-hydrothermal circulation at mid-ocean ridges. *J. Geophys. Res.* **86**, 2737–2755.

GREGORY R. T., CRISS R. E. and TAYLOR H. P., JR. (1989) Oxygen isotope exchange kinetics of mineral pairs in closed and open systems: applications to problems of hydrothermal alteration of igneous rocks and Precambrian iron formations. *Chem. Geol.* **75**, 1–42.

HOFFMAN S. E., WILSON M. and STAKES D. S. (1986) Inferred oxygen isotope profile of Archean oceanic crust, Onverwacht Group, South Africa. *Nature* **321**, 55–58.

HOLEMAN J. N. (1968) The sediment yield of major rivers of the world. *Water Resource Res.* **4**, 737–747.

HOLLAND H. (1984) *The Chemical Evolution of the Atmosphere and Oceans.* Princeton University Press.

HOLSER W. T., SCHIDLOWSKI M., MACKENZIE F. T., and MAYNARD J. B. (1988) Biogeochemical cycles of carbon and sulfur. In *Chemical Cycles in the Evolution of the Earth* (eds. C. B. GREGOR, R. M. GARRELS, F. T. MACKENZIE and J. B. MAYNARD), pp. 105–174, Wiley Interscience, New York.

HOPSON C. A., COLEMAN R. G., GREGORY R. T., PALLISTER J. S. and BAILEY E. H. (1981) Geologic section through the Samail ophiolite and associated rocks along a Muscat-Ibra transect. *J. Geophys. Res.* **86,** 2527–2544.

JACOBSEN S. B. and WASSERBURG G. J. (1979) The mean age of mantle and crustal reservoirs. *J. Geophys. Res.* **84,** 7411–7427.

KASTING J. F. (1989) Long-term stability of the Earth's climate. *Paleogeogr. Paleoclimat. Paleoecol.* (*Global Planet. Change Sec.*) **75,** 83–95.

KERRICH R. (1987) The stable isotope geochemistry of Au-Ag vein deposits in metamorphic rocks. In *Stable Isotope Geochemistry of Low Temperature Fluids* (ed. T. K. KYSER); *Mineral. Assoc. Canada Short Course 13,* pp. 287–336.

KNAUTH L. P. and EPSTEIN S. (1976) Hydrogen and oxygen isotope ratios in nodular and bedded cherts. *Geochim. Cosmochim. Acta* **40,** 1095–1108.

LANPHERE M. A., COLEMAN R. G. and HOPSON C. A. (1981) Sr isotopic tracer study of the Samail ophiolite, Oman. *J. Geophys. Res.* **86,** 2709–2720.

LOHMANN K. C. and WALKER J. C. G. (1989) The $\delta^{18}O$ record of Phanerozoic abiotic marine calcite cements. *Geophys. Res. Lett.* **16,** 319–322.

LUZ B., KOLODNY Y. and KOVACH H. (1984) Oxygen isotope variation in phosphate of biogenic apatites, III. conodonts. *Earth Planet. Sci. Lett.* **69,** 255–262.

MCCULLOCH M. T., GREGORY R. T., WASSERBURG G. J. and TAYLOR H. P., JR. (1981) Sm-Nd, Rb-Sr, $^{18}O/^{16}O$ isotopic systematics in an oceanic crustal section: Evidence from the Samail ophiolite. *J. Geophys. Res.* **86,** 2721–2736.

MUEHLENBACHS K. (1986) Alteration of the oceanic crust and the $^{18}O$ history of seawater. In *Stable Isotopes in High Temperature Geological Processes* (eds. J. W.

VALLEY, H. P. TAYLOR, JR., and J. R. O'NEIL); *Rev. Mineral. 16,* pp. 425–444.

MUEHLENBACHS K. and CLAYTON R. N. (1976) Oxygen isotope composition of oceanic crust and its bearing on seawater. *J. Geophys. Res.* **81,** 4365–4369.

PALMER M. R. and EDMOND J. M. (1989) The strontium isotope budget of the modern ocean. *Earth Planet. Sci. Lett.* **92,** 11–26.

PETERMAN Z. E., HEDGE C. E. and TOURTELOT H. A. (1970) Isotopic composition of strontium in seawater throughout Phanerozoic time. *Geochim. Cosmochim. Acta* **34,** 105–120.

POPP B. N., ANDERSON T. E. and SANBERG P. A. (1986) Brachiopods as indicators of original isotopic compositions in some Paleozoic limestones. *Geol. Soc. Amer. Bull.* **97,** 1262–1269.

SMITH H. S., O'NEIL J. R., and ERLANK A. J. (1984) Oxygen isotope compositions of minerals and rocks and chemical alteration patterns in pillow lavas from the Barberton greenstone belt, South Africa. In *Archean Geochemistry* (eds. A. KRONER, G. N. HANSON and A. M. GOODWIN), pp. 115–137. Springer-Verlag, New York.

TURCOTTE D. L. and SCHUBERT G. (1982) *Geodynamics: Applications of Continuum Physics to Geological Problems.* Wiley, New York.

VEIZER J., FRITZ P. and JONES B. (1986) Geochemistry of brachiopods: oxygen and carbon isotopic records of Paleozoic oceans. *Geochim. Cosmochim. Acta* **50,** 1679–1696.

WALKER J. C. G. and LOHMANN K. C. (1989) Why the isotopic composition of seawater changes with time. *Geophys. Res. Lett.* **16,** 323–326.

YODER H. (1976) *Generation of Basaltic Magma.* National Academy of Science: Washington. 265.

Stable Isotope Geochemistry: A Tribute to Samuel Epstein
© The Geochemical Society, Special Publication No. 3, 1991
Editors: H. P. Taylor, Jr., J. R. O'Neil and I. R. Kaplan

# Oxygen and hydrogen isotope compositions of oceanic plutonic rocks: High-temperature deformation and metamorphism of oceanic layer 3

DEBRA S. STAKES

Department of Geological Sciences, University of South Carolina, Columbia, SC 29208, U.S.A.

**Abstract**—Oxygen and hydrogen isotopic data from three suites of modern oceanic plutonic rocks are presented: (a) dredged gabbro, diorite, and aplite from the southern Mid-Atlantic Ridge; (b) dredged gabbro, plagiogranite, diorite, ferrogabbro, and a quartz monzonite from five fracture zones in the western Indian Ocean; and (c) a 500-meter core of olivine gabbro, norite, troctolite, ferrogabbro, and trondjemite drilled from the intersection of the Atlantis II fracture zone and the Southwest Indian Ridge. Essentially all samples bear isotopic and mineralogic evidence of high to moderate temperature hydrothermal metamorphism by seawater. Maximum temperatures of alteration are above 600°C; lower temperatures of alteration, greenschist and below, are not characteristic. Whole-rock samples and plagioclase separates have undergone $^{18}O$ depletions associated with deformation and development of metamorphic mineral assemblages. The stratigraphic control provided by the drill core allows detailed correlation between depth and $^{18}O/^{16}O$ effects, as well as the correlation with pervasive deformation textures and major faults that provided the permeability for seawater to penetrate deeply into oceanic layer 3. The abundance of hydrous alteration minerals can be correlated with the water-rock ratio. Igneous pyroxene has not undergone appreciable isotopic exchange with seawater except under conditions of dynamic recrystallization. Rather, it is either relict or is replaced by amphibole in isotopic equilibrium with plagioclase. Silicic igneous rocks have apparently undergone isotopic exchange in the same range of temperatures as metagabbros. There is some evidence of local assimilation of hydrothermally altered metagabbro by late-stage magma. Isotopic evidence is provided for the presence of a hydrous fluid enriched in $^{18}O$ by up to 4.5 per mil and depleted in D by 30 per mil compared to seawater. This fluid is either an evolved seawater-hydrothermal fluid, perhaps derived from a late hydrous magma, or a hybrid resulting from mixing between magmatic water and seawater during the waning stages of magmatic activity.

## INTRODUCTION

PLUTONIC ROCKS ARE a major constituent of the oceanic crust and presumably comprise most of oceanic layer 3. Detailed petrologic and isotopic studies of oceanic gabbros have suggested that metamorphic recrystallization is related to deformation and/or interaction with seawater during the progressive cooling of the gabbroic sequence (STAKES *et al.*, 1991; MEVEL, 1988; STAKES and VANKO, 1986; BATIZA and VANKO, 1985; ITO and ANDERSON, 1983; BONATTI *et al.*, 1975). The controls on the initial penetration of seawater into the lower crust, the extent and temperatures of seawater circulation, and the possible interaction between high-temperature metamorphism and late-stage magmatic processes can be inferred from the stable isotopic compositions of modern oceanic plutonic rocks.

This study presents a wealth of new oxygen and hydrogen isotopic data from three suites of oceanic plutonic rocks. Drilled and dredged gabbroic and silicic rocks from the western Indian Ocean comprise one of the largest suites of plutonic rocks. These are complemented by a suite of evolved rocks—diorites, aplites, and plagiogranites—from the southern Mid-Atlantic Ridge. This study will

investigate whether seawater penetrates and extensively alters these sections of lower oceanic crust at high temperatures, and whether high-temperature shear zones play an important role in the metamorphism of the lower crust.

## SAMPLE SUITES ANALYZED FOR THIS STUDY

Petrography and mineral identification for each suite of rocks are from previous studies (ENGEL and FISHER, 1975; FREY *et al.*, 1991; STAKES *et al.*, 1991; VANKO and STAKES, 1991). Additional microprobe analyses are provided for samples from the Indian Ocean suites. These analyses were performed on the fully automated Cameca SX-50 electron microprobe at the University of South Carolina, using natural minerals for standards. Special efforts were made to determine plagioclase zonation, evidence of secondary or recrystallized pyroxene, and intergrown minerals in hydrothermal coronas. Trace minerals were identified using the Kevex EDS system on the microprobe. All three suites of samples contain evolved silicic rocks comprised of plagioclase, quartz, and other minerals. These silicic rocks are referred to as aplites or plagiogranites unless biotite or phlogopite is identified as an accessory mineral. Silicic rocks containing mica are referred to as trondjemites.

*Samples from 22°S on the Mid-Atlantic Ridge*

Gabbros, diorites, and an aplite dredged from a fracture zone at 22°S on the Mid-Atlantic Ridge (MAR) were an-

D. S. Stakes

Table 1. Oxygen isotopic composition of dredged rocks.

| Sample no. | Rock type | Mineralogy | WR | PLAG | AMPH | PX | QTZ | Other |
|---|---|---|---|---|---|---|---|---|
| **A. MAR 22°S** | | | | | | | | |
| **SILICIC ROCKS:** | | | | | | | | |
| 12-32G | FE-DI | f, ol, cpx, ap, hb, mt, ilm | 7.1 | 6.3 | 4.6 | | 7.4 | |
| 12-32W | PLGT DK | q, ab | 7.0 | 5.9 | | | 7.0 | |
| 12-22 | FE-DI | f, ol, cpx, hb, mt, ilm, ap | 6.6 | 6.5 | | | | |
| 12-11C | FE-DI | f, ol, cpx, ap, ilm, hb, mt | 3.7 | 4.2 | 2.5 | | | |
| 12-11FG | FE-DI | f, ol, px, ap, hb, mt, ilm | 4.4 | 4.9 | 3.3 | | | |
| 12-24 | Q-DI | f, q, cpx, hb, ilm, ap, xn | 5.1 | 4.6 | 4.6 | | 6.4 | |
| 12-3D | GB | f, hb | 6.3 | 6.2 | 3.8 | | | |
| 12-16 | FE-DI | f, hb, cpx | 6.2 | 6.4 | 5.1 | | 6.7 | |
| 12-36 | FE-DI | f, hb | 6.4 | 5.3 | | | 7.4 | |
| **GABBROS:** | | | | | | | | |
| 5-38 | OL-GB | f, ol, cpx, ilm | 5.7 | 5.6 | | 5.7 | | 5.3OL |
| 5-9 | OL-GB | f, ol, cpx, mt, ilm, chl | 5.7 | 5.9 | | 5.5 | | |
| 5-62 | OL-GB | f, ol, cpx, mt, ilm | 5.9 | 6.0 | | 5.6 | | |
| **B. INDIAN OCEAN** | | | | | | | | |
| **SILICIC ROCKS:** | | | | | | | | |
| ANTP125-4B | GR DB | f, hb, kf, q, ap | 5.4 | 6.4 | 4.4 | | | |
| ANTP125-4C | Q-MZ DK | f, hb, q, kf, bt, ap, sp | 7.5 | 7.3 | 4.7 | | 8.7 | |
| ANTP125-10 | DI | f, hb | 2.8 | 4.5 | 2.5 | | | |
| ANTP125-13 | PLGT | f, hb, q, chl | 5.0 | 6.4 | 4.6 | | | |
| ANTP125-14 | S-DI | f, hb, tc, bt | 5.3 | 5.7 | 1.4 | | | |
| ANTP125-16 | PLGT | f, hb, q, ap, sp | 4.4 | 3.9 | | | 5.7 | |
| **GABBROS:** | | | | | | | | |
| ANTP125-2(2) | PX GB | f, cpx, opx, hb | 5.2 | 5.9 | 5.4 | 5.3 | | |
| ANTP125-8 | FETI GB | f, cpx, opx, tc, chl | 5.7 | 6.5 | | 5.7 | | |
| ANTP126-1(4) | OL GB | f, ol, cpx, hb, opx, tc, chl | 4.9 | 5.4 | | 5.5 | | |
| ANTP130-1(2) | OL GB | f, ol, cpx, sm | 6.2 | 6.3 | | 5.7 | | |
| ANTP130-4 | GB | f, ol, cpx, act, tc, chl, z | 7.8 | 7.0 | 5.6 | 5.6 | | 13.4 Z |
| ANTP130-6 | OL GB | f, ol, tc | 6.0 | 6.6 | | 5.5 | | |
| CIR82-1 | PX GB | f, cpx, opx, hb, chl | 5.0 | 5.2 | 3.7 | 5.3 | | |
| CIR97B | OL GB | f, ol, cpx, hb, opx, chl, tc | 4.7 | 5.3 | | 5.2 | | |
| CIR97D | OL GB | f, ol, cpx, tc, chl, sm | 5.0 | 5.0 | | 5.2 | | |
| **AMPHIBOLITIZED GABBROS:** | | | | | | | | |
| ANTP113-1(1) | PX GB | f, cpx, hb, | 3.8 | 4.5 | 4.6 | | | |
| ANTP125-1 | HB GB | f, cpx, hb, opx, ap | 2.3 | 3.1 | 1.5 | 5.0 | | |
| ANTP130-1(1) | OL GB | f, ol, cpx, tc, mt | 4.9 | 4.1 | 4.1 | 5.1 | | |
| ANTP130-3 | HB GB | f, hb, cpx | 5.3 | 4.9 | 4.7 | 5.2 | | |
| ANTP130-8 | PX GB | f, cpx, hb, opx, tc, chl, z | | 5.3 | | 5.4 | | |
| CIR97ZZ | PX GB | f, hb, cpx | 3.7 | 3.5 | 3.4 | | | |
| CIR97C | HB GB | f, hb | 4.9 | | 4.7 | | | |
| CIR97F(2) | HB GB | f, hb, ilm | 4.1 | 4.5 | 4.1 | | | |
| CIR97X | S-GB | f, hb, ab | 4.7 | 4.6 | 4.9 | | | |

Notes: f = feldspar; ol = olivine; cpx = clinopyroxene; hb = hornblende; opx = orthopyroxene; act = actinolite; tc = talc; chl = chlorite; sm = smectite; ap = apatite; z = zeolite; ilm = ilmenite; mt = magnetite; ab = albite; bt = biotite; q = quartz; sp = titanite; kf = K-feldspar; GB = gabbro; PX = pyroxene; S-GB = deformed gabbro; FETI = ferrogabbro; PLGT = plagiogranite; DI = diorite; Q-MZ DK = quartz monzonite dike; GR DB = granophyric diabase.

alyzed for oxygen isotopes. Complete petrographic and geochemical descriptions of these samples are provided in FREY *et al.* (1991) and a summary is provided here. The isotopic results for both whole rock and mineral separates are provided in Table 1. All the gabbros and diorites from 22°S have cumulate textures. Samples 5-9, 5-38, and 5-62 are petrographically the freshest olivine gabbros obtained, and contain cumulate plagioclase, olivine, and pyroxene. Ilmenite, magnetite, and sulfides are accessory minerals. Trace amounts of chlorite were observed in microfractures cutting plagioclase in sample 5-9. The plagioclase compositions in 5-9, and 5-38 are very uniform at An62 and An69, respectively. The plagioclase in sample 5-62 is variable in grain size and strongly zoned with cores of An56.

Samples 12-22, 12-11C, 12-11FG, 12-30, and 12-32G are characterized as ferrodiorites by FREY et al. (1991), although they have lower SiO$_2$ than typical diorites. These samples contain sodic plagioclase (An30-An8), olivine partially to completely altered to amphibole and magnetite, pyroxene partially altered to amphibole, primary brown hornblende partially altered to green amphibole, magnetite, ilmenite, and apatite. Relict olivine is preserved only in sample 12-32 and is very Fe-rich (Fo14), similar to the ferrogabbros of ODP Hole 735B (discussed below). Samples of quartz-diorite (12-16, 12-24, 12-36) are composed of quartz, sodic plagioclase (An10), pyroxene partially altered to amphibole, primary green amphibole with minor apatite, ilmenite, and xenotime. An aplite dike (12-32W) that cross-cuts ferrodiorite sample 12-32G is composed of quartz and albite (An2) in a sugary, equigranular texture with grain-size that decreases toward the center of the vein. The amphiboles may in part be xenocrysts from the host diorite.

## Samples from Indian Ocean fracture zones

A suite of 24 gabbroic rocks dredged from five fracture zones in the western Indian Ocean were analyzed for oxygen and hydrogen isotopes. Geographic distribution and detailed mineral chemistry of the complete set of dredge hauls is described in ENGEL and FISHER (1975) and BLOOMER et al. (1989). Rocks from the Vema (ANTP130), Argo (ANTP125, ANTP126, CIR82), Marie Celeste (CIR97), and Melville (ANTP113) fracture zones were selected for study. Detailed studies of primary mineral compositions in gabbroic rocks led BLOOMER et al. (1989) to suggest that these represent cumulates in small sills or chambers emplaced laterally from a central axial magma chamber. Boundary layer crystallization and partial resorption of wall rock are suggested to play a role in the extensive mineral variability observed in these samples.

Most of the samples included in this isotopic study are described by ENGEL and FISHER (1975), with a comparison to ophiolitic samples presented in STAKES et al. (1984). Detailed mineralogy and isotopic results are presented in Table 1. The samples include olivine gabbros (ANTP130B-1(2A), -4, -6; ANTP126-1(4); CIR97B, -D), two pyroxene gabbros (ANTP125-2(2); CIR82-1), and a Ti-ferrogabbro (ANTP125-8), all of which contain minor to trace amounts of secondary hydrous minerals. The mineralogy of these hydrous minerals is controlled by the primary mineral being replaced during static hydrous or coronitic alteration (STAKES et al., 1984).

Amphibolitized gabbros are extensively replaced by metamorphic minerals, dominantly hornblende or actinolite. Sample ANTP125-1 contains metamorphic pyroxene and brown hornblende that may have formed during high-temperature deformation, now obscured by extensive hydrous alteration. Plagioclase is variable in composition (An46-An29) with rims containing up to 3% Or and small needles of apatite. Augite gabbros (ANTP113-1(1); CIR97ZZ) similarly contain intermediate plagioclase (An53-An48) and amphibole ranging from actinolite to edenitic or magnesio-hornblende in composition. Sample

CIR97ZZ, in addition, shows evidence of a deformed plagioclase mosaic (An40) cross-cut by a vein of ferroan pargasitic hornblende. Olivine-bearing rocks (e.g. 130B-1(1), Fo68) and orthopyroxene-bearing rocks (e.g. 130B-8) contain talc-magnetite pseudomorphs in addition to plagioclase (An64-An52) with local sodic rims and hornblende replacing both the plagioclase and most clinopyroxene. Pyroxene symplectites and small plagioclase grains may be artifacts of an early episode of ductile deformation.

The hornblende-rich gabbros (ANTP130-3; CIR97C; -F(2)) and the cataclastic anorthosite (CIR97X) are predominantly composed of plagioclase of intermediate composition (An58-An45) and aluminous hornblende, with zones of ductile deformation similar to those in the amphibolitized gabbros. These samples also exhibit a later cataclastic deformation characterized by the formation of more sodic plagioclase (An39-An8) in overgrowths, granulated zones, or network veins.

Silicic rocks from the Indian Ocean dredge suites were all collected from the Argo Fracture Zone (ANTP125) and include a diorite (10) and a mylonitized diorite (14), aplite or trondjemite (13, 16), and a granophyric diabase host (4B) for a dikelet of quartz monzonite (4C). The latter two samples are unusual in containing rims of orthoclase. The quartz monzonite dikelet, in addition, contains zircon and biotite, and is described in detail in ENGEL and FISHER (1975). The primary minerals include sodic plagioclase (An18-An36), ferro-edenitic hornblende, and variable amounts of quartz.

## Samples from ODP Leg 118, Hole 735B

Cored gabbros, ferrogabbros, and trondjemites recovered from ODP Hole 735B in 1987 represent 500 m of oceanic layer 3 that formed at the Southwest Indian Ridge 18 km from its intersection with the Atlantis II Fracture Zone. The lithostratigraphy and igneous mineralogy of these samples are described in detail in DICK et al. (1991) and NATLAND et al. (1991). The primary lithostratigraphy is illustrated in Fig. 1, with core numbers and depth in the core. Most of the core (61%) is chemically uniform, massive olivine gabbro with minor cryptic variations. Plagioclase is moderately anorthitic (An58) while the olivine and clinopyroxene are both magnesian (Mg# = 81, Fo74, respectively). A small unit of gabbronorite caps the section while the lower 80 m contains intercalated troctolite and microgabbro. The grain size is highly variable, and contacts between the six lithologic units are frequently sheared and deformed.

The remainder of the core is comprised of abundant Ti-ferrogabbro rich in ilmenite and magnetite, together with small volumes of late felsic veins and intrusives. The oxide-rich gabbros are interpreted to be derived by extensive high-iron differentiation of the olivine gabbros, followed by mechanical concentration of the Fe-rich fractionate into permeable shear zones by filter pressing and deformation. This is associated with the latter stages of cooling and crystallization at a spreading axis (NATLAND et al., 1991; DICK et al., 1991). DICK et al. (1991) refer to these oxide-rich gabbros as products of "syndeformational magmatic fractionation."

Late felsic intrusives include trondjemite and aplite that are mineralogically and stratigraphically associated with diopside-plagioclase veins. The felsic veins and intrusives typically contain biotite, phlogopite, and zircon. Both the felsic intrusives and the diopside-bearing veins have characteristically suffered from low-temperature alteration (greenschist to zeolite grade), obscuring primary mineral relationships (STAKES et al., 1991). DICK et al. (1991) suggest that the felsic intrusions are the silicic complement to the ferrogabbros, forming by magmatic hydrofracture in brecciated zones that dominate the lower half of the core, presumably as a result of localization of the late hydrous magmas. NATLAND et al. (1991) suggest that liquid immiscibility played a role in the formation of the silicic differentiates. STAKES et al. (1991) describe textural features more consistent with assimilation or partial resorption of hydrothermally altered gabbroic wall rock. The largest trondjemite horizon is found between cores 53R and 56R and contains partially resorbed xenoliths of gabbro, distinguished by euhedral sodic plagioclase mantling partially digested calcic plagioclase.

The metamorphic history and stratigraphy of the drill-core is described in detail by STAKES et al. (1991) and VANKO and STAKES (1991). The core is dissected by ductile deformation zones that are apparently related to normal faulting (CANNAT et al., 1991a,b). The textural log from STAKES et al. (1991) is provided in Fig. 1, as a compilation of ductile deformation from faintly foliated (Type I) to mylonitic (Type V). Metamorphic mineral assemblages suggest that ductile deformation was initiated under granulite to amphibolite grade conditions and terminated in lower amphibolite conditions. A crack and vein network that dominates the upper half of the core resulted from brittle failure at the conclusion of the ductile deformation. A histogram provided in Fig. 1 illustrates the relationship between extensional veins oriented perpendicular to the metamorphic foliation and intensity of deformation. The veins related to deformation are either hornblende-bearing or hornblende- and sodic plagioclase-bearing, and are the most abundant vein type in the upper 250 m of core. Similar amphibole veins are also present sporadically in the lower 50 m of core. Hydrous or coronitic alteration of the gabbro to assemblages including cummingtonite, talc, hornblende of variable composition, sodic plagioclase, Mg-rich chlorite, clinozoisite, and phlogopite is correlated with penetration by brittle cracks and veins.

The felsic intrusions and diopside-bearing leucocratic veins are abundant in the lower half of the core, spacially associated with brecciated horizons (see Fig. 1). The largest leucocratic veins are found in the undeformed horizon between cores 60 and 75. Within this horizon diopside not only appears in monomineralic veins but also as a replacement of igneous pyroxene and plagioclase. Most of the veins in the lower 250 m of core represented in the histogram of Fig. 1 are diopside-plagioclase or their altered equivalent. The brecciated horizons are the only portion of the core that exhibit mineral assemblages characteristic of greenschist- and zeolite-grade metamorphism, including epidote, sphene, chlorite, actinolite, thomsonite, and analcime. Continued alteration by cold seawater within some of the brecciated horizons is demonstrated by the presence of late, low-temperature carbonate-smectite veins (see Fig. 1).

## RESULTS OF ISOTOPIC ANALYSES

Oxygen and hydrogen isotopic analyses were performed on whole rocks and mineral separates. Results are reported in standard $\delta$-notation relative to SMOW; NBS-28 has a $\delta^{18}O = +9.6$ on this scale. Minerals were mechanically separated and then hand-picked and cleaned with acetone prior to isotopic analyses. Traces of carbonate were removed by reaction with cold dilute hydrochloric acid. In addition, quartz separates were cleaned with cold hydrofluoric acid to insure purity. When possible, multiple generations of feldspar and amphibole were separated from single samples, based on grain size and optical properties.

Results of isotopic analyses from the dredged rocks are provided in Table 1. These analyses were performed at the California Institute of Technology using fluorine gas as a reagent. Samples from Hole 735B (Table 2) are distinguished as veins versus matrix, and these subsamples separated where possible. Other samples are from homogeneous bulk rock, some of which include veinlets too small to separate. Mineral separates from Hole 735B include plagioclase, clinopyroxene, metamorphic diopside, hornblende, olivine, epidote, and biotite. Homogenous whole-rock powders were produced during the cruise for the purpose of shipboard chemical analyses. Isotopic analyses performed on these powders were reported in STAKES et al. (1991) and are provided in Fig. 1. All of these analyses were performed at the University of South Carolina using CIF₃ as a reagent. Hydrogen isotopic analyses (Table

FIG. 1. Metamorphic and deformation stratigraphy for ODP Hole 735B (after STAKES et al., 1991). From left to right the columns represent: (1) Depth (in meters below seafloor) and core number (1 to 87) using lithostratigraphic designations from DICK et al. (1991): Unit I = gabbro norite; Unit II = compound olivine and oxide gabbro; Unit III = disseminated oxide-olivine gabbro; Unit IV = massive oxide olivine gabbro; Unit V = massive olivine gabbro; Unit VI = compound olivine, oxide, and troctolitic gabbro. (2) Textural type as an indicator of extent of synkinematic recrystallization showing structural domains and major mylonite zones (M): I = weakly deformed with no penetrative deformation; II = well-foliated with limited plagioclase recrystallization; III = well-foliated with extensive plagioclase recrystallization and gneissic layering; IV = intercalated gneissic and mylonitic layering; V = mylonitic. (3) Histogram of number of veins per core, with patterned intervals representing heavily veined brecciated horizons; the veins are dominantly hornblende-bearing to bottom of Core 54, diopside-bearing below Core 54, and carbonate veins are indicated by arrows. (4) Profile of $\delta^{18}O$ vs. depth, with symbols as follows: filled circles = whole-rock powders; × = vein hornblende; filled square = vein plagioclase; open square = matrix plagioclase; open triangle pointing up = whole-rock plagioclase; open triangle pointing down = whole-rock hornblende.

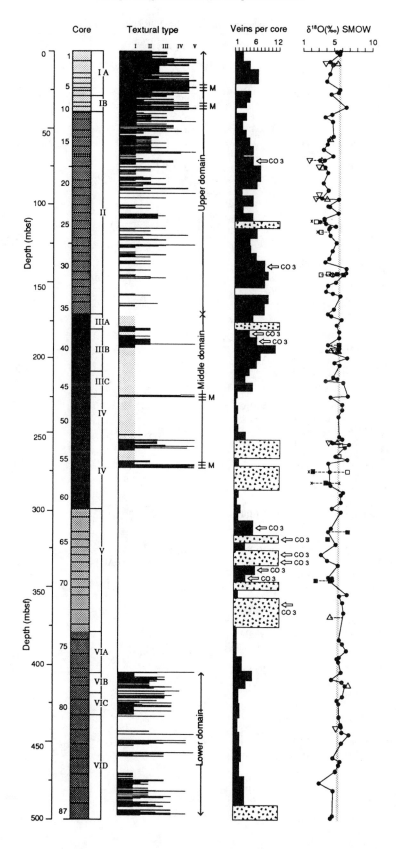

Table 2. Oxygen isotope data for ODP Hole 735B.

| CORE-SEC | Interval | Depth | WR | PLAG | AMPH | DI | CPX | Other |
|---|---|---|---|---|---|---|---|---|
| 2-2 | 36-39 | 8.4 | VEIN | 4.8 | 4.2 | | | |
| 4-2 | 37-43 | 19.4 | | 6.5 | | | | |
| 10-1 | 37-39 | 36.6 | | 6.6 | 6.1 | | 5.8 | |
| 12-1 | 114-117 | 40.5 | | 4.6 | 4.5 | | 4.1(A) | |
| 12-2 | 135-139 | 42.2 | 3.6 | 4.7 | | | | |
| 15-1 | 90-93 | 57.1 | 4.2 | 4.4 | | | | |
| 16-1 | 151-154 | 63.3 | | 4.9 | 1.9 | | | |
| 18-3 | 5-8 | 71.6 | 3.2 | 3.2 | 1.6 | | | |
| 19-1 | 124-128 | 75.9 | 3.8 | 3.4 | 2.9 | | | |
| 19-3 | 5-9 | 77.7 | | | | | | |
| 22-1 | 56-62 | | | | 3.2 | | | |
| 22-1 | 69-73 | 94.7 | | | 3.3 | | | |
| 22-1 | 142-147 | 95.5 | 3.3 | 3.9 | 3.0 | | | |
| 22-3 | 112-115 | 98.2 | VEIN | 4.0 | 3.6 | | | |
| 24-1 | 128-131 | 107.4 | | 5.3 | 2.1 | | 3.4(A) | |
| 24-2 | 47-51 | 108.1 | 3.6 | | | | | |
| 25-1 | 12-17 | 110.6 | Ca-plg | 4.9 | | | | |
| | | | Na-plg | 2.4 | 1.9 | | | |
| 26-2 | 8-12 | 117.1 | | 3.3 | 2.7 | | 5.1 | |
| 31-2 | 100-104 | 146.1 | 4.1 | | | | | |
| | | | VEIN | 5.3 | | | | |
| 31-3 | 31-33 | 146.7 | 3.6 | 3.5 | 5.3 | | | |
| | | | VEIN | 5.7 | | | | |
| 33-1 | 137-141 | 154.8 | | 4.4 | 4.0 | 2.5 | | |
| 36-1 | 117-119 | 173.0 | VEIN | 5.8 | | | | |
| 35-6 | 114-117 | 171.9 | 4.3 | | | | 5.4 | |
| 38-4 | 140-143 | | | 5.7 | | | 5.8 | |
| 40-2 | 73-78 | 192.2 | 4.2 | | | | | |
| | | | VEIN | 6.1 | | | | |
| 40-3 | 34-39 | 193.3 | VEIN | | | 1.9 | | |
| 41-1 | 42-50 | 196.9 | 4.2 | 4.5 | 4.8 | | 5.2 | |
| 41-3 | 67-71 | 200.1 | VEIN | 6.9(A) | | | | |
| 44-4 | 41-49 | 215.5 | 3.9 | | | | | |
| 53-4 | 5-15 | 256.9 | 4.7 | 5.3 | 4.4 | | | |
| 55-1 | 59-69 | 265.3 | 5.3 | 3.2 | 4.2 | | | |
| 56-1 | 54-61 | 270.7 | 4.3 | | | | | |
| 57-2 | 11-18 | 276.4 | 4.4 | 4.0 | 5.3 | | 5.5 | |
| 57-4 | 0-6 | 277.9 | VEIN | 6.6 | | | | |
| 58-3 | 8-16 | 283.3 | 4.4 | | | | | |
| | | | VEIN | 3.9 | 2.1 | | 5.6 | |
| 60-4 | 105-112 | 295.5 | VEIN | 7.34(A) | 4.0 | 1.7 | | |
| | | | | | 2.6ACT | | | |
| 61-3 | 48-58 | 299.0 | 4.7 | | | | | |
| 63-1 | 107-113 | 309.4 | VEIN | 4.3 | 4.9HB | 1.7 | | |
| | | | | | 2.5ACT | | | |
| 63-5 | 70-77 | 311.1 | VEIN | 5.6 | 5.4 | | | |
| | | | MATRIX | 4.9 | | | | |
| 63-6 | 94-98 | 313.4 | VEIN | 6.8 | | 4.0 | | |
| | | | MATRIX | 6.3 | | | | |
| 63-7 | 80-87 | 314.6 | 4.2 | | | | | |
| | | | VEIN C | 4.1 | | 2.4 | | |
| | | | VEIN F (A) | 7.0 | | | | |
| 64-3 | 95-104 | 319.3 | VEIN | 4.1 | | | | |
| 66-4 | 14-19 | 329.4 | 3.4 | | | | | |
| 68-2 | 68-75 | 337.2 | | 7.4 | | 1.1 | | |
| 69-1 | 41-48 | 341.5 | VEIN | 4.8 | | | 5.2 | |
| 69-3 | 86-96 | 334.5 | 4.9 | 7.2 | | | | |
| 70-1 | 39-49 | 346.4 | VEIN | 4.7 | | 2.7 | | |
| 70-1 | 130-140 | 347.3 | 5.7 | 5.3 | | 5.2 | | 4.8OL |
| 70-2 | 11-13 | | VEIN C | 5.0 | | 2.9 | | |
| | | | VEIN F | 6.6 | | | | |
| 72-7 | 42-47 | 360.1 | | 4.7 | | | | |
| 73-6 | 60-65 | 372.9 | | 7.5 | 5.4 | | | |

Table 2. (Continued)

| CORE-SEC | Interval | Depth | WR | PLAG | AMPH | DI | CPX | Other |
|---|---|---|---|---|---|---|---|---|
| 74-5 | 104-109 | 382.3 | | 6.5 | | | 5.1 | |
| 75-1 | 0-6 | 385.2 | 6.0 | | | | | |
| 76-2 | 121-126 | 396.5 | 5.5 | | 4.9 | | 4.3 | |
| 77-5 | 15-19 | 409.1 | 4.7 | | | | | |
| 78-3 | 110-119 | 413.4 | 6.6 | | | | | |
| | | | VEIN | 6.8 | | | | |
| 79-4 | 46-49 | 419.5 | VEIN | 6.0 | | 2.6 | | |
| 79-6 | 69-77 | 422.5 | 6.4 | 7.2 | | | 5.7 | 4.9OL |
| 80-7 | 27-34 | 433.1 | 5.8 | | | | | |
| 81-2 | 23-31 | 436.1 | VEIN | 7.9 | 6.0 | | | |
| 81-4 | 60-68 | 438.4 | 6.3 | | 6.0 | | | |
| 81-6 | 87-90 | 441.3 | | 6.3 | 5.3 | | | |
| | | NAPL | VEIN | 5.8 | 5.7 | | | |
| 82-2 | 58-65 | 445.1 | 7.2 | | 5.7 | | | |
| 82-7 | 21-29 | 451.8 | 6.2 | 6.2 | | | 5.6 | |
| 83-5 | 36-46 | 460.1 | 5.1 | | | | | 5.4BT |
| 84-2 | 70-78 | 464.2 | 5.7 | | | | | |
| 84-6 | 0-8 | 468.7 | VEIN | 6.5 | | 1.8 | | 3.8EP |
| 85-4 | 17-25 | 476.0 | 3.0 | | | | | |
| 85-6 | 11-15 | 478.6 | | 5.0 | | 1.4 | | 3.5EP |
| 86-6 | 15-18 | 489.4 | | 7.5 | | 1.0 | | |
| 86-6 | 91-96 | 490.1 | | 7.7 | 5.3 | | 5.3 | |
| 87-5 | 79-86 | 497.4 | 4.9 | 4.7 | 3.8 | 5.7 | | |
| | | | VEIN | | 3.4 | | | |
| 87-7 | 7-14 | | MATRIX | 3.0 | | | | |
| | | | VEIN C | 4.5 | | 1.4 | | |
| | | | VEIN F | 6.2 | | | | |

Notes: VEIN C = coarse-grained vein mineral; VEIN F = fine grained vein mineral; Minerals: PLAG = plagioclase; AMPH = amphibole; CPX = clinopyroxene (igneous or dynamic recrystallization); DI = secondary diopside; OL = olivine; EP = epidote; BT = biotite; ACT = actinolite; HB = dark green to brown hornblende.

3) were performed on hornblende separates from Indian Ocean dredged samples and the Hole 735B gabbros. These analyses were all performed at the U.S. Geological Survey in Menlo Park using an RF induction furnace to liberate the water from the mineral and reducing this to hydrogen by reaction with a heated uranium furnace.

The $\delta^{18}O$ of mid-ocean ridge basalt is relatively constant (+5.8; TAYLOR, 1968), and plutonic rocks that have crystallized from such magmas with no seawater involvement would have a whole-rock value similar to this. Isotopic exchange among the crystallizing phases, however, can continue with plagioclase (and quartz) becoming enriched, and pyroxene or hornblende becoming depleted in $^{18}O$ with decreasing temperatures. The result of closed-system crystal fractionation of olivine would produce evolved magmas (ferrogabbros, diorites, plagiogranites) that are slightly enriched in $^{18}O$. Such $^{18}O$ enrichments with no complication by seawater are typically less than one per mil, and have only been documented in a limited number of suites of oceanic island basalts and their differentiates (see TAYLOR, 1986, for a summary). The mineralogical

and isotopic effects of sub-seafloor metamorphism on oceanic layer 3 has been described for ophiolitic rocks and for suites of oceanic gabbros (see MUEHLENBACHS, 1986, for a review). At temperatures above about 250°C, the plutonic rocks are depleted in $^{18}O$, with plagioclase exchanging at a rate approximately five times that of pyroxene (see GREGORY et al., 1989; GREGORY and CRISS, 1986). An additional complicating factor is that the effect of seawater interaction is not merely an isotopic exchange: at temperatures below granulite grade, calcic plagioclase is replaced by more sodic compositions and pyroxene is replaced by amphibole. These metamorphic alteration minerals would presumably be in isotopic equilibrium with the local fluid phase, either seawater or an $^{18}O$-enriched derivative.

*MAR plutonic rocks*

The $^{18}O$ values of the whole-rock powders from the MAR 22°S plutonic rocks vary from +3.7 to +7.0, covering a range anticipated for both fresh and hydrothermally altered rocks. Silicic rocks include the isotopically heavier values, consistent with

Table 3. Hydrogen and oxygen isotopic compositions of hornblendes (per mil relative to SMOW).

| Sample | $\delta^{18}O$ | $\delta D$ | |
|--------|------|-----|---|
| **DREDGED GABBROS:** | | | |
| ANTP125-1 | 1.5 | −43 | |
| ANTP113-1(1) | 4.6 | −43 | |
| ANTP125-4B | 4.4 | −57 | Host for qtz-monzonite dikelet |
| ANTP125-2(2) | 5.4 | −38 | |
| ANTP130-3 | 4.7 | −46 | |
| CIR97C | 4.6 | −41 | |
| CIR97X | 4.7 | −46 | |
| CIR97F(2) | 4.1 | −45 | |
| CIR97ZZ | 3.4 | −37 | |
| **ODP DRILLCORE GABBROS:** | | | |
| 22-1, 69-73 | 3.2 | −49 | |
| 55-1, 59-69 | 4.2 | −66 | Trondjemite with xenoliths |
| 57-2, 11-18 | 5.3 | −59 | Trondjemite with xenoliths |
| 70-1, 130-134 | 5.2 | −43 | |
| 76-2, 121-126 | 4.9 | −44 | |
| 81-4, 60-68 | 6.0 | −54 | |
| 81-6, 87-90 | 5.3 | −50 | Vein |
| 87-5, 79-86 | 3.4 | −63 | Vein with diopside |

the slight $^{18}O$ enrichments predicted for closed-system fractionation. The quartz separates from the silicic rocks have $\delta^{18}O$ values that are normal to depleted compared to continental granitic rocks (+7.4 to +6.4). Plagioclase separates from these rocks vary from +4.2 to +6.5, comprising fresh and depleted values. In contrast, pyroxene separates are very limited in range, +5.5 to +5.7, consistent with primary igneous values. Values for amphibole, +4.6 to +2.5, are all slightly depleted in $^{18}O$ compared to what would be expected for primary igneous phases.

*Indian Ocean dredged rocks*

Within the suite of plutonic rocks dredged from the Indian Ocean fracture zones two groups of gabbros are considered separately: *gabbros* with limited coronitic alteration, and *amphibolitized gabbros* that are extensively replaced by secondary plagioclase and hornblende. The gabbros have whole-rock isotopic compositions that are either normal or depleted in $^{18}O$ compared to pristine gabbros. The single exception is ANTP130-4, where both the whole-rock and the plagioclase are enriched in $^{18}O$, likely associated with replacement of the plagioclase by an $^{18}O$-enriched zeolite ($\delta^{18}O$ = +13.4). The other plagioclase separates in the gabbroic rocks

vary from slightly $^{18}O$-depleted values ($\delta^{18}O$ = +5.0) to slightly enriched values ($\delta^{18}O$ = +6.6). Similar to the MAR suite, the pyroxene isotopic compositions are less variable than those observed for plagioclase, ranging from $\delta^{18}O$ = +5.2 to +5.7. Amphiboles in the gabbros are either identical to the pyroxenes (two samples) or strongly depleted in $^{18}O$ (one sample).

Within the group of amphibolitized gabbros, all whole-rock samples, all plagioclase separates, and all amphibole separates are strongly depleted in $^{18}O$. Pyroxene separates are isotopically uniform, but slightly depleted in $^{18}O$ compared to the gabbro average composition. The silicic rocks from this suite are extremely heterogeneous in isotopic composition. The quartz-monzonite dikelet, its granophyric diabase host, and one of the plagiogranite samples all contain $^{18}O$-rich plagioclase. In contrast, the diorite and the second plagiogranite are extremely depleted in $^{18}O$. Quartz from the $^{18}O$-depleted plagiogranite is three per mil heavier than that separated from the monzonite dikelet, even though the quartz-plagiclase fractionations are similar ($\Delta$ = 1.8 and 1.4, respectively). The amphibole $^{18}O/^{16}O$ ratios are within the same range as observed in the MAR suite.

*ODP Leg 118 Site 735B samples*

The whole-rock $\delta^{18}O$ variations in the drillcore are illustrated in Fig. 1. In the upper half of the core the gabbros are uniformly and pervasively depleted in $^{18}O$, except in limited undeformed regions (STAKES *et al.*, 1991). In the lower half of the core, most zones are slightly enriched in $^{18}O$ or undepleted, except in brecciated portions of the core. Plagioclase separated from the upper half of the core (down to sample 735B-118-58) has a normal igneous value or is depleted in $^{18}O$. The only exceptions are two veins which contain plagioclase partially altered to zeolites. Felsic veins typically show extensive low-temperature alteration, making their origin (metamorphic versus igneous) ambiguous (VANKO and STAKES, 1991; STAKES *et al.*, 1991). Plagioclases in the lower half of the core are extremely variable, from enriched values of $\delta^{18}O$ = +7.9 to values as low as +3.0.

With only one exception, the amphiboles in the upper half of the core are strongly depleted in $^{18}O$. In contrast, in the lower half of the core, the amphiboles commonly have $\delta^{18}O$ > +5, mirroring the general $^{18}O$ enrichment in the associated plagioclase and the bulk rock. In the lower half of the core diopside occurs as a replacement of igneous pyroxene and plagioclase, and is more common as a mafic vein mineral than is hornblende (VANKO and STAKES, 1991). Except for one sample, diopside is lower in $\delta^{18}O$ (+1.5 to +3.0) than the pyroxenes in fresh gabbros. The igneous clinopyroxene, in contrast, commonly retains an igneous isotopic composition, falling below $\delta^{18}O$ = +5.0 in only a few samples. The presence of $^{18}O$-depleted pyroxene is optically correlated with syn-deformational recrystallization.

### Hydrogen isotope compositions of amphibole separates

Most hornblende separates have relatively uniform $\delta D$ values between −37 and −50 (Table 3). However, one hornblende sample from the dredged suite and several from the drillcore have $\delta D$ values that are up to 15 per mil lighter than this range. Chemical composition plays a role in determining the $\delta D$ value, with Fe-rich minerals typically lower in deuterium. The hornblende separates from the drillcore are relatively Fe-rich pargasites, ferroan pargasites, and edenites. However the low-D hornblendes are not consistently richer in iron than the other hornblende samples. The most consistent attribute of the low-D hornblendes is their association with the silicic differentiates. The only low-D sample from the dredged rocks is from the host for the quartz-monzonite dikelet. The lowest-D samples from the drillcore are from trondjemite horizons containing partially digested gabbro xenoliths.

### FACTORS THAT CONTROL THE ISOTOPIC COMPOSITION OF OCEANIC PLUTONIC ROCKS

The oxygen isotopic compositions of the oceanic plutonic rocks reflect pervasive seawater metamorphism that has resulted in modest to extensive depletions in $^{18}O$. The paucity of isotopically pristine gabbroic rocks, even within the drillcore, suggests that much of oceanic layer 3 has been modified by seawater metamorphism. In the following discussion, the relationship of the $^{18}O$ depletion to secondary mineralogy and deformation will be examined to address the question of the mechanism of seawater penetration into the crystalline oceanic crust.

### Mineralogy and $^{18}O/^{16}O$ composition

STAKES et al. (1991) show a rough correlation between the quantity of primary pyroxene replaced by amphibole (used as an alteration index) and the $^{18}O$-depletion of the ODP Leg 118 gabbros. The static hydrous replacement of pyroxene is only one of a series of predictable mineralogical replacements that is characteristic of these suites of rocks. Both undeformed and dynamically recrystallized pyroxenes are replaced by amphibole. Olivine is replaced by talc and tremolite or cummingtonite (low percentage of replacement), and olivine and plagioclase margins are replaced by chloritic or micaceous coronas (high percentage of replacement). These replacement assemblages are typically depleted in $^{18}O$ compared to the original mineral phase. Coexisting plagioclase is similarly depleted in $^{18}O$, and presumably is also partially replaced by secondary plagioclase (although this is not optically conspicuous).

For both the Indian Ocean dredged rocks (Table 1) and the Hole 735B drillcore (Table 2), the presence of chlorite and talc is commonly (though not perfectly) correlated with low $\delta^{18}O$ values in gabbroic rocks that are mineralogically only slightly altered. The presence of zeolites or analcime, in contrast, is always associated with high $\delta^{18}O$ values in plagioclase. Much of the mineralogical replacement can be considered dissolution-reprecipitation associated with static hydration of the rocks, and the $^{18}O/^{16}O$ effects associated with these mineralogical replacements is highly variable and dependent on the quantity of secondary minerals ($\approx$ quantity of external fluid involved?).

### Deformation and $^{18}O/^{16}O$ depletions

Many of the dredged gabbros exhibit high-temperature deformation textures. Several workers have noted a relationship between the amounts of various metamorphic minerals and the deformation (VANKO and BATIZA, 1982; BATIZA and VANKO, 1985; STAKES and VANKO, 1986; ITO and CLAYTON, 1983). Within the set of amphibolitized gabbros from the dredged Indian Ocean rocks, several samples (e.g. ANTP125-1; CIR97ZZ) have textures that suggest early high-temperature ductile deformation that has been subsequently obscured by metamorphic replacement. The best example of this is ANTP125-1, in which even the pyroxene has been partially recrystallized. The plagioclase and pyroxene from this sample are the most $^{18}O$-depleted of any of the dredged samples.

The $^{18}O$ depletions in the pyroxenes from these amphibolitized gabbros are likely related to recrystallization under dynamic conditions, although some of the isotopic effects may also be attributable to amphibole impurities in the mineral separates. This is in contrast to the lack of isotopic exchange observed in the pyroxene separates from the undeformed gabbros. Samples that exhibit evidence of brittle deformation, possibly post-dating ductile deformation (*e.g.* CIR97X), show more extensive hydrous alteration, with no relict pyroxene. These correlations of metamorphic replacement, isotopic exchange, and deformation together suggest that high-temperature shear zones play a central role in providing the pathways for seawater to penetrate into the lower oceanic crust.

*Stratigraphic control on $^{18}O/^{16}O$ and deformation*

The Site 735B drillcore samples provide an unsurpassed opportunity to assess the relationship between major shear zones and penetration of seawater into the lower oceanic crust. The relationship between deformation and mineralogical alteration was observed on every scale. Even the smallest volume of hydrous alteration minerals in a single thin section can be observed to be associated with crosscutting healed microfractures (STAKES *et al.*, 1991). The deformation index (Textural type, Fig. 1), quantity of veins, and depletions in whole-rock $\delta^{18}O$ are all roughly coherent.

In the upper half of the core, the crosscutting vein network is consistently orthogonal to the metamorphic foliation and correlated with the final stages of extensional deformation. The host rock for this deformation-related vein network is consistently depleted in $^{18}O$. The veins in the upper half of the core are mostly also depleted in $^{18}O$, with the few high-$^{18}O$ vein minerals probably a result of deposition at lower temperatures. The significant oxygen isotopic shifts in the upper half of the drillcore are clearly related to deformation-enhanced penetration of seawater and subsequent metamorphic replacements. The stratigraphic relationships of the ODP drillcore permit us to associate the textural deformation and isotopic exchange effects to the existence of major listric normal faults (CANNAT *et al.*, 1991a,b; DICK *et al.*, 1991).

*Plagioclase-pyroxene/amphibole $^{18}O/^{16}O$ fractionations*

Isotopic compositions for plagioclase coexisting with pyroxene or amphibole for (a) dredged samples and (b) drillcore samples are provided in Figs. 2 and 3, respectively. Plagioclase-pyroxene fractionations at igneous temperatures are about 0.5 per mil, and the data-points for fresh gabbroic rocks would be expected to fall near such an equilibrium line, as shown in the two diagrams. Equilibrium at some lower temperature would similarly produce a linear array above this line (larger $\Delta$ values). Plagioclase-pyroxene pairs (open symbols) on both plots lie along a steeply dipping array that represents

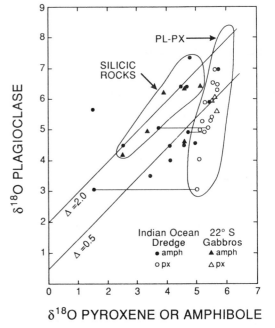

FIG. 2. Oxygen isotopic compositions for coexisting pairs of plagioclase and either pyroxene (open symbols) or amphibole (filled symbols) for dredged rocks. Unperturbed igneous rocks would fall close to the high-temperature equilibrium fractionation line indicated by $\Delta = 0.5$, and lower temperatures of equilibration would be expected to have higher $\Delta$ values (*e.g.* the $\Delta = 2$ line). Silicic rocks include diorites, plagiogranites, aplites, and a quartz monzonite. PL-PX = plagioclase-pyroxene pairs, which form a steeply dipping array as a result of depletion of $^{18}O$ in the plagioclase while largely preserving igneous $\delta^{18}O$ values of the pyroxene.

$^{18}O$ depletion of plagioclase together with virtual preservation of the igneous $\delta^{18}O$ values of the coexisting pyroxene. Such trends are characteristic of open-system isotopic exchange in hydrothermally altered plutonic rocks (GREGORY and TAYLOR, 1981; TAYLOR, 1974, 1977, 1983; TAYLOR and FORESTER, 1979; GREGORY and CRISS, 1986) and are the most sensitive indicators of water-rock interactions.

Very few of the plutonic rocks studied (only the 22°S olivine gabbros and a few drillcore samples) have $\delta^{18}O$ values characteristic of fresh, unaltered gabbroic rocks, even in those samples which contain only modest quantities of secondary minerals. Only two of the drillcore samples have igneous $\delta^{18}O$ values and plagioclase-pyroxene pairs that fall along the $\Delta = 0.5$ per mil "equilibrium line." In the remaining samples both the plagioclase and the pyroxene are depleted $^{18}O$. The "equilibrium pairs" with $^{18}O$-depleted pyroxene likely are a result of

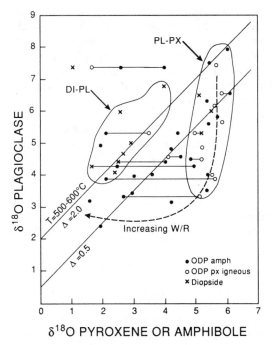

FIG. 3. Oxygen isotopic compositions for coexisting pairs of plagioclase and either pyroxene (open symbols), diopside (×'s) or amphibole (filled symbols) for samples from ODP Leg 118 Hole 735B. PL-PX and lines for Δ = 0.5 and Δ = 2.0 are the same as in Fig. 2, with Δ = 0.5 representing igneous temperatures and Δ = 2.0 indicating metamorphic temperatures. DI-PL = coexisting secondary diopside and plagioclase. Dashed line tracks progressive alteration of the gabbroic rocks: (a) at low water/rock ratios (W/R) the only evidence of alteration is the preferential $^{18}O$ depletion of plagioclase relative to pyroxene; (b) with increasing W/R, pyroxene is increasingly replaced by low-$^{18}O$ amphibole; and (c) at high W/R veins are filled with plagioclase, hornblende, and/or diopside in apparent isotopic equilibrium at metamorphic temperatures.

enhanced isotopic exchange associated with ductile deformation and hydrothermal recrystallization at very high temperatures. For plagioclase-pyroxene pairs that fall below the "equilibrium line," amphibole is typically depleted in $^{18}O$ compared to pyroxene.

Some plagioclase-amphibole pairs (filled symbols) also fall along the same limits of steeply dipping arrays as observed for plagioclase-pyroxene. However, most of the plagioclase-amphibole pairs, especially in the drillcore samples, fall either near the igneous equilibrium band or in the region that represents lower temperatures of equilibration (above and to the left of the Δ = 0.5 line). The apparent close approach to equilibrium of the plagioclase-amphibole pairs underscores the observation that, in the absence of dynamic recrystalliza-

tion, the only mafic minerals that monitor the fluid $\delta^{18}O$ value are those that are new metamorphic minerals; the unrecrystallized pyroxene does not undergo any appreciable isotopic exchange. This isotopic exchange/replacement apparently begins at near-igneous temperatures, consistent with the Δ values of the few plagioclase-recrystallized pyroxene pairs.

Most plagioclase-amphibole pairs plot within the field between the Δ = 0.5 and Δ = 2.0 lines. Points that fall above and to the left of this field are samples that either (1) contain plagioclase that has been enriched in $^{18}O$ at low temperatures or (2) are fractionated rocks from the MAR. The plagioclase-diopside (metamorphic) pairs from the Site 735B drillcore samples fall within this same field, except for the three veins with strongly $^{18}O$-enriched plagioclase. Such samples are not thought to represent equilibrium pairs. The diopside coexisting with the high-$^{18}O$ plagioclase is frequently partially altered to actinolite, suggesting a low-temperature overprint for both minerals.

Plagioclase-diopside fractionation has been experimentally calibrated by MATTHEWS et al. (1983), using the formula

$$\Delta(\text{plag-px}) = 1.58 - 1.09(\beta)\ 10^6 T^{-2},$$

where $\beta$ is the mole fraction of An in the plagioclase.

The precise temperature estimate is dependent upon the composition of the plagioclase assumed to be in equilibrium with the diopside. Analyzed plagioclase compositions in this work vary from An = 30 to An = 0, but the mineral grains frequently show evidence of zonation and late low temperature alteration. For the purpose of this calculation, a plagioclase composition of An = 20 is used, consistent with the least altered plagioclase-diopside veins. Based on this composition, estimated temperatures of formation vary from 622 to 265°C (excluding values for plagioclase with $\delta^{18}O > +6.5$). More sodic plagioclase compositions would result in higher temperature estimates.

Using the above temperatures of formation and the $\Delta(\text{plag-}H_2O)$ fractionation equation from O'NEIL and TAYLOR (1967), the isotopic composition of the fluid phase can be calculated. The fluid $\delta^{18}O$ and the temperatures of formation are plotted in Fig. 4. The calculated fluid compositions vary from near seawater ($\delta^{18}O = +0.4$) at low temperatures to $^{18}O$-enriched values ($\delta^{18}O = +4.6$) at the highest temperatures. The range of temperatures and isotopic compositions suggests mixing between seawater and either a strongly $^{18}O$-shifted hydrothermal endmember or a hydrous fluid exsolved from the magma.

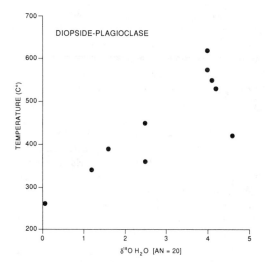

FIG. 4. Calculated isotopic temperatures of formation of diopside-plagioclase veins based on the calibration curves of MATTHEWS (1983) and corrected to an average plagioclase composition of An20. The isotopic composition of the aqueous fluid coexisting with each pair is calculated from the temperature and the plagioclase $\delta^{18}O$ value, using the equilibrium equation from O'NEIL and TAYLOR (1967).

*Hydrogen isotope compositions*

The D/H ratios of the amphibole separates provide additional evidence about the nature of the aqueous fluids that exchanged with these rocks. Using the hornblende-water fractionation curve of SUZUOKI and EPSTEIN (1976), the range of $\delta$D values in Fig. 5 for "seawater metamorphism" would require temperatures of formation of about 400 to 500°C. Lower values of $\delta$D require either lower temperatures of formation (down to 300°C) or a fluid depleted in deuterium compared to seawater. A lower temperature of formation is discounted as an explanation for the low $\delta$D hornblende values, as these samples are characterized by euhedral brown to green aluminous hornblende petrographically and chemically similar to hornblendes in the other samples. The alternative is that these hornblendes record the presence of a different hydrous fluid. This hydrous fluid could have been: (1) "primary" (derived from a deep-seated magmatic source); (2) a metamorphic dehydration water; or (3) water liberated from hydrous rocks as they are incorporated into a magma during assimilation, thereby mixing with any available magmatic water (see TAYLOR, 1986, and Fig. 5).

Primary hornblendes from most igneous rocks have $\delta$D values in the range −80 to −60 (TAYLOR and SHEPPARD, 1986). The low $\delta$D hornblendes

from the Indian Ocean gabbros fall in a range intermediate between such "magmatic water" values and the "metamorphic water" values as defined from the other hornblende separates. This range of values could represent a mixture of hornblendes from magmatic and metamorphic origins. The $\delta$D of the $H_2O$ in a magma (and presumably of its derivative fluid phase) can also be increased by isotopic fractionation during formation of methane (TAYLOR, 1986), and $CH_4$ has in fact been identified within fluid inclusions in these gabbros (VANKO and STAKES, 1991). The intermediate $\delta$D values could also result from a hybrid fluid derived from assimilation of rocks previously altered by seawater-hydrothermal fluids, a derivation supported by the petrographic evidence of partially digested xenoliths.

## CONCLUSIONS

(1) The oxygen isotopic compositions of seafloor gabbros and their differentiates, representing portions of oceanic layer 3, record pervasive high-temperature interactions with seawater. Temperatures of metamorphism are typically in excess of 600°C, but most assemblages record equilibrium temperatures of 400–600°C. The range of temperatures estimated from plagioclase-diopside and plagioclase-hornblende pairs is identical for both metamorphic veins and late-stage silicic differentiates.

(2) Plagioclase-pyroxene pairs are rarely equilibrated except under conditions of dynamic recrystallization. Rather, plagioclase is preferentially de-

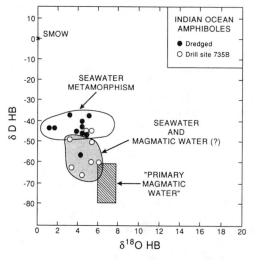

FIG. 5. Oxygen and hydrogen isotopic compositions of hornblende separates (HB) from Indian Ocean plutonic rocks. Primary magmatic hornblendes would be expected to fall into cross-hatched region.

pleted in $^{18}O$, and pyroxene is either relict or is replaced by amphibole in equilibrium with the plagioclase. Many of the plutonic rocks exhibit textural evidence of local ductile deformation, commonly obscured by later hydrous alteration. The effects of plagioclase $^{18}O$-depletion, hornblende replacement of pyroxene, and isotopic equilibration of hornblende and plagioclase can be correlated with aqueous fluid-rock ratios.

(3) The penetration of fluid into the lower oceanic crust and the degree of isotopic equilibration of the coexisting minerals are directly correlated with increased deformation and increased local permeability. Evidence of assimilation of metagabbro by late-stage intrusives suggests that high-grade metamorphism and the latest-stage magmatic processes may be contemporaneous in time (cooling history) and space (permeable ductile shear zones).

(4) Gabbros from ODP Leg 118, Site 735B, comprise the first drillcore samples from intact oceanic layer 3. Plagioclase-diopside veins from the lower portions of this core record temperatures of formation up to 620°C from an aqueous fluid strongly enriched in $^{18}O$ (up to 4.5 per mil) compared to normal seawater.

(5) Hydrogen isotopic analyses of hornblende separates fall into two groups: one comprised solely of a seawater-metamorphic origin, and a second group that suggests the presence of mixing between a magmatically derived fluid that has a $\delta D$ value at least 20 to 30 per mil lighter than the seawater-derived metamorphic fluid. It is possible that some of the magmatic fluid itself may ultimately have been derived from seawater.

(6) Volumetrically, the most important hydrothermal-metamorphic processes recorded by the mineral assemblages and isotopic compositions of the plutonic rocks took place under amphibolite-facies conditions. Greenschist and zeolite grade minerals are only found locally, suggesting that pervasive fluid penetration diminished as the temperatures declined.

*Acknowledgements*—The author thanks Fred Frey and Geoffrey Thompson for providing samples from the 22°S MAR collection and copies of their unpublished mineral and petrographic data. Assistance in hydrogen isotope analyses were provided by Lanny Adami and Doug White at the U.S.G.S. Oxygen isotope analyses were performed by Leon Ember at the University of South Carolina. Mineral separates for the ODP samples were produced by Mian Hong. Illustrations were produced by Jack Gerstner. The author benefited from valuable discussions with D. Vanko, J. R. O'Neil, H. P. Taylor, Jr., and J. Natland. H. P. Taylor, Jr. also provided a thorough and extremely useful review of the manuscript. This work was supported by NSF Grant OCE-8902586.

## REFERENCES

BATIZA R. and VANKO D. A. (1985) Petrologic evolution of large failed rifts in the Eastern Pacific: petrology of volcanic and plutonic rocks from the Mathematician Ridge area and the Guadalupe Trough. *J. Petrol.* **26**, 564–602.

BLOOMER S. H., NATLAND J. H. and FISHER R. L. (1989) Mineral relationships in gabbroic rocks from fracture zones of Indian Ocean ridges: evidence for extensive fractionation, parental diversity and boundary-layer recrystallization. In *Magmatism in the Ocean Basins* (eds. A. D. SAUNDERS and M. J. NORRY); *Geol. Soc. Spec. Publ.* **42**, pp. 107–124.

BONATTI E., HONNOREZ J., KIRST P. and RADICATTI F. (1975) Metagabbros from the Mid-Atlantic Ridge at 6°N: contact-hydrothermal-dynamic metamorphism beneath the axial valley. *J. Geol.* **83**, 61–78.

CANNAT M., MÉVEL C. and STAKES D. (1991a) Stretching of the deep crust at the slow spreading Southwest Indian Ridge. In *The Geology, Geophysics and Metallogeny of the Present-Day Oceans* (eds. J. FRANCHETEAU, O. ELDHOLM and P. MILES); *Tectonophysics* **190**, pp. 73–94.

CANNAT M., MÉVEL C. and STAKES D. (1991b) Normal ductile shear zones at an oceanic spreading ridge: tectonic evolution of the Site 735B gabbros, Southwest Indian Ocean. In *Leg 118, Scientific Results, Proc. Ocean Drilling Program* (eds. P. T. ROBINSON and R. VON HERZEN). College Station, Ocean Drilling Program 415–430.

CRISS R. E., GREGORY R. T. and TAYLOR H. P., JR. (1987) Kinetic theory of oxygen isotopic exchange between minerals and water. *Geochim. Cosmochim. Acta* **51**, 1099–1108.

DICK H. J. B., MEYER P., BLOOMER S., KIRBY S., STAKES D. and MAWER C. (1991) Lithostratigraphic evolution of an in-situ section of oceanic layer 3. In *Leg 118, Scientific Results, Proc. Ocean Drilling Program* (eds. P. T. ROBINSON and R. VON HERZEN). College Station, Ocean Drilling Program 439–515.

ENGEL C. G. and FISHER R. L. (1975) Granitic to ultramafic rock complexes of the Indian Ocean ridge system, western Indian Ocean. *Geol Soc. Amer. Bull.* **86**, 1553–1578.

FREY F., CARROLL B. M. and THOMPSON G. (1991) Geochemistry and petrology of 22°S coarse-grained rocks and related aplite (in prep.).

GREGORY R. T. and CRISS R. E. (1986) Isotopic exchange in open and closed systems. In *Stable Isotopes in High-Temperature Geological Processes* (eds. J. W. VALLEY, H. P. TAYLOR, JR. and J. R. O'NEIL); *Reviews in Mineralogy* **16**, pp. 91–128. Mineralogical Society of America.

GREGORY R. T. and TAYLOR H. P. JR. (1981) An oxygen isotope profile in a section of Cretaceous oceanic crust, samail ophiolite, Oman: Evidence for $\delta^{18}O$ buffering of the oceans by deep (>5 km) seawater-hydrothermal circulation at mid-ocean ridges. *J. Geophys. Res.* **86**, 2737–2755.

GREGORY R. T., CRISS R. E. and TAYLOR H. P., JR. (1989) Oxygen isotope exchange kinetics of mineral pairs in closed and open systems: applications to problems of hydrothermal alteration of igneous rocks and Precambrian iron formations. *Chem. Geol.* **75**, 1–42.

ITO E. and ANDERSON A. T., JR. (1983) Submarine metamorphism of gabbros from the Mid-Cayman Rise: petrographic and mineral constraints on hydrothermal processes at slow-spreading ridges. *Contrib. Mineral. Petrol.* **82**, 371–388.

ITO E. and CLAYTON R. N. (1983) Submarine metamorphism of gabbros from the Mid-Cayman Rise: an oxygen isotopic study. *Geochim. Cosmochim. Acta* **47**, 535–546.

MATTHEWS A., GOLDSMITH J. R. and CLAYTON R. N. (1983) Oxygen isotope fractionation involving pyroxenes: the calibration of mineral-pair geothermometers. *Geochim. Cosmochim. Acta* **47**, 631–644.

MÉVEL C. (1988) Metamorphism in oceanic layer 3, Gorringe Bank, Eastern Atlantic. *Contrib. Mineral. Petrol.* **100**, 496–509.

MUEHLENBACHS K. (1986) Alteration of the oceanic crust and the 18O history of seawater. In *Stable Isotopes in High-Temperature Geological Processes* (eds. J. W. VALLEY, H. P. TAYLOR, JR. and J. R. O'NEIL); *Reviews in Mineralogy* **16**, pp. 425–444. Mineralogical Society of America.

NATLAND J. H., MEYER P. S., DICK H. J. B. and BLOOMER, S. H. (1991) Magmatic oxides and sulfides in gabbroic rocks from ODP Hole 735B and the later development of the liquid line of descent. In *Leg 118, Scientific Results, Proc. Ocean Drilling Program* (eds. P. T. ROBINSON and R. VON HERZEN). College Station, Ocean Drilling Program 75–112.

O'NEIL J. R. and TAYLOR H. P., JR. (1967) The oxygen isotope and cation exchange chemistry of feldspars. *Amer. Mineral.* **52**, 1414–1437.

STAKES D. S. and VANKO D. A. (1986) Multistage hydrothermal alteration of gabbroic rocks from the failed Mathematician Ridge. *Earth Planet. Sci. Lett.* **79**, 75–92.

STAKES D. S., TAYLOR H. P., JR. and FISHER R. L. (1984) Oxygen isotope and geochemical characterization of hydrothermal alteration in ophiolite complexes and modern oceanic crust. In *Ophiolites and Oceanic Lithosphere* (eds. I. G. GASS, S. J. LIPPARD and A. W. SHELTON), pp. 199–214. Blackwell Scientific Publications, Oxford.

STAKES D., CANNAT M., MÉVEL C. and CHAPUT T. (1991) Metamorphic history of ODP Site 735B, Southwest Indian Ocean. In *Leg 118, Scientific Results, Proc. Ocean Drilling Program* (eds. P. T. ROBINSON and R. VON HERZEN). College Station, Ocean Drilling Program 153–180.

SUZUOKI T. and EPSTEIN S. (1976) Hydrogen isotope fractionation between OH-bearing minerals and water. *Geochim. Cosmochim. Acta* **40**, 1229–1240.

TAYLOR B. E. (1986b) Magmatic volatiles: isotopic variation of C, H and S. In *Stable Isotopes in High-Temperature Geological Processes* (eds. J. W. VALLEY, H. P. TAYLOR, JR. and J. R. O'NEIL); *Reviews in Mineralogy* **16**, pp. 185–226. Mineralogical Society of America.

TAYLOR H. P., JR. (1968) The oxygen isotope geochemistry of igneous rocks. *Contrib. Mineral. Petrol.* **19**, 1–17.

TAYLOR H. P., JR. (1974) Oxygen and hydrogen isotope evidence for large-scale circulation and interaction between ground waters and igneous intrusions, with particular reference to the San Juan volcanic field, Colorado. In *Geochemical Transport and Kinetics* (eds. A. W. HOFFMAN *et al.*); *Carnegie Inst. Washington, Publ.* **634**, pp. 299–324.

TAYLOR H. P., JR. (1977) Water-rock interactions and the origin of $H_2O$ in granitic batholiths. *J. Geol. Soc. Lond.* **133**, 509–558.

TAYLOR H. P., JR. (1983) Oxygen and hydrogen isotope studies of hydrothermal interactions at submarine and subaerial spreading centers. In *NATO Symposium Volume on Hydrothermal Processes at Seafloor Spreading Centers*, (eds. P. A. RONA *et al.*), pp. 83–139. Plenum, New York.

TAYLOR H. P., JR. (1986) Igneous rocks: II: Isotopic case studies of circumpacific magmatism. In *Stable Isotopes in High-Temperature Geological Processes* (eds. J. W. VALLEY, H. P. TAYLOR, JR. and J. R. O'NEIL); *Reviews in Mineralogy* **16**, pp. 273–317. Mineralogical Society of America.

TAYLOR H. P., JR. and FORESTER R. W. (1979) An oxygen and hydrogen isotope study of the Skaergaard intrusion and its country rocks: a description of a 55-m.y. old fossil hydrothermal system. *J. Petrol.* **20**, 335–419.

TAYLOR H. P., JR. and SHEPPARD S. M. F. (1986) Igneous rocks: I: Processes of isotopic fractionation and isotope systematics. In *Stable Isotopes in High-Temperature Geological Processes* (eds. J. W. VALLEY, H. P. TAYLOR, JR. and J. R. O'NEIL); *Reviews in Mineralogy* **16**, pp. 277–271. Mineralogical Society of America.

VANKO D. A. and BATIZA R. (1982) Gabbroic rocks from the Mathematician Ridge failed rift. *Nature* **300**, 742–744.

VANKO D. A. and STAKES D. S. (1991) Petrology of altered lithologies and evidence for fluids interacting with oceanic layer 3: petrographic, mineral, chemical, fluid inclusion, and oxygen isotopic results, ODP Hole 735B, Southwest Indian Ridge. In *Leg 118, Scientific Results, Proc. Ocean Drilling Program*. (eds. P. T. ROBINSON and R. VON HERZEN). College Station, Ocean Drilling Program 180–215.

Stable Isotope Geochemistry: A Tribute to Samuel Epstein
© The Geochemical Society, Special Publication No. 3, 1991
Editors: H. P. Taylor, Jr., J. R. O'Neil and I. R. Kaplan

# The hydrogen and oxygen isotope history of the Silurian-Permian hydrosphere as determined by direct measurement of fossil water

L. Paul Knauth and Sarah K. Roberts

Department of Geology, Arizona State University, Tempe, AZ 85287-1404, U.S.A.

**Abstract**—Hydrogen and oxygen isotope analyses of fluid inclusions in 236 halite samples from undeformed Permian, Silurian, and Devonian bedded salt deposits are most readily interpreted in terms of connate evaporite brines trapped during initial halite precipitation or during early diagenesis. The synsedimentary fluids may represent evaporated sea water, evaporated meteoric water, or any mixture between the two depending upon the interplay between marine flooding and continental runoff in the original depositional environment.

$\delta^{18}O$ values for Devonian, Silurian, and Permian fluid inclusions have the same range and approach the same maximum values. Silurian values are not 4 to 5.5 per mil depleted in $^{18}O$ relative to Permian values as expected if the oceans were 4 to 5.5 per mil lower in the Silurian as widely claimed. The data indicate that $\delta^{18}O$ of sea water did not vary by more than 1–2 per mil during the interval Silurian-Permian, strongly contradicting interpretations of sea water history based on $\delta^{18}O$ analyses of carbonates.

As a group, $\delta D$ for Silurian samples is about 20 per mil lower than values for Permian samples, and the Devonian samples have intermediate values. The possibility arises that the inclusions are recording a progressive deuterium enrichment of the hydrosphere between the Silurian and the Permian.

## INTRODUCTION

THE OXYGEN ISOTOPE history of ocean water is important to many areas of geochemistry. The present ocean is 5.5 per mil depleted in $^{18}O$ relative to the total reservoir of oxygen in the crust and mantle, and the process or processes that produced this large depletion may have varied with time. Continental weathering and rock/water interactions at sea floor spreading centers affect $\delta^{18}O$ of the oceans, so evidence of past changes in $\delta^{18}O$ of sea water might carry major implications for tectonism, or even for questions of ocean origin and growth through time. In addition, estimates of paleotemperatures and diagenetic environments based upon isotopic analyses of ancient carbonates, cherts, phosphates, and clays depend critically upon the isotopic history of the hydrosphere.

Muehlenbachs and Clayton (1976) argued that the current 5.5 per mil $^{18}O$ depletion of ocean water relative to the whole earth value is basically fixed at mid-ocean spreading centers where sea water is cycled through hot basalts. Gregory and Taylor (1981) presented further evidence for this rock/water buffering and argued that it would be operative as long as worldwide spreading rates are greater than one $km^2/yr$. Assuming that these processes have worked throughout geologic time, $\delta^{18}O$ of sea water should be invariant within about ±1 per mil.

At present, it is not clear whether the sedimentary rock record is in accord with this model for constancy in the isotopic history of ocean water. In a general way, $\delta^{18}O$ of cherts, carbonates, and phosphates decreases for progressively older samples (e.g. Perry, 1967; Knauth and Lowe, 1978; Veizer and Hoefs, 1976; Karhu and Epstein, 1986). Archean examples are up to 12 per mil lower in $^{18}O$ than their Phanerozoic counterparts, and changes on the order of 5 per mil occur within the Paleozoic alone. Of particular interest is the remarkable 4 to 5 per mil "jump" in $\delta^{18}O$ for carbonates between the Devonian and Mississippian shown in Fig. 1 (Fritz, 1971; Veizer et al., 1986; Popp et al., 1986a,b; Carpenter and Lohmann, 1989). All of these authors have attributed the lower values of the early Paleozoic to a change in $\delta^{18}O$ of the oceans.

Isotopic variations in the sedimentary rock record are difficult to interpret because there are at least three major variables that can strongly influence $\delta^{18}O$ of a phase that precipitates from an aqueous fluid: (1) $\delta^{18}O$ of the fluid, including the problems of whether the fluid was sea water or had a component of low-$^{18}O$ meteoric water; (2) temperature, which is important because sedimentary temperatures are low and isotopic fractionation is quite sensitive to temperature in the low-temperature range; and (3) diagenetic and metamorphic recrystallization, which can lead to obliteration of the original isotopic record. Various authors have dealt in various ways with these problems. There appears to be a consensus that petrographic examination can screen out altered and recrystallized samples,

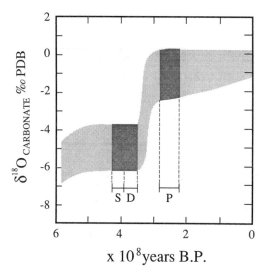

x $10^8$ years B.P.

FIG. 1. Oxygen isotope history of Phanerozoic carbonates according to VEIZER et al. (1986). Changes in $\delta^{18}O$ of carbonates putatively correspond to changes in $\delta^{18}O$ of sea water. Salt samples for this investigation bracket the time interval proposed for the dramatic change in $\delta^{18}O$ of sea water.

but there is much controversy over the importance of temperature versus possible changes in the past $\delta^{18}O$ of sea water. KARHU and EPSTEIN (1986) attempted to resolve the problem by analyzing co-existing phosphate-chert pairs, but this has also not settled the controversy (cf. PERRY, 1990).

Instead of analyzing the precipitated phases in ancient sedimentary rocks, we have attempted to evaluate the isotopic history of sea water by direct analysis of samples of the ancient hydrosphere preserved as fluid inclusions in undeformed bedded salt deposits. The background, analytical methods, and approach for using such samples to evaluate past changes in both $\delta^{18}O$ and $\delta D$ of the hydrosphere were given in KNAUTH and BEEUNAS (1986). In short, fluid inclusions in halite crystals in some bedded salt deposits (excluding deformed, totally recrystallized, and diapiric salt) are most readily interpreted as connate evaporite brines trapped during initial halite precipitation or during early diagenesis. The fluids may represent evaporated sea water, evaporated meteoric water, or any mixture between the two depending upon the interplay between marine flooding and continental runoff in the original depositional environment. In spite of this range of source waters and the fact that the inclusions represent fluids isotopically altered by evaporation, it is nevertheless possible to evaluate isotopic changes

in sea water, especially changes as large as those proposed by several of the authors above.

We have analyzed fluid inclusions from three giant bedded salt deposits that span the age range during which $\delta^{18}O$ of the oceans may have changed by 4 to 5.5 per mil (Fig. 1). As discussed in KNAUTH and BEEUNAS (1986), changes this large should be readily detectable from isotopic analyses of fluid inclusions in halite. An underlying assumption of our approach is that the general range of isotopic compositions expected for a giant evaporite deposit is represented by data for the Permian salt deposits of the Palo Duro Basin, Texas. Since publication of KNAUTH and BEEUNAS (1986), the data base for fluid inclusions in this evaporite deposit has been greatly expanded. We first review general results for the Palo Duro Basin in order to defend our assumptions and to understand better the meaning of isotopic measurements of fluid inclusions in halite.

## ANALYTICAL PROCEDURE

Backlighted core samples of bedded salt were scanned for fluid inclusions with a hand-lens. The smallest possible piece of halite containing fluid inclusions was quarried out along cleavage planes using a small chisel and a razor-blade. For the larger inclusions it was often possible to cleave away surrounding salt to within one millimeter of the inclusion.

All samples were examined under a polarizing binocular microscope to insure that no cracks had penetrated to the inclusions and to verify the purity of the salt with respect to organic matter, oil, anhydrite, hydrous minerals, or the presence of rarely observed gas bubbles in the inclusions which might indicate leakage.

For inclusions larger than about 2–3 mm, a pyrex capillary tube was forced into the inclusion. The capillary tube was flame-sealed at both ends after the inclusion fluid was drawn in. Total water was extracted from the capillary brine using the technique given in KNAUTH and BEEUNAS (1986). Large inclusions were sampled only in the Permian salt and are so indicated by a "C" suffix on the depth listings in Table 1.

For the smaller inclusions, total water was extracted from the screened solid salt samples using the vacuum volatilization method of KNAUTH and BEEUNAS (1986). Isotopic analyses of extracted water were done using a variant of the method of KISHIMA and SAKAI (1980) (see KNAUTH and BEEUNAS, 1986, for details). Results are reported in the standard $\delta$-notation. Routine accuracy using this method is probably better than ±0.5 per mil for $\delta^{18}O$ and ±5.0 per mil for $\delta D$.

## PALO DURO BASIN

Isotopic analyses of 182 samples from ten wells in the Palo Duro evaporites are given in Table 1 and are shown in Fig. 2. The envelope drawn around the data excludes five points which are clearly atypical. These atypical data are reproducible and may have significance for the evaporite sedimentology but will not be discussed further here. The other data overlap completely the initial data of KNAUTH and BEEUNAS (1986).

The salt beds sampled in the Palo Duro Basin range in age from Mid- to Upper Permian and were therefore deposited over a time interval on the order of 30 million years. Halite interbedded with anhydrite, minor clastic layers, and carbonate occurs over a depth interval of 600 meters. Halite-anhydrite interbeds often occur in cycles, and it is clear that the evaporites represent numerous, repeated incursions of sea water into a shallow, coastal basin. An individual cycle may involve simple flooding by sea water followed by evaporation to total desiccation. In another case, flooding may occur before complete desiccation of the previous cycle is achieved. Upon renewed evaporation, halite might precipitate and trap remnants of the parent fluid (in this case, initially a mixture of sea water and partially evaporated sea water). In other cases, runoff from the surrounding area and/or local precipitation could flood the evaporite flat with meteoric waters. Virtually any mixture of sea water with meteoric water at any stage of partial evaporation is possible for depositional fluids in this type of setting. HOVORKA (1990) has documented petrographic and sedimentologic evidence of this interplay for the Palo Duro evaporites.

KNAUTH and BEEUNAS (1986) give the isotopic systematics expected for the mixed marine-meteoric system of this sort. Briefly, data which lie toward the positive, upper-right end of the $\delta D$-$\delta^{18}O$ data array in Fig. 2 approach the isotopic composition of halite-facies, evaporated sea water. During the initial evaporation of sea water, the lighter isotopes are removed and the residual fluid becomes enriched in $^{18}O$ and D. However, upon further evaporation, the residual fluid apparently evolves isotopically along a curved trajectory toward progressively lower $\delta D$ and $\delta^{18}O$ (GONFIANTINI, 1965; HOLSER, 1979; PIERRE et al., 1984). The cause of this reversal is not fully understood, but its validity is not an issue for this discussion. Evaporated sea water will clearly be enriched in $^{18}O$, and possibly in D relative to normal sea water. For halite that forms in a mixed marine-meteoric system, fluid inclusions with the most positive $\delta$-values are the ones with the greatest component of sea water evaporite brine, whether the trajectory reversal is valid or not.

$\delta$-values near the negative end of the array are very close to the meteoric water line. These samples are interpreted as having formed on a desiccated

flat that was flooded by meteoric waters. The influx of fresh water dissolved the previously deposited salt to the point of halite saturation. Upon subsequent evaporation, halite precipitated immediately in water which had undergone only a small amount of evaporation and therefore had become only slightly enriched in $^{18}O$ and D relative to the meteoric water line. $\delta$ values intermediate between the positive and negative ends of the array in Fig. 2 are interpreted as various mixtures of evaporated marine-meteoric fluids.

In order to test the concept that the isotopic composition of fluid inclusions is preserved in ancient halite and is related to the depositional environment, analyses were made of a suite of samples that records the transition from a marine dominated system to a meteoric-water dominated system. Sedimentologic and petrographic arguments for this transition are given by HOVORKA (1990). The isotopic results are given in Fig. 3.

The interval shown is overlain by clastic redbeds and represents progradation of surrounding continental clastic deposits over the evaporite section. On the basis of sedimentologic interpretations, the top of the salt cycle was repeatedly reworked by the influx of meteoric waters as the environment gradually shifted from predominantly marine to continental HOVORKA (1990). The transition is clearly recorded in the isotopic data in Fig. 3; $\delta^{18}O$ decreases from just under +5 to below −6, a change in $\delta^{18}O$ of over 10 per mil. $\delta D$ shifts concurrently from values around 0.0 to below −45. As shown in Fig. 4, values for this one interval span the entire range of $\delta$ values encountered in the whole Palo Duro sample suite. The strong correspondence between isotopic composition and depositional environment is a compelling argument that the inclusions are accurately recording major changes in the nature of the parent evaporite fluids and that they have not been altered since the Permian.

## PALO DURO DATA AS A REFERENCE

There are no modern evaporite deposits on the scale of those in the Silurian, Devonian, and Permian examined here. It is therefore not possible to examine in a modern setting the range of isotopic compositions associated with all the possible flooding and evaporation scenarios that surely occurred during deposition of a 0.6 km-thick evaporite deposit like that sampled in the Palo Duro Basin. Considering the large number of data, it is likely that the data domain in Fig. 2 is representative of that of the most typical evaporite waters that oc-

Table 1. Isotopic analyses of fluid inclusions in halite.

Permian Palo Duro Basin

| County | Well | Depth (m) | $\delta^{18}O$† | $\delta D$† | County | Well | Depth (m) | $\delta^{18}O$† | $\delta D$† |
|--------|------|-----------|------|-----|--------|------|-----------|------|-----|
| DO | S | 255.8C | 0.8 | −20 | DS | JF | 722.4C | 1.9 | −24 |
| DS | D | 409.0 | −5.2 | −55 | | | 742.1C | 1.6 | −31 |
| | | 409.3C | −5.3 | −51 | | | 746.6 | 3.1 | −17 |
| | | 409.3C | −2.9 | −44 | | | 751.8C | 1.6 | −37 |
| | | 409.3C | 3.5 | −10 | | | 773.6C | −0.7 | −34 |
| | | 410.2C | 3.9 | −16 | | | 784.9 | 0.8 | −26 |
| | | 421.8 | 1.7 | −23 | | | 786.2 | 0.3 | −27 |
| | | 422.7C | 0.9 | −30 | | | 800.2 | 1.3 | −12 |
| | | 423.1 | 2.5 | −17 | | | 800.3 | 0.7 | −19 |
| | | 423.4 | 1.4 | −43 | | | 800.4 | 1.7 | −14 |
| | | 423.5 | 0.5 | −32 | | | 800.4 | 1.6 | −30 |
| | | 423.6 | −1.6 | −51 | | | 860.7 | −5.4 | −45 |
| | | 729.3 | 3.3 | −21 | | | 861.1 | 3.3 | −23 |
| | | 733.3C | 3.6 | −3 | O | M | 351.7 | 3.8 | −26 |
| | | 734.9C | −0.7 | −19 | | | 470.6 | 2.8 | −13 |
| | | 742.9 | 0.6 | −18 | | | 470.6C | 2.8 | −12 |
| | | 752.0C | 0.5 | −27 | | | 470.6C | −0.2 | −20 |
| | | 752.0 | 1.3 | −33 | | | 471.8 | 1.5 | −26 |
| | | 753.0C | 0.6 | −25 | | | 483.7 | 1.7 | −21 |
| | | 754.7C | 1.4 | −29 | | | 483.8 | 1.5 | −27 |
| | | 786.1 | 0.0 | −26 | | | 484.5 | 0.9 | −30 |
| | | 786.1C | 0.6 | −33 | | | 484.6 | 1.9 | −18 |
| | | 786.2C | −1.0 | −30 | | | 492.3 | 1.3 | −18 |
| | | 803.0 | 0.8 | −16 | | | 494.6 | 2.0 | −15 |
| | | 864.4C | 2.7 | −21 | | | 494.7 | −0.2 | −37 |
| | | 864.4C | 2.6 | −37 | | | 494.7 | 0.5 | −58 |
| | | 864.4C | 2.0 | −36 | | | 494.8 | 1.7 | −6 |
| | GF | 389.4 | −0.3 | −53 | | | 494.9 | 1.1 | −18 |
| | | 389.4 | −1.1 | −50 | | | 494.9 | 1.6 | −23 |
| | | 389.4 | 4.1 | −25 | | | 499.6 | 1.6 | −26 |
| | | 389.7 | 0.4 | −1 | | | 499.8 | 2.3 | −26 |
| | | 394.8C | 1.8 | −29 | | | 499.8 | 1.6 | −21 |
| | | 707.2C | 1.9 | −24 | | | 515.4 | −0.5 | −29 |
| | | 705.0C | −0.3 | −29 | | | 513.5C | 0.2 | −29 |
| | | 705.0 | 1.7 | −13 | | | 525.7C | 1.0 | −35 |
| | | 710.4C | 1.1 | −41 | | | 525.8C | 0.7 | −30 |
| | | 710.5 | −0.5 | −26 | | | 525.8C | −1.9 | −32 |
| | | 712.1C | 1.9 | −14 | | | 915.5 | 4.3 | −11 |
| | | 712.1C | 2.8 | −28 | | | 915.5 | 3.9 | −27 |
| | | 742.2C | 0.9 | −28 | | | 915.5 | 2.8 | −33 |
| | | 742.2C | 1.6 | −18 | | | 921.0 | 3.9 | −10 |
| | | 757.3 | 2.0 | −19 | | | 921.0 | 2.8 | −17 |
| | | 758.9 | 3.0 | −27 | R | HO | 415.9 | 3.9 | −5 |
| | | 768.7 | 2.3 | −33 | | | 425.0 | 2.8 | −7 |
| | | 773.6C | −1.3 | −33 | | | 425.0 | 4.4 | −11 |
| | JF | 417.1 | −5.8 | −53 | | RW | 206.0 | −5.4 | −45 |
| | | 418.0 | −5.9 | −54 | | | 206.1 | −4.6 | −54 |
| | | 418.2 | −6.3 | −56 | | | 206.1 | −5.0 | −81 |
| | | 418.2 | −3.5 | −41 | | | 206.7 | −6.2 | −53 |
| | | 418.4 | −5.7 | −54 | | | 210.5 | −2.9 | −36 |
| | | 418.4 | −0.9 | −27 | | | 217.8C | 1.6 | −22 |
| | | 419.2 | −6.2 | −54 | | | 217.8 | 0.0 | −34 |
| | | 419.7C | 0.1 | −27 | | | 217.8 | −0.7 | −33 |
| | | 421.0 | 1.7 | −8 | | | 217.8 | 0.3 | −17 |
| | | 422.7 | −1.0 | −35 | | | 221.2 | 0.9 | −22 |
| | | 423.6 | 3.4 | −11 | | | 403.9 | 2.7 | −20 |
| | | 424.3 | 0.8 | −24 | | | 403.9 | 2.2 | −10 |
| | | 442.4 | 4.4 | 7 | | | 403.9 | 1.2 | −36 |
| | | 442.2 | 3.0 | −1 | | | 408.0 | 2.4 | −30 |
| | | 443.1 | 4.1 | −2 | | | 512.2 | 2.2 | −21 |
| | | 443.1 | 2.5 | −12 | | | 512.2C | 3.1 | −31 |
| | | 443.2 | 3.9 | −2 | | | 565.7 | 0.9 | −36 |
| | | 443.3 | 4.2 | −1 | | | 565.7 | 0.2 | −48 |
| | | 707.2C | 1.3 | −28 | | | 574.2 | 0.8 | −27 |
| | | 722.2 | 1.2 | −18 | | | 574.2 | 3.4 | −25 |
| | | 722.4 | 2.2 | −14 | | | 869.1C | 1.9 | −11 |
| | | 722.4C | 1.8 | −20 | | | 869.1C | 2.3 | −12 |

Table 1. (Continued)

### Permian Palo Duro Basin

| County | Well | Depth (m) | $\delta^{18}O$† | $\delta D$† | County | Well | Depth (m) | $\delta^{18}O$† | $\delta D$† |
|--------|------|-----------|-----------------|-------------|--------|------|-----------|-----------------|-------------|
| SW | G | 318.7 | −6.2 | −45 | SW | G | 812.1 | 1.2 | −80 |
| | | 323.0 | −6.8 | −55 | | | 812.1 | −1.5 | −75 |
| | | 321.6C | −4.1 | −56 | | | 812.9 | 2.2 | −20 |
| | | 321.6C | −4.0 | −44 | | | 853.0C | 2.4 | −29 |
| | | 323.0 | −3.6 | −41 | | H | 388.8C | 1.2 | −22 |
| | | 356.4 | 3.8 | −27 | | | 395.8C | 5.4 | −2 |
| | | 370.8C | 5.6 | −8 | | | 396.5 | 4.1 | −8 |
| | | 373.0 | 6.1 | −4 | | | 780.1 | −1.2 | −30 |
| | | 374.6 | 3.8 | −12 | | | 819.4 | 1.3 | −27 |
| | | 375.0 | 5.7 | −7 | | | 819.9 | 1.7 | −17 |
| | | 377.6 | 4.6 | −1 | | | 831.3 | 1.7 | −15 |
| | | 378.0 | 4.1 | 0 | | | 831.3 | −0.8 | −44 |
| | | 388.8 | 4.1 | 0 | | Z | 348.3C | 2.0 | −19 |
| | | 390.7 | 3.4 | −6 | | | 786.4 | 0.9 | −22 |
| | | 398.7 | 2.3 | −27 | | | 786.4 | 1.3 | −12 |
| | | 399.0 | 3.3 | −15 | | | 805.8 | 3.1 | −10 |
| | | 399.1 | 3.6 | −27 | | | 833.7C | 1.9 | −28 |
| | | 739.9 | 0.9 | −33 | | | 833.7C | 2.1 | −34 |
| | | 764.8C | 0.0 | −36 | | | 834.2 | 1.5 | −27 |
| | | 765.0 | 1.5 | −25 | | | 846.2 | 2.3 | −16 |
| | | 765.0C | −1.6 | −26 | | | 847.0 | 1.0 | −26 |
| | | 765.0C | 1.9 | −12 | | | 847.0 | −0.1 | −28 |
| | | 765.0C | −1.4 | −27 | | | 854.7 | 0.4 | −18 |
| | | 765.0C | 1.9 | −6 | | | 856.5 | 1.5 | −14 |

### Silurian Michigan Basin

| County | Well | Depth (m) | $\delta^{18}O$† | $\delta D$† | County | Well | Depth (m) | $\delta^{18}O$† | $\delta D$† |
|--------|------|-----------|-----------------|-------------|--------|------|-----------|-----------------|-------------|
| GT | NC | 2283.3 | 6.9 | −59 | MD | DC | 2483.8 | 2.5 | −73 |
| | | 2283.3 | 5.3 | −58 | | | 2486.9 | 0.2 | −66 |
| K | NX | 2025.7 | 3.3 | −48 | | | 2559.1 | −2.0 | −43 |
| | | 2036.4 | 4.9 | −46 | | | 2559.1 | −1.8 | −43 |
| | | 2036.4 | 5.5 | −45 | | | 2612.1 | 5.7 | −31 |
| | NP | 1868.4 | 4.4 | −52 | | | 2612.1 | 5.5 | −26 |
| | | 1868.9 | 4.4 | −52 | | | 2613.1 | 5.9 | −26 |
| | PA | 2046.1 | 5.2 | −30 | | | 2618.8 | 5.8 | −44 |
| | | 2120.2 | 2.8 | −45 | | | 2618.8 | 5.6 | −53 |
| | | 2123.3 | 5.0 | −54 | N | SB | 1566.7 | 4.9 | −32 |
| | | 2125.4 | 4.7 | −51 | | | | | |
| | | 2127.8 | 5.8 | −49 | | | | | |

### Devonian Alberta Basin

| Formation | Depth (m) | $\delta^{18}O$ | $\delta D$ | Formation | Depth (m) | $\delta^{18}O$ | $\delta D$ |
|-----------|-----------|----------------|------------|-----------|-----------|----------------|------------|
| MU | 679.2-A | 1.3 | −30 | MU | 677.3-G | 1.6 | −30 |
| | 679.2-B | 1.6 | −20 | | 677.3-H | 1.8 | −18 |
| | 679.2-C | 1.7 | −26 | | 681.8 | 1.7 | −19 |
| | 679.2-D | 1.6 | −25 | | Slide 3A | 2.2 | −16 |
| | 679.2-F | 4.0 | −24 | PE | 998.5-A | 1.3 | −16 |
| | 679.2-G | 4.7 | −22 | | 998.5-B | 1.6 | −16 |
| | 679.2-H | 1.2 | −27 | | 998.5-C | 1.6 | −15 |
| | 690.7-A | 2.4 | −31 | | 998.5-B1 | 1.5 | −15 |
| | 690.7-B | 0.7 | −43 | | 222.1-E | 2.4 | −7 |
| | 690.7-C | 3.0 | −31 | | 222.1-F | 3.2 | −7 |
| | 677.3-A | 1.1 | −24 | | 222.1-G | 2.1 | −25 |
| | 677.3-B | 1.3 | −26 | | 466.6-C | −1.3 | −77 |
| | 677.3-C | 1.4 | −29 | | 466.6-D | 0.0 | −65 |
| | 677.3-D | 1.4 | −29 | | 466.6-E | −1.2 | −57 |
| | 677.3-E | 0.9 | −32 | | 466.6-F | −1.1 | −62 |
| | 677.3-F | 2.6 | −27 | | | | |

† $\delta^{18}O$ and $\delta D$ relative to SMOW.
   **Permian Palo Duro Basin** County: DO = Donley, DS = Deaf Smith, O = Oldham, R = Randall, SW = Swisher; Well: S = Sawyer, D = Detten, GF = G. Friemel, JF = J. Friemel, M = Mansfield, HO = Holtzclaw, RW = Rex White, G = Grabbe, H = Harmon, Z = Zeeck; Depth: C = capillary sample.
   **Silurian Michigan Basin** County: GT = Grand Traverse, K = Kalkaska, MD = Midland, N = Nawago; Well: NC = NMEC-ST-FIFE 1-20, NX = NMEX-ST KALK 2, NP = NMEP-ST 1-18, PA = PanAm Simpson 2, DC = Dow Chemical Salt #8, SB = Sun Bradley #4.
   **Devonian Alberta Basin** Formation: MU = Muskeg, PE = Prairie Evaporite.

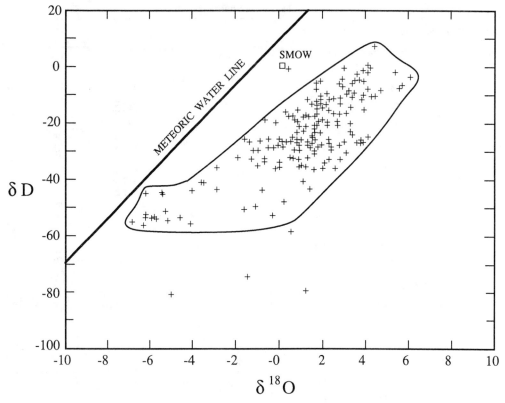

FIG. 2. Isotopic analyses of Permian fluid inclusions from the Palo Duro Basin, Texas. This data array is considered representative of the range of isotopic compositions of a giant, shallow-water, bedded salt deposit. The salt accumulated during repeated floodings of an evaporite basin over tens of millions of years. The isotopic variations are a result of the evaporation trajectory of sea water and mixing of various stages of evaporated sea water with renewed influxes of sea water and influxes of meteoric water, all followed by renewed evaporation to halite facies.

curred in the Palo Duro Basin. If the Palo Duro evaporites are representative of typical saline giants, then a similar domain with respect to the position of the meteoric water line is probable for any saline giant throughout geologic time. However, the isotopic composition of the meteoric waters that enter an evaporating basin is likely to depend on the specific geographic setting and various climatic variables. In the case of the Palo Duro evaporites, $\delta^{18}O$ and $\delta D$ values have a typical minimum value of about $-7$ and $-55$, respectively. In other basins of other geologic ages these minimum values may have been different, depending on the average isotopic composition of the local meteoric water. Because of this, the $\delta^{18}O$-$\delta D$ domain for these other evaporites may have been more or less elongated. The shape of this domain could also be affected by the amount of meteoric water present in the evaporating brine. Nevertheless, the concept that data for evaporite brines will define some domain to the right of

the meteoric water line similar to the Palo Duro domain provides a basis for exploring the possibility that the meteoric water line was strongly displaced in the Silurian and/or Devonian. If ocean water was 4–5.5 per mil lower in the Silurian than in the Permian and the same type of evaporation processes that created the Palo Duro Basin were active, then the domain of fluid inclusion data would plot as shown by the shaded domain in Fig. 4. Many of the data would lie above the modern meteoric water line and maximum $\delta^{18}O$ values would be only about $+1$ per mil enriched relative to SMOW. The data could be kept below the modern meteoric water line if $\delta D$ were also dramatically different, but this would also produce a major offset of the domain relative to the Palo Duro data.

## COMPARISON OF SILURIAN, DEVONIAN, AND PERMIAN DATA

Data for the Devonian and Silurian fluid inclusions are given in Table 1 and are shown together

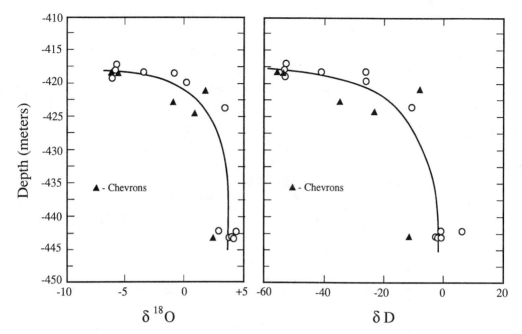

FIG. 3. Isotopic composition versus stratigraphic position for the transition from marine-dominated to meteoric water runoff-dominated salt in the Upper Seven Rivers unit of the Permian salt in the Palo Duro Basin (J. Friemel well). Much of the salt toward the top of this section was reworked (dissolved-reprecipitated) by meteoric waters. The overlying horizon is made up of clastic deposits that flooded the evaporite flats.

with the data envelope for the Palo Duro evaporites in Fig. 5. Although there are fewer data for the Devonian and Silurian, it is clear that the data domains for the older deposits are not strongly shifted to lower $\delta^{18}O$ values. Both Permian and Silurian $\delta^{18}O$ values approach a maximum value of about +6, and the Devonian data approach +5. None of the Silurian or Devonian data plot above, or even near, the meteoric water line. $\delta D$ values for the Devonian samples strongly overlap the Permian data, but may be slightly lower as a group than the Permian counterparts. The Silurian data are lower as a group in $\delta D$ relative to either of the other two groups, and this will be considered as a separate issue below.

*Oxygen isotope variations*

If the same types of processes operated to produce the fluid inclusions in these evaporite deposits, then these data are fatal to the idea that $\delta^{18}O$ of ocean water changed by 4–5 per mil between the Silurian and Permian. Evaporation processes in the Silurian would have to have enriched residual brines in $^{18}O$ by an additional 4–5 per mil in order for the maximum values to coincide with the Permian maximum values. Additionally, all three age groups appear to approach a +6 per mil enrichment relative

to ocean water, the maximum value proposed by LLOYD (1966) that evaporating sea water can reach. For $\delta^{18}O$ of ocean water to have been 4–5.5 per mil lower in the Devonian and Silurian, Lloyd's maximum value would need to be specially extended to 10–11.5 per mil for the Silurian and Devonian in order for the data fields to coincide as shown. There is no inherent reason why the maximum evaporative enrichment in $^{18}O$ should be tied to the numerical value for $\delta^{18}O$ of sea water, so this is unlikely.

Because of the variable number of samples in the three age groups, there is not a complete overlap of $\delta^{18}O$. A number of Permian samples are significantly lower in $\delta^{18}O$ than any of the Devonian or Silurian samples. This is probably because selected horizons were targeted within the Permian salts where sedimentologic evidence had suggested synsedimentary reworking of the salts by meteoric waters. While prominent on the diagram, these horizons are minor in abundance and probably would not have been sampled if only a limited number of samples were available. Because of the sampling limitations for the older data, it cannot be stated that $\delta^{18}O$ is exactly coincident for the three age groups. Also, because of the multitude of evaporation processes that can

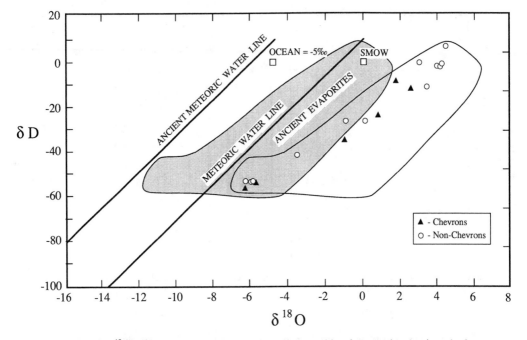

FIG. 4. δD-δ$^{18}$O array for the data shown in Fig. 3. The transition from marine-dominated salt to meteoric water runoff-dominated salt spans the data domain for the Permian reference domain. Some of the most $^{18}$O- and D-depleted salts are chevron-zoned crystals, indicating that these light values represent connate fluids and not later meteoric waters that somehow penetrated the salt.

The shaded domain is the hypothetical position of isotopic compositions that would result if a giant salt deposit formed under similar conditions in a hydrosphere where sea water was depleted in $^{18}$O by 5.5 per mil relative to SMOW. Many fluid inclusion data would plot above the position of the modern meteoric water line and maximum δ$^{18}$O would be less than +2.

go on in evaporite environments it is unlikely that the data for any two saline giants would be identical. These uncertainties mean that δ$^{18}$O of the parent sea water for the data domains in Fig. 5 could easily have varied by ±1 per mil, but not by 4–5.5 per mil. Although this approach cannot yet yield the exact isotopic composition of past ocean water, it is sensitive to the large variations that have been previously proposed, and appears to be sufficient to rule out the large changes that have been advocated for the interval Silurian-Permian on the basis of isotopic analyses of carbonates. Secular variations in δ$^{18}$O of Paleozoic shelf carbonates are probably better interpreted in terms of climatic temperature variations, diagenetic alteration, and possible meteoric water contributions to the coastal or epieric sea environments in which these carbonates formed.

*Preservation of fluid inclusions in halite*

O'NEIL *et al.* (1986) analyzed the isotopic composition of fluid inclusions in Permian bedded salt from the Delaware Basin, New Mexico, and concluded that the inclusions were a mixture of me-

teoric water and connate brine. They suggested that relatively recent meteoric ground waters had partially penetrated the salt deposit. As argued in the previous sections, all giant, shallow-water marine evaporite deposits are likely to contain mixed meteoric-marine fluids at the time of deposition and early burial, so it is not clear that isotopic data alone can be used to decide if bedded salt has been penetrated by later waters. The issue is of utmost importance to the present investigation; if later fluids have penetrated the salt, then the fluids are not synsedimentary fluids and cannot be used to obtain information about the ancient hydrosphere.

The problem is typified by the data in Fig. 3. An alternative explanation is that the clastic sequence over the salt interval might be interpreted as a subsurface conduit which allowed later meteoric waters to enter the basin. Water descending below this conduit might somehow have entered the salt and been preserved as fluid inclusions. We offer four arguments that the inclusions analyzed throughout this investigation are synsedimentary evaporite fluids, and not later groundwaters that have penetrated the salt.

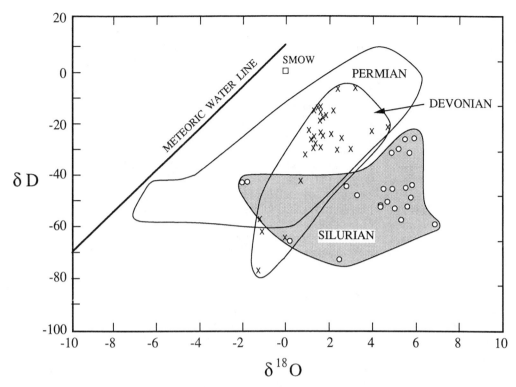

FIG. 5. Isotopic data for Devonian and Silurian fluid inclusions compared with the Permian reference domain. The range of $\delta^{18}O$ values is similar for all three age groups, but $\delta D$ is lower for the Silurian inclusions. The possible trend of increasing D with time can be explained if $\delta D$ of sea water has increased with time.

(1) Fluid inclusions in salt are completely isolated within individual halite crystals, and are not interconnected even if they are lodged near grain boundaries. Brine therefore cannot move in a salt deposit in response to gravity or to pressure differences that normally drive subsurface movement of basinal fluids.

Water *can* move in a salt deposit in response to recrystallization, deformation of the salt, or fracturing. Examples of each of these have been documented in diapiric salt by TESORIERO and KNAUTH (1988), KNAUTH et al. (1980), and KNAUTH and KUMAR (1983). Many of the samples analyzed here contained locally recrystallized salt. This was most evident where chevron-zoned crystals were partially obliterated by coarser crystals of halite. However, the coarse crystals of the recrystallized halite are often truncated by deposition of the overlying halite layers (HOVORKA, 1990). This indicates that the recrystallization was early; fluid inclusions trapped in this second generation halite represent synsedimentary evaporite fluids, not basinal fluids that entered the salt during deep burial.

The salt beds from which these samples were

taken are undeformed, unfractured, and have not undergone wholesale recrystallization. In any case, recrystallization at depth is very likely an expulsion mechanism for water in salt, not a mechanism for water entry. Salt recrystallized at depth has the lowest water content of any known terrestrial rock (KNAUTH and KUMAR, 1981). All of the salts sampled here were water-rich (average water content of Palo Duro halite is 0.5 wt%; FISHER, 1985).

A mechanism involving inclusion migration within single KCl crystals in response to a strong thermal gradient was documented in laboratory experiments by ANTHONY and CLINE (1974), and a widespread misconception has apparently developed that fluid inclusions can migrate through natural salt beds in response to the natural geothermal gradient. OLANDER (1982) clarified the mechanism whereby inclusions might migrate within single NaCl crystals in response to a strong thermal gradient around nuclear waste cannisters but indicated that such inclusions become immobilized at grain boundaries. Migration across grain boundaries has never been demonstrated in laboratory experiments or under natural conditions. In any case, the natural geothermal gradient is far below the thermal gradients used to induce fluid inclusion migration in laboratory experiments. The speculation that the geothermal gradient can move water into or through salt under natural conditions remains to be demonstrated.

(2) Many of the inclusions are arrayed in chevron zonations which point stratigraphically upward. This is a well-documented synsedimentary texture indicating preservation of the originally precipitated crystals (WARDLAW and SCHWERDTNER, 1966). The isotopic composition of the chevrons is typically similar to that of co-existing non-chevron salt. For example, throughout the interval in Fig. 3 the salt contains abundant vertically oriented chevron-zoned fluid inclusions. Many of the salt crystals, including the chevron-zoned crystals, are displacive halite crystals with respect to mudstone lamellae. In other words, halite displaced delicate layers of clay during crystal growth. Many of these displacive crystals are chevron-zoned crystals pointing stratigraphically upward. These textures and fabrics are diagnostic of synsedimentary halite crystal growth, not recrystallization during deep burial. Unless the standard criteria used to interpret these evaporite fabrics are seriously in error, the inclusions were trapped before deposition of the overlying clastic sequence. The data in Fig. 3 are therefore best interpreted in terms of connate fluids and not in terms of water percolating downward from the overlying clastic sequence.

(3) DAS et al. (1990) have analyzed the fluid inclusion chemistry and argued that the inclusions in the same Silurian deposits represent syndepositional or early diagenetic brines. Several of the Silurian samples analyzed by DAS et al. (1990) were splits from the same core samples analyzed here. ROEDDER et al. (1987) analyzed the fluid inclusion chemistry of the Palo Duro salts but did not reach conclusions regarding the origin of the fluids. Their data show that the fluids are never simple NaCl brines as might be expected if meteoric ground waters penetrated the salt, but instead are strongly concentrated brines. BEIN et al. (1991) refined and reanalyzed the same data set and concluded that the inclusions are syndepositional evaporite fluids. Many of the isotopic data reported here are for sample splits of the actual fluids analyzed by BEIN et al. (1991). Large fluid inclusions that can be multiply sampled in this manner for both isotopic and chemical analysis are most prevalent in the locally recrystallized salt, the salt type most suspect of not preserving syndepositional fluids. The fact that even these inclusions are best interpreted chemically as

syndepositional evaporite brines is strong evidence that the salt beds as a whole have not been penetrated by later fluids.

(4) Formation water in deep sedimentary basins often has chemical and isotopic compositions that can be reasonably interpreted as having a component of evapo-concentrated sea water (CARPENTER, 1978; KNAUTH, 1988). Penetration of subsurface salt beds by this water via some unknown mechanism might possibly yield fluid inclusions with the observed chemistry and isotopic composition. However, if this occurred in the case of the Paleozoic samples analyzed here, the Devonian data should be isotopically lighter as a group than the Silurian data because Alberta Basin formation waters are strongly depleted in both D and $^{18}O$ relative to Michigan Basin formation waters. The reverse is observed, so this possibility is unlikely. Also, KNAUTH and BEEUNAS (1986) have shown that the Palo Duro fluid inclusions are isotopically dissimilar from formation waters in the Palo Duro Basin; the inclusions cannot represent intrusions of water presently in the Palo Duro deep aquifers.

*Gypsum dehydration waters*

Gypsum is normally considered to be a primary precipitate in marine evaporite deposits. During burial, gypsum converts to anhydrite with release of water. All sulfate in the samples analyzed here is in the form of anhydrite. O'NEIL et al. (1986) and KNAUTH and BEEUNAS (1986) explored the isotope systematics associated with the potential water release from gypsum. The latter authors concluded that this had not had a major effect on the isotopic composition of the Permian fluid inclusions at Palo Duro. HOVORKA (1990) has subsequently argued on the basis of petrographic studies that the gypsum-anhydrite conversion in the Palo Duro evaporites occurred at or near the sediment water interface. The likely mechanism involved back reaction of more evapo-concentrated brine with gypsum precipitated during earlier stages of evaporation. The water is released back into the evaporite brine and does not appear as a halo of fluid inclusions in salt around the gypsum pseudomorphs.

In the salt cores of the Michigan Basin, dense arrays of brine inclusions are often found immediately above or beneath anhydrite bands. These were specifically sampled on the chance that these inclusions might represent water released in the subsurface from the sulfate layer when it was originally gypsum. However, data for these inclusions do not define any specific part of the Silurian data array. It is possible that all of the Silurian inclusions nevertheless represent water released from gypsum, and that this is the reason the Silurian data array is different from the Devonian data array. Since gypsum hydration water is enriched in $^{18}O$ by about +5.5 per mil relative to its parent brine (SOFER, 1978), it is possible under this scenario that the parent evaporite fluids are all displaced about 5.5 per mil to the left of the array shown in Fig. 5. In this case, the position of the Silurian data array relative to that of the Permian arises via a sampling bias, and Silurian sea water could indeed have been depleted in $^{18}O$ relative to Permian sea water. A similar argument might be made for the Devonian data. However, neither Devonian nor Silurian fluid inclusions are simple NaCl brines (DAS *et al.,* 1990; BRODYLO and SPENCER, 1987) as would be expected if water from gypsum were simply released into halite. All are concentrated brines requiring evaporative processes. Also, this putative mechanism would not lead to chevron zonations with halite crystals. While it is possible that release of water from gypsum has somewhat altered the isotopic composition of the inclusions, it is very unlikely that this is the major control, and it is equally unlikely that all Silurian samples just happened to be sampled from inclusions that originated purely through gypsum dehydration while none were encountered in almost 200 samples of Permian halite.

*Hydrogen isotope variations*

The most striking difference in the three data sets in Fig. 5 is the overall depletion in D of the Silurian data relative to the Permian and Devonian data. A shift upward of about 20 per mil in $\delta D$ would bring the Silurian domain coincident with the Permian reference domain. One interpretation of the data is therefore that the Silurian parent waters were depleted in D about 20 per mil relative to the Permian waters. The Devonian $\delta$-values may also be somewhat lower relative to the Permian, and it is possible to read into Fig. 5 a progression in which $\delta D$ increases going from Silurian to Devonian and Permian.

Although the oxygen isotope history of the oceans has been extensively debated, the hydrogen isotope history has generally been considered an intractable problem. Many sedimentary minerals do contain structural water and fluid inclusions, but these have never been considered as indicators of sea water isotopic composition. The rock record therefore offers no indication of hydrogen isotope evolution with which the fluid inclusion data can be compared.

In principle, it is likely that the hydrosphere has undergone some enrichment in D over geologic time. Photodissociation of water in the upper atmosphere yields free hydrogen which can escape from the Earth. Protium should escape preferentially to deuterium, and recombination of the residual, D-enriched hydrogen gas with oxygen causes the hydrosphere to become enriched in D. The fractionation of hydrogen isotopes during the complicated dissociation-escape-recombination processes is unknown. The effect today on $\delta D$ of the hydrosphere is surely small because such a small amount of water is involved at any given time relative to the mass of the entire hydrosphere. It is difficult to imagine that this process could account for the large shifts shown in Fig. 5, but the possibility cannot be dismissed because so little is known about the current process or how it may have varied in the past.

Another possibility relates to the process whereby basalts become hydrated at mid-ocean ridges and release water at subduction zones. Part of the water that hydrates mid-ocean ridge basalts is returned via dehydration reactions at subduction zones and part may be recycled through the mantle and outgassed again at spreading centers. It is not clear, however, that a steady state has been achieved; a clear demonstration has never been made that water subducted equals water emitted at spreading centers. It is conceivable that the hydrosphere was outgassed early in Earth history and that it is being slowly returned to the crust and mantle by hydration of ocean crust and incomplete dehydration at subduction zones. The hydrogen isotope fractionation between hydroxyl in hydrous minerals and water is normally such that the lighter isotopes are preferentially taken into the mineral, so this process works in the right direction to account for the shift shown in Fig. 5. Unlike the photodissociation process, this one has the potential of working on a scale large enough to cause changes in $\delta D$ as large as those suggested by the fluid inclusion data.

Unlike the Permian and Devonian salt samples, many of the Silurian samples contain enough dissolved gas to yield microscopic bubbles when small chips are dissolved in water. The possibility arises that the Silurian samples are depleted in D because they have been contaminated by water that has exchanged with, or been derived from, D-depleted organic matter. Every sample was microscopically screened for freedom from any visible impurity, but the sample aliquots actually analyzed could not be tested for dissolved gases by the water dissolution method. Additional confirmation of the D-deple-

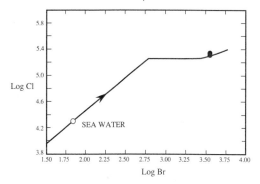

FIG. 6. Two Cl-Br analyses of brine encountered in the Silurian salt of the Retsof Mine, New York. The correspondence of these data with the trajectory shown for the evaporation of sea water makes this brine a good candidate for connate evaporate brine.

tion in Silurian salt is desirable and has been provided by a fortuitous occurrence of brine in the Retsof salt mine of the International Salt Company (now Akzo Salt Inc.) in western New York.

The Retsof Mine is a large mine in bedded Silurian salt that is generally recrystallized (T. LOWENSTEIN, pers. comm.). For the first time in 20 years, a brine "pocket" was encountered in late 1987 (A. G. GEARY, International Salt Co., written comm., 1987). The seep area was quickly grouted to stop further entry of brine into the mine, but multiliter quantities were sampled by the mine engineers. Seeps in salt mines can represent a variety of water sources, including external aquifers which could potentially enter a mine along fractures. The chemical analysis supplied by International Salt Company gives the following concentrations (mg/l): Na = 26,815; Cl = 217,775; Ca = 73,705; Mg = 8,365; K = 12,650; Br = 3,600; S.G. = 1.254. Figure 6 shows the Br-Cl data together with the trajectory for the evaporation of sea water (CARPENTER, 1978). Although the use of chemical analyses to determine the source of brines is a controversial subject, the agreement of the Br-Cl data with the sea water evaporation trend makes this brine a good candidate for evaporite brine trapped in the Retsof salt since the Silurian. The other chemical data are consistent with a marine evaporite brine that has been involved in dolomitization reactions, precipitation of anhydrite, and possible K exchange with clays (using the treatment of CARPENTER, 1978). The most likely explanation for the Retsof brine is that it is "connate water," a remnant of the parent Silurian evaporite brine trapped within the salt. Dewatering of the salt during recrystallization may have contributed to the brine, but this released fluid

would also have been parent Silurian evaporite brine. Isotopic data for the Retsof leak are shown in Fig. 7. The isotopic composition of this Silurian sample is just like those of the Silurian samples from Michigan and plots below the data fields for the Devonian and Permian. This result supports the interpretation that the fluid inclusions are recording a Silurian signal that is really depleted in D relative to the younger samples.

## CONCLUSIONS

1. New isotopic analyses of fluid inclusions in Permian halite confirm the earlier results of KNAUTH and BEEUNAS (1986), and support the interpretation that the inclusions are connate brines trapped at the time of halite precipitation or during early diagenesis. The fluids represent evaporated sea water, meteoric water, or any mixture between the two depending upon the interplay between marine flooding and continental runoff in the original depositional environment.

2. $\delta^{18}O$ of fluid inclusions from Devonian and Silurian bedded salts falls within the range of the Permian data. Maximum $\delta^{18}O$ of all three groups approaches a "limiting" value of about +6; Silurian values are not 4 to 5.5 per mil depleted in $^{18}O$ relative to Permian values as expected if the oceans were 4 to 5.5 per mil lower in the Silurian. The data indicate that sea water did not vary by more than

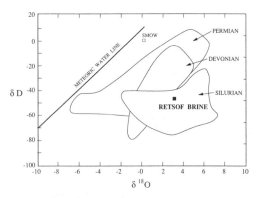

FIG. 7. Isotopic datum for the Retsof brine in relation to the fluid inclusion data. The isotopic composition of this large brine sample is similar to that of fluid inclusions in the Michigan Basin Silurian salt. The Retsof sample is large enough to analyze by conventional methods. This lends support to the interpretation that Silurian evaporite brines are depleted in D relative to younger evaporite brines and that the observed depletion is not some quirk associated with the analysis of small water samples in halite or special conditions in the Michigan Basin that might alter the isotopic composition of fluid inclusions.

1-2 per mil during the interval Silurian-Permian, strongly contradicting interpretations of sea water history based on oxygen isotopic analyses of carbonates. Secular variations in $\delta^{18}O$ of Paleozoic carbonates are therefore probably best interpreted in terms of climatic temperature variations, diagenetic alteration, and/or possible contributions of meteoric water to the original coastal or epieric sea depositional environment, and not in terms of lower $^{18}O$ content of past sea water.

3. $\delta D$ for the Silurian samples is about 20 per mil lower than for the Permian samples, and the Devonian samples have intermediate values. A viable interpretation of these differences is that the Earth's hydrosphere became progressively enriched in deuterium between the Silurian and the Permian.

*Acknowledgements*—Devonian samples were generously provided by Ron Spencer, University of Calgary. Many of the Permian samples were selected and transmitted by Sue Hovorka, Texas Bureau of Economic Geology. We thank both for sharing sedimentologic information about the samples. Sarah Larimer carefully prepared every sample. Her painstaking efforts are gratefully acknowledged. We thank A. G. Geary and Akzo Salt Inc. for the Retsof Mine brine sample, chemical data, and permission to publish the Retsof results. We also thank personnel at the University of Michigan core lab for their cooperation and generosity. Editorial comments by Jim O'Neil improved the manuscript. Funding was by NSF EAR-8618369 and Battelle Memorial Institute Contract #E 512-08100.

## REFERENCES

ANTHONY T. R. and CLINE H. E. (1974) Thermomigration of liquid droplets in salt. In *Fourth Symposium on Salt* (ed. A. H. COOGAN); *Northern Ohio Geol. Soc. 1*, pp. 313–321.

BEIN A., HOVORKA S. D., FISHER R. S. and ROEDDER E. (1991) Fluid inclusions in bedded Permian halites, Palo Duro Basin, Texas, U.S.A.: evidence for modification of seawater in evaporite brine-pools and subsequent early diagenesis. *J. Sediment. Petrol.* **61**, 1–14.

BRODYLO L. A. and SPENCER R. J. (1987) Depositional environment of the Middle Devonian Telegraph Salts, Alberta, Canada. *Bull. Canadian Petrol. Geol.* **3**, 455–474.

CARPENTER A. B. (1978) Origin and chemical evolution of brines in sedimentary basins. *Oklahoma Geol. Surv. Cir.* **79**, 60–77.

CARPENTER S. J. and LOHMANN K. C. (1989) $\delta^{18}O$ and $\delta^{13}C$ variations in Late Devonian marine cements from the Golden Spike and Nevis Reefs, Alberta, Canada. *J. Sediment. Petrol.* **59**, 792–814.

DAS N., HORITA J. and HOLLAND H. D. (1990) Chemistry of fluid inclusions in halite from the Salina Group of the Michigan Basin: implications for Late Silurian seawater and the origin of sedimentary brines. *Geochim. Cosmochim. Acta* **54**, 319–327.

FISHER R. S. (1985) Amount and nature of occluded water in bedded salt, Palo Duro Basin, Texas. *Bur. Econ. Geol., Univ. Texas Austin, Geol. Cir. 85-4.*

FRITZ P. (1971) Geochemical characteristics of dolomites and the $^{18}O$ content of Middle Devonian oceans. *Earth Planet. Sci. Lett.* **11**, 277–282.

GONFIANTINI R. (1965) Effetti isotopici nell'evaporazione di acque salate. *Atti. della Soc. Tosc. Sc. Nat., Ser. A* **LXXII**, 3–22.

GREGORY R. T. and TAYLOR H. P. (1981) An oxygen isotope profile in a section of Cretaceous oceanic crust, Samail ophiolite, Oman: evidence for $\delta^{18}O$ buffering of the oceans by deep (<5 km) seawater—Hydrothermal circulation at mid-ocean ridges. *J. Geophys. Res.* **86**, 2737–2755.

HOLSER W. (1979) Trace elements and isotopes in evaporites. In *Marine Minerals* (ed. R. G. BURNS); *Reviews in Mineralogy*, pp. 295–346. Mineralogical Society of America.

HOVORKA S. D. (1990) Sedimentary processes controlling halite deposition, Permian Basin, Texas. Ph.D. dissertation. Univ. Texas at Austin.

KARHU J. and EPSTEIN S. (1986) The implication of the oxygen isotope records in coexisting cherts and phosphates. *Geochim. Cosmochim. Acta* **50**, 1745–1756.

KISHIMA N. and SAKAI H. (1980) Oxygen-18 and deuterium determination on a single water sample of a few milligrams. *Anal. Chem.* **52**, 356–358.

KNAUTH L. P. (1988) Origin and mixing history of brines, Palo Duro Basin, Texas, U.S.A. *Appl. Geochem.* **3**, 455–474.

KNAUTH L. P. and BEEUNAS M. A. (1986) Isotope geochemistry of fluid inclusions in Permian halite with implications for the isotopic history of ocean water and the origin of saline formation waters. *Geochim. Cosmochim. Acta* **50**, 419–433.

KNAUTH L. P. and KUMAR M. B. (1981) Trace water content of salt in Louisiana salt domes. *Science* **213**, 1005–1007.

KNAUTH L. P. and KUMAR M. B. (1983) Isotopic character and origin of brine leaks in the Avery Island salt mine, South Louisiana, U.S.A. *J. Hydrology* **66**, 343–350.

KNAUTH L. P. and LOWE D. R. (1978) Oxygen isotope geochemistry of cherts from the Onverwacht Group (3.4 billion years) Transvaal, South Africa, with implications for secular variations in the isotopic composition of cherts. *Earth Planet. Sci. Lett.* **41**, 209–222.

KNAUTH L. P., KUMAR M. B. and MARTINEZ J. D. (1980) Isotope geochemistry of water in Gulf Coast Salt Domes. *J. Geophys. Res.* **85**, 4863–4871.

LLOYD R. M. (1966) Oxygen isotope enrichment of sea water by evaporation. *Geochim. Cosmochim. Acta* **30**, 801–814.

MUEHLENBACHS K. and CLAYTON R. N. (1976) Oxygen isotope composition of the oceanic crust and its bearing on seawater. *J. Geophys. Res.* **81**, 4365–4369.

OLANDER D. R. (1982) A model of brine migration and water transport in rock salt supporting a temperature gradient. *Nucl. Tech.* **58**, 256–270.

O'NEIL J. R., JOHNSON C. M., WHITE L. D. and ROEDDER E. (1986) The origin of fluids in the salt beds of the Delaware Basin, New Mexico and Texas. *Appl. Geochem.* **1**, 265–271.

PERRY E. C. (1967) The oxygen isotope chemistry of ancient cherts. *Earth Planet. Sci. Lett.* **3**, 62–66.

PERRY E. C., JR. (1990) Comment on "The implication of the oxygen isotope records in coexisting cherts and phosphates" by J. Karhu and S. Epstein. *Geochim. Cosmochim. Acta* **54**, 1175–1179.

PIERRE C., ORTLIEB L. and PERSON A. (1984) Supratidal evaporitic dolomite at Ojo de Liebre lagoon: mineralogical and isotopic arguments for primary crystallization. *J. Sediment. Petrol.* **54,** 1049–1061.

POPP B. N., ANDERSON T. F. and SANDBERG P. A. (1986a) Textural, elemental, and isotopic variations among constituents in Middle Devonian limestones, North America. *J. Sediment. Petrol.* **56,** 715–727.

POPP B. N., ANDERSON T. F. and SANDBERG P. A. (1986b) Brachiopods as indicators of original isotopic compositions in Paleozoic limestones. *Geol. Soc. Amer. Bull.* **97,** 1262–1269.

ROEDDER E., D'ANGELO, DORRZAPF A. F. and ARUSCAVAGE P. (1987) Composition of fluid inclusions in Permian salt beds, Palo Duro Basin, Texas, U.S.A. *Chem. Geol.* **61,** 79–90.

SOFER Z. (1978) Isotopic composition of hydration water in gypsum. *Geochim. Cosmochim. Acta* **42,** 1141–1149.

TESORIERO A. J. and KNAUTH L. P. (1988) The distribution of trace water around brine leaks in the Avery Island salt mine: implications for the natural migration of water in salt. *Nucl. Chem. Waste Management* **8,** 189–197.

VEIZER J. and HOEFS J. (1976) The nature of $O^{18}/O^{16}$ and $C^{13}/C^{12}$ secular trends in sedimentary carbonate rocks. *Geochim. Cosmochim. Acta* **40,** 1387–1395.

VEIZER J., FRITZ P. and JONES B. (1986) Geochemistry of brachiopods: oxygen and carbon isotopic records of Paleozoic oceans. *Geochim. Cosmochim. Acta* **50,** 1679–1696.

WARDLAW N. C. and SCHWERDTNER W. N. (1966) Halite anhydrite seasonal layers in the Middle Devonian Prairie Evaporite Formation, Saskatchewan, Canada. *Bull. Geol. Soc. Amer.* **77,** 331–342.

Stable Isotope Geochemistry: A Tribute to Samuel Epstein
© The Geochemical Society, Special Publication No. 3, 1991
Editors: H. P. Taylor, Jr., J. R. O'Neil and I. R. Kaplan

# Oxygen isotopes in phosphates of fossil fish—Devonian to Recent

YEHOSHUA KOLODNY and BOAZ LUZ

Department of Geology, The Institute of Earth Sciences, The Hebrew University of Jerusalem, Jerusalem, Israel

**Abstract**—The isotopic composition of oxygen in the phosphate of apatite ($\delta^{18}O_p$) was determined in 159 fish bones and teeth from museum collections throughout the world. The fossils were both marine and fresh water, ranging in age from Devonian to the Recent. In 45 of those we also determined the isotopic composition of oxygen and carbon of the lattice carbonate in apatite ($\delta^{18}O_c$ and $\delta^{13}C$). In most cases the isotopic results are compatible with previously available geological information: the difference between marine and fresh water, the indication of previously known warm and cold time periods, and the ranking of fishes from warm to cold according to their inferred life habitat. The relationship between $\delta^{18}O_p$ and $\delta^{18}O_c$ suggests early diagenetic replacement of an originally phosphatic phase by carbonate fluor apatite (CFA). The correlated latitudinal variation in $\delta^{18}O$ of meteoric water and temperature should result in a small variation of $\delta^{18}O_p$ in fresh-water fish. The large range in $\delta^{18}O_p$ of Recent fish is the outcome of the "altitude effect" (DANSGAARD, 1964), *i.e.* of the existence of post orogenic high altitudes.

## INTRODUCTION

THE "ESTIMATION OF the paleotemperatures of ancient oceans by measurement of the oxygen isotope distribution between calcium carbonate and water" has been heralded as "one of the most striking and profound achievements of modern nuclear geochemistry" (CRAIG, 1965). The idea was initiated by H. C. Urey and it was the group led by Sam Epstein that provided geologists with the first reliable values for temperatures of the past (EPSTEIN *et al.,* 1951, 1953; UREY *et al.* 1951; EPSTEIN and LOWENSTAM, 1953; LOWENSTAM and EPSTEIN, 1954). In the almost four decades since, the great bulk of paleothermometric studies have centered on measuring $\delta^{18}O$ of carbonate secreting organisms, mainly molluscs and foraminifera (*e.g.* EMILIANI, 1955; SAVIN, 1977). The applicability of the carbonate-water paleotemperature scale is, however, restricted for the most part to the Cenozoic and late Mesozoic record because of poor preservation of older fossils (SAVIN, 1982). Furthermore, practically all paleotemperature determinations were limited to marine fossils, again because well-preserved carbonate land-fossils are scarce and because of the difficulty in estimating the isotopic composition of continental water in which the animal grew.

The possibility of measuring $\delta^{18}O$ in biogenic apatites was first demonstrated by TUDGE (1960) and further developed by LONGINELLI (1965), LONGINELLI and NUTI (1973a,b), and KOLODNY *et al.* (1983). A major advantage of the phosphate oxygen paleothermometer is that isotope exchange between phosphate oxygen and water is very rapid in biochemical enzyme catalyzed reactions but is extremely slow in inorganic systems (KOLODNY *et al.,* 1983). Thus, the problem of preservation in the

case of apatitic fossils should become less acute than it is with calcium carbonate. The apatite-water thermometer has been calibrated with living, marine and fresh-water, fish. It has been applied to the analysis of conodonts of the North American Paleozoic (LUZ *et al.,* 1984), of fossil fishes from the Cretaceous and Tertiary of Israel and other Mediterranean countries (KOLODNY and RAAB, 1988), and of phosphorites from the entire geological record (SHEMESH *et al.,* 1988). We present here the results of a survey of $\delta^{18}O$ analyses of fossil fishes from many parts of the world which sample a time period of about 400 million years: from the Devonian, the time of appearance of the first fish, to the Recent.

## SAMPLES AND ANALYTICAL METHODS

The sample set was obtained by contribution of Museums, as well as by donations of individuals from several universities. In Table 1 the sources are identified as following:

| | |
|---|---|
| AGF | A. G. Fisher, USC, Los Angeles |
| AMNH | American Museum of Natural History, New York |
| AT | A. Tintori, University of Milan, Italy |
| BB | B. Buchardt, Kopenhagen University, Denmark |
| BM | The British Museum, London |
| FA | F. Albarède, CRPG, Vandoeuvre-les-Nancy, France |
| MNH | Muséum National d'Histoire Naturelle, Paris |
| FMNH | Field Museum of Natural History, Chicago |
| LACM | Natural History Museum of Los Angeles County, Los Angeles (J. D. Stewart) |
| NHT | N. H. Trewin, University of Aberdeen |
| UCLA | The UCLA fossil collection, Los Angeles |

The samples designated KLN and KR were collected

Table 1. Isotopic composition of oxygen in phosphate of fossil fishes.

| Source | Locality | Description | Strat. age | Abs. age | $\delta^{18}O$ marine | $\delta^{18}O$ fresh |
|--------|----------|-------------|------------|----------|------------|-----------|
| 1. AGF | Pacific Oc. | *Stenella longirostric* | Recent | 0 | 19.7 | |
| 2. AGF | Iowa | Fish unident. | Recent | 0 | | 14.4 |
| 3. KLN | L. Kinnereth | *Nirogrex terraesanctae* | Recent | 0 | | 19.4 |
| 4. KLN | Mediterranean | *Epinephelus sp.* | Recent | 0 | 22.3 | |
| 5. KLN | Gulf of Elat | *Scarus sp.* | Recent | 0 | 23.3 | |
| 6. KLN | Gulf of Elat | *Scarus sp.* | Recent | 0 | 22.7 | |
| 7. KLN | Gulf of Elat | *Variola louti* | Recent | 0 | 22.2 | |
| 8. KLN | Bardawil | *Sparus aurata* | Recent | 0 | 25.2 | |
| 9. KLN | L. Inari | *Salvelinus namaycush* | Recent | 0 | | 11.1 |
| 10. KLN | L. Baikal | *Perca* | Recent | 0 | | 6.0 |
| 11. KLN | L. Baikal | *Coregorius* | Recent | 0 | | 7.3 |
| 12. KLN | L. Baikal | *Cottus* | Recent | 0 | | 9.0 |
| 13. KLN | L. Karaun | *Salmo* | Recent | 0 | | 14.9 |
| 14. KLN | Dan pond | *Salmo gairdneri* | Recent | 0 | | 15.4 |
| 15. LACM | Off Calif. | *\*Dermochelys* | Recent | 0 | 21.4 | |
| 16. LACM | Off Calif. | *\*Dermochelys* | Recent | 0 | 21.3 | |
| 17. AMNH | Idaho | *Osteichthian* unident. | Pleistocene | 1 | | 11.3 |
| 18. AMNH | Florida | *Lepisosteus spatula* | Pleistocene | 1 | | 21.5 |
| 19. LACM | Nebraska | *Stizostedion canadense* | Pleistocene | 1 | | 15.0 |
| 20. FA | S. France | *Synodontaspis acutissima* | M. Pliocene | 2 | 21.9 | |
| 21. LACM | California | clupeid skeleton | Miocene | 5 | 21.1 | |
| 22. AMNH | Florida | *Myliobatis sp.* | Pliocene | 5 | 20.9 | |
| 23. UCLA | California | Fish, unident. | Miocene | 8 | 21.5 | |
| 24. LACM | California | clupeid skeleton | Miocene | 8 | 19.9 | |
| 25. LACM | California | clupeid skeleton | Miocene | 8 | 20.9 | |
| 26. LACM | California | myliobatid tooth | Miocene | 8 | 21.1 | |
| 27. AMNH | Nebraska | *Achtioptorygian* unident. | Miocene | 9 | | 13.7 |
| 28. FA | S. France | *Mitsukurina lineata* | M. Miocene | 14 | 20.9 | |
| 29. AGF | Maryland | tooth | Miocene | 15 | 19.3 | |
| 30. AGF | Maryland | tooth | Miocene | 15 | 20.5 | |
| 31. AGF | Maryland | shark tooth | Miocene | 15 | 21.3 | |
| 32. AGF | Maryland | fish bone | Miocene | 15 | 21.7 | |
| 33. AGF | Maryland | shark tooth | Miocene | 15 | 21.7 | |
| 34. AGF | Maryland | fish vertebra | Miocene | 15 | 21.4 | |
| 35. AGF | Maryland | shark tooth | Miocene | 15 | 21.3 | |
| 36. AMNH | Florida | *Carcharodon megalodon* | Miocene | 15 | 20.2 | |
| 37. LACM | Calif. | *\*Chelonid* | Miocene | 15 | 22.2 | |
| 38. LACM | Calif. | *Psephophorus* | Miocene | 15 | 21.7 | |
| 39. LACM | Calif. | *Isurus planus* | Miocene | 15 | 22.1 | |
| 40. LACM | Calif. | **Otariidae | Miocene | 15 | 21.2 | |
| 41. LACM | Calif. | myliobatid tooth | Miocene | 15 | 21.6 | |
| 42. LACM | Calif. | *Cetorhinus* tooth | Miocene | 15 | 21.3 | |
| 43. LACM | Calif. | *Psephophorus* | Miocene | 15 | 22.2 | |
| 44. FA | Saudi Arabia | *Myliobatis sp.* | Miocene | 16 | 14.3 | |
| 45. AGF | Maryland | *Myliobatis sp.* | Miocene | 16 | 21.0 | |
| 46. AGF | Baja Calif. | shark tooth | Oligocene | 25 | 19.0 | |
| 47. BB | Belgium | *Myliobatis sp.* | Oligocene | 30 | 20.1 | |
| 48. BB | England | *Myliobatis sp.* | L. Eocene | 35 | 18.4 | |
| 49. BB | England | *Myliobatis sp.* | Eocene | 40 | 19.3 | |
| 50. FA | Paris Basin | *Striatolamia macrota* | L. Eocene | 43 | 17.5 | |
| 51. BB | England | *Myliobatis sp.* | Eocene | 44 | 18.2 | |
| 52. BB | England | *Myliobatis sp.* | Eocene | 44 | 18.1 | |
| 53. FA | North Peru | *Isurus praecursor* | M. Eocene | 46 | 19.4 | |
| 54. FA | Togo | *Synodontaspis sp.* | M. Eocene | 46 | 19.6 | |
| 55. FA | Togo | *Synodontaspis koerti* | M. Eocene | 46 | 18.5 | |
| 56. FA | Togo | Sawfish (rostrum) | M. Eocene | 46 | 18.8 | |
| 57. FA | Togo | Teleostid (vertebra) | M. Eocene | 46 | 19.4 | |
| 58. FA | Togo | Teleostid (bone) | M. Eocene | 46 | 18.8 | |
| 59. FA | Togo | *Synodontaspis koerti* | M. Eocene | 46 | 19.4 | |
| 60. BB | Belgium | *Squatina prima; St. striata* | Eocene | 50 | 15.2 | |
| 61. FA | Morocco | *Striatolamia striata* | M. Eocene | 52 | 18.9 | |
| 62. AMNH | Wyoming | *Amia uintaensis* | M. Eocene | 50 | | 11.0 |

Table 1. (Continued)

| Source | Locality | Description | Strat. age | Abs. age | $\delta^{18}O$ marine | $\delta^{18}O$ fresh |
|---|---|---|---|---|---|---|
| 63. AMNH | S. Carolina | *Myliobatis mordax* | Eocene | 50 | 21.3 | |
| 64. KR | Morocco | Shark unident. | E. Eocene | 55 | 18.6 | |
| 65. KR | Italy | Fish unident. | E. Eocene | 55 | 18.7 | |
| 66. BB | U.K. | *Squatina prima; St. striata* | E. Eocene | 55 | 17.8 | |
| 67. BB | U.K. Oldhaven Beds | *Striatolamia striata* | Paleocene | 60 | 16.5 | |
| 68. BB | U.K. Oldhaven Beds | *Striatolamia striata* | Paleocene | 60 | 16.3 | |
| 69. BB | U.K. Oldhaven Beds | *Squatina prima; St. striata* | Paleocene | 60 | 15.5 | |
| 70. AMNH | N. Mexico | *Lepisosteus sp.* | Paleocene | 60 | | 15.3 |
| 71. FA | Morocco | *Synodontaspis tingitana* | Danian | 62 | 19.6 | |
| 72. FA | Morocco | *Myliobatis sp.* | Danian | 62 | 24.2 | |
| 73. AMNH | Wyoming | *Lepisosteus sp.* | M. Paleocene | 63 | | 12.3 |
| 74. BB | Denmark | *Striatolamia sp.* | Danian | 65 | 19.7 | |
| 75. FA | Bolivia | *Pucapristis branisi* | Maastrichtian | 68 | 21.9 | |
| 76. FA | Morocco | *Cretolemna maroccana* | Maastrichtian | 68 | 19.3 | |
| 77. AMNH | Wyoming | garfish | Maastrichtian | 70 | | 12.7 |
| 78. LACM | Montana | *Lepisosteid* | Maastrichtian | 70 | | 13.4 |
| 79. LACM | Calif. | *Plotosaurus tuckeri* | Maastrichtian | 70 | 22.3 | |
| 80. LACM | Calif. | *Enchodus* | Maastrichtian | 70 | 22.1 | |
| 81. KR | Israel | Teleostid, unident. | Maastrichtian | 74 | 19.8 | |
| 82. KR | Israel | *Squatina ? sp.* | Maastrichtian | 74 | 20.3 | |
| 83. FA | N. Jersey | *Scapanorhynchus texanus* | Campanian | 75 | 20.2 | |
| 84. KR | Morocco | *Lamna biauriculata* | L. Campanian | 75 | 19.5 | |
| 85. KR | Jordan | *Squalicorax pristodontus* | Campanian | 77 | 18.4 | |
| 86. KR | Israel | *Enchodus bursuaxi* | Campanian | 77 | 20.0 | |
| 87. KR | Israel | *Enchodus bursuaxi* | Campanian | 77 | 19.7 | |
| 88. KR | Israel | *Enchodus libycus* | Campanian | 77 | 19.1 | |
| 89. KR | Israel | *Squalicorax kaupi* | Campanian | 77 | 18.7 | |
| 90. KR | Israel | *Lamna biauriculata* | Campanian | 77 | 19.3 | |
| 91. FA | Morocco | *Cretolamna appendiculata* | Campanian | 75 | 18.9 | |
| 92. AMNH | S. Dakota | Teleostid, unident. | Campanian | 77 | 18.1 | |
| 93. LACM | Alabama | *cf. Mawsonia* | Campanian | 77 | 21.3 | 21.3 |
| 94. AMNH | Montana | *Lepisosteus sp.* | L. Cretaceous | 80 | | 13.4 |
| 95. LACM | S. Dakota (Pierre) | *Platecarpus ictericus* | E. Campanian | 83 | 19.7 | |
| 96. LACM | S. Dakota (Pierre) | *Tylosarurus proriger | E. Campanian | 83 | 18.5 | |
| 97. LACM | S. Dakota (Pierre) | *Enchodus petrosus* | E. Campanian | 83 | 19.9 | |
| 98. LACM | Kansas (Niobrara) | *Platecarpus ictericus* | Santon.-Campan. | 84 | 19.7 | |
| 99. KR | Israel | *Scapanorhynchus sp.* | Santon.-Campan. | 84 | 18.3 | |
| 100. KR | Israel | *Scapanorhynchus rapax* | Santon.-Campan. | 84 | 18.6 | |
| 101. LACM | S. Dakota | *Ptychodus mortoni* | Santon.-Campan. | 85 | 18.1 | |
| 102. AMNH | Kansas | *Ptychodus mortoni* | Santon.-Campan. | 85 | 18.6 | |
| 103. KR | Israel | *Scapanorhynchus ? rapax* | Santon.-Campan. | 85 | 18.3 | |
| 104. LACM | Kansas | *Inocentrus vulgaris* | L. Santonian | 86 | 18.1 | |
| 105. LACM | Kansas | *Squalicorax falcatus* | L. Coniacian | 87 | 18.8 | |
| 106. LACM | Kansas | *Tylosaurus | L. Coniacian | 87 | 18.1 | |
| 107. LACM | Kansas (Niobrara) | *Lepisosteus sp.* | L. Coniacian | 87 | 19.3 | 19.3 |
| 108. LACM | Kansas | *Protosphyraena pernicosa* | L. Coniacian | 87 | 19.7 | |
| 109. KR | Israel | *Squalicorax falcatus* | E. Coniacian | 88 | 18.0 | |
| 110. KR | Sinai, Egypt | *Palaeobalistum ? sp.* | Turonian | 90 | 17.2 | |
| 111. LACM | Kansas | *Ptychodus whipplei* | M. Turonian | 90 | 18.0 | |
| 112. LACM | Kansas | *Squalicorax falcatus* | M. Turonian | 90 | 19.3 | |
| 113. KR | Israel | Teleostid, unident. | Cenomanian | 93 | 17.4 | |
| 114. KR | Israel | Shark, vertebra | Cenomanian | 95 | 17.8 | |
| 115. KR | Israel | Pycnodontidae, bone | Cenomanian | 95 | 17.9 | |
| 116. KR | Israel | *cf. Eubiodectes* | Cenomanian | 95 | 17.8 | |
| 117. KR | Israel | *Pachyamia* | Cenomanian | 95 | 17.8 | |
| 118. FA | Angola | *Cretolamna appendiculata* | Cenomanian | 98 | 18.8 | |
| 119. FA | Texas | *Cretolamna appendiculata* | Albian | 103 | 19.5 | |
| 120. FA | France | *Protolamna sokolovi* | Aptian | 108 | 17.2 | |
| 121. KR | Israel | Pycnodontidae, tooth | Aptian-Albian | 113 | 17.9 | |
| 122. AMNH | N.E. Brasil | *Rhacolepis buccalis* | Aptian | 115 | 19.2 | |
| 123. AMNH | N.E. Brasil | *Tharrhias arpinis* | Aptian | 115 | 18.3 | |
| 124. KR | Israel | Pycnodontidae, tooth | Berr.-Valangin. | 138 | 18.1 | |

Table 1. (Continued)

| Source | Locality | Description | Strat. age | Abs. age | $\delta^{18}O$ marine | $\delta^{18}O$ fresh |
|---|---|---|---|---|---|---|
| 125. MNH | Spain | *"Anaethalion" vidali* | Berr.-Valangin. | 138 | 18.1 | |
| 126. FA | Oman | *Asteracanthus sp.* | L. Jurassic | 150 | 19.7 | |
| 127. MNH | France | *Loptolepis coryphaenides* | Toarcian | 185 | 17.3 | |
| 128. PO | Feltville Fm. | *Ischypterus* | E. Jurassic | 208 | | 17.9 |
| 129. FA | S. France | *Hybodus sp.* | Triassic | 215 | | 14.2 |
| 130. BM | U.K. | *Nemacanthus monilifer* | Triassic (Rhaet.) | 215 | 16.8 | |
| 131. BM | U.K. | *Hybodont teeth* | Triassic (Rhaet.) | 215 | 17.0 | |
| 132. AT | Italy | *Pholidophorus gervasutii* | Norian | 215 | 17.7 | |
| 133. AT | Italy | *Paralepidotus ornatus* | Norian | 215 | 19.6 | |
| 134. AT | Italy | *Paralepidotus ornatus* | M. Norian | 220 | 20.2 | |
| 135. AT | Italy | *Parapholidophores nybelini* | M. Norian | 220 | 18.0 | |
| 136. AT | Italy | *Paralepidotus ornatus* | M. Norian | 220 | 19.9 | |
| 137. AMNH | N. Jersey | *Semionotus sp.* | L. Triassic | 220 | | 17.0 |
| 138. AT | Italy | *Paleobates latissimus* | L. Carnian | 228 | 17.3 | |
| 139. AT | Italy | *Ptycholepis scales* | Landinian | 232 | 16.4 | |
| 140. AT | Italy | Fish scales | E. Landinian | 235 | 17.9 | |
| 141. AMNH | Texas | Xenacanth shark; unident. | Permo-Triassic | 245 | | 20.5 |
| 142. MNH | France | Fish, unident. | E. Permian | 280 | | 15.9 |
| 143. FMNH | Nebraska | Arthrodira tooth | Pennsylvanian | 300 | 19.7 | |
| 144. BM | Northumberland | *Strepsodus sp.* | L. Carboniferous | 315 | | 14.8 |
| 145. BM | Northumberland | *Gyracanthus sp.* | L. Carboniferous | 315 | | 17.3 |
| 146. BM | Ireland | *Psephodus ps.* | E. Carboniferous | 350 | 17.4 | |
| 147. AMNH | Quebeck | *Bothriolepis canadensis* | L. Devonian | 370 | | 16.0 |
| 148. AMNH | Iowa | *Synthotodus trisulcatus* | L. Devonian | 370 | | 17.2 |
| 149. AMNH | Ohio | *Dinichthys terrelli* | L. Devonian | 370 | 18.2 | |
| 150. MNH | Latvia | *Asterolepis* | Devonian | 380 | | 16.4 |
| 151. BM | Scotland | *Coccosteus cuspidatus* | M. Devonian | 380 | | 15.8 |
| 152. NHT | Scotland | *Dipterus* | M. Devonian | 380 | | 15.5 |
| 153. NHT | Scotland | *Coccosteus* | M. Devonian | 380 | | 14.3 |
| 154. NHT | Scotland | *Homosteus* | M. Devonian | 380 | | 18.1 |
| 155. BM | N.S.W | Arthrodira | Devonian (Ems.) | 390 | 19.0 | |
| 156. MNH | Spitzbergen | Fish, unident. | E. Devonian | 400 | | 13.5 |
| 157. BM | Shropshire | Acanthodian spine | E. Devonian | 400 | | 13.8 |
| 158. BM | Shropshire | 'thelodont' scales | E. Devonian | 400 | | 15.8 |
| 159. AGF | Corwallis Is. | Heterostracan fish | Silurian | 410 | 15.9 | |

\* Marine reptiles ($\delta^{18}O_p$ of marine reptiles agrees well with $\delta^{18}O_p$ of fish-KOLODNY and RAAB, 1988)
\*\* Walrus

by the authors and are described in KOLODNY *et al.* (1983) and KOLODNY and RAAB (1988), respectively. Those marked FA are referred to in GRANDJEAN *et al.* (1987, 1988), AT in TINTORI *et al.* 1985), and NHT in TREWIN (1985, 1986). All identifications were given by the contributors, who also supplied us with a stratigraphic age of the fossil and its habitat (marine vs. fresh water). Stratigraphic ages were translated into absolute age by use of the Geologic Time Scale (PALMER, 1983). We aimed at obtaining the best preserved and least cemented teeth and bone samples. These were crushed, dissolved in nitric acid, and bismuth phosphate was prepared from them according to the TUDGE (1960) procedure (see KOLODNY *et al.*, 1983, and SHEMESH *et al.*, 1988, for details). The BiPO$_4$ was dried, fluorinated at 150°C in stainless steel vessels, converted to CO$_2$, and analyzed mass-spectrometrically. The standard reproducibility of our results is ±0.3 per mil. Throughout this paper we refer to $\delta^{18}O$ of phosphate oxygen as $\delta^{18}O_p$ and to $\delta^{18}O$ of CO$_2$ derived from apatite as $\delta^{18}O_c$.

The analysis of $\delta^{18}O_c$ and $\delta^{13}C$ in apatite CO$_2$ was carried out by acid extraction (KOLODNY and KAPLAN, 1970)

after all calcite was preferentially dissolved (SILVERMAN *et al.*, 1959). All $\delta^{18}O$ results are reported in per mil with respect to SMOW, and $\delta^{13}C$ in per mil with respect to PDB.

## RESULTS AND DISCUSSION

### Paleothermometry—$\delta^{18}O_p$ analyses

Table 1 is a summary of a brief sample description, absolute age of the fishes, their localities, identification of their life habitat, and the isotopic composition of oxygen in phosphate ($\delta^{18}O_p$). Table 2 is a similar summary of $\delta^{18}O_c$ and $\delta^{13}C$ in the structural carbonate of apatite. Figures 1, 2, and 3 summarize this information graphically.

Whereas the analytical reproducibility of $\delta^{18}O_p$ is as reported about ±0.3 per mil, it is more difficult to estimate the degree of "geological noise" which

Table 2. Isotopic composition of oxygen and carbon in apatite carbonate and the coexisting phosphate.

| Sample* | $\delta^{18}O_p$ | $\delta^{18}O_c$ | $\delta^{13}C$ |
|---------|------|------|------|
| *Recent* | | | |
| 14. *Salmo* | 15.4 | 20.6 | −3.8 |
| *Tunus* | 21.0 | 32.7 | −10.3 |
| *Tunus* | 21.0 | 37.1 | −4.2 |
| *Bothus* | 23.0 | 25.7 | −4.4 |
| *Saurida* | 23.2 | 24.6 | −3.7 |
| *Fistularia* | 23.2 | 26.2 | −3.7 |
| *Rhinobates* | 22.0 | 26.2 | −5.3 |
| *Siganus* | 22.4 | 26.4 | −4.1 |
| *Iago* | 22.1 | 28.5 | −7.0 |
| *Pempheris* | 22.9 | 28.6 | −4.6 |
| *Diplodus* | 22.9 | 24.7 | −7.6 |
| *Mustelus* | 22.7 | 25.6 | |
| *Cottus* | 9.0 | 26.0 | −6.3 |
| *Fossil* | | | |
| 17. Osteichthian | 11.3 | 20.7 | −3.7 |
| 18. *Lepisosteus* | 21.5 | 31.5 | −0.5 |
| 22. *Myliobatis* | 20.9 | 29.3 | −4.3 |
| 27. *Achtioptorygian* | 13.7 | 21.7 | −6.7 |
| 36. *Carcharodon* | 20.2 | 29.0 | −4.6 |
| 62. *Amia* | 11.0 | 16.3 | −5.0 |
| 63. *Myliobatis* | 21.3 | 28.5 | −3.3 |
| 64. *Lamna* | 18.1 | 25.9 | −2.2 |
| 73. *Lepisosteus* | 12.3 | 17.2 | −5.2 |
| 77. garfish | 12.7 | 19.8 | −2.3 |
| 88. *Enchodus* | 19.7 | 26.4 | −3.3 |
| 89. *Squalicorax* | 18.7 | 26.2 | −5.1 |
| 92. Teleostid | 18.1 | 21.3 | −4.7 |
| 94. *Lepisosteus* | 13.4 | 18.0 | −1.9 |
| 99. *Scapanorhynchus* | 18.3 | 24.8 | −2.3 |
| 102. *Ptychodus* | 18.6 | 23.3 | −3.7 |
| 103. *Scapanorhynchus* | 18.3 | 25.0 | −1.7 |
| 113. Teleostid | 17.4 | 24.2 | −3.6 |
| 122. *Enneles* | 19.2 | 26.0 | −8.3 |
| 130. *Nemacanthus* | 16.8 | 23.3 | −3.5 |
| 131. Hybodont | 17.0 | 23.5 | −3.4 |
| 137. *Semionotus* | 17.0 | 21.5 | −3.3 |
| 144. *Strepsodus* | 14.8 | 21.5 | −2.4 |
| 145. *Gyracanthus* | 17.3 | 22.9 | −3.8 |
| 146. *Psephodus* | 17.4 | 20.7 | −2.8 |
| 147. *Bothriolepis* | 16.0 | 22.1 | −3.6 |
| 148. *Synthotodus* | 17.2 | 24.5 | −1.6 |
| 149. *Dinichthys* | 18.2 | 21.7 | −6.6 |
| 151. *Coccosteus* | 15.8 | 11.6 | −12.2 |
| 152. *Dipterus* | 15.5 | 28.2 | 3.3 |
| 153. *Coccosteus* | 14.3 | 24.4 | −0.5 |
| 155. Arthrodira | 19.0 | 20.2 | −1.2 |

\* For sample number identification, see Table 1.

should be assigned to our data. Two sets of samples may help in such an estimate. Samples 86–89 are all fish bones of Campanian age from the Zefa-Ef'e area in Israel. They come from a narrow stratigraphic sequence, and their $\delta^{18}O_p$ ranges between 19.1 and 20. Similarly, samples 54–59 come from

Kpogame in Togo, all of Middle Eocene age, and yield $\delta^{18}O_p$ between 18.5 and 19.6.

It is significant to note in this context that when Recent fish bones were analyzed (KOLODNY et al., 1983) the spread of $\delta^{18}O_p$ values for six fish specimens of different species from the Gulf of Elat was one per mil (22.3 to 23.3), whereas the spread of $\delta^{18}O_p$ for four specimens of *Sparus aurata* from a single catch from the Bardawil Lagoon was 1.6 per mil (23.6 to 25.2). The difference in noise thus reflects a real difference in the fishes habitat. The Bardawil Lagoon is highly variable both in salinity, water isotopic composition, and temperature, while the Gulf of Elat is a more homogeneous water body.

Hence, it seems safe to assume that the spread of about one per mil observed in different samples from both Togo and Israel reflects, to a large degree, a real environmental variability—either a temperature range of their habitat of a few degrees or a small variation in the isotopic composition (hence salinity) of the sea water. Since no specific information is available on the habitats of the different fossil fishes, such a range should be taken as a rough estimate of the "geological noise" in question.

Figure 1 shows the change of $\delta^{18}O$ in phosphate of marine and fresh-water fishes since the Devonian to the present. The $\delta^{18}O$ can be translated into environmental temperatures by means of the phosphate paleotemperature equation (LONGINELLI and NUTI, 1973a):

$$t\ (°C) = 111.4 - 4.3(\delta^{18}O_p - \delta^{18}O_w) \qquad (1)$$

where $\delta^{18}O_p$ and $\delta^{18}O_w$ are $\delta^{18}O$ of the solid phosphate and the water, respectively. Following estimates of $\delta^{18}O_w$ of pre-glacial ocean water (e.g. Savin, 1977) we assume a value of −1 for it. The temperatures calculated by this transformation are shown on the right-hand ordinate axis. The following points may be noted in Fig. 1:

(a) No clear and simple time trend is evident from the plot. The calculated isotopic temperatures for the entire range of 400 My vary between 4 and 35°C.

More detailed examination of the $\delta^{18}O$ variation in the last 150 My (Fig. 2) shows a variation similar to the paleotemperature changes deduced for the same time from the isotopic analysis of foraminifera (SAVIN, 1977). Specifically, the temperature maxima ($\delta^{18}O$ minima) of the Albian (100 My) and the Middle Eocene (50 My) stand out, as do the temperature minimum of the Maastrichtian (70 My), as well as the general cooling trend of the last 100 My. Obviously one cannot expect a perfect correlation between paleotemperature curves like those

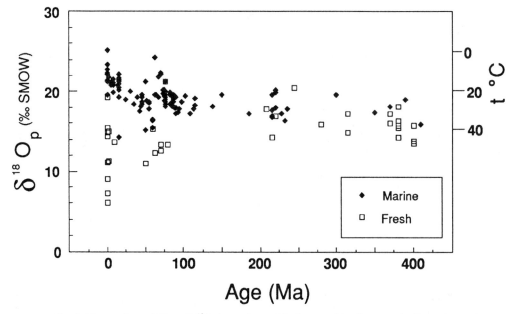

FIG. 1. The secular variation of $\delta^{18}O_p$ in marine and fresh water fishes between the Devonian and the present. The right-hand ordinate denotes temperatures calculated from Eqn. (1), assuming $\delta^{18}O_w = -1$.

of DOUGLAS and WOODRUFF (1981) and that of Fig. 2. In their case the assemblages are benthic and thus record bottom temperatures. These are probably related to a general cooling trend of the high latitudes. Our sample on the other hand includes specimens of different species and genera which cover both a broad geographic range and a wide range of depth habitats, so it is expected to be more noisy. A large part of our samples comes from intermediate latitudes (North America and Europe);

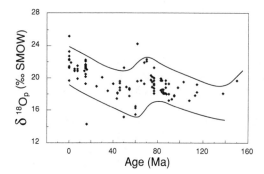

FIG. 2. The secular variation of $\delta^{18}O_p$ in marine fishes in the last 150 My. The envelope marks broad secular temperature trends. Note the general cooling trend in the last 60 My, as well as thermal maxima around 100 My (Albian) and 50–60 My (Eocene), and a thermal minimum around 70 My (Maastrichtian).

indeed, the young (post-Eocene) cooling trend resembles more the high latitude trend detected by SHACKLETON and KENNETT (1975), not the equatorial warming of DOUGLAS and SAVIN (1975). It is likely that when single species fish assemblages from limited geographic areas are sampled through geologic time, a more self-consistent paleothermometric pattern would emerge. A modest beginning in this direction was the study of KOLODNY and RAAB (1988). That study dealt with Cretaceous to Eocene fish remains from the southern Tethys and arrived at temperature curves which show similar trends to previous estimates, though the absolute temperatures are consistently higher than those from contemporaneous carbonates. In fact, the temperature estimates which are derived from $\delta^{18}O_p$ measurements are in considerably better agreement with climate model simulations for the Cretaceous-Eocene (MANABE and BRYAN, 1984) than the previous estimates based on $\delta^{18}O$ of planktonic foraminifera (CROWLEY, 1991).

The isotopic composition of pre-Cretaceous marine fishes does not sharply deviate from the pattern of younger age. The $\delta^{18}O_p$ values remain within the rather narrow limits of 17 and 20. This variation is translated into a temperature range of 35 to 20°C, respectively. The very few samples with $\delta^{18}O$ outside this range will be dealt with separately, below.

(b) No case has been detected where $\delta^{18}O_p$ of a

fresh-water fish fossil is higher than that of a contemporaneous marine fish. Obviously this is the result of the basic relationship between sea water and meteoric water (EPSTEIN and MAYEDA, 1953), the latter being the distillation product of the former. The observed relationship suggests, however, that the analyzed fishes did not undergo significant, post-depositional, isotopic exchange, at least not to the degree that their original, depositional signature would have been erased. The last conclusion might have been doubted in view of the fact that the difference between marine and fresh-water fishes is significantly larger for recent fish than it is for ancient, *e.g.*, Devonian fossils (Fig. 1). This could be interpreted as resulting from increased isotopic exchange for the old fossils. However, in such a case, there is no reason why in some instances marine fossils would not exchange to a degree that they became more $^{18}O$ depleted than their fresh-water contemporaries. Similarly, fresh-water fishes may become more $^{18}O$ enriched than marine fossils of the same age. In fact, a slight overlap between marine and fresh-water values is permitted; the Pleistocene fossil gar *Lepisosteus spatula* from Florida (sample #18) has $\delta^{18}O$ of 21.5, which is within the lower range of marine values. Such an isotopic composition is easily understood for a fish from a low latitude, where meteoric water is "heavy," and was even heavier during the Pleistocene (mean present-day Florida rain has a $\delta^{18}O$ of $-2$ to 0; YURTSEVER and GAT, 1981), and evaporation is intensive.

(c) The range of fresh-water fossil fishes $\delta^{18}O_p$ is much narrower than that of Recent fishes. The first isotopically, very light fishes are of Pleistocene age. This observation of a change in the range between the present and the bulk of the fossil record may be compared with the essentially similar spread (though changing values) of the marine fishes (Fig. 1). We shall deal with this observation below.

In two cases the isotopic analyses of marine fossil fishes are "misbehaved" in the sense that they show surprisingly low $\delta^{18}O$ values:

(1) Samples 67, 68, and 69 are Tertiary sharks *Squatina* and *Striatolamia*, with unexpectedly low $\delta^{18}O$. This regularity applies to several specimens of *Striatolamia striata* and *Sq. prima*, whereas closely related *Striatolamia macrota* and *Myliobatis* have normal values, similar to other fossils of the same age. Table 3 summarizes 40 analyses of $\delta^{18}O$ of sharks and stresses the aforementioned differences. One may speculate that the $^{18}O$ depletion is a species-related feature resulting in the disequilibrium $^{18}O$ depletion ("vital effect") or that it is their

Table 3. $\delta^{18}O_p$ of sharks from the Cretaceous—Tertiary (*Squatina-Sq., and Striatolamia—S.*).

| Squatina sp. S. striata, Sq. prima. | S. macrota | Myliobatis |
|---|---|---|
| 14.2 | 18.1 | 18.1 |
| 14.6 | 17.9 | 19.3 |
| 17.8 | 18.8 | 18.6 |
| 17.9 | 17.2 | 17.4 |
| 15.4 | 18.5 | 18.4 |
| 15.7 | 17.7 | 20.1 |
| 19.0 | 18.3 | 18.2 |
| 15.4 | 19.1 | 17.5 |
| 15.3 | 19.2 | 20.5 |
| 16.8 | 18.7 | 18.8 |
| 17.3 | 18.8 | 18.0 |
| 18.0 | 18.1 | |
| 16.3 | | |
| 15.3 | | |
| 16.5 | | |
| 14.9 | | |
| 15.6 | | |
| Average: 16.2 | 18.3 | 18.6 |

bone structure which makes some sharks more sensitive to diagenesis or that some feature of their habitat makes those species more likely to undergo fresh-water diagenesis (see discussion below).

(2) Sample 129 is a Triassic *Hybodus* from South France. Its $\delta^{18}O$ is 14.2, clearly not a marine value. This sample has been studied by GRANDJEAN *et al.* (1987). They found here an extremely high $^{87}Sr/^{86}Sr$ ratio (0.708629), much too high for Triassic sea water, a non-seawater REE pattern and a low Sr content (425 ppm). The bulk REE pattern has been confirmed by GRANDJEAN and ALBARÈDE (1989) who analyzed this sample by an ion probe and showed a clear enrichment in the middle REE. Such pattern is interpreted by Grandjean and her co-workers as reflecting deposition in estuarine or near shore conditions. Although GRANDJEAN *et al.* (1987) identify the fossil as marine, MACFARLANE (1923, pp. 192–193) claims that in the Triassic *Hybodus* was ". . . at least partially if not wholly freshwater," and ". . . wavering between a lake and sea environment." Even if the *Hybodus* in question spent most of his life in sea water, fresh-water early diagenesis could have affected its final isotopic composition. The Triassic *Hybodus* has also been studied by FTIR spectroscopy (SHEMESH, 1990). Of all analyzed fossil fishes it showed the second highest crystallinity index, suggesting its severe recrystallization.

Thus, in both of these cases we raise the possibility that it is fresh-water early diagenesis which altered $\delta^{18}O$ of the "misbehaved" fossils.

Both GRANDJEAN *et al.* (1987) and SHAW and WASSERBURG (1985) interpret geochemical signals recorded in fossil fish bones and teeth as reflecting depositional environments. Their approach is principally based on mass balance considerations. Thus GRANDJEAN *et al.* (1987) suggest that because the bulk of the REE in apatitic fossils should be acquired by the fossil early diagenetically, soon after death, some transitional carrier phase (oxyhydroxides, organic debris?) is required. Very fast (postdepositional) REE enrichment is indicated also by the combined REE and U-Th isotopic studies of BERNAT (1975). Such reasoning does, however, not demand that the addition of REE must occur on the sea-floor. If a marine environment is replaced by fresh water while a marine fish bone undergoes diagenesis, *i.e.*, if it undergoes transformation to carbonate fluorapatite (CFA), it may acquire both a low $\delta^{18}O$ of its phosphate oxygen and an unpredictable REE signature depending on the nature of the sediments within which it is buried. We shall return to this discussion below.

We now consider several cases in Table 1, which deserve special attention:

*Questionable marine fishes.* Two samples have been marked in Table 1 as both marine and fresh water (93, 107). We followed this procedure for those cases where our paleontological information was not unequivocal, identified by our contributor as "? fresh water" or "? marine." Such is the case with the Mid-Campanian coelacanth identified as *Mawsonia.* It had been marked as "? fresh water" when contributed by J. D. Stewart. It comes from a marine unit in Alabama, which also contains terrestrial dinosaurs. Such coelacanths have tended to be fresh water or near shore where previously discovered (J. D. STEWART, written comm.). Cretaceous coelacanths are also known from shallow marine deposits (CARROLL, 1988, p. 148). $\delta^{18}O$ of the phosphate oxygen in the *Mawsonia* bone is 21.3, clearly a marine value.

The gar *Lepisosteus* from the Coniacian Niobrara Fm. is similarly identified; gars are usually fresh water, occasionally brackish, rarely in marine water (NELSON, 1976, p. 63). Even the Pleistocene *Lepisosteus spatula* from Florida, which was discussed above, was not necessarily a purely fresh-water fish; it is euryhaline, and while it generally spends its time in large river systems it may also be found in coastal waters (L. ROE, written comm.). The *Lepisosteus* in case here, comes however from the same unit in the Smoky Hill Chalk Member of the Niobrara Fm. and from the same locality in Trego County, Kansas, as two clearly marine fishes—the pelagic shark *Squalicorax* and *Protosphyraena.* The

$\delta^{18}O_p$ value of the gar is intermediate between its two, clearly marine, neighbors. Hence, the simple conclusion from the isotopic analysis of the *Mawsonia* and *Lepisosteus* is that both fishes were marine in the Cretaceous. Our suggestion that early diagenesis of apatitic fossils involves practically complete dissolution-recrystallization (see below), casts some doubt on such a simple solution. If that suggestion is correct, then a fresh-water fish which drifted into the sea sank there to the floor, and became fossilized might not be distinguishable from a marine fish which is found in the same assemblage. The decision as to whether a certain species was fresh water or sea dwelling in the geological past must in such cases be resolved by using additional, often field, evidence. Thus the re-occurrence of *Mawsonia* and *Lepisosteus* with marine $\delta^{18}O_p$ values would serve as a strong support to our suggestion that indeed both these fishes were marine in the Cretaceous.

The Holost *Pachyamia* from the Cenomanian of Israel is an analogous case (# 117). Again, this is a fish presently known to be related to fresh water species (Y. KHALIFA, pers. comm.), but again, it is isotopically undistinguishable from the clearly marine fossils of *Eubiodectes* and the Pycnodontidae (samples 114, 115, 116) which occur in the same area. In this case there seems to be independent paleontological evidence (S. WENZ, pers. comm.) that the Pachyamia was indeed a marine fish in the Cretaceous.

*Isotopic analysis of inoceramids.* The interpretation of Cretaceous paleotemperatures and paleosalinities has been severely complicated by the seemingly conflicting results of the isotopic analysis of carbon and oxygen of inoceramids, oysters, baculites, and other cephalopods from the Campanian and Maastrichtian Pierre Shale of the Western Interior Seaway. TOURTELOT and RYE (1969) were the first to find that inoceramids had generally much lower $\delta^{18}O$ values (as low as $-9.5$ PDB) than did the cephalopods. Whereas their results were confirmed by several investigators (SCHOLLE and KAUFFMAN, 1975; SCHOLLE, 1977; PRATT 1984, 1985; ARTHUR *et al.,* 1985; WRIGHT, 1987) the interpretation of the discrepancy varied between explaining it by a "vital effect" (TOURTELOT and RYE, 1969) to referring the $^{18}O$ depletion in inoceramids to fresh-water influx (PRATT, 1984, 1985; ARTHUR *et al.,* 1985). Accordingly, the paleogeographical interpretations varied: RYE and SOMMER (1980) suggested that the Western Interior Seaway has been brackish to normal in its salinity, whereas WRIGHT (1987) used practically the same data to claim a stratified water body in the Interior Seaway. Sample

104 offers a case to re-examine the $\delta^{18}O$ values in inoceramids from a different angle. We analyzed here an Inoceramus together with the fish often found living inside its shell, the *Inocentrus vulgaris.* Whereas the inoceramid we analyzed yields a low $\delta^{18}O$ value (−7.9 PDB, not in Table 1), the fish shows a perfectly normal $\delta^{18}O_p$ (18.1 SMOW). Hence, we must conclude that both the Inoceramus and the co-habitant fish lived in normal seawater at normal marine temperatures; apparently the inoceramids did not record their environment properly. The initial explanation of TOURTELOT and RYE (1969) seems to be in agreement with our data.

*Two sites of oxygen in apatite; $\delta^{18}O_p - \delta^{18}O_c$*

Practically all low temperature, sedimentary apatites (phosphorites, apatitic fossils) are francolites, or carbonate fluorapatites (CFA). The location of the carbonate in the CFA lattice of phosphorites is apparently mainly governed by the distorted $(CO_3 \cdot F)^{-3}$ tetrahedron replacing a tetrahedral $PO_4^{-3}$ ion (BORNEMAN-STARYNKEVITCH and BELOV, 1940; ALTSCHULER et al., 1952; BACQUET et al., 1980). The status of the carbonate ion in bone is much less clear and is still largely unsolved (LOWENSTAM and WEINER, 1989, p. 152; NEWESELY, 1989). The main difficulty with carbonate-containing bone apatites is deciding whether the carbonate forms an integral part of the crystal structure or is external to it, *i.e.* adsorbed on the surface of the crystals or in a separate phase. If the carbonate ions replace ions in the structure, it probably occurs in two sites: one in which it replaces hydroxyl and a second site where it substitutes for phosphate ions (NEWESELY, 1989). It is during diagenesis and aging that the poorly ordered, phosphatic bones are transformed into the much better ordered CFA structure.

The occurrence of structurally bound carbonate within the apatite lattice opened the possibility of using the isotopic composition of both the oxygen and the carbon in this carbonate as isotopic thermometers and/or tracers (KOLODNY and KAPLAN, 1970; MCARTHUR et al., 1980, 1986; BENMORE et al., 1983; GLENN et al., 1988). SHEMESH et al. (1983, 1988) made use of the simplicity of analytical separation between the oxygen in $PO_4^{-3}$ ($\delta^{18}O_p$) and the one in $CO_3^{-2}$ ($\delta^{18}O_c$) and treated these two coexisting(?) sites as two cogenetic oxygen-bearing phases. It was found that $\delta^{18}O_p$ is very well correlated with $\delta^{18}O_c$. This correlation has been explained as reflecting, at least in part, post-depositional isotopic exchange between the two oxygen-bearing phases. The possibility has also been explored that the linear

correlation and its slope reflect non-equilibrium exchange conditions, under which the carbonate oxygen has been altered by an aqueous phase more significantly than its phosphate oxygen counterpart.

On Fig. 3 we plot the variation with age of both $\delta^{18}O_p$ and $\delta^{18}O_c$. Also shown are the values of $(\delta^{18}O_p + 9.5)$, which is a good approximation of the expected value for $\delta^{18}O_c$, if it behaves similarly to a carbonate (both the carbonate paleotemperature equation of EPSTEIN et al., 1953, and Eqn. 1 have a similar slope, with different intercepts; see discussion in SHEMESH et al., 1983). As evident from Fig. 3, in some Cenozoic fish $\delta^{18}O_c$ is indeed close to the $(\delta^{18}O_p + 9.5)$ values. In many other cases, however, especially in the older fish fossils, $\delta^{18}O_c$ is considerably lower than the expected value, thus suggesting its lower resistivity to post-depositional isotopic alteration.

The good correlation between $\delta^{18}O_p$ and $\delta^{18}O_c$ which is observed in phosphorites is absent in living fish (Fig. 4). Whereas the phosphate oxygen reflects well the temperature and the water isotopic composition of the environment in which the fish lived, $\delta^{18}O_c$ has apparently no relation to these parameters. Neither are the isotopic compositions of the two oxygens in living fish-bones related to the "expected" [$\delta^{18}O_p = \delta^{18}O_c - 9.5$] straight line. An analogous plot of data from fossil fishes (Fig. 5) shows a somewhat better correlation between $\delta^{18}O_p$ and $\delta^{18}O_c$. Almost all points plot to the left of the [$\delta^{18}O_p = \delta^{18}O_c - 9.5$] straight line. Thus, the relationships depicted on Fig. 5 can be explained by a shifting of the carbonate towards lower $\delta^{18}O$ values by post-depositional interaction with meteoric water. In the above reasoning we consider the plot of Fig. 5 as intermediate between the initial conditions of living fish (Fig. 4) and the "end point" towards which such an assemblage is altered—that of a strong correlation between $\delta^{18}O_p$ and $\delta^{18}O_c$ as expressed by the phosphorite relationship.

The proposed changes in $\delta^{18}O_p$ and $\delta^{18}O_c$ of fish apatite upon fossilization require that the bone mineral undergoes a thorough mineralogical reorganization. Several lines of evidence support such an assumption: SHEMESH (1990) observed a sharp difference between the infrared spectra of bones of living and fossil fish. He attributed these differences to the recrystallization of carbonate-hydroxy-apatite into francolite (CFA). Several studies of REE in apatitic fossils (SHAW and WASSERBURG, 1985; GRANDJEAN et al., 1987, 1988; GRANDJEAN and ALBARÈDE 1989) stressed the dramatic increase of REE concentration in fish bones from very low levels in apatite from living animals to hundreds of parts per million in fossils. The enrichment occurs

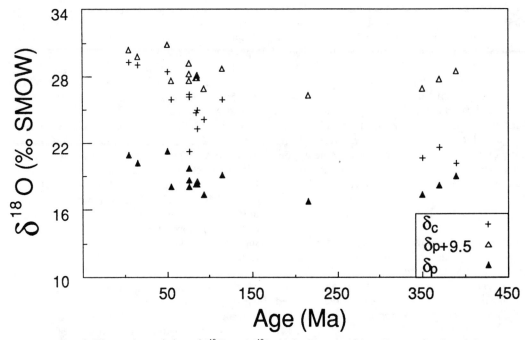

FIG. 3. The secular variation of $\delta^{18}O_p$ and $\delta^{18}O_c$ in fossil marine fishes. Empty triangles mark estimates of $\delta^{18}O_c$ from $\delta^{18}O_p$ ($\delta^{18}O_c(est) = \delta^{18}O_p + 9.5$). Note the good agreement between the estimated and measured $\delta^{18}O_c$ for young fishes, and the divergence between the two values (due to alteration) for older samples.

apparently very rapidly after the sinking of the fish debris to the sea floor. All these changes suggest that upon sinking to the sea floor, fish fragments undergo dissolution and replacement recrystallization. In effect *every fossil fish is a pseudomorph after a fish bone,* the original phase being hydroxy apatite and the replacing one—francolite (CFA). It is quite likely that during that replacement the iso-topic composition of oxygen both in the carbonate and the phosphate of apatite are re-equilibrated. Possibly the recrystallization is bacterially mediated (SOUDRY and CHAMPETIER, 1983) so as to reset $\delta^{18}O_p$. Fossil fish fragments may yield $\delta^{18}O_p$ values which reflect the habitat of the fishes because in most cases organisms die and are buried (and fossilized) in environments which are not dissimilar

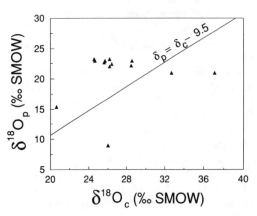

FIG. 4. Relationship between $\delta^{18}O_p$ and $\delta^{18}O_c$ in living fishes. None of the points plot on the expected line of $\delta^{18}O_p = \delta^{18}O_c - 9.5$.

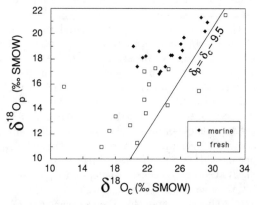

FIG. 5. Relationship between $\delta^{18}O_p$ and $\delta^{18}O_c$ in fossil marine and fresh-water fishes. Note that in most cases measured $\delta^{18}O_c$ is lower than expected from the ($\delta^{18}O_p = \delta^{18}O_c - 9.5$) relationship.

to their life environments. In oscillating or schizo-haline environments on the one hand, and at river mouths on the other, one may, however, expect cases in which a marine fish would undergo re-crystallization in fresh water or vice versa. In our listing of "misbehaved" fossils we cite several such possibilities (the Tertiary sharks *Squatina* and *Striatolamia,* the Triassic *Hybodus,* the Cretaceous *Pachyamia*).

The variation of $\delta^{18}O_c$ with time (Fig. 3) also demonstrates the susceptibility of oxygen in the carbonate site of apatite to isotopic alteration. Whereas the changes in $\delta^{18}O_p$ are a rather smooth function of age, $\delta^{18}O_c$ fluctuates sharply. A similar conclusion is suggested by comparing $\delta^{18}O_p$ and $\delta^{18}O_c$ of two specimens of *Coccosteus* from the Middle Devonian of Scotland (samples 151 and 153, Table 2). The two samples show a rather small difference in their $\delta^{18}O_p$ values (15.8 vs. 14.3) whereas the respective $\delta^{18}O_c$ are almost 13 per mil apart (11.6 and 24.4, respectively).

### Freshwater fishes

*The Orcadian Basin fishes.* Three fossils (samples 152–154) come from the very well-studied Fish-Beds of the Orcadian Basin (Achanarras and Wey-dale) in Scotland (TREWIN, 1985, 1986). The habitat of these fishes has been interpreted as rather large, more than 65 m deep, post-orogenic fresh-water lakes. The fish mass mortality has been explained as being caused by hydrogen sulfide poisoning; the high $H_2S$ content of the bottom water is also the suggested cause of the scarcity of bottom dwelling fishes as compared to the abundance of surface wa-ter dwellers. Thus, the very abundant *Dipterus* and *Coccosteus* (samples 152 and 153) were both swim-ming in the upper waters of the lake (TREWIN, 1986), whereas *Homosteus* (154) is interpreted as a bottom feeder. Indeed, the $\delta^{18}O_p$ values of the fish bones are 14.3 and 15.5 for the two surface swim-mers, and 18.1 for the *Homosteus.*

Scotland was located between 20 and 30°S of the Devonian equator (SMITH *et al.,* 1973). The Or-cadian lakes were fed by waters from the surround-ing mountains. TREWIN (1986) notes that "the landscape of the Devonian landmass was still mountainous," but the accompanying sketch sug-gests rather low mountains (see sketch in TREWIN, 1985, 1986). The isotopic composition of the De-vonian lake water may be constrained within nar-row limits. In fresh-water lakes density stratification depends only on the temperature-depth gradient. One can hence assume that the difference in $\delta^{18}O_p$

between bottom dwelling fish and surface dwellers (paleontologically identified) depends only on tem-perature difference at constant $\delta^{18}O_w$. From Eqn. (1) $\delta^{18}O_w$ can be derived for any given temperature. The lower limit for $\delta^{18}O_w$ is calculated from $\delta^{18}O_p$ of the bottom dweller *Homosteus* assuming a tem-perature of 4°C (the lowest bottom temperature of any fresh-water lake, HUTCHINSON, 1957). The up-per limit can be estimated from $\delta^{18}O_p$ of the surface dwellers and an assumption that the temperature of the upper water body was 37°C. Hence, $\delta^{18}O_w$ of the Orcadian water was within the limits of $-7$ $< \delta^{18}O_w < -3$. Conditions can be further con-strained. Near-freezing winter temperatures have probably prevailed within land masses even during the more "equable" stages of Earth history (SLOAN and BARRON, 1990). Hence, bottom water tem-perature was close to 4°C, and $\delta^{18}O_w$ was closer to the lower estimate of $-7$. If one assumes $\delta^{18}O_w = -6$ (SMOW), then the estimated temperatures would be higher by about 4°C. Accordingly, the temperature of the water in which the surface dwellers lived was between 20 and 15°C. The emerging set of conditions is rather typical of a ver-tical temperature distribution in temperate lakes during summer stratification and stagnation (HUTCHINSON, 1957). The relationships between the three Orcadian fishes are thus in good agreement with the expected values and do not suggest post-depositional alteration.

*The young and isotopically light fishes.* The broader range of $\delta^{18}O_p$ in young fresh-water fishes could also be interpreted as a result of late, post-depositional changes. There is, however, no reason why fish bones which were formed with a broad range of $\delta^{18}O_p$ should converge to a narrower one with time. Moreover, $\delta^{18}O_p$ of pre-Cretaceous fresh-water fish is higher than about $+12$, whereas in younger fossils values as low as $+6$ are reached. Such a pattern is not to be expected if all samples underwent increasing post-depositional re-equili-bration with time.

It must be stressed that the broad range of $\delta^{18}O_p$ of young fresh-water fishes reflects a broad sampling scheme; thus, the most $^{18}O$-depleted samples are fishes from Lakes Baikal, Lake Inari in Finland, and a lake in Idaho. We shall now consider the expected change with latitude of $\delta^{18}O$ values in a solid authigenic precipitate—carbonate or phos-phate. The isotopic composition of oxygen in rain-water changes regularly with latitude, altitude, dis-tance from the coast, and intensity of precipitation. An early set of worldwide data has been analyzed by DANSGAARD (1964) who showed that $\delta^{18}O$ of precipitation is linearly correlated with the annual mean surface air temperature. Actually this correlation is a combined summary of the so-called latitude, altitude, and amount effects, and the suggested change is one of 0.69 per mil per one °C. The DANSGAARD (1964) relationship has been strongly influenced by high latitude stations, whereas JOUZEL et al. (1987) noted that the relationship essentially vanishes at high temperatures. A multiple linear regression analysis of a larger data set suggested to YURTSEVER and GAT (1981) that for continental areas $\delta^{18}O$ decreases by about 0.1 to 0.15 per degree latitude, and since temperature decreases with increasing latitude, $\delta^{18}O$ decreases by about 0.25 to 0.4 per mil per °C. The best fit suggested by YURTSEVER and GAT (1981, p. 116) is given in Eqn. (2):

$$\delta^{18}O_w = -11.99 + 0.338t \qquad (2)$$

where $\delta^{18}O_w$ is the weighted mean average isotopic composition of precipitation water, and $t$ is average monthly temperature at the collection site. The isotopic composition of the solid should not change with latitude similarly with $\delta^{18}O_w$, since both $\delta^{18}O_c$ and $\delta^{18}O_p$ are related to temperature by an expression of the type of Eqn. (1). In both cases $\delta^{18}O$ of the solid ($\delta^{18}O_s$) is related to $t$ by a function of the type

$$t = A - 4.3(\delta^{18}O_s - \delta^{18}O_w). \qquad (3)$$

For both apatite and calcite the slope of Eqn. (3) in the low temperature region is $-4.3$; i.e., $\delta^{18}O$ will increase by $1/4.3 = 0.23/°C$. By combining Eqns. (2) and (3) one obtains the expected change of the isotopic composition of a solid precipitated from a meteoric water body as a function of the average air temperature in the area where that water body exists:

$$\delta^{18}O_s = 0.10t - 12 + A/4.3 \qquad (4)$$

where $A$ is the same constant as in Eqn. (3). Thus the $\delta^{18}O$ of calcitic or apatitic shells varies rather little with latitude (or surface temperature). The present-day air surface temperature gradient between the equator and latitude 70° of about 30°C would result in a $\delta^{18}O$ range in apatite (or calcite) of about 3 per mil. In the case of Cretaceous or Eocene climates, when the Equator-to-Pole surface temperature gradients were substantially reduced to perhaps one-half the present-day gradient, (BARRON, 1983; SLOAN and BARRON, 1990), this would result in an even smaller variation in the oxygen isotopic composition of shells and skeletons.

The narrow range of $\delta^{18}O_p$ of pre-Pleistocene fishes should hence be considered as largely con-

firming our expectations. It is the very $^{18}O$ depleted fish fossils of young geological age that require explanation. The explanation may be provided by another regularity of the isotope systematics of the hydrological cycle, which has been referred to (YURTSEVER and GAT, 1981) as the altitude effect. Rain at the cool, high altitudes is depleted in $^{18}O$ in comparison to coastal rains. In the present postorogenic period, when high altitudes are abundant, many water bodies (such as lakes) in low regions get their water supply from water in the mountains. Such water bodies are then characterized by "too light" water in comparison with the values expected from surface temperatures. Thus, at Lake Baikal the average monthly surface temperature is about 10°C; hence, the expected $\delta^{18}O_w$ would be about $-8.5$ to $-9$. In fact $\delta^{18}O$ of Lake Baikal water is about $-16$, as the source of water is from rain falling upon the surrounding (up to 3000 m high) mountains (the Barguzin Range, the Sayan) not upon Lake Baikal itself, hence the very low $\delta^{18}O$ values of Lake Baikal fish bones (+6 to +9). They were deposited from a combination of both $^{18}O$-depleted and warm waters.

If high standing mountains are a relatively short-lived phenomenon in Earth history, and if most of Phanerozoic time has not been post orogenic, then it should not be surprising that for most of that time the range of $\delta^{18}O_p$ in fossil fishes is indeed rather narrow. Following that logic the $^{18}O$-depleted fishes between 70 and 50 Ma ago (samples 62, 73, 77, 78) from Wyoming and Montana may reflect conditions which followed the Laramide orogeny.

The above discussion is not an attempt to deny that part of the difference in the spread of $\delta^{18}O_p$ values may be due to a bias in sampling: in present day conditions we know there is a Lake Baikal; hence, one goes and samples it. In the geological past such sampling is much less likely. On the other hand, the opposing effects of temperature of precipitation and water composition upon $\delta^{18}O_p$ (and $\delta^{18}O_c$) should make the observed pattern less surprising.

## SUMMARY

Isotopic analysis of oxygen in the phosphate of fossil marine and fresh-water fish is apparently the best paleo-environmental recorder among sedimentary phosphates. Fish are clearly a better recorder than phosphorites. This has been demonstrated by the isotopic analysis of phosphorites and fish from the Miocene Monterey Formation of California (KASTNER et al., 1990). The $\delta^{18}O_p$ values for phosphorites from the Monterey (14.9 to 20.8) are significantly lower and have a larger range than those of Miocene fish bones from the same and related formations (19.9 to 21.5). Thus, the temperatures which are indicated by fish bone analysis are both lower and "more reasonable" than the temperatures derived from the analysis of phosphorites.

The range of temperatures indicated by the isotopic analysis of $\delta^{18}O_p$ in phosphorites seems clearly too high for surface or bottom temperatures of ancient seas and lakes (SHEMESH *et al.,* 1988; KOLODNY and LUZ, 1991). They are, however, quite acceptable as burial-diagenetic temperatures or temperatures of incipient metamorphism. In contrast, the temperatures indicated by fish-bone analysis are compatible with what might be expected from surface environments.

When discussing our results above, we stressed the problems one encounters upon critical examination of our data. These include the possibility of diagenetic changes, "vital effects," and possible long-range preservation problems. Thus, it is quite clear that $\delta^{18}O_p$ in fishes is not an *ideal* recorder. On the other hand it is quite possible that it is the *best* recorder presently available. The final judgment on how good it is in comparison with other paleothermometers will have to wait until a sufficiently large data base is available for inter-calibration.

*Acknowledgements*—The reported results could not have been obtained without the generous cooperation of many paleontologists who contributed the samples and shared with us their knowledge. For some of them that meant sacrificing fossils for irreversible destruction. We hope that our results do at least partly compensate those friends for their loss. Among the contributors were Drs. B. Buchardt, Forey of the BM, D. Goujet of MNH, M. C. McKenna and J. Maisey of the AMNH, J. D. Stewart of LACM, A. Tintori, and N. H. Trewin of the University of Aberdeen. We wish to single out A. G. Fisher and F. Albarède who not only shared samples with us, but also enlightened us in many aspects of result interpretation. The analytical work was carried out by R. Nissan with her usual devotion.

## REFERENCES

ALTSCHULER Z. S., CISNEY E. A. and BARLOW I. H. (1952) X-ray evidence of the nature of carbonate-apatite (abstr.). *Geol. Soc. Amer. Bull.* **63,** 1230–1231.

ARTHUR M. A., DEAN W. E., POLLASTRO R., SCHOLLE P. A. and CLAYPOOL G. E. (1985) A comparative geochemical study of two transgressive pelagic limestone units, Cretaceous Western Interior basin, U.S. In *Fine-grained Deposits and Bio-facies of the Cretaceous Western Interior Seaways: Evidence of Cyclic Sedimentary Processes* L. M. PRATT, E. G. KAUFFMAN and F. B. ZELT (eds); *Society of Economic Paleontologists and Mineralogists 1985 Midyear meeting, Golden Colorado, Field trip guidebook* **4,** pp. 16–27.

BACQUET G., VO QUANG T., BONEL G. and VIGNOLES M. (1980) Resonance paramagnetique du centre F dans les fluorapatites carbonatees de type B. *J. Solid State Chem.* **33,** 189–195.

BARRON E. J. (1983) A warm, equable Cretaceous: the nature of the problem. *Earth-Sci. Rev.* **19,** 305–338.

BENMORE R. A., COLEMAN M. L. and MCARTHUR J. M. (1983) Origin of sedimentary francolite from its sulphur and carbon isotope composition. *Nature* **302,** 516–518.

BERNAT M. (1975) Les isotopes de l'uranium et du thorium et les terres rares dans l'environnement marin. *Cah. ORSTOM Ser. Geol.* **7,** 68–83.

BORNEMAN-STARYNKEVITCH I. D. and BELOV N. V. (1940) Isomorphic substitutions in carbonate-apatite. *Compte Rendus (Dokl.) de l'Academie des Sciences de l'URSSS* **26,** 804–806.

CARROLL R. L. (1988) *Vertebrate Paleontology and Evolution.* W. H. Freeman and Co.

CRAIG H. (1965) The measurement of oxygen isotope paleotemperatures. In *Stable Isotopes in Oceanographic Studies and Paleotemperatures.* (ed. E. TONGIORGI), pp. 161–182. Consiglio Nazionale delle Richerche, Laboratorio de Geologia Nucleare. Pisa.

CROWLEY T. J. (1991) Past $CO_2$ changes and tropical climates. *Palaeogeogr., Palaeoclimatol, Palaeoecol.* (in press).

DANSGAARD W. (1964) Stable isotopes in precipitation. *Tellus* **16,** 436–468.

DOUGLAS R. G. and SAVIN S. M. (1975) Oxygen and carbon isotope analyses of Tertiary and Cretaceous microfossils from Shatsky Rise and other sites in the North Pacific Ocean. *DSDP Init. Rep.* **32,** 509–520.

DOUGLAS R. G. and WOODRUFF F. (1981) Deep sea benthic foraminifera. In *The Sea, Vol. 7* (ed. C. EMILIANI), pp. 1233–1327. Wiley-Interscience.

EMILIANI C. (1955) Pleistocene temperatures. *J. Geol.* **63,** 538–578.

EPSTEIN S. and LOWENSTAM H. A. (1953) Temperature-shell growth relations of recent and interglacial Pleistocene shoal-water biota from Bermuda. *J. Geol.* **61,** 424–438.

EPSTEIN S. and MAYEDA T. (1953) Variations in $O^{18}$ content of waters from natural sources. *Geochim. Cosmochim. Acta* **27,** 213–224.

EPSTEIN S., BUCHSBAUM R., LOWENSTAM H. A. and UREY H. C. (1951) Carbonate-water isotopic temperature scale. *Geol. Soc. Amer. Bull.* **62,** 417–425.

EPSTEIN S., BUCHSBAUM H. A., LOWENSTAM H. A. and UREY H. C. (1953) Revised carbonate-water isotopic temperature scale. *Geol. Soc. Amer. Bull.* **64,** 1315–1326.

GLENN C. R., ARTHUR M. A., YEH H. W. and BURNETT W. C. (1988) Carbon isotopic composition and lattice-bound carbonate of Peru-Chile margin phosphorites. In *The Origin of Marine Phosphorite. The Results of the R. V. Robert D. Conrad Cruise 23-06 to the Peru Shelf.* (eds. W. C. BURNETT and P. N. FROEHLICH); *Mar. Geol.* **80,** pp. 287–307.

GRANDJEAN P. and ALBARÈDE F. (1989) Ion probe measurement of rare earth elements in biogenic phosphates. *Geochim. Cosmochim. Acta* **53,** 3179–3183.

GRANDJEAN P., CAPPETTA H., MICHARD A. and ALBARÈDE F. (1987) The assessment of REE patterns and $^{143}Nd/^{144}Nd$ ratios in fish remains. *Earth Planet. Sci. Lett.* **84,** 181–196.

GRANDJEAN P., CAPPETTA H. and ALBARÈDE F. (1988)

The REE and $\epsilon$Nd of 40–70 Ma old fish debris from the West-African platform. *Geophys. Res. Lett.* **15**(4), 389–392.

HUTCHINSON G. E. (1957) *A Treatise on Limnology.* John Wiley and Sons, London.

JOUZEL J., RUSSEL G. L., SUOZZO R. J., KOSTER R. D., WHITE J. W. C. and BROECKER W. S. (1987) Simulations of the HDO and $H_2^{18}O$ atmospheric cycles using the NASA GISS general circulation model: the seasonal cycle for present-day conditions. *J. Geophys. Res.* **92**, 14,739–14,760.

KASTNER M., GARRISON R. E., KOLODNY Y., SHEMESH A. and REIMERS C. E. (1990) Simultaneous changes of oxygen isotopes in $PO_4^{-3}$ and $CO_3^{-2}$ in apatite, with emphasis on the Monterey Formation California. In *Genesis of Neogene to Modern Phosphorites* (eds. BURNETT W. C. and S. R. RIGGS), pp. 312–324. Cambridge University Press.

KOLODNY Y. and KAPLAN I. R. (1970) Carbon and oxygen isotopes in apatite $CO_2$ and coexisting calcite from sedimentary phosphorite. *J. Sediment. Petrol.* **40**, 954–959.

KOLODNY Y. and LUZ B. (1991) Phosphate deposits, formation and diagenetic history. In *Isotopic Signatures and Sedimentary Records* (eds. N. CLAUER and S. CHAUDHURI). Springer-Verlag (in press).

KOLODNY Y. and RAAB M. (1988) Oxygen isotopes in phosphatic fish remains from Israel: paleothermometry of tropical Cretaceous and Tertiary shelf waters. *Palaeogeogr., Palaeoclimatol., Palaeoecol.* **64**, 59–67.

KOLODNY Y., LUZ B. and NAVON O. (1983) Oxygen isotope variations in phosphate of biogenic apatite. I: Fish bone apatite—rechecking the rules of the game. *Earth Planet. Sci. Lett.* **64**, 398–404.

LONGINELLI A. (1965) Oxygen isotopic composition of orthophosphate from shells of living marine organisms. *Nature* **207**, 716–719.

LONGINELLI A. and NUTI S. (1973a) Revised phosphate-water isotopic temperature scale. *Earth Planet. Sci. Lett.* **19**, 373–376.

LONGINELLI A. and NUTI S. (1973b) Oxygen isotope measurements of phosphate from fish teeth and bones. *Earth Planet. Sci. Lett.* **20**, 337–340.

LOWENSTAM H. A. and EPSTEIN S. (1954) Paleotemperatures of the Post-Aptian Cretaceous as determined by the oxygen isotope method *J. Geol.* **62**, 207–248.

LOWENSTAM H. A. and WEINER S. (1989) *On Biomineralization.* Oxford University Press, New York.

LUZ B., KOLODNY Y. and KOVACH J. (1984) Oxygen isotope variations in phosphate of biogenic apatites, III. Conodonts. *Earth Planet. Sci. Lett.* **69**, 255–262.

MACFARLANE J. M. (1923) *The Evolution and Distribution of Fishes.* The Macmillan Co.

MANABE S. and BRYAN K. (1984) $CO_2$-induced change in a coupled ocean-atmosphere model and its paleoclimatic implications. *J. Geophys. Res.* **90**, 11,689–11,707.

MCARTHUR J. M., COLEMAN M. L. and BREMNER J. M. (1980) Carbon and oxygen isotopic composition of structural carbonate in sedimentary francolite. *J. Geol. Soc. London* **137**, 669–673.

MCARTHUR J. M., BENMORE R. A., COLEMAN M. L., SOLDI C., YEH H.-W. and O'BRIEN G. W. (1986) Stable isotopic characterisation of francolite formation. *Earth Planet. Sci. Lett.* **77**, 20–34.

NELSON J. S. (1976). *Fishes of the World.* John Wiley and Sons.

NEWESELY H. (1989) Fossil bone apatite. *Appl. Geochem.* **4**, 233–245.

PALMER A. R. (1983) The decade of North American geology 1983 geologic time scale. *Geology* **11**, 503–504.

PRATT L. M. (1984) Influence of paleoenvironmental factors on preservation of organic matter in middle Cretaceous Greenhorn Formation of Pueblo, Colorado. *Amer. Assoc. Petrol. Geol. Bull.* **68**, 1146–1159.

PRATT L. M. (1985) Isotopic studies of organic matter and carbonate in rocks of the Greenhorn marine cycle. In *Fine-grained Depositsa and Biofacies of the Cretaceous Western Interior Seaway: evidence of Cyclic Sedimentary Processes* (eds. L. M. PRATT, E. G. KAUFFMAN and F. B. ZELT); *Society of Economic Paleontologists and Mineralogists 1985 Midyear meeting; Golden, Colorado, Field trip guidebook* **4**, pp. 38–48.

RYE D. M. and SOMMER M. A. (1980) Reconstructing paleotemperature and paleosalinity regimes with oxygen isotopes. In *Skeletal Growth of Equatic Organisms* (eds. D. C. RHOADS and R. A. LUTZ), pp. 169–202. New York, Plenum Press.

SAVIN S. M. (1977) The history of the Earth's surface temperature during the past 100 million years. *Ann. Rev. Earth Planet. Sci.* **5**, 319–355.

SAVIN S. M. (1982) Stable isotopes in climatic reconstructions. In *Climate in Earth History*, pp. 164–171. National Academy Press.

SCHOLLE P. A. (1977) Chalk diagenesis and its relation to petroleum exploration: oil from chalks, a modern miracle. *Amer. Assoc. Petrol. Geol. Bull.* **61**, 982–1009.

SCHOLLE, P. A. and KAUFFMAN E. G. (1975) Paleoecological implications of stable isotope data from Upper Cretaceous limestones and fossils from the U. S. Western Interior (abstr.). *North America Paleontology Convention* II, 24.

SHACKLETON N. J. and KENNETT J. P. (1975) Paleotemperature history of the Cenozoic and the initiation of Antarctic glaciation: oxygen and carbon isotope analyses in DSDP Sites 277, 279, and 281. *DSDP Init. Rep.* **29**, 743–755.

SHAW H. F. and WASSERBURG G. J. (1985) Sm-Nd in marine carbonates and phosphorites: implications for Nd isotopes in seawater and crustal ages. *Geochim. Cosmochim. Acta* **49**, 503–508.

SHEMESH A. (1990) Crystallinity and diagenesis of sedimentary apatites. *Geochim. Cosmochim. Acta* **54**, 2433–2438.

SHEMESH A., KOLODNY Y. and LUZ B. (1983) Oxygen isotope variations in phosphate of biogenic apatites. II. Phosphorite rocks. *Earth Planet. Sci. Lett.* **64**, 405–416.

SHEMESH A., KOLODNY Y. and LUZ B. (1988) Isotope geochemistry of oxygen and carbon in phosphate and carbonate of phosphorite francolite. *Geochim. Cosmochim. Acta* **52**, 2565–2572.

SILVERMAN S. R., FUYAT R. K. and WEISER J. D. (1959) Quantitative determination of calcite associated with carbonate bearing apatite. *Amer. Mineral.* **37**, 211–222.

SLOAN L. C. and BARRON E. J. (1990) "Equable" climates during Earth history? *Geology* **18**, 489–492.

SMITH A. G., BRIDEN J. C. and DREWRY G. E. (1973) Phanerozoic world maps. In *Organisms and Continents through Time* (ed. N. F. HUGHES); *Spec. Paper Paleontol.* **12.**

SOUDRY D. and CHAMPETIER Y. (1983) Microbial processes in the Negev phosphorites (southern Israel). *Sedimentol.* **30,** 411–423.

TINTORI A., MUSCIO G. and NARDON S. (1985) The Triassic fossil fishes localities in Italy. *Riv. It. Paleontol. Strat.* **91,** 197–210.

TOURTELOT H. A. and RYE R. O. (1969) Distribution of oxygen and carbon isotopes in fossils of Late Cretaceous age, Western Interior region of North America. *Geol. Soc. Amer. Bull.* **80,** 1903–1922.

TREWIN N. H. (1985) Mass mortalities of Devonian fish—the Achanarras Fish Bed, Caithness. *Geology Today* (Mar–Apr.), 45–49.

TREWIN N. H. (1986) Palaeoecology and sedimentology of the Achanarras fish bed of the Middle Old Red Sandstone, Scotland. *Trans. Roy. Soc. Edinburgh. Earth Sci.* **77,** 21–46.

TUDGE A. P. (1960) A method of analysis of oxygen isotopes of orthophosphates: its use in the measurement of paleotemperatures. *Geochim. Cosmochim. Acta* **18,** 81–93.

UREY H. C., LOWENSTAM H. A., EPSTEIN S. and MCKINNEY U. (1951) Measurements of paleotemperatures and temperatures of the Upper Cretaceous of England, Denmark and the south-eastern U.S. *Geol. Soc. Amer. Bull.* **62,** 399–416.

WRIGHT E. K. (1987) Stratification and paleocirculation in the Late Cretaceous Western Interior Seaway of North America *Geol. Soc. Amer. Bull.* **99,** 480–490.

YURTSEVER Y. and GAT J. R. (1981) Atmospheric waters. In *Stable Isotope Hydrology,* (eds. J. R. GAT and R. GONFIANTINI), Chap. 6, Tech. Rept. Ser., Intl. Atom. Energy Agency, Vienna 210, 103–142.

Stable Isotope Geochemistry: A Tribute to Samuel Epstein
© The Geochemical Society, Special Publication No. 3, 1991
Editors: H. P. Taylor, Jr., J. R. O'Neil and I. R. Kaplan

# Dolomitization of the Hope Gate Formation (north Jamaica) by seawater: Reassessment of mixing-zone dolomite

Lynton S. Land

Department of Geological Sciences, University of Texas, Austin TX 78713, U.S.A.

**Abstract**—Deposition of the Hope Gate Formation, which forms a prominent reef terrace along the coastline of north Jamaica, took place near the Pliocene-Pleistocene boundary, based on $^{87}Sr/^{86}Sr$ ratios of a mineralogically unaltered biolithite. $^{87}Sr/^{86}Sr$ ratios of some isolated dolomite samples are consistent with coeval seawater values, but most samples are less radiogenic. Dolomite crystals are characterized by relatively narrow ranges in strontium concentration ($300 \pm 50$ ppm) and $\delta^{18}O$ ($+3.1 \pm 0.4$ per mil PDB), both of which are consistent with precipitation from seawater (using a $D_{Sr} = 0.06$), but not with precipitation from mixed water. The observed range in $^{87}Sr/^{86}Sr$ can be explained if both surface seawater and seawater that had interacted with underlying Miocene chalk were responsible for dolomite precipitation. Lowered $\delta^{13}C$ values of Hope Gate dolomite ($+0.9$) relative to precursor biolithites ($+3.0$) suggest that the oxidation of organic carbon, possibly accompanying sulfate reduction, also modified the seawater that caused dolomitization. Because the concentration of magnesium in seawater exceeds the concentration of either calcium or bicarbonate, and because seawater is nearly calcite-saturated, precipitation of dolomite causes undersaturation with $CaCO_3$. Replacement of $CaCO_3$ by dolomite thus proceeds automatically if the difficulty in nucleating and/or growing dolomite can be overcome. Porosity is generated because the volume of dolomite precipitated is less than the volume of $CaCO_3$ dissolved as long as large amounts of new $CO_2$ are not supplied. Dolomitization by seawater can thus be self-sustaining, following porosity channels generated by the process itself, as long as the seawater "pump" is maintained.

## INTRODUCTION

THE ZONE OF MIXING between seawater and meteoric water is one hydrogeochemical environment which has been advocated to account for extensively dolomitized rocks. The Hope Gate Formation of north Jamaica (LAND, 1973) was one of the first examples described where mixing-zone dolomitization was proposed. Although the applicability of the mixing-zone model to larger scale, more ancient examples has been questioned (*e.g.,* HARDIE, 1987), no author, to my knowledge, has proposed an alternative explanation for the Hope Gate Formation. Additionally, many other Quaternary and late Cenozoic dolomites, similar to the Hope Gate in both petrography and geochemistry, have subsequently been described (SUPKO, 1977; SIBLEY, 1980; KALDI and GIDMAN, 1982; WARD and HALLEY, 1985; AHARON *et al.,* 1987; HUMPHREY, 1988). Most authors have advocated dolomitization in the mixing-zone for these occurrences, but some have proposed dolomitization by normal or evaporated seawater. Because of virtually identical petrography and geochemistry, a single explanation presumably applies to all.

Two new lines of evidence have stimulated a reassessment of the mixing-zone hypothesis as applied to the Hope Gate Formation. First, $^{87}Sr/^{86}Sr$ ratios not only "date" the time of deposition of Hope Gate biolithites to approximately the Plio-Pleistocene boundary, older than was previously

assumed, but $^{87}Sr/^{86}Sr$ analyses of the dolomite also prove that significant amounts of yet "older" strontium were incorporated in most of the dolomite which now constitutes the rocks. The allochthonous strontium must have been derived from underlying units. Secondly, the discovery of dolomite forming in modern Jamaican reefs from near-normal seawater (MITCHELL *et al.,* 1987) suggests other models. The possibilities that Hope Gate dolomite is marine in origin, or that an original marine precipitate was modified by subsequent interaction with meteoric water, must also be considered.

## LATE CENOZOIC EVOLUTION OF NORTH JAMAICA

During the Cenozoic, central and western Jamaica consisted of a carbonate platform which accumulated mostly foraminiferal packstones and wackestones, including local scleractinian biolithites. Toward the end of the Oligocene and beginning of the Miocene, a shelf margin approximately 10 km south of the present north coast shed reef debris onto a north-facing slope on which pelagic chalk (the Miocene Montpelier Formation) accumulated. $^{87}Sr/^{86}Sr$ ratios of chalk which is subaerially exposed, and chalk which has been recovered in piston cores taken offshore in water depths up to 4200 m (LAND, 1979), range from .7083 to .7088 (Table 1). Because it is unlikely that erosion has removed much overburden, the highest ratios probably record the end

Table 1. Analytical data for Miocene chalk

| Sample | $^{87}Sr/^{86}Sr$ | $\delta^{13}C$ | $\delta^{18}O$ | % dolomite |
|---|---|---|---|---|
| Onshore outcrop sample | | | | |
| A | 0.70845 | −8.0 | −3.5 | 0 |
| F | 0.70834 | +0.6 | +1.7 | 0 |
| M′ | 0.70851 | −0.3 | +0.1 | 5 |
| 8a | 0.70883 | 0.0 | −1.2 | 0 |
| 8c | 0.70883 | −1.7 | −0.9 | 0 |
| S2 | 0.70847 | 1.9 | 3.6 | 100 |
| Offshore samples | | | | |
| 477 | 0.70847 | +1.3 | +0.8 | 0 |
| 628 | 0.70838 | +1.4 | +0.3 | 0 |
| 458 | 0.70850 | +1.3 | +0.3 | 0 |

Sample locations from Fig. 1 and LAND, 1979, his Fig. 1.

of sedimentation, perhaps as the result of uplift, which is thought to have occurred in Late Middle Miocene at approximately 12 Ma (HENDRY, 1987; LAND, 1991). Biolithites of the Hope Gate Formation were deposited unconformably on the Miocene Chalk (Fig. 1), which has undergone considerable meteoric modification since uplift (LAND, 1979).

## METHODS

$^{87}Sr/^{86}Sr$ data were obtained by dynamic multicollection on samples immersed for 72 hours in three rinses with 0.2 N sodium acetate to remove exchangable strontium, rinsed several times with distilled water, and dissolved in dilute acetic acid prior to isolation of strontium by column chromatography. Replication is better than 30 ppm, and within-run precision is better than 20 ppm. Carbon and oxygen isotopes were determined by phosphoric acid digestion at 25°C relative to PDB, and are reproducible to ±0.2 per mil. Mineralogy was determined by X-ray diffraction. Calcium, magnesium, and strontium were analyzed by inductively coupled argon plasma atomic emission spectroscopy, and replicates and multiple analyses of the NBS #88b standard indicate precision better than ±5%.

## THE HOPE GATE FORMATION

### Age

In 1968, while searching for fossil sclerosponges (HARTMAN and GOREAU, 1970) the late T. F. Goreau chanced upon a small outcrop of "chalky" *Halimeda* grainstone (quarry B-1 of LAND, 1973, his Fig. 1), which contains deep water species including *Halimeda cryptica.* The grainstone appears to have been a local sand channel within the reef, which became so densely cemented by Mg-calcite marine cement as to almost entirely preclude subsequent diagenesis. Not only are the primary textures, mineralogy, and bulk chemistry of both allochems and cement preserved in these samples, but the original $^{87}Sr/^{86}Sr$ cannot be very different

from the ocean in which Hope Gate reefs grew. Except for this small outcrop, the Hope Gate formation is entirely dolomite plus calcite.

Fourteen analyses from several samples, using various dissolution techniques involving various pretreatments to minimize extraneous strontium, yield an $^{87}Sr/^{86}Sr$ ratio of 0.709064 ± 0.000014. When compared to the value for modern seawater obtained during the interval when these analyses were being accumulated (0.709167 ± 0.000016, 16 analyses), it is clear from known secular changes in ocean $^{87}Sr/^{86}Sr$ (DePAOLO, 1986; HODELL et al., 1990) that the seaward-most exposures of the Hope Gate Formation must have been deposited in latest Pliocene or earliest Pleistocene time. Exposure surfaces of the Hope Gate formation exhibit extensive microkarst, local karst collapse features, and locally extensive horizontal (water-table) caves which display multiple levels of occupation. These geomorphic features are much more in accord with exposure for approximately 2 Ma subsequent to deposition as evidenced by the $^{87}Sr/^{86}Sr$ data, than would be true if the Hope Gate had a late Pleistocene age as previously supposed (LAND, 1973).

### Petrography

The petrography of Hope Gate biolithites is virtually identical to other late Cenozoic dolomites which have been described (e.g., SIBLEY, 1982). Fine-grained, sub-micron-sized dolomite mimetically replaces red algae and benthic foraminifera, and single crystals replace echinoderm allochems, faithfully preserving internal microarchitecture (Fig. 2). Mimetic replacement suggests that dolomite replacement occurred while the allochems were still Mg-calcite, and that dolomite nucleated syntaxially on the skeletal crystals and grew into voids (some submicroscopic) generated by dissolution of the Mg-

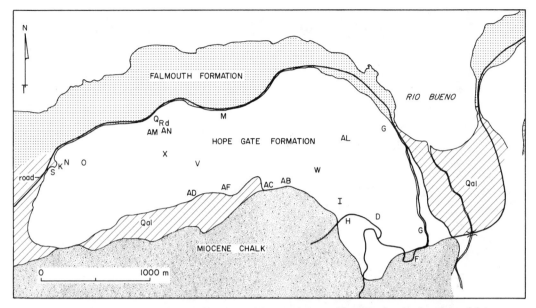

FIG. 1. Map of the study area along the north central coast of Jamaica showing locations of the samples analyzed. Hope Gate reefs form a geomorphic terrace deposited unconformably on chalk of the Middle Miocene Montpelier Formation. The Hope Gate Formation is overlain unconformably by the Falmouth Formation, a reef terrace formed 125,000 years ago during the last interglacial stage when sea level was six meters above its present level.

calcite substrate. Similarly, originally micritic areas are preferentially dolomitized. Since Mg-calcite micrite dominates modern Jamaican biolithites (*e.g.*, LAND and MOORE, 1980), epitaxial nucleation of dolomite on primary Mg-calcite is again suggested (see MITCHELL *et al.*, 1987, their Fig. 4).

The coarsest-grained (<100 microns) "limpid" dolomite isopachously lines aragonite dissolution voids and large primary intergranular pores, many of which were subsequently filled by spar calcite. The average chemistry of the spar calcite ($\delta^{18}O$ = −3.5, $\delta^{13}C$ = −6.7, $^{87}Sr/^{86}Sr$ = 0.70884) is consistent with precipitation from meteoric water, some of the $CaCO_3$ being derived autochthonously from dissolution of aragonite within the reefs themselves, but most being allochthonous from the Miocene chalk.

The presence of intimately associated "sparry" calcite and "limpid" dolomite cements (ignoring minor subsequent cave and soil features), together with relatively low strontium and sodium concentrations of the dolomite, constituted the primary petrographic and geochemical arguments for mixing-zone dolomitization (LAND, 1973). Rare alternating zones of calcite and dolomite (LAND, 1973, his Fig. 9; WARD and HALLEY, 1985, their Fig. 5; HUMPHREY, 1988, his Fig. 4) seem to support the hypothesis that precipitation of limpid dolomite was

associated with meteoric influx. But the volume of "limpid" dolomite in the reefs is small, and alternating zones of calcite and dolomite are rare. It is the origin of the fine-grained mimetic dolomite which preceeded the pore-filling dolomite and spar calcite, and which constitutes most of the dolomite in the rocks, which is the primary issue.

## FIRST-CYCLE MIXING-ZONE PRECIPITATION OF DOLOMITE

Table 2 presents data collected subsequent to 1973, mostly from localities shown in Fig. 1. In order to test the hypothesis that Hope Gate dolomite was a first-cycle precipitate from mixtures of seawater and meteoric water, the composition of meteoric water which might have been available to infiltrate the reefs must be constrained. Hope Gate reefs grew on uplifted Miocene chalk which was subsequently considerably modified by meteoric diagenesis (LAND, 1979). We can estimate the composition of meteoric water which accompanied diagenesis of the chalk and is hypothesized to have discharged through Hope Gate reefs. Specifically, the $^{87}Sr/^{86}Sr$ of the water would have reflected the $^{87}Sr/^{86}Sr$ of the surficial chalk. Rain infiltrating the chalk would have rapidly become saturated with the most soluble phases, probably fine nannofossils,

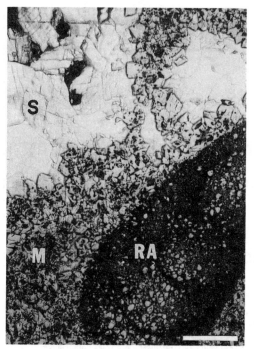

FIG. 2. Back-scattered electron micrograph of typical Hope Gate biolithite. Red algal grain (RA) was replaced mimetically by extremely fine-grained dolomite, suggesting that the dolomite directly replaced Mg-calcite. Matrix dolomite (M) is somewhat coarser-grained and probably also grew epitaxially on primary Mg-calcite micrite. Coarse "limpid" dolomite fills a moldic pore formed by the dissolution of an aragonite allochem and is overlain by spar calcite (S) of meteoric origin. A few dolomite crystals are zoned, and "hollow" rhombs are common, probably formed by epitaxial growth of a more stable phase and subsequent dissolution of the more Ca-rich and defect-ridden core. Scale bar is 100 microns.

near the land surface, and therefore would have an $^{87}Sr/^{86}Sr$ of about 0.7085 (Table 1). This is exactly the ratio found today in the Pear Tree river, a small river just east of the study area, having its headwaters in the Miocene Montpelier Formation.

The ionic composition of meteoric water in Hope Gate time, controlled by the partial pressure of $CO_2$ in the soil and the bedrock lithology, would probably have been similar to the ground water in this area today, which contains between 40 and 75 ppm dissolved calcium (O'NEIL, 1964; F.A.O., 1974). Groundwater today contains about 20 ppb Sr (O'NEIL, 1964), yielding a molar Sr/Ca ratio of about 0.00032, only slightly higher than the Sr/Ca ratio of outcropping (altered) chalk (LAND, 1979, his Fig. 4). In Hope Gate time, the recently uplifted chalk would have contained approximately 1200 ppm Sr (LAND, 1979, his Table 2), yielding a Sr/

Ca of .0014. Judging from studies of Holocene aquifers where mineralogic stabilization reactions are in progress (HARRIS and MATTHEWS, 1968; BUDD, 1988) the Sr/Ca of groundwater is several times elevated over the Sr/Ca of the host sediments because of the precipitation of low-strontium calcite. Therefore, accepting a calcium concentration of the water of about 75 ppm, and a molar Sr/Ca about three times that of the primary chalk, meteoric water in Hope Gate time is estimated to have contained at most 0.5 ppm Sr.

### $^{87}Sr/^{86}Sr$ data

Combining estimates of the Sr/Ca ratio in meteoric water infiltrating Hope Gate reefs, and its strontium isotopic composition, Fig. 3 depicts possible mixtures which could account for the observed strontium isotopic composition of Hope Gate dolomite. If Hope Gate dolomite is a first-cycle precipitate from mixtures of seawater having a $^{87}Sr/^{86}Sr$ ratio of 0.70906 and meteoric water having an $^{87}Sr/^{86}Sr$ of 0.7085, then precipitation of dolomite must have taken place from a wide range of mixtures, from essentially pure seawater to mixtures containing only a few percent seawater. Most samples, however, could have precipitated in the range of 10 to 40% seawater, similar to the range of overlapping dolomite supersaturation and calcite undersaturation predicted from theoretical solubility equilibria for mixtures of seawater and meteoric water (PLUMMER, 1975). The most radiogenic samples, those inconsistent with mixing-zone precipitation, might be explained if meteoric water had undergone rock/water interaction with the Hope Gate reefs (say by aragonite dissolution) prior to mixing, thus shifting the $^{87}Sr/^{86}Sr$ ratio of the meteoric water toward coeval seawater values. The increased strontium concentrations which would result from this scenario are not substantiated, however, and no gradients of increased $^{87}Sr/^{86}Sr$ toward the present coast (away from the Miocene chalk) have been detected (Table 2).

### Strontium concentration data

The range in strontium concentrations of Hope Gate dolomite is quite restricted (Table 2, Fig. 4). Unfortunately, lack of assurance of the distribution coefficient for strontium between dolomite and solution makes interpretation of this fact somewhat tenuous. Known Holocene marine dolomite (BEHRENS and LAND, 1972; PATTERSON, 1972; MITCHELL et al., 1987) contains approximately 600 ppm Sr. Given a constant molar Sr/Ca for seawater of

Table 2. Analytical data for Hope Gate dolomite and limestone

| Sample | $f_{Mg}$[1] | ppm Sr | $^{87}Sr/^{86}Sr$ | $\delta^{13}C$ | $\delta^{18}O$ | % dolomite[2] |
|--------|------|--------|------------|------------|------------|------------|
| Dolomite concentrates | | | | | | |
| C | | | 0.70899 | 1.0 | 3.1 | 60 |
| D | | | 0.70901 | 1.6 | 3.3 | 50 |
| G | 0.417 | 240 | 0.70901 | 0.8 | 2.9 | 45 |
| I | 0.416 | 330 | 0.70907 | 1.6 | 3.4 | 70 |
| K | 0.429 | 270 | 0.70897 | 1.6 | 3.4 | 95 |
| M | 0.419 | 270 | 0.70901 | 1.6 | 3.5 | 70 |
| Mc | 0.421 | 295 | 0.70897 | 1.1 | 3.2 | 95 |
| N | 0.419 | 295 | 0.70897 | 1.6 | 3.6 | 90 |
| Qrd | 0.387[3] | 285 | 0.70906 | −2.6 | 2.5 | 60 |
| Q30 | 0.416 | 325 | 0.70895 | 0.2 | 3.2 | 90 |
| Q40 | 0.419 | 305 | 0.70892 | 0.1 | 3.3 | 85 |
| Q45 | 0.389[3] | 340 | 0.70893 | 0.3 | 2.9 | 65 |
| W | 0.419 | 295 | 0.70904 | 0.8 | 3.2 | 45 |
| X | 0.416 | 435 | 0.70889 | 0.8 | 2.9 | 45 |
| AB | 0.346[3] | 220 | 0.70900 | −0.9 | 2.2 | 55 |
| AF | 0.421 | 270 | 0.70888 | −0.7 | 2.5 | 55 |
| AM | 0.429 | 330 | 0.70884 | 0.6 | 3.2 | 70 |
| AN | 0.435 | 325 | 0.70889 | 0.4 | 2.3 | 45 |
| Limestones | | | | | | |
| H | | | 0.70884 | −10.1 | −2.9 | trace |
| O | | | 0.70884 | −8.3 | −3.3 | 5 |
| V | | | 0.70881 | −9.4 | −3.3 | 5 |
| AC | | | 0.70881 | −4.6 | −1.6 | trace |
| AL | | | 0.70889 | −6.5 | −2.6 | trace |
| AD | | | 0.70892 | −9.6 | −2.6 | 5 |

[1] Molar Mg/(Ca + Mg).
[2] Before concentration by leaching with EDTA.
[3] Still contained detectable calcite by X-ray diffraction.

0.0092, this transforms to a distribution coefficient of 0.14 (based on the Sr/Ca of dolomite, not Sr/[Ca + Mg]), nearly identical to the distribution coefficient for calcite which applies to most biogenic marine calcite and to rapidly precipitated laboratory calcite (KINSMAN, 1969). This is not surprising since strontium in the dolomite lattice probably substitutes almost entirely for calcium and not for magnesium. Because the distribution coefficient of strontium in calcite is known to be lower than 0.14 under conditions of slower, more nearly equilibrium precipitation (LORENS, 1981), it is logical to suppose that a lower distribution coefficient might also apply to dolomite precipitated under more nearly equilibrium conditions. Figure 4 shows that Hope Gate dolomite could have precipitated as a first-cycle phase from solutions containing more than about 50% meteoric water using a distribution coefficient of 0.14. Alternatively, marine-dominated solutions are required, and mixing-zone conditions precluded, if distribution coefficients as low as 0.05 apply.

*Oxygen isotope data*

One of the most puzzling aspects of Hope Gate (and other Quaternary) dolomite is the relatively uniform and $^{18}O$-enriched compositions in comparison to presumed normal marine precipitates. Average Hope Gate $\delta^{18}O$ dolomite is approximately +3.1 (PDB), whereas dolomite having a slightly more Ca-rich composition, and interpreted to have precipitated from normal seawater (MITCHELL *et al.*, 1987; LUND, 1989), is between 0.0 and +2.0. Oxygen isotope data thus do not support significant involvement of first-cycle meteoric water in the precipitation of Hope Gate dolomite. Two possible explanations could account for the somewhat $^{18}O$-enriched composition of Hope Gate dolomite relative to presumed marine precipitates:

1) The dolomite-water fractionation factor used (+3.8 relative to calcite, which includes the differences in phosphoric acid fractionation factors between the two minerals at 25°C, *i.e.,* ΔPDB) is too low, and should be closer to 4.5 or even 5 per mil.

2) Hope Gate dolomite precipitated from mixtures of seawater and/or meteoric water which had been buffered toward $\delta^{18}O$-enriched values because of rock/water interaction with underlying strata.

Figure 5 demands that if the second explanation is correct, then the most enriched dolomites must have precipitated from about half seawater and half

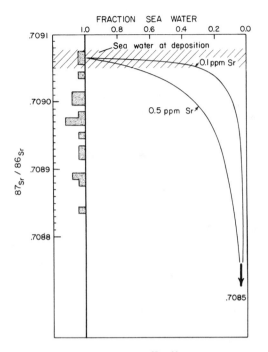

FIG. 3. Fraction of seawater ($^{87}$Sr/$^{86}$Sr = 0.70906) and meteoric water ($^{87}$Sr/$^{86}$Sr = 0.7085) necessary to precipitate Hope Gate dolomite (analyses from Table 2 presented as a histogram on left) for two assumed strontium concentrations of meteoric water (0.1 and 0.5 ppm). The range of mixtures characterized by overlapping dolomite supersaturation and calcite undersaturation is typically between 0.1 and 0.5, depending on variables such as $CO_2$ partial pressure and K-dolomite (PLUMMER, 1975). All but the most radiogenic dolomite samples could have precipitated under appropriate mixing conditions. Some samples contain large amounts of allochthonous (Miocene) strontium, whereas others contain none.

meteoric water which had been buffered at $\delta^{18}O$ = +3.5 (SMOW) by reaction with the Miocene chalk. In the case of Jamaica, this scenario is possible, considering that the $\delta^{18}O$ of the original chalk was approximately +1 (Table 1, and LAND, 1979, his Table 1), and that water which reached equilibrium with the chalk at 25°C would have a $\delta^{18}O$ slightly greater than +3. In the case of other Quaternary localities, however, where large upflow masses of reactive pelagic carbonates are absent, this explanation is less satisfactory. In addition, such large $^{18}O$-enrichments have never been documented in modern meteoric aquifers, and would require extremely low water/rock ratios.

If the fractionation factor between dolomite and calcite is larger than 3.8 per mil, then Hope Gate dolomite could have precipitated directly from seawater, as well as from mixtures of seawater and/or meteoric water which had undergone substantial

chalk/water interaction. The oxygen isotopic data in no way support significant involvement of first-cycle meteoric water in dolomite precipitation. If mixtures of meteoric water and seawater were involved, oxygen isotopic data demand not only that the $\delta^{18}O$ of the mixtures was similar to, or slightly enriched relative to, modern surface seawater, but that the mixtures did not vary more than about 1.5 per mil over the time Hope Gate dolomite precipitated. It is difficult to understand how mixtures of seawater and rock-buffered meteoric water could maintain such limited compositional ranges over the duration of Hope Gate dolomitization.

*Other data*

Other chemical parameters which have been analyzed include $\delta^{13}C$ of both dolomite and calcite,

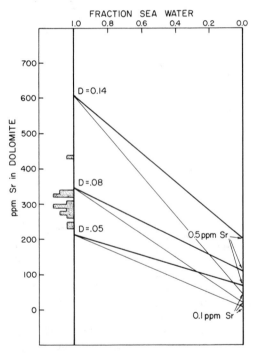

FIG. 4. Strontium concentration in Hope Gate dolomite (data from Table 2 presented as a histogram on left axis) versus fraction seawater in meteoric water-seawater mixtures for three different distribution coefficients, $D$ ($m$[Sr/Ca]$_{dolomite} = D*m$[Sr/Ca]$_{water}$), and two assumed strontium concentrations in meteoric water (0.1 and 0.5 ppm). Hope Gate dolomite could have formed as a first-cycle mixing-zone precipitate in the range 10 to 50% seawater if $D$ = 0.14. Marine-dominated mixtures must have been responsible if lower $D$'s apply, unless Sr/Ca ratios of mixtures were elevated due to the dissolution of Sr-rich aragonite and Mg-calcite in the primary reefs. The relatively narrow range of strontium values observed, and their generally non-radiogenic nature, dispute such a scenario.

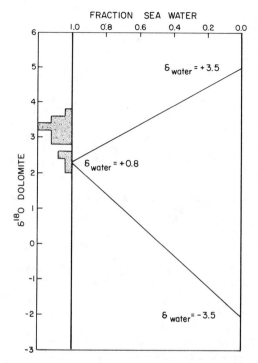

FIG. 5. $\delta^{18}O$ of Hope Gate dolomite (data from Table 2 presented as a histogram on the left axis) versus fraction seawater ($\delta^{18}O = 0.8$ SMOW). Mixing lines are shown for both first-cycle coastal meteoric water (−3.5 SMOW), and for water buffered at 25°C by primary Miocene chalk (+3.5 SMOW). Equilibrium dolomite precipitates could be heavier than the values calculated if the dolomite-water fractionation factor used (+3.8 PDB relative to calcite) is actually larger. In either case, precipitation of Hope Gate dolomite from mixtures of seawater and first-cycle meteoric water is precluded. If meteoric water is involved, the water must have been buffered to relatively $^{18}O$-enriched values by the $^{18}O$-enriched Miocene chalk.

and a few sodium determinations. The average $\delta^{13}C$ of Hope Gate dolomite is +0.9 (PDB), as compared to +3.0 for the precursor reefs (LAND, 1973, his Table 2) and +1.5 for the original Miocene chalk (LAND, 1979, his Table 1). Subaerially exposed Miocene chalk today has a wide range of $\delta^{13}C$ values, averaging −2.3. Clearly, Hope Gate dolomite precipitation incorporated additional $^{12}C$ than was present in the precursor sediments, a scenario consistent with (but not unique to) meteoric-marine mixing. Too many variables exist, however, to constrain a narrow range of mixtures. The average $\delta^{13}C$ of Hope Gate calcite (−6.7) is very different from Hope Gate dolomite (+0.9), and proves that the bulk of the fine-grained dolomite cannot be a meteoric precipitate co-genetic with (meteoric) calcite.

Limited sodium analyses support substantially less sodium in Hope Gate dolomite (*ca.* 500 ppm)

than in modern marine examples (>1000 ppm, LAND and HOOPS, 1973). Too much uncertainty exists in assuring that sodium is a lattice constituent, and in assigning a distribution coefficient, to use sodium to constrain the magnitude of possible meteoric-marine mixing. If kinetic factors affect the distribution coefficient of strontium in carbonates, then similar factors likely affect distribution coefficients for other elements, including sodium.

One final relevant calculation is the volume of water necessary to accomplish the required diagenesis. As previously documented (LAND, 1973, p. 76), Hope Gate diagenesis involved not only the elimination of primary aragonite and Mg-calcite, but the addition of approximately 15% by volume dolomite cement which reduced average porosities from about 20% to about 5%. Using PHREEQE (PARKHURST *et al.*, 1980) and a pK-dolomite of 17.23, a minimum of 67 cm$^3$ of seawater (0.15 cm$^3$ dolomite/2.224 cm$^3$ dolomite precipitated per liter of seawater, Table 3) is required to precipitate 15 volume percent dolomite in one cm$^3$ of reef. Assuming a mixture of 20% seawater and 80% meteoric water, approximately ⅓ liter is required, involving approximately 2500 exchanges of pore water using an average porosity during cementation of 12%. If the reefs grew and underwent diagenesis in an interval of 80,000 years (80 m thick reef which grew at a rate of one meter per 1000 years, LAND, 1974), then only one pore volume exchange would need to occur every 30 years (assuming the modelled equilibrium was achieved) to accomplish the observed dolomite cementation. Even allowing for only 1% efficiency of dolomite precipitation, a flow rate of three pore volumes per year is hardly excessive, especially in this relatively high relief setting.

Based on these data (and assumptions), Hope Gate dolomite apparently could have precipitated from mixtures of approximately 20% meteoric water and seawater, provided (1) that a distribution coefficient for strontium of 0.14 applies; (2) that all the meteoric water was buffered to relatively $^{18}O$-enriched values by interaction with the underlying reactive chalk, but that some was buffered back to coeval $^{87}Sr/^{86}Sr$ values; and (3) that the range of mixtures which caused precipitation was quite restricted. These relatively uniform conditions must have been maintained over sufficient time for at least 2500 pore volume exchanges to take place.

## STABILIZATION OF PRIMARY MARINE DOLOMITE IN METEORIC WATER

The finding that dolomite is forming from seawater in modern and late Pleistocene biolithites

Table 3. Results of equilibrating seawater[1] with calcite + dolomite[2]

| | Open to $CO_2$ | | Closed to $CO_2$ | |
|---|---|---|---|---|
| | Cal + Dol | Cal + Dol + C[3] | Cal + Dol | Ca + Dol + C[3] |
| pH | 7.51 | 7.52 | 6.79 | 6.16 |
| $pCO_2$ | −3.50 | −3.50 | −2.07 | −0.78 |
| Dol ppt'd[4] | 2.224 | 2.318 | 2.206 | 2.273 |
| Cal dissv'd[4] | 2.451 | 2.398 | 2.462 | 2.427 |
| porosity[5] | 0.227 | 0.080 | 0.256 | 0.154 |

[1] from PARKHURST et al. (1980, p. 55). pH = 8.32, $pCO_2$ = $10^{-3.50}$. PHREEQE was modified to calculate activity coefficients by the B-dot method. Simulations using PHRQPITZ (PLUMMER et al., 1988) produce similar results.

[2] pK dolomite = 17.23, pK calcite = 8.51.

[3] 0.015 moles organic carbon, which resulted in reduction of approximately 25% of the original sulfate. This would produce dolomite with a $\delta^{13}C$ of approximately −1.3 (assuming −20 organic matter), which is more $^{13}C$ depleted than is actually observed. Increasing sulfate-reduction would result in dolomite progressively more depleted in $^{13}C$, and eventually, no increase in porosity.

[4] $cm^3$ per kilogram of water using a molar volume of 65.64 $cm^3$ $mole^{-1}$ for Hope Gate dolomite (based on unit cell measurements by X-ray diffraction) and 36.94 $cm^3$ $mole^{-1}$ for calcite.

[5] $cm^3$ per kilogram of water. Increasing sulfate reduction results in increased dolomite precipitation and decreased calcite dissolution. Changes in pK dolomite and/or dolomite stoichiometry cause only minor changes in the amount of porosity produced.

(MITCHELL et al., 1987), and the observation of extensive hydrodynamic flow of seawater through both modern and late Pleistocene reefs (LAND et al., 1989), suggests another possible origin for Hope Gate dolomite involving meteoric water. If considerable amounts of dolomite, similar to that observed forming today (MITCHELL et al., 1987; LUND, 1989), had been emplaced contemporaneously with deposition, by direct precipitation from seawater, the dolomite might have recrystallized when meteoric water infiltrated the reefs as they grew seaward. No "water volume" problem exists to accomplish porosity reduction because of demonstrably adequate (although not explained) flow of seawater through the reefs (LAND et al., 1989). This scenario can be modelled using an algorithm evolved from that presented by LAND (1980) or advocated by BANNER and HANSON (1990).

The original dolomite is presumed to have contained 600 ppm Sr having an $^{87}Sr/^{86}Sr$ ratio of 0.70906, and to have a $\delta^{18}O$ of +2 and a $\delta^{13}C$ of +2. Using values for meteoric water of 0.1 ppm Sr, $^{87}Sr/^{86}Sr$ = 0.7085, $\delta^{18}O$ = +1.3, and $\delta^{13}C$ = −25, the results of the simulation are shown in Fig. 6.

Because of the rock/water ratio of the constituents modelled (12% porosity), oxygen is most sensitive to modification, and carbon least sensitive. Fifty pore-volume exchanges of fluid of any reasonable oxygen isotopic composition are sufficient to equilibrate primary dolomite with the imposed water assuming that equilibration takes place during each pore volume exchange. Clearly, the water which was responsible for precipitation of the dolomite

that now constitutes the rocks must have been in oxygen isotopic equilibrium with the existing dolomite. Even granted that sufficient volumes of mixed water having a $\delta^{18}O$ of +1.3 were available, approximately 150 pore volume exchanges are necessary to lower $^{87}Sr/^{86}Sr$ ratios to average Hope Gate values (0.70896), 500 to lower the strontium content to Hope Gate values using a $D$ = 0.06, and more than 2000 pore volume exchanges to reach acceptable $\delta^{13}C$ values.

Therefore, using basic conservation-of-mass requirements and reasonable approximations of possible solution compositions, an original marine dolomite could have been reset to the values observed today in the Hope Gate Formation only if several thousand pore volume exchanges took place in order to satisfy the carbon mass-balance. Except for $\delta^{13}C$, the water involved must have been in equilibrium with the observed dolomite ($\delta^{18}O_{water}$ = +1.3, 6 ppm Sr if $D$ = 0.06, and $^{87}Sr/^{86}Sr$ between 0.70916 and 0.70884). These constraints are not too different from those demanded by direct precipitation from mixed waters. Except for the most rock-dominated component (carbon), the dolomite must essentially be an equilibrium precipitate from the water which caused stabilization (recrystallization). Except in the case of the most rock-dominated component, carbon, the precursor composition was not important.

## DIRECT PRECIPITATION FROM MODIFIED SEAWATER

The two scenarios outlined above are not satisfactory for several reasons. Although the oxygen

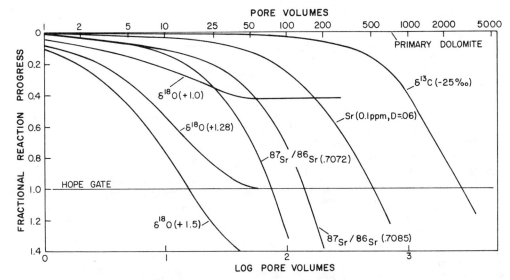

FIG. 6. Modelled evolution of dolomite chemistry as an initial marine precipitate (PRIMARY DOLOMITE, FRACTIONAL REACTION PROGRESS = 0) is recrystallized by meteoric water. REACTION PROGRESS is relative to observed average Hope Gate dolomite composition (FRACTIONAL REACTION PROGRESS = 1.0). In order to "reset" $\delta^{13}C$ values, for which rock/water ratios are highest, the $\delta^{18}O$ of the imposed water, together with its strontium concentration and $^{87}Sr/$ $^{86}Sr$ ratio, must be in equilibrium with the replacement product. Several possible water compositions are shown. Therefore, except for the component with the highest rock/water ratio, no difference between primary precipitation and replacement can be discerned.

isotopic fractionation between dolomite and water is not known with certainty, it is unlikely that water more depleted in $^{18}O$ than modern surface seawater could have precipitated Hope Gate dolomite. Therefore, either seawater was the dolomitizing solution, or seawater and/or meteoric water buffered to elevated $\delta^{18}O$ values by reaction with Miocene chalk is required. The limited range of $\delta^{18}O$ dolomite values observed (Fig. 5), the lack of correlation of $\delta^{18}O$ with other measured variables (Table 2), and the unlikelihood of large volumes of rock-buffered ($^{18}O$-enriched) meteoric water being available, all make it difficult to invoke mixtures of seawater and meteoric water.

A similar conclusion can be reached with respect to strontium concentrations in the dolomite. Many authors have advocated a distribution coefficient for strontium in slowly precipitated dolomite (and calcite) considerably lower than 0.14, and values of 0.06 (BAKER and BURNS, 1985) or even lower (BAKER et al., 1982; VAHRENKAMP and SWART, 1990) have been suggested. If a distribution coefficient of 0.06 is appropriate, then precipitation of Hope Gate dolomite from near-normal seawater is possible, and precipitation from meteoric/marine mixtures ruled out (Fig. 4). The precipitation of low-strontium dolomite directly from seawater may not be unreasonable, as the precipitation of low-

strontium calcite from seawater has been documented (FREEMAN-LYNDE et al., 1986; SALLER, 1986).

The $^{87}Sr/^{86}Sr$ data, however, demand that allochthonous (presumably Miocene) strontium be incorporated in most of the dolomite crystals. The apparent need to precipitate dolomite from seawater, and simultaneously to import extraneous strontium, can be achieved if the seawater had been modified by interaction with underlying Miocene chalk. There is no reason to suppose that unmodified surface seawater must be the sole agent of dolomitization. In fact, Jamaican surface seawater apparently precipitates more Ca-rich ($Mg_{0.38}$) and Sr-rich (600 ppm) dolomite than the dolomite that characterizes the Hope Gate Formation. Seawater which had interacted with Miocene chalk would have been characterized by $^{87}Sr/^{86}Sr$ ratios approaching those of the chalk, and slightly elevated strontium and $\delta^{18}O$ relative to seawater in which the reefs grew. Only the increased strontium concentration of seawater which had been modified by chalk/water interaction appears to be incompatible with this hypothesis. Either the strontium concentration of seawater resulting from chalk/water interaction did not rise because of rapid back-precipitation of calcite at a $D = 0.14$, or a distribution coefficient of strontium in dolomite somewhat less than 0.06 may apply (BAKER *et al.*, 1982; VAH-RENKAMP and SWART, 1990).

One further modification of seawater is compatible with these data and may have favored dolomitization. Small amounts of organic carbon in the underlying chalk and in Hope Gate reefs themselves may have undergone oxidation, possibly accompanying sulfate reduction. Many cases of dolomite precipitation in organic-rich marine sediments have been reported (*e.g.,* GARRISON *et al.,* 1984). Both increased alkalinity and reduction in sulfate concentrations may favor dolomite precipitation (BAKER and KASTNER, 1981). The slightly [13]C depleted values of Hope Gate dolomite relative to the precursor sediments suggest that the oxidation of organic carbon (not necessarily soil carbon), possibly accompanying sulfate reduction, was involved in the dolomitization process. Massive sulfate reduction (and, of course, methanogenesis) is precluded by the paucity of organic matter in these high energy deposits, and by relatively small changes in $\delta^{13}C$ that took place as the precursor sediments were dolomitized relative to the large change in Mg/Ca which occurred.

The coincidence of calcite undersaturation and dolomite oversaturation has been one of the strengths of the mixing-zone model, permitting replacement to take place as dolomite precipitates occupy voids caused by calcite dissolution (PLUMMER, 1975). Seawater is grossly oversaturated with dolomite because of its high Mg/Ca ratio, but is much closer to calcite saturation. Once precipitation of dolomite is initiated, calcite undersaturation is necessitated. The rate-limiting step is certainly dolomite precipitation, not calcite dissolution. Provided that large quantities of new $CO_2$ are not introduced, the volume of calcite dissolved exceeds the volume of dolomite precipitated (Table 3). In this way precipitation of dolomite from seawater generates porosity, and dolomite "fronts" can continue to advance at the expense of limestones. As long as the "pump" is maintained, fresh seawater is continuously funnelled into porous zones at the sites of reaction and in more porous, previously dolomitized strata. Porosity (and permeability?) should continue to increase as long as the reaction proceeds, and dolomitization by circulating seawater can thus proceed to completion, and then advance as a "front" into adjacent limestones. Calcite undersaturation is also favored by small amounts of sulfate reduction in carbonate sediments (WALTER and BURTON, 1990) and by aerobic respiration and sulfide oxidation. Thus, calcite undersaturation in seawater can be achieved in several ways other than as a result of dolomite precipitation,

and the need for mixing with meteoric water is diminished.

The precipitation of dolomite from seawater may be an extremely common phenomenon, as evidenced by numerous pore water analyses which show lowered Mg/Ca ratios with increased depth (*e.g.,* GEISKES, 1981), and the relatively common occurrence of dolomite in deep-sea sediments (*e.g.,* LUMSDEN, 1988). In the absence of an advective seawater pump, the amount of dolomite formed is limited by diffusion (*e.g.,* COMPTON and SIEVER, 1986), so that dolomite is rarely an abundant phase in modern sediments, although it may be much more common than is currently recognized.

Near-normal seawater is hypothesized to have dolomitized Hope Gate reefs. Thermal buoyancy, dispersion due to meteoric discharge, tidally induced flow, and/or yet undocumented (geostrophic?) forces (LAND *et al.,* 1989) circulated seawater through the reefs. The presence of a massive seawater pump, whatever its cause, is the primary cause of massive dolomitization. In the case of the Hope Gate Formation, some of the seawater had undergone previous chalk/water interaction so as to achieve lowered [87]Sr/[86]Sr ratios (Fig. 7). Increased alkalinity, possibly accompanied by minor sulfate reduction, and evidenced by slight [13]C depletion is also likely. Extensive sulfate reduction is not supported by the generally rock-buffered character of the carbon isotopic data and is not evidenced in water analyses where active dolomitization by seawater is hypothesized (FANNING *et al.,* 1981).

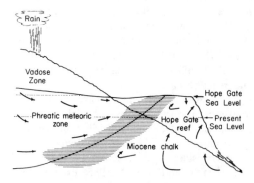

FIG. 7. Cross section of the study area showing the inferred environment of dolomitization. Dolomite precipitated in Hope Gate reefs from coeval surface seawater and from seawater which had interacted with underlying Miocene chalk. Emplacement of meteoric spar followed dolomitization (Phreatic meteoric zone). Precipitation of small amounts of coarse-grained "limpid" dolomite spar in the mixing-zone one (horizontal pattern) may also have taken place.

## CONCLUSION

Meteoric water was probably not involved in the precipitation of most Hope Gate dolomite. It is difficult to accept that relatively large volumes of water having a $\delta^{18}O$ near +1 and more importantly, a limited range in $\delta^{18}O$ of only about one per mil could have been generated as the result of mixing seawater with rock-buffered meteoric water. The oxygen isotopic data strongly support seawater as being the dolomitizing agent. If a distribution coefficient for Sr in dolomite near 0.06 is accepted, strontium concentration data are also consistent with seawater as the dolomitizing solution, provided that "slow" precipitation is invoked. Again, a relatively narrow range of data argues against mixing of disparate solutions. A few of the $^{87}Sr/^{86}Sr$ ratios also support coeval seawater as the sole agent of dolomitization, but many values prove that import of allochthonous strontium took place. Circulation of seawater through underlying units to derive the extraneous strontium is the most reasonable explanation. Modified seawater may be a more effective dolomitizing agent than is surface seawater, accounting for the chemical differences between Hope Gate dolomite and modern Jamaican dolomite (MITCHELL et al., 1987).

In Hope Gate time, surface seawater may have precipitated minor (?) amounts of dolomite ($Mg_{.38}$) similar to that observed in modern Jamaican reefs (MITCHELL et al., 1987). This extremely metastable phase was subsequently replaced by, or syntaxially overgrown by, the more stable phase ($Mg_{.42}$) characteristic of the rocks today. Presumably, the more stoichiometric phase was favored by some combination of slower precipitation, and/or precipitation from sulfate-depleted and/or otherwise "modified" seawater. The removal of "organic coatings" or "crystal poisons" (phosphate?) in oxygen-depleted seawater may have provided suitable substrates on Mg-calcites and Ca-rich ($Mg_{.38}$) dolomite for epitaxial dolomite nucleation and crystal growth, and is another "modification" which cannot be discounted.

Subsequent infiltration of the reefs by meteoric water resulted in dissolution of all metastable phases which had not been replaced by dolomite (aragonite, Mg-calcite, and $Mg_{.38}$ dolomite) and the emplacement of meteoric spar. The "hollow rhombs" (Fig. 2), and perhaps even the calcite-dolomite intergrowths (LAND, 1973, his Fig. 9; WARD and HALLEY, 1985, their Fig. 5; HUMPHREY, 1988, his Fig. 4) may be due to the preferential dissolution of the more unstable $Mg_{.38}$ phase followed by epitaxial nucleation of meteoric spar. If this is true, then alternating calcite-dolomite zones do not provide conclusive evidence for mixing-zone conditions.

## RELEVANCE TO OTHER DOLOMITES

The Hope Gate Formation is remarkably similar to many other late Cenozoic dolomites in the Caribbean, including those from the Netherlands Antilles (LAND, 1973; SIBLEY, 1982), Mexico (WARD and HALLEY, 1985), Grand Cayman Island (B. JONES, pers. commun.), Barbados (HUMPHREY, 1988), and the subsurface of the Bahamas (SUPKO, 1977; SWART et al., 1987; VAHRENKAMP, 1988). Based on very limited data, nearly coeval deposits in the Pacific and Indian oceans are also known (AISSAOUI, 1986; AHARON et al., 1987, and refs. therein). Limited $^{87}Sr/^{86}Sr$ data from several of these deposits (AHARON et al., 1987; SWART et al., 1987; VAHRENKAMP, 1988; unpubl. data) support dolomitization of coeval or older strata by seawater at a time not too different from the Pliocene-Pleistocene boundary. It is tempting to invoke an "event" to account for these very similar deposits, widely separated in space, but apparently not widely separated in time.

SIBLEY (1980) suggested a climatic "event" to account for the Pliocene Seroe Domi dolomite of Bonaire. Changes in sea-level are a more appealing world-wide "event" which might trigger dolomitization. Several authors (KALDI and GIDMAN, 1982; WARD and HALLEY, 1985; VAHRENKAMP, 1988) have suggested that dolomitization was triggered by a fall in sea level. The transition from marine (deposition and dolomitization) conditions to meteoric (stabilization and spar emplacement) conditions is certainly favored by such circumstances. Alternatively, a transgression followed by a period of relatively stable aggradation may favor dolomitization, as porous sediments accumulate rapidly, and as coastal hydrology (including seawater circulation) stabilizes.

We should be careful, however, not to generalize about the contemporaneity of these very similar Cenozoic deposits at this stage of our knowledge. Similarity in $^{87}Sr/^{86}Sr$ data from dolomite support neither contemporaneous deposition nor contemporaneous dolomitization, and allochthonous strontium seems to characterize many dolomites (Fig. 3; GAO and LAND, 1991). Clearly, continued investigation of the effects of modified seawater on the dolomitization process, both in the laboratory and in the field, is warranted. Especially important is an increased understanding of the behavior of more stoichiometric phases, such as are found in the subsurface of the Bahamas (VAHRENKAMP,

1988), which exhibit very low strontium concentrations and maintain enriched $^{18}O$ signatures. If these phases can also be shown to be due to primary precipitation from, or stabilization in, near-normal seawater (LAND, 1985), then reassessment of a great many ancient examples will be necessary.

*Acknowledgements*—Sam Epstein introduced me to stable isotopes (probably(?) unbeknownst to him during nighttime "invasions" of his laboratories). Although I was not fortunate enough to have formally been one of his students, Sam's stimulation through the years, and the initial analyses of the Hope Gate he performed, have been invaluable. The discovery of dolomite in modern reef samples collected by Todd Mitchell was accomplished during routine(!) analysis of Mg-calcite and aragonite cements on the electron probe obtained with NSF grant EAR-8319716. This discovery stimulated continued work on Jamaican dolomite with the assistance of the Petroleum Research Fund of the American Chemical Society, PRF-19316-AC2. Strontium isotopic analyses were mediated by NSF grant EAR-8618226. Additional support during the last 20 years has been provided by the Geology Foundation of the University of Texas at Austin and the Discovery Bay Marine Laboratory. Many students and colleagues have contributed during this period, with perceptive questions and sometimes-polite skepticism. In particular I wish to thank recent students Jim Anderson, Dave Budd, Harris Cander, Guoqiu Gao, Sue Hovorka, Julie Kupecz, Dave Leary, Holly Lund, Matt McCullough, Todd Mitchell, and Jay Vogt.

## REFERENCES

AHARON P., SOCKI R. A. and CHAN L. (1987) Dolomitization of atolls by sea water convective flow: Test of a hypothesis at Niue, South Pacific. *J. Geol.* **95**, 187–203.

AISSAOUI D. M. (1986) Diagenese carbonatee en domaine recifal. Theses, Univ. Paris Sud, 369 p.

BAKER P. A. and BURNS S. J. (1985) Occurrence and formation of dolomite in organic-rich continental margin sediments. *Bull. Amer. Assoc. Petrol. Geol.* **69**, 1917–1930.

BAKER P. A. and KASTNER M. A. (1981) Constraints on the formation of sedimentary dolomite. *Science* **213**, 214–216.

BAKER P. A., GIESKES J. M. and ELDERFIELD H. (1982) Diagenesis of carbonates in deep sea sediments—Evidence from Sr/Ca ratios and interstitial dissolved $Sr^{++}$ data. *J. Sediment. Petrol.* **52**, 71–82.

BANNER J. L. and HANSON G. N. (1990) Calculations of simultaneous isotopic and trace element variations during water-rock interaction with applications to carbonate diagenesis. *Geochim. Cosmochim. Acta* **54**, 3123–3137.

BEHRENS E. W. and LAND L. S. (1972) Subtidal Holocene dolomite, Baffin Bay, Texas, *J. Sediment. Petrol.* **42**, 155–161.

BUDD D. A. (1988) Aragonite-to-calcite transformation during fresh-water diagenesis of carbonates: Insights from pore-water chemistry. *Bull. Geol. Soc. Amer.* **100**, 1260–1270.

COMPTON J. S. and SIEVER R. (1986) Diffusion and mass balance of Mg during early dolomite formation, Monterey Formation. *Geochim. Cosmochim. Acta* **50**, 125–135.

DEPAOLO D. J. (1986) Detailed record of the Neogene Sr isotopic evolution of seawater from DSDP site 590B. *Geology* **14**, 103–106.

FANNING K. A., BYRNE R. H., BRELAND J. A., BETZER P. A., MOORE W. S. and ELSINGER R. J. (1981) Geothermal springs of the West Florida continental shelf. *Earth Planet. Sci. Lett.* **52**, 345–354.

F.A.O. [Food and Agriculture Organization of the United Nations] (1974) Development and management of water resources, Jamaica, Dry Harbour mountains-north coast basin. *AGG:DP/JAM/70/512, Tech. Rept.* **3**, Rome, 139p.

FREEMAN-LYNDE, R. P., WHITLEY K. E. and LOHMANN K. C. (1986) Deep-marine origin of equant spar cements on Bahama escarpment limestones. *J. Sediment. Petrol.* **56**, 799–811.

GAO G. and LAND L. S. (1991) Early Ordovician Cool Creek Dolomite, Middle Arbuckle Group, Slick Hills, SW Oklahoma, U.S.A.: Origin and modification. *J. Sediment. Petrol.* **61**, 161–173.

GARRISON R. E., KASTNER M. and ZENGER D. H. (1984) *Dolomites of the Monterey Formation and Other Organic-rich Units.* Pacific Sect. Soc. Econ. Paleon. and Mineral.

GIESKES J. M. (1981) Deep-sea drilling interstitial water studies: Implications for chemical alteration of oceanic crust, Layer I and II. In *The Deep Sea Drilling Program: A Decade of Progress* (ed. J. E. WARME et al.); Soc. Econ. Paleon. Mineral. Spec. Publ. 32, pp. 149–167.

HARDIE L. A. (1987) Dolomitization: A critical view of some current views. *J. Sediment. Petrol.* **57**, 166–183.

HARRIS W. H. and MATTHEWS R. K. (1968) Subaerial diagenesis of carbonate sediments: Efficiency of the solution-precipitation process. *Science* **160**, 77–79.

HARTMAN W. D. and GOREAU T. F. (1970) Jamaican coralline sponges: Their morphology, ecology and fossil relatives. Symp. Zool. Soc. London **25**, 205–243.

HENDRY M. D. (1987) Tectonic and eustatic control on late Cenozoic sedimentation within an active plate boundary zone. *Bull. Geol. Soc. Amer.* **99**, 718–728.

HODELL D. A., MEAD G. A. and MUELLER P. A. (1990) Variation in the strontium isotopic composition of seawater (8 Ma to present): Implications for chemical weathering rates and dissolved fluxes to the oceans. *Chem. Geol.* **80**, 291–307.

HUMPHREY J. D. (1988) Late Pleistocene mixing-zone dolomitization, Southeastern Barbados, West Indies. *Sedimentology* **35**, 327–348.

KALDI J. and GIDMAN J. (1982) Early diagenetic dolomite cements: Examples from the Permian Lower Magnesian Limestone of England and the Pleistocene carbonates of the Bahamas. *J. Sediment. Petrol.* **52**, 1073–1085.

KINSMAN D. J. J. (1969) Interpretation of $Sr^{+2}$ concentrations in carbonate minerals and rocks. *J. Sediment. Petrol.* **39**, 486–508.

LAND L. S. (1973) Contemporaneous dolomitization of Middle Pleistocene reefs by meteoric water. *Bull. Marine Sci.* **23**, 64–92.

LAND L. S. (1974) Growth rate of a West Indian (Jamaican) reef. *Proc. 2nd Intl. Coral Reef Symp. Brisbane, Australia* **2**, 409–412.

LAND L. S. (1979) Chert-chalk diagenesis: The Miocene island slope of North Jamaica. *J. Sediment. Petrol.* **49**, 223–232.

LAND L. S. (1980) The isotopic and trace element geochemistry of dolomite: The state of the art. In *Concepts and Models of Dolomitization* (eds. D. H. ZENGER, J. B. DUNHAM and R. L. ETHINGTON); *Soc. Econ. Paleon. Mineral Spec. Publ. 28*, pp. 87–110.

LAND L. S. (1985) The origin of massive dolomite. *J. Geol. Educ.* **33,** 112–125.

LAND L. S. (1991) Some aspects of the Late Cenozoic evolution of North Jamaica as revealed by strontium isotopic stratigraphy. *J. Geol. Soc. Jamaica* (in press).

LAND L. S. and HOOPS G. K. (1973) Sodium in carbonate sediments and rocks: A possible index to the salinity of diagenetic solutions. *J. Sediment. Petrol.* **43,** 614–617.

LAND L. S. and MOORE C. H. (1980) Lithification, micritization and syndepositional diagenesis of biolithites on the Jamaican island slope. *J. Sediment. Petrol.* **50,** 357–370.

LAND L. S., LUND H. J. and McCULLOUGH M. L. (1989) Dynamic circulation of interstitial seawater in a Jamaican fringing reef. *Carbonates Evaporites* **4,** 1–7.

LORENS R. B. (1981) Sr, Cd, Mn and Co distribution coefficients in calcite as a function of calcite precipitation rates. *Geochim. Cosmochim. Acta* **45,** 553–561.

LUMSDEN D. N. (1988) Characteristics of deep-marine dolomite. *J. Sediment. Petrol.* **58,** 1023–1031.

LUND H. J. (1989) Marine dolomite in a fore-reef hardground, Discovery Bay, Jamaica. M.A. thesis, Univ. Texas, Austin. 98 p.

MITCHELL J. T., LAND L. S. and MISER D. E. (1987) Modern marine dolomite cement in a north Jamaican fringing reef. *Geology* **15,** 557–560.

O'NEIL T. J. (1964) Chemical interactions due to mixing of meteoric and marine waters in a Pleistocene reef complex, Rio Bueno, Jamaica. M.A. Thesis, Louisiana State Univ. 186 p.

PARKHURST D. L., THORSTENSON D. C. and PLUMMER L. N. (1980) PHREEQE: A computer program for geochemical calculations. *U.S. Geol. Survey Water-Res. Invest.* **80–96,** 210 p.

PATTERSON R. J. (1972) Hydrology and carbonate diagenesis of a coastal sabkha in the Persian Gulf. Ph.D. dissertation, Princeton Univ., 473 p.

PLUMMER L. N. (1975) Mixing of seawater with calcium carbonate ground water. In *Quantitative Studies in the Geological Sciences* (ed. E. H. WHITTEN); *Geol. Soc. Amer. Mem. 142,* pp. 219–236.

PLUMMER L. N., PARKHURST D. L., FLEMING D. W. and DUNKLE S. A. (1988) A computer program incorporating Pitzer's equations for calculation of geochemical reactions in brines. *U. S. Geol. Survey Water-Res. Invest.* **88–4153,** 310 p.

SALLER A. H. (1986) Petrologic and geochemical constraints on the origin of radiaxial calcite, Enewetak Atoll. *J. Sediment. Petrol.* **56,** 743–762.

SIBLEY D. F. (1980) Climatic control of dolomitization, Seroe Domi Formation (Pliocene), Bonaire. In *Concepts and Models of Dolomitization* (eds. D. H. ZENGER, J. B. DUNHAM and R. L. ETHINGTON); *Soc. Econ. Paleon. Mineral. Spec. Publ. 28,* pp. 247–258.

SIBLEY D. F. (1982) The origin of common dolomite fabrics: Clues from the Pliocene. *J. Sediment. Petrol.* **52,** 1087–1100.

SUPKO P. R. (1977) Subsurface dolomites, San Salvador, Bahamas. *J. Sediment. Petrol.* **47,** 1063–1077.

SWART P. K., RUIZ J. and HOLMES C. (1987) The use of strontium isotopes to constrain the timing and mode of dolomitization of upper Cenozoic sediments in a core from San Salvador, Bahamas. *Geology* **15,** 262–265.

VAHRENKAMP V. K. (1988) Constraints on the formation of platform dolomites: A geochemical study of Late Tertiary dolomite from Little Bahama Bank, Bahamas. Ph.D. dissertation, Univ. Miami, 328 p.

VAHRENKAMP V. K. and SWART P. K. (1990) New distribution coefficient for the incorporation of strontium into dolomite and implications for the formation of ancient dolomites. *Geology* **18,** 387–391.

WALTER L. M. and BURTON E. A. (1990) Dissolution of recent platform carbonate sediments in marine pore fluids. *Amer. Jour. Sci.* **290,** 601–643.

WARD W. C. and HALLEY R. B. (1985) Dolomitization in a mixing-zone of near-seawater composition, late Pleistocene, northeastern Yucatan Peninsula. *J. Sediment. Petrol.* **55,** 407–420.

WHITEKAR F. F. and SMART P. L. (1990) Active circulation of saline groundwaters in carbonate platforms: Evidence from the Great Bahama Bank. *Geology* **18,** 200–203.

Stable Isotope Geochemistry: A Tribute to Samuel Epstein
© The Geochemical Society, Special Publication No. 3, 1991
Editors: H. P. Taylor, Jr., J. R. O'Neil and I. R. Kaplan

# Fossil meteoric groundwaters in the Delaware Basin of southeastern New Mexico

STEVEN J. LAMBERT

Geochemistry Division 6233, Sandia National Laboratories, Albuquerque, NM 87185, U.S.A.

**Abstract**—$^{18}O/^{16}O$ and D/H ratio measurements have been made on groundwaters sampled from the Rustler Formation (Ochoan, Permian) and related rocks in the northern Delaware Basin of southeastern New Mexico. Most confined Rustler Formation waters at the WIPP site and to the west in Nash Draw and confined waters from the Capitan Limestone constitute one population in $\delta D/\delta^{18}O$ space, while unconfined groundwaters inferred to originate as modern surface recharge waters constitute a distinctly different and non-overlapping population. A likely explanation for this distinction is that meteoric recharge to most of the Rustler and Capitan units took place in the geologic past under climatic conditions significantly different from those of the present. Available tritium and radiocarbon data are consistent with this hypothesis, and the apparent age of confined groundwaters is in excess of 12,000 radiocarbon years, suggesting that recharge took place under wetter conditions in the late Pleistocene. Water at the Rustler/Salado contact at the WIPP site is of meteoric origin but has experienced isotopic alteration that increases with decreasing permeability. Rustler dolomites have not recrystallized in isotopic equilibrium with Rustler Formation water. The absence of modern meteoric recharge to the Rustler Formation at and near the WIPP site indicates that the hydrologic system there is not at steady state. Instead, the system is responding to the cessation of local recharge, this cessation occurring more than 10,000 years ago.

## INTRODUCTION

### Rationale and objectives

UNDERSTANDING THE GEOLOGIC history of the Rustler Formation in the northern Delaware Basin of southeastern New Mexico is relevant to the evaluation of the ability of the bedded evaporite environment at the Waste Isolation Pilot Plant (WIPP) to contain waste radionuclides for long periods of time. The Rustler is important because it (1) is the uppermost evaporite-bearing unit in the Ochoan (Permian) sequence, (2) is experiencing active dissolution where it crops out west of the WIPP site, (3) immediately overlies the Salado Formation where the WIPP is being excavated, and (4) contains interbeds of brittle fractured rock that carry the most abundant and regionally persistent occurrences of groundwater associated with Delaware Basin bedded evaporites. The rates and directions of flow in a groundwater system such as the Rustler Formation are inferred from determinations of permeability and potentiometric head in individual boreholes. Groundwater geochemistry, however, provides information on the nature of processes governing recharge, groundwater residence time, the degree of connection among individual groundwater occurrences, and identification of discharge areas. Stable isotope studies of the Rustler groundwaters contribute to this supplemental information.

To facilitate the interpretation of groundwater flow in the Rustler Formation, isotopic compositions of other geologically and economically important Delaware Basin groundwaters were also determined, including those from the overlying Dewey Lake Red Beds, the Capitan Limestone bordering the Delaware Basin evaporites (both the vadose zone represented in Carlsbad Caverns and the phreatic zone to the east), the Ogallala Sandstone underlying much of the southern Great Plains, near-surface alluvium, and a spring discharging from local shallow-seated gypsum karst. The part of the Delaware Basin in southeastern New Mexico and west Texas relevant to this study is shown in Fig. 1, which illustrates large-scale geographic relationships among various water occurrences. Figure 2 shows the locations of boreholes and other features near the WIPP site, including Nash Draw, a solution-subsidence valley formed by the partial dissolution of outcropping Rustler evaporites.

### Previous work

LAMBERT (1978) first documented the stable isotope compositions of confined groundwaters in the Capitan Limestone and the Rustler Formation and concluded that they are of meteoric origin. However, stable isotope ratios of most Capitan groundwaters under confined hydrologic conditions were distinctly different from those of other local meteoric groundwaters whose origins could be traced by observation and inference to infiltration of modern precipitation. In particular, groundwaters from Carlsbad Caverns, where active meteoric recharge is observed, were isotopically distinct from tightly clustered $\delta D$ and $\delta^{18}O$ values of groundwaters from buried portions of the Capitan, extending from the

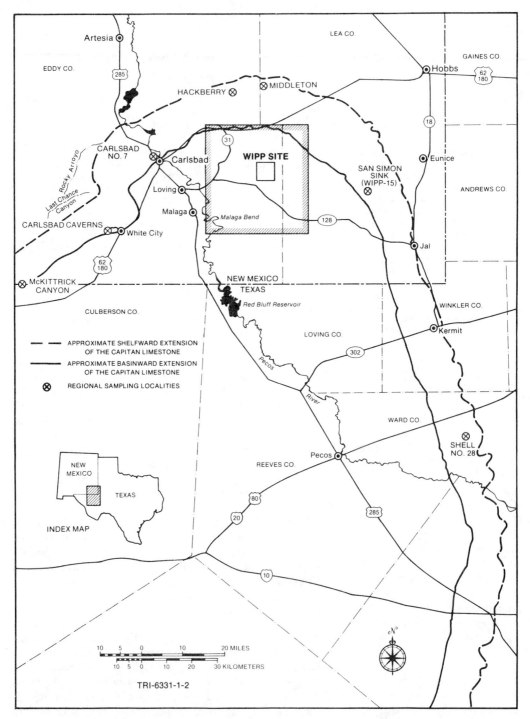

FIG. 1. Regional map of the Delaware Basin, southeastern New Mexico and West Texas. Approximate positions of basinward and shelfward extensions of the Capitan Limestone are taken from HISS (1975). Hachured rectangle is the area covered by Fig. 2.

city of Carlsbad eastward and southward into west Texas (Fig. 1). LAMBERT (1978) concluded that (except for Carlsbad Caverns) a $\delta^{18}O$ value of $-7$ and a $\delta D$ value of $-50$ are good approximations to local meteoric water in the Delaware Basin, and the Caverns are part of a hydrologic system independent of the rest of the Capitan, with their enrichment in D and $^{18}O$ reflecting the water's origin from air-

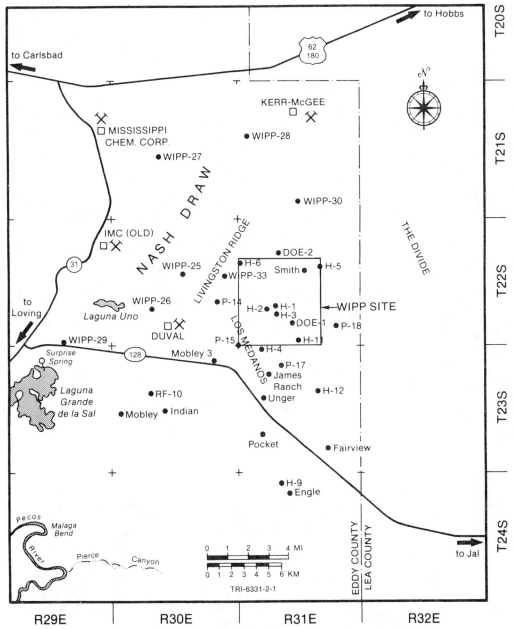

FIG. 2. Map of northern Delaware Basin, southeastern New Mexico. Detailed map of the area enclosed by hachures in Fig. 1 showing sampling localities, mostly boreholes. Modified from MERCER (1983).

mass conditions different from those which produce other Delaware Basin rains. This implied that most of the eastern (deeper) Capitan groundwaters were probably recharged under climatic conditions different from those prevalent in the Guadalupe Mountains (Fig. 1). At the time, no estimates were available of ages of recharge for Delaware Basin groundwaters. Similarly, it was not known to what

degree climatic and recharge conditions in the northern Guadalupe Mountains represented those in other parts of the northern Chihuahuan Desert throughout the northern Delaware Basin. Until recently (LAMBERT, 1987) the time of groundwater recharge to the Rustler Formation and the overlying Dewey Lake Red Beds was unknown, but independent paleoclimatic evidence indicated wetter conditions, more conducive to recharge, at various times in the Pleistocene, ranging from 10,000 to 600,000 years ago (VAN DEVENDER, 1980; BACHMAN, 1984).

MERCER (1983) summarized the stratigraphy and hydraulic properties of the five members of the Rustler Formation, two of which are 8-m thick locally fractured dolomite units carrying groundwater under confined conditions. The distribution of halite removal by dissolution and the conversion of anhydrite to gypsum in the Rustler Formation across Nash Draw and the WIPP site was described in more detail by SNYDER (1985). In addition, the regional aspects of dissolution of Ochoan evaporites have been discussed by LAMBERT (1983).

## METHODS

### Sample collection

Several boreholes (Fig. 2) penetrate the three principal water-bearing units above the main evaporite sequence at the WIPP site: the Magenta and Culebra dolomite members of the Rustler Formation, and the zone near the contact between the Rustler and the underlying Salado Formation. In addition, some boreholes allowed sampling of local water-bearing horizons in the Dewey Lake Red Beds immediately overlying the Rustler Formation. The Culebra dolomite member of the Rustler Formation appears to be the most regionally pervasive and consistent water-producing horizon (MERCER, 1983). The Rustler/Salado contact was studied because it represents the uppermost horizon of Salado halite dissolution.

Readily accessible accumulations of water (springs, streams, and pools) were grab-sampled; subsurface sampling from wells required special equipment and procedures, primarily because of the low productivity. From the beginning of the WIPP project in late 1975 to 1980, all samples from wells were bailed or swabbed during hydrologic testing. Well-water samples resulting from pump tests in 1980 and 1981 were collected using the criteria and procedures described by LAMBERT and ROBINSON (1984). From 1981 to the present well-water samples were collected by subcontractor organizations whose sampling criteria were based on those of LAMBERT and ROBINSON (1984), although procedures differ in detail.

In several boreholes core samples of the water-bearing carbonate rock were available along with water samples. Oxygen isotope ratios of host rocks in most recent contact with the water were used to evaluate the degree of isotope exchange between carbonate and water, as an indicator of secondary precipitation. Because most waters were sampled from cased wells perforated in production zones isolated by packers, contact of water samples with rocks other than the producing horizons was avoided.

### Analytical procedures

Water was first distilled in vacuum so that no salinity correction was necessary. Because the principal solutes in most water samples were sodium chloride and calcium sulfate, the effect of fractionation between vapor and low-volatility hydrous residue was small. The quantitatively distilled water was analyzed for oxygen isotope composi-

tion by the $CO_2$-equilibration technique at 25.4°C (EPSTEIN and MAYEDA, 1953).

Hydrogen gas was quantitatively produced from water samples by reaction with uranium metal at 800°C (BIGELEISEN et al., 1952). The hydrogen was collected by means of a Toepler pump and the HD/HH ratio was determined by mass spectrometry.

Ratios of the stable oxygen and carbon isotopes in carbonates were measured on the carbon dioxide liberated using a modification of the method described by EPSTEIN et al. (1964), in which $CO_2$ collected after one hour is attributed to calcite, and $CO_2$ collected after three hours is attributed to dolomite, allowing the determination of δ-values for both of these carbonates in a mixture. For all the carbonate samples a three-day reaction time yielded at least 60% of the gas and acceptably reproducible δ-values.

All stable isotope data are reported in per mil in the usual delta (δ) notation, expressed relative to internationally accepted references. Mean values of replicate analyses were used in the interpretations. The $\delta^{18}O$ and $\delta^{13}C$ values of pure calcite samples were precise to ±0.1 per mil or less, but the variation in measurements of dolomites was typically ≤ ±0.4 per mil.

Typical confidence limits (at the 95% level) for replicate analyses of water $\delta^{18}O$ values were about 0.25 per mil, whereas confidence limits for replicate δD analyses were typically ±2.5 per mil.

## DISCUSSION

### Hydrologic context for groundwaters

Distinctions made on more than one basis (isotopic as well as hydraulic) allow the identification of fossil as well as actively recharged groundwater systems. The occurrences of waters in the Delaware Basin are here categorized according to four types.

*Vadose-zone waters.* The most readily accessible sampling points in the unsaturated (vadose) zone were standing pools receiving dripwater in Carlsbad Caverns, in the northern Guadalupe Mountains (Fig. 1). The dominant mechanism of recharge to Carlsbad Caverns pools is vertical infiltration into near-surface outcrops of overlying dolomite of the Tansill and Yates Formations. Residence times of several weeks to months have been reported, "with no apparent relationship to depth below the surface" (WILLIAMS, 1983).

*Near-surface waters.* Samples of near-surface waters came from a geographically widespread area in the Delaware Basin (Fig. 1). Stormwaters were collected at the surface in the city of Carlsbad and at the WIPP-29 borehole site. A major through-flowing stream that drains the region, the Pecos River, was sampled at Lake Carlsbad. The surface elevations at these sampling sites (Table 1) are representative of the surface elevation over much of southeastern New Mexico and Texas. Surprise Spring, an intermittent spring issuing from the Tamarisk member of the Rustler Formation near the north end of Laguna Grande de la Sal (Fig. 2)

Table 1. Waters from the Vadose Zone and the surface

| Location | Sampling date | Elev.[1] (ft asl) | $\delta D$ ‰ SMOW | $\delta^{18}O$ ‰ SMOW | Analyst[2] |
|---|---|---|---|---|---|
| *Carlsbad Caverns Pools* | | | | | |
| Green Lake Green Lake Room | 29 Aug 76 | 3575 | −24 | −3.6 | (a) |
| Mirror Lake Big Room | 29 Aug 76 | 3660 | −28 | −4.3 | (a) |
| Longfellow's Bathtub Big Room | 29 Aug 76 | 3660 | −29 | −4.2 | (a) |
| Celery Stalk Pool Big Room | 29 Aug 76 | 3660 | −20 | −3.0 | (a) |
| Devil's Spring Main Corridor | 09 Jun 77 | 4100 | −30 | −4.4 | (a) |
| Horsehead Lake New Mexico Room | 09 Jun 77 | 3672 | −39 | −4.8 | (a) |
| Lake of the Clouds | 09 Jun 77 | 3311 | −33 | −5.1 | (a) |
| Junction/Rope Pool Left-Hand Tunnel | 09 Jun 77 | 3641 | −32 | −6.3 | (a) |
| Lower Cave Pool | 09 Jun 77 | 3625 | −17 | −1.7 | (a) |
| Music Room Main Corridor | 21 Dec 77 | 4100 | −32 −31 | −4.0 −4.0 | (b), (c) (b), (c) |
| Naturalist's Room Lower Cave | 21 Dec 77 | 3575 | −24 −23 | −3.5 | (b), (c) (b) |
| Grass Skirt Pool New Mexico Room | 21 Dec 77 | 3670 | −37 −37 | −4.2 −3.7 | (b), (c) (b), (c) |
| *Stream, Storm, and Spring Waters* | | | | | |
| Pecos River Lake Carlsbad | 08 Jun 77 | 3111 | −36 | −3.6 | (a) |
| McKittrick Canyon stream | 13 Jun 84 | 6000 | −49 −50 | −8.1 −8.1 | (d) (d) |
| Carlsbad storm Rodeway Inn | 05 May 77 | 3150 | −80 | −10.3 | (a) |
| Carlsbad storm Rodeway Inn | 11 Aug 77 | 3150 | −18 −19 | | (b) (b) |
| Storm, WIPP-29 1750–1815 h | 26 Aug 80 | 2975 | −18 −20 | −2.3 | (b), (c) (b) |
| Surprise Spring SW Nash Draw | 20 Dec 77 | 2950 | −31 −30 | −1.8 −1.2 −1.0 | (b), (c) (b), (c) (c) |

[1] Cavern elevations were provided by Dr. G. AHLSTRAND, National Park Service. Other elevations were taken from U.S.G.S. topographic maps.

[2] Analysts as follows:

    (a) $\delta D$ and $\delta^{18}O$, J. R. O'NEIL, U.S. Geological Survey.

    (b) $\delta D$, C. J. YAPP, Univ. of New Mexico.

    (c) $\delta^{18}O$, LAMBERT and HARVEY, (1987).

was also sampled. Because of its location in southwestern Nash Draw, it is a likely discharge for some of the groundwater in the Rustler Formation. A local stream that drains a portion of the southern Guadalupe Mountains was sampled in McKittrick Canyon, together with the travertine it has deposited in historic times.

*Shallow groundwaters.* Shallow groundwaters, commonly under perched or water-table conditions, include groundwaters from alluvium, the late Permian Dewey Lake Red Beds, Triassic rocks, and the late Cenozoic Ogallala Formation. Groundwaters nearest the surface and under water-table conditions have a greater probability of receiving recharge by direct infiltration from the surface than do groundwaters under confined conditions.

*Confined groundwaters of the Capitan Limestone and Rustler Formation.* The Capitan Limestone east of the Pecos River contains groundwater under confined conditions (*i.e.,* water levels in wells rise above an upper confining horizon) in its cavernous porosity. Direct vertical infiltration into this portion of the Capitan is inhibited by the overlying soluble evaporites of low permeability (SNYDER and GARD, 1982; BACHMAN, 1985).

In the water-bearing gypsiferous dolomite members of the Rustler Formation (Magenta and Culebra) near the WIPP site, potentiometric levels increase and permeabilities are lower toward the east or northeast. Except locally in Nash Draw, Rustler groundwater is under confined conditions (MERCER, 1983). Where the potentiometric levels are higher to the east and northeast, the low-permeability overburden is thicker and the overall Rustler Formation permeability is generally lower. Thus, the observed relatively high potentiometric levels may not be caused by significant amounts of recharge by vertical infiltration.

### Vadose-zone waters

The elevations of sampling stations, dates of collection, and isotopic compositions of waters from Carlsbad Caverns are given in Table 1 and their isotopic compositions are plotted in Fig. 3. Data for Carlsbad Caverns waters generally lie on or near the meteoric field. Some caverns waters have apparently undergone some kinetically induced isotopic fractionation due to partial evaporation from the surface of free-standing water in the humid speleal environment. The isotopic compositions of Carlsbad Caverns waters are probably derived from meteoric recharge to the unsaturated zone, allowing for some scatter arising from partial evaporation and recent seasonal variations.

### Near-surface waters

Isotopic compositions of near-surface waters from the northern Delaware Basin are given in Table 1, including $\delta D$ and $\delta^{18}O$ values for storms in May and August, the Pecos River at Lake Carlsbad in June, the McKittrick Canyon stream, and Surprise Spring. Figure 3 shows the positions of these data in $\delta D/\delta^{18}O$ space, together with the meteoric field and the Carlsbad Caverns field.

The $\delta D$ values of the summer stormwaters (26 Aug 80 and 11 Aug 77) are statistically indistinguishable. They are probably more representative of modern rainfall than the springtime stormwater from Carlsbad on 5 May 77 (which is much more depleted in D and $^{18}O$), because most of the Delaware Basin precipitation occurs during the summer (HUNTER, 1985). Isotopic compositions of individual precipitation events are given here only to illustrate the range of seasonal isotopic effects in the Delaware Basin. A more reliable estimate of seasonally averaged isotopic compositions of local me-

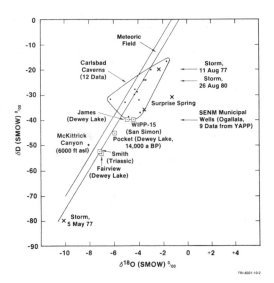

FIG. 3. Stable-isotope compositions of near-surface waters and shallow groundwaters in southeastern New Mexico. The "meteoric field" in this and following $\delta D/\delta^{18}O$ plots is taken to be the area between the lines defined by CRAIG (1961) and EPSTEIN et al. (1965, 1970).

teoric water might be obtained from perennial streams and springs, as suggested by FRIEDMAN et al. (1964), or from groundwaters that can be shown to originate from direct infiltration under prevalent climatic conditions.

The isotopic composition of the Pecos River, sampled at Lake Carlsbad in June, probably represents the period of highest runoff feeding the river's tributaries upstream and falls near the field of most other surface-derived waters. Its isotopic composition is probably influenced by upstream precipitation at higher elevations and by evaporation.

The spring-fed stream in McKittrick Canyon has a $\delta^{18}O$ value of $-8.1$. If such a stream has a relatively constant isotopic composition, as discussed by FRIEDMAN et al. (1964), then its isotopic composition may represent a seasonal average for modern meteoric water at an elevation of 6000 ft in southeastern New Mexico.

### Shallow groundwaters

Groundwater under water-table conditions was sampled from the alluvial fill of San Simon Sink (SANDIA NATIONAL LABORATORIES and UNIVERSITY OF NEW MEXICO, 1981). Groundwaters sampled from the Dewey Lake Red Beds and Triassic rocks may be either under confined or perched conditions. The isotopic compositions of these shallow groundwaters are given in Table 2, and the data are plotted in Fig. 3. Isotopic compositions of

Table 2. Waters from shallow wells (post-Rustler units)

| Location | Sampling date | Depth[1] (ft) | $\delta D$ ‰ SMOW | $\delta^{18}O$ ‰ SMOW | Analyst[2] |
|---|---|---|---|---|---|
| James Ranch prob. Dewey Lake[3] | 11 Dec 75 | 166.4 | −40 | −5.0 | (a) |
| Smith Livingston Ridge prob. Triassic[4] | 09 Jun 76 | 167.3 | −52 | −7.2 | (a) |
| Fairview prob. Dewey Lake[5] | 11 Dec 76 | 361.3 | −53 | −7.1 | (a) |
| WIPP-15 (alluvium) San Simon Sink | 12 Mar 77 | 445–540 | −37 −40 | −4.5 | (b), (c) |
| Pocket Dewey Lake[6] | 11 Nov 83 | 223.9 | −45 | −6.0 | (d) |

[1] Depth of slotted interval in casing, or total depth of well.
[2] Analysts as follows:
  (a) $\delta D$ and $\delta^{18}O$, J. R. O'NEIL, U.S. Geological Survey.
  (b) $\delta D$, C. J. YAPP, Univ. of New Mexico.
  (c) $\delta^{18}O$, LAMBERT and HARVEY (1987).
  (d) $\delta D$, $\delta^{18}O$, Hydro Geo Chem, Tucson, AZ.
[3] "Ranch Headquarters Well," 23.31.6.444 as listed by COOPER and GLANZMAN (1971). Previously considered a Rustler well by LAMBERT (1978).
[4] 22.31.15.130a as listed by COOPER and GLANZMAN (1971).
[5] 23.31.26.340 as listed by COOPER and GLANZMAN (1971).
[6] "Walker Well," 23.31.29.113 as listed by COOPER and GLANZMAN (1971).

groundwaters from the Ogallala Sandstone in the High Plains province of Texas (NATIV and SMITH, 1987) were used for comparison, because the High Plains province, due east of the Delaware Basin, has latitudes, elevations, topography, vegetative cover, and climatic conditions similar to those of the Delaware Basin.

*Groundwater in alluvium.* The San Simon Sink (WIPP-15) water was sampled through slotted well-casing open to alluvium. The water-table conditions at WIPP-15 probably represent a greater degree of interconnection with surficial recharge than do confined conditions.

*Groundwater in the Dewey Lake Red Beds.* Groundwater occurrences in the Dewey Lake Red Beds near the WIPP site were described as localized, laterally discontinuous, perched or semiperched, developed in lenticular "sands," and probably depend largely on locally favorable conditions for recharge (MERCER, 1983). The isotopic compositions of Dewey Lake groundwaters vary significantly.

The isotopic composition of the James Ranch well is near the meteoric field and the WIPP-15 point. The well's proximity to a large area of sand dunes (MERCER, 1983) implies that infiltration can readily proceed there, and thus its $\delta D$ and $\delta^{18}O$ values probably represent modern recharge. The $\delta D$ and $\delta^{18}O$ values of the water from Pocket well (Table 2; Fig. 3) are significantly more negative than those from the James Ranch well and from alluvium in San Simon Sink. LAMBERT (1987) found that the

apparent radiocarbon age of Pocket water is 14,000 radiocarbon years, using the interpretive numerical model of EVANS *et al.* (1979). Its age suggests that its $\delta D$ and $\delta^{18}O$ values, which are lower than those of James Ranch and WIPP-15 waters, are less affected by modern recharge. The $\delta D$ and $\delta^{18}O$ values of Fairview water (Table 2) are significantly more negative than those of most other shallow groundwaters, including those having probable hydraulic connections with the surface at elevations of 3000 to 4000 ft, such as at WIPP-15 and James Ranch.

*Groundwater in Triassic rocks.* The isotopic composition of water from the Smith well, which appears to tap a water-producing horizon in the Triassic (COOPER and GLANZMAN, 1971), is indistinguishable from that of Dewey Lake water from Fairview (Table 2; Fig. 3). Its $\delta D$ and $\delta^{18}O$ values are significantly different from those of probably modern recharge to local groundwaters (WIPP-15 and James Ranch).

*Groundwater in sandstone of the Ogallala Formation.* The $\delta D$, $\delta^{18}O$, and tritium values of groundwaters from the Ogallala Formation and related units underlying the Southern High Plains of Texas were reported by NATIV and SMITH (1987). Only those High Plains groundwaters having $\delta D$ values more positive than −42 have significant levels of tritium (>10 Tritium Units; 1 TU = 1 tritium atom in $10^{18}$ hydrogen atoms), indicating that demonstrably modern (post-1950) recharge on the High Plains is relatively enriched in deuterium (Fig.

4). Values less than about 10 TU are not considered conclusively indicative of a large degree of hydraulic connection with the surface since about 1950 (ISAACSON *et al.*, 1974). Since the elevations, climate, and vegetative cover are similar in the Southern High Plains and the northern Delaware Basin, it is here inferred that conditions governing recharge of groundwaters are probably also similar.

Figure 5 shows the isotopic relations for High Plains Ogallala waters reported by NATIV and SMITH (1987), not including those judged by them to be contaminated. These data points do not deviate significantly from the meteoric field, supporting the contention that these waters have not undergone significant partial evaporation prior to recharge. Although the waters having >10 TU occur in the more positive half of the range of $\delta D$ and $\delta^{18}O$ values, that half of the range also contains waters having <10 TU. This suggests that the prevalent climatic conditions governing modern Ogallala recharge on the High Plains, represented by more positive $\delta$-values, began prior to 1950 when atmospheric tritium was less abundant. The low levels of tritium in waters with $\delta D$ values more negative than −42, however, indicate that such waters contain only a minimal component recharged from the atmosphere since 1950. Thus, NATIV and SMITH's (1987) Ogallala waters having $\delta D$ values more negative than about −42 may represent recharge prior to the time when present recharge and climatic conditions were established in the High Plains.

C. J. YAPP (unpubl. data) has measured several $\delta D$ values for water from the Ogallala Formation from eastern New Mexico. These samples were from wells in Ogallala Sandstone and/or Quaternary alluvium. The Ogallala groundwater in this region is under water-table conditions (NICHOLSON and

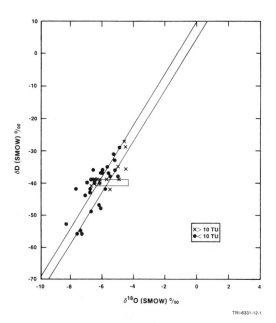

FIG. 5. Stable-isotope compositions of groundwaters from the Southern High Plains, Texas. Data are from NATIV and SMITH (1987). The $\delta D$ range of Ogallala groundwaters (rectangle) from southeastern New Mexico analyzed by YAPP (unpublished) is shown for comparison.

CLEBSCH, 1961). The $\delta D$ values are −39 to −41 (Fig. 3), well within the population of Ogallala $\delta D$ values of the High Plains groundwaters having significant tritium levels (Fig. 5).

*Isotopic signature of modern Delaware Basin recharge*

Occurrences of groundwater in San Simon Sink, parts of the Ogallala Formation, and probably the Dewey Lake at James Ranch have demonstrable or inferred degrees of hydraulic connection with the surface, and their stable isotope compositions are typical of demonstrably modern meteorically derived recharge to groundwater in the northern Delaware Basin at elevations between 3000 and 4000 ft. Recharge to Carlsbad Caverns pools in the unsaturated zone of the Capitan Limestone is responsive to rainfall (WILLIAMS, 1983), but the seasonal variations in the isotopic compositions of vadose water are not known.

The seasonally averaged isotopic composition of modern recharge to groundwater systems in the north-central Delaware Basin is inferred to have a $\delta D$ value more positive than −42 (Fig. 4). Modern Delaware Basin groundwaters having $\delta D$ values more negative than about −42 generally originate as precipitation at higher elevations (*e.g.,* McKittrick Canyon). Summer precipitation in the

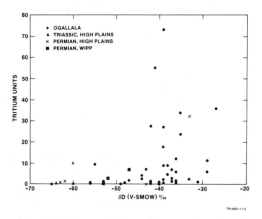

FIG. 4. Tritium and deuterium concentrations in groundwaters from the Southern High Plains, Texas, and the Delaware Basin, southeastern New Mexico. High Plains data are from NATIV and SMITH (1987).

Delaware Basin and surrounding areas is believed to be more abundant than that in winter over periods of several years (HUNTER, 1985) and thus may be volumetrically more important in recharging local shallow groundwater systems. Hence, groundwaters at lower elevations having δ-values more negative than those of modern recharge are likely to have been recharged under a different climatic regime, rather than during modern winters or at higher elevations.

### Confined groundwaters in the Capitan Limestone

The stratigraphy and hydrology of the Capitan Limestone have been described in detail by HISS (1975). In the Guadalupe Mountains near Carlsbad Caverns, the elevation of the water table is approximately 3100 ft (BJORKLUND and MOTTS, 1959). This is at least 200 ft below the lowest surveyed level of the accessible vadose zone in Carlsbad Caverns (JAGNOW, 1979). East of the Pecos River, where the Capitan is buried (Fig. 1), water in the Capitan is under confined (artesian) conditions, making recharge by direct vertical infiltration unlikely.

The isotopic compositions of waters from four wells in the eastern (confined) part of the Capitan, whose locations are shown in Fig. 1, are given in Table 3. The small range of δ-values for waters from these wells, relative to the larger range in isotopic compositions of caverns waters, indicates that isotopic mixing and homogenization have been much more efficient in the confined zone than in the unsaturated zone. Such homogenization probably results from longer flow paths, longer residence times, or both.

Water from McKittrick Canyon (Table 1) is similar in δD and $δ^{18}O$ to eastern confined Capitan waters. This might imply that water from the southern Guadalupe Mountains recharges the confined zones in the eastern parts of the Capitan (e.g., Middleton and Shell No. 28). However, HISS (1975) described the West Laguna Submarine Canyon, a local thinning of the Capitan between the Hackberry and Middleton wells (Fig. 1), as an efficient hydraulic constriction near the northern apex of the Capitan limestone.

Confined hydraulic conditions in the Capitan preclude a direct connection to the surface through the overlying evaporite section. The stable isotope compositions of Capitan groundwaters east of Carlsbad are significantly different from those of modern recharge at lower elevations in the Delaware Basin (Fig. 6) and were probably recharged under different climatic conditions than those that now govern recharge.

### Groundwaters in the Rustler Formation

*Rustler groundwaters confined within dolomite layers.* MERCER (1983) has summarized the general hydrology of the water-bearing gypsiferous dolomite units in the Rustler Formation. Groundwater flow in the Magenta, based on density-corrected potentiometric contours, is westward from the WIPP site toward Nash Draw; Culebra flow is dominantly southward over the WIPP site, then westward. Culebra transmissivity values vary from about $10^{-1}$ $ft^2$/day east of the WIPP site to $10^3$ $ft^2$/day in Nash Draw. Transmissivity values in the Magenta where saturated are about an order of magnitude smaller (MERCER, 1983). Static water-levels are about 100 ft higher in the Magenta than in the Culebra at H-1, H-2, and H-3 (MERCER, 1983) where halite, gypsum, or anhydrite has not been removed from the intervening Tamarisk member by dissolution (SNYDER, 1985); hence, this potentiometric differential indicates a poorly developed vertical connection.

Isotopic compositions of waters from the Rustler Formation are given in Table 3, and plotted in Fig. 6. The plot includes data for waters from the Magenta, Culebra, and Tamarisk members (i.e., Surprise Spring), and shows that with the exception of WIPP-29 Culebra and Surprise Spring, all Rustler well waters are tightly clustered in $δD/δ^{18}O$ space on or near the meteoric field, spanning no more than 12 per mil in δD and no more than 2.2 per mil in $δ^{18}O$. Despite their mutual hydraulic isolation, Magenta and Culebra waters have isotopic compositions that are indistinguishable from one another. These isotopic compositions do not overlap the range of modern meteoric recharge, represented by the modern Ogallala groundwaters.

The two discrete populations of isotopic compositions are divisible according to the hydrologic conditions they represent. The Rustler groundwaters under confined conditions which have meteoric isotopic signatures are more depleted in D and $^{18}O$ than other Delaware Basin groundwaters from the vadose zone, perched bodies, or the water table. Thus, the dichotomy in stable isotope compositions of the Rustler waters and modern Delaware Basin recharge at comparable elevations is consistent with the hypothesis that the confined Rustler groundwaters are not currently receiving significant recharge.

The isotopic compositions of groundwaters under confined conditions from the Rustler occupy the same general position in $δD/δ^{18}O$ space as do the data points for confined groundwaters from the eastern portion of the Capitan Limestone. The tight clustering of δ-values of waters from a widespread

Table 3. Waters from confined units

| Location[1] | Sampling date | Depth[2] (ft) | δD‰ SMOW | δ$^{18}$O‰ SMOW | Analyst[3] |
|---|---|---|---|---|---|
| *Magenta Dolomite member, Rustler formation* | | | | | |
| *Collected by USGS* | | | | | |
| H-1 | 04 Jun 76 | 563–589 | −48 | −6.8 | (a) |
| H-2A | 22 Feb 77 | 513 | −46 | −6.3 | (a) |
| H-3 | 10 May 77 | 557–608 | −53 | −7.3 | (a) |
| *Collected by Lambert and Robinson* | | | | | |
| WIPP-25 | 17 Sep 80 | 302–328 | −44 | −6.2 | (b), (c) |
| | | | −43 | | (b) |
| WIPP-27 | 25 Sep 80 | 176–194 | −46 | −6.3 | (b), (c) |
| | | | −47 | | (b) |
| H-3B1 (= H-3) | 01 Jul 85 | 557–608 | | −6.7 | (c) |
| | | | | −6.7 | (c) |
| *Culebra Dolomite member, Rustler formation* | | | | | |
| *Collected by USGS* | | | | | |
| H-1 | 02 Jun 76 | 676–699 | −50 | −7.0 | (a) |
| H-2B | 22 Feb 77 | 623–645 | −53 | −7.2 | (a) |
| H-2C | 16 Mar 77 | 623–645 | −53 | −6.9 | (a) |
| H-3 | 17 Mar 77 | 672–694 | −53 | −7.0 | (a) |
| H-6B | 19 Dec 78 | 604–627 | −49 | | (b) |
| | | | −47 | | (b) |
| H-9A | 05 Feb 80 | 647–677 | −48 | | (b) |
| | | | −49 | | (b) |
| H-9B | 05 Feb 80 | 647–677 | −51 | | (b) |
| | | | −51 | | (b) |
| P-14 | 14 Mar 77 | 573–595 | −48 | −6.3 | (a) |
| P-15 | 10 May 77 | 413–435 | −52 | −7.3 | (a) |
| Indian[4] prob. Culebra | 08 Jun 76 | 203.6 | −46 | −6.3 | (a) |
| Mobley[5] prob. Culebra | 08 Jun 76 | 89.0 | −44 | −6.9 | (a) |
| Mobley #3[6] prob. Culebra | 08 Jun 76 | 318.4 | −44 | −5.9 | (a) |
| *Collected by Lambert and Robinson* | | | | | |
| WIPP-25 | 20 Aug 80 | 447–472 | −43 | −6.4 | (b), (c) |
| | | | −44 | | (b) |
| WIPP-26 | 24 Aug 80 | 186–209 | −43 | −6.5 | (b), (c) |
| | | | −44 | | (b) |
| WIPP-27 | 05 Sep 80 | 292–318 | −44 | −6.1 | (b), (c) |
| | | | −47 | | (b) |
| WIPP-28 | 11 Sep 80 | 420–446 | −46 | −6.6 | (b), (c) |
| | | | −46 | | (b) |
| WIPP-29 | 28 Aug 80 | 012–042 | −27 | −0.5 | (b), (c) |
| | | | −27 | −0.4 | (b), (c) |
| WIPP-30 | 06 Sep 80 | 631–654 | −50 | −7.1 | (b), (c) |
| | | | −50 | | (b) |
| *Collected by HGC* | | | | | |
| H-3 [*sic*] | 11 Jun 84 | 672–694 | −54 | | (d) |
| | | | −56 | | (d) |
| | | | −53 | | (d) |
| | | | −54 | | (d) |
| H-3B3 | 04 Feb 85 | 672–694 | −53 | | (d) |
| | | | −53 | | (d) |
| H-4C | 10 Aug 84 | 490–516 | −51 | | (d) |
| | | | −53 | | (d) |
| H-9 [*sic*] | 06 Oct 83 | 647–677 | −54 | −8.0 | (e) |
| DOE-1 | 20 Apr 83 | 821–843 | −48 | −6.1 | (e) |
| Engle | 11 Oct 83 | 423.6 | −52 | −7.2 | (e) |
| RF-10 (H-13) | 06 Oct 83 | 172–207 | −45 | −7.3 | (e) |
| *Collected by WQSP* | | | | | |
| H-4B | 25 Jul 85 | 498–522 | | −6.7 | (d) |
| | | | | −6.5 | (d) |

Table 3. (Continued)

| Location[1] | Sampling date | Depth[2] (ft) | δD ‰ SMOW | δ¹⁸O ‰ SMOW | Analyst[3] |
|---|---|---|---|---|---|
| H-5B | 27 Aug 85 | 897–920 | | −6.8 | (d) |
| | | | | −6.8 | (d) |
| H-6B | 15 Sep 85 | 604–627 | | −7.1 | (d) |
| H-11B3 | 04 Jun 85 | 710 | | −6.8 | (d) |
| | | | | −6.8 | (d) |
| H-12 | 09 Aug 85 | 825–852[7] | | −6.9 | (d) |
| | | | | −7.2 | (d) |
| | | | | −6.8 | (d) |
| DOE-1 | 24 Apr 85 | 821–843 | −58 | −6.8 | (d) |
| | | | −55 | −6.9 | (d) |
| | | | −54 | −7.0 | (d) |
| DOE-2 | 11 Mar 85 | 822–848 | −51 | −6.9 | (d) |
| | | | −51 | −6.8 | (d) |
| | | | −53 | −7.1 | (d) |
| | | | −53 | | (d) |
| Engle | 04 Mar 85 | WL = 423.6 | −54 | −7.0 | (d) |
| | | | −57 | −7.0 | (d) |
| | | | −53 | | (d) |

*Rustler/Salado contact zone*

*Collected by USGS*

| Duval Nash Draw mine shaft collector ring | 09 Dec 75 | ≈350 | −48 | −6.4 | (a) |
|---|---|---|---|---|---|
| H-1 | 23 Feb 77 | 824 | −29 | 1.6 | (a) |
| H-2C | 23 Feb 77 | 764 | −41 | −2.9 | (a) |
| H-3 | 23 Feb 77 | 821 | −38 | 0.2 | (a) |
| H-4C | 16 Mar 79 | 626 | −57 | −4.0 | (a) |
| H-5C | 16 May 79 | 1041 | −44 | −1.9 | (a) |
| H-6C | 09 Apr 79 | 721 | −53 | −4.9 | (a) |
| P-14 | 24 Feb 77 | 687 | −64 | −9.0 | (a) |
| P-17 | 11 May 79 | 715 | −50 | −1.4 | (a) |

*Collected by Lambert and Robinson*

| WIPP-25 | 17 Jul 80 | 565 | −52 | −7.1 | (b), (c) |
|---|---|---|---|---|---|
| | | | −52 | | (b) |
| WIPP-26 | 23 Jul 80 | 309 | −46 | −6.7 | (b), (c) |
| | | | −47 | | (b), (c) |
| WIPP-28 | 31 Jul 80 | 531 | −58 | −7.0 | (b), (c) |
| | | | −57 | | (b) |
| WIPP-29 | 24 Jul 80 | 143 | −47 | −7.0 | (b), (c) |
| | | | −48 | | (b) |
| WIPP-30 | 17 Jul 80 | 749 | −53 | −7.1 | (b), (c) |
| | | | −51 | | (b) |

*Capitan Limestone*

| Carlsbad #7 | 12 Dec 75 | 143[8] | −54 | −7.9 | (a) |
|---|---|---|---|---|---|
| Shell #28 | 13 Dec 75 | 5100 | −56 | −7.7 | (a) |
| Middleton | 10 Dec 75 | 1700 | −55 | −7.5 | (a) |
| Hackberry | 12 Dec 75 | 3900 | −46 | −6.5 | (a) |

[1] For collection methodologies used by the various indicated agencies, see the following:
USGS: Mercer and Orr (1979); MERCER (1983)
Lambert and Robinson: LAMBERT and ROBINSON (1984)
HGC: HYDRO GEO CHEM (1984)
WQSP: COLTON and MORSE (1985).

[2] Sampling depth or depth interval, from local datum (typically ground level), isolated by packers, casing, perforations, or combinations thereof. WL = depth to water level.

[3] Analysts as follows:
  (a) δD and δ¹⁸O, J. R. O'NEIL, U.S. Geological Survey.
  (b) δD, C. J. YAPP, Univ. of New Mexico.
  (c) δ¹⁸O, LAMBERT and HARVEY (1987).
  (d) δD and δ¹⁸O, LAMBERT and HARVEY (1987).
  (e) δD and δ¹⁸O, Hydro Geo Chem, Tucson, AZ.

[4] 23.30.21.122 as listed by COOPER and GLANZMAN (1971).

[5] "South Well," 23.30.19.123 as listed by COOPER and GLANZMAN (1971).

[6] "Little Windmill Well," 23.30.2.444a as listed by COOPER and GLANZMAN (1971).

[7] Open-hole; no packers or perforations.

[8] Cased to 118 ft depth (HENDRICKSON and JONES, 1952).

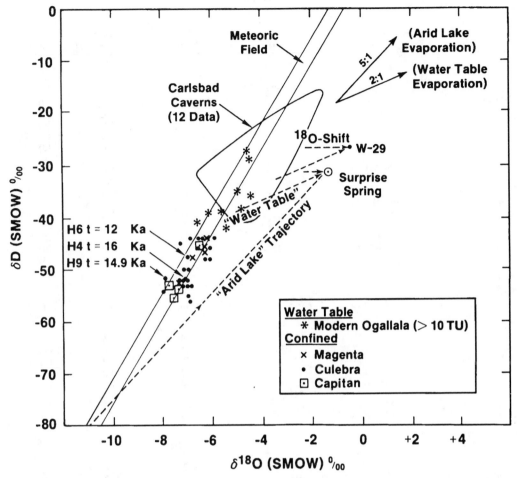

FIG. 6. Stable-isotope compositions of confined groundwaters from the Rustler Formation and Capitan Limestone. The isotopic compositions of demonstrably modern Ogallala groundwaters containing significant (>10 TU) tritium are shown for comparison.

geographic area indicates homogeneous conditions of recharge, long flow paths, long residence times, or a combination thereof, in the confined Capitan and in both the Culebra and Magenta; the last two units are not well connected, except at WIPP-25 and WIPP-27 in Nash Draw (Fig. 2).

WIPP-29 Culebra and Surprise Spring (in the southwestern part of Nash Draw) neither lie near the meteoric field nor bear any similarity to any of the other waters in Nash Draw. At this time it is not possible to determine a unique cause for the isolation of WIPP-29 Culebra and Surprise Spring in δD/δ¹⁸O space. Their isotopic compositions, however, show that they are not derived by direct flowage from other Rustler waters, either in Nash Draw or the WIPP site. Discharge from Surprise Spring and its relation with WIPP-29 are discussed below.

*Rustler/Salado contact zone.* Groundwater flow in the Rustler/Salado contact zone (the "brine aquifer" of ROBINSON and LANG, 1938) as described by MERCER (1983) is southwest across the WIPP site toward Nash Draw. Stable isotope data for waters from the zone near the Rustler/Salado contact are given in Table 3 and are plotted in Fig. 7. There is no overlap between any of the data for Rustler/Salado contact waters and the field of modern recharge. Also, δ-values of waters from the Rustler/Salado contact in and near Nash Draw are clustered near the meteoric field. δ-values of waters from farther east near the WIPP site deviate significantly from the meteoric field. The cause of this deviation is probably related to the eastward decrease in transmissivity (*i.e.,* effective water/rock ratio), from $10^1$ to $10^{-4}$ ft²/day. Partial evaporation is not a plausible cause for the deviation from the meteoric field, because water from the zone near the Rustler/Salado contact is under confined conditions in Nash Draw and at the WIPP site (MERCER, 1983).

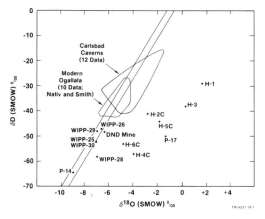

FIG. 7. Stable-isotope compositions of groundwaters from the Rustler/Salado contact.

The geographic distribution of isotopic variations of Rustler/Salado contact waters is shown in Fig. 8. The contours depict arithmetic deviations of the $\delta^{18}O$ values from the mean regional meteoric value of $-7$, represented by the isotopic compositions of meteoric Rustler/Salado contact waters in the high-permeability region of Nash Draw. These contours generally parallel the dissolution/subsidence scarp that defines the eastern boundary of Nash Draw. The zero contour is offset about 1.5 to 3 km east of the scarp, and roughly corresponds to the division between higher values of transmissivity to the west ($>10^{-2}$ ft$^2$/day) and lower values ($<10^{-2}$ ft$^2$/day) to the east.

Superimposed on the contours of oxygen isotope shift in Fig. 8 are the boundaries of zones delineated by SNYDER (1985) according to the uppermost occurrence of halite in the Rustler Formation. The zones are, from southeast to northwest: (1) top of halite in the Forty-niner member, above the Magenta Dolomite, (2) top of halite in the Tamarisk member, between the Magenta and Culebra Dolomites, (3) top of halite in the lower (unnamed) member, below the Culebra Dolomite, and (4) top of halite in the Salado Formation, with no halite in the Rustler Formation. The contours roughly parallel the boundaries of Rustler halite zones, and the $+3$ per mil contour partly coincides with the western-most occurrence of Rustler halite. The west-to-east increase in isotopic deviation indicates that circulation of meteoric fluids is more restricted toward the east, reflecting a smaller water/rock ratio. This is consistent with Mercer's conclusion that the extreme variability (*i.e.,* east-to-west increase) of transmissivities in the various parts of the Rustler Formation results from the size and number of fractures, which in turn are related to the degree of evaporite dissolution within the Rustler Formation.

The $\delta D/\delta^{18}O$ trend for waters from zones of lower permeability, represented by H-1, H-2C, H-3, H-4C, H-5C, H-6C, and P-17 in Fig. 7, intersects with the meteoric field at isotopic compositions representative of much of the Rustler, reflecting a meteoric origin. Greater displacements from the meteoric field along this trend are generally correlative with smaller water/rock ratios. This trend is reminiscent of that resulting from water/rock interactions with small water/rock ratios, but whether such interactions consist of isotopic exchange between small amounts of meteoric water and mineral sources such as gypsum and polyhalite, or mixing with evaporite brines as proposed by KNAUTH and BEEUNAS (1986) and O'NEIL *et al.* (1986), is not known.

*The age of Rustler groundwaters*

LAMBERT (1987) found that application of the model of EVANS *et al.* (1979) to 12 of 16 selected Rustler groundwaters gave significantly large negative radiocarbon ages, reflecting the addition of excess modern (anthropogenic) carbon, introduced during drilling operations and contaminating the native fluid. The remaining four groundwaters have the following apparent ages (in radiocarbon years): H-4, 16,100; H-9, 14,900; H-6, 12,100 (all Culebra); Pocket (Dewey Lake), 14,000. These apparent ages are statistically indistinguishable from one another.

The stable isotope compositions of these dated groundwaters are marked in Fig. 6 and are distinct from those of the tritium-bearing Ogallala groundwaters inferred to have been recharged under present regional climatic conditions. Given that these groundwaters could contain traces of contaminant $^{14}C$, their apparent radiocarbon ages are regarded as minimum times of isolation from the atmosphere. These residence times probably represent the time of cessation of recharge at the close of an interval of wetter climate in the Pleistocene. Independent evidence of wetter Pleistocene climate in southeastern New Mexico has been presented by VAN DEVENDER (1980), who determined from packrat middens in Rocky Arroyo east of Carlsbad (Fig. 1) that a juniper-oak plant community existed there 10,500 to 10,000 years ago, at an elevation of about 3600 ft, where desert scrub communities have been stable for the last 4,000 years.

A limited number of high-precision tritium measurements are also available for Culebra and Dewey Lake groundwaters near the WIPP site. Figure 9 shows the geographic distribution of wells whose waters were analyzed for tritium. Tritium values from the WIPP site and the area immediately south range from $-0.08$ to $+2.8$ TU. Such low but mea-

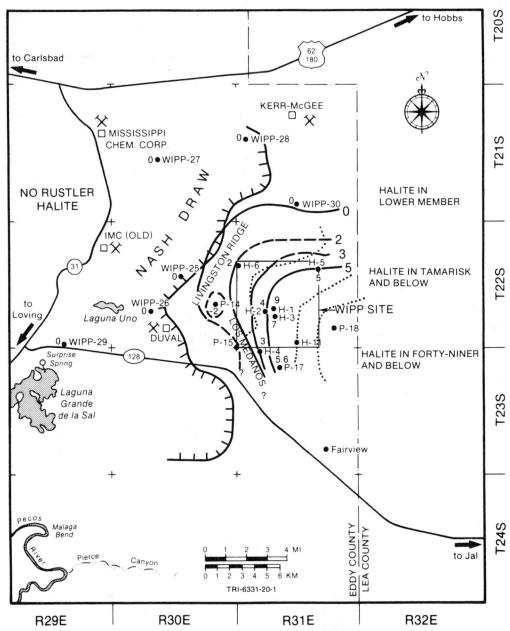

FIG. 8. Contour map of oxygen-isotope deviation in confined groundwaters at the Rustler/Salado contact, relative to $\delta^{18}O = -7$. Dotted lines are boundaries of SNYDER (1985) delineating the occurrences of halite in various members of the Rustler.

surable tritium counts are generally considered indistinguishable from zero, according to EVANS *et al.* (1979). Thus, the tritium data from seven localities show conclusively that the travel time between the surface and the Culebra or parts of the Dewey Lake has been greater than 40 years, since these waters do not contain the tritium spike that was introduced into the atmosphere by post-1950 nuclear detonations.

The radiocarbon dates show that the time of isolation from the atmosphere for groundwaters at four widely separated locations (Fig. 9) has been at least 12,000 years; in the absence of a statistically significant difference among the four radiocarbon dates, a significant north-to-south age gradient cannot be inferred. The age range 12,000 to 16,000 radiocarbon years is tentatively considered the minimum residence time of the Rustler, Dewey

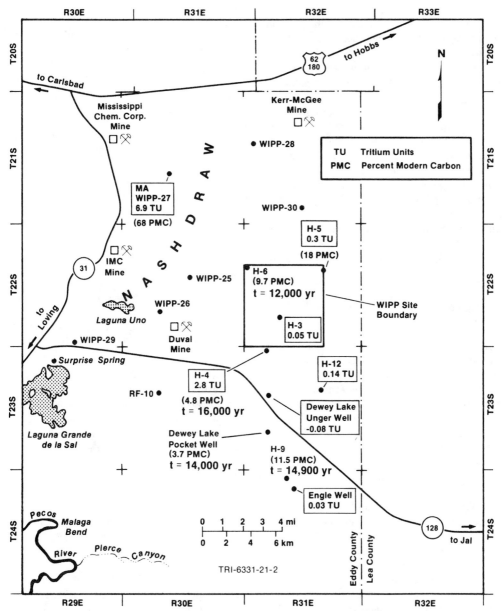

FIG. 9. Tritium and radiocarbon in Rustler and Dewey Lake groundwaters. Unless otherwise specified as Dewey Lake or Magenta (MA), measurements apply to water from the Culebra member of the Rustler Formation. Tritium Units (TU, 1 part tritium in $10^{18}$ total hydrogen) enclosed in rectangles. The PMC values at H-5 and WIPP-27 are probably contaminated.

Lake, Triassic, and Capitan groundwaters having similar stable isotope compositions throughout the northern Delaware Basin. Water at least this old is therefore a significant component of the confined Culebra waters having more negative meteoric δ-values. Despite differences in depth (Dewey Lake vs. Culebra), geographic position along a north-south line (H-4, H-6, and H-9 in the Culebra), and two and one-half orders of magnitude variation in

Culebra transmissivity (0.65, 33, and 110 ft²/day for H-4, H-6, and H-9, respectively; BEAUHEIM, 1987, 1989), carbon isotope systematics indicate uniform late Pleistocene ages for these four borehole samples. Holocene recharge and mixing have not been rapid enough to result in post-Pleistocene radiocarbon ages.

The isotopic data indicate that the Rustler groundwaters at the WIPP site and probably over much of Nash Draw are not now receiving significant amounts of modern meteoric recharge. The four late Pleistocene apparent ages derived from radiocarbon measurements of waters more depleted in $^{18}$O and D relative to modern recharge suggest that the isotopically lighter population represents southeastern New Mexico paleowater, distinct from recharge under modern climatic conditions, analogous to the findings of GAT and ISSAR (1974) for groundwater in the Sinai Desert. Even if the $\delta$D, $\delta^{18}$O, and percent modern carbon (PMC) values of radiocarbon-dated groundwater resulted from mixing of more than one reservoir, the hydrogen, oxygen, and carbon isotope data constitute compelling evidence that at least some of the confined groundwaters in the Delaware Basin having $\delta$D values more negative than $-42$ and $\delta^{18}$O values more negative than $-5.5$ at elevations of about 3000–4000 ft are not 100% modern.

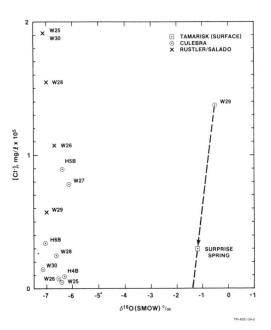

FIG. 10. Dissolved chloride versus $\delta^{18}$O for Rustler groundwaters in Nash Draw and at the WIPP site.

*Discharge from Surprise Spring and WIPP-29 Culebra*

Waters from Surprise Spring and WIPP-29 Culebra, the southwestern-most groundwater sampling point in Nash Draw (Fig. 2) both exhibit a profound difference in isotopic composition from other Rustler waters. Both have a significant deviation from a meteoric $\delta$D/$\delta^{18}$O signature (see Fig. 6). MERCER (1983) argued, on hydraulic evidence, that Surprise Spring has no connection with the underlying Culebra member. Taken together, the solute and the stable isotope evidence confirm the independent behavior of Surprise Spring.

The WIPP-29 area is strategically located between Surprise Spring and points upgradient at the WIPP site and in Nash Draw. Hence, the WIPP-29 area (Fig. 2), where the top of the Culebra member is 12 feet beneath the surface, would intercept hypothetical flow paths from the Culebra to Surprise Spring, assuming the hydraulic conductivity is continuous along each path. The degree to which Surprise Spring discharges water from the Culebra and Rustler/Salado contact zone can be evaluated using the chloride/$\delta^{18}$O systematics for the Culebra and Rustler/Salado zones at the WIPP site and Nash Draw, in relation to Surprise Spring, as depicted in Fig. 10. Evaporation will increase the solute concentrations and will also make the $\delta^{18}$O and $\delta$D values more positive (CRAIG et al., 1963). Figure 10 shows that it is not possible to derive Surprise Spring water directly by evaporation of Culebra or basal brine-aquifer water having more chloride than Surprise Spring (30,000 mg/l). Such evaporation would indeed enrich the residual solution in $^{18}$O, but would not dilute the chloride. Furthermore,

derivation of WIPP-29-like Culebra water from any of the waters would require (1) a greater increase in total dissolved solids than could be achieved by evaporation alone, for the observed degree of evaporation-induced isotope shift (see CRAIG et al., 1963), and (2) a mechanism for evaporating water from a zone confined at its upper surface, since the Culebra at WIPP-29 is at least partially confined. Whereas the first requirement can be easily met by evaporite dissolution along the flow path, the second requirement is more demanding, since the condition of even partial confinement, by definition, precludes an unconfined surface from which water can evaporate.

Derivation of Surprise Spring directly from the nearby Culebra, represented by WIPP-29, would entail a reduction in chloride from 138,000 to 30,000 mg/l. This could be accomplished by dilution, but would require water with a $\delta^{18}$O value of $-1.4$ (as indicated by the [Cl$^-$] = 0 intercept of the dashed line in Fig. 10). Water of this isotopic composition is in principle obtainable in the summer months (Table 1), but the required dilution factor of 4.6 in chloride alone would then make local surficial recharge a much more abundant component than water derived directly from WIPP-29.

The anomalous isotopic compositions of WIPP-29 Culebra and Surprise Spring waters are probably related to locally derived recharge from the surface, with enrichment in $^{18}$O due to partial evaporation or rock-water interaction. HUNTER (1985) argued for locally derived surface runoff recharging the Rustler in the vicinity of WIPP-29, originating as spillage of water imported from the Ogallala for potash refining. Less than 300 ft from WIPP-29, for example, is a small, relatively permanent pond that came into being since the beginning of local potash-refining activity. Laguna Uno (Fig. 2), upgradient from WIPP-29, is of similar origin (HUNTER, 1985).

Water having an isotopic composition similar to that of Surprise Spring or WIPP-29 Culebra might be derived by oxygen isotope shift (see CRAIG, 1966) from the inferred modern meteoric water represented by the James Ranch, San Simon, and many Ogallala data, along a nearly horizontal trajectory labelled "$^{18}$O-shift" in Fig. 6. Given the high local water/rock ratio (transmissivity = $10^3$ ft$^2$/day as reported by MERCER, 1983), this is unlikely.

The origin of the WIPP-29 Culebra water and the Surprise Spring discharge water as spillage from nearby refineries would make them susceptible to kinetic fractionation by partial evaporation. One hypothetical $\delta D/\delta^{18}O$ trajectory is drawn through the WIPP-29 Culebra and Surprise Spring points in Fig. 6 with a slope of five, based on results of HOY and GROSS (1982) for two analyses of standing water from Bitter Lakes near Roswell, New Mexico. This trend is labelled "Arid-Lake Trajectory" and intersects the meteoric field in the $\delta D$ range $-70$ to $-80$, not the $-50$ characteristic of the rest of the Rustler. As suggested above, such a mechanism of evaporation does not appear warranted by local conditions.

HUNTER (1985) proposed that Ogallala-derived imported water spilled on the surface in southwestern Nash Draw recharges a local water table. Evaporation taking place in the unsaturated zone above a water table would move the isotopic composition of the residual liquid along a $\delta D/\delta^{18}O$ trajectory having a slope of approximately two (ALLISON, 1982), rather than about five for evaporation from a free water surface. By such evaporation, it is possible to derive waters having isotopic compositions similar to those of WIPP-29 Culebra and Surprise Spring from waters having $\delta D$ and $\delta^{18}O$ values similar to those of modern Ogallala groundwaters, as illustrated by the trajectory labelled "Water-Table" in Fig. 6. Therefore, local processes can account for the origin of Surprise Spring and WIPP-29 Culebra waters. However, imported Ogallala water cannot be distinguished from local modern recharge solely on the basis of isotopic compositions, due to their probable similarities.

*Isotopic compositions of carbonates*

Several samples of carbonate rock coexisting with water, including Magenta and Culebra reservoir

rock from the Rustler Formation and surficial travertine deposits in McKittrick Canyon, were collected in order to evaluate the degree of rock/water interaction taking place in carbonate/water systems in the Delaware Basin, and to determine reasonable origins for the carbonates. The $\delta^{13}C$ and $\delta^{18}O$ values of carbonates, together with cumulative $CO_2$ yields, are given in Table 4.

*McKittrick Canyon travertine.* Calcite was sampled from the outermost layers of the travertine deposit coexisting with the water sampled from McKittrick Canyon (Fig. 1, Table 1), and its $\delta^{18}O$ and $\delta^{13}C$ values determined. The outermost (youngest) layers of an active travertine deposit are assumed to represent calcite deposition in isotopic equilibrium with its coexisting water. The travertine system sampled in this study consists of a small pond, approximately 10 ft wide and 20 ft long, recharged by an upstream spillway (a natural sluice) and discharging into another spillway downstream. The presumed-active travertine and its coexisting water were sampled from the upper sluice. $\delta^{18}O$ and $\delta^{13}C$ values for other nearby surficial calcites were determined as well.

*Rustler Formation carbonates.* Magenta and Culebra dolomite reservoir rock was sampled from several cored holes that produced water. The radioiodide tracejector tests of MERCER and ORR (1979) indicated that only a fraction of the total unit thickness produces most of the water. This zone is inferred to have a higher fracture density; such rock does not provide competent core, but falls out of the core barrel as poorly sorted angular to subrounded rubble. The most fractured zones were sampled in hopes that they would be most likely to have experienced rock/water interaction due to local maxima in rock surface-areas.

$\delta^{18}O$ values of all dolomites, both Magenta and Culebra, fall into a very narrow range, with a mean of +33.4; the mean $\delta^{13}C$ value is +6.1. Dolomite $\delta$-values are independent of depth and geographic location, indicating either uniformity of geochemical conditions governing Permian deposition or a widespread episode of uniform postdepositional alteration.

The $\delta^{13}C$ values of Rustler dolomites are higher than those of most of the lacustrine Pleistocene dolomites from the west Texas high plains, reported by PARRY et al. (1970). Although one of their values was as high as +5.8, none of their dolomites with $\delta^{18}O$ values comparable to those in the Rustler had $\delta^{13}C$ values as high as in the Rustler. PARRY et al. (1970) suggested that their dolomites formed under conditions in which evaporation is extreme, with or without a calcite precursor.

Table 4. Stable-isotope composition of carbonates

| Sample name[1] | Extraction | Yield, %[2] | $\delta^{13}C$ ‰ PDB | $\delta^{18}O$ ‰ SMOW |
|---|---|---|---|---|
| *Culebra Dolomites* | | | | |
| H-4B 509/517 | 3-day | 45 (D) | 5.8 | 34.3 |
| | 6-day | 19 (D) | 5.8 | 35.1 |
| | | 64 (Σ) | | |
| | 3-day | 41 (D) | 5.3 | 33.4 |
| H-5B 912 | 3-day | 32 (D) | 5.8 | 32.3 |
| | 6-day | 23 (D) | 5.8 | 32.5 |
| | | 55 (Σ) | | |
| | 3-day | 41 (D) | 5.9 | 32.6 |
| H-6B 616 | 3-day | 41 (D) | 5.9 | 33.4 |
| | 6-day | 24 (D) | 6.1 | 33.9 |
| | | 65 (Σ) | | |
| | 3-day | 45 (D) | 5.9 | 33.4 |
| WIPP-25 461 | 3-day | 44 (D) | 6.2 | 33.7 |
| | 6-day | 21 (D) | 6.3 | 34.2 |
| | | 65 (Σ) | | |
| | 3-day | 48 (D) | 6.1 | 33.7 |
| WIPP-26 198/208 | 3-day | 49 (D) | 5.7 | 34.3 |
| | 6-day | 24 (D) | 5.7 | 34.8 |
| | | 73 (Σ) | | |
| | 3-day | 49 (D) | 5.4 | 33.9 |
| WIPP-27 307/308 | 3-day | 40 (D) | 6.1 | 33.7 |
| | 6-day | 25 (D) | 6.2 | 34.0 |
| | | 65 (Σ) | | |
| | 3-day | 42 (D) | 5.9 | 33.6 |
| WIPP-28 431 | 3-day | 44 (D) | 5.9 | 33.4 |
| | 6-day | 27 (D) | 6.0 | 33.7 |
| | | 71 (Σ) | | |
| | 3-day | 42 (D) | 5.8 | 33.2 |
| WIPP-29 35 | 3-day | 52 (D) | 5.5 | 33.4 |
| | 6-day | 22 (D) | 5.6 | 33.8 |
| | | 74 (Σ) | | |
| | 3-day | 53 (D) | 5.4 | 33.4 |
| | 3-day | 52 (D) | 5.4 | 33.3 |
| WIPP-30 640.2–640.3 | 3-day | 44 (D) | 6.0 | 33.4 |
| | 6-day | 21 (D) | 6.0 | 34.2 |
| | | 65 (Σ) | | |
| | 3-day | 44 (D) | 5.8 | 33.0 |
| WIPP-33 549.8–550.3 | 1-hour | 7 (C) | −2.8 | 24.7 |
| | 2-hour | 8 (C) | −2.9 | 24.5 |
| | 2-hour | 7 (C) | −2.9 | 24.5 |
| *Magenta Dolomites* | | | | |
| WIPP-25 328.8–328.9 | 3-day | 24 (D) | 6.5 | 33.1 |
| | 6-day | 12 (D) | 5.9 | 32.0 |
| | | 36 (Σ) | | |
| | 3-day | 28 (D) | 6.5 | 33.1 |
| WIPP-28 293.7–294.1 | 3-day | 44 (D) | 6.6 | 33.1 |
| | 6-day | 9 (D) | 6.6 | 33.4 |
| | | 53 (Σ) | | |
| | 3-day | 45 (D) | 6.6 | 33.0 |
| | 6-day | 6 (D) | 6.6 | 33.5 |
| | | 51 (Σ) | | |
| | 3-day | 53 (D) | 6.6 | 32.5 |
| WIPP-30 536.5–536.7 | 3-day | 42 (D) | 7.2 | 33.1 |
| | 6-day | 22 (D) | 7.4 | 33.3 |
| | | 64 (Σ) | | |
| | 3-day | 45 (D) | 7.2 | 33.1 |
| | 6-day | 13 (D) | 7.4 | 33.5 |
| | | 58 (Σ) | | |

Table 4. (Continued)

| Sample name[1] | Extraction | Yield, %[2] | $\delta^{13}C$ ‰ PDB | $\delta^{18}O$ ‰ SMOW |
|---|---|---|---|---|
| *Travertine (McKittrick Canyon)* | | | | |
| Sluice crust | overnight | 90 (C) | −7.9 | +22.9 |
| Dry crust # 1 | overnight | 90 (C) | −8.5 | +23.4 |
| Dry crust # 2 | overnight | 85 (C) | −7.1 | +24.3 |
| Dry crust # 3 | overnight | 88 (C) | −6.7 | +24.5 |
| Dry crust # 4 | overnight | 93 (C) | −7.3 | +23.7 |

[1] Hole name and core depth, in feet. Hyphenated intervals are precisely known. Intervals delineated by "/" indicate that the sample originated from somewhere in the rubble between the tabulated depths. Single footages are given for rubble whose depth is known only to the nearest foot.
[2] (D) = weight % dolomite
(C) = weight % calcite
(Σ) = cumulative yield after 6-day reaction.

## Isotope exchange between carbonates and water

Apparent oxygen isotope fractionation factors ($\alpha$-values) for the coexisting carbonate/water pairs were calculated, using mean $\delta^{18}O$ values if replicate determinations were available, according to the relationship

$$\alpha = \frac{\frac{\delta^{18}O(\text{calcite})}{1000} + 1}{\frac{\delta^{18}O(\text{water})}{1000} + 1}. \qquad (1)$$

The calculated values of $\alpha$ are given in Table 5. No representative water sample was collected from WIPP-33, so the water $\delta^{18}O$ value is the mean of $\delta^{18}O$ values of confined Rustler waters from the other boreholes described in Table 5.

*Dolomite/water.* Except for WIPP-29 Culebra, whose isotopic composition deviates from the meteoric field (Fig. 6), the calculated dolomite/water fractionation factors are between 1.0395 and 1.0409. The equilibrium fractionation factor for $^{18}O/^{16}O$ partitioning between dolomite and water at ambient temperatures is not precisely known, because of extremely low exchange rates in experiments at low temperatures (*e.g.,* NORTHROP and CLAYTON, 1966). WEBER (1964) estimated that it is about 1.037. If this is the case, these dolomite-water pairs clearly cannot be in oxygen isotope equilibrium.

Regardless of the origin of the dolomites, they appear not to have participated in significant isotopic exchange with the water they contain at present. This does not preclude dissolution of dolomite, which leaves no material to preserve the isotopic record and which has probably occurred during the development of secondary porosity in the Rustler.

*Calcite/water.* The calculated $^{18}O/^{16}O$ fractionation factors for coexisting calcite and water allowed oxygen isotope equilibrium temperatures of calcite formation to be calculated, according to the equation of O'NEIL *et al.* (1969), and modified by FRIEDMAN and O'NEIL (1977):

Table 5. Carbonate/water isotopic fractionation factors

| Locality | $\delta^{18}O$ (carbonate) ‰ | $\delta^{18}O$ (water) ‰ | $\alpha$ (carbonate/water) calculated |
|---|---|---|---|
| *Calcites* | | | |
| *McKittrick Canyon* *Travertine* | | | |
| Sluice crust | 22.9 | −8.1[1] | 1.0313 |
| *Culebra Mbr., Rustler Fm.* | | | |
| WIPP-33 | 24.6 | −6.6[2] | 1.0314 |
| *Dolomites* | | | |
| *Magenta Mbr., Rustler Fm.* | | | |
| WIPP-25 | 33.1 | −6.2 | 1.0395 |
| *Culebra Mbr., Rustler Fm.* | | | |
| H-4B | 34.0 | −6.6 | 1.0408 |
| H-5B | 32.6 | −6.8 | 1.0396 |
| H-6B | 33.5 | −7.1 | 1.0408 |
| WIPP-25 | 33.6 | −6.4 | 1.0404 |
| WIPP-26 | 34.1 | −6.5 | 1.0409 |
| WIPP-27 | 33.8 | −6.1 | 1.0400 |
| WIPP-28 | 33.3 | −6.6 | 1.0402 |
| WIPP-29 | 33.4 | −0.5[3] | 1.0339 |
| WIPP-30 | 33.3 | −7.1 | 1.0406 |

[1] Measured on water sample from upper sluice.
[2] Mean value from Culebra, other boreholes in this table.
[3] Deviates from meteoric signature.

$$1000 \ln \alpha = 2.78(10^6 T^{-2}) - 2.89. \quad (2)$$

A temperature of 14.1°C was calculated for the formation of McKittrick Canyon travertine in the sluice crust from the apparent $^{18}O/^{16}O$ fractionation factor for calcite in the sluice crust and the water running down the sluice (Table 5). This is a reasonable value for ambient conditions, indicating that the coexisting carbonate and water are very nearly at isotopic equilibrium. From the $\delta^{18}O$ values of the other travertines (Table 4) and the assumed temperature (14°C), $\delta^{18}O$ values were calculated for waters from which the older travertines were formed. These values range from −6.6 to −7.7. The total range −6.6 to −8.1 may be quite reasonable for the oxygen isotope composition of modern meteoric water at the elevation of McKittrick Canyon (6000 ft), and may reflect some seasonal variations.

Rustler calcite has been found only in the Culebra core from borehole WIPP-33, drilled in a surficial depression about 10 ft deep. The borehole stratigraphy, described by BACHMAN (1985), includes dissolution cavities in the subsurface Rustler gypsum; partial collapse of some of these cavities led to subsidence at the surface.

This cavity collapse resulted in conditions favorable to the local dissolution of the original dolomite and precipitation of secondary calcite in the Culebra. Calcite $\delta^{13}C$ and $\delta^{18}O$ values of −2.9 and +24.6, respectively, are much lower than those of the dolomites. The observed calcite-water $^{18}O/^{16}O$ fractionation factor, 1.0314, yields a temperature of crystallization of 13.8°C according to Eqn. (2). This reasonable temperature is consistent with the formation of calcite in oxygen isotope equilibrium with water having a $\delta^{18}O$ value of about −7, in a system where the water/rock ratio was large. The profound difference between the calcite $\delta^{13}C$ value (−2.9) and those of surrounding dolomites (about +6) implies that the calcite carbon was not derived from dissolved dolomites, but may have been influenced by introduced aqueous carbon species. The age of formation of the calcite is unknown.

## CONCLUSIONS

### Fossil groundwater in the Rustler Formation

Seasonally integrated modern precipitation that recharges groundwater in the northern Delaware Basin is represented by groundwaters in water-table and perched systems, which are inferred to have an existing hydraulic connection with the surface. The isotopic compositions of waters from wells in alluvium, the Ogallala Sandstone, and parts of the Dewey Lake Red Beds indicate that modern recharge water in the northern Delaware Basin has a

$\delta D$ value more positive than about −42, and a $\delta^{18}O$ value generally more positive than −5.5. Groundwaters under hydraulically confined conditions in the Rustler Formation have more negative $\delta$-values that do not overlap with those of demonstrably modern recharge. The differences in isotopic composition between the two populations indicate that modern recharge in the northern Delaware Basin is minimally contributing to the confined groundwaters.

Evidence of isotopic exchange between Ochoan rock and typical meteoric Rustler-type water has been found only in a local collapse structure. Interactions between Rustler groundwater and its host rock result mainly in the dissolution rather than recrystallization of dolomite, but calcite has locally precipitated in isotopic equilibrium with Rustler groundwater.

Among the confined Rustler Formation groundwaters, tritium concentrations show a residence time greater than about 40 years, and radiocarbon dating shows isolation from the atmosphere for at least 12,000 to 16,000 years. The climatic conditions that formerly governed Rustler recharge, inferred from contemporaneous packrat middens, were probably different from those at present. The difference in isotopic compositions between Rustler waters and waters receiving demonstrably modern active recharge from precipitation at surface elevations < 4000 ft is consistent with the hypothesis that the last major recharge event for Rustler waters was in the late Pleistocene. This hypothesis also applies to other confined groundwaters in the northern Delaware Basin that have stable isotope compositions similar to those of the three radiocarbon-dated Rustler waters and the one dated Dewey Lake water, and which have no hydraulic connection with mountainous recharge areas at elevations >4000 ft. Thus, confined groundwaters in the Capitan and Rustler formations may have been recharged under similar climatic conditions.

The stable isotope compositions of groundwater systems in the Delaware Basin appear to reflect at least two generations of meteoric recharge: localized recharge under modern climatic conditions and more widespread paleorecharge to groundwaters now under confined conditions. The cessation of recharge to the Rustler Formation in the late Pleistocene left a fossil groundwater system. Continued groundwater movement, suggested by potentiometric contours and inferred southward flowlines, implies that discharge may now exceed recharge.

### Discharge from the Rustler Formation

Stable isotope, solute, and hydraulic evidence indicate that Surprise Spring and the near-surface water in the Culebra at WIPP-29 are part of a shallow groundwater system, probably largely under water-table conditions, derived from surface water largely imported by potash refiners and recharging the Rustler through local gypsum karst developed above the Culebra. Any possible contribution from confined waters in east-central Nash Draw and the WIPP site is overwhelmed by the surficial contribution. This local system may increase in importance with an increase in rainfall recharging the local gypsum karst. At the present time, Rustler water from the WIPP site does not appear to be discharging at the surface in southwestern Nash Draw.

*Paleoclimatic and hydraulic implications*

An important implication of fossil water in the Rustler Formation is that hydraulic measurements of the present system are indicative of only modern transient conditions. These measurements, then, may not be relevant to the past steady-state conditions of the Rustler Formation (>10,000 years ago), nor will they necessarily be relevant over the next 10,000 years if the climate changes. The packrat-midden evidence shows that in the immediate vicinity of the Delaware Basin, a wetter climate prevailed more than 10,000 years ago. The correspondence between the climatic transition from wetter to drier and the residence time of some Rustler and Dewey Lake groundwaters (12,000 to 16,000 years) is probably significant.

*Acknowledgements*—This work was supported by the U.S. Department of Energy, contract number DE-AC04-76DP00789. Dixie Harvey provided some of the necessary analytical laboratory support. The U.S. Geological Survey laboratory of Jim O'Neil provided many of the early data in this study, which have since been published. The incisive questions and suggestions of Tyler Coplen and Crayton Yapp helped to make many of these discussions and arguments more precise. In addition, Paul Knauth, Rick Beauheim, and Al Lappin helped clarify some of the discussion. The manuscript benefitted from the critical comments of Regina Hunter, Bill Casey, and Jim O'Neil. Final preparation of the manuscript was partially supported by the Department of Energy Office of Basic Energy Sciences (Geosciences).

## REFERENCES

ALLISON G. B. (1982) The relationship between $^{18}O$ and deuterium in water in sand columns undergoing evaporation. *J. Hydrology* **55**, 163–169.

BACHMAN G. O. (1984) Regional geology of the Ochoan evaporites, northern part of the Delaware Basin. *New Mexico Bur. Mines Mineral Resources Circ.* **184**, 1–22. Socorro, NM.

BACHMAN G. O. (1985) Assessment of near-surface dissolution at and near the Waste Isolation Pilot Plant (WIPP), southeastern New Mexico. *SAND84-7178*, pp. 1–33. Sandia National Laboratories, Albuquerque, NM.

BEAUHEIM R. L. (1987) Interpretations of single-well hydraulic tests conducted at and near the Waste Isolation Pilot Plant (WIPP) site, 1983–1987. *SAND87-0039*, pp. 1–169. Sandia National Laboratories, Albuquerque, NM.

BEAUHEIM R. L. (1989) Interpretations of single-well hydraulic tests of the Culebra Dolomite conducted in the vicinity of the Waste Isolation Pilot Plant (WIPP) site, 1988–1989. *SAND89-0869*. Sandia National Laboratories, Albuquerque, NM.

BIGELEISEN J., PERLMAN M. L. and PROSSER H. C. (1952) Conversion of hydrogenic materials to hydrogen for isotopic analysis. *Anal. Chem.* **24**, 1356–1357.

BJORKLUND L. J. and MOTTS W. S. (1959) Geology and ground-water resources of the Carlsbad area, New Mexico. *US Geol. Surv. Open-file Rept.*, 1–322.

COLTON I. D. and MORSE J. G. (1985) Water quality sampling plan. *WIPP-DOE-215*. U.S. Department of Energy, Albuquerque, NM.

COOPER J. B. and GLANZMAN V. M. (1971) Geohydrology of Project Gnome site, Eddy County, New Mexico. *U.S. Geol. Surv. Prof. Pap.* **712-A**, A1–A24.

CRAIG H. (1961) Isotopic variations in meteoric waters. *Science* **133**, 1702–1703.

CRAIG H. (1966) Isotopic composition and origin of the Red Sea and Salton geothermal brines. *Science* **154**, 1544–1548.

CRAIG H., GORDON L. I. and HORIBE Y. (1963) Isotopic exchange effects in the evaporation of water, I. Low-temperature experimental results. *J. Geophys. Res.* **68**, 5079–5087.

EPSTEIN S. and MAYEDA T. (1953) Variation of O-18 content of waters from natural sources. *Geochim. Cosmochim. Acta* **4**, 213–224.

EPSTEIN S., GRAF D. L. and DEGENS E. T. (1964) Oxygen isotope studies on the origin of dolomites. In *Isotopic and Cosmic Chemistry* (eds. H. CRAIG, S. L. MILLER and G. J. WASSERBURG), pp. 169–180. North Holland.

EPSTEIN S., SHARP R. P. and GOW A. J. (1965) Six-year record of oxygen and hydrogen isotope variations in South Pole firn. *J. Geophys. Res.* **70**, 1809–1814.

EPSTEIN S., SHARP R. P. and GOW A. J. (1970) Antarctic ice sheet: Stable isotope analyses of Byrd station cores and interhemispheric climatic implications. *Science* **168**, 1570–1572.

EVANS G. V., OTLET R. L., DOWNING R. A., MONKHOUSE R. A. and RAE G. (1979) Some problems in the interpretation of isotope measurements in United Kingdom aquifers. *Proc. Int. Symp. Isotope Hydrol.*, STI/PUB/493 **2**, 679–707. Intl. Atomic Energy Agency, Vienna.

FRIEDMAN I. and O'NEIL J. R. (1977) Compilation of stable isotope fractionation factors of geochemical interest. *U.S. Geol. Surv. Prof. Pap.* 440-KK.

FRIEDMAN I., REDFIELD A. C., SCHOEN B. and HARRIS J. (1964) The variation of the deuterium content of natural waters in the hydrologic cycle. *Rev. Geophys.* **2**(1), 177–224.

GAT J. R. and ISSAR A. (1974) Desert isotope hydrology: water sources of the Sinai Desert. *Geochim. Cosmochim. Acta* **38**, 1117–1131.

HENDRICKSON G. E. and JONES R. S. (1952) Geology and ground-water resources of Eddy County, New Mexico. *New Mexico Bur. Mines Mineral Resources Groundwater Rept.* **3**, 1–169.

HISS W. L. (1975) Stratigraphy and ground-water hydrology of the Capitan Aquifer, southeastern New Mexico and western Texas. unpub. Ph.D. dissertation, Univ. of Colorado, Boulder.

HOY R. N. and GROSS G. W. (1982) A baseline study of oxygen 18 and deuterium in the Roswell, New Mexico, groundwater basin. *New Mexico Water Resources Res. Inst. Rept.* **144**, 1–95. Las Cruces, NM.

HUNTER R. L. (1985) A regional water balance for the Waste Isolation Pilot Plant (WIPP) site and surrounding area. *SAND84-2233*, 1–83. Sandia National Laboratories, Albuquerque, NM.

HYDRO GEO CHEM (1984) Water quality sampling criteria for pumped wells. pp. 1–38. Hydro Geo Chem, Inc., Tucson, Arizona.

ISSACSON R. E., BROWNELL L. E., NELSON R. W. and ROETMAN E. L. (1974) Soil-moisture transport in arid site vadose zones. *Proc. Intl. Symp. Isotope Hydrol. 1973*, 97–114. Intl. Atomic Energy Agency (Vienna).

JAGNOW D. H. (1979) *Cavern Development in the Guadalupe Mountains.* Cave Research Foundation, Columbus, Ohio.

KNAUTH L. P. and BEEUNAS M. A. (1986) Isotope geochemistry of fluid inclusions in permian halite with implications for the isotopic history of ocean water and the origin of saline formation waters. *Geochim. Cosmochim. Acta* **50**, 419–434.

LAMBERT S. J. (1978) Geochemistry of Delaware Basin groundwaters. In *Geology and Mineral Deposits of Ochoan Rocks in Delaware Basin and Adjacent Areas* (ed. G. S. AUSTIN); *New Mexico Bur. Mines Mineral Resources Circ. 159*, pp. 33–38.

LAMBERT S. J. (1983) Evaporite dissolution relevant to the WIPP site, northern Delaware Basin, southeastern New Mexico. *Mat. Res. Soc. Symp. Proc.* **15**, 291–298.

LAMBERT S. J. (1987) Feasibility study: Applicability of geochronologic methods involving radiocarbon and other nuclides to the groundwater hydrology of the Rustler Formation. *SAND86-1054*, 1–72. Sandia National Laboratories, Albuquerque, NM.

LAMBERT S. J. and HARVEY D. M. (1987) Stable-isotope geochemistry of groundwaters in the Delaware Basin of southeastern New Mexico. *SAND87-0138*, 1–218. Sandia National Laboratories, Albuquerque, NM.

LAMBERT S. J. and ROBINSON K. L. (1984) Field geochemical studies of groundwaters in Nash Draw, southeastern New Mexico. *SAND83-1122*, 1–38. Sandia National Laboratories, Albuquerque, NM.

MERCER J. W. (1983) Geohydrology of the proposed Waste Isolation Pilot Plant site, Los Medaños area, southeastern New Mexico. *U.S. Geol. Surv. Water-Resources Inv. Rept.* **83-4016**, 1–113.

MERCER J. W. and ORR B. R. (1979) Interim data report on the geohydrology of the proposed Waste Isolation Pilot Plant site, southeast New Mexico. *U.S. Geol. Surv. Water-resources Inv. Rept.* **79-98**, 1–178.

NATIV R. and SMITH D. A. (1987) Hydrogeology and geochemistry of the Ogallala Aquifer, southern High Plains. *J. Hydrology* **91**, 217–253.

NICHOLSON A., JR. and CLEBSCH A., JR. (1961) Geology and groundwater conditions in southern Lea County, New Mexico. *New Mexico Bur. Mines Mineral Resources Ground-water Rept.* **6**, 1–123.

NORTHRUP D. A. and CLAYTON R. N. (1966) Oxygen-isotope fractionations in systems containing dolomite. *J. Geology* **74**, 174–196.

O'NEIL J. R., CLAYTON R. N. and MAYEDA T. K. (1969) Oxygen isotope fractionation in divalent metal carbonates. *J. Chem. Phys.* **51**, 5547–5558.

O'NEIL J. R., JOHNSON C. M., WHITE L. D. and ROEDDER E. (1986) The origin of fluids in the salt beds of the Delaware Basin, New Mexico and Texas. *Appl. Geochem.* **1**, 265–272.

PARRY W. T., REEVES C. C., JR. and LEACH J. W. (1970) Oxygen and carbon isotope composition of West Texas lake carbonates. *Geochim. Cosmochim. Acta* **34**, 825–830.

ROBINSON T. W. and LANG W. B. (1938) Geology and ground-water conditions of the Pecos River Valley in the vicinity of Laguna Grande de la Sal, New Mexico, with special reference to the salt content of the river water. *12th and 13th Biennial Repts., New Mexico State Engineer*, pp. 77–100.

SANDIA NATIONAL LABORATORIES and UNIVERSITY OF NEW MEXICO (1981) Basic data report for drillhole WIPP 15 (Waste Isolation Pilot Plant—WIPP). *SAND79-0274*, 1–31 (with appendices). Sandia National Laboratories, Albuquerque, NM.

SNYDER R. P. (1985) Dissolution of halite and gypsum, and hydration of anhydrite to gypsum, Rustler Formation, in the vicinity of the Waste Isolation Pilot Plant, southeastern New Mexico. *U.S. Geol. Surv. Open-file Rept.* **85-229**, 1–11.

SNYDER R. P. and GARD L. M., JR. (1982) Evaluation of breccia pipes in southeastern New Mexico and their relation to the Waste Isolation Pilot Plant (WIPP) site, with a section on drill-stem tests by J. W. Mercer. *U.S. Geol. Surv. Open-file Rept.* **82-968**, 1–73.

VAN DEVENDER T. R. (1980) Holocene plant remains from Rocky Arroyo and Last Chance Canyon, Eddy County, New Mexico. *Southwestern Naturalist* **25**, 361–372.

WEBER J. N. (1964) Oxygen isotope fractionation between coexisting calcite and dolomite. *Science* **145**, 1303–1305.

WILLIAMS P. W. (1983) The role of the subcutaneous zone in karst hydrology. *J. Hydrology* **61**, 45–67.

# Part C.
# Climatology and Glaciology

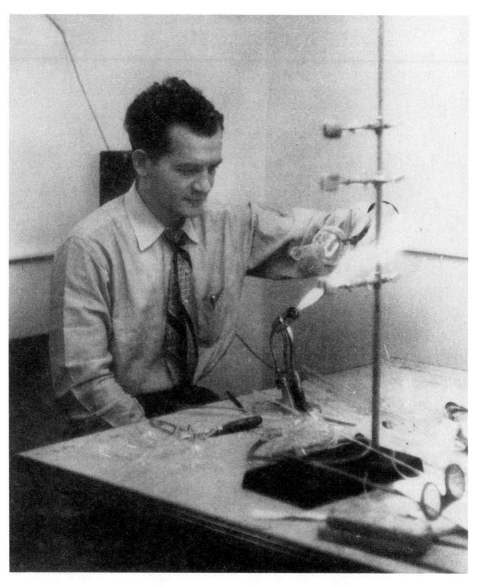

Sam at the glass blowing table in the early 1950's.

Stable Isotope Geochemistry: A Tribute to Samuel Epstein
© The Geochemical Society, Special Publication No. 3, 1991
Editors: H. P. Taylor, Jr., J. R. O'Neil and I. R. Kaplan

# The heavy isotope enrichment of water in coupled evaporative systems*

JOEL R. GAT[1,2] and CARL BOWSER[1]

[1]Department of Geology and Geophysics, University of Wisconsin—Madison, Madison, WI 53706, USA
[2]Department of Environmental Sciences and Energy Research, The Weizmann Institute of Science,
76 100 Rehovot, Israel

**Abstract**—The enrichment of heavy isotopic species of hydrogen and oxygen in a coupled series of evaporative steps is limited by the feedback of atmospheric moisture. A number of feedback schemes involving the admixture of evaporated moisture into the atmosphere is examined. The humidity is found to be the controlling parameter, so that high degrees of enrichment of the heavy isotopes are an attribute of the arid zones. The relation $\delta_L - \delta_a = \dfrac{\epsilon}{h}$ describes a limiting situation, beyond which no further heavy isotope enrichment can occur.

## INTRODUCTION

THE CHANGES IN the isotopic composition of a water body exposed to evaporation are well documented (DINCER, 1968; MERLIVAT, 1970; GAT, 1981, 1991; GONFIANTINI, 1986). The evaporation flux is depleted in the heavy isotopic species $H_2{}^{18}O$ and HDO relative to the water pool; as a result, the residual waters are enriched in the heavy isotopes. The isotopic composition is expressed in $\delta$ units in per mil relative to mean ocean water (CRAIG, 1961), using the notation $\delta_{18}$ for the heavy oxygen species and $\delta_D$ for the hydrogen isotopes.

Based on the Craig-Gordon linear resistance model (CRAIG and GORDON, 1965), the isotopic composition of the evaporating flux is given as

$$\delta_E = \frac{\alpha^* \delta_L - h\delta_a - \epsilon}{(1-h) + \Delta\epsilon/1000} \sim \frac{\delta_L - h\delta_a - \epsilon}{(1-h)} \quad (1)$$

where $h$ is the relative humidity, normalized to the saturated vapor pressure at the surface of the liquid; $\delta_a$ is the isotopic composition of atmospheric moisture, $\delta_L$ that of the liquid and $\alpha^*$ the equilibrium fractionation factor from which the value of $\epsilon^*$ is derived as follows: $\epsilon^* = (1 - \alpha^*)10^3$; $\epsilon = \epsilon^* + \Delta\epsilon$ where $\Delta\epsilon = (1 - h)C_K$, and $C_K$ is a parameter which expresses the nonequilibrium fractionation which occurs at the air/water interface due to the diffusion of the isotopic water molecules.

Equation (1) can be rewritten in the following form:

$$\delta_E - \delta_L \sim \frac{h(\delta_L - \delta_a) - \epsilon}{(1-h)} \quad (1a)$$

from which it is apparent that there cannot be any further fractionation due to the evaporation process once

$$\delta_L - \delta_a \geq \epsilon/h. \quad (1b)$$

This interesting relation will be further discussed below.

If $F_+$ stands for the influx and $\delta_+$ is the weighted average isotopic composition of $F_+$—if further, $E$ is the evaporation flux and $F_-$ is the outflow which is assumed to be unfractionated with respect to the water body's isotopic composition so that $\delta(F_-) = \delta_L$—then the isotopic balance of the water body (of volume $V$) is given at hydrologic steady state, when $V = $ constant and $F_+ = F_\pm + E$, by the expression

$$V\frac{d\delta_L}{dt} = F_+\delta_+ - F_-\delta_L - E\delta_E \quad (2)$$

On introducing the value for $\delta_E$ from Eqn. (1) into Eqn. (2) one obtains

$$\frac{d\delta_L}{dt} = \frac{F_+}{V}(\delta_+ - \delta_L) - \frac{E}{V}\frac{[h(\delta_L - \delta_a) - \epsilon]}{(1-h)} \quad (3)$$

whose steady-state solution (from the isotopic point of view) yields the following expression for the enrichment of the heavy isotopes in the water body relative to the influx:

$$\Delta = \delta_{ss} - \delta_+ = \frac{\left\{\delta_a - \delta_+ + \dfrac{\epsilon}{h}\right\}}{\left[1 + \dfrac{F_+}{E}\dfrac{(1-h)}{h}\right]}. \quad (4)$$

According to this equation and for given values of $\delta_a$ and $\delta_+$, the determining parameters for the heavy isotope enrichment are, on the one hand, the inherent fractionation factors associated with the

---

* Contribution No. 5, Department of Environmental Science and Energy Research, The Weizmann Institute of Science.

phase transition, namely $\epsilon^*$ and $C_K$, and, on the other hand, the humidity term which is the only ambient parameter which appears explicitly in this formulation. However, the ambient temperature appears in a hidden way since both $\epsilon^*$ and $h$ are a function of the prevailing temperature at the surface. Moreover, the wind and turbulence regime at the water/air interface controls the value of parameter $C_K$ (MERLIVAT and COANTIC, 1975).

In an isolated evaporating system which does not influence its environment, $h$ and $\delta_a$ are fixed by the meteorological situation. The value of $\delta_+$ is determined by the hydrologic setting of the lake or system. In the case of a midcontinental setting, the precipitation and runoff (which together make up the $\delta_+$ term) and the atmospheric moisture are often in isotopic equilibrium (CRAIG and HORIBE, 1967; MATSUI et al., 1983), so that $\delta_a = \delta_+ - \epsilon^*$.

Equation (4) can then be further simplified:

$$\Delta = \delta_{ss} - \delta_+ = \frac{(1 - h)(\epsilon^* + C_K)}{\left[ h + (1 - h) \dfrac{F_+}{E} \right]}. \quad (4a)$$

In this paper, however, we will be discussing coupled systems which are not isolated, but where a feedback between the evaporation process and the environment takes place through either one or both of the following coupling mechanisms:

- the introduction of the heavy waters from one such evaporative system into a downstream water body;
- admixture of the evaporated moisture into the ambient air, which then affects downwind evaporative systems.

The first of these effects we can call a "string-of-lakes" effect, which exercises its control through the influx term $\delta_+$. The second mechanism obviously constitutes a coupling by means of the atmosphere, affecting the parameters $h$ and $\delta_a$. Either of these feedbacks changes the value of $(\delta_a - \delta_+)$, and thus, according to Eqn. (4), the degree of enrichment of the heavy isotopic species in an evaporative element which is situated downstream (or downwind), will be smaller than if such an element were situated in an unperturbed environment.

Figure 1 shows a number of feedback schemes for a series of evaporative ponds. Three variants of hydrologically coupled strings-of-lakes with different atmospheric feedbacks are shown, as well as systems which are coupled only atmospherically but which differ in the composition of the liquid input to the downwind evaporation systems.

In the following sections the direction and magnitude of the isotopic changes in these systems will be discussed.

## THE "STRING-OF-LAKES" EFFECT

Let us consider a series of evaporating elements, numbered $1 \cdots n$, whose outflow constitutes the influx into the consecutive element in the series. Examples of such a system are a series of lakes or reservoirs situated along a river, or the case of arid zone hydrologic systems where water moves from the rain, through stages of surface flows and soil waters into either plants, discharge ponds, or groundwaters, with some evaporation occurring all along the hydrologic path. Let us assume further, as a first approximation, that the evaporation exerts a negligibly small effect on the atmospheric moisture, so that each of the evaporation elements interacts with an atmosphere characterized by a given value of humidity "$h$" and of the atmospheric moisture's isotopic composition, $\delta_a$ (model C, Fig. 1). It is then evident from Eqn. (4), which describes the buildup of the heavy isotopes in each evaporation step, that the heavy isotope enrichment downstream falls short of that of the primary element, for the simple reason that the term $(\delta_a - \delta_{+,n})$ $< (\delta_a - \delta_{+,0})$ because $\delta_{+,n}$, the $\delta$ value for the input to the $n$th element, is a larger number than $\delta_{+,0}$.

The enrichment in the heavy isotopic species of the $n$th element of such a series, according to Eqn. (4), and assuming that $\delta_{+,n} = \delta_{L,(n-1)}$, is given by the expression

$$\Delta_{n,n-1} = \delta_{L,n} - \delta_{L,n-1} = \frac{\left( \delta_a - \delta_{L,n-1} + \dfrac{\epsilon}{h} \right)}{\left[ 1 + \dfrac{F_+}{E} \dfrac{(1 - h)}{h} \right]}. \quad (5)$$

Using the shorthand notation of $a \equiv \dfrac{F_+}{E} \dfrac{(1 - h)}{h}$, this value of $\Delta_{n,n-1}$ is related to the first element in the series $\Delta_{1,0}$ in the following manner:

$$\Delta_{n,n-1} = \left[ \prod^{(n-1)} \frac{a_x}{1 + a_x} \right] \Delta_{1,0}. \quad (5a)$$

If one can assume in a simplified version that all elements are similar in the hydrologic sense so that $a_1 = a_2 = \cdots$, then Eqn. (5a) simplifies and becomes a power series:

$$\Delta_{n,n-1} = \left( \frac{a}{1 + a} \right)^{n-1} \Delta_{1,0}. \quad (5b)$$

The overall, summed-up enrichment of the heavy isotopic species along the series is given by the expression

## Model A

Feedback to atmosphere: constant input

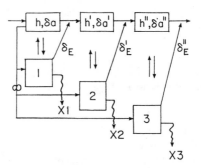

## Model B1

Feedback to atmosphere: equilibrium input at each stage

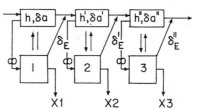

## Model B2

With Rayleigh rainout

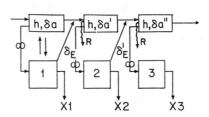

## Model C

String-of-lakes, no feedback to atmosphere

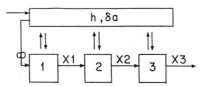

## Model D1

String-of-lakes, with feedback to atmosphere

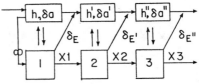

## Model D2

String-of-lakes with counter-current atmospheric flow

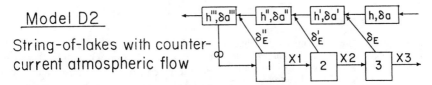

FIG. 1. Flow schemes for coupled evaporation elements with varied feedback loops. In each scheme the upper series of boxes represents the atmospheric reservoir and the lower series of boxes (numbered consecutively) represent the evaporation elements.

$$\Delta_{n,0} = \delta_{L_n} - \delta_{+,0} = \left[ 1 + \sum_{1}^{n-1} \left( \frac{a}{1+a} \right)^x \right] \Delta_{1,0}. \quad (6)$$

The buildup of isotopically heavy species as a function of the humidity for different values of $F_+/E$ (up to the limiting case of $F_+/E \to 1$) is shown in Fig. 2.

Evidently, not only is the heavy isotope enrichment of a single evaporation element a function of the parameters that make up "$a$," but also the amplification of the heavy isotope enrichment in a series of evaporative elements.

The maximum heavy isotope enrichment achieved in an infinite series of elements is simply

$$\Delta_{\infty,0} = (1 + a)\Delta_{1,0} = (\delta_a - \delta_{+,0}) + \frac{\epsilon}{h}. \quad (6a)$$

Not too surprisingly, this corresponds to the condition set forth in Eqn. (1a). This final degree of heavy isotope enrichment is no longer a function of the hydrologic parameters $F_+/E$. However, as shown in Fig. 3, the rate at which this limiting value is approached bears an inverse relation to "$a$" (or to $F_+/E$ for a given value of $h$).

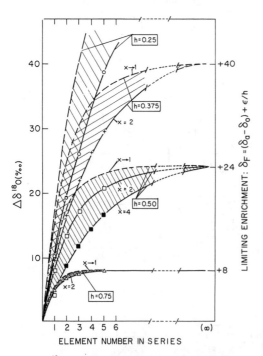

FIG. 2. $^{18}$O enrichment along the elements of an evaporative series (string-of-lakes) for different humidity values and a range of $X = F_+/E$: open symbols—for $X = 2$; filled symbols—for $X = 4$; the limits of $X \to 1$ (terminal lakes' system) are shown by stippled lines. The ultimate enrichment obtainable as $n \to \infty$ is shown on the right-hand margin: $\delta_f = (\delta_a - \delta_{0,+}) + \epsilon/h$.

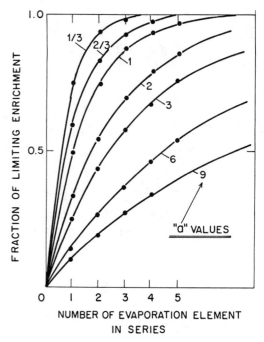

FIG. 3. The fraction of the ultimate enrichment achieved along a string-of-lakes, for a range of values of $a = X \dfrac{(1-h)}{h}$ according to the formula: $f_{(n)} = \sum_{x=1}^{x=n} \dfrac{a^{(x-1)}}{(1+a)^x}$.

The ultimate heavy isotope enrichment is very considerable when humidity is low but is more restrained at humidities above 50%, when the atmospheric flux becomes increasingly important. Indeed, humidity is the controlling parameter, and already the second or third evaporation element of a series (provided that evaporation is a dominant component of the water balance in each of them) enables one to assess the humidity rather accurately, as can be seen in Fig. 2. This attribute of the string-of-lakes effect makes the isotopic composition of remnants of highly evaporative systems, such as desert plants or carbonate nodules, valuable paleoclimatic indicators, since they provide a rather clear indication of the prevailing humidity with relatively little interference from other changeable climate parameters.

It should be noted that a desert river which continually loses water by evaporation, such as described by FONTES and GONFIANTINI (1967), can be considered an example of a "string-of-lakes" of infinite extent. Such a system finally approaches high $\delta$ values even though each incremental element shows a high throughflow ratio and a small enrichment.

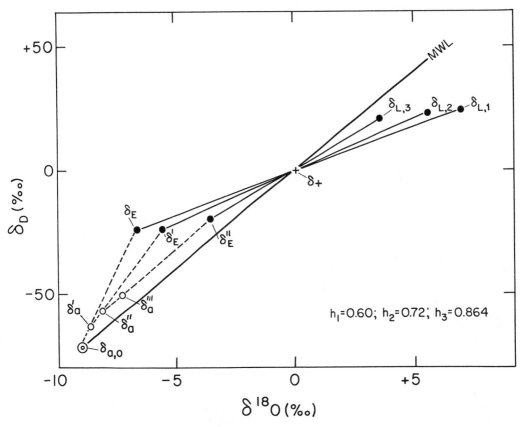

FIG. 4. $\delta_D - \delta_{18}$ plot of the steady-state isotopic values in consecutive evaporation elements $n = 1$ ... 3, for a group of lakes which are all fed by the same input water ($\delta_+$), with buildup of atmospheric humidity by the evaporation flux ($\delta_E$) according to model scheme A; for $X = 2$ and $b = 1.2$.

The value of the ultimate enrichment of the heavy isotopic species given by the relation $\delta_1 = (\delta_a - \delta_{+,0} + \epsilon/h)$ depends on the value of the atmospheric parameters $h$ and $\delta_a$, but one also must take note of the mechanism of fractionation of the final stage of enrichment, as this determines the value of $\Delta\epsilon$, specifically the value of $C_K$. As shown by ALLISON et al. (1983), the value of $C_K$ is considerably larger when evaporation takes place through a fully developed boundary layer. Such is the case when evaporation occurs from within the soil column or from leaves, and $C_K$ may then be doubled compared to the case of evaporation occurring from a freely exposed water surface. This effect is very pronounced for the enrichment in $^{18}O$, whereas the deuterium values are relatively less affected: the range of $(\epsilon^* + C_K)$ for the two extreme mechanisms of evaporation vary between the values of $C_K^{18} = 24$–39 per mil for $^{18}O$, and within the limits of $C_K^D = 85$–98 per mil in the case of deuterium. The last evaporation stage plays a most pronounced role in the string-of-lakes.

In $\delta_{18} - \delta_D$ space, the changing isotopic composition along the series of evaporative elements describe an "evaporation line," whose slope can be derived from Eqn. (4) as

$$S = \frac{\left[\delta_a - \delta_+ + \dfrac{\epsilon}{h}\right]_D}{\left[\delta_a - \delta_+ + \dfrac{\epsilon}{h}\right]_{18}}. \qquad (7)$$

As described by GAT (1971) this slope becomes independent of $h$ when the atmospheric moisture and the inflow are in isotopic equilibrium; under these conditions the slope merges into the value

$$S = \frac{(\epsilon^* + C_K)_D}{(\epsilon^* + C_K)_{18}}. \qquad (7a)$$

Obviously, then, the shift in the relative values of $C_K$ as the evaporative mechanism changes, as discussed in the last section, will manifest itself in a change of slope of the evaporation line.

It will be shown below that this rule of a single evaporation line for a string-of-lakes is violated once an atmospheric feedback occurs. Indeed, this is one

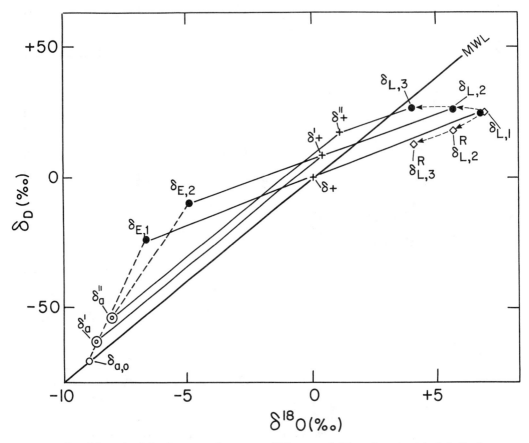

FIG. 5. Isotopic relation for evaporating systems which are coupled through an atmospheric feedback, and with isotopic equilibrium between the liquid input ($\delta_{+,n}$) and atmospheric moisture ($\delta_{a,n}$). Dots correspond to model B1 with an increasing humidity of $h_{(1)} = 0.6$, $h_{(2)} = 0/72$, and $h_{(3)} = 0.864$ (*i.e.*, $b = 1.2$) and for $X = F_+/E = 2$. Diamonds indicate system with "Rayleigh" rainout at constant humidity of $h = 0.6$ (model B2).

property of the system that can be used as a diagnostic for the occurrence of such feedbacks.

### COUPLING OF EVAPORATION SYSTEMS THROUGH ATMOSPHERIC FEEDBACK MECHANISMS

Since atmospheric moisture plays a dominant role in the isotopic change which accompanies the evaporation process, especially at high humidities where it limits the isotopic buildup, it is not surprising to find that the incorporation of the evaporated moisture flux into the atmosphere affects the buildup of heavy isotopes in an evaporating system. Furthermore, it has been shown that such a process imprints on the meteoric waters an isotopic signature which enables one to quantify this feedback interaction.

In principle, one can conceive of a large variety of air-water interaction schemes between atmo-

spheric moisture and evaporating waters. We will first discuss just a few representative and idealized systems, shown in Fig. 1, which span the situations actually encountered. Subsequently, some real systems will be discussed in light of these models.

*Constant input model*

The simplest model is that of a group of lakes situated downwind one from another, each of which is being fed by a stream of identical isotopic composition (Scheme A, Fig. 1). Although not too realistic from a hydrological point of view, we will use this scheme to explore the dependence of the heavy isotope enrichment on the feedback parameters (since in this scheme it is only the atmospheric component which changes along the flowpath).

We assume, as before, that the lake system is in hydrologic and isotopic steady state for a through-

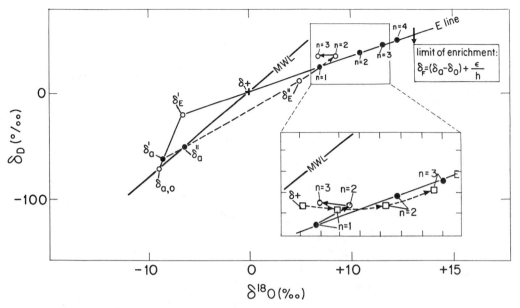

FIG. 6. Steady-state heavy isotope enrichment along a string-of-lakes, assuming $X = 2$, $h_{initial} = 0.6$, and with the initial inflow ($\delta_+$) in isotopic equilibrium with atmospheric water vapor ($\delta_{a,0}$). Filled circles: $\delta_{ss}$ values for model C (without humidity buildup). Open circles: $\delta_{ss}$ values for model D1, with humidity buildup due to the evaporation flux, for $b = 1.2$. The atmospheric $\delta$ values ($\delta_E$ and $\delta_a$) correspond to the case of model D1. Open squares are $\delta_{ss}$ values for the reverse, countercurrent system (model D2) (shown in inset only).

flow ratio $F_+/E = X$. For the sake of simplicity, it is assumed that the input ($\delta_+$) is in isotopic equilibrium with the atmospheric humidity in the first

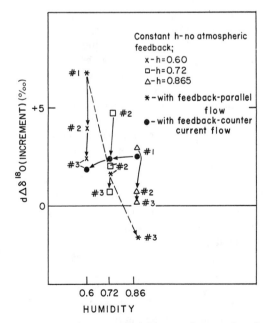

FIG. 7. The incremental enrichment along a string-of-lakes for the case of parallel and countercurrent air and water flow as a function of humidity.

element $\delta_a^{(1)}$; i.e., $\delta_+ = \delta_a^{(1)} + \epsilon^*$. It is also assumed that the difference ($h' - h$) is made up of evaporated moisture of composition $\delta_E$ where $b = h'/h$ is the ratio of the humidity in successive elements. The following set of equations then describes the heavy isotope buildup in the different elements of the system:

for element $n = 1$

$$\delta_L^{ss} = \frac{(1 - h)(\epsilon^* + C_K)}{[h + (1 - h)X]} + \delta_+ \tag{8}$$

$$\delta_E = \frac{[\delta_L^{ss} - h\delta_a^{(1)} - \epsilon^* - (1 - h)C_K]}{(1 - h)} \tag{9}$$

for the $n$th element

input value (as before): $\quad \delta_+ = \delta_a^{(1)} + \epsilon^*$

atmospheric moisture: $\quad \delta_a^{(n)}$

$$= \frac{1}{b}\delta_a^{(n-1)} + \left(1 - \frac{1}{b}\right)\delta_E^{(n-1)} \tag{10}$$

$$h^{(n)} = b_n h^{(n-1)} \tag{11}$$

$$\delta_{ss}^n = \frac{h^{(n)}(\delta_a^n) + \epsilon^* + (1 - h^{(n)})C_K}{h^{(n)} + (1 - h^{(n)})X_n} + \delta_+. \tag{12}$$

Solutions for the case of $X = 2$ and $b = 1.2$ are

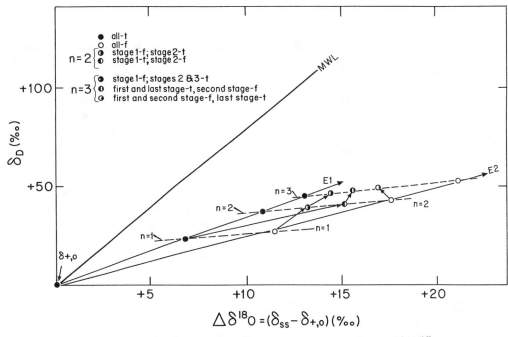

FIG. 8. The heavy isotope enrichment along a series of evaporation elements with different evaporation mechanism, *i.e.,* a turbulent (t) or fully developed (f) boundary layer. Line #1 (with filled circles) is the evaporation line for open water surface elements (t); line #2 (open circles) is the evaporation line for systems with a diffusive (f) boundary layer. Note the locus lines for successive stages of the evaporative series, from $n = 1 \ldots 3$, etc.

shown on a $\delta_D$ versus $\delta_{18_O}$ diagram in Fig. 4. Evidently the controlling parameter in this case is the humidity; as the humidity increases, the heavy isotope buildup in the evaporation system is reduced. Most interesting, however, is the increase of the deuterium excess value of atmospheric moisture ("$d$"—defined by DANSGAARD, 1964, as $d = \delta_D - 8\delta_{18}$), which initially increases (by about 8 per mil for elements $n = 2, 3$) but then reverses its value and at the limit of $h \to 1$ returns to the initial Meteoric Water Line.

One can note further that the initial increase in "$d$" of the atmospheric reservoir is inversely related to the ratio of influx to evaporation, *i.e.,* the value of $X$. Somewhat counter-intuitively, the "$d$" value of the evaporated moisture is largest for a throughflow system with a large $Fx/E$ ratio, whereas at the lower limit, as $X \to 1$ (which is the situation of a terminal lake system) the isotopic composition of re-evaporated moisture is located on the MWL; obviously then, $\delta_E = \delta_+$ (at steady state).

The slope of the evaporation line increases for each successive element, and it is once more the increasing humidity which is the dominant parameter in this respect.

*Atmosphere/input equilibrium systems*

Scheme B (Fig. 1), where the input into any downwind evaporation element is in isotopic equilibrium with the local (higher) moisture, is a more realistic model. This scheme can be considered in two variants, namely with a continuous humidity buildup from element $n = 1$ to $n$, and a second one of more or less constant humidity, due to rainout of the added moisture. In the latter case it is, of course, reasonable to assume that the isotopic composition changes according to a Rayleigh law as rainout proceeds. Since in this scheme the input into each of the evaporation elements is in isotopic equilibrium with the atmospheric waters, the mathematical formulation of $\delta_L$ is even more simple than in the previous model (Table 1, GAT, 1991).

The following are the relevant formulations of the isotopic composition for these two variants of the scheme. In both cases the equations for $\delta_L^{ss}$, $\delta_E$, and $\delta_a$ in the first element ($n = 1$) are the same as in scheme A, given above. For the case of a humidity buildup downwind, so that $h^{(n)} = bh^{(n-1)}$, the following equations apply to element "$n$" in the series:

atmospheric input:

$$\delta_a^{(n)} = \frac{1}{b} \delta_a^{(n-1)} + \left(1 - \frac{1}{b}\right) \delta_E^{(n-1)}; \quad h^{(n)} = bh^{(n-1)}$$

liquid input:

$$\delta_+^{(n)} = \delta_a^{(n)} + \epsilon^*$$

$$\delta_{L,ss}^{(n)} = \frac{(1 - h^{(n)})(\epsilon^* + C_K)}{[h^{(n)} + (1 - h^{(n)})X_n]} + \delta_+^{(n)} \quad (13)$$

$$\delta_E^{(n)} = \frac{\delta_{L,ss}^{(n)} - h^{(n)} \delta_a^{(n)} - \epsilon}{(1 - h^{(n)})}. \quad (14)$$

For the case where rainout keeps the humidity constant, the expression for the atmospheric input is changed (according to a Rayleigh formulation):
atmospheric input:

$$\delta_a^{(n)} = \frac{1}{b} \delta_a^{(n-1)} + \left(1 - \frac{1}{b}\right) \delta_E^{(n-1)} + \epsilon^* \ln\left(\frac{1}{b}\right);$$

$$h^{(n)} = h$$

liquid input:

$$\delta_+^{(n)} = \delta_a^{(n)} + \epsilon^*$$

Figure 5 shows the data for the singular case of the parameter $X = 2$ and $b = 1.2$ for these two situations. It is to be noted that the buildup of the "$d$" excess is larger compared to model A, simply because the inflow term $\delta_+$ is already characterized by a high "$d$" value. Being equilibrium systems, the slopes of the evaporation lines are fixed by Eqn. (7a) and do not vary as a function of humidity.

*Fully coupled systems*

The effect of humidity buildup along a string-of-lakes, in parallel to the streamflow, is shown in Fig. 6. In comparison to the system without the atmospheric buildup it is evident that the humidity buildup (and to a lesser extent the change in the value of $\delta_a$) limits the heavy isotope enrichment in the downstream elements. Actually, a reversal in the trend of increasing $\delta_{18}$ values is noted further downstream.

In contrast, when the air and runoff streams run countercurrently (as is the case of the Amazon basin; GAT and MATSUI, 1991), the final heavy isotope enrichment approaches that of the string-of-lakes without feedback. The process of heavy isotope enrichment is reversed, however, with the larger increases occurring in the final stages of the flow-system, where humidity is lower (Fig. 7).

This latter case exemplifies once more the overriding importance of humidity on the degree of heavy isotope enrichment in these evaporative systems.

## DISCUSSION: EVAPORATIVE SYSTEMS IN THE ARID ENVIRONMENT

The high enrichment of heavy isotopic species of water is an attribute of rather dry and warm climates. The buildup of high atmospheric moisture levels is not likely in arid zones, and evaporation can play a major role in every link of the hydrologic cycle. Indeed, very heavy waters have been described in the arid environment, such as residual surface waters in the desert (FONTES and GONFIANTINI, 1967) or the water in fruits and leaves of arid zone plants (NISSENBAUM et al., 1974).

A closer look at these systems reveals that they represent a series of linked evaporative systems. In the case of the very heavy water in plants, for example, these evaporation steps occur consecutively: during the fall of rain droplets to the ground, on the surface and within the soil column, during the irrigation process when it applies (evaporation from either sprinkler droplets or from flooded surface plots), and finally during the transpiration process by the stomata-mediated evaporation processes. Two of these steps, namely evaporation from within the soil column and evaporation from leaves, occur through a "fully developed" boundary layer (as defined by ALLISON et al., 1983) which favors $^{18}O$ enrichment relative to that of the deuterium.

As a general rule one can observe a monotonous heavy isotope enrichment along the hydrologic path. Yet at times a reversal of the enrichment process can be observed even under arid conditions. The most commonly encountered situation is that related to the buildup of salinity, in which case humidity (apparently) increases due to the salt effect on the saturated vapor pressure over the evaporating waters, an effect discussed before, e.g., by GONFIANTINI (1965), GAT (1979), and others. The relatively low heavy isotope enrichment in a terminal evaporative system such as the Dead Sea (where one could have expected some extremely positive $\delta$ values) is one illustration of this effect (GAT, 1984).

Another situation where a reversal in the heavy isotope enrichment occurs along the flow path is in the case where the mechanism of evaporation changes, i.e., where an evaporation step with a fully developed boundary layer precedes evaporation from an open water surface, as shown in Fig. 8.

## CONCLUSION

Even though possible scenarios for linking lake and evaporation systems are numerous, it is found that heavy isotope enrichment in such coupled systems is severely constrained by the atmospheric feedback loop. Evidently, in addition to the hydrologic setting of the evaporation process it is mainly the humidity which controls the degree of heavy isotope enrichment, and hence it is the latter for which the enrichment is a measure. In any event, the value defined in Eqn. (1b) remains as the ultimate enrichment barrier regardless of circumstances.

## REFERENCES

ALLISON G. B., BARNES C. J. and HUGHES M. W. (1983) The distribution of deuterium and $^{18}O$ in dry soil, 2. Experimental. *J. Hydrol.* **64,** 377–397.

CRAIG H. (1961) Standards for reporting concentrations of deuterium and oxygen-18 in natural waters. *Science* **133,** 1833–1834.

CRAIG H. and GORDON L. I. (1965) Deuterium and oxygen 18 variations in the ocean and the marine atmosphere. In *Proc. Conf. on stable isotopes in oceanographic studies and paleotemperatures, Spoletto,* (ed. E. TONGIORGI), pp. 9–130.

CRAIG H. and HORIBE Y. (1967) Isotope characteristics of marine and continental water vapour. *Trans. Amer. Geophysical Union* **48,** 135.

DANSGAARD W. (1964) Stable isotopes in precipitation. *Tellus* **16,** 436–468.

DINCER T. (1968) The use of Oxygen-18 and deuterium concentration in the water balance of lakes. *Water Resources Res.* **4,** 1289–1305.

FONTES J. CH. and GONFIANTINI R. (1967) Comportment isotopiques au cour de l'evaporation de deux bassins sahariens. *Earth Planet. Sci. Lett.* **3,** 258–266.

GAT J. R. (1971) Comments on the stable isotope method in regional groundwater investigations. *Water Resources Res.* **7,** 980–993.

GAT J. R. (1979) Isotope hydrology of very saline surface waters. In *Isotopes in Lake Studies,* pp. 151–162. IAEA, Vienna.

GAT J. R. (1981) Lakes. In *Stable Isotope Hydrology: Deuterium and Oxygen-18 in the Water Cycle* (eds. J. GAT and R. GONFIANTINI); *IAEA, Tech. Rept. Ser. 210,* pp. 203–222.

GAT J. R. (1984) The stable isotope composition of Dead Sea waters. *Earth Planet. Sci. Lett.* **71,** 361–376.

GAT J. R. (1991) Stable isotopes and the water balance of fresh and saline lakes. In *Lakes II* (ed. A. LERMAN). Springer-Verlag (in press).

GAT J. R. and MATSUI E. (1991) Atmospheric water balance in the Amazon Basin: an isotopic evapo-transpiration model. *J. Geophys. Res.* (in press).

GONFIANTINI R. (1965) Effecti isotopoci nell evaporazioni di acqua salate, *Atti. Soc. Toscana Sci. Nat.* **A72,** 550.

GONFIANTINI R. (1986) Environmental isotopes in lake studies. In *Handbook of Environmental Isotope Geochemistry* (eds. D. FONTES and P. FRITZ), Vol. 2, pp. 113–168. Elsevier.

MATSUI E., SALATI E., RIBEIRO M. N. G., REIS C. M., TANCREDI A. C. S. N. F. and GAT J. R. (1983) Precipitation in the Central Amazon Basin: the isotopic composition of rain and atmospheric moisture at Belem and Manaus. *Acta Amazonica* **13,** 307–369.

MERLIVAT L. (1970) Quantitative aspects of the study of water balance in lakes using the Deuterium and Oxygen-18 concentration in water. In *Isotope Hydrology 1970,* pp. 89–107. IAEA, Vienna.

MERLIVAT L. and COANTIC M. (1975) Study of mass transfer at the air-water interface by an isotopic method. *J. Geophys. Res.* **80,** 3455–3464.

NISSENBAUM A., LIFSHITZ A. and STEPEK Y. (1974) Detection of citrus fruit adulteration using the distribution of natural isotopes. *Lebensmittel-Wissensch, Tech.* **7,** 152–154.

Stable Isotope Geochemistry: A Tribute to Samuel Epstein
© The Geochemical Society, Special Publication No. 3, 1991
Editors: H. P. Taylor, Jr., J. R. O'Neil and I. R. Kaplan

# The elusive climate signal in the isotopic composition of precipitation

JAMES R. LAWRENCE

Department of Geosciences, University of Houston, Houston, TX 77204-5503, U.S.A.

and

JAMES W. C. WHITE

Institute of Artic and Alpine Research and Department of Geological Sciences,
University of Colorado, Boulder, CO 80302, U.S.A.

**Abstract**—The hydrogen and oxygen isotopic compositions of precipitation contain a climate signal. Two climate signals that are present in precipitation show up as a correlation between isotopic composition and temperature and a correlation between isotopic composition and the amount of precipitation. The temperature signal is strongest in polar continental regions and the amount signal is strongest in tropical regions. In temperate regions both signals are present, making retrieval of climate information more difficult.

An investigation of eight locations where long-term collections of isotopic data exist has revealed that correlations between climate parameters and isotopic values are usually limited to certain seasons of the year. Only parts of a year may show a good amount-isotope or temperature-isotope signal from one seasonal period in a year to the same seasonal period in other years. The result is that most locations yield poor correlations for whole-year periods on a year-to-year basis.

A detailed study of a seven-year collection of individual precipitation events in southeastern New York state has shown that year-to-year correlations between the isotopic composition of precipitation and both temperature and the amount of precipitation exist. These year-to-year correlations are limited to specific seasons of the year. The temperature signal is strongest in the months January to April. The amount signal is strongest in the months May to August. No simple climate signal was detected in September to December precipitation. The temperature signal in the January to April precipitation is best understood in the context of changes of atmospheric circulation patterns that changed the loci of storm tracks. The amount signal in the May to August precipitation is best understood in the context of changes in atmospheric circulation patterns that determined frontal positioning during rainfall events.

## INTRODUCTION

EVER SINCE UREY (1947) recognized that light elements partition their isotopes as a function of temperature the utilization of isotope data to unravel past climates has led to numerous discoveries. For example, EMILIANI (1955) demonstrated that shifts in the isotopic composition of oxygen in microfossil shells in deep-sea cores are a result of changes in ocean temperature and changes in the volume of the polar ice caps. The sawtoothed profile of the Pleistocene isotope record reflects several cycles of slow growth and then rapid melting of the ice caps. A review by SAVIN (1977) outlines the history and major discoveries in this subfield for the Cenozoic Era.

A detailed record of climate change during the lastest ice age was discovered in the oxygen and hydrogen isotopic compositions of ice cores in both Greenland (DANSGAARD and TAUBER, 1969; DANSGAARD *et al.*, 1969) and Antartica (EPSTEIN *et al.*, 1970). The isotope ratios were lower when the climate was colder. This effect is primarily a reflection of the capacity of air to hold $H_2O$. An air mass moving from a warm ocean to the polar regions progressively loses $H_2O$, and the condensate has both a higher $^{18}O/^{16}O$ and a higher D/H ratio than the vapor that remains. This process, which can be modelled as a Rayleigh distillation, ultimately yields very low isotope ratios that are lowest when the ambient temperature is lowest.

A detailed evaluation of the equilibrium and non-equilibrium factors that determine the isotopic composition of precipitation is given by DANSGAARD (1964). Two major factors correlate with the isotopic ratios: temperature and the amount of precipitation. The best temperature correlation is observed in continental regions nearer to the poles, whereas the correlation with amount of rainfall is best in tropical regions. In temperate latitudes both factors are important.

The search for a climate-isotope signal in temperate regions has focused predominately on stable isotope studies of tree rings. EPSTEIN *et al.* (1976) discovered a correlation between the isotopic composition of ground water and the isotopic composition of tree ring cellulose. Because the former reflects local climate (*e.g.*, FRIEDMAN *et al.*, 1964) tree rings theoretically should provide a record of local climate changes. A study by EPSTEIN and YAPP (1976) of tree rings from a Bristle Cone Pine in eastern California uncovered a major isotopic shift that could be correlated with the Little Ice Age in Europe. Several other investigators (SCHIEGEL, 1974; WILSON and GRINSTED, 1975; GRAY and THOMPSON, 1976) have also shown correlations between local climate changes and the isotopic ratios of tree rings.

WHITE (1983) and WHITE *et al.* (1985) have attempted to understand how the isotopic signal is recorded in tree rings. They discovered that the isotopic ratios of the tree rings reflect the ratios in the sap present in the tree during the growing season, and this led to the classification of trees into three categories: dry site, wet site, and intermediate site. Dry-site trees get their water only from rain. Wet-site trees get their water predominantly from ground waters. Intermediate-site trees get their water from both, the proportions depending on the depth of the water table. Most trees are in the intermediate category. These studies revealed that care must be taken in interpreting the isotopic signal found in tree rings.

With the above restrictions in mind, WHITE (1983) and LAWRENCE and WHITE (1984) reported a correlation between the isotopic composition of May to August rain over a four-year period and the isotopic composition of two dry-site trees. They further showed that for a time period of six years, the isotopic ratio of May to August rain correlated with the amount of May to August rain. Finally, they showed that for time periods of 11 and 21 years, the isotopic ratios of tree rings in two dry-site trees correlated with the amount of May to August rain (LAWRENCE and WHITE, 1984). Unfortunately, studies carried back 80 years on one of the dry-site trees did not show a continued good correlation, and the correlation was particularly poor in the middle part of the 80-year interval (J. W. C. WHITE, unpubl. data). This period of poor correlation with isotope studies was also the same interval over which standard tree rings width studies also yielded a poor correlation with rainfall amount.

Paleoclimates can also be studied using $^{18}O/^{16}O$ ratios of fresh-water fossils (BUCHARDT and FRITZ, 1980; FRITZ and POPLAWSKI, 1974; ABELL, 1986; YAPP, 1979; MAGARITZ and HELLER, 1980). The main problem with fresh-water fossils is that the $^{18}O/^{16}O$ shifts in such fossils are mainly determined by two counteracting effects. A shift to colder climates usually means lower $\delta^{18}O$ values in the fresh waters in which the organisms live and thereby in their shells. But this same shift in climate increases the $^{18}O/^{16}O$ fractionation between the water and the carbonate shell. An additional problem is that in dry areas evaporation tends to raise the $^{18}O/^{16}O$ ratio of surface waters.

It is essential to discover in detail how climatic changes and meteorological factors induce changes in the isotopic composition of precipitation. Success in unraveling past climate changes may depend on locating places on the Earth's surface that display a simple isotope-climate relationship. The report that follows focuses on identifying and evaluating these factors in a variety of localities. The data base consists of the data set of the International Atomic Energy Agency (IAEA, 1969, 1970, 1971, 1973, 1975, 1979, 1983, 1986) and a collection of isotopic analyses of precipitation from storms collected over a seven-year period in southeastern New York state.

## GLOBAL RELATIONSHIPS IN THE ISOTOPIC RATIOS OF PRECIPITATION

Because the objective of this report is in part to identify places on Earth where the climate-isotope relationship in precipitation is simple, we first look at isotope data on a global scale. The only global set of data that exists is that compiled by the International Atomic Energy Agency (IAEA), first evaluated in detail by DANSGAARD (1964). Subsequently, the data have been available both on magnetic tape and in IAEA technical reports. It can be seen that the isotopic composition of precipitation is strongly dependent on climate by looking at the average distribution of oxygen isotopes in precipitation on a global scale in January and July. Figures 1 and 2 show contour maps of oxygen isotope values based on average values for January and July, respectively. Over 80 stations involving a few to several years of samples were used to construct the contours. The data of FRIEDMAN *et al.* (1964) and LAWRENCE (1970) for North America were helpful in estimating contours in mountainous areas.

The most noticeable isotopic shift occurs in the continental regions, particularly at high latitudes. The isotope values are much lower in the northern hemisphere in January than in July. The gradients in $^{18}O/^{16}O$ ratios on the northern continents are also very steep in January, particularly near ocean-continent boundaries. These low isotope values reflect the extremely cold temperatures over the northern continents in January, and the steep isotopic gradients reflect large temperature gradients.

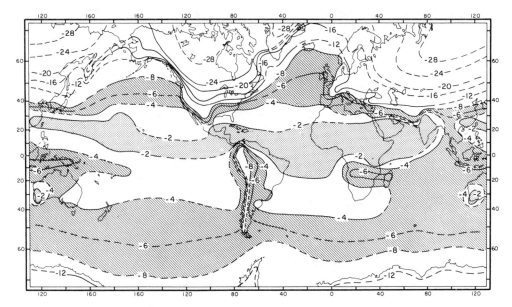

FIG. 1. Contours of $\delta^{18}O$ values relative to Standard Mean Ocean Water (SMOW) of the average precipitation in the month of January. Data obtained from the International Atomic Energy Agency (IAEA).

Low isotope ratios and steep gradients undoubtedly exist over the Antarctic continent in July, but there are insufficient data to draw contours with confidence.

The areas on Earth that exhibit the smallest changes in oxygen isotope ratios are the oceans. This is expected because temperature changes are minimal over the oceans. In both January to July oxygen isotopic gradients are somewhat steeper over tropical and subtropical continental regions than over the oceans (Figs. 1 and 2).

Simple geographic relationships between climate and the isotopic composition of precipitation can be seen. Temperature-isotope relationships for northern continental locations ($\delta^{18}O = 0.69T - 13.6$, $\delta D = 5.6T - 100$) are determined by plot-

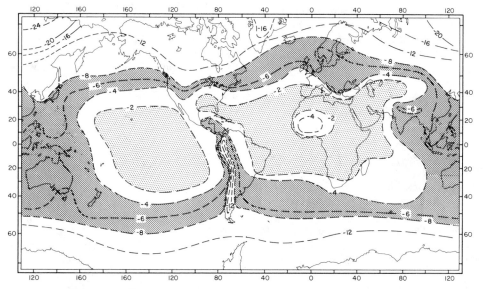

FIG. 2. Contours of $\delta^{18}O$ values relative to SMOW of the average precipitation in the month of July. Data obtained from the IAEA.

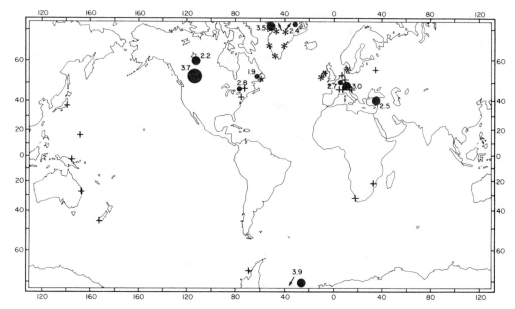

FIG. 3. Locations of IAEA weather stations where significant correlations exist between the hydrogen isotopic composition of monthly precipitation and the average monthly temperature. The numbers next to the dots give the slope, $A$, in the relationship, $\delta D = AT + B$ where $T$ is temperature in degrees Celcius and $\delta D$ is the hydrogen isotopic composition of precipitation expressed in per mil deviations from SMOW. The size of the dots is related to the coefficient of determination, $r^2$, of the relationship. The smallest dots indicate an $r^2$ value between 0.5 and 0.6, the middle sized dots $r^2$ between 0.6 and 0.7, and the large dot $r^2$ greater than 0.7. The * marks show the locations of IAEA precipitation collection stations used by DANSGAARD (1964) to determine temperature-isotope relationships. The + marks show the location of IAEA precipitation collection stations with long records.

ting the mean annual temperature of a locality against the mean annual isotopic composition of its precipitation (DANSGAARD, 1964). Many of the locations used by DANSGAARD (1964) are shown in Figs. 3 and 4. Additional locations in northern Greenland off these maps were also used. Locations in Antarctica also fit this relationship. Over other areas of the Earth temperature-isotope correlations are much worse and no meaningful relationships were found.

An amount-isotope relationship was also noted by DANSGAARD (1964) in the tropics, particularly in the Pacific Ocean. He noted that the farther east the samples were taken, the lower was the precipitation and the higher the isotope ratio. He attributed these differences mainly to differing condensation temperatures, differing degrees of evaporation on falling rain drops, and differing stages of condensation. All of these factors can be related to the positioning of the rain collection stations in the subtropical high pressure area in the Pacific. The air on the eastern flank of the subtropical high has cooler and dryer air than air on the southern and western flanks. Figure 5 displays the average hydrogen isotopic composition of precipitation as a

function of the average amount of annual precipitation for tropical island stations. The locations of these stations are given in Fig. 4.

## TEMPORAL RELATIONSHIPS IN THE ISOTOPIC RATIOS OF PRECIPITATION

The goal of this report is to stimulate interest in searching for locations on the Earth's surface where temporal changes in the isotopic composition of precipitation can be simply related to temporal climatic changes. The analysis of the isotopic values of precipitation has now been going on long enough so that year-to-year relationships can be investigated. Following a review of the climate-isotope relationships within a year we will evaluate year-to-year relationships.

### Temporal relationships within annual periods

By evaluating monthly precipitation samples analyzed by the IAEA, LAWRENCE (1980) discovered temporal relationships between the isotopic composition of precipitation and temperature within a single year. Pearson's product-moment correlation coefficient is utilized, and Fig. 3 displays the locations on the Earth's surface where there are good

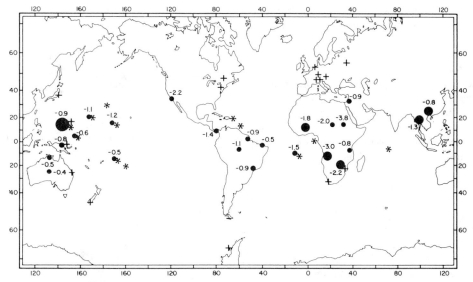

FIG. 4. Locations of IAEA weather stations where significant correlations exist between the hydrogen isotopic composition of monthly precipitation and the amount of monthly precipitation. The numbers next to the dots give the slope, $A$, in the relationship, $\delta D = AX + B$ where $X$ is the amount of monthly precipitation in centimeters and $\delta D$ is the hydrogen isotopic composition of precipitation expressed in per mil deviations from SMOW. The size of the dots is related to the coefficient of determination, $r^2$, of the relationship. The smallest dots indicate an $r^2$ value between 0.3 and 0.4, the middle size dots $r^2$ between 0.4 and 0.5, and the large dot $r^2$ greater than 0.5. The * marks show the locations of IAEA precipitation collection stations used to develop the amount-isotope relationship shown in Fig. 5. The + marks show the location of IAEA precipitation collection stations with long records.

correlations between monthly temperatures and the isotopic composition of monthly precipitation. The larger dots indicate the better correlations and the number gives the slope of the relationship. All IAEA stations not represented by a dot had $r^2$ values less than 0.5. As can be seen, the good temporal correlations are found only in northern continental regions and one Antarctic station. Note that the slopes in these temporal relationships are lower than the slope of the geographic relationship (5.6) given by DANSGAARD (1964). This difference exists mostly because at any of the given locations winter storms tend to be warmer than the average temperature, and summer storms tend to be colder than the average temperature.

Correlations were also found within a year between the amount of precipitation and its hydrogen isotopic composition (LAWRENCE, 1980; IAEA, 1981; see Fig. 4). IAEA stations with $r^2$ values greater than 0.3 are shown. Once again, larger dots indicate better correlations and the numbers indicate the slope of the correlation with amounts expressed in centimeters of precipitation. Good correlations between the amount of precipitation and hydrogen isotope values are found only in the tropics. DANSGAARD (1964) first noted and evaluated this relationship and labelled it the "amount" effect.

*Temporal relationships from year to year*

The recording of an isotope-climate signal at a single location over time periods ranging from years to centuries is the ultimate goal of stable-isotope paleoclimatologists. The climate signal may be limited to a tree's growing season for dry-site trees (WHITE, 1983; LAWRENCE and WHITE, 1984; WHITE *et al.*, 1985) or to periods of several years as represented by ground waters. Trees which utilize

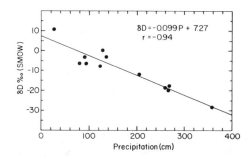

FIG. 5. The average $\delta D$ value of the annual precipitation from oceanic islands plotted as a function of the average amount of annual rainfall. The island stations are distant from continents, within 30° of the equator, and at elevations less than 120 meters.

ground waters, fresh-water fossils, and dripstone deposits in caves are all sensitive to the isotope-climate signal of local ground waters. With this in mind, below we investigate year-to-year variations in the isotopic composition of precipitation.

There are only a few locations where precipitation samples have been gathered for long enough time periods that we can look for correlations between climate and isotope values. These locations are IAEA precipitation collection stations and one station maintained by us at Mohonk Lake, New York, U.S.A. The locations of these stations are shown on Figs. 3 and 4. Eight of these stations will be investigated here.

We illustrate a simple method of looking for a climate-isotope relationship. Time periods of two to twelve months from one year to another will be investigated, and time periods of two to six months will give us seasonal comparisons from year to year. Average isotope values for these seasonal periods

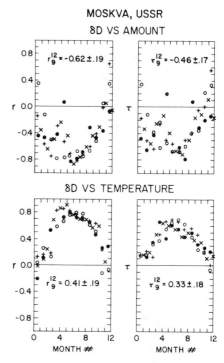

FIG. 7. The correlations of hydrogen isotope values of precipitation with precipitation amounts and temperatures for Moskva, U.S.S.R. See Fig. 6 caption for more detail.

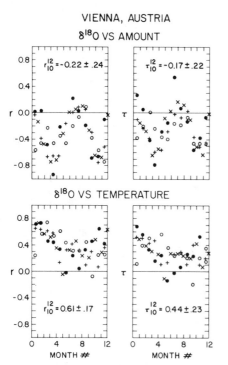

FIG. 6. The correlations of oxygen isotope values of precipitation with precipitation amounts and temperatures for Vienna, Austria. The correlation coefficients plotted are the familiar Pearson product-moment correlation coefficient ($r$) and Kendall's rank correlation coefficient (Tau) (DEMIRMEN, 1976). Comparisons are for seasonal values from year to year. The symbols for the seasons are as follows: closed circles = two months, $\times$ = three months, $+$ = four months, open circles = six months. The $r$ and Tau values listed separately are the mean and standard deviation of annual comparisons.

will be compared to either the average temperatures or the total amount of precipitation for these seasonal periods. Correlations will be determined using statistical methods that derive the familiar Pearson product-moment correlation coefficient, as well as Kendall's rank correlation coefficient. The Kendall coefficient is being used because proper use of the Pearson coefficient requires an assumption of bivariate normality of compared data sets (DEMIRMEN, 1976) which climatic and isotope data usually do not have.

Correlation coefficients for seasonal isotope values versus total seasonal precipitation or average seasonal temperature from year to year for eight locations around the world are shown in Figs. 6 to 13. Pearson's coefficients are shown on the left-hand side of the figures and Kendall's on the right-hand side. Correlation coefficients range from 1.0 to −1.0, respectively, with these limits representing perfect positive correlation and perfect negative correlation of the variables (0.0 represents no correlation). For most locations correlations were determined for all seasons of the year. This was possible when continuous records were available for several years. In instances where records were fragmented, only seasons in the range 1 to 12 could be correlated. In other

GRONINGEN, NETHERLANDS
δ¹⁸O VS AMOUNT

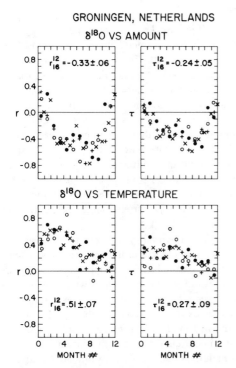

δ¹⁸O VS TEMPERATURE

FIG. 8. The correlations of oxygen isotope values of precipitation with precipitation amounts and temperatures for Groningen, Netherlands. See Fig. 6 caption for more detail.

words, it was not possible to compare seasons going from the end of one year into the next. The position of a season on the time axis in the diagrams is the month number of the mid period of the season. For example, the January to February season is plotted at 1.5 on a given diagram and the September to December season is plotted at 10.5 on the same diagram.

The numerical $r$ (Pearson) and Tau (Kendall) correlation coefficient values given in each diagram represent 12-month year-to-year correlations. The subscript gives the number of years used in determining the correlation. The superscript gives the number of 12-month periods averaged. For example, January to December is one twelve-month period, whereas February to January is another, and so on. The plus or minus value after the numerical average $r$ or Tau value is the standard deviation of the average. For locations where isotope records are fragmented, only the 12-month period from January to December could be compared from year to year. In that instance the superscript has a value of unity.

The most outstanding feature of the correlations shown in Figs. 6 to 13 is the variability of correlation

between isotope values and amount or temperature from one part of a year to another. Some seasons show good correlations from one year to the next while other seasons show very little correlation, or in a few instances the opposite correlation. The net effect of this variability is that year-to-year correlations of 12-month periods are weak for most locations.

Examination of Figs. 6 to 13 shows that each location displays a unique pattern of correlations. At Vienna, Austria (Fig. 6), correlations of amount and $^{18}O/^{16}O$ ratios are highly seasonal, with the strongest correlations occurring around the equinoxes. Temperature-isotope correlations are good in cold months and weaker the rest of the year. At Moskva (Moscow), U.S.S.R. (Fig. 7), a very different pattern is seen. Both amount-isotope and temperature-isotope correlations are strongest in the warm months of the year. At Groningen, Netherlands (Fig. 8), the amount-isotope pattern of correlations is similar to that at Moskva, with generally weaker correlations; the temperature-isotope pattern at Groningen is similar to that of Vienna, but with generally weaker correlations.

At Mohonk, New York, U.S.A., a location that

MOHONK LAKE, NY
δD VS AMOUNT

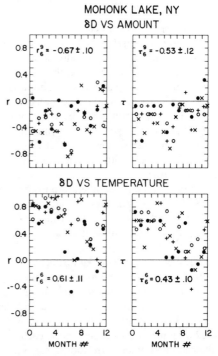

δD VS TEMPERATURE

FIG. 9. The correlations of hydrogen isotope values of precipitation with precipitation amounts and temperatures for Mohonk Lake, New York, U.S.A. See Fig. 6 caption for more detail.

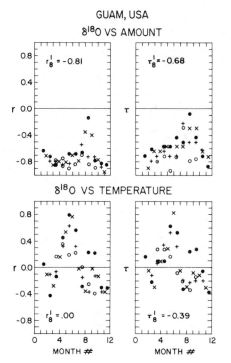

FIG. 10. The correlations of oxygen isotope values of precipitation with precipitation amounts and temperatures for Guam. See Fig. 6 caption for more detail.

Tokyo, Japan, which is a nearby location at a higher latitude (Fig. 12). These correlations at Tokyo are strongest in the summer. The temperature-isotope correlations are better in the summer and autumn.

The last station to be examined, Argentine Island, U.K., lies in the southern hemisphere on the edge of the Antarctic continent. Here, the amount-isotope and temperature-isotope correlations display sinusoidal patterns that tend to mirror each other. Although moderately weak, the best correlations occur around the equinoxes. The amount-isotope correlation changes from positive around the fall equinox to negative around the spring equinox. The temperature-isotope correlations are best during the spring.

One final observation concerning the eight locations is that the scatter in correlation coefficients appears in part to be related to the number of years of observations. Those locations with a large number of years of isotope data such as Groningen, Netherlands (Fig. 8), Tokyo, Japan (Fig. 12), and Argentine Island, U.K. (Fig. 13), exhibit much less scatter in correlation coefficients for any given season than the other locations examined. Continued collection of isotope data by the IAEA is therefore

will be examined in detail below, the amount-isotope correlation (Fig. 9) shows considerable scatter, although the correlation is generally negative and best near the summer soltice. Overall, the correlation for 12-month comparisons at Mohonk is the best of all eight stations with the exception of Guam (Fig. 10). The temperature-isotope correlation at Mohonk is particularly good in the winter months but weakens in other seasons, especially autumn. At a nearby location, Ottawa, Canada (Fig. 11), correlations between amount and isotope values are weaker than at Mohonk. Temperature-isotope correlations at Ottawa as at Mohonk are stronger in the colder months, although the winter seasons crossing from one year to another are not represented.

The best year-to-year correlations are at Guam (Fig. 10). The correlation between amount and oxygen isotope values is strong for all months of the year, with the possible exception of August-September. This high degree of correlation shows up in the 12-month year-to-year correlation coefficient. The temperature-isotope correlations, however, are generally weak and opposite for different seasons of the year. Considerably weaker correlations between $\delta^{18}O$ values and amount are observed at

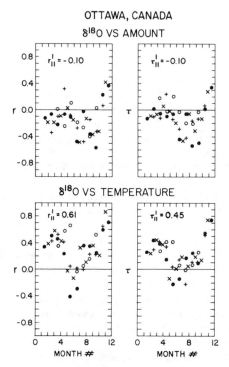

FIG. 11. The correlations of oxygen isotope values of precipitation with precipitation amounts and temperatures for Ottawa, Canada. See Fig. 6 caption for more detail.

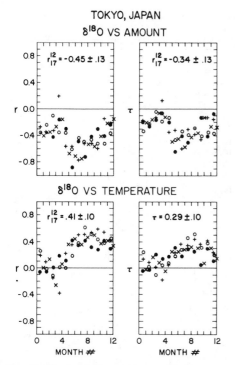

FIG. 12. The correlations of oxygen isotope values of precipitation with precipitation amounts and temperatures for Tokyo, Japan. See Fig. 6 caption for more detail.

York, than at the other sites examined, because precipitation from individual storms was collected over a seven-year period. Mohonk Lake is located near New Paltz in southeastern New York state. A set of precipitation samples was collected there from May 1977 to December 1983. The isotopic analyses from this sample collection are listed in Table 1.

The objective here is to demonstrate that changes in the isotopic composition of precipitation are related to changes in atmospheric circulation patterns. This can only be achieved by examining the meteorological conditions existing at the time the precipitation fell. Such an examination of isotopic data was undertaken by LAWRENCE et al. (1982) for precipitation samples collected in Mohonk Lake from storms from July 1977 to June 1979. It was shown that the track taken by a storm relative to the collection station had a very important effect on the isotopic composition of the precipitation. The more seaward and southerly the paths, and the colder the temperatures at Mohonk, the lower were the D/H ratios.

Examination of the seven-year data set in Table 1 reveals some year-to-year isotopic variations that can be directly related to changes in atmospheric

very important. Unfortunately, a large number of IAEA stations have very fragmented records.

The unique patterns of correlation seen at the different locations are almost certainly related to atmospheric circulation patterns that are characteristic of that location on the Earth's surface. Positioning with respect to continental land masses and oceans must be very important, because the heat budget of the atmosphere is strongly influenced by the distribution of land and ocean masses. Atmospheric circulation patterns respond seasonally to changes in this heat budget. Local orographic or ocean circulation effects may also be important. Because of this, it is important that we examine changes in isotopic values at any given location with respect to changes in meteorological conditions at that location. In the next section we take a closer look at changes in atmospheric circulation patterns at one location from one year to the next and relate them to isotopic changes in precipitation.

## Detailed relationships at Mohonk Lake, New York

A more detailed examination of climate-isotope relationships is possible at Mohonk Lake, New

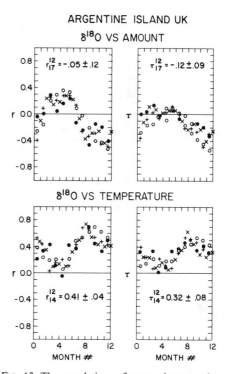

FIG. 13. The correlations of oxygen isotope values of precipitation with precipitation amounts and temperatures for Argentine Island, U.K. See Fig. 6 caption for more detail.

Table 1. Hydrogen isotopic composition of precipitation

| Date | Amount (cm) | δD (per mil) | Date | Amount (cm) | δD (per mil) |
|------|-------------|--------------|------|-------------|--------------|
| | | | 1977 | | |
| 5/4–5 | 2.3 | −38 ± 3 | 8/31 | 0.4 | −29 |
| 5/9–10 | 3.4 | −64 ± 1 | 9/13–14 | 1.3 | −18 |
| 5/18 | 0.5 | −16 ± 3 | 9/16–17 | 3.2 | −46 |
| 6/6–10 | 6.3 | −53 | 9/20–21 | 4.5 | −50 |
| 6/18 | 1.6 | −37 ± 2 | 9/23–26 | 10.4 | −65 |
| 6/25 | 1.1 | −29 ± 3 | 10/1–2 | 5.7 | −43 |
| 6/29 | 0.7 | −39 ± 1 | 10/8–9 | 3.4 | −11 |
| 7/6 | 0.7 | −35 ± 2 | 10/14–15 | 1.5 | −21 |
| 7/8 | 0.4 | −21 ± 2 | 10/16–17 | 2.5 | −14 |
| 7/17 | 0.4 | −12 ± 1 | 10/19–20 | 1.3 | −47 |
| 7/19 | 0.5 | −25 ± 1 | 11/7–9 | 13.2 | −44 |
| 7/25 | 1.8 | −33 ± 1 | 11/25–26 | 3.1 | −88 |
| 8/1–2 | 0.3 | −22 | 11/29–12/1 | 2.6 | −62 |
| 8/3 | 0.4 | −44 | 12/9 | 0.5 | −66 |
| 8/5 | 0.5 | −35 | 12/12–15 | 3.8 | −40 |
| 8/12 | 0.7 | −14 | 12/18–19 | 1.3 | −146 |
| 8/17 | 1.0 | −26 | 12/20–21 | 2.3 | −58 |
| 8/22 | 0.4 | −39 | 12/25 | 0.8 | −73 |
| | | | 1978 | | |
| 1/1–2 | 0.8 | −113 | 7/10 | 0.8 | −40 ± 2 |
| 1/6–9 | 6.4 | −48 | 7/17–18 | 0.8 | −38 ± 1 |
| 1/13–14 | 3.0 | −116 | 7/23 | 0.6 | −28 ± 1 |
| 1/17–18 | 3.5 | −96 | 7/28–29 | 0.7 | −20 ± 1 |
| 1/19–20 | 2.3 | −145 | 7/31–8/1 | 1.0 | −56 ± 3 |
| 1/25–26 | 4.0 | −75 ± 1 | 8/4 | 0.5 | −45 ± 2 |
| 2/6–7 | 1.9 | −138 | 8/6–7 | 3.4 | −38 ± 2 |
| 3/3 | 0.8 | −123 | 8/11–12 | 0.9 | −44 ± 2 |
| 3/14 | 3.3 | −30 | 8/24–25 | 1.9 | −7 ± 1 |
| 3/16 | 0.4 | −130 | 8/28 | 0.5 | −17 ± 2 |
| 3/25–27 | 6.0 | −55 | 8/31 | 4.1 | −45 ± 1 |
| 4/19–20 | 3.2 | −55 ± 2 | 9/12 | 0.8 | −24 ± 2 |
| 5/4–5 | 2.0 | −134 ± 2 | 9/18–19 | 5.9 | −35 ± 1 |
| 5/8 | 2.0 | −50 ± 2 | 9/22–23 | 0.6 | −12 |
| 5/9 | 1.9 | −34 ± 1 | 10/4 | 0.6 | −25 |
| 5/14–15 | 5.0 | −31 ± 2 | 10/6 | 1.8 | −29 |
| 5/16–18 | 4.9 | −67 ± 2 | 10/25–27 | 1.0 | −22 |
| 5/24–25 | 5.9 | −57 ± 2 | 11/7–8 | 0.4 | −37 |
| 5/31 | 1.0 | −22 ± 1 | 11/17–18 | 2.8 | −31 |
| 6/3 | 1.8 | −51 ± 4 | 11/23–24 | 1.7 | −67 |
| 6/7–8 | 2.3 | −21 ± 4 | 11/29–30 | 0.8 | −161 |
| 6/9 | 1.1 | −62 ± 2 | 12/3–4 | 1.1 | −83 |
| 6/13 | 0.4 | −38 ± 2 | 12/8–10 | 3.6 | −84 |
| 6/21 | 1.8 | −21 ± 4 | 12/21–22 | 2.4 | −92 |
| 7/3–4 | 2.8 | −84 ± 5 | 12/24–25 | 3.8 | −112 |
| | | | 1979 | | |
| 1/1–4 | 7.1 | −62 | 3/29 | 0.6 | −55 |
| 1/5–6 | 0.5 | −165 ± 5 | 4/2–3 | 0.7 | −30 |
| 1/7–8 | 5.8 | −84 ± 5 | 4/4–5 | 0.6 | −66 |
| 1/12–14 | 1.5 | −76 ± 5 | 4/8–10 | 3.2 | −64 |
| 1/17–18 | 0.6 | −99 | 4/14–15 | 2.8 | −63 |
| 1/20–21 | 7.4 | −87 | 4/26–28 | 4.4 | −37 |
| 1/24–26 | 5.5 | −86 | 5/3–4 | 0.6 | −24 ± 4 |
| 2/7–8 | 0.8 | −127 | 5/12–14 | 1.5 | −42 ± 2 |
| 2/19 | 0.6 | −170 | 5/18–20 | 0.9 | −37 |
| 2/23–25 | 4.3 | −69 | 5/23–25 | 10.2 | −43 ± 2 |
| 2/25–27 | 2.5 | −109 | 5/26 | 0.7 | −48 |
| 3/2 | 0.5 | −72 | 6/5 | 2.6 | −42 ± 4 |
| 3/6–7 | 3.4 | −45 | 6/11 | 4.4 | −43 ± 2 |
| 3/10–11 | 1.5 | −110 | 6/18 | 0.9 | −19 ± 2 |
| 3/14 | 0.3 | −39 | 6/30 | 0.5 | −25 ± 4 |
| 3/24–25 | 2.1 | −46 | 7/1 | 1.2 | −21 |

Table 1. (Continued)

| Date | Amount (cm) | δD (per mil) | Date | Amount (cm) | δD (per mil) |
|------|-------------|--------------|------|-------------|--------------|
| | | | 1979 | | |
| 7/16 | 2.8 | −60 | 10/1 | 4.6 | −81 |
| 7/18 | 0.7 | −58 | 10/3 | 2.3 | −46 |
| 7/24 | 0.3 | −34 | 10/5 | 4.0 | −28 |
| 8/2 | 1.1 | −34 | 10/10 | 0.8 | −185 |
| 8/10 | 1.9 | −25 | 10/12 | 0.7 | −86 |
| 8/11 | 1.5 | −55 | 10/28 | 0.5 | −83 |
| 8/12–13 | 4.3 | −54 | 11/2–3 | 3.9 | −35 |
| 8/18–19 | 1.8 | −30 | 11/9–10 | 1.2 | −23 |
| 8/24–25 | 2.2 | −21 | 11/11–12 | 0.6 | −112 |
| 8/29 | 0.6 | −27 | 11/25–26 | 3.2 | −30 |
| 9/6 | 10.1 | −47 | 12/6 | 0.8 | −120 |
| 9/14 | 1.5 | −38 | 12/13 | 0.8 | −130 |
| 9/21–22 | 4.3 | −49 | 12/24–25 | 2.8 | −37 |
| 9/28–29 | 1.6 | −30 | | | |
| | | | 1980 | | |
| 1/11 | 1.8 | −31 | 7/2 | 1.2 | −36 |
| 2/16 | 1.9 | −134 | 7/5 | 3.5 | −36 |
| 2/22 | 0.8 | −98 ± 5 | 7/21 | 3.8 | −14 ± 3 |
| 3/8 | 1.2 | −40 | 7/22–23 | 1.1 | −50 |
| 3/9–10 | 1.1 | −75 | 7/29 | 0.4 | −16 |
| 3/13–14 | 2.9 | −86 | 8/1 | 0.9 | −16 ± 2 |
| 3/17–18 | 2.3 | −10 | 8/2–3 | 2.0 | −41 ± 3 |
| 3/21–22 | 8.1 | −70 | 8/5 | 1.9 | −12 ± 1 |
| 3/24–25 | 1.9 | −28 | 8/15 | 0.8 | −27 ± 1 |
| 3/29–30 | 1.5 | −98 | 9/5 | 0.6 | −22 |
| 4/4 | 1.5 | −66 | 9/6 | 0.8 | −37 |
| 4/9 | 6.9 | −28 | 9/17–18 | 3.7 | −27 |
| 4/14–15 | 1.3 | −45 | 9/25–26 | 0.7 | −34 |
| 4/27–30 | 6.7 | −45 | 10/2–3 | 1.3 | −37 |
| 5/11–12 | 1.4 | −27 | 10/3 | 1.6 | −94 |
| 5/13 | 0.7 | −46 | 10/10–11 | 1.1 | −25 |
| 5/18–19 | 1.0 | −27 | 10/25 | 4.9 | −73 ± 5 |
| 5/21 | 0.9 | −70 | 11/9 | 0.6 | −56 |
| 6/7 | 1.4 | −16 ± 2 | 11/17–18 | 3.6 | −92 |
| 6/15 | 0.6 | −5 ± 2 | 11/24 | 3.7 | −54 |
| 6/20 | 0.4 | −35 ± 2 | 11/27–28 | 2.2 | −54 |
| 6/29–30 | 5.7 | −48 ± 2 | 12/15–17 | 1.4 | −105 |
| | | | 1981 | | |
| 1/6–7 | 0.8 | −149 | 6/21–22 | 2.0 | −40 |
| 2/1–2 | 4.6 | −29 | 6/25 | 0.7 | −40 |
| 2/8–9 | 0.8 | −114 | 7/1–3 | 3.5 | −24 |
| 2/10–11 | 2.9 | −34 | 7/4–5 | 4.3 | −54 |
| 2/19–21 | 3.8 | −63 | 7/20–21 | 3.4 | −19 ± 1 |
| 2/23–24 | 3.0 | −47 | 7/28–29 | 0.9 | −33 |
| 3/30 | 0.8 | −25 | 8/11–12 | 0.8 | −43 ± 3 |
| 4/1–2 | 2.1 | −57 | 8/30 | 2.0 | −14 ± 6 |
| 4/5–6 | 0.6 | 0 | 9/1 | 1.3 | −13 ± 1 |
| 4/9 | 0.6 | −16 | 9/8 | 4.5 | −63 |
| 4/14 | 2.0 | −36 | 9/14–15 | 0.7 | −31 |
| 4/23–24 | 1.1 | −15 | 9/15–16 | 0.8 | −53 |
| 4/28–29 | 1.2 | −36 | 9/22–23 | 1.2 | −22 |
| 4/29 | 1.1 | −45 | 10/1–2 | 1.6 | −20 |
| 5/2 | 0.5 | −82 | 10/6–7 | 0.7 | −26 ± 1 |
| 5/10–12 | 10.7 | −54 | 10/18–19 | 1.0 | −27 |
| 5/15–16 | 1.2 | −42 | 10/23–24 | 2.7 | −50 |
| 5/29 | 1.5 | −18 | 10/26–28 | 3.8 | −52 ± 1 |
| 6/3–4 | 0.5 | −30 | 11/6 | 1.0 | −41 |
| 6/12–13 | 0.8 | −56 | 11/15–18 | 1.2 | −65 |
| 6/14 | 1.7 | −71 | 11/19–20 | 1.5 | −40 |
| 6/15 | 1.1 | −58 | 12/1–2 | 3.2 | −53 |
| 6/20 | 0.9 | −30 | 12/14 | 1.7 | −170 |

Table 1. (Continued)

| Date | Amount (cm) | δD (per mil) | Date | Amount (cm) | δD (per mil) |
|------|-------------|--------------|------|-------------|--------------|
| | | 1981 | | | |
| 12/15 | 2.1 | −160 | 12/23 | 1.4 | −29 |
| 12/17–18 | 0.7 | −105 | 12/27 | 0.9 | −60 |
| | | 1982 | | | |
| 1/1 | 1.7 | −105 | 6/17 | 1.1 | −28 |
| 1/4 | 6.1 | −60 | 6/22–23 | 1.4 | −81 |
| 1/13–14 | 1.3 | −155 | 6/29 | 2.3 | −49 |
| 1/23 | 1.9 | −74 | 7/20 | 3.5 | −35 |
| 1/30–2/1 | 2.9 | −11 | 7/28 | 3.3 | −37 |
| 2/3–4 | 4.3 | −49 | 7/29 | 0.5 | −25 |
| 2/9 | 1.4 | −126 | 7/31 | 0.7 | −32 |
| 2/19–20 | 1.0 | −106 | 8/9 | 1.9 | −46 |
| 3/4–5 | 1.1 | −56 | 8/9 | 0.9 | −26 |
| 3/6–8 | 2.2 | −105 | 8/17 | 0.4 | −49 |
| 3/9 | 0.5 | −75 | 8/25 | 2.1 | −42 |
| 3/17 | 1.3 | −26 | 9/2 | 0.5 | −46 |
| 3/26 | 0.8 | −48 | 9/2–3 | 0.5 | −25 |
| 3/31 | 1.7 | −24 | 9/15–16 | 3.9 | −20 |
| 4/3 | 3.3 | −28 | 9/22 | 0.6 | −75 |
| 4/6 | 2.0 | −129 | 9/22–23 | 2.9 | −68 |
| 4/17–18 | 2.0 | −43 | 9/27 | 1.9 | −50 |
| 4/26 | 3.6 | −70 | 10/7–9 | 1.3 | −43 |
| 5/19 | 0.7 | −30 | 10/13–14 | 0.9 | −44 |
| 5/20 | 0.6 | −43 | 11/4–5 | 3.7 | −57 |
| 5/22–24 | 2.1 | −30 | 11/12–13 | 3.0 | −42 |
| 5/29 | 3.9 | −64 | 11/28–29 | 1.1 | −58 |
| 5/31 | 1.1 | −50 | 12/16 | 2.9 | −32 |
| 6/2 | 1.1 | −56 | 12/19–20 | 0.4 | −84 |
| 6/5–7 | 10.0 | −65 | 12/23–24 | 0.9 | −48 |
| 6/13–14 | 3.7 | −54 | | | |
| | | 1983 | | | |
| 1/5–6 | 0.9 | −29 | 5/29–30 | 2.0 | −22 |
| 1/10–11 | 3.5 | −42 | 5/30 | 1.6 | −21 |
| 1/15 | 1.8 | −72 | 6/4 | 3.5 | −41 |
| 1/23 | 3.6 | −53 | 6/6–7 | 3.5 | −29 |
| 1/30 | 0.7 | −96 | 6/27–29 | 3.9 | −46 |
| 2/2–3 | 4.0 | −62 | 7/24 | 2.3 | −63 |
| 2/6–8 | 2.7 | −105 | 8/11–12 | 3.8 | −32 |
| 2/11–12 | 2.5 | −170 | 8/18 | 0.6 | −7 |
| 3/1–2 | 1.4 | −78 | 8/28 | 1.3 | −40 |
| 3/5 | 0.5 | −65 | 8/29 | 0.5 | −43 |
| 3/7–9 | 4.7 | −56 | 8/29 | 0.6 | −34 |
| 3/10–11 | 1.8 | −90 | 8/30–31 | 0.5 | −51 |
| 3/12 | 0.7 | −148 | 9/21 | 5.9 | −58 |
| 3/18–20 | 6.3 | −42 | 9/22 | 0.6 | −28 |
| 3/21 | 2.9 | −63 | 9/30 | 0.9 | −89 |
| 3/27–28 | 2.9 | −73 | 10/5 | 1.0 | −20 |
| 4/3 | 3.1 | −55 | 10/12 | 2.7 | −27 |
| 4/7–8 | 0.5 | −32 | 10/13–14 | 0.6 | −21 |
| 4/8 | 0.6 | −49 | 10/18–19 | 1.4 | −95 |
| 4/10–11 | 4.7 | −68 | 10/23–24 | 2.8 | −47 |
| 4/15–16 | 7.8 | −67 | 11/10–11 | 2.9 | −54 |
| 4/19–20 | 3.4 | −137 | 11/15–16 | 1.9 | −62 |
| 4/24–26 | 6.1 | −71 | 11/21 | 1.9 | −37 |
| 4/30 | 0.4 | −10 | 11/23–25 | 4.6 | −82 |
| 5/1–2 | 0.7 | −61 | 11/28–29 | 2.5 | −41 |
| 5/8–9 | 1.2 | −44 | 12/4 | 1.8 | −98 |
| 5/15 | 3.4 | −18 | 12/6–7 | 2.7 | −70 |
| 5/16 | 0.5 | −86 | 12/12–14 | 8.3 | −35 |
| 5/19–20 | 1.2 | +2 | 12/22 | 2.3 | −97 |
| 5/26–27 | 4.4 | −46 | 12/28–29 | 2.6 | −58 |

circulation patterns. These year-to-year relationships are best revealed when one season of a year is compared to the same season of another year. In the discussions that follow each year is broken up into three seasons: January to April, May to August, and September to December. In part, the justification for this breakdown can be seen by examining Fig. 9. The January to April time period shows the best correlations between temperature and isotope values. The May to August time period was chosen for a combination of reasons. Firstly, this time period is when trees form most of the cellulose that goes into tree rings. Dry-site trees use only hydrogen from growing season precipitation to form these tree rings (WHITE, 1983; WHITE et al., 1985). Therefore, any climate signal present in May to August precipitation will be recorded in the tree-ring cellulose (LAWRENCE and WHITE, 1984). Secondly, the best correlations between amount and isotopic values are for this time period, although considerable scatter is observed (Fig. 9).

Changes in storm tracks are most easily correlated with the isotopic composition of precipitation from one year to the next in the January to April time period. In Fig. 14 the storm tracks for January to April for the years 1978 to 1983 are shown along with the average isotopic composition of the storms. The numbers on each of the storm tracks give the time sequence of the storms. As can be seen, the year with the most coastal storm track positioning (1978) gives the lowest isotope values, whereas the most inland storm positioning (1981) gives the highest isotope values. Other years have intermediate positioning and intermediate isotope values (see Fig. 14). In 1982 and 1983, however, the average storm positions were different yet the average isotope values are the same. A temperature difference between 1982 and 1983 accounts for this apparent discrepancy. In 1982 the average temperature was lower than in 1983.

Although storms were more coastal in 1983 than in 1982, it was warmer at Mohonk Lake and storms were weaker. The greater number of dashed lines shown in the 1983 map indicates that storms were weak and difficult to track. In a detailed analysis of winter storms GEDZELMAN and LAWRENCE (1982) describe how isotopic changes in storms are related to storm structure. The farther up a warm frontal surface moist air has to move before reaching the precipitation site, the lower the isotope values at the precipitation site. Therefore, on average, colder winters have better developed warm frontal surfaces and thus exhibit lower isotope values.

Year-to-year variations of isotopic composition in the May to August time period relate best to the average position of fronts during the precipitation event. In Fig. 15 the average positions of fronts at the midpoint of all precipitation events for the years 1977 to 1983 are shown. The error bars represent the standard error of the mean position of the fronts. For six of the seven years a clear relationship between frontal position and the average hydrogen isotopic composition of the precipitation is evident. When Mohonk was located south of the mean frontal position, 1977 and 1980, δD values were high. When Mohonk was located north of the mean frontal position, 1978 and 1982, δD values were low. When Mohonk was located near the average position of the fronts, 1979 and 1980, δD values were intermediate. GAMBELL and FRIEDMAN (1965) observed such a relationship for a single storm in which precipitation formed along a cold front.

The year 1981 is anomalous. A greater number of warm fronts produced precipitation than in other years. This is partly reflected in the more east-west positioning of the average frontal positions compared with the other years. The abundance of warm fronts in 1981 suggests better development of extratropical cyclones. The summer rain patterns can be classified as cyclonic or convective; the cyclonic patterns display the lower isotopic values (GEDZELMAN et al., 1987). Finally, the September to December time periods for the years 1977 to 1982 were investigated in an attempt to find correlations between isotopic composition of precipitation and atmospheric circulation patterns, but no good correlations were found. This time period also showed weaker correlations with amount or temperature than did the other seasons (Fig. 9).

## CONCLUSIONS

The aim of this paper was to focus attention on finding locations where the climate-isotope relationship in precipitation is simple. Under such conditions proxy recorders of climate such as tree rings, dripstone deposits in caves, and fresh-water fossils might be utilized to give past climatic information. To date, it can be seen from the examination of IAEA isotope data that year-to-year correlations of isotope values with precipitation amount and temperature are generally poor if whole-year time periods are considered. The exceptions are amount-isotope correlations at Guam and possibly at Mohonk Lake, New York. The conclusion that can be drawn is that proxy recorders of climate that obtain their isotopic imprint from ground waters may only be used successfully in certain specific locations. If the "good" sites are to be discovered, long-term precipitation collections will have to be carried out at many more localities in the future.

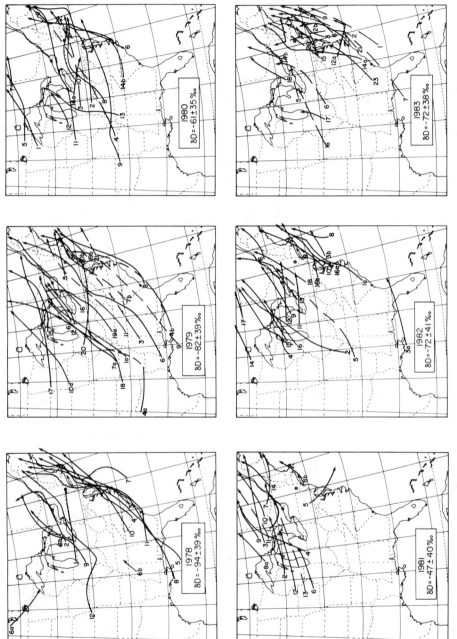

Fig. 14. Storm tracks, showing loci of the low pressure centers of extratropical cyclones occurring between January and April for the years 1978 to 1983. The numbers at the beginning of the tracks give the time sequence of storms for each year. Dashed storm tracks indicate weaker storms which were more difficult to plot. The average hydrogen isotopic composition (unweighted) and standard deviation of all of the storms for each year are also given expressed in δD. The location of Mohonk Lake, New York is shown by an × within a circle.

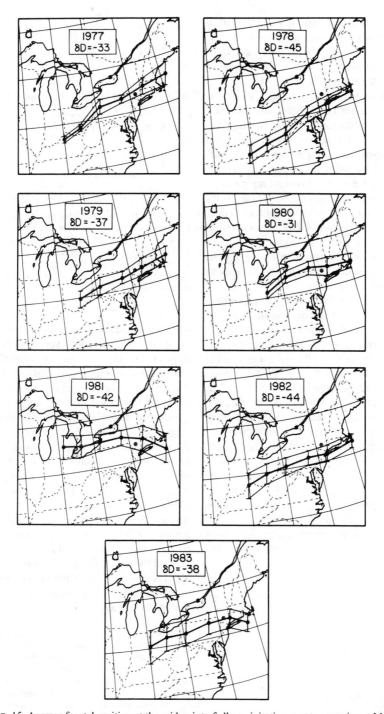

FIG. 15. Average frontal position at the mid point of all precipitation events occurring at Mohonk Lake, New York for the time period May to August for the years 1977 to 1983. The error bars give standard error of the mean position of the fronts. The location of Mohonk Lake is indicated by an × within a circle. The average δD value (unweighted) of all storms for each year is also given.

In order to further demonstrate the potential of Guam and Mohonk Lake as locations to make further paleoclimate studies, the isotope data from these locations were modelled to simulate a ground water isotope-climate signal (Figs. 16 and 17). Twelve-month totals of precipitation are plotted as a function of time for both Guam and Mohonk Lake, and these rolling totals exhibit considerable change over time. Plotted above these values in each figure are twelve-month rolling means of the annual isotope values. Visually, it can be seen that a good correlation exists between the two rolling parameters. The Pearson, Kendall, and Spearman correlation coefficients (DEMIRMEN, 1976) for each data set are given, and the values of the correlation coefficients are typically high. This suggests that proxy recorders of climate that utilize ground waters in these areas may provide climatic information about past precipitation patterns.

Another possibility for retrieving climatic information from proxy recorders of isotopic signals in precipitation is to find proxy recorders that only utilize part of a year's precipitation. Tree rings from trees that grow on dry sites offer such a possibility (WHITE, 1983; LAWRENCE and WHITE, 1984; WHITE et al., 1985). Of the stations examined in this report, Moskva, U.S.S.R., seems to offer the best prospect for isotopic studies of dry-site trees. Both temperature and precipitation amounts show good correlations with the isotopic composition of summer rain. During cooler and wetter summers in Moskva, isotope values are lower than in warmer and drier summers (Fig. 7). If other proxy recorders utilize only one season's precipitation, several other locations may also offer good prospects.

Isotopic studies of precipitation from individual storms collected over long periods should be un-

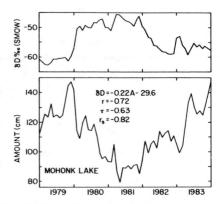

FIG. 17. The rolling twelve-month weighted mean of hydrogen isotopic composition of precipitation from Mohonk Lake, New York plotted as a function of time. The rolling twelve-month precipitation amounts are also plotted. The Pearson, Kendall, and Spearman correlation coefficients (DEMIRMEN, 1976) of the compared parameters are also given.

dertaken at more locations. In this way whole-year comparisons from year to year may be discovered to yield good correlations with climatic variables. The polar regions are particularly promising. If individual storms are studied and isotope changes can be related to changes in meteorological parameters, the isotope data already produced from ice cores might yield a much better understanding of polar climate change. The tropical regions of the Earth are another promising area because a strong amount-isotope correlation may be present at some locations. Such an isotopic relationship may be related to changes in atmospheric circulation patterns, which in turn may be related to changes in the temperatures of the oceans' surface waters. The possibility of discovering a historical record of the El Niño in the Pacific Ocean is exciting. Isotopic studies of fresh-water fossils may offer good prospects because seasonal temperature variations are minimal in the tropics.

*Acknowledgements*—This paper is dedicated to two men whose pursuit of scientific knowledge made this paper possible. Sam Epstein inspired both the authors, especially in their early careers. He shared that special wisdom he possesses. Dan Smiley loved nature and had a broad-based and deep curiosity. His entire life was dedicated to recording everything he could about natural phenomena around the Mohonk Preserve. He collected most of the samples used in this report and provided the detailed weather records that went with them. His recent death saddened us deeply.

We owe a special thanks to Stan Gedzelman, our long-time colleague, for a thorough review of this paper, which improved its content considerably. We thank John Butler for his assistance in the statistical treatment of the data and Paula Lazov for her careful analytical work.

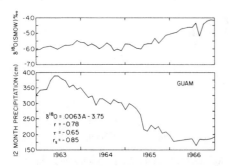

FIG. 16. The rolling twelve-month weighted mean of oxygen isotopic composition of precipitation from Guam, plotted as a function of time. The rolling twelve-month precipitation amounts are also plotted. The Pearson, Kendall, and Spearman correlation coefficients (DEMIRMEN, 1976) of the compared parameters are also given.

This research was sponsored by grants ATM-77-19217, ATM-79-18920, ATM-81-16371, ATM-83-13954, and ATM-85-41987 from the Climate Dynamics Section of the National Science Foundation.

## REFERENCES

ABELL P. I. (1986) Oxygen isotope ratios in modern gastropod shells: a data base for paleoclimatology. *Chem. Geol.* **58**, 183–193.

BUCHARDT B. and FRITZ P. (1980) Environmental isotopes as environmental and climatic indicators. In *Handbook of Environmental Isotope Geochemistry*, Vol. 1, pp. 473–532. Elsevier.

DANSGAARD W. (1964) Stable isotopes in precipitation. *Tellus* **16**, 436–468.

DANSGAARD W. and TAUBER H. (1969) Glacier oxygen-18 content and Pleistocene ocean temperatures. *Science* **166**, 499–502.

DANSGAARD W., JOHNSEN S. F., MOLLER J. and LANGWAY C. C. (1969) One thousand centuries of climatic record from Camp Century on the Greenland ice sheet. *Science* **166**, 377–381.

DEMIRMEN F. (1976) Rank: A fortran IV program for computation of rank correlations. *Computers Geosci.* **1**, 221–229.

EMILIANI C. (1955) Pleistocene temperatures. *J. Geol.* **63**, 538–578.

EPSTEIN S. and YAPP C. J. (1976) Climatic implications of the D/H ratio of hydrogen in C-H groups in tree cellulose. *Earth Planet. Sci. Lett.* **30**, 252–261.

EPSTEIN S., SHARP R. P. and GOW A. J. (1970) Antarctic ice sheet: Stable isotope analyses of Byrd Station cores and interhemispheric climatic implications. *Science* **168**, 1570–1572.

EPSTEIN S., YAPP C. J. and HALL J. H. (1976) The determination of the D/H ratio of non-exchangeable hydrogen in cellulose extracted from aquatic and land plants. *Earth Planet. Sci. Lett.* **30**, 241–251.

FRIEDMAN I., REDFIELD A. C., SCHOEN B. and HARRIS J. (1964) The variation of the deuterium content of natural waters in the hydrologic cycle. *Rev. Geophys.* **2**, 177–224.

FRITZ P. and POPLAWSKI S. (1974) $^{18}O$ and $^{13}C$ in the shells of freshwater mollusks and their environment. *Earth Planet. Sci. Lett.* **24**, 91–98.

GAMBELL A. W. and FRIEDMAN I. (1965) Note on the great variation of deuterium/hydrogen ratios in rainfall for a single storm event. *J. Appl. Meteorol.* **4**, 533–535.

GEDZELMAN S. D. and LAWRENCE J. R. (1982) The isotopic composition of cyclonic precipitation. *J. Appl. Meteorol.* **21**, 1385–1404.

GEDZELMAN S. D., LAWRENCE J. R., WHITE J. W. C. and SMILEY D. (1987) The isotopic composition of precipitation at Mohonk Lake, New York: The amount effect. *J. Geophys. Res.* **92**, 1033–1040.

GRAY J. and THOMPSON P. (1976) Climatic information from $^{18}O/^{16}O$ ratios of cellulose in tree rings. *Nature* **262**, 481–482.

IAEA (1969) Environmental isotope data No. 1: World survey of isotope concentration in precipitation (1953–1963). *Tech. Rept. Series No. 96.* International Atomic Energy Agency, Vienna, Austria.

IAEA (1970) Environmental isotope data No. 2: World survey of isotope concentration in precipitation (1964–1965). *Tech. Rept. Series No. 117.* International Atomic Energy Agency, Vienna, Austria.

IAEA (1971) Environmental isotope data No. 3: World survey of isotope concentration in precipitation (1966–1967). *Tech. Rept. Series No. 129.* International Atomic Energy Agency, Vienna, Austria.

IAEA (1973) Environmental isotope data No. 4: World survey of isotope concentration in precipitation (1968–1969). *Tech. Rept. Series No. 147.* International Atomic Energy Agency, Vienna, Austria.

IAEA (1975) Environmental isotope data No. 5: World survey of isotope concentration in precipitation (1970–1971). *Tech. Rept. Series No. 165.* International Atomic Energy Agency, Vienna, Austria.

IAEA (1979) Environmental isotope data No. 6: World survey of isotope concentration in precipitation (1972–1975). *Tech. Rept. Series No. 192.* International Atomic Energy Agency, Vienna, Austria.

IAEA (1981) Statistical treatment of environmental isotope data in precipitation. *Tech. Rept. Series No. 206.* International Atomic Energy Agency, Vienna, Austria.

IAEA (1983) Environmental isotope data No. 7: World survey of isotope concentration in precipitation (1976–1979). *Tech. Rept. Series No. 226.* International Atomic Energy Agency, Vienna, Austria.

IAEA (1986) Environmental isotope data No. 8: World survey of isotope concentration in precipitation (1980–1983). *Tech. Rept. Series No. 264.* International Atomic Energy Agency, Vienna, Austria.

LAWRENCE J. R. (1970) $^{18}O/^{16}O$ and D/H ratios of soils, weathering zones and clay deposits. Ph.D. thesis, CIT.

LAWRENCE J. R. (1980) D/H and $^{18}O/^{16}O$ ratios in precipitation. In *Carbon Dioxide Effects Research Assessment Program: Proceedings of the International Meeting on Stable Isotopes in Tree-ring Research*, pp. 122–124. NTIS, Springfield, VA.

LAWRENCE J. R. and WHITE J. W. C. (1984) Growing season precipitation from D/H ratios of Eastern White Pine. *Nature* **311**, 558–560.

LAWRENCE J. R., GEDZELMAN S. D., WHITE J. W. C., SMILEY D. and LAZOV P. (1982) Storm trajectories in the Eastern U.S.: D/H isotopic composition of precipitation. *Nature* **296**, 638–640.

MAGARITZ M. and HELLER J. (1980) A desert migration indicator-oxygen isotopic composition of land snail shells. *Paleogeogr. Paleoclimatol. Paleoecol.* **32**, 153–162.

SAVIN S. M. (1977) The history of the earth's surface temperature during the past 100 million years. *Ann. Rev. Earth Planet. Sci.* **5**, 319–355.

SCHIEGEL W. E. (1974) Climatic significance of deuterium abundance in growth rings of Picea. *Nature* **251**, 582–584.

UREY H. C. (1947) The thermodynamic properties of isotopic substances. *J. Chem. Soc. (London)*, 562–581.

WHITE J. W. C. (1983) The climate significance of D/H ratios in White Pine in the northeastern United States. Ph.D. dissertation, Columbia University.

WHITE J. W. C., COOK E. R., LAWRENCE J. R. and BROECKER W. S. (1985) The D/H ratios of sap in trees: Implications for water sources and tree ring D/H ratios. *Geochim. Cosmochim. Acta* **49**, 237–246.

WILSON A. T. and GRINSTED M. J. (1975) Paleotemperatures from tree rings and the D/H ratio of cellulose as a biochemical thermometer. *Nature* **257**, 387–388.

YAPP C. J. (1979) Oxygen and carbon isotope measurements of land snail shell carbonate. *Geochim. Cosmochim. Acta* **43**, 629–635.

Stable Isotope Geochemistry: A Tribute to Samuel Epstein
© The Geochemical Society, Special Publication No. 3, 1991
Editors: H. P. Taylor, Jr., J. R. O'Neil and I. R. Kaplan

# Stable oxygen and hydrogen isotope ratios in shallow ground waters from India and a study of the role of evapotranspiration in the Indian monsoon

R. V. KRISHNAMURTHY* and S. K. BHATTACHARYA

Physical Research Laboratory, Ahmedabd 380 009, India

**Abstract**—We have measured the $\delta D$ and $\delta^{18}O$ values of shallow ground waters along a traverse in the east-northwest parts of India that come under the direct influence of the Indian monsoon. On the premise that shallow ground waters represent an "averaged contemporary precipitation," their isotopic ratios can be interpreted as proxy indicators of the $\delta D$ and $\delta^{18}O$ values of the local precipitation. The isotopic ratios thus measured suggest that, as in many other parts of the world, the rain-out process basically follows a Rayleigh-type distillation with a $\delta^{18}O$ inland gradient of about $-2$ per mil per 1000 km between the coastal Calcutta and inland Delhi. However, the gradient appears to be smaller than what would be expected for a pure Rayleigh process where the vapor reduction factor in Delhi is more than half. This reduced gradient can arise if the original parcel of water vapor is augmented by additional vapor transport through evapotranspiration. A simple box model has been employed to take this into account. This model suggests that up to 40% of water that has precipitated has to be put back into the vapor system to explain the observed isotopic trend. This estimate of 40% is not farfetched when compared to values estimated based on other hydrological balance calculations and is also similar to the 35% obtained in European precipitations. The $\delta D$-$\delta^{18}O$ line of the shallow ground waters along this traverse is expressed by the equation $\delta D = 6.4 \, \delta^{18}O - 1$; significantly different from the Meteoric Water Line (MWL) of $\delta D = 8 \, \delta^{18}O + 10$. However, if twelve of the samples that lie close to large irrigation systems and rivers are disregarded, the relationship is found to be of the form $\delta D = 7.12 \, \delta^{18}O + 3$, which is similar to the relationship obtained for the direct precipitation in three IAEA stations in India. These data lend support for the argument that the shallow ground waters serve as good proxy records of the isotopic composition of local precipitation.

## INTRODUCTION

AT ANY GIVEN LOCATION the distribution of stable oxygen and hydrogen isotopes in precipitation is influenced by several factors (DANSGAARD, 1964); to name a few: the "temperature effect" that causes the isotopic ratio to change proportionally with the surface air temperature; the "amount effect" in which there is a negative correlation between the $\delta$ values and the amount of precipitation; and the "altitude effect" that causes a depletion of the heavier isotope with increasing altitude where the precipitation falls (YURTSEVER, 1975; FRIEDMAN and SMITH, 1976; EHHALT et al., 1963). In spite of these several local effects that have to be taken into account while interpreting the isotope ratio in precipitation, it is fortunate that on a global scale and also to a large extent on a regional scale, the rain-out process can be explained by means of a simple mechanism. This simple mechanism, as indicated by DANSGAARD (1964), turns out to be a Rayleigh-type distillation where from an initial oceanic reservoir water vapor is generated and lost through successive steps of precipitation as this parcel of vapor moves polewards. The distribution of the oxygen and hydrogen isotopic ratio in such a condensation process can be expressed as

$$R_p = \alpha R_0 F^{\alpha-1} \tag{1}$$

where $R_p$ = the isotopic ratio of precipitation at a point away from the source region, $R_0$ = the isotopic ratio of the initial vapor mass, $F$ = the vapor reduction factor at the point where $R_p$ is being calculated, and $\alpha$ = the fractionation factor between the vapor and the liquid phases. Note that this expression assumes constancy of $\alpha$ at every stage of condensation.

Since the fractionation causes the liquid phase to be higher in the concentration of the heavier isotope, one of the main consequences of a process such as the Rayleigh distillation is the "continental effect." Because of this effect the $\delta$ values of precipitation become progressively more negative as one moves away from the oceanic source region. That this trend has been observed in the majority of cases is a strong support for the Rayleigh distillation hypothesis of precipitation.

## SAMPLES AND EXPERIMENTAL METHODS

In all, more than 80 samples encompassed by a triangular sector Ahmedabad-Calcutta-Delhi were collected and analysed (KRISHNAMURTHY, 1984; BHATTACHARYA et al., 1985). However, for the present study which attempts

---

* *Present address:* Division of Geological and Planetary Sciences, California Institute of Technology, Pasadena, CA 91125, U.S.A.

to estimate the role of evapotranspiration, only 55 of these are relevant. These 55 samples cover a distance of approximately 1400 km, and form a roughly rectangular track between coastal Calcutta and inland Delhi. The sampled area falls in the "monsoon trough" and directly experiences the influence of the Indian southwestern monsoon that operates between June and September every year (SIKKA, 1977; ANANTHAKRISHNAN, 1977; PISHAROTY, 1965; RAO, 1981). Significantly, this area also experiences the "monsoon depressions" which are characterised by severe precipitation events accompanied by strong winds. The samples came from open dug wells of depth no more than ten meters from the surface. Care was taken to ensure that the wells were situated as far away as possible from irrigation systems, rivers, or lakes. Samples were collected in pre-cleaned dry glass or plastic bottles and filled to the brim and sealed to avoid evaporation. Dug well samples were collected by sending an air-filled bottle upside down to the bottom part of the water column and then tilting it. All the samples were analysed within about a month after arrival in the laboratory to minimize errors that might be caused by storage over long periods of time. Sample locations are indicated in Fig. 1.

The $\delta^{18}O$ values were determined by a slight modification of the standard technique first suggested by EPSTEIN and MAYEDA (1953). The $\delta D$ values were determined by reduction of the water sample over hot uranium metal (BIGELEISEN et al., 1952; FRIEDMAN and HARDCASTLE,

1970). Samples were analysed in batches of five, and with each batch a calibrated laboratory standard was analysed. The $\delta$ values are reported with respect to SMOW in the usual way and the overall precision determined by repeated analysis of the laboratory standard is $\pm0.1$ and $\pm1.5$ per mil for $\delta^{18}O$ and $\delta D$, respectively.

## RESULTS AND DISCUSSION

### Oxygen isotope ratios

The $\delta^{18}O$ values of the ground waters as a function of distance from Calcutta are plotted in Fig. 2. The data points other than the solid circles come from localities that do have large rivers and irrigation systems close by and so might have influenced the ground water samples. The "continental effect" causing the depletion in $^{18}O$ with distance, that is going inland from the coastal Calcutta, is clearly evident. This is to be expected in a typical Rayleigh distillation process where during the monsoon, air masses collect moisture in and around the Bay of Bengal and release as rain when they are carried by the prevailing winds inland in a northwest-west direction. The inland gradient in $\delta^{18}O$ is

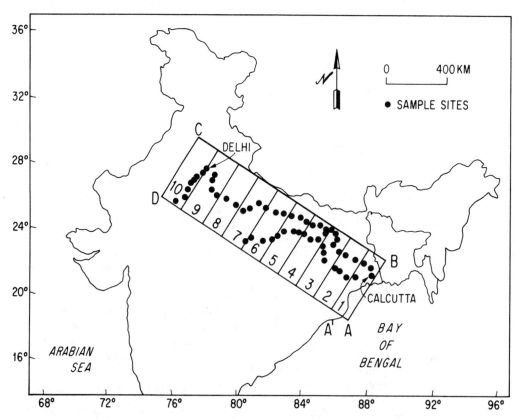

FIG. 1. Map of part of India showing the ground water sample sites. Each filled circle represents one sampling location. The rectangular box ABCD and the sub-boxes (1–10) were constructed to model the contribution of evapotranspiration. See text for details.

found to be −2 per mil per 1000 km. This is comparable to an inland gradient in $\delta^{18}O$ of −2.8 per mil per 1000 km observed in the analysis of over 900 samples of municipal water supplies of 480 stations in West Germany (FORSTEL and HUTZEN, 1983). An inland gradient of −3 per mil per 1000 km has been reported by SONNTAG *et al.* (1976) for the precipitation in the European continent. However, this $\delta^{18}O$ change with respect to distance is much less than the −6 per mil per 1000 km seen for the shallow ground water samples along a traverse from Ahmedabad to Delhi in the northwestern part of India (BHATTACHARYA *et al.*, 1985). One factor that can reduce the inland gradient is the recycling of the vapor mass through processes such as evapotranspiration. This has the effect of restoring the vapor content of the airmasses and increasing its isotopic composition over what it would normally be. Apparently, recycling of water vapor within the basin is responsible for the low $\delta^{18}O$ inland gradient of −0.75 per mil per 1000 km in the Amazon basin (SALATI *et al.*, 1979).

### δD-δ¹⁸O relationship

Figure 3 shows the $\delta D$-$\delta^{18}O$ relationship for the ground water samples analysed. The relationship when *all* the samples are considered is

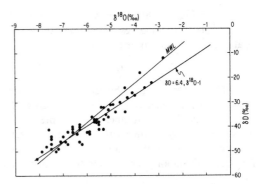

FIG. 3. The δD-δ¹⁸O relationship in the ground water samples. The meteoric water line (MWL) is also shown for comparison.

$$\delta D = 6.4 \, \delta^{18}O - 1 \quad (r = 0.95, \, n = 55).$$

BHATTACHARYA *et al.* (1985) have found a δD-δ¹⁸O relationship given by

$$\delta D = (6.8 \pm 0.1) \, \delta^{18}O + (2.2 \pm 0.4)$$

by taking into consideration the analysis of ground waters from several other stations, including the ones reported here. However, if only the samples

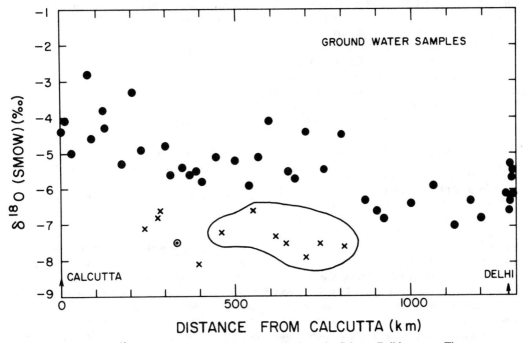

FIG. 2. The δ¹⁸O values of the ground water samples along the Calcutta-Delhi traverse. The zero point is set at Calcutta on the eastern coast where the vapor mass originates and propagates inland towards Delhi. The points other than the filled circles represent sampling locations that are presumably influenced by large artificial irrigation systems, rivers, etc. They may thus have contribution other than local precipitation.

indicated in Fig. 2 by filled circles are used, because of the likely mixed sources of the other ones, the relationship is found to be (Fig. 4)

$$\delta D = 7.12 \, \delta^{18}O + 3 \quad (r = 0.92, \, n = 43).$$

It is interesting to note that this relationship is quite similar to that calculated by BHATTACHARYA et al. (1985) for the limited number of direct precipitations measured by the International Atomic Energy Agency (IAEA) for the stations in New Delhi, Bombay, and Shillong. They found the relationship to be

$$\delta D = (7.2 \pm 0.1) \, \delta^{18}O + (5.1 \pm 0.1).$$

This similarity adds strength to the argument that the $\delta$ values of the shallow ground water samples along the Calcutta-Delhi sector, ignoring those with anomalous values, quite reasonably represent an averaged precipitation in the region. Therefore, the value of $\sim$7.2 can be taken as characteristic of the $\delta D$-$\delta^{18}O$ slope for the average Indian monsoonal precipitation. While this relationship deviates slightly from the well-known Meteoric Water Line (MWL) $\delta D$-$\delta^{18}O$ relationship (CRAIG, 1961), it should be noted that correlation lines with slope less than eight are not rare, especially on a regional scale where local effects play an important role. For example, GAT and DANSGAARD (1972) found a slope close to the "evaporation line" in their study of water samples from Israel and Jordan. In continental Europe the slope of the $\delta D$-$\delta^{18}O$ line has been reported to be 7.6 and 6.0 for the winter and summer precipitations, respectively (ROZANSKI et al., 1982). Even in tropical island stations such as Barbados, Canton, Johnston, and Wale, the least-square fit linear relationship has a slope of 6.17.

*Role of evapotranspiration in the Indian monsoon*

The distribution of oxygen and hydrogen isotope ratios in precipitation along the sector Calcutta-Delhi as inferred from an analysis of shallow ground waters can be explained by treating the rain-out process in this sector as a Rayleigh-type distillation. However, the $\delta^{18}O$ change with distance or the $\delta^{18}O$ gradient inland is less than what one might expect for a pure Rayleigh-type distillation. We arrive at this by following the methods used by ROZANSKI et al. (1982) for interpreting the stable isotope composition of European precipitation. The sector under investigation is approximated by a rectangle and divided into ten boxes of equal size (Fig. 1), with each box measuring $350 \times 140$ km. The construction of the rectangle is mainly dictated by the disposition of the monsoon trough and that of the

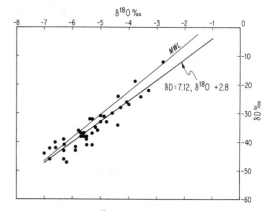

FIG. 4. The $\delta D$-$\delta^{18}O$ relationship in the ground water samples obtained after removing those with multiple contribution (irrigation systems, rivers, etc). These latter samples are shown in Fig. 2 by symbols other than filled circles.

boxes by the need to distribute the sample locations and metereological stations as uniformly as possible. An assumption is introduced that the atmospheric circulation over the rectangular area is essentially zonal in character. This simplifies the situation by restricting the calculation of only the vapor flux entering the first box, i.e. along the boundaries AB and AA'. The vapor flux across the above boundaries can be calculated using the following relation (DEWAN and DATTA, 1976):

$$W = t/g \int_{P_{1000}}^{P_{500}} (L_i U_i X_i) dp \qquad (2)$$

where

$W$ = vapor flux

$t$ = time period for which the flux is to be calculated

$g$ = acceleration due to gravity

$L_i$ = the distance across which the flux enters i.e. AB and AA'

$u_i$ = wind component normal to the sides AB and AA'

$x_i$ = the humidity mixing ratio.

The integration is performed between the heights 1000 and 500 mb since the moisture content above the 500 mb level is negligible. Adopting values of 5 m/sec for $u_i$ and 12.3 g/kg for $x_i$ (RANGARAJAN and MANI, 1982; DESAI and SUBRAMANIAN, 1978) the value of W, the vapor flux entering the first box turns out to be $1.57 \times 10^{12}$ tons per season (June to September). It must be noted that the value of the flux is strongly dependent on the values used for $u_i$ and $x_i$. We feel nevertheless that the value obtained by us is quite reasonable. This quantity of vapor flux entering the first box is allowed to undergo a Rayleigh distillation so that condensation takes place in each box by successive removal of the initial vapor mass. Equation (1) will then govern the isotopic ratio of the system. We can slightly modify Eqn. (1) to accomodate a varying $\alpha$, the fractionation factor from box to box. The modified expression for the isotopic composition of the condensate, *i.e.* rain at a distance from the coast, can be written as

$$R_{p(i)} = \alpha_i R_{(i-1)} F_i^{\alpha i - 1} \quad (3)$$

where

$R_{p(i)}$ = isotopic ratio of the precipitation in the $i$th box

$R_{(i-1)}$ = isotopic ratio of the vapor entering the $i$th box

$F_i$ = The vapor reduction factor within a single box

$\alpha_i$ = the fractionation factor in the $i$th box as applicable at temperatures at the average cloud base at 880 mb level.

Equation (3) also allows a step-wise development of $R$ from box to box. In a step-wise treatment of $R$ from box to box, proper amount of vapor can be put back by evapotranspiration before it goes into the next box so that the $R_{2-1}$ term includes the contribution of evapotranspired water as well. A simplifying assumption is to be made that the evapotranspired component is isotopically identical to the fraction left behind as precipitation (ZIMMERMAN *et al.*, 1967).

The remaining water vapor fraction $F(n)$ in box number $n$ is calculated using the equation

$$F(n) = \frac{W - \sum_{i=1}^{n} (P_i - E_{i-1})}{W} \quad (4)$$

where

$W$ = water vapor flux into the first box

$P_i$ = the precipitation flux in the $i$th box

$E_{i-1}$ = the evapotranspiration flux in the $(i-1)$th box.

The value of $P_i$ was estimated for each box using the rainfall data recorded by the meteorological stations lying in the $i$th box. Table 1 shows the $F_n$, $P_i$, and $\alpha_i$ values for each of the ten boxes without taking into account contribution by evapotranspiration, i.e., setting the $F_i$ terms in Eqn. (4) to zero. The initial isotopic composition of the vapor in box 1 was set so that the condensate in the first box will have a $\delta^{18}O$ value of $-4.4$, the value for the ground

Table 1. The precipitation $(P_i)$, fraction remaining in vapor $(F_n)$ and the fractionation factor for each of the ten boxes. $P_i$ and $F_n$ are for conditions of no evapotranspiration

| Box No. | $P_i$ (10¹² tons/season) | $F_n$ | $\alpha_i$ |
|---|---|---|---|
| 1 | 0.05 | 0.968 | 1.00970 |
| 2 | 0.05 | 0.936 | 1.00966 |
| 3 | 0.049 | 0.905 | 1.00962 |
| 4 | 0.047 | 0.875 | 1.00958 |
| 5 | 0.047 | 0.845 | 1.00954 |
| 6 | 0.048 | 0.814 | 1.00950 |
| 7 | 0.042 | 0.788 | 1.00946 |
| 8 | 0.035 | 0.766 | 1.00942 |
| 9 | 0.038 | 0.741 | 1.00938 |
| 10 | 0.031 | 0.721 | 1.00934 |

water in Calcutta and its neighborhood. Figure 5 shows the isotopic composition in precipitation, due to a Rayleigh process, as a function of distance from Calcutta for three initial vapor fluxes entering the first box. The three fluxes—1.19, 1.57, and 1.95 $\times 10^{12}$ tons per season—allow for an error in the estimate of the initial flux by ±25%. Also shown by the straight line is the best fit line of the experimental $\delta^{18}O$ data of ground water samples. Clearly, a pure Rayleigh-type distillation does not allow for the observed trend. The line based on experimental $\delta^{18}O$

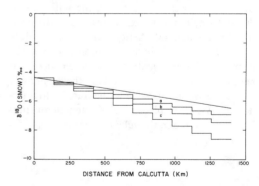

FIG. 5. The measured $\delta^{18}O$ values in ground water samples and that estimated due to a pure Rayleigh-type distillation as the vapor mass travels from coastal Calcutta towards inland Delhi. The histograms a,b,c would be the isotopic trend in local precipitation for an initial seasonal vapor mass, respectively, of 1.95, 1.57, and 1.19 $\times 10^{12}$ tons entering Calcutta and then being lost as precipitation in each of the ten boxes shown in Fig. 1. The fraction of vapor remaining in each box after removal of the condensate is given in Table 1 and was calculated using the actual rainfall data available from the metereological stations within each box. The straight line represents the measured $\delta^{18}O$ values in the ground water samples. If only a pure Rayleigh-type distillation operated, the experimental line would be expected to pass through one of the histograms.

values behaves as though the vapor reduction factor is offset by additional contribution to the overlying vapor mass. As stated earlier, one process that is likely to do so is evapotranspiration. Therefore, the $P_i$ values obtained for each box may be regarded as the residual left after what has been put back by evapotranspiration.

A series of calculations can be done to estimate the fraction of the condensate in each box that needs to be put back into the overlying vapor mass so as to obtain a reasonable agreement between the calculated and observed $\delta^{18}O$ values. Figure 6 shows the results of these calculations, where it is seen that if a 40% evapotranspiration for each box is allowed, the agreement between the calculated and observed trend is pretty good. The figure of 40% compares well with a similar one quoted for the north Indian region by DATTA and DEWAN (1975) and RAMA (1980). This is also comparable with the 35% estimate for European precipitation (ROZANSKI et al., 1982). It is significant, too, that the area considered here is in the fertile Ganges basin, which is abundant with vegetation and thus can be very conducive to the process of evapotranspiration.

Although an estimate of the evapotranspiration flux that is comparable with the existing estimates for this region could be made, it must be emphasized that this figure is dependent, as far our model is considered, on the two parameters $W$ and $P_i$ in the equations utilised. Of these, $W$, the initial vapor flux entering the first box, is sensitive to the wind speed that enters into the calculation. The values adopted by us are those we have been able to obtain from available information. The closer these two parameters are to the actual values, the greater will be the precision assignable to the fraction that undergoes evapotranspiration. The potential for studies of this nature in the subcontinent is clearly evident.

## CONCLUSIONS

Stable oxygen and hydrogen isotope ratio of shallow ground waters along the track Calcutta-Delhi in northern India appears to be a good proxy indicator of the isotopic composition of local precipitation. Since this track is well served by the Indian monsoon, such a study can be used to understand more about the isotopic distribution in precipitation in a monsoonal system. The present study, admittedly of limited coverage, suggests that the rain-out process in this traverse can be regarded as a Rayleigh-type distillation. The Rayleigh distillation is apparently modified by additional vapor introduction to the cloud system through evapo-

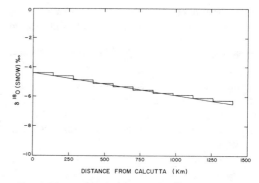

FIG. 6. The measured ground water $\delta^{18}O$ values (straight line) and the calculated $\delta^{18}O$ values (histogram) of precipitation taking into account a 40% vapor feed back through evapotranspiration. The initial vapor mass entering Calcutta is set at $1.57 \times 10^{12}$ tons per season (June-September).

transpiration from the ground or vegetation cover. A simple box model can be used to estimate the fraction that is added to the overlying vapor mass by this process. If the various input parameters of the model are accepted, the evapotranspiration flux is estimated to be 40%, a figure comparable to the previous estimates.

*Acknowledgements*—We thank Dr. S. K. Gupta for the collection of a majority of the samples and Dr. R. Ramesh for discussions. We would also like to put on record the vision of Prof. Rama which greatly prompted this study. RVK gratefully acknowledges NSF grant EAR-8504096.

## REFERENCES

ANANTHAKRISHNAN R. (1977) Some aspects of the monsoon circulation and monsoon rainfall. In *Monsoon Dynamics* (ed. T. N. KRISHNAMURTI), Birkhauses-Verlag.

BHATTACHARYA S. K., GUPTA S. K. and KRISHNAMURTHY R. V. (1985) Oxygen and hydrogen isotope ratios in groundwaters and rivers from India. *Proc. Ind. Acad. Sci. (Earth Planet. Sci.)* **94**, 283–295.

BIGELEISEN J., PERIMAN M. C. and PROSSER H. C. (1952) Conversion of hydrogenic materials to hydrogen for isotopic analysis. *Anal. Chem.* **24**, 1356–1357.

CRAIG H. (1961) Isotopic variations in meteoric waters. *Science* **133**, 1702–1703.

DANSGAARD W. (1964) Stable isotopes in precipitation. *Tellus* **16**, 436–467.

DATTA P. K. and DEWAN B. N. (1975) A study of water potential over India during monsoon season. *Proc. 2nd World Cong. Intl. Wat. Res. Assn., New Delhi* **3**, 493–496.

DESAI B. N. and SUBRAMAINAN S. K. (1978) Air masses up to 500 mb level over the Indian summer monsoon trough area. *Ind. J. Meteorol. Hydrol. Geophys.* **29**, 54–60.

DEWAN B. N. and DATTA R. K. (1976) Subdivision-wise study of water potential over India during south-west monsoon. *Proc. Symp. Tropical Monsoon, Indian Inst. Trop. Meteorol.*, Pune.

EHHALT D., KNOTT K., NAGEL, J. F. and VOGEL J. C. (1963) Deuterium and oxygen-18 in rain water. *J. Geophys. Res.* **68**, 3775–3780.

EPSTEIN S. and MAYEDA T. (1953) Variations of $^{18}$O content of waters from natural sources. *Geochim. Cosmochim. Acta* **4**, 213–221.

FORSTEL H. and HUTZEN H. (1983) Oxygen isotope ratios in German groundwater. *Nature* **304**, 614–616.

FRIEDMAN I. and HARDCASTLE K. (1970) A new technique for pumping hydrogen gas. *Geochim. Cosmochim. Acta* **34**, 125–129.

FRIEDMAN I. and SMITH G. (1976) Deuterium content of snow cores from Sierra Nevada area. *Science* **196**, 467–469.

GAT J. R. and DAANSGAARD W. (1972) Stable isotope survey of the fresh water occurrences in Israel and the Northern Jordan Rift. *J. Hydrolo.* **16**, 177–192.

KRISHNAMURTHY R. V. (1984) Stable isotope studies on sedimentary deposits and groundwaters and their climatic implications. Ph.D. thesis, Gujarat Univ, India.

PISHAROTI P. R. (1965) Evaporation from the Arabian Sea and the Indian southwest monsoon. *Proc. Symp. Meteorolo. Results of the Intl. Indian Ocean Expedition, Bombay.*

RAMA V. (1980) Increasing the rainfall over India? *Mausam* **31**, 324–325.

RANGARAJAN S. and MANI A. (1982) Total precipitable water in the atmosphere over India. *Proc. Indian Acad. Sci.* **91**, 189–207.

RAO K. N. (1981) Tropical cyclones of the Indian Seas. In *World Survey of Climatology* (eds. H. ARAKAWA and K. TAKAHASHI), Vol 9, pp. 257–281.

ROZANSKI K. (1985) Deuterium and oxygen-18 in European groundwaters-links to atmospheric circulation in the past. *Isotope Geosci.* **52**, 349–363.

ROZANSKI K., SONNTAG C. and MUNNICH K. O. (1982) Factors controlling stable isotope composition of European precipitation. *Tellus* **34**, 142–150.

SALATI E., OALL'OLIO A., MATSUI E. and GAT J. R. (1979) Recycling of water in the Amazon basin, an isotope study. *Water Resources Res.* **15**, 1250–1258.

SIKKA D. R. (1977) Some aspects of the life, history, structure and movement of monsoon depressions. In *Monsoon Dynamics* (ed. T. N. KRISHNAMURTI). Birkhauses-Verlag.

SONNTAG C., NEUREUTHER P., KALINKE C., MUNNICH K. O., KLITZCH E. and WEISTROFFER K. (1976) Zur palaeoklimatik der Sahara: kontinental effekt im D und O-18 Gehalt pluvial pluvialer Saharawasser *Naturewiss.* **63**, 749–765.

YURTSEVER Y. (1975) World survey of stable isotopes in precipitation, *Internal Report,* IAEA, Vienna.

ZIMMERMAN U., MUNNICH K. O. and ROETHER W. (1967) Downward movement of soil movement traced by means of hydrogen isotopes. In *Isotope Techniques in the Hydrological Cycle; Geophys. Monogr. 11.* Amer. Geophys. Union.

Stable Isotope Geochemistry: A Tribute to Samuel Epstein
© The Geochemical Society, Special Publication No. 3, 1991
Editors: H. P. Taylor, Jr., J. R. O'Neil and I. R. Kaplan

# Stable isotopic composition of waters in a small Piedmont watershed

DAVID B. WENNER,[1] PETER D. KETCHAM[1] and JOHN F. DOWD[2]

Department of Geology[1] and School of Forest Resources,[2] The University of Georgia, Athens, GA 30602, U.S.A.

**Abstract**—The oxygen isotopic compositions of rainfall, soil water, groundwater, and streamflow were measured over a one-year period from 1988–1989 at a 23 hectare forested watershed in the Georgia Piedmont. Rainfall was collected at an open area within the watershed and soil water was collected using zero tension and tension lysimeters from four different 5 m$^2$ plots. Groundwater was collected from two wells; streamflow samples were collected from two flumes on a perennial stream draining the watershed. During this period, the isotopic composition of the rainfall was quite variable; individual rainfall events had $\delta^{18}O$ values varying up to 11 per mil and the volume weighted monthly averages ranged from $-1.2$ in summer to $-7.1$ per mil in winter. Significant isotopic dampening of the infiltrating rainfall occurred as shallow as 30 cm in the soil. At greater depths (60 and 120 cm), homogenization was even more complete. This homogenization process occurred as downwardly percolating rainfall exchanged isotopically with a much larger volume of more tightly bound, relatively immobile water in the soil matrix. This process is most apparent with the zero tension lysimeter data, which have $\delta^{18}O$ values intermediate between rain water and the soil matrix water as sampled by the tension lysimeters. During the winter of 1988 when soil moisture was high, these soil waters were similar isotopically to groundwater, which remained isotopically uniform over the year. This suggests that most groundwater recharge occurs only during this (wet) period. The $\delta^{18}O$ of the baseflow in the perennial stream is also uniform, but slightly $^{18}O$-enriched compared to groundwater adjacent to the stream channel. This difference is likely due to discharge of evaporated waters from an upstream pond. $^{18}O$-enrichment by evaporation was very evident in a downstream pond.

## INTRODUCTION

A NUMBER OF investigators have used naturally occurring tracers, such as the stable isotopic composition of rainfall, to evaluate the relationship between rainfall, runoff, and groundwater in small forested watersheds (*e.g.,* FRITZ *et al.,* 1976; SKLASH *et al.,* 1976; KENNEDY *et al.,* 1986; DEWALLE *et al.,* 1988; MCDONNELL *et al.,* 1990). These studies assume that the isotopic signature of the various hydrologic components such as rainfall, soil water in different horizons, and groundwater, all of which can potentially contribute to streamflow, are distinct and remain that way so that their relative contributions can be determined from streamflow using simple mixing models. Most studies, however, have not examined the assumption that the isotopic signatures of these various hydrologic components are distinct and remain identifiable.

The study presented here was designed to monitor the stable isotopic composition of rainfall and waters from upper parts of the unsaturated zone, saturated zone, and the nearby fluvial system over a period of one year. It was undertaken in a small loblolly pine watershed within the N.E. Georgia Piedmont. The specific objectives of this study were to

(1) document the event and seasonal fluctuations in the isotopic compositions of rainfall that reach the ground;

(2) examine how these isotopic signals are propagated into upper parts of the soil zone;

(3) assess whether the isotopic data can be used to constrain the flow mechanisms responsible for downward movement of water through the soil;

(4) ascertain if isotopic data can define what portion of the rainfall recharges the groundwater;

(5) assess what isotopic similarities and differences exist among waters in the upper parts of the soil and the much deeper groundwaters; and

(6) determine how the isotopic composition of the groundwater and base flow of a nearby perennial stream compare.

## FIELD SITE DESCRIPTION AND SAMPLING METHODS

*Site description*

The present study involves collection and $^{18}O$-isotopic analysis of water samples within a small 23 hectare forested watershed located in the Georgia Piedmont, approximately 33 km northeast of Athens, near the town of Comer (Fig. 1). Typical slopes for the site range from 6 to 10 percent, but are steeper near the perennial stream.

Individual rainfall event samples were collected from a meteorological area within the watershed, whereas waters from upper parts of the unsaturated zone were obtained from both tension and zero tension lysimeters located within four representative, 5 m$^2$ instrumented plots. Also within this watershed, samples of the saturated zone were obtained from two wells. Stream samples were obtained from one H-flume located on the perennial stream upstream from a pond and downstream from the instru-

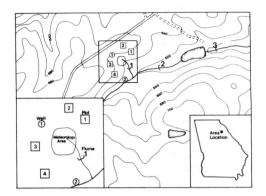

FIG. 1. Site location and experimental design.

mented plots, and one H-flume located at the outflow of
the pond.

The site containing the four instrumented plots consists
of a three-hectare sub-watershed drained by an ephemeral
stream, which in turn drains into a first-order perennial
stream that discharges, approximately 0.5 km downstream
from the test site, into a 1.2 hectare man-made pond. The
sub-watershed is located in a 22-year-old loblolly (*Pinus
taeda*) plantation. The trees are from 12 to 15 m tall.

The four instrumented test plots (each 5 m² in area)
were selected to represent the different geographic and topographic settings and soil types of the area. Three of the
four plots (1, 2, and 4; see Fig. 1) occur within a typical,
highly weathered Piedmont soil (Cecil series). Such soils
form from the gneissic bedrock underlying the area. The
A horizon is a reddish brown sandy clay loam, 5 to 20 cm
thick, averaging about 13% clay. Below the A horizon is
an A/B transition, usually 10 to 20 cm thick. The Bt horizon, a red clay and red clay loam, averages about 47%
clay and extends from the base of the A/B transition to
depths of 1 m. Below this is saprolite approximately 7 m
deep. Plot 3 is located in a small drainage area and is
atypical in that a buried sand-rich A-horizon occurs due
to slumping. This sandy horizon extends more than 0.5
m deep.

*Instrumentation*

Each of the 5 m² plots shown in Fig. 1 contain the
following equipment for collecting water samples:

(1) Four zero-tension lysimeters similar to that described by JORDAN (1968) were placed horizontally within
the walls of open pits at depths of 30 and 60 cm below
the surface. These lysimeters were designed to sample waters flowing under locally saturated conditions along preferential flow pathways within the unsaturated zone.

(2) Six 1-bar solution-cup (tension) lysimeters, placed
vertically at depths of 30, 60, and 120 cm, were used to
sample the more tightly bound waters in the soil matrix.

The 23 hectare watershed also contains the following sampling equipment (see Fig. 1):

(1) A meteorological weather station with a non-evap-
orative rainfall collector.
(2) Three flumes to measure discharge and to collect
samples. Flume 1, located on an ephemeral stream close
to the instrumented plots, never flowed during the study

period and no samples were collected. Flume 2 is an H-
flume located on the perennial stream below the site but
above a 1.2 hectare pond. Flume 3 is an H-flume located
at the overflow of the pond.

(3) Two wells to sample waters from the saturated zone.
Well 1 is approximately 10 m deep with the lower 1.5 m
screened in gneissic bedrock. The watertable in this well
lies approximately 6.5 m below the surface. Well 2 is situated approximately 300 m down-gradient from well 1,
six meters from the perennial stream. It is 8.5 m deep and
screened in the saprolite. The watertable here is 3.2 m
below the surface.

*Sampling procedures*

Sampling of rainfall and waters from the unsaturated
zone, the saturated zone, and the fluvial system began in
late January 1988 and was concluded in late January 1989.
During this period, northeast Georgia experienced drought
conditions that made sampling more variable than anticipated. Rainfall samples were collected as soon as possible
after each event. Whenever collection was not possible
before another event, samples representing the multiple
event were obtained.

When conditions permitted, waters from the unsaturated
zone were collected weekly from the 1-bar solution cup
(tension) lysimeters located in the test plots. During most
of the year, weekly sampling from the lysimeters was not
possible because of low soil moisture. Only during February, March, and part of April 1988, and late January
1989, was the soil moisture consistently high enough to
permit weekly sampling. During other periods, sampling
was only possible after large storm events. To collect samples from the tension lysimeters, a manual pump was used
to apply a partial vacuum (approximately 0.6 bar). About
48 hours later, 5 to 40 ml of water was obtained and placed
in air-tight glass bottles. Tests conducted on the suction
lysimeters demonstrated that no measurable isotopic
changes occurred to the water during movement through
the porous cup or while it was standing in the partially
evacuated lysimeters (FEILD, 1990).

The two observation wells were also sampled weekly.
Sampling protocol was to bail three times the well volume,
then allow the well to return to its pre-bailed levels. After
recovery, the wells were sampled with a bailer. This procedure follows ENVIRONMENTAL PROTECTION AGENCY
(1986) guidelines for well sampling. Samples were stored
in air-tight bottles.

Stream samples were collected as grab samples from the
outlets of flumes 2 and 3 and stored in air-tight bottles.

*Sample analysis*

Three hundred and fifty five samples were analyzed for
$\delta^{18}O$, and these are reported in per mil relative to SMOW.
The complete data set is reported by KETCHAM (1989).
The $CO_2$ equilibration technique described by EPSTEIN
and MAYEDA (1953) was used in preparation of samples
for oxygen isotopic analysis. Isotopic analyses were performed with a Finnigan MAT, model delta E isotope ratio
mass spectrometer.

## WEATHER PATTERNS, 1983–1989

The isotopic composition of waters in the subsurface reflects the rainfall from the past as well as

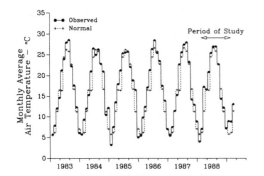

FIG. 2. Monthly average air temperatures (observed) for the period 1983 to 1989 at Athens, Georgia, compared to long-term average (normal) monthly temperatures.

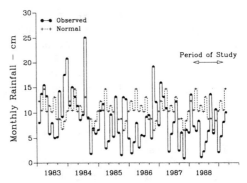

FIG. 3. Monthly average rainfall (observed) for the period 1983 to 1989 at Athens, Georgia, compared to long-term average (normal) monthly rainfall.

the present, and thus it is useful to examine the weather conditions several years prior to and during the time of the study.

Monthly average air temperature data from the closest NOAA weather station in Athens, Georgia (33 km away) is displayed in Fig. 2. For the years prior to this study (1983–1987), monthly average temperatures were from 1 to 6°C above normal. This trend continued through the study period. Of particular importance to this study is the fact that during the last week of December 1988, and extending into February 1989, an unusual shift in the jet stream caused near record high temperatures for most of the southeastern United States. These anomalous temperatures are not evident in Fig. 2 for the month of December 1988, because temperatures for the first part of the month were below normal. The anomalously high average monthly temperatures for January and February 1989 are very apparent in Fig. 2.

Because $\delta^{18}O$ values of rainfall are dependent upon temperature (*e.g.*, YURTSEVER and GAT, 1981), these unusually warm air temperatures almost certainly account for the departure from the normal seasonal isotopic rainfall trends discussed below and shown in Fig. 4.

Rainfall volumes for the period 1983 through 1987 were above average in 1983 and most of 1984 and well below average from late 1984 onward (Fig. 3). In 1983, the yearly rainfall volume was 9.93 cm above normal (50.1 cm). The following four years (1984 through 1987), however, were below normal by 0.8, 12.3, 35.9, and 36.3 cm, respectively. For the study period, monthly rain volumes were 44.9 cm below normal, the lowest within the six-year period. In particular, the months of May, June, and December were extremely dry, having rainfall volumes of 24, 39, and 5%, respectively, below normal. The small amount of rainfall during the whole

1988–89 winter period caused recharge to groundwater to be abnormally low. Normally, recharge below the root zone occurs during winter because of low evapotranspiration rates. This study was conducted during a period of abnormal weather conditions, and thus some of the results observed in this report may be atypical.

## DISCUSSION OF ISOTOPIC DATA

### Rainfall

Isotopic data and volumes for individual rainfall events are presented in Fig. 4. Also shown are the monthly weighted averages calculated using the formula given by YURTSEVER and GAT (1981):

$$WA = \frac{\sum (V*\delta)}{\sum (V)} \qquad (1)$$

where

WA = monthly weighted average
$V$ = volume of rainfall from a single event
$\delta$ = isotopic value for a single rainfall event.

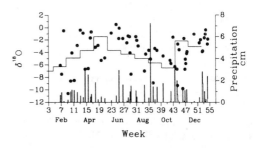

FIG. 4. Oxygen isotopic composition of individual rainfall events (dots), their volumes (spikes), and the volume weighted monthly $\delta^{18}O$ values (line).

As Fig. 4 shows, the $\delta^{18}O$ values of the 64 individual rainfall events are quite erratic, although as a general rule relatively large events are more $\delta^{18}O$ depleted than smaller rainfalls (KETCHAM, 1989).

The monthly weighted average rainfall data shown in Fig. 4 display the typical winter-summer cyclic isotopic variation observed in many continental localities (*e.g.,* GAT and DANSGAARD, 1972), although the later part of the study period (late December 1988 through February 1989) is anomalously $^{18}O$-enriched. This $^{18}O$-enrichment was almost certainly caused by the abnormally warm air temperatures in the southeastern U.S.A. during this period.

*Waters in the forest soil*

*Zero tension lysimeters.* Four zero tension lysimeters were installed in each of the pits (two at 30 cm and two at 60 cm) at each of the plots in July 1988. These lysimeters collect water flowing rapidly through the unsaturated zone along open pathways such as root-soil interfaces, cracks, faunal tunnels, or other zones of extremely high hydraulic conductivity. If these pathways become active, it usually occurs only during large (>2 cm) rainfall events.

Soil moisture during the period after installation was generally low (MILLER, 1989) and sample collection was infrequent. Relatively short period rainfall events of 2.5 cm or more produced samples in some of the zero tension lysimeters within 24 hours of the event. Of the 16 zero tension lysimeters installed, only five produced samples. These five lysimeters were in contact with tree roots. It can probably be assumed that they collected water that flowed along soil/root interfaces.

In all four cases studied, the waters from the zero tension lysimeters differed isotopically from the rainfall event that produced the flow (see Fig. 5). In three instances (November 23, 1988, and January 2 and 18, 1989), the $\delta^{18}O$ values of the waters collected by the zero tension lysimeters were intermediate between the rainfall and waters collected from the tension lysimeters. On November 1, 1988, soil moisture was too low to obtain water from the tension lysimeters. On November 23, 1988, the rainwater $\delta^{18}O$ values were depleted relative to the waters in the zero tension lysimeters. For January 2 and 18, 1989, the $\delta^{18}O$ values of the rainfall were enriched compared to water collected in zero tension lysimeters. The direction of isotopic change in waters collected by the zero tension lysimeters indicates that mixing must occur between rain water flowing along preferential flow paths and the water

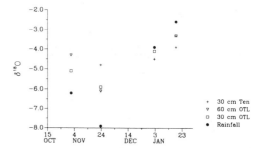

FIG. 5. $\delta^{18}O$ values of waters from zero tension lysimeters (OTL), rainfall events, and tension lysimeters (Ten).

in the soil matrix. This soil matrix water is probably more tightly bound and probably relatively immobile. Our results indicate that approximately equal proportions of these two "types" of waters underwent mixing.

Because large volumes of water are moving to depth quickly, it might be inferred that macropore flow (BEVAN and GERMANN, 1982) is occurring. However, true macropore flow is a turbulent process with little contact between water in the macropores and water in the soil matrix (SKOPP, 1981). If true closed-system macropore flow existed during infiltration, the $\delta^{18}O$ value of the rain water should not change its isotopic composition upon reaching the zero tension lysimeters at depth. However, our studies clearly indicate that mixing does occur, implying that little if any classic macropore flow occurs in the structured soils of the Piedmont.

*Tension lysimeters.* Tension lysimeters are designed to sample soil water bound less tightly than about 0.6 bar. Such waters may not be directly associated with any specific rainfall event. It is not well understood what the exact spatial extent is of the waters that tension lysimeters actually sample because the partial vacuum applied to the lysimeter permits all of the less strongly bound water of the soil matrix in the vicinity of the porous cup to flow into the lysimeter. Because mixing can occur between this water and the more tightly bound water during movement to and through the cup, any precise understanding of the water in the soil matrix cannot be made by this method of sampling. Clearly, it is possible that a water sample collected by a tension lysimeter may not be the same as the bulk water in the soil matrix. To overcome this problem, many investigators (*e.g.,* BARNES and ALLISON, 1988) extract all of the water in the soil by vacuum distillation or some other technique. This approach, however, may not provide water samples that are hydrologically important because a substantial portion of moisture in a clay-rich soil is so tightly bound within and between fine-grained clay particles as to be almost completely immobile. For these soils, for example, the water bound more tightly than that which will be driven off by heating the soil to 105°C ($H_2O^+$) is as much as 4 wt%. The approach used in this study to sample the unsaturated zone with tension lysimeters may actually be the best method for studying the hydrologically and botanically important water. A significant portion of the soil water is more tightly bound than the wilting point and is unavailable to plants in the clay-rich Piedmont soils (PERKINS, 1987).

### Data from individual plots

For a given depth, there is considerable inter-plot variability in the isotopic composition of waters obtained from the tension lysimeters (see Fig. 6). The magnitude of this variability diminishes with depth, as is evident by comparison between waters from 30 cm (Fig. 6A) with those at 120 cm (Fig. 6C). It is also clear that the smallest isotopic variation among the different plots at any depth occurs during weeks 4 through 12, and the greatest variation occurs during weeks 48 through 52. Further, at 30 cm depth, plot 4 samples are almost invariably the most [18]O-enriched, whereas samples from plot 3 are the most [18]O-depleted.

Soil moisture was too low to collect soil water samples with suction lysimeters for much of the study period. After March, samples could not be regularly collected until the following December. In September soil moisture was near the threshold of the ability of the lysimeters to collect water, and some lysimeters yielded samples. Soil texture differences between plots caused marked soil moisture differences. Plot 3, for example, which is sandy to 60 cm, was always drier and yielded less sample. The other three plots had more typical Piedmont soils with significant amounts of clay below 40 cm. These plots were moister than plot 3. The high clay content causes the soil to have a higher porosity and relatively low permeability. This low permeability inhibits water movement and tends to immobilize relatively large water volumes. In contrast, sandy soils are more permeable and contain smaller amounts of more tightly bound water.

The isotopic data obtained from the tension lysimeters at 30 cm are consistent with the differing amounts of soil moisture observed in the soil. In the clay-rich soil underlying plot 4, mixing between a more abundant, largely immobile, [18]O-enriched water and an [18]O-depleted infiltrating water can account for the tension lysimeter waters from this plot generally being the most [18]O enriched (see Fig. 6).

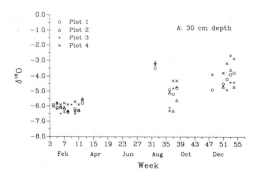

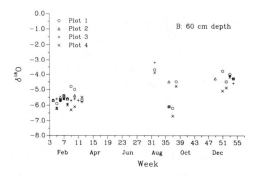

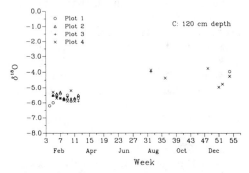

FIG. 6. Comparison of $\delta^{18}O$ values of waters from tension lysimeters from individual plots at 30 cm (A), 60 cm (B), and 120 cm (C) depths.

In the sand-rich soils at plot 3, which contain less tightly bound (largely immobile) water, it might be expected that the $\delta^{18}O$ values of waters collected by the tension lysimeters isotopically would be similar to the infiltrating rain. This is what is observed when comparing the rainfall data for weeks 4–12 (Fig. 4) with lysimeter waters for this same period (Fig. 6).

### Data averaged for four plots

Because the four plots are representative of the various soil types within the watershed, it is meaningful to average the data from the individual plots to obtain some insight on the behavior of water movement through the soil in the whole watershed. These data are presented in Fig. 7. Early in the study, from January 16 until March 25, 1988 (weeks 3 through 13), when the soil moisture was at or near field capacity, the average isotopic composition of water from the 30, 60, and 120 cm lysimeters exhibited a narrow range despite the extreme isotopic variability of the rain events (see Fig. 4). The weighted average rainfall $\delta^{18}O$ value during this period was $-6.4$. However, the four plot average $\delta^{18}O$ values were no more negative than $-6.2$ and only a few waters at the 30 cm depth were this depleted in $^{18}O$. During this period, the $\delta^{18}O$ values at 60 and 120 cm remained relatively uniform at $-5.7$. Thus, the overall trend was for infiltrating waters to become more $^{18}O$ enriched with depth. At no time was there an isotopically distinct front from any rainfall event that would indicate a piston flow process such as observed in other studies (ZIMMERMANN et al., 1967; SHARMA and HUGHES, 1985; BARNES and ALLISON, 1988).

These results suggest that some mechanism was buffering the isotopic composition of the water as it percolated through the soil. This process occurs to a large extent before the infiltrating water reached 30 cm. The most obvious explanation for this buffering process is the same one advanced to explain the zero tension data: that infiltrating rainfall mixes with a much larger volume of less mobile water in the soil matrix. This less mobile soil matrix water appears to be relatively $^{18}O$ enriched during the early winter (weeks 3 to 13) because the tension lysimeters collected waters of about $-6.2$ per mil, whereas average weighted rainfall during this period was more depleted ($-6.7$ per mil).

These $^{18}O$-enriched, less mobile soil matrix waters might be inherited from the previous summer-fall's rainfall input which was almost certainly more $^{18}O$ enriched, perhaps augmented by evaporation processes in upper parts of the soil (e.g., BARNES and ALLISON, 1988).

For the latter part of the study period, from late March 1988 and onward, evapotranspiration rates generally exceeded infiltration and few samples were collected from the lysimeters. Of all the samples obtained during this period, only a small percentage of water reached 120 cm deep. Almost certainly little, if any, of this summer rainfall ever reached the saturated zone. During this period, when the monthly weighted rainfall $\delta^{18}O$ values were relatively $^{18}O$ enriched (most were more positive than $-5.7$ per mil), the waters collected by the tension lysimeters were in most instances more $^{18}O$ depleted with depth (e.g., see data for weeks 32, 36, 38, 52, 53, 54 in Fig. 7). This is the opposite of what is

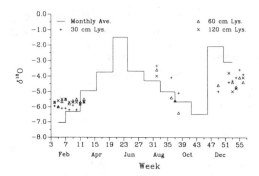

FIG. 7. Comparison of four plot average $\delta^{18}O$ values of waters from tension lysimeters at 30, 60, and 120 cm depths to volume weighted monthly rainfall (line).

observed during weeks 3 to 13 when soil moisture was near field capacity. This pattern of enrichment or depletion is consistent between the tension lysimeters within the various plots as well as in the zero-tension lysimeters discussed previously. It appears that during the latter part of the study period, infiltrating rainfall may have mixed with a more $^{18}O$-depleted, less-mobile water in the soil matrix. The apparent pattern of $^{18}O$-enriched water occurring in the soil matrix during the early 1988 winter period and a more $^{18}O$-depleted water residing in soil matrix in summertime is out of phase with the normal cyclic isotopic rainfall pattern reaching the surface. This implies that some or perhaps much of the water in the soil matrix may remain isolated or largely unexchanged isotopically for long periods time, perhaps many months or more.

In short, it appears that isotopic exchange almost certainly occurs between infiltrating water and less mobile water in the soil matrix. In the clay-rich Bt horizon of the soil, which lies 20 to 40 cm below the surface, this less mobile soil matrix water may be volumetrically quite significant. GVIRTZMAN and MAGARITZ (1986), for example, suggest that up to 55% of the total amount of water in a loess-type soil is "immobile." The clay content of their loess soil is lower than the clay content of a typical Piedmont soil. With clay-rich soils, it is not difficult to see how "new" infiltrating water very quickly takes on the isotopic characteristics of the less mobile "old" water in the soil matrix.

### Waters in the saturated zone

Waters from the saturated zone nearest the test plots (well 1) had a nearly constant $\delta^{18}O$ value $= -5.7 \pm 0.1$ throughout the sampling period (Fig. 8). This isotopic composition is virtually the same as that observed in the 60 and 120 cm tension ly-

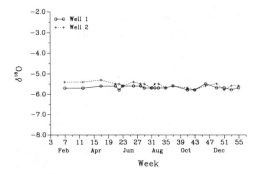

FIG. 8. $\delta^{18}O$ values of groundwaters from two wells.

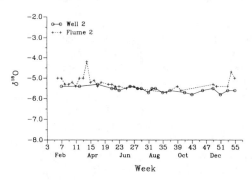

FIG. 9. Comparison of the $\delta^{18}O$ values of the perennial stream sampled at Flume 2 and groundwater at Well 2.

simeters during the first two months of the study period (weeks 4 to 13; see Fig. 7). Waters collected from the tension lysimeters during the remainder of the study period, from April 1988 and onward, however, are not at all similar to waters in the saturated zone. These observations are consistent with the hypothesis that only winter rainfall, and likely only that from "normal" winters when temperatures are seasonal, ever reaches the watertable. This winter recharge occurs because evapotranspiration is high during the rest of the year; very little summer rainfall moves through the soil, even to depths of 120 cm or more. Any significant contribution of summer rainfall to the groundwater should produce more isotopic variation in waters from the saturated zone than we see.

The saturated zone $\delta^{18}O$ values from well 2 near the perennial stream showed slightly more variation than in well 1 (see Fig. 8). This difference may be because this well is shallower and/or closer to the perennial stream, making it more likely to receive waters of differing isotopic compositions from various upslope areas.

### Waters from the fluvial system

During base flow, samples from the perennial stream sampled at flume 2 were somewhat $^{18}O$-enriched (up to 0.5 per mil) compared to water from well 2 (Fig. 9). This type of enrichment could be explained by evaporation from a lake located approximately 1 km upstream from flume 2 (not shown in Fig. 1). Water discharging from this lake would then have mixed with groundwater emerging in the stream channel to produce the observed isotopic compositions of the base flow in the perennial stream. The $^{18}O$-enriched "spikes" in the streamflow pattern shown in Fig. 9 appear to reflect direct channel precipitation of relatively high $^{18}O/^{16}O$ rainfall and/or somewhat larger amounts of discharge of an upstream pond.

The $\delta^{18}O$ values of the water collected from the spillway at flume 3 show a significant $^{18}O$ enrichment during the period from February to June 1988 (after which flow over the spillway ceased) compared to the $^{18}O/^{16}O$ of waters from the perennial stream feeding it (see Fig. 10). This trend almost certainly reflects evaporation from the lake. Short-term excursions from these patterns at both flumes 2 and 3 reflect input from large rainfall events (>1.0 cm) directly into the stream channel and pond. During weeks 8, 17, and 18, large volume, $^{18}O$-depleted rainfall events produced sharp $^{18}O$-depletion trends of the lake waters. During weeks 14 and 19, two smaller, $^{18}O$-enriched rain events produced a positive $^{18}O$ peak to the patterns for the perennial stream and the lake.

### SUMMARY AND CONCLUSIONS

These studies reveal that despite the large and erratic isotopic variations (up to 11 per mil for oxygen) of individual rainfalls and a seasonal weighted

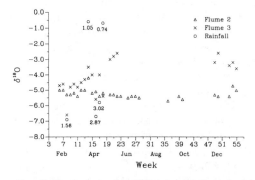

FIG. 10. Comparison of the $\delta^{18}O$ values for the perennial stream sampled at Flume 2 with values sampled at Flume 3, immediately downstream from a 1.2 hectare pond, and selected rainfall events. Rainfall volumes (cm) are printed below each rainfall symbol.

monthly variation ranging from −1.2 per mil in summer to −7.1 in winter, the variable isotopic composition of this rainfall becomes largely homogenized at depths as shallow as 30 cm in the soil. The homogenization process is more complete at depths of 60 cm and at 120 cm. This homogenization or buffering process is especially evident during the first two and one-half months of the study period, from January to March 1988, when soil moisture was greatest.

At times of ground water recharge during "normal" winters when evapotranspiration rates are minimal, these unsaturated zone waters are very similar isotopically to the waters in the saturated zone some ten meters deeper. This suggests that winter rainfall is largely responsible for recharging the watertable in a forested watershed in the southern Piedmont.

The homogenization or buffering process occurring within the upper parts of the soil almost certainly involves extensive mixing between rainfall infiltrating the ground and a much larger volume of water already present in the soil. This mixing process is most clearly demonstrated in instances where water moves rapidly through the soil along preferential pathways and can be collected by zero tension lysimeters. Such infiltrating waters partially exchange with isotopically different waters that are more tightly bound within the soil matrix and can only be collected by tension lysimeters.

The isotopic compositions of these soil matrix waters in four representative 5 m$^2$ plots in the watershed are themselves quite variable (ranging from 0.5 to 2 per mil) at any given depth. These differences appear to be related to the amount of soil moisture, which is in turn controlled by variations in the size fractions of material in the soil. Clay-rich soils have a greater soil moisture content than more sand-rich soil. We find that the more clay-rich soils, which contain a greater amount of this less mobile water, seem to buffer the isotopic composition of the infiltrating water to the greatest extent. In contrast, infiltrating waters appear to be buffered less in the more sand-rich soils.

The $\delta^{18}O$ values of waters in the saturated zone and the base flow of the perennial stream draining the watershed were observed to be quite uniform during the year-long sampling period. However, the stream samples were on average 0.5 per mil enriched in $^{18}O$ compared to waters from the saturated zone. This difference indicates that most of the stream water originates from groundwaters flowing into the channel, perhaps mixing with water discharging from an upstream pond undergoing evaporation. Waters from the outflow of a downstream pond in the watershed show significant $^{18}O$-enrichment due to summertime evaporation. Both the downstream pond and stream showed short-term isotopic fluctuations due to direct channel precipitation.

The results presented here may in some cases invalidate mixing models that attempt to identify the various components contributing to stormflow. Such models generally assign distinct isotopic compositions to various components of the hydrologic cycle. Two-component models, used for example by FRITZ et al. (1976), SKLASH et al. (1976), KENNEDY et al. (1986), and McDONNELL et al. (1990), distinguish "old" water (the total water in the ground) and "new" water (that added during any rainfall event). Three-component models (e.g., DEWALLE et al., 1988) assign distinct isotopic compositions to groundwater, soil water, and channel precipitation. Our results indicate that most "new" water very quickly loses its isotopic identity when percolating through the upper parts of the soil, and thus the volumetric significance of this "new" water becomes questionable. Three-component models that distinguish soil water from groundwater have little meaning since much of the water in soil appears to be isotopically indistinguishable from groundwater.

*Acknowledgements*—This work was supported by Parshall B. Bush of the Cooperative Extension Service of the University of Georgia with funding by the National Agricultural Pesticide Impact Assessment Program—USDA, and administered by Forest Pest Management, State and Private Forestry, USDA Forest Service, Atlanta, GA.

## REFERENCES

BARNES C. J. and ALLISON G. B. (1988) Tracing of water movement in the unsaturated zone using stable isotopes of hydrogen and oxygen. *J. Hydrol.* **100**, 143–176.

BEVEN K. and GERMANN P. (1982) Macropores and water flow in soils. *Water Res.* **18**, 1131–1325.

DEWALLE D. R., SWISTOCK B. R. and SHARPE W. E. (1988) Three-component tracer model for stormflow on a small Appalachian forested catchment. *J. Hydrol.* **104**, 301–310.

ENVIRONMENTAL PROTECTION AGENCY (1986) RCRA—Groundwater monitoring technical enforcement guidance document (TEGD). QSWER 9950.1.

EPSTEIN S. and MAYEDA T. (1953) Variation of $\delta^{18}O$ content of water from natural sources. *Geochim. Cosmochim. Acta* **4**, 213–224.

FEILD J. B. (1990) Plot tracer study in a Georgia Piedmont *Pinus taeda* (L.) Plantation. M.S. thesis, University of Georgia.

FRITZ P., CHERRY J. A., WEYER K. U. and SKLASH M. (1976) Storm runoff analysis using environmental isotope and major ions. In *Interpretation of Environmental Isotope and Hydrochemical Data in Groundwater Hydrology.* Proc. Adv. Group Meeting, Vienna, 1975, IAEA.

GAT J. R. and DANSGAARD W. (1972) Stable isotopes

survey of fresh water occurrences in Israel and the Northern Jordan Rift. *J. Hydrol.* **16,** 177.

GVIRITZMAN H. and MAGARITZ M. (1986) Investigation of water movement in the unsaturated zone under an irrigated area using environmental tritium. *Water Resources Res.* **22,** 635–642.

JORDAN C. F. (1968) A Simple, tension-free lysimeter. *Soil Sci.* **105,** 81–86.

KENNEDY V. C., KENDALL C., ZELLWEGER G. W., WYERMAN T. A. and AVANZINO R. J. (1986) Determination of the composition of stormflow using water chemistry and environmental isotopes, Mattole River Basin, California. *J. Hydrol.* **84,** 107–140.

KETCHAM P. (1989) Studies of groundwater movement in north Georgia Piedmont by natural oxygen-18 tracing. M.S. thesis, University of Georgia.

MCDONNELL J. J., BONELL M., STEWART M. K. and PEARCE A. J. (1990) Deuterium variations in storm rainfall implication for stream hydrograph separation. *Water Resources Res.* **26,** 455–458.

MILLER J. H. (1989) Fate of lindane in a Georgia Piedmont *Pinus Taeda* plantation. M.S. thesis, University of Georgia.

PERKINS H. F. (1987) Characterization data for selected Georgia soils. *GA. Agric. Exp. Stns. Spec. Bull. 43.*

SHARMA M. L. and HUGHES M. W. (1985) Groundwater recharge estimation using chloride deuterium and oxygen-18 profiles in deep coastal sands of Western Australia. *J. Hydrol.* **81,** 93–109.

SKLASH M. G., FARVOLDEN R. N. and FRITZ P. (1976) A conceptual model of watershed response to rainfall, developed through the use of oxygen-18 as a natural tracer. *Canadian J. Earth Sci.* **13,** 271–283.

SKOPP J. (1981) Comment on "micro-, meso-, and macroporosity of soil." *Soil Sci. Soc. Amer. J.* **45,** 1246.

YURTSEVER Y. and GAT J. R. (1981) Stable isotope hydrology. Deuterium and Oxygen-18 in the water cycle. *IAEA. Vienna. Tech. Rept.* **210,** Chap. 6.

ZIMMERMANN U., EHHALT D. and MUNNICH K. O. (1967) Soil-water movement and evapotranspiration: changes in the isotopic composition of the water. In *Isotopes in Hydrology.* IAEA, Vienna, 567–585.

Stable Isotope Geochemistry: A Tribute to Samuel Epstein
© The Geochemical Society, Special Publication No. 3, 1991
Editors: H. P. Taylor, Jr., J. R. O'Neil and I. R. Kaplan

# Isotopic changes during the formation of depth hoar in experimental snowpacks

Richard A. Sommerfeld,[1] Clark Judy[2] and Irving Friedman[3]

[1]U.S.D.A. Forest Service, 240 West Prospect Road, Fort Collins, CO 80526, U.S.A.
[2]Morrison-Knudsen, 1120-Lincoln Street, Denver, CO 80203, U.S.A.
[3]U.S. Geological Survey, Denver Federal Center, MS 963, Denver CO 80225, U.S.A.

**Abstract**—Depth hoar in snow was produced experimentally by imposing a thermal gradient on snow in two different types of experimental apparatus. One experiment was performed in an open-top container in a freezer, five in an apparatus with a closed top. In all six experiments, samples of the snow were analyzed for $HDO/H_2O$ ratios; in two, $H_2^{18}O/H_2^{16}O$ ratios were also determined. In all six experiments fractionation was similar. Snow strata that lost mass were depleted in the lighter isotopes, while strata that gained mass were enriched. Results indicate that the isotopic fractionation was the result of diffusion processes as well as change-of-state processes, that there is diffusive mixing of the water molecules on the surfaces of the ice crystals, and that there may be vapor communication over distances larger than one crystal diameter.

## INTRODUCTION

DEPTH HOAR IS a type of snow with distinctive crystal shapes (AKITAYA, 1974). It forms in snow with densities less than about 0.3 g cm$^{-3}$ at temperature gradients larger than 1°C cm$^{-1}$. The high rate of vapor transport forced by the temperature gradient causes the snow to recrystallize entirely in a few days. The snow crystals under these conditions exhibit the skeletal forms characteristic of high growth rates (HOBBS, 1974). These are modified into conical shapes by the fact that the crystals grow on the bottom and sublimate at the top in a process called "hand to hand" by YOSIDA *et al.* (1955).

The micro-structure of the snow can affect the process by affecting the local thermal gradients (SOMMERFELD, 1983; GUBLER, 1985). Such effects may be important in determining the rate of vapor transport of water vapor and of volatile material in snowpacks, and in determining the rate at which depth hoar forms.

During the discussion of the mechanisms of material transport from the bottom to the top of the snowpack, and ultimately to the freezer coils, we will be concerned with the effects of the differing transport mechanisms on the various isotopic forms of water, namely HDO, $H_2^{16}O$, $H_2^{18}O$. Experimentally, the isotopic ratios

$$\frac{HDO}{H_2O} \quad \text{and} \quad \frac{H_2^{18}O}{H_2^{16}O}$$

are determined mass spectrometrically and expressed in per mil in delta notation:

$$\delta D \text{ or } \delta^{18}O = \frac{R_{sample} - R_{standard}}{R_{standard}} \times 1000$$

where $R$ = ratio of heavy isotopic species to light isotopic species. We will here consider changes in these two $\delta$ values, as compared with that in the original snow. In addition, we will also discuss the ratio of the changes in deuterium to the changes in oxygen-18. This latter ratio will be expressed as the "slope of the linear regression line connecting the points in a $\delta D$ vs. $\delta^{18}O$ plot."

The possibility of fractionation of the light ($H_2^{16}O$) and heavy (HDO, $H_2^{18}O$) molecules during the metamorphism of snow suggested that measurements of $\delta D$ and $\delta^{18}O$ of snow might provide information on the mechanism of depth-hoar formation. If a strict crystal-to-crystal movement of material occurred, there could be no change in the isotopic composition of the snow. After a period of time, the entire mass of the lower crystal would be deposited on the lower side of the next crystal above it. If the isotopic composition of the snow changed, an alternative theory of depth-hoar formation would be needed. The changes in these ratios compared to the original snow give information on the transport processes.

Because the vapor pressure of the lighter molecule $H_2^{16}O$ is higher than that of the heavier molecules $H_2^{18}O$ and HDO, the vapor will be enriched in the light molecules relative to the solid in equilibrium with it. This difference in vapor pressure results in the vapor being lower in $\delta D$ by 122 per mil and in $\delta^{18}O$ by 11.8 per mil at 0°C, and by 160 per mil and 13.4 per mil at −20°C (FRIEDMAN and O'NEIL, 1977). This process will result in a slope of 10 to 13 for a $\delta D$ vs. $\delta^{18}O$ plot of samples of the vapor, or from the solid condensed from it. During a Rayleigh distillation process it is assumed that, at any

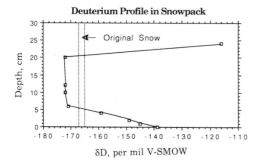

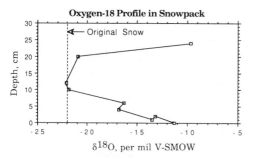

FIG. 1. Isotopic profiles of $\delta D$ (top) and $\delta^{18}O$ (bottom) for the open-box experiment.

instant of time, the vapor is in isotopic equilibrium with the condensed phase that is emitting the vapor.

We performed a simple experiment in which the vapor coming off snow was collected on a surface cooled by dry ice. Isotopic analysis showed that the vapor had 110 per mil less deuterium than the snow from which it sublimed, yielding a fractionation factor of 1.11. MOSER and STICHLER (1970) obtained a fractionation factor of 1.10 to 1.11 for a similar study. In both experiments the period of time that the sublimation occurred was short, and therefore the process studied was probably a transient-state study. A basic question is whether fractionation occurs in the steady state. If temperature gradient metamorphism is strictly "hand to hand," no change in composition would occur. After a period of time the entire mass of the lower crystal would be deposited on the lower side of the crystal above it. For this process to be effective in the steady state, the solid phase must be mixed. Because self-diffusion in ice is about 1/1000 as rapid as molecular diffusion in the vapor, the amount of isotopic separation due to vapor pressure differences between the isotopic molecules will be greatly reduced from the values of approximately 130 per mil for deuterium and 12 per mil for oxygen-18 that would be expected if the molecules in the solid mixed rapidly.

The existence of a quasi-liquid film on the surface of snow crystals at temperatures above −30°C has

been postulated and can help explain the existence of isotopic fractionation during the sublimation of snow. Even though this process results in only a small isotopic fractionation, the cascading of many such change-of-state events, as the vapor travels vertically through the snowpack, might result in relatively, large isotopic changes, with slopes of the $\delta D$ vs. $\delta^{18}O$ plots having values greater than five.

A discussion of isotopic fractionation caused by diffusion is given in the companion paper (FRIEDMAN *et al.*, this volume).

## EXPERIMENTS

Both undisturbed and sieved snow were exposed to temperature gradients. At the initiation and at times during the course of each experiment, a vertical series of samples was taken and analyzed for $\delta D$ by the method described by WOODCOCK and FRIEDMAN (1963) and for $\delta^{18}O$ by the technique of O'NEIL and EPSTEIN (1966). The deuterium results are precise to ±1 per mil, while the $\delta^{18}O$ analyses are precise to ±0.2 per mil.

*Open box experiment*

An open-top box 25 × 25 × 25 cm was constructed from 50 mm thick styrofoam. This was placed on a heat source maintained at −1.2°C in a freezer at −24°C and filled with snow. The temperatures at four different levels were monitored with thermistors. The lower 15 cm of snow had a gradient of 1.05°C cm⁻¹ while the upper 10 cm had a lower gradient of about 0.80°C cm⁻¹. The nonlinearity of the gradient was probably the result of air being able to mix into the upper layer of the open box. After the experiment proceeded for 31 days, the false front of the container was removed, the first 50 mm of snow in a plane parallel to the front was discarded to eliminate border effects, and samples were taken for isotopic analysis.

The average density of the snow increased from 0.14 to 0.19 g cm⁻³ during the 31-day duration of the study. There was a 276 g (about 10%) loss of total mass from the container to the freezer walls, which is equal to a layer of water 2 mm deep. Most of the lower 30–50 mm of the original snow was lost by sublimation into the upper part, and adhesion to the walls of the box prevented settling. The results of the isotopic analyses are shown in Fig. 1. Frost collected from the freezer walls was 10 per mil lower in $\delta D$ than the original snow.

A plot of $\delta D$ vs $\delta^{18}O$ (Fig. 2) has a slope of three in

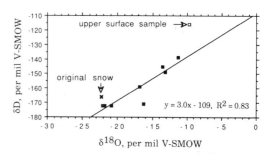

FIG. 2. Plot of $\delta D$ vs. $\delta^{18}O$ for the open-box experiment.

contrast to the slope of about 10 to 13 to be expected if the mass-transport process took place under an equilibrium Rayleigh distillation process. This is in agreement with the results of SOMMERFELD et al. (1987).

*Closed box experiments*

An apparatus similar to that described in SOMMERFELD (1983) was constructed. This apparatus housed ten polyethylene bags of snow of dimensions 30 × 30 × 10 cm. A special lid had ten aluminum blocks that fitted into the bags with a clearance of less than 3 mm. The lid was provided with a circulating coolant to maintain its temperature at about −15°C. The bottom surface of the apparatus was a heated plate whose temperature was controlled between −1 and −2°C. The entire apparatus was insulated with 100 mm of styrofoam and was placed in a cold room maintained at −10°C. The lid was allowed to settle with the upper surface of the snow to limit sublimation losses from the samples and to maintain a more uniform thermal gradient. The thermal gradient was monitored by six thermocouples placed in a central bag. The boundary temperatures were controlled to ±0.1°C. The resulting gradients were almost linear and constant with time (SOMMERFELD, 1983).

*January, 1987.* Ten bags were placed in the apparatus on January 8, 1987. Nine samples of the original snow were analyzed to determine the variability of the original snow. They showed a range in $\delta D$ of −176 to −194, and in $\delta^{18}O$ of −22 to −26. The variability in these samples was much larger than in the snow used in the open box experiment described above.

The experiment was conducted for 13 days at an average gradient of 0.5°C cm⁻¹. Samples for isotopic analysis were taken on January 11 and January 21. During this time the density increased from 0.220 to 0.242 g cm⁻³. Qualitatively, the lower portion of the snow was about 7 per mil higher in $\delta D$ and about 3 per mil higher in $\delta^{18}O$ than the average at the end of the experiment.

The slope of the $\delta D$ vs. $\delta^{18}O$ plot should not be affected by the original variability in either isotopic species. There is relatively little scatter in this plot in Fig. 3, and the slope decreased from 4.9 for the original snow to 4.2 and 3.7 for the two sample dates, in agreement with the results of the open box experiments and with SOMMERFELD et al. (1987). The low value of 4.9 for the initial snow samples is the result of metamorphism that occurred before the snow was collected for the experiments.

*February, 1987.* A second set of samples was collected on February 18, 1987. They were placed in the apparatus under a thermal gradient of 0.45°C cm⁻¹ for 28 days. During this period the density of the samples increased from 0.279 to 0.308 g cm⁻³. Samples for analysis of $\delta D$ were removed on February 23, March 3, 10, and 17. Although the scatter in the data is large, the lower 5 cm show an increase in $\delta D$ associated with mass loss, and the upper part shows a somewhat smaller decrease associated with mass gain.

*March, 1987.* A third experiment was initiated on March 23, 1987, and terminated 50 days later. The initial density was 0.200 g cm⁻³ which increased to 0.254 g cm⁻³ at the end of the experiment. The temperature gradient averaged 0.595°C cm⁻¹ throughout the experiment.

There is somewhat less scatter in this set of samples than in the previous set, but the variation in isotopic composition was still high. Here there is a clear increase in $\delta D$

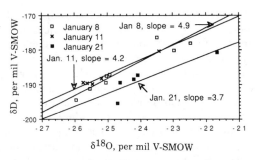

FIG. 3. Plot of $\delta D$ vs. $\delta^{18}O$ for the closed-box experiments, January 1987.

in the lower 5 cm and a smaller decrease in the upper 15 cm.

*February, 1988.* An attempt was made to eliminate the natural variability of the snow by mixing a sample of snow and sieving into the sample bags. This experiment was initiated on February 12, 1988, and terminated on March 9. During this 25-day period, the density of the snow increased from 240 to 251 kg m⁻³ under a thermal gradient of 54°C m⁻¹.

Samples were collected for $\delta D$ analysis at the initiation, and on February 25 and March 3. Samples from three bags were taken at selected levels for isotopic analysis. Each set of three samples from each level was combined for the analysis in an attempt to further reduce the variability. Fractionation was similar to that observed in the February 1987 experiment but the measurements showed less scatter as expected.

*March, 1988.* The last experiment was initiated on March 14 and run to April 13, 1988. Sieved snow was used and densities and thermal gradients were essentially identical to those of the previous experiment. Samples were taken for analysis at the initiation and on April 4 and April 13, again combining samples from three bags for each level. The lower 5 cm became significantly enriched in deuterium while the upper 15 cm became depleted.

## DISCUSSION

Clearly, fractionation of the isotopic species occurred in the open-box experiment. The bottom 5 to 10 cm of the snow was depleted in the lighter species as the snow sublimated from the lower to the upper crystals. The upper 5 cm of the snow was also depleted in the lighter species. We verified that this was caused by sublimation and deposition of vapor to the freezer walls, where the deposited ice was enriched in the lighter species.

The results from the 1987 series of experiments with a closed-top apparatus were less clear. Apparently, the snow used in the open-top experiment was unusually uniform in isotopic composition. The large variability in isotopic composition of the snow in 1987 made interpretation difficult when the results were plotted on coordinates similar to those of the open-box experiment. Two problems were associated with this variability: (1) the initial samples, and probably most of the other samples, had initial vertical gradients in isotopic composition; and (2) the average isotopic compositions among the samples varied significantly. However, the curves seemed to show depletion of the lighter species at the bottom and enrichment of the lighter species at the top, similar to the results of SOMMERFELD et al. (1987). To test this impression we assumed that the average isotopic composition of each bag would not change during the course of the experiment because with the closed top, very little mass is lost. We calculated the difference between the average for each sample and the average composition of the bottom 5 cm and of the top 15 cm. If our impression is correct, then the difference for the lower layer should increase with time as the lighter isotopic species is depleted and the $\delta$ values should become increasingly negative with time. The results are shown in Table 1. In each case, the regression line is consistent with isotopic fractionation. The correlation is better in some experiments than others where there is large scatter. In the 1988 experiments, the snow was mixed and sieved to make it more homogeneous, which improved the results.

## COMPARISON WITH NATURAL SNOWPACK

In a companion paper in this volume, FRIEDMAN et al. describe the results of isotopic measurements carried out on natural snowpacks. The snowpack that most closely resembled our experimental snowpack is their "plastic-pack." This snowpack was deposited on soil that had been covered with a plastic sheet to prevent the transfer of moisture from the ground to the snowpack. However, the plastic sheet did not prevent the formation of a temperature gradient in the snow caused by the transfer of heat from the soil to the snow above it.

The plastic-packs from Fairbanks, Alaska, in both 1985 and 1986, developed a characteristic depth-hoar profile. However, the slope of the $\delta$D vs. $\delta^{18}$O plot gave values of 8 and 11, in contrast to the value of 3 from the experimental snowpack.

This difference might be explained by the greater length of time that the natural packs were exposed to a temperature gradient ($\sim$150 days), as compared to the 31 days for the experimental pack. This would allow additional time for diffusion in the solid to increase the efficiency of the Rayleigh process, which, in turn, would increase the slope. Another factor might be the differences in temperature as well as thermal gradient between the experimental and natural snowpack.

Table 1. Slopes of the regression lines of the $\delta$D vs. $\delta^{18}$O plots for experiments of 1987–1988

| Experiment | 0–5 cm | | 5–20 cm | |
|---|---|---|---|---|
| | Slope | $R^2$ | Slope | $R^2$ |
| January 1987 | 0.24 | 0.86 | −0.14 | 0.59 |
| February 1987 | 0.15 | 0.28 | −0.06 | 0.14 |
| March 1987 | 0.25 | 0.89 | −0.12 | 0.64 |
| February 1988 | 0.12 | 0.97 | −0.04 | 0.64 |
| March 1988 | 0.18 | 0.99 | −0.18 | 0.99 |

The upper surfaces of the natural and experimental packs show very different isotopic changes. This can be explained by several factors, including the very different relative humidity (rH) of the two environments. The removal of material to the freezer coils would tend to reduce the rH to low values, in contrast to the natural environment, where the rH would have been high. The high rH, combined with the fact that the water vapor in the air would have an isotopic composition in equilibrium with that of the snow, would act to reduce the change in isotopic composition at the top of the natural pack.

The interchange between water vapor in the atmosphere and the natural snowpack would be an important factor in maintaining an equilibrium slope of about ten. In the absence of this interchange in the experimental pack, kinetic processes would tend to predominate, yielding lower slopes for the $\delta$D vs. $\delta^{18}$O plot.

## CONCLUSIONS

The fact that fractionation is observed within the body of the snow shows that vapor transport in snow under a thermal gradient involves processes other than "hand to hand" sublimation. Because diffusion in the solid is slow, it is unlikely to be important in the time scale of these experiments. However, ice is known to exhibit surface premelting at temperatures above −10°C and perhaps to temperatures as low as −30°C (HOBBS, 1974). The quasi-liquid layer on the surface of ice is mobile and exhibits chemical characteristics similar to those of liquid water (CONKLIN et al., 1989; SOMMERFELD et al., 1991). Diffusion within this layer could mix the upper parts of the ice crystals, where sublimation occurs. Thus, the quasi-liquid layer would make the substrate appear more like a liquid than a solid for the water molecules. The resulting slopes of the $\delta$D vs. $\delta^{18}$O plots are 3 to 4, within the range that EHHALT and KNOTT (1964) and CRAIG and GORDON (1965) predicted for evaporation from the liquid.

Another possible explanation for the observed fractionation is diffusion in the vapor, where the communication distance is several crystal diameters. This would allow fractionation because of the different gas diffusion rates of the different isotopic species. For this mechanism, the ratio of the separation factors would be about two.

We speculate that both mechanisms are important. The fact that the $\delta D$ vs. $\delta^{18}O$ plot has a slope of three to four argues that the quasi-liquid layer is important. In addition, the fact that sieved snow fractionates at about the same rate as natural snow indicates that the micro structure of the snow is not of primary importance in the fractionation process. On the other hand, the top layers of the snow were at $-10°C$ or colder where the thickness of the quasi-liquid layer is very reduced (HOBBS, 1974). The fact that the fractionation in the upper layers is not much different than in the warmer lower layers indicates that a mechanism not involving the quasi-liquid layer is also active.

*Acknowledgements*—The authors wish to thank Professor James Meiman for his help and encouragement in carrying out the open-box experiments. We also thank Kenneth Hardcastle for his help in carrying out the deuterium analysis, and Jim Gleason for making the oxygen-18 analyses.

## REFERENCES

AKITAYA E. (1974) Studies on depth hoar. Contributions from the Institute of Low Temperature Science, *Ser. A., No. 26*, pp. 1–67. Hokkaido University, Sapporo, Japan.

CONKLIN M., SOMMERFELD R. and LAIRD K. (1989) The uptake of $SO_2$ on ice surfaces. (abstr.). *Eos* **70**, 1020.

CRAIG H. and GORDON L. I. (1965) Deuterium and oxygen-18 variations in the oceans and marine atmosphere. *Symposium on Marine Geochemistry, Narragansett Marine Laboratory, Univ. of Rhode Island Occ. pub. #3-1965.*

EHHALT D. and KNOTT K. (1964) Kinetische Isotopentrennung bei der Verdampfung von Wasser. *Tellus* **17**, 389–397.

FRIEDMAN I. and HARDCASTLE K. (1970) A new technique for pumping hydrogen gas. *Geochim. Cosmochim. Acta* **34**, 125–126.

FRIEDMAN I. and O'NEIL J. R. (1977) Fractionation factors of geochemical interest. In *Data of Geochemistry,* 6th edn., Chap. KK; *U.S. Geol. Surv. Prof. Pap. 440.*

GIDDINGS C. J. and LACHAPELLE E. R. (1962) The formation rate of depth hoar. *J. Geophys. Res.* **67**, 2377–2383.

GUBLER H. (1985) Model for dry snow metamorphism by interparticle vapor flux. *J. Geophy. Res.* **90**, 8081–8092.

HOBBS P. V. (1974) *Ice Physics.* Oxford University Press.

JUDY C., MEIMAN J. R. and FRIEDMAN I. (1970) Deuterium variations in an annual snowpack. *Water Resources Res.* **6**, 125–129.

MERLIVAT L. (1970) L' étude quantitative de bilans de lacs à l'aide des concentrations en deuterium et oxygen-18 dans l'eau. In *Isotope Hydrology 1970,* pp. 89–107. International Atomic Energy Agency, Vienna.

MOSER J. and STRICHLER W. (1970) Deuterium measurements on snow samples from the Alps. In *Isotope Hydrology 1970,* pp. 43–55. International. Atomic Energy Agency, Vienna.

O'NEIL J. R. and EPSTEIN S. (1966) A method for oxygen isotopic analysis of milligram quantities of water and some of its applications. *J. Geophys. Res.* **71**, 4955–4961.

SOMMERFELD R. A. (1983) A branch grain theory of temperature gradient metamorphism in snow. *J. Geophys. Res.* **88**, 1484–1494.

SOMMERFELD R. A., FRIEDMAN I. and NILLES M. (1987) The fractionation of natural isotopes during temperature gradient metamorphism of snow. In *Seasonal Snowcovers: Physics Chemistry, Hydrology* (eds. H. G. JONES and W. J. ORVILLE-THOMAS); *NATO-ASI series C, 211,* pp. 95–106.

SOMMERFELD R. A., LAIRD S. K. and RECTOR H. (1991) D, NO adsorption on ice at low concentrations (in prep.).

STEWART M. K. (1974) Stable isotope fractionation due to evaporation and isotopic exchange of falling waterdrops: Applications to atmospheric processes and evaporation of lakes. *J. Geophys. Res.* **80**, 1133–1146.

WOODCOCK A. H. and FRIEDMAN I. (1963) The deuterium content of raindrops. *J. Geophys. Res.* **68**, 4477–4494.

YOSIDA Z. *et al.* (1955) Physical studies on deposited snow. I. Thermal properties. *Contributions from the Institute of Low Temperature Science, Ser. A.,* No. 7, pp. 19–74. Hokkaido University, Sapporo, Japan.

Stable Isotope Geochemistry: A Tribute to Samuel Epstein
© The Geochemical Society, Special Publication No. 3, 1991
Editors: H. P. Taylor, Jr., J. R. O'Neil and I. R. Kaplan

# Isotopic changes during snow metamorphism

Irving Friedman,[1] Carl Benson[2] and Jim Gleason[1]

[1]U.S. Geological Survey, Denver Federal Center, MS 963, Denver, CO 80225, U.S.A.
[2]Geophysical Institute, University of Alaska, Fairbanks, AK 99775-0800, U.S.A.

**Abstract**—Mechanisms of metamorphism of snow were investigated by examining the deuterium and oxygen-18 content of snowpacks deposited in Fairbanks, Alaska. This location was chosen because of the very large thermal gradient in the snowpack. Experiments were carried out for nine years by sampling two or more adjacent snowpack regimes. The first snowpack was deposited on bare ground (soil-pack). The second snowpack was deposited on ground that was covered by a plastic sheet to prevent water-vapor transfer from the ground to the snow above it (plastic-pack). The third snowpack was deposited on a nearby wooden table (table-pack). The table-pack did not experience the thermal gradient between top and bottom that was developed by the first two, and is used as a sample of the original unaltered snow. All sampling was carried out in the spring, after snow metamorphism had occurred, but before melting of the snow. Although all of the snowpacks lying on the soil or plastic developed a typical depth-hoar profile, none of the table-packs showed evidence of metamorphism associated with the development of depth-hoar. All of the snowpacks displayed variations of isotopic composition with depth associated with isotopic differences between individual precipitation events. In all of the vertical sections, the bottommost 5 to 20 cm of the soil-packs was enriched in deuterium relative to the table-packs, indicating that water molecules depleted in deuterium (and oxygen-18) had been removed from this portion of the snowpack. This isotopically light material appears to have been incorporated in the snow immediately above this bottom portion of the soil-pack, which was lower in $\delta D$ and $\delta^{18}O$ relative to the corresponding portion of the table-pack. Isotopic analyses of the water vapor that left the soil and was condensed as ice under the plastic sheet have $\delta D$ and $\delta^{18}O$ values more positive than any of the snow. The transfer of water from the soil to the immediately overlying 10–20 cm of snow played a part in changing the isotopic composition of the natural soil-packs. The slopes of the lines joining the bottom samples of the table-pack and soil-pack in a $\delta D$ vs. $\delta^{18}O$ plot ranged from 3 to 4.3, in contrast to the slopes found in $\delta D$ vs. $\delta^{18}O$ plots of all of the samples from the table-packs, which ranged from 7.4 to 8.8, characteristic of the Meteoric Water Line. Slopes of 2 are characteristic of diffusive isotope separation processes, and the low slopes found in the bottom samples indicate the role of diffusion transport of water both from the soil to the overlying snowpack, and also within the snow. Higher slopes were found in the remainder of the samples and are the result of fractionation due to change-of-state processes, as well as the exchange of water vapor present in the atmosphere above the snow with water vapor in the snowpack.

## INTRODUCTION

THE ISOTOPIC CHANGES that accompany the metamorphism of snow under natural conditions have received little attention. EPSTEIN *et al.* (1965) observed that the $^{18}O$ content of depth-hoar was higher than that of the remainder of the snowpack. MACPHERSON and KRAUSE (1967) determined that percolating melt water homogenized the $\delta^{18}O$ of the snow. JUDY *et al.* (1970) showed that changes in the $\delta D$ of the snow occurred as the snow pack aged, resulting in a greatly reduced variability of $\delta D$ from the original snowfalls.

Because deuterium and oxygen-18 are fractionated in slightly different ways during processes that are mass dependent (for example, diffusion), we hoped that a study of both isotopes in natural snowpacks might yield information on the mechanisms of depth-hoar formation. Depth hoar constitutes a weak layer at the bottom of the snowpack and has long been studied for its role in producing avalanches on steep slopes (BADER *et al.,* 1939;

YOSIDA *et al.,* 1955). Depth hoar is also responsible for the formation of recognizable annual layers in the dry snow strata of polar ice sheets (SORGE, 1935; BENSON, 1962).

The study was carried out on samples of the seasonal snowpack collected in Fairbanks, Alaska by one of us (C.B.). The site at Fairbanks is ideal for such a study because the snowpack lasts for a long time (150–200 days) at temperatures well below freezing ($-40°C$ is common) and has a very large thermal gradient ($1°C/cm$ is common) established between the ground at its base and the air above it. The resulting depth hoar has exceptionally low density (0.19 to 0.20 g/cm$^3$ compared with 0.28 to 0.30 g/cm$^3$ in alpine regions), and it can spread upwards through the entire snowpack before winter is over (TRABANT and BENSON, 1972; STURM, 1989).

## EXPERIMENTAL

All collections were made at the end of winter in March and early April, before melting of the snow began. Snow samples were taken with a set of stainless steel sample tubes inserted horizontally into the vertical walls of pits dug through the snow pack. The 500 cm³ samples were weighed and density values were calculated. The samples were emptied into plastic bags in the field and sealed until they could be melted and poured into tightly sealed bottles to minimize evaporation of the melted snow. They were then sent to the U.S. Geological Survey laboratories in Denver for $\delta D$ and $\delta^{18}O$ analysis.

The $\delta D$ analyses were made by reacting 5 $\mu l$ samples of water with hot uranium metal. The hydrogen gas produced by this reaction was analyzed for deuterium using a double collector Nier-type mass spectrometer of 15 cm radius. All results are expressed in delta units relative to Vienna Standard Mean Ocean Water (V-SMOW), where

$$\delta D = \frac{\left(\dfrac{D}{H}\right)_{sample} - \left(\dfrac{D}{H}\right)_{standard}}{\left(\dfrac{D}{H}\right)_{standard}} \times 1000$$

and were normalized to zero for Vienna Standard Mean Ocean water (V-SMOW), and −428 for Standard Light Antarctic Precipitation (SLAP). The deuterium analyses were carried out in replicate, with a two sigma of 0.8 per mil.

The $\delta^{18}O$ analysis were made by equilibrating a 5 ml sample of water with $CO_2$, purifying the $CO_2$, and analyzing the purified gas on a double collecting Nier-type mass spectrometer. After making appropriate corrections the results are given in delta units relative to V-SMOW, with a two sigma of 0.1 per mil. The results have been normalized to zero for V-SMOW and −55.5 for SLAP:

$$\delta^{18}O = \frac{\left(\dfrac{^{18}O}{^{16}O}\right)_{sample} - \left(\dfrac{^{18}O}{^{16}O}\right)_{standard}}{\left(\dfrac{^{18}O}{^{16}O}\right)_{standard}} \times 1000$$

The analytical results are presented in Table 1.

## COLLECTION PROTOCOL

Experiments were carried out by sampling two or more adjacent snowpack regimes as described by TRABANT and BENSON (1972):

(1) The snowpack resting on bare ground is referred to as "soil-pack."

(2) The snowpack on ground that was covered with a plastic sheet to prevent water vapor transfer from the ground to the snow above it is referred to as "plastic-pack."

(3) An adjacent pack resting on a wooden table in a wind-sheltered area in a spruce forest is referred to as "table-pack." This pack did not experience the thermal gradient between top and bottom developed by the first two packs, because it had cold air below as well as above. The fundamental assumption is that negligible vapor flux occurs within the snowpack resting on the table, and there is no possibility of vapor transfer into it from the soil. Thus, the table snowpack was treated as a control each year and the other snowpacks were compared to it.

All sampling was carried out before melting occurred. In 1966, 1972, 1974, 1975, 1976, and 1982, only the soil-packs and table-packs were sampled and were analyzed for deuterium. In addition to deuterium, the 1974, 1982, 1985 and 1986 samples were also analyzed for oxygen-18. In 1985 the sampling protocol was extended to include the plastic-pack, in addition to the soil-pack and table-packs. Samples of ice from the underside of the plastic sheet were collected in 1975, 1985, and 1986.

## RESULTS

### Physical changes in the snowpack

In most years we observed that the table-packs were thinner than the adjacent soil and plastic-packs (Figs. 1 through 9). The table-packs underwent some horizontal creep, resulting in the formation of snow cornices at the outer edges of the table. Although part of the reduction in thickness of the table pack was due to this horizontal movement, the depth hoar is mechanically stronger than fine-grained compact snow against a static force, even though it is extremely fragile against a dynamic force (KO-JIMA, 1956; AKITAYA, 1974). Thus, depth hoar on the ground does not settle under the load of overlying snow as fast as the fine-grained compact snow on the tables. The effect of this on our experimental setup was discussed by STURM (1989). The different compaction rate of the table-packs complicates comparisons between similar portions of the table-pack and of the other two snowpacks. The further up from the bottom that such comparisons are made, the more uncertain that any chosen horizontal horizon in the table-pack is equivalent to that in the soil-pack or plastic-pack. Therefore we have restricted comparisons between the table-pack and the other packs to the lowest and next-to-lowest sampled horizons.

Although all of the soil and plastic-snowpacks developed a typical depth-hoar profile, none of the table-packs developed depth-hoar, emphasizing the importance of a thermal gradient in the snowpack for depth-hoar development to occur. Every year that that we have compared the table-packs and soil-packs, we have found that the table-pack had a higher density at the bottom but a lower density at the top. A summary of the density distribution of the soil-packs and table-packs during 11 winters between 1966 and 1987 is shown in normalized form in Fig. 16 (from STURM, 1989).

Figures 1–9 are plots of $\delta D$ vs. depth in the snow pack for all collections, while Figs. 10–13 are plots of $\delta D$ vs. $\delta^{18}O$ for 1974, 1982, 1985, and 1986. Because the lowest sample from each of the soil-packs had suffered large changes in isotopic composition from soil moisture, as discussed below, the least mean squares solution to the data sets in Figs. 10–13 have not included data for this lowest soil-pack sample.

## Isotopic composition of snow

All of the snowpacks display variations of isotopic composition with depth associated with isotopic differences between individual precipitation events. During the winter, as the snowpacks that experienced a thermal gradient (soil-pack, plastic-pack) aged, physical changes occured that modified these initial isotopic differences (JUDY et al., 1970).

## Soil moisture

Measurement of soil moisture in Fairbanks over many years has shown that the moisture content at the beginning of snow accumulation is about 30% by dry weight and is reduced to less than 10% by March (TRABANT and BENSON, 1972; STURM, 1989). Calculations show that about 1 cm of water equivalent is transferred from the soil to the overlying snowpack during the winter. This is about 10% of the total snowpack.

Ice that accumulated on the underside of the plastic-ground cover was collected in 1975, 1985, and 1986. In all three cases, the isotopic composition of this water was enriched in the heavier isotopes as compared to the snowpacks. We ascribe this to the fact that the soil moisture is a mixture of precipitation that fell as summer rain as well as winter snow. The summer rain can be expected to be enriched in the heavier isotopes, because the condensation temperature of the summer rain is higher than that of the winter snow, resulting in less loss of the heavier isotopic molecules from the cloud system that is undergoing precipitation (FRIEDMAN et al., 1964).

This soil moisture was important in modifying the isotopic composition of the bottom of the soil-pack. However, as will be discussed later, the bottom soil-pack samples are not simply soil moisture, nor mixtures of soil moisture and pre-existing snow, but can be modelled by mixtures of soil moisture and snow that has undergone heavy-isotope enrichment after deposition.

## $\delta D$ vs. depth

In all of the $\delta D$ vs. depth plots (Figs. 1–9) the one or two lowest samples from the base of the soil-packs are higher in $\delta D$ relative to the corresponding table-pack. Inasmuch as the lower section of the soil-pack had a lower density than the corresponding section of the table-pack, this indicates that material that was depleted in deuterium (and oxygen-18) had been removed from this portion of the soil-pack. This heavy-isotope–depleted material appears to have been incorporated in the snow immediately above this bottom portion of the soil-pack, the 10 to 20 cm layer, which is depleted in deuterium and oxygen-18 relative to the corresponding portion of the table-pack.

## $\delta D$ vs. $\delta^{18}O$

On a $\delta D$-$\delta^{18}O$ plot of the 1974, 1982, and 1986 data (Figs. 10, 11, and 13) the table- and soil-pack data plot very close to each other. However, in a similar plot of the 1985 data (Fig. 12) the soil-pack data displays a small shift relative to the table-pack data.

The relation between the $\delta D$ and $\delta^{18}O$ values of the basal samples from the soil-pack and from the table-pack from the 1974, 1982, 1985, and 1986 collections is shown in Fig. 14. We have joined the plotted values of the bottom samples from the soil and from the table-packs, inferring that the samples from the table-pack represent the starting snow unaltered by processes that originated in the soil, and that the sample from the base of the soil-pack has been changed isotopically by such processes. In all of the four cases plotted, the basal soil-pack sample had been enriched by about 15 per mil in deuterium and about 3.3 per mil in oxygen-18.

On a $\delta D$ vs. $\delta^{18}O$ plot, the slopes of the lines that join the values of the basal samples in the table- and soil-pack range from 3 to 4.3, in contrast to the slopes found for all of the remaining samples (see Figs. 10–13), which range from 7.4 to 8.8. These higher slopes are characteristic of isotope separation processes that depend upon the change of state between solid and vapor. The slope of the line joining the bottom samples from the 1986 *plastic*-pack and *table*-packs is 2.8. As will be discussed later, slopes of 2 to 5 are characteristic of diffusive isotope separation processes and indicate the role of diffusive transport of water both from the soil to the overlying snowpack, as well as within the lower portion of the snowpack itself.

A $\delta D$ vs. $\delta^{18}O$ plot of the samples collected from the interval 10–20 cm for these same years is shown in Fig. 15. The slopes of the lines joining the corresponding soil and table points for each year range from 7.4 to 13, indicating that changes in isotopic composition of samples from this level in the snow-

Table 1. Isotopic data on snow packs

| Year | Location | Depth (cm) | δ$^{18}$O | δD | Year | Location | Depth (cm) | δ$^{18}$O | δD |
|---|---|---|---|---|---|---|---|---|---|
| 1966[1] | soil | 0–10 | —[2] | −158 | 1973[4] | table | 0–4 | — | −153 |
| | | 10–20 | — | −165 | | | 4–8 | — | −174 |
| | | 20–30 | — | −205 | | | 8–10.5 | — | −179 |
| | | 30–41 | — | −160 | | | 10.5–13.5 | — | −148 |
| | | 41–43 | — | −174 | | | 13.5–17.0 | — | −117 |
| | | 43–49 | — | −174 | | | 17.0–20.5 | — | −115 |
| | | 49–53 | — | −150 | | | 20.5–23.0 | — | −138 |
| | | 53–60 | — | −153 | | | 23.0–26.0 | — | −184 |
| | | 60–65 | — | −172 | | | 26.0–29.5 | — | −196 |
| | | 65–73 | — | −225 | | | 29.5–32.8 | — | −202 |
| | table | 0–4 | — | −167 | | | 32.8–35.9 | — | −215 |
| | | 4–9 | — | −162 | | | 39–42 | — | −175 |
| | | 9–16 | — | −171 | | | 42–46 | — | −183 |
| | | 16–26 | — | −207 | 1974[5] | soil | 0–5 | −19.0 | −154 |
| | | 26–33 | — | −156 | | | 0–5 | −19.6 | −154 |
| | | 33–40 | — | −167 | | | 5–10 | −21.9 | −157 |
| | | 50–56 | — | −164 | | | 10–13 | −20.8 | −154 |
| | | 56–60 | — | −169 | | | 13–15 | −22.1 | −154 |
| | | 60–67 | — | −194 | | | 15–20 | −23.3 | −161 |
| 1972[3] | soil | 2–5 | — | −166 | | | 20–25 | −26.1 | −190 |
| | | 5–10 | — | −179 | | | 25–30 | −28.3 | −204 |
| | | 10–15 | — | −185 | | | 30–35 | −28.1 | −206 |
| | | 15–20 | — | −186 | | | 35–40 | −31.6 | −245 |
| | | 20–25 | — | −213 | | | 45–50 | −29.0 | −220 |
| | | 25–30 | — | −202 | | table | 0–5 | −24.4 | −184 |
| | | 30–35 | — | −198 | | | 0–6 | −24.8 | −179 |
| | | 35–40 | — | −165 | | | 0–5 | −24.3 | −177 |
| | | 40–43 | — | −181 | | | 5–10 | −22.5 | −166 |
| | | 43–48 | — | −195 | | | 10–15 | −20.0 | −144 |
| | | 48–55 | — | −179 | | | 15–20 | −24.1 | −178 |
| | | 55–60 | — | −146 | | | 20–25 | −28.1 | −208 |
| | | 60–65 | — | −218 | | | 25–30 | −28.0 | −203 |
| | table | 1–5 | — | −175 | | | 30–35 | −29.1 | −218 |
| | | 5–7 | — | −183 | | | 35–40 | −31.0 | −250 |
| | | 7–10 | — | −179 | | | 40–45 | −29.0 | −222 |
| | | 10–15 | — | −209 | | | 45–50 | −26.1 | −201 |
| | | 15–20 | — | −224 | 1975[6] | soil | 0–5 | — | −172 |
| | | 20–25 | — | −196 | | | 5–8 | — | −185 |
| | | 25–30 | — | −191 | | | 8–10 | — | −192 |
| | | 29–33 | — | −198 | | | 10–14 | — | −197 |
| | | 34–40 | — | −202 | | | 14–18 | — | −200 |
| | | 40–45 | — | −170 | | | 18–22 | — | −200 |
| | | 45–50 | — | −150 | | | 22–25 | — | −199 |
| | | 50–56 | — | −182 | | | 25–29 | — | −198 |
| 1973[4] | soil | 0–4 | — | −146 | | | 29–34 | — | −201 |
| | | 5–10 | — | −156 | | | 34–38 | — | −206 |
| | | 10–14 | — | −160 | | | 35–41 | — | −214 |
| | | 14–18 | — | −159 | | | 42–48 | — | −261 |
| | | 18–20 | — | −147 | | | 48–54 | — | −137 |
| | | 20–24 | — | −149 | | table | 0.5–6.5 | — | −201 |
| | | 24–28 | — | −165 | | | 7–13 | — | −202 |
| | | 28–31 | — | −191 | | | 13–19 | — | −199 |
| | | 31–35 | — | −204 | | | 19–25 | — | −195 |
| | | 35–39 | — | −214 | | | 25–31 | — | −203 |
| | | 39–43 | — | −204 | | | 32–38 | — | −249 |
| | | 43–47 | — | −176 | | | 38–44 | — | −191 |
| | | | | | | | 44–56 | — | −136 |
| | | | | | | | 48.5–54.5 | — | −177 |
| | | | | | | under plastic | | — | −147 |

Table 1. (Continued)

| Year | Location | Depth (cm) | δ¹⁸O | δD | Year | Location | Depth (cm) | δ¹⁸O | δD |
|---|---|---|---|---|---|---|---|---|---|
| 1976[7] | soil | 0–4 | — | −144 | 1985[9] | table | 0–6 | −22.6 | −169 |
| | | 4–7 | — | −166 | | | 4–10 | −25.6 | −183 |
| | | 1.5–4.5 | — | −140 | | | 11–17 | −18.0 | −134 |
| | | 4–7 | — | −158 | | | 18–24 | −19.7 | −147 |
| | | 7–10 | — | −167 | | | 25–31 | −21.6 | −164 |
| | | 10–13 | — | −171 | | | 34–40 | −25.9 | −194 |
| | | 13–16 | — | −165 | | | 41–47 | −26.6 | −204 |
| | | 16–19 | — | −163 | | | 49–55 | −23.7 | −183 |
| | | 19–22 | — | −170 | | | 56–62 | −21.9 | −170 |
| | | 22–25 | — | −188 | | | 64–70 | −23.0 | −177 |
| | | 25–28 | — | −199 | | plastic | 1–7 | −21.2 | −170 |
| | | 28.5–31.5 | — | −193 | | | 5–11 | −24.3 | −180 |
| | | 35.5–35.5 | — | −217 | | | 10–16 | −20.6 | −151 |
| | table | 0–3 | — | −164 | | | 16–22 | −18.6 | −133 |
| | | 0–3.5 | — | −162 | | | 21–27 | −20.6 | −152 |
| | | 3.5–7 | — | −172 | | | 28–34 | −23.2 | −174 |
| | | 7–10 | — | −161 | | | 34–40 | −25.9 | −194 |
| | | 10–13 | — | −166 | | | 40–46 | −26.4 | −201 |
| | | 19–22 | — | −191 | | | 46–52 | −25.7 | −200 |
| | | 22–25 | — | −216 | | | 52–58 | −23.9 | −181 |
| | | 25–28 | — | −164 | | | 58–64 | −25.1 | −191 |
| 1982[8] | soil | 1–7 | −21.5 | −184 | | | 64–70 | −18.5 | −139 |
| | | 9–15 | −25.8 | −211 | | | 69–75 | −21.0 | −156 |
| | | 17–23 | −26.4 | −214 | | | 74–80 | −22.6 | −172 |
| | | 23–29 | −25.0 | −193 | | | 1–7 | | −163 |
| | | 27–33 | −23.8 | −182 | | under plastic | | −13.4 | −117 |
| | | 33–39 | −24.0 | −189 | | | | — | −118 |
| | | 32–38 | −21.4 | −174 | | | | −12.9 | −115 |
| | table | 1–7 | −24.8 | −197 | 1986[10] | soil | 0–6 | −21.8 | −176 |
| | | 6–12 | −26.9 | −211 | | | 7–13 | −24.2 | −181 |
| | | 11–17 | −27.2 | −213 | | | 14–20 | −19.5 | −142 |
| | | 16–22 | −24.8 | −192 | | | 18–24 | −19.5 | −138 |
| | | 23–29 | −23.5 | −184 | | | 24–25 | −21.3 | −168 |
| | | 28–34 | −25.4 | −205 | | | 26–29 | −26.0 | −198 |
| 1985[9] | soil | 2–8 | −18.0 | −155 | | table | 1–7 | −25.1 | −190 |
| | | 9–15 | −23.6 | −183 | | | 4–10 | −21.2 | −159 |
| | | 14–20 | −21.4 | −162 | | | 10–16 | −20.7 | −155 |
| | | 21–27 | −18.3 | −144 | | | 12–18 | −23.0 | −179 |
| | | 27–33 | −20.6 | −164 | | plastic | 1–7 | −22.2 | −182 |
| | | 33–39 | −23.2 | −182 | | | 7–13 | −22.5 | −174 |
| | | 38–44 | −25.6 | −207 | | | 9–15 | −21.7 | −159 |
| | | 45–51 | −26.2 | −209 | | | 14–20 | −19.7 | −145 |
| | | 52–58 | −24.5 | −198 | | | 16–22 | −21.0 | −156 |
| | | 58–64 | −24.4 | −200 | | | 24–25 | −22.0 | −171 |
| | | 64–70 | −19.3 | −156 | | | 25–28 | −24.6 | −198 |
| | | 69–75 | −21.3 | −177 | | under plastic | | −17.7 | −145 |
| | | 71–77 | −22.5 | −185 | | | | | |

[1] Samples collected March 22, 1966.
[2] Dash indicates no measurements were made.
[3] Samples collected March 27, 1972.
[4] Samples collected March 25, 1973.
[5] Samples collected March 16, 1974.
[6] Samples collected March 27, 1975.
[7] Samples collected April 3, 1976.
[8] Samples collected March 12, 1982.
[9] Samples collected March 18, 1985.
[10] Samples collected March 19, 1986.

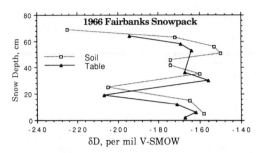

FIG. 1. A plot of $\delta D$ vs. vertical position in the soil-pack and table pack for the 1966 snowpack sampled in the spring before melting occurred.

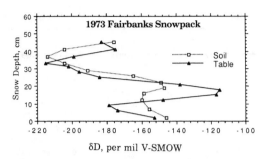

FIG. 3. A plot similar to Fig. 1, but for the 1973 snowpack.

pack was determined predominately by vapor-pressure fractionation, or by exchange with atmospheric water vapor, as will be discussed later. The $\delta D$ vs. $\delta^{18}O$ slope for the 10–20 cm interval for 1986, but for the plastic-pack and table-pack samples, is 12, showing that similar processes have occurred in these levels of both the plastic-pack and soil-pack.

## DISCUSSION

The isotopic data from the 1985 and 1986 plastic-packs resembles that from the table-packs, and differs from the soil-packs. This indicates that the plastic sheet intercepted an agent that would normally act on the snowpack above the soil. The plastic sheet prevented transfer of moisture from the soil to the snow above it. The moisture condensed under the plastic sheet was sampled in 1975, 1985, and 1986. In all cases this condensed moisture, which normally would have moved into the snow above it in the soil-pack, is very enriched in deuterium and oxygen-18 relative to the snow. In Figs. 12 and 13 we have plotted the data obtained from samples of this under-plastic condensate. From these figures it would appear that the bottom soil-pack samples are a simple mixture of this condensate with the lowest *plastic* sample, but not with

the lowest *table* sample. Therefore, the agents that acted to change the isotopic composition of the base of the soil-pack are not only dilution or mixing with the soil-derived moisture, but fractionation associated with transport of water within the snowpack itself.

This transport can occur by several mechanisms. (1) Surface diffusion along the snow crystal surfaces and transfer of material from crystal-to-crystal at the contact between crystals can be expected to fractionate both deuterium and oxygen-18. (2) Vapor transport from the bottom crystals to the top crystals, along the vapor pressure gradient generated by the temperature gradient in the snow pack, will result in an isotopic fractionation that is caused by two processes. The first process is the change of state from solid to vapor, while the second is molecular diffusion during vapor transport.

### Fractionation during change of state

The vapor pressure of the lighter isotopic molecule ($H_2{}^{16}O$) is higher than that of the heavier isotopic molecules (HDO and $H_2{}^{18}O$); therefore, the vapor will be enriched in the light molecules relative to the solid in equilibrium with it. EPSTEIN *et al.* (1965) observed that depth hoar was enriched in

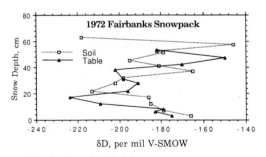

FIG. 2. A plot similar to Fig. 1, but for the 1972 snowpack.

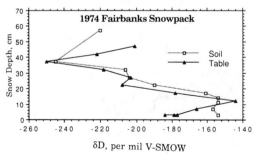

FIG. 4. A plot similar to Fig. 1, but for the 1974 snowpack.

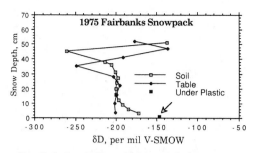

FIG. 5. A plot similar to Fig. 1, but for the 1975 snowpack. The $\delta D$ of the frost condensed under a plastic sheet covering the soil is also shown.

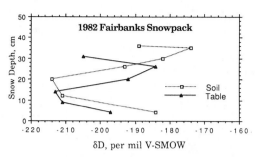

FIG. 7. A plot similar to Fig. 1, but for the 1982 snowpack.

$^{18}O$ and suggested that this was the result of partial recondensation of vapor generated within the depth hoar accompanied by the escape of residual vapor impoverished in $^{18}O$. The difference in vapor pressure of the isotopic molecules results in the vapor being lower in $\delta D$ by 122 per mil and in $\delta^{18}O$ by 11.8 per mil at 0°C, and by 160 and 13.4, respectively, at −20°C (FRIEDMAN and O'NEIL, 1977). The slope of $\delta D$ vs. $\delta^{18}O$ for metamorphosed snowpack samples should be between 10 and 12 (the ratio of the vapor pressures of the isotopic molecules) if this process was the dominant transport agent. The solid-vapor fractionation due to the vapor pressure difference between the isotopic molecules can, in the steady state, only be effective in isotopic separation if one or both of the following processes occur.

(1) First is fractionation during sublimation of snow. In order for this process to be effective in isotope separation, the rate of self-diffusion in the solid must be rapid compared to the rate of molecular diffusion in the vapor. In other words, the solid must "mix" so that the surface layer of the solid undergoing sublimation will not be unduly enriched in the heavier isotopic species due to the preferential loss of the lighter isotopic species to the vapor. This would result in sublimation occurring "layer-by-

layer" with no resulting isotopic fractionation. Because self-diffusion in ice is about 1/1000 as rapid as molecular diffusion in the vapor, the amount of isotopic separation due to vapor pressure differences between the isotopic molecules will be greatly reduced from the values of approximately 130 per mil for deuterium and 12 per mil for oxygen-18 that would to be expected if the molecules in the solid were well mixed.

(2) The second process is the condensation of vapor produced in the snowpack on growing ice crystals. If partial condensation of rising vapor occurs at each growing crystal, then the crystals receiving the condensate would be enriched in the molecules having the lowest vapor pressure (the heavier molecules). Under our extreme conditions, virtually all of the ice present at the base of the Alaskan snowpack passes from solid to vapor and back into the solid phase during the winter, according to TRABANT and BENSON (1972) and STURM (1989). These authors documented this by showing that the number of grains decreased from about 400 per $cm^3$ at the beginning of the winter to about 40 at the end, and these few crystals grew to much larger sizes (up to 1 cm) than the original

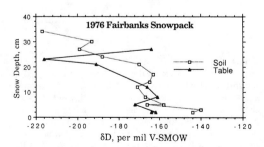

FIG. 6. A plot similar to Fig. 1, but for the 1976 snowpack.

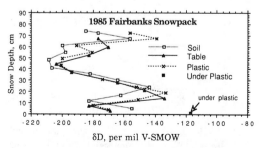

FIG. 8. A plot of $\delta D$ vs. vertical position in the soil-pack, table-pack, and plastic-pack for the 1985 snowpack sampled in the spring before melting occurred. The $\delta D$ of the frost condensed under the plastic sheet covering the soil is also shown.

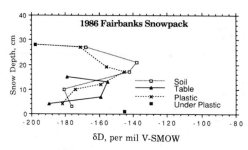

FIG. 9. A plot similar to Fig. 8, but for the 1986 snow-pack.

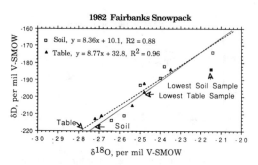

FIG. 11. A plot similar to Fig. 10, but for the 1982 snow-pack.

crystals (<1 mm). This order-of-magnitude decrease in the number of grains means that only one in ten grew to become large depth-hoar crystals by subli-mation while the remainder vanished. In effect, al-most all of the snow in the depth hoar will have sublimed, passed into the vapor state, and then condensed on a relatively few ice crystals. Even though this change-of-state process operating at re-duced efficiency results in only a small isotopic fractionation, the cascading of many such change-of-state events, the "hand-to-hand" transfer mech-anism of YOSIDA *et al.* (1955), as the vapor travels vertically through the snowpack can result in rel-atively large isotopic changes, with slopes of the δD vs. δ¹⁸O changes having values in the range of 10 to 12.

*Atmospheric water vapor*

Air moved in-and-out of the snowpack due to changes in temperature and atmospheric pressure (TRABANT and BENSON, 1972; GJESSING, 1977). Atmospheric water vapor will have an isotopic composition that is approximately in equilibrium with that of the "average" snow, and this water va-por can exchange with vapor produced in the snow. This exchange will act to maintain the δD-δ¹⁸O slope at values of about eight, similar to that in the original snow, and will be more effective in the upper, rather than lower, portion of the snowpack, inasmuch as the upper portion experiences the largest amount of air exchange.

*Isotopic fractionation due to molecular diffusion*

Molecular diffusion of water along the surfaces of crystals can result in isotopic fractionation. This diffusive separation is a function of the ratio of the relative masses of the diffusing molecules, and the separation factor $\epsilon$ is equal to $1 - \alpha$, where $\alpha$ is the fractionation factor defined as $\alpha = \dfrac{R_{\text{initial phase}}}{R_{\text{final phase}}}$, where

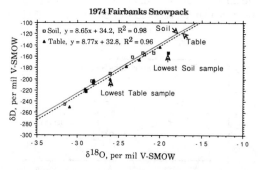

FIG. 10. A plot of δD vs. δ¹⁸O for the soil-pack and table-pack for the 1974 snowpack sampled in the spring before melting occurred. The straight lines are the linear least mean square solutions to the soil-pack and to the table-pack data. The data from the lowest soil sample were not included in the calculation of the linear least mean square solution to the soil-pack data.

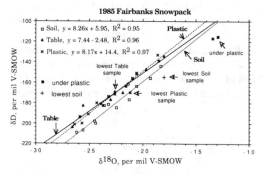

FIG. 12. A plot of δD vs. δ¹⁸O for the soil-pack, table-pack, and plastic-pack for the 1985 snowpack sampled in the spring before melting occurred. The isotopic compo-sition of the ice collected from the underside of the plastic sheet is also plotted. The straight lines are the linear least mean square solutions to the soil-pack, table pack, and plastic-pack data. The data from the lowest soil-pack and the lowest plastic-pack samples were not included in the calculation of the linear least mean square solution to the corresponding soil-pack and plastic-pack data.

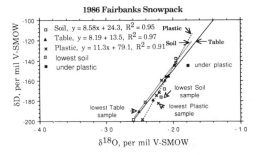

FIG. 13. A plot of δD vs. δ$^{18}$O for the soil-pack, table-pack, and plastic-pack for the 1986 snowpack sampled in the spring before melting occurred. The isotopic composition of the ice collected from the underside of the plastic sheet is also plotted. The straight lines are the linear least mean square solutions for the soil-pack, table-pack, and plastic-pack data. The data from the lowest soil-pack and the lowest plastic-pack samples were not included in the calculation of the linear least mean square solution to the corresponding soil-pack and plastic-pack data.

$R$ is the ratio of the concentration of heavy to light isotopes:

$$\epsilon_{deuterium} = 1 - \alpha_D = 1 - \sqrt{\frac{19}{18}} = .0274$$

$$\epsilon_{oxygen\text{-}18} = 1 - \alpha_O = 1 - \sqrt{\frac{20}{18}} = .0540.$$

The ratio of the two separation factors given above is 1.97 and will be equal to the slope of the δD vs. δ$^{18}$O plot of the samples undergoing such a diffusive separation.

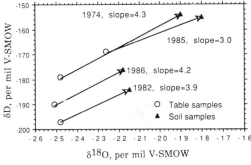

FIG. 14. A plot of the δD vs. δ$^{18}$O for the samples from the bottom of the soil-pack and table-pack of the 1974, 1982, 1985, and 1986 snowpacks. Lines are drawn to connect the corresponding soil-pack and table-pack samples from each year. The arrows indicate the direction of the changes, from the original snow in the table-packs to the metamorphosed snow in the soil-packs. The slopes of these lines are also shown.

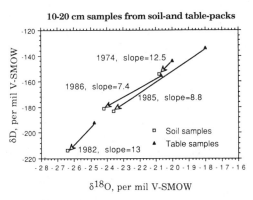

FIG. 15. A plot similar to Fig. 14, but for samples from 10–20 cm above the bottom of the snowpacks.

Molecular diffusion of water vapor through the air during the transport of vapor from bottom to top of the snowpack will also result in fractionation. EHHALT and KNOTT (1964) found that the separation factors $\epsilon$ are given by

$$\epsilon_{deuterium} = 1 - \alpha_D$$

$$= 1 - \sqrt{\frac{19(18 + 29)}{18(19 + 29)}} = .01664$$

$$\epsilon_{oxygen\text{-}18} = 1 - \alpha_O$$

$$= 1 - \sqrt{\frac{20(18 + 29)}{18(20 + 29)}} = .03236.$$

The ratio of the two separation factors is 1.95.

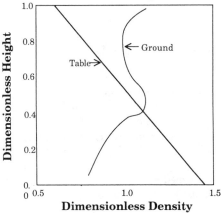

FIG. 16. A plot, in normalized form (from STURM, 1989), of the density distribution of the soil and table-packs during 11 winters between 1966 and 1987.

Experimental determination of the fractionation factors for diffusion of water vapor in air was determined by MERLIVAT (1970) and STEWART (1974), and gave separation factors of .024 for deuterium and .0289 for oxygen-18. The ratio of these separation factors is 1.20.

EHHALT and KNOTT (1964) and CRAIG and GORDON (1965) predicted values of between three and five for the case of evaporation from a liquid, where similar vapor pressure differences and molecular transport phenomena can be expected, but where mixing in the liquid phase is more rapid than in the solid snow.

In a laboratory study of snow metamorphism, SOMMERFELD et al. (this volume) observed that the slope of the $\delta D$ vs. $\delta^{18}O$ of all of the samples from the experimental snowpack that had been exposed to a temperature gradient was 3.0. In this experiment, the snowpack was not in contact with normal atmospheric water vapor, but was contained in a freezer, with the result that vapor was continuously being removed from the snow and transferred to the freezer coils. This one-directional flow of water vapor resulted in the experimental snowpack having a slope of 3.0, in contrast to the values of 10 to 13 found for the natural snowpacks. In another laboratory study of snow metamorphism, SOMMERFELD et al. (1986) found that the slope varied from 4.0 to 4.5, again much lower than that of the natural snowpack. In this later study the snow was sealed in plastic bags and isolated from the atmosphere.

SOMMERFELD et al. (1986) found that the effective diffusion coefficient of water vapor in snowpacks exposed to a temperature gradient was approximately twice that of water vapor in air. This result indicates that hand-to-hand water transport along the surface of snow crystals and from crystal-to-crystal is an important factor in vapor transport in the snow pack.

*Relative importance of soil-added water and heat transport in the metamorphism of snow*

In both 1985 and 1986 the plastic-packs experienced about the same degree of metamorphism as did the soil-packs. Inasmuch as water from the underlying soil could not enter the plastic-packs, water from the underlying soil was not *directly* involved in the metamorphism of these packs. The major driving-force in this metamorphic change was heat transfer from the soil to the snow. In a natural snowpack, in addition to conduction, an important agent in this heat transfer is the latent heat transfer associated with the water vapor as it moves from the ground and condenses in the snowpack. In the

experiment where a plastic sheet prevented the direct transfer of vapor from the ground to the snow, the vapor from the soil was condensed on the underside of the plastic, transferring heat to the plastic, and thereby to the snow above. In this case heat transport by water vapor was still effective in inducing the recrystallization of the snow, although water molecules from the soil did not reach the snow.

The primary factor in snow metamorphism is the addition of heat from the ground to the overlying snowpack. This heat is transferred along a thermal gradient from the warm ground to the cooler snow. The intensity of this gradient is determined by a number of climatic factors, including the timing of the first permanent snow cover, the temperature at which each snowfall occurs, and the intensity and duration of cold events during the winter.

This temperature gradient acts to transfer both heat and water from the external environment of the soil to the snowpack. In addition, it acts to redistribute water within the snowpack by diffusive transport. Each of these processes acts somewhat differently on the isotopic water species and allows us to separate the processes.

## CONCLUSIONS

1. A thermal gradient within the snowpack is necessary for the development of depth hoar. This is shown by the development of depth hoar in the plastic-pack, which developed a thermal gradient, but not in the table-pack where no thermal gradient existed.

2. Transfer of water from the underlying soil to the snowpack is not necessary for depth-hoar formation. This was shown by the development of depth hoar in the plastic-pack, where the plastic sheet prevented water from the soil from reaching the overlying snow.

3. Although atmospheric water vapor interacts with the natural snowpack, this interaction is not necessary for depth-hoar development to occur. The experimental snowpacks, particularly in the experiments of SOMMERFELD et al. (1986), were not in contact with atmospheric water vapor but did develop depth hoar.

4. Atmospheric water vapor interacts with the natural snowpack and is responsible for some isotopic alteration of the snowpack.

5. Fractional condensation of water vapor (produced by sublimation of the snow), on growing snow crystals as the vapor moves vertically through the snowpack, results in isotopic fractionation.

6. The efficiency of the Rayleigh process during

sublimation is reduced due to the low (diffusive) rate of mixing of water molecules within the snow crystals, and isotopic fractionation during the sublimation of snow is therefore not an important process.

7. Transport of water vapor by diffusion is an important process. However, we do not know the relative importance of diffusion through the intergranular atmosphere as compared to diffusion along a liquid water film as described by DASH (1990).

8. In the lowest portion of the natural snowpack, diffusive processes are most important in mass-transfer, while further up in the snowpack change-of-state processes and vapor advection usually predominate. These differences may be due to the fact that the amount of advected atmospheric water vapor in the snowpack decreases in proportion to the depth below the snow-atmosphere interface.

*Acknowledgements*—We thank Ms. Augusta Warden for performing the $\delta^{18}O$ measurements. We also thank Matthew Sturm and Dennis Trabant for assistance in the field. One of us (C.B.) also received initial support from a grant from Dr. Terris Moore, former president of the University of Alaska, and from NSF grants G-22224 and DPP 79-26425. Additional support was provided by DOE Grant DE-RG-06-84ER60245 and by the State of Alaska.

## REFERENCES

AKITAYA E. (1974) Studies on depth hoar. *Contributions from The Institute of Low Temperature Science Series A, No. 26*, pp. 1–67. Hokkaido University, Sapporo, Japan.

BADER H., HAEFELI R., NEHER E., ECKEL O. and THAMS C. (1939) Der Schnee und seine metamorphose. *Beitrage zur Geologie der Schweiz, Geotechnische Serie. Hydrologie*. Lieferung 3, Bern [Snow and its metamorphism. Translation No. 14, 1954, of the U.S. Army Cold Regions Research and Engineering Lab. (CRREL) Hanover, N.H.].

BENSON C. S. (1962) Stratigraphic studies in the snow and firn of the Greenland ice sheet. *SIPRE. (CRREL) Res. Rep. 70* (Published version of PhD. dissertation, Calif. Inst. of Technology, 1960; summarized in: *Folia Geographica Danica* Tom IX, 13–37, 1961).

CRAIG H. and GORDON L. I. (1965) Deuterium and oxygen-18 variations in the oceans and marine atmosphere. *Symp. Marine Geochem., Narragansett Marine Laboratory, Univ. of Rhode Island Occ. pub. #3-1965*.

DASH J. G. (1990) Thermomolecular pressure in surface melting: Motivation for frost heave. *Science* **246**, 1591–1593.

EHHALT D. and KNOTT K. (1964) Kinetische Isopentrennung bei der Verdampfung von Wasser. *Tellus* **17**, 389–397.

EPSTEIN S., SHARP R. P. and GOW A. J. (1965) Six-year record of oxygen and hydrogen isotope variations in South Pole firn. *J. Geophys. Res.* **70**, 1809–1814.

FRIEDMAN I. and O'NEIL J. R. (1977) Fractionation factors of geochemical interest. In *Data of Geochemistry*, 6 edn., Chap. KK; *U.S. Geol. Surv. Prof. Pap.* 440.

FRIEDMAN I., REDFIELD A. C., SCHOEN B. and HARRIS J. (1964) The variation of the deuterium content of natural waters in the hydrologic cycle. *Rev. Geophys.* **2**, 177–224.

GJESSING Y. T. (1977) The filtering effect of snow. *Symp. Isotopes Impurities in snow and ice; IASH-AISH Publ. 118*, pp. 199–203.

JUDY C., MEIMAN J. R. and FRIEDMAN I. (1970) Deuterium variations in an annual snowpack. *Water Resources Res.* **6**, 125–129.

KOJIMA K. (1956) Viscous compression of natural snow— Layer II. *Low Temperature Science Contributions. Series A, No. 15*, pp. 117–135. Hokkaido University, Sapporo, Japan.

MACPHERSON D. and KRAUSE H. (1967) $O^{18}/O^{16}$ ratios in snow and ice of the Hubbard and Kaskawulsh glaciers. In *Isotope Techniques in the Hydrologic Cycle; Geophys. Monogr. 11*, pp. 180–194. American Geophysical Union, Washington, D.C.

MERLIVAT L. (1970) L'étude quantitative de bilans de lacs à' l'aide des concentrations en deuterium et oxygen-18 dans l'eau. In *Isotope Hydrology 1970*, pp. 89–107. International Atomic Energy Agency, Vienna.

SOMMERFELD R. A., FRIEDMAN I. and NILLES M. (1986) The fractionation of natural isotopes during temperature gradient metamorphism of snow. *Chemistry of Seasonal Snowpacks*. NATO Advanced Study Institute, Les Arcs, France, July 1986.

SORGE E. (1935) Glaziologische untersuchungen in Eismitte. In *Wissenschaftliche Ergebnisse der Deutschen Grönland Expedition Alfred Wegener 1929 and 1930-31*. Leipzig: F. A. Brockhaus, **3**, 62–270.

STEWART M. K. (1974) Stable isotope fractionation due to evaporation and isotopic exchange of falling waterdrops: Applications to atmospheric processes and evaporation of lakes. *J. Geophys. Res.* **80**, 1133–1146.

STURM M. (1989) The role of convection in heat and mass transport in the subarctic snow cover. Ph.D. dissertation, University of Alaska, Fairbanks.

TRABANT D. and BENSON C. (1972) Field experiments on the development of depth hoar. In *Studies in Mineralogy and Precambrian Geology* (ed. B. R. DOE and D. K. SMITH), *Geol. Soc. Amer. Mem. 135*, pp. 309–322.

YOSIDA Z., OURA H., KUROIWA D., HUZIOKA T. and KOJIMA K. (1955) Physical studies on deposited snow— I Thermal properties. *Contributions from The Institute of Low Temperature Science, No. 7*, pp. 19–74. Mokkaido University, Sapporo, Japan.

Stable Isotope Geochemistry: A Tribute to Samuel Epstein
© The Geochemical Society, Special Publication No. 3, 1991
Editors: H. P. Taylor, Jr., J. R. O'Neil and I. R. Kaplan

# The glacial/interglacial temperature range of the surface water of the oceans at low latitudes

CESARE EMILIANI

Department of Geological Sciences, University of Miami, Coral Gables, FL 33124, U.S.A.

and

DAVID B. ERICSON*

Lamont-Doherty Geological Observatory, Palisades, NY 10964, U.S.A.

**Abstract**—The isotopic and micropaleontological evidence pertinent to the glacial/interglacial temperature range of the surface water of the ocean at low latitudes is reassessed. We conclude that the maximum range is 7.8°C in the Caribbean-equatorial Atlantic, 5.5°C in the northern Indian Ocean, and 3.6°C in the equatorial Pacific. The intertropical, area-weighted average is 5.0°C. The negligible range reported by CLIMAP may be due to faulty calibration.

## INTRODUCTION

EARLY ISOTOPIC AND micropaleontological work (EMILIANI, 1955; ERICSON and WOLLIN, 1956) demonstrated a large isotopic and micropaleontological change between the hypsithermals and bathythermals of the Late Quaternary. Since then much work has been done in an attempt to reconstruct the true history of the ice ages (see review by MIX, 1987). Different methods and different interpretations have produced conclusions that are at variance with each other. This disagreement requires scrutiny.

## THE ISOTOPIC EVIDENCE

The isotopic evidence, graphically summarized by BROECKER (1986, Figs. 1 and 2), is reported in Table 1. We notice that the benthic foraminifera give similar $\delta^{18}O$ values (1.6–1.8) around the world, while the planktic foraminifera exhibit marked variations from region to region. SHACKLETON (1967) and SHACKLETON and OPDYKE (1973), assuming that the bottom temperature in the ocean remained constant during the Quaternary, assigned the entire isotopic range measured on benthic foraminifera to the change in isotopic composition of the ocean water related to glaciation. This would require the equatorial Pacific to have been warmer during the ice ages than during the interglacial ages. Evidence now indicates that bottom water temperature did not remain constant. Table 2 shows that there has been a decrease of 1–2°C in the bottom

temperature of the world ocean since the last hypsithermal.

The world ocean bottom water consists of a mixture of the warmer (2.5°C), more saline (34.9 per mil) North Atlantic deep water and the colder (−0.5°C), less saline (34.6 per mil) Antarctic bottom water. During interglacial ages, bottom water consists mainly of North Atlantic deep water, while it may consist mainly of Antarctic bottom water during glacial ages. If so, the observed temperature decrease of 1–2°C in the bottom water of the world ocean (Table 2) may herald the initiation of the next ice age.

The temperature changes of the bottom water between the hypsithermals and bathythermals of the Quaternary were considerably larger, amounting to 5.7°C in the Atlantic, 3.8°C in the Indian Ocean, and 2.7°C in the equatorial Pacific (LABEYRIE et al., 1987). These data, together with the isotopic data of Table 1, would indicate a surface temperature change of 5.6°C in the Caribbean-equatorial Atlantic, 3.9°C in the northern Indian Ocean, and 2.6°C in the eastern equatorial Pacific. The actual surface temperature change, however, may have been even larger. ANDERSON and STEINMETZ (1981), in fact, showed that coccoliths in a Caribbean core exhibit a glacial/interglacial isotopic range of 2.8 per mil, which is 40% greater than that given by the shallow planktic foraminiferal species *Globigerinoides rubra* and *Globigerinoides sacculifera*. The ratios of the isotopic compositions of different foraminiferal species to each other remain approximately constant worldwide. If the ratio of the isotopic composition of the coccoliths to that of *G. rubra* and *G. sacculifera* also remained constant, the glacial/interglacial temperature change could

---

* *Present address:* 466 Commercial Street, Provincetown, MA 02657, U.S.A.

Table 1. Oxygen isotopic change ($\delta^{18}O$ in per mil relative to PDB-1) between bathythermal 2 and hypsithermal 1 (data from BROECKER, 1986)

| Region | Foraminifera | |
| --- | --- | --- |
| | Planktic | Benthic |
| North Atlantic | 1.7–2.4 | 1.8 |
| Caribbean | 1.9–2.1 | 1.8* |
| Equatorial Atlantic | 1.6–1.8 | 1.6–1.8 |
| South Atlantic | 1.1–1.6 | 1.6–1.7 |
| Northern Indian Ocean | 1.5–2.1 | 1.8 |
| Eastern Equatorial Pacific | 1.1–1.5 | 1.6–1.8 |
| Western Equatorial Pacific | 1.0–1.2 | — |

\* Inferred from the adjacent equatorial Atlantic.

have been 40% greater than that given by *G. rubra* and *G. sacculifera,* or 7.8°C in the Caribbean-equatorial Atlantic, 5.5°C in the northern Indian Ocean, and 3.6°C in the equatorial Pacific.

Coccolithophoridae do not deposit their calcite in isotopic equilibrium with ambient sea water. Isotopic disequilibrium for the five species used by ANDERSON and STEINMETZ (1981) amounts to +1 per mil and is not affected by downcore changes in the relative abundances of the five species (four *Gephyrocapsa* and one *Syracosphaera*). As observed in other taxa (benthic foraminifera, echinoderms, corals, etc.), the disequilibrium effect is constant and independent of temperature. Because disequilibrium does not change with changing temperature (*cf.* DUDLEY *et al.,* 1986, Figs. 1 and 2), the glacial/interglacial isotopic range measured by ANDERSON and STEINMETZ (1981) is real and has an important bearing on the actual glacial/interglacial temperature range of the surface seawater at low latitudes.

Coccolithophoridae occur most abundantly in

the top 50 m of ocean water. Most are eurythermal. Reproduction is rapid (one to two cell divisions per day). While some taxa (*e.g. Umbellosphaera*) exhibit seasonality even at subtropical latitudes (OKADA and MCINTYRE, 1979), *Gephyrocapsa* (which is the most abundant taxon in the core studied by ANDERSON and STEINMETZ, 1981) and *Syracosphaera* do not (see OKADA and MCINTYRE, 1979, Fig. 7). Planktic foraminifera, on the other hand, exhibit marked seasonality at subtropical and higher latitudes, with *Globigerinoides rubra* as a dominant summer species (TOLDERLUND and BÉ, 1971; WILLIAMS *et al.,* 1981). At low latitudes where the temperature difference between the warmer and the colder times of the year is a few degrees centigrade at most, *Globigerinoides sacculifera* appears to prefer the warmer season, while *G. rubra* exhibits no apparent seasonality (Table 3).

It is likely that during the ice ages the temperature difference between the warmer and colder seasons at low latitudes was more pronounced than today. If so, planktic foraminifera, especially *G. rubra* and *G. sacculifera* which occupy a shallow habitat, may have developed a stronger seasonality and deposited their shells predominantly during the warmer portion of the year. A reduction in the amplitude of the glacial/interglacial isotopic signal to the values listed in Table 1 would result.

## THE NON-ISOTOPIC EVIDENCE

The glacial/interglacial surface temperature range can also be assessed by using temperature tolerance limits. The species *Globorotalia menardii, Pulleniatina obliquiloculata,* and *Sphaeroidinella dehiscens* have sharply restricted temperature tolerance limits (Table 4) and are, therefore, particularly useful. These are deeper water species that repro-

Table 2. Temperature decrease of the bottom water of the ocean since the last hypsithermal. Water corrections from CRAIG and GORDON (1965). The isotopic temperatures were calculated using the revised Epstein equation published by YAPP (1979). Data from the following references: (1) DUPLESSY *et al.* (1975); (2) DUPLESSY *et al.* (1980); (3) STREETER and SHACKLETON (1979); (4) RUDDIMAN and MCINTYRE (1971); (5) SHACKLETON (1974); (6) DUPLESSY (1978)

| Genus | Location | | Depth (m) | $\delta^{18}O$ (per mil) | Taxonomic corr. (per mil) | Water corr. (per mil) | $\delta^{18}O$ (corrected) | Isotopic temp. (°C) | Ambient temp. (°C) | Temp. decrease (°C) | Ref. |
| --- | --- | --- | --- | --- | --- | --- | --- | --- | --- | --- | --- |
| *Cibicides* | Norwegian-Greenland Sea | | 1668–3139 | +3.88 | +0.64 | +0.1 | 4.42 | 0.4 | −1.4 | 1.2 | (1) |
| *Cibicides* | 54°38′N | 16°21′W | 2209 | +2.59 | +0.64 | +0.1 | 3.13 | 4.5 | 3.3 | 1.2 | (2) |
| *Uvigerina* | 44°01′N | 24°32′W | 3331 | +3.00 | 0.00 | +0.1 | 2.90 | 5.3 | 2.8 | 2.5 | (3) |
| *Uvigerina* | 41°00′N | 32°55′W | 3371 | +3.22 | 0.00 | +0.1 | 3.12 | 4.6 | 2.8 | 1.8 | (4) |
| *Uvigerina* | 47°01′N | 129°34′W | 2650 | +3.35 | 0.00 | −0.2 | 3.55 | 3.1 | 1.3 | 1.8 | (5) |
| *Uvigerina* | 47°31′S | 79°52′E | 3193 | +3.52 | 0.00 | −0.2 | 3.72 | 2.6 | 0.8 | 1.8 | (5) |
| *Nonion* | 43°49′S | 51°19′E | 3284 | +3.13 | +0.34 | −0.2 | 3.67 | 2.7 | 0.6 | 2.1 | (6) |

Table 3. Seasonal distribution of *G. rubra* and *G. sacculifera* in the equatorial Atlantic (data from JONES, 1967)

| Season | Surface temperature (°C) | Surface salinity (per mil) | Max. standing crop (no. of individuals per 1000 m³ of seawater) | |
| --- | --- | --- | --- | --- |
| | | | *G. rubra* | *G. sacculifera* |
| September | 25–26 | 35.0–35.7 | 6000 | 10,000 |
| April–May | 27–29 | 34.8–35.6 | 4000–7000 | 15,000–30,000 |

duce near the surface during the winter (DEUSER *et al.,* 1981; WILLIAMS *et al.,* 1981). Because shell deposition begins near the surface (EMILIANI, 1971; WILLIAMS *et al.,* 1981), a species would disappear if surface winter temperature drops below the threshold for reproduction and initial shell growth of that species. Table 5 shows the depth at which temperature is 18.5°C, together with the relative abundances of *G. menardii* and temperature data. As may be seen, the 18.5°C isothermal surface deepens from east to northwest in the equatorial Atlantic, reaching its maximum depth in the Caribbean. DURAZZI (1981) showed that the minimum isotopic depth of *G. menardii* exhibits the same trend.

The absence of *Globorotalia menardii, Pulleniatina obliquiloculata,* and *Sphaeroidinella dehiscens* from the equatorial-tropical Atlantic and the Caribbean during the last ice age (ERICSON and WOLLIN, 1956) indicates that winter temperature dropped below 18.5°C, a decrease of at least 7°C for the equatorial-tropical Atlantic and about 8°C for the Caribbean.

Some species that grow during the summer at high northern latitudes become winter species at lower latitudes. A conspicuous example is *Globigerina bulloides* (TOLDERLUND and BÉ, 1971, Figs. 4 and 5). Other species remain summer species but disappear when summer temperature is too high. *Globigerina quinqueloba,* a typical summer species in the northern North Atlantic (TOLDERLUND and BÉ, 1971), is not found if summer temperature is higher than 22°C (PHLEGER *et al.,* 1953, Table 38; KIPP, 1976, Fig. 5). This species can be used to assess the glacial/interglacial range of summer surface temperature. Because *G. quinqueloba* is present during bathythermal 2 in equatorial Atlantic core 246 (PHLEGER *et al.,* 1953, Table 17; *cf.* with EMILIANI, 1955, Fig. 6), we conclude that summer temperature in the equatorial Atlantic at that time was lower than 22°C, indicating a drop of at least 4.5°C.

In the equatorial Pacific, *Globorotalia menardii* and *Pulleniatina obliquiloculata* remain abundant downcore (10 to 40% and 5 to 20%, respectively—

see ARRHENIUS, 1952, Appendix, plates 2.58–2.62). This indicates that winter temperature did not drop below 18.5°C in the eastern equatorial Pacific. Present surface temperature ranges from 25 to 27°C in the area of the cores described by Arrhenius. *Sphaeroidinella dehiscens* is present mainly in interglacial times, indicating that temperature may have dropped below 23°C in glacial times. A glacial/interglacial range of >3°C is thus suggested. Table 6 shows the temperature change from bathythermal 2 to hypsithermal 1 based on oxygen isotope analysis of planktic foraminifera (increased by 1.4 to account for the coccolith evidence) and on the temperature tolerances of stenothermal species.

## A PROBLEM WITH CLIMAP?

CLIMAP (1976, 1981) determined the relative abundances (percentages) of planktic foraminifera in a large number of gravity and piston core tops, and related these percentages to the temperature prevailing at the surface. Having thus calibrated the composition of the core-top foraminiferal faunas, CLIMAP determined the faunal composition in core samples below the tops, dating from bathythermal 2 (18,000 y BP), and proceeded to reconstruct temperature conditions at that time. Their reconstructions showed that "large areas of the tropics and subtropics within all oceans had sea-surface temperatures as warm as, or slightly warmer, than today" (CLIMAP, 1981, p. 9). Similar conclusions, with some notable regional exceptions, were reached by PRELL (1985). These conclusions

Table 4. Temperature tolerance limits for three species of planktic foraminifera (data from PHLEGER *et al.,* 1953; KIPP, 1976)

| Species | Lowest tolerable temperatures (°C) | |
| --- | --- | --- |
| | Winter | Summer |
| *Globorotalia menardii* | 18.5 | 22.5 |
| *Pulleniatina obliquiloculata* | 18.5 | 22.5 |
| *Sphaeroidinella dehiscens* | 23.0 | 26.0 |

Table 5. Percentages of *Globorotalia menardii* in CLIMAP's core top samples between latitudes 2°S and 23°N in the Atlantic. Samples 52 and 56 are not included here because below the $R_0$ level of VINCENT and BERGER (1981, p. 1087). Data from IMBRIE and KIPP (1971)

| Sample No. | Core No. | Lat. | Long. | Depth (m) | % of G. menardii | Surface seasonal temp. range (°C) | Subsurface temp. (°C) 100 m | 200 m | Depth at which temp. = 18.5°C |
|---|---|---|---|---|---|---|---|---|---|
| 42 | V22–204 | 15°01'N | 23°14'W | 1723 | 9.2 | 21.5–26.5 | 15.5 | 17.5 | 70 |
| 44 | V10–89 | 23°02'N | 43°48'W | 3523 | 1.1 | 23.0–26.0 | 21.9 | 18.5 | 190 |
| 45 | V12–79 | 1°31'S | 11°47'W | 3823 | 5.4 | 23.3–26.0 | 16.0 | 12.5 | 110 |
| 48 | A180–72 | 0°36'N | 21°47'W | 3841 | 6.9 | 24.0–27.5 | 21.1 | 12.5 | 110 |
| 49 | V16–21 | 17°17'N | 48°25'W | 3975 | 0.9 | 24.5–27.0 | 23.0 | 16.0 | 190 |
| 50 | A180–76 | 0°46'S | 26°02'W | 3512 | 5.4 | 25.0–27.0 | 22.5 | 12.5 | 120 |
| 53 | V14–5 | 0°51'N | 32°51'W | 3255 | 7.8 | 26.0–27.0 | 24.0 | 12.0 | 130 |
| 57 | V20–230 | 1°57'S | 39°02'W | 3294 | 1.3 | 26.0–27.5 | 25.5 | 12.0 | 145 |
| 58 | V20–7 | 11°33'N | 60°31'W | 1018 | 3.1 | 26.0–27.5 | 24.0 | 14.5 | 180 |
| 59 | V20–234 | 5°19'N | 33°02'W | 3133 | 3.6 | 26.5–27.0 | 22.5 | 12.0 | 200 |
| 60 | V18–21 | 4°14'N | 47°45'W | 2374 | 12.4 | 26.5–27.0 | 26.5 | 12.0 | 150 |
| 61 | V12–122 | 17°00'N | 74°24'W | 2800 | 7.5 | 26.5–28.0 | 25.5 | 16.0 | 210 |

are in disagreement with both the isotopic and the nonisotopic evidence discussed above, suggesting that there may be a problem with CLIMAP.

The problem may derive from faulty calibration. All core top samples used for calibration were verified to be Holocene in age by the usage of micropaleontological criteria (IMBRIE and KIPP, 1971). At latitudes below 20° in the North Atlantic and the Caribbean, the Holocene (Ericson's Zone Z) is characterized by the presence of *Globorotalia menardii* which, in modern sediments, comprises more than 5% of the planktic foraminiferal fauna (PHLEGER *et al.*, 1953, p. 62, Fig. 14; BERGER *et al.*, 1985, Tables 4A and 4B). Table 7 shows the relative abundance of *G. menardii* in deep-sea cores from the Caribbean and the tropical-equatorial Atlantic that have been accurately analyzed both isotopically (EMILIANI, 1955; IMBRIE *et al.*, 1973; BERGER *et al.*, 1985) and micropaleontologically (PHLEGER *et al.*, 1953; IMBRIE and KIPP, 1971; BERGER *et al.*, 1985). The modern age of the core top is assured and, in all cases except one, *G. menardii* is more than 5% (Table 7). The single exception, core INMD-97 with 4.0% of *G. menardii* at the top, shows, however, 6% of *G. menardii* 4–5 cm below top (last hypsithermal).

When cores from the equatorial Atlantic-Caribbean region are analyzed micropaleontologically,

the percentage of *G. menardii* is seen to drop rapidly from more than 5% at or near the top of Zone Z to 0 at the bottom. Because of the steepness of the micropaleontological and isotopic gradients through Zone Z, the absence (by local submarine erosion) or loss (by coring) of even a few centimeters at the top coupled with bioturbation will produce an assemblage that still contains *G. menardii* and, therefore, belongs to Zone Z by definition, yet is not representative of hypsithermal or even modern conditions (modern surface temperatures in the Caribbean-equatorial Atlantic region are about 1°C cooler than during hypsithermal 1—see EMILIANI, 1955, Figs. 7–9). Indeed, 5 out of the 11 Atlantic core tops located between the equator and the tropic and used by IMBRIE and KIPP (1971) for their CLIMAP calibration contain less than 5% of *G. menardii* (Table 5). This indicates that the corresponding faunas were not related to the present surface temperatures, but to the lower temperature obtaining during earlier Holocene or even late Pleistocene times. In higher latitudes and in regions of upwelling, where the sedimentation rates are higher, this problem is less acute and the CLIMAP temperatures are probably closer to reality.

## CONCLUSION

We conclude that temperature during the last bathythermal was 8°C colder than during the last

Table 6. Bathythermal/hypsithermal temperature range (°C) of the surface water of the ocean

| Method | Caribbean | Eq. Atlantic | N. Indian | Eq. Pacific |
|---|---|---|---|---|
| Isotopes | 7.8 | 7.8 | 5.5 | 3.6 |
| Temp. tolerances | >8 | >7 | — | >3 |

Table 7. Percentage of *Globorotalia menardii* at the top of Caribbean core V12-122, tropical-equatorial Atlantic box cores (INMD-97 through INMD-115), and equatorial Atlantic piston core 246. Data from the following references: (1) IMBRIE and KIPP (1971); (2) BERGER *et al.* (1985); (3) PHLEGER *et al.* (1953)

| Core No. | Lat. | Long. | Depth (m) | Thickness of Zone Z (cm) | % of *G. menardii* at top of core | Ref. |
|---|---|---|---|---|---|---|
| V12-122 | 17°00'N | 74°24'W | 2800 | 40 | 7.5 | (1) |
| INMD-97 | 16°39'N | 46°08'W | 3619 | 21 | 4.0 | (2) |
| INMD-101 | 6°57'N | 26°27'W | 4093 | 21 | 10.0 | (2) |
| INMD-104 | 4°15'N | 21°55'W | 3279 | 25 | 11.7 | (2) |
| 246 | 0°48'N | 31°28'W | 3210 | 30 | 8.0 | (3) |
| INMD-109 | 5°27'S | 15°58'W | 3895 | >31 | 17.3 | (2) |
| INMD-110 | 10°02'S | 13°23'W | 1959 | 23 | 10.0 | (2) |
| INMD-111 | 12°39'S | 13°51'W | 3069 | 14 | 13.0 | (2) |
| INMD-113 | 15°15'S | 14°58'W | 3471 | 16 | 5.0 | (2) |
| INMD-115 | 17°38'S | 16°13'W | 3427 | 14 | 6.7 | (2) |

hypsithermal in the Caribbean-equatorial Atlantic, 5.5°C colder in the northern Indian Ocean, and 3.6°C colder in the equatorial Pacific. The intertropical, area-weighted average is 5.0°C. This value is identical to that obtained by RIND and PETEET (1985), who reviewed the non-isotopic evidence from low latitudes and simulated climate during bathythermal 2 using model II of HANSEN *et al.* (1983). In order to reproduce the observed snowline depressions at low latitudes and the widespread tropical aridity evidenced by pollen analysis, they had to lower the mean surface temperature of the ocean by 5–6°C. MIX and PISIAS (1988) stress that cooling of the deep ocean during the glacial ages implies a stronger thermohaline circulation. Indeed, increased vertical circulation with a doubling of the coccolith and foraminiferal productivity, was demonstrated by BROECKER *et al.* (1958) for the Atlantic and by ARRHENIUS (1952) for the Pacific.

We believe that the CLIMAP data base should be recalibrated using box cores instead of gravity or piston core tops and that the truly modern age of the tops be assessed by either oxygen isotope analysis at one cm intervals (as in EMILIANI, 1955, Figs. 8–10) or by accelerator $^{14}$C dating, or both. The fact that different taxonomic groups (foraminifera, radiolaria, coccolithophoridae) give concordant, even though inaccurate, surface temperatures when subjected to the Imbrie-Kipp method of analysis (MOLFINO *et al.,* 1982) strengthens the need for recalibration. CLIMAP's data base could then be reanalyzed using the method advocated by MALMGREN and KENNETT (1976, 1978) which, according to them, is more sensitive to variations in the significant, stenothermal and stenohaline species. LIDZ (1966) showed that the micropaleontological signal can be amplified if ratios of warm to cold steno species are used. Perhaps this technique too could be incorporated in the new analysis.

*Acknowledgements*—Preparation of this paper was supported by NSF Grant No. OCE-8900288, Marine Geology and Geophysics Program. Contribution No. 61 from The Harold C. Urey Laboratory for Isotopic Paleotemperature Research, Department of Geological Sciences, University of Miami.

## REFERENCES

ANDERSON T. F. and STEINMETZ J. C. (1981) Isotopic and biostratigraphical records of calcareous nannofossils in a Pleistocene core. *Nature* **294**, 740–744.

ARRHENIUS G. (1952) Sediment cores from the East Pacific. *Swedish Deep-Sea Exped. 1947–1948, Repts., Vol. 5, Fasc. 1* (with Appendix).

BERGER W. H., KILLINGLEY J. S., MELTZER C. V. and VINCENT E. (1985) Two-step deglaciation: $^{14}$C-dated high-resolution $\delta^{18}$O records from the tropical Atlantic Ocean. *Quatern. Res.* **23**, 258–271.

BROECKER W. S. (1986) Oxygen isotope constraints on surface ocean temperatures. *Quat. Res.* **26**, 121–134.

BROECKER W. S., TUREKIAN K. K. and HEEZEN B. C. (1958) The relation of deep-sea sedimentation rates to variations in climate. *Amer. J. Sci.* **256**, 503–517.

CLIMAP PROJECT MEMBERS (1976) The surface of the ice-age earth. *Science* **191**, 1131–1137.

CLIMAP PROJECT MEMBERS (1981) Seasonal reconstructions of the earth's surface at the last glacial maximum. *Geol. Soc. Amer. Map and Chart Ser., MC-36.*

CRAIG H. and GORDON L. I. (1965) Deuterium and oxygen-18 variations in the ocean and the marine atmosphere. In *Stable Isotopes in Oceanographic Studies and Paleotemperatures* (ed. E. TONGIORGI), pp. 9–130. Consiglio Nazionale delle Ricerche, Laboratorio di Geologia Nucleare, University of Pisa, Italy.

DEUSER W. G., ROSS E. H., HEMLEBEN C. and SPINDLER M. (1981) Seasonal changes in species composition, numbers, mass, size, and isotopic composition of planktonic Foraminifera settling into the deep Sargasso Sea. *Paleogeogr. Palaeoclim. Palaeoecol.* **33**, 103–127.

DUDLEY W. C., BLACKWELDER P., BRAND L. and DU-

PLESSY J.-C. (1986) Stable isotopic composition of coccoliths. *Mar. Micropaleontol.* **10**, 1–8.

DUPLESSY J.-C. (1978) Isotope studies. In *Climatic Change* (ed. J. GRIBBIN), pp. 46–67. Cambridge University Press.

DUPLESSY J.-C., CHENOUARD L. and VILA F. (1975) Weyl's theory of glaciation supported by isotopic study of Norwegian core K 11. *Science* **288**, 1208–1209.

DUPLESSY J.-C., MOYES J. and PUJOL C. (1980) Deep water formation in the North Atlantic during the last ice age. *Nature* **286**, 479–482.

DURAZZI J. T. (1981) Stable-isotope studies of planktonic foraminifera in North Atlantic core tops. *Palaeogeogr. Palaeoclim. Palaeoecol.* **33**, 157–172.

EMILIANI C. (1955) Pleistocene temperatures. *J. Geology* **63**, 538–578.

EMILIANI C. (1971) Depth habitats and growth stages of pelagic foraminifera. *Science* **173**, 1122–1124.

ERICSON D. B. and WOLLIN G. (1956) Correlations of six cores from the equatorial Atlantic and the Caribbean. *Deep-Sea Res.* **3**, 104–125.

HANSEN J., RUSSELL G., RIND D., STONE P., LACIS A., LEBEDEFF S., RUEDY R. and TRAVIS L. (1983) Efficient three-dimensional global models for climate studies, models I and II. *Monthly Weather Rev.* **111**, 609–662.

IMBRIE J. and KIPP N. G. (1971). A new micropaleontological method for quantitative paleoclimatology: application to a Late Pleistocene core. In *The Late Cenozoic Glacial Ages* (ed. K. K. TUREKIAN), pp. 71–181. Yale University Press.

IMBRIE J., VAN DONK J. and KIPP N. G. (1973) Paleoclimatic investigation of a late Pleistocene Caribbean core: comparison of isotopic and faunal methods. *Quat. Res.* **3**, 10–38.

JONES J. I. (1967) Significance of distribution of planktonic foraminifera in the equatorial Atlantic undercurrent. *Micropaleontol.* **13**, 489–501.

KIPP N. G. (1976) New transfer function for estimating past sea-surface conditions from sea-bed distribution of planktonic foraminiferal assemblages in the North Atlantic. *Geol. Soc. Amer. Mem.* **145**, p. 3–41.

LABEYRIE L. D., DUPLESSY J. C. and BLANC P. L. (1987) Variations in the mode of formation and temperature of oceanic deep waters over the past 125,000 years. *Nature* **327**, 477–482.

LIDZ L. (1966) Deep-sea Pleistocene biostratigraphy. *Science* **154**, 1448–1452.

MALMGREN B. A. and KENNETT K. P. (1976) Principal component analysis of Quaternary planktic Foraminifera in the Gulf of Mexico: paleoclimatic applications. *Mar. Micropaleontol.* **1**, 299–306.

MALMGREN B. A. and KENNETT J. P. (1978) Test size variation in *Globigerina bulloides* in response to Quaternary palaeoceanographic changes. *Nature* **275**, 123–124.

MIX A. C. (1987) The oxygen-isotope record of glaciation. In *The Geology of North America; Vol. K-3, North America and Adjacent Oceans during the Last Deglaciation,* (eds. W. F. RUDDIMAN and H. E. WRIGHT JR.),

pp. 111–135. Geological Society of America, Boulder, Colorado.

MIX A. C. and PISIAS N. G. (1988) Oxygen isotope analyses and deep-sea temperature changes: implications for rates of oceanic mixing. *Nature* **331**, 249–251.

MOLFINO B., KIPP N. G. and MORLEY J. J. (1982) Comparison of foraminiferal, coccolithophorid, and radiolarian paleotemperature equations: assemblage coherency and estimate concordancy. *Quat. Res.* **17**, 279–313.

OKADA H. and MCINTYRE A. (1979) Seasonal distribution of modern coccolithophores in the western North Atlantic Ocean. *Mar. Biol.* **54**, 319–329.

PHLEGER F. B., PARKER F. L. and PEIRSON J. F. (1953) North Atlantic foraminifera. *Swedish Deep-Sea Exped. 1947–1948, Repts., Vol. 7, Fasc. 1.*

PRELL W. L. (1985) The stability of low-latitude sea-surface temperatures: an evaluation of the CLIMAP reconstruction with emphasis on the positive SST anomalies. *U.S. Dept. Energy, Tech. Rept. 25.*

RIND D. and PETEET D. (1985) Terrestrial conditions of the last glacial maximum and CLIMAP sea-surface temperature estimates: are they consistent? *Quat. Res.* **24**, 1–22.

RUDDIMAN W. F. and MCINTYRE A. (1971) Oceanic mechanisms for the amplification of the 23,000-year ice volume cycle. *Science* **212**, 617–627.

SHACKLETON N. J. (1967) Oxygen isotope analyses and Pleistocene temperatures reassessed. *Nature* **215**, 15–17.

SHACKLETON N. J. (1974) Attainment of isotopic equilibrium between ocean water and the benthonic foraminiferal genus *Uvigerina:* isotopic changes in the ocean during the last glacial. *Coll. Intern. CNRS* **219**, 203–209.

SHACKLETON N. J. and OPDYKE N. D. (1973) Oxygen isotope and paleomagnetic stratigraphy of equatorial Pacific core V28-238: oxygen isotopes temperatures and ice volumes on a $10^5$ and $10^6$ year scale. *Quat. Res.* **3**, 39–55.

STREETER S. S. and SHACKLETON N. J. (1979) Paleocirculation of the deep North Atlantic: a 150,000 year record of benthic foraminifera and $\delta^{18}$O. *Science* **203**, 168–171.

TOLDERLUND D. S. and BÉ A. W. H. (1971) Seasonal distribution of planktonic foraminifera in the western North Atlantic. *Micropaleontol.* **17**, 297–329.

VINCENT E. and BERGER W. H. (1981) Planktonic Foraminifera and their use in paleoceanography. In *The Oceanic Lithosphere* (ed. C. Emiliani), pp. 1025–1119. John Wiley & Sons, New York.

WILLIAMS D. F., BÉ A. W. H. and FAIRBANKS R. G. (1981) Seasonal stable isotopic variations in living planktonic foraminifera from Bermuda plankton tows. *Palaegeogr. Palaeoclim. Palaeoecol.* **33**, 71–102.

YAPP C. J. (1979) Oxygen and carbon isotope measurements of land snail shell carbonate. *Geochim. Cosmochim. Acta* **43**, 629–635.

Stable Isotope Geochemistry: A Tribute to Samuel Epstein
© The Geochemical Society, Special Publication No. 3, 1991
Editors: H. P. Taylor, Jr., J. R. O'Neil and I. R. Kaplan

# Is the Postglacial artificial?

CESARE EMILIANI, DAVID A. PRICE*, and JOANNE SEIPP†

Department of Geological Sciences, University of Miami, Coral Gables, FL 33124, U.S.A.

**Abstract**—Interglacial temperature maxima for which radiometric dating has provided absolute ages appear to have occurred at times of high orbital eccentricity, high axial obliquity, and when northern summer occurred at perihelion. The present high-temperature interval (the Postglacial) is anomalous for, today, eccentricity is low, obliquity is intermediate, and northern summer occurs at aphelion. It is suggested that the Postglacial may have been caused not by natural events but by widespread forest burning by prehistoric humans. A new technique is described that can test this hypothesis. It involves simultaneously determining the concentration of inorganic particulate carbon in deep-sea sediments and its isotopic composition.

## INTRODUCTION

THE PEAKS OF THE oxygen isotopic curve obtained from deep-sea cores, corresponding to major interglacials, occurred at times when both the eccentricity and obliquity of the Earth's orbit were high and when northern summer occurred at perihelion (EMILIANI, 1978, Fig. 2). On the other hand, the minima, corresponding to major glaciations, occurred at times when both eccentricity and obliquity were low (the Earth's orbital position during northern summer was evidently unimportant at times of low eccentricity). Isotopic stages 1, 3, and 4 are different. The glaciation of stage 4, as shown by the isotopic curve, was considerably less significant than that of stage 2 and of the earlier even stages. This apparently resulted from obliquity being low but not eccentricity (BERGER, 1978). Stage 3, with conditions intermediate between glacial and interglacial, coincided with a time of low eccentricity, high obliquity, and the occurrence of northern summer at aphelion. As for stage 1, which exhibits an isotopic maximum as high as those of stages 5, 7, and 9, there is no coincidence of high eccentricity, high obliquity, and the occurrence of northern summer at perihelion.

Today, the northern ice is gone (Greenland excepted) and temperature is high, but eccentricity is low, obliquity is intermediate, and northern summer is occurring at aphelion. The Postglacial should not have happened: semi-glacial or glacial conditions should have continued until the next coincidence of the three astronomical parameters, not due to occur for another 60,000 (or perhaps 160,000) years (BERGER, 1978, Fig. 4e). The present should

have been the longest ice age of all, with a total duration of 100,000 years or more.

## THE POSTGLACIAL

Instead of a continuing ice age, deglaciation began about 16,000 years ago. Oxygen isotopic analysis of Gulf of Mexico cores indicates that the waning of the North American ice sheet accelerated between 16,000 and 12,000 y BP, with giant floods down the Mississippi Valley (KENNETT and SHACKLETON, 1975; EMILIANI et al., 1975, 1978; LEVENTER et al., 1982; SHAW, 1989). Tundra was rapidly replaced by coniferous and broadleaf forests in both Europe and North America during the Allerød-Two Creeks interval (12,000 to 11,000 y BP). The discharge of the Mississippi decreased by 30% between 11,000 and 10,000 y BP, when retreating ice opened the St. Lawrence waterway (EMILIANI, 1957; BROECKER et al., 1989). After a minor readvance (Cochrane, 8500 y BP), possibly an ice surge, deglaciation went to completion.

The Allerød-Two Creeks interval was a time of affluence for prehistoric humans, who had spread through both the Old and the New World, finding abundant wildlife everywhere. Prehistoric humans appear to have used fire extensively to flush animals out of the forests. A 200 km-long burnt layer, dating from 12,550 y BP, has been found along the Nile valley (WENDORF and SAID, 1970); and carbon-rich sediment layers dating from 11,000 to 10,000 y BP are found along a belt reaching from western North America through Europe to eastern Siberia (see BRACKENRIDGE, 1981, for a summary). The use of fire continued as agriculture developed, to clear land and for slash-and-burn cultivation.

Forest fires produce both carbon particles (graphitic carbon) and soot (particles consisting of carbon plus organics, resulting from incomplete combustion). Soot and graphitic carbon particles range

* *Present address:* VG Instruments, 32 Commerce Center, Cherryhill Drive, Danver, MA 01923, U.S.A.

† *Present address:* PIECO MIAMI Inc., 8105 W 20th Ave., Miami, FL 33014, U.S.A.

in radius from 0.01 to 1 $\mu$m. Graphitic carbon and mineral particles (dust) in this size range scatter, rather than absorb, solar radiation. Soot, with the virtual portion of the index of refraction as high as 0.7 (BACH, 1976), is, on the other hand, a powerful absorber of both solar radiation and radiation backscattered from the ground (ANDREAE, 1983). It has the effect of warming up the lower troposphere (ENSOR et al., 1971; KELLOGG, 1980) as it is mainly confined to this atmospheric layer (CRESS, 1982). Is it possible that, by burning forests each summer, the expanding human population caused the disappearance of the ice from the northern continents and created in fact an artificial interglacial?

We suggest that the burning of a few percent of the mid-latitude forest each year may have been sufficient to terminate the last ice age. Some 1.04 $\times$ 10$^5$ km$^2$ of timberland, representing 1.1% of the country's surface, were burned in the United States by wildfires in 1968, destroying 10.9 $\times$ 10$^6$ tons of plant matter (BACH, 1976). For a particle production efficiency of 0.032 (TURCO et al., 1983), 3.5 $\times$ 10$^{11}$ g or 3.5 $\times$ 10$^{11}$ cm$^3$ (density $\sim$1 g/cm$^3$) of particles were produced. For a residence time in the atmosphere of one week (JAENICKE, 1981) and a mean particle radius of 0.05 $\mu$m (TURCO et al., 1983), the surface covered by the standing crop of particles in 1968 was 3.5 $\times$ 10$^{15}$ cm$^2$ (cf. ROSEN and NOVAKOV, 1983) or 3.7% of the surface of the United States. Albedo was proportionally reduced, depending upon the background terrain.

In late glacial times, the summer system of prevailing winds would tend to transport smoke particles over the residual ice sheets to the north in both North America and Eurasia, thus reducing the ice sheet albedo by several percent. In addition, forest fires are likely to have occurred mainly during the summer, providing a greater concentration of particles during the ablation season, with particles surviving for a while on the ice surface and continuing to affect albedo even after removal from the atmosphere. An important, related factor contributing to the temperature increase is the rapid addition of $CO_2$ to the atmosphere from the reduction in biomass (REINERS and WRIGHT, 1977) and as a release from the warming ocean surface. The forest fires also would have had the effect of destroying a major habitat of the northern megafauna.

Once the northern ice was gone, the Earth would have been in an interglacial mode in spite of the adverse astronomical configuration. The subsequent climatic evolution appears to have been largely conditioned by such human activities as deforestation and the injection of pollutants into the atmosphere. The climatic effects of these activities

have been the object of numerous investigations. Contrary to the simple forest burning of prehistoric humans, these activities are multiform as well as inadvertent and, therefore, should tend to cancel out. Should one effect become climatically dominant, however, climate will be driven in the corresponding direction. In the short range (decades to centuries), continued $CO_2$ injection into the system and the time delay in ocean floor carbonate sediment reaction may lead to warmer temperatures and ice melting; in the longer range, when the tropical forest is removed and injection of pollutants in the atmosphere is reduced, glacial conditions could be reestablished. Here, we are not considering, of course, the "nuclear winter" of TURCO et al. (1983), which would result from a massive and instantaneous injection of smoke particles into the troposphere. (It should be noticed that, as the Earth is already in a glacial mode, a "nuclear winter" followed by rapid glaciation may require a much more modest nuclear event than the one envisioned by TURCO et al., 1983.)

## AN EXPERIMENT TO TEST THE HYPOTHESIS

The suggestion that the Postglacial may be artificial is subject to experimental verification. SMITH et al. (1973) found significant amounts (0.02 to 0.1 dry weight percent) of elemental carbon particles in the top 5–15 cm in deep-sea cores from the North Pacific and the North Atlantic, as well as much smaller amounts (<0.01 dry weight percent) at lower latitudes. We applied for, and received, a grant from the National Science Foundation to study the downcore distribution of carbon particles and compare it with the trend of the oxygen isotopic curve. We hoped that this study would yield a record of forest burning stretching back several hundred thousand years, against which the known climatic oscillations could then be gauged. At the same time, this study would test the suggestion that the postglacial may be artificial. For a start, of course, we had to develop a technique to isolate the smoke particles from all other sediment components, including kerogen. For a while this seemed to be an impossible task, but eventually we succeeded. The technique we have developed is straightforward and allows us to simultaneously determine the concentration and the isotopic composition of carbon particles in deep-sea sediments. This technique is detailed in Table 1.

The work we proposed to do on deep-sea cores could not be done, however, because a series of actions by the provost's office engulfed our depart-

Table 1. Preparation of Globigerina-ooze samples for elemental carbon analysis

1. Dry samples at 80°C
2. Weigh
3. Determine bulk density
4. Disintegrate in triple distilled water
5. Add 10 cc of 1 N HCl
6. Heat to 80°C in water bath for 30 minutes
7. Rinse five times (centrifuge) in distilled water
8. Dry at 80°C in oven
9. Weigh and determine the percent of carbonate and salt
10. Add 5 cc of 1 N HF and 1 cc of 1 N HCl
11. Heat to 80°C in water bath for 30 minutes
12. Dry at 80°C in oven
13. Weigh and calculate the percent of silicates
14. Make concoction of 30% $H_2O_2$ and KOH to make pH 12
15. Add 10 cc of concoction to well ground, dry sample
16. Let stand for 24 hrs at room temperature
17. Rinse five times (centrifuge) in distilled water
18. Dry in oven at 80°C
19. Transfer residue to glass tube
20. Add 0.5 g of cuprous oxide
21. Flame to convert to $CO_2$
22. Analyze the $CO_2$ gas in mass spectrometer

Calibrated mass 44 peak height gives amount of $CO_2$ in sample, while the 45/44 ratio gives the carbon isotopic composition.

ment, destroying its infrastructure. Because it was not possible for us to complete the proposed research, we have decided to publish at least the technique that we have developed (Table 1) so that others may benefit (cf. WOLBACH and ANDERS, 1989, footnote).

*Acknowledgements*—This research was supported by NSF Grant No. ATM-8506649, Climate Dynamics Program. Contribution No. 59 from the Harold C. Urey Laboratory for Isotopic Paleotemperature Research, Department of Geological Sciences, University of Miami.

## REFERENCES

ANDREAE M. O. (1983) Soot carbon and excess fine potassium: long-range transport of combustion-derived aerosols. *Science* **220**, 1148–1151.

BACH W. (1976) Global air pollution and climate change. *Rev. Geophys. Space Phys.* **14**, 429–474.

BACH W., PANKRATH J. and WILLIAMS J., eds. (1980) *Interactions of Energy and Climate*. D. Reidel.

BERGER A. (1978) Long-term variations of caloric insolation resulting from the Earth's orbital elements. *Quat. Res.* **9**, 139–167.

BRAKENRIDGE G. R. (1981) Terrestrial paleoenvironmental effects of a Late-Quaternary-age supernova. *Icarus* **46**, 81–93.

BROECKER W. S., KENNETT J. P., FLOWER B. P., TELLER J. T., TRUMBORE S., BONANI G. and WOLFLI W. (1989) Routing of meltwater from the Laurentide ice sheet during the younger Dryas episode. *Nature* **341**, 318–321.

CRESS T. S. (1982) Altitudinal variations of aerosol size distributions over northern Europe. In *Atmospheric Aerosols—Their Formation, Optical Properties, and Effects* (ed. A. DEEPAK), pp. 51–61. Spectrum Press, Hampton, VA.

EMILIANI C. (1957) Temperature and age analysis of deep-sea cores. *Science* **125**, 383–387.

EMILIANI C. (1978) The cause of the ice ages. *Earth Planet. Sci. Lett.* **37**, 347–354.

EMILIANI C., GARTNER S., LIDZ B., ELDRIDGE K., ELVEY D. K., HUANG T. C., STIPP J. J. and SWANSON M. F. (1975) Paleoclimatological analysis of Late Quaternary cores from the northeastern Gulf of Mexico. *Science* **189**, 1083–1088.

EMILIANI C., ROOTH C. and STIPP J. J. (1978) The Late Wisconsin flood into the Gulf of Mexico. *Earth Planet. Sci. Lett.* **41**, 159–162.

ENSOR D. S., PORCH W. M., PILAT M. J. and CHARLSON R. J. (1971) Influence of atmospheric aerosol on albedo. *J. Appl. Meteorol.* **10**, 1303–1306.

JAENICKE R. (1981) Atmospheric aerosols and global climate. In *Climatic Variations and Variability: Facts and Theories* (ed. A. BERGER), pp. 577–597. D. Reidel.

KELLOGG W. W. (1980) Aerosols and climate. In *Interactions of Energy and Climate* (eds. W. BACH, J. PANKRATH and J. WILLIAMS), pp. 281–296. D. Reidel.

KENNETT J. P. and SHACKLETON N. J. (1975) Laurentide ice sheet meltwater recorded in Gulf of Mexico deep-sea cores. *Science* **188**, 147–150.

LEVENTER A., WILLIAMS D. F. and KENNETT J. P. (1982) Dynamics of the Laurentide ice sheet during the last deglaciation: evidence from the Gulf of Mexico. *Earth Planet. Sci. Lett.* **59**, 11–17.

REINERS W. A. and WRIGHT H. E., JR. (1977) Impact of prehistoric and present fire patterns on the carbon dioxide content of the atmosphere. In *Global Chemical Cycles and their Alteration by Man* (ed. W. STUMM), pp. 121–135. Abakon Verlagsgesellsch., Berlin.

ROSEN H. and NOVAKOV T. (1983) Combustion-generated carbon particles in the Arctic atmosphere. *Nature* **306**, 768–770.

SHAW J. (1989) Drumlins, subglacial meltwater floods, and ocean responses. *Geology* **17**, 853–856.

SMITH D. M., GRIFFIN J. J. and GOLDBERG E. D. (1973) Elemental carbon in marine sediments: a baseline for burning. *Nature* **241**, 268–270.

TURCO R. P., TOON O. B., ACKERMAN T. P., POLLACK J. B. and SAGAN C. (1983) Nuclear winter: global consequences of multiple nuclear explosions. *Science* **222**, 1283–1292.

WENDORF F. and SAID R. (1970) Egyptian prehistory: some new concepts. *Science* **169**, 1161–1171.

WOLBACH W. S. and ANDERS E. (1989) Elemental carbon in sediments: Determination and isotopic analysis in the presence of kerogen. *Geochim. Cosmochim. Acta* **53**, 1637–1647.

# Part D.
# Paleoenvironment and Archaeology

One of Sam's major scientific contributions was utilizing D/H and $^{13}C/^{12}C$ ratios from the nitrated cellulose of tree rings to monitor climatic records on Earth.

Stable Isotope Geochemistry: A Tribute to Samuel Epstein
© The Geochemical Society, Special Publication No. 3, 1991
Editors: H. P. Taylor, Jr., J. R. O'Neil and I. R. Kaplan

# Osteocalcin as the recommended biopolymer for $^{14}$C age dating of bone and $\delta^{13}$C and $\delta^{15}$N paleodietary reconstruction

HENRY O. AJIE and ISAAC R. KAPLAN

Department of Earth and Space Sciences, Institute of Geophysics and Planetary Physics,
University of California, Los Angeles, CA 90024-1567, U.S.A.

**Abstract**—Osteocalcin, a gamma-carboxyglutamic acid containing bone protein is tightly bound to the hydroxyapatite matrix of bone and is relatively more stable than the dominant collagen. Its distribution in nature is limited to vertebrates. Osteocalcin and collagen have been isolated from modern and fossil bone samples of different organisms in different depositional environments for analysis of their $\delta^{13}$C, $\delta^{15}$N, and $^{14}$C content. We present evidence suggesting that osteocalcin is a more suitable protein fraction for obtaining accurate $^{14}$C age estimates and/or $\delta^{13}$C and $\delta^{15}$N for paleodietary reconstruction from bone samples.

## INTRODUCTION

THE EARLIEST DESCRIPTIONS of diet in prehistoric humans were based upon inferences from artifact assemblages or anecdotal accounts of midden constituents. Column sampling performed with proper statistical controls is adequate for measuring quantities of small, well-preserved, and evenly distributed food remains such as seed, shell, or fish bone (TREGANZA and COOKE, 1948; MEIGHAN, 1972). It is less accurate, however, at predicting quantities of larger, unevenly distributed components such as animal bone. Similar problems are encountered with faunal analyses where spotty distribution patterns are complicated by non-representation of bones due to diagenesis, butchering patterns, or scavenger activity. Plant remains pose unique problems. They infrequently are preserved in archaeological sites and when present, mostly represent uneaten foodstuffs.

In contrast to standard midden analyses, trace element and stable isotope analysis of human bone collagen provide a direct means for estimating the contribution of broad categories of food items to the diet. This is possible because the slight, but detectable differences in the isotopic composition of different food types are ultimately reflected in bone collagen (DENIRO and EPSTEIN, 1978, 1981; SCHOENINGER and DENIRO, 1984; CHISHOLM et al., 1982; MINAGAWA et al., 1986). The following sections discuss the basis for using stable carbon and nitrogen isotope ratios for dietary reconstruction.

### Carbon isotope ratios

Carbon isotope ratios discriminate C$_3$ plants from C$_4$ and CAM (Crassulacean acid metabolism) plants and also differentiate marine from terrestrial organisms. Different classes of plants have different carbon isotope ratios, depending on the type of biochemical reaction they utilize to obtain their carbon. C$_3$ plants use a different enzymatic pathway to fix atmospheric carbon during photosynthesis than do C$_4$ plants. The enzyme responsible for the C$_3$ pathway discriminates $^{13}$CO$_2$ to a greater extent than that for C$_4$ plants (BENDER, 1968, 1971), resulting in lower $\delta^{13}$C values ranging from $-22$ to $-33$ (mean $-25$), whereas those of C$_4$ plants fix carbon with a $\delta^{13}$C of $-9$ to $-16$ (mean $-12$). CAM plants, which have the ability to use both C$_3$-like and C$_4$-like photosynthetic pathways, tend under natural conditions to resemble C$_4$ plants in their isotopic composition (BENDER et al., 1973; OSMOND et al., 1973). These differences have been exploited by many researchers to document the introduction of plants from one isotopic group into an environment where the natural vegetation consists of plants of another isotopic type. This has been particularly useful in documenting the progression of maize (a C$_4$ plant) agriculture in the New World (VAN DER MERWE and VOGEL, 1977; BENDER, 1968; DENIRO and EPSTEIN, 1981; VAN DER MERWE, 1982; SCHWARCZ et al., 1985).

Carbon isotopes can also discriminate between marine and terrestrial organisms (TAUBER, 1981; CHISHOLM et al., 1982, 1983). This is possible due to the different isotopic composition of the carbon source in each environment. Marine organisms use seawater bicarbonate, which is approximately 7 per mil more positive than atmospheric carbon dioxide. Thus, the mean $\delta^{13}$C value of organic carbon in marine organisms is $-18$ compared to the mean $\delta^{13}$C value of $-25$ for terrestrial C$_3$ plants. Unfortunately, marine $\delta^{13}$C values may be mimicked in a terrestrial animal that feeds on a mixture of C$_3$ and C$_4$ land plants. Due to this complication, it is sometimes impossible to assess the marine contribution to the diet in any human population that utilizes both marine foods and large quantities of maize or other $C_4$ plants, by use of the $^{13}C/^{12}C$ isotope method alone.

### Nitrogen isotope ratios

Studies on animals raised on diets of known nitrogen composition demonstrate that the $\delta^{15}N$ of animal tissues is determined by the $\delta^{15}N$ of their diets (DENIRO and EPSTEIN, 1981). $\delta^{15}N$ values of bone collagen was shown to be about 3 per mil more positive than that of the diet. The nitrogen isotopic composition of diet ultimately depends on the composition of nitrogen compounds available for uptake by plants at the base of the food chain. Subsequently, it was shown that nitrogen isotope ratios distinguish between marine and terrestrial foods in the diet (SCHOENINGER et al., 1983; SCHOENINGER and DENIRO, 1984). Animals utilizing marine food sources are more enriched in $^{15}N$ than animals feeding on land plant sources, because the nitrogen sources utilized during protein synthesis in the two systems have a different nitrogen isotope composition. Marine plants have $\delta^{15}N$ values which are about 8 per mil heavier than those of terrestrial plants. These differences are then reflected in the food chain, with organisms feeding directly on either phytoplankton or land plants showing about a 3 per mil enrichment in $^{15}N$ over the starting $^{15}N/^{14}N$ ratio at each trophic level (DE-NIRO and EPSTEIN, 1981; MINAGAWA et al., 1986; SCHOENINGER and DENIRO, 1984; SCHOENINGER, 1985). This has the effect of magnifying the differences between marine and terrestrial foods, as humans tend to feed on marine organisms higher in the food chain (fish) than on land animals (herbivores).

As with carbon isotopes, overlap in $\delta^{15}N$ ratios of marine and land animals may be observed under certain conditions. Organisms inhabiting estuaries or coral reef environments are likely to have $\delta^{15}N$ values similar to those of terrestrial organisms, due to high nitrogen fixation rates (CAPONE and CARPENTER, 1982; SCHOENINGER and DENIRO, 1984). If food from these environments is incorporated into the diet, there will be an apparent under-representation of the marine components. Consumption of large quantities of $\delta^{15}N$-depleted legumes (VIRGINIA and DELWICHE, 1982) might also skew marine/terrestrial contrasts, although this has yet to be documented in human populations (SCHWARCZ et al., 1985).

The combined application of carbon and nitrogen isotope ratios may resolve discrepancies resulting from the use of only one isotope (SCHOENINGER et al., 1983). However, there are certain conditions when the application of both isotopic techniques will still be inconclusive. For example, combined $\delta^{13}C$ and $\delta^{15}N$ analyses sometimes do not permit a thorough dietary reconstruction of the native inhabitants of tropical island such as the Bahamas, where a diet consisting of $C_4$ agricultural products and marine resources are gathered from both coral reefs and the open ocean (KEEGAN and DENIRO, 1988). A similar situation is likely to be found in coastal Peru, where archaeological populations are known to have cultivated both maize and non-legumes while also exploiting marine resources. Under such conditions, resolution of dietary contributions becomes difficult.

### Radiocarbon dating

Radiocarbon measurement is usually achieved by measuring the indigenous carbon extracted and purified from a suitable fraction of the material. This measurement is then used to derive the age of the material. Radiocarbon measurement for bones has conventionally been achieved by scintillation measurement of the $\beta$-disintegration of $^{14}C$ atoms in the mineral phase (usually hydroxyapatite) or the organic fraction (usually collagen). Each of these phases has been observed to have its associated problems for radiocarbon measurements (HEDGES and LAW, 1989). The exchange of carbon atoms of the mineral phase with ground water poses a serious problem in the use of hydroxyapatite. Contamination through secondary deposition and recrystallization of indigenous carbonate further complicates the use of hydroxyapatite. An indigenous organic fraction, such as collagen, which constitutes >90% of bone organic matter is considered to be more suitable for radiocarbon measurements of bone.

The development of the Accelerator Mass Spectroscopy (AMS) now makes it feasible to utilize milligram amounts of organic materials for $^{14}C$ dating and to refine existing, or develop new, pretreatment strategies for the $^{14}C$ dating of bone, including the direct dating of Holocene and Pleistocene hominid skeletal samples. This has been especially useful in dating bone fragments where only small quantities are available. In cases where the majority of the intact collagen remains, it is widely agreed that accurate $^{14}C$ age estimates can be obtained on this purified organic extract. However, accepted methods used to chemically pretreat bone samples can, in some cases, yield unreliable $^{14}C$ age determinations when applied to fossil bones characterized by low to trace amounts of organic residues which do not exhibit a collagen-like amino acid pattern. The lack of effective pretreatment procedures for biochemically degraded bone limits the application of ${}^{14}C$ dating on bone samples from most tropical environments older than a few thousand years. These environments include regions from which valuable late Pleistocene hominid fossil bones derive. The use of collagen or any other fraction as a dating tool, therefore, should be approached with caution for the following reasons:

1) The sensitivity to contamination by modern carbon increases exponentially (1% contamination has 6,000 year effect for a bone 37,000 years old; HEDGES and LAW, 1989).

2) Carbon containing compounds from allochthonous environments may become physically and chemically mixed during diagenesis with carbon compounds indigenous to bone. Because the burial and fossilization environments represent a variety of different conditions, no patterns of interaction which occur are able to predict the origin of such exogenous contaminants.

Another bone protein, osteocalcin, which comprises 10–20% of the total non-collagenous protein of bone is tightly bound to the mineral phase and is present in bone of all vertebrate animals (HAUSCHKA, 1977; HAUSCHKA and GALLOP, 1977; HAUSCHKA et al., 1982, 1983; GUNDBERG et al., 1984). The properties of osteocalcin (see below) give it certain advantages over collagen in the study of fossil organic materials.

Osteocalcin is distinguished from collagen by its content of two or three (depending on species) residues of the vitamin K-dependent amino acid, gamma-carboxyglutamic acid (Gla). This amino acid is formed in the protein as a result of post-translational carboxylation of specific glutamic acid residues at specific sequence positions (GUNDBERG et al., 1984). The number of Gla residues in human osteocalcin is reported to be two (POSER et al., 1980). Some characteristic properties of osteocalcin relevant to the analysis of $\delta^{13}C$, $\delta^{15}N$ and ${}^{14}C$ in this study include:

1) It is a non-collagenous protein of low molecular weight (~6000 daltons) containing 46–50 amino acid residues per molecule. The amino acid sequence has been determined for more than a dozen vertebrate species (PRICE et al., 1976; HAUSCHKA et al., 1982) and has been reported to show strong conservation over hundreds of millions of years of divergent evolution (ULRICH et al., 1987).

2) It binds strongly to the hydroxyapatite (HAUSCHKA, 1977), the major mineral component of bone. In this bound form, the protein is very stable in part because of the buffering action of hydroxyapatite and partly due to the decreased accessibility to exogenous proteinases. Osteocalcin has been isolated from bovid bones 12,000 years and older (ULRICH et al., 1987).

3) The protein is most abundant in bone (up to 2 mg/g), with lower amounts in dentin and cementum; enamel is devoid of osteocalcin (HAUSCHKA et al., 1983, 1989). Osteocalcin has not been detected in any living groups other than vertebrates, and because of its content of Gla, it is strongly bound to the bone (ZYTKOVICZ and NELSESTUEN, 1976). Therefore, it is less likely that osteocalcin extracted from fossil bone will be contaminated by other protein or complex organic matter from the environment.

4) Osteocalcin can be isolated from bone free from high molecular weight proteins, humic and fulvic acids, polysaccharides, or other common soil contaminants (this study).

Dietary assessment ($\delta^{13}C$, $\delta^{15}N$) and ${}^{14}C$ measurements assume that no changes have occurred in the isotopic composition of the body carbon and nitrogen post-mortem, except by ${}^{14}C$ decay. However, post-mortem alterations that can change the isotopic configuration of the body carbon are often commonly observed in collagen, especially in buried bones (STAFFORD et al., 1987). Post-mortem alteration (diagenesis) is most frequently induced by adverse environmental conditions resulting in degradation, modification, leaching, replacement, or contamination of collagen by similar or dissimilar exogenous organic materials. Depending on the extent of the diagenesis, bones are usually classified as "well-preserved," "moderately preserved," or "poorly preserved." Well-preserved bone contains collagen having identical characteristics to those of modern fresh bone. In moderately preserved bone, the elemental C/N ratio of collagen may be different due to preferential loss of some amino acids. In poorly preserved bone, collagen is extensively degraded, and in extreme cases it is undetectable (by the absence of hydroxyproline in amino acid analysis).

Major diagenetic problems associated with collagen from poorly preserved bones are contamination and partial degradation leading to alteration of isotopic content. Introduction of contaminants in the form of exogenous free amino acids and proteins, humic and fulvic acids, and polysaccharides may occur through ground water or soil contact and microbial action. These may react with the indigenous polypeptides of collagen, for example, through condensation reaction between sugar residues and amino groups, to provide exogenous contamination. Protein hydrolysis in acidic or alkaline aqueous environments and proteolytic attack resulting from bacterial action causes fragmentation and may allow the more soluble components to be leached out. For bone materials where diagenetic effects have significantly reduced and/or altered the collagen content, serious questions can be raised concerning the effectiveness of a preparative protocol for the isolation and purification of a meaningful indigenous organic fraction (HEDGES and LAW, 1989). To overcome these difficulties, we have examined the isotopic and biogeochemical characteristics of osteocalcin in a series of bone samples exhibiting wide variability in their residual collagen content.

## PROCEDURES

### Bone preparation procedures

Bone samples are cleaned by ultrasonication in an ice-cold tris buffered protease inhibitor cocktail (TPIC) (GUNDBERG et al., 1984), containing the following: benzamidine, 5 mM; 6-aminocaproic acid, 10 mM; p-hydroxymercuribenzoic acid, 100 $\mu$M; phenylmethylsulfonyl fluoride, 30 $\mu$M; and tris HCl, 20 mM; pH 7.8. The bone samples are then rinsed several times with ice-cold distilled water and freeze-dried. The dry bone is powdered in liquid nitrogen with a diamond mortar to a size less than 710 $\mu$M. The powder is then homogenized in ice-cold TPIC (1 g/20 ml) for 30 minutes and allowed to settle. Decanting and re-homogenization with distilled water is continued until the supernatant is clear and colorless. In some cases, to remove contaminating pigments, the powder is allowed to settle in ice-cold 1 M HCl at 4°C for 20 minutes and then washed with distilled water to neutrality, and finally soaked in ice-cold 0.125 M NaOH at 4°C for 30 minutes; and again washed with distilled water to neutrality and lyophilized. These last procedures of alternate soaking in acid and base results in extractive loss and a reduced yield of osteocalcin.

### Preparation of osteocalcin and collagen

Two methods are employed for the extraction and purification of osteocalcin. The first method is a modification of the EDTA procedure of GUNDBERG et al. (1984); the second is a modification of the formic acid procedure of POSER et al. (1980). As both methods produce the same high quality product and the second is considerably simpler, because it avoids problems of complete EDTA removal by dialysis, we recommend using it and describe it briefly below.

Demineralization of bone (typically 10–50 g) is accomplished in 20% formic acid (10 ml/g bone), followed by dialysis (Spectrapor 1 membrane tubing, molecular weight cutoff 6000–8000, Spectrum Medical Industries, Los Angeles, CA) against deionized water for four days at 4°C with daily changes of water. The content of the dialysis

tubing is centrifuged and the supernatant reduced to a volume of 20 ml by freeze-drying. This is followed by gel filtration of the soluble extract on sephacryl S-200 in 6 M GuHCl. Elution of osteocalcin is monitored by absorbance at 276 nm. The pooled osteocalcin fraction is freeze-dried, dissolved in 0.07 M $NH_4HCO_3$ (1 mg/ml) and eluted from a DEAE ion exchange column with a 700 ml linear gradient of 0.7 M $NH_4HCO_3$ (GUNDBERG et al., 1984). Fractions of 5 ml are collected, and protein is monitored by ultraviolet light adsorption at $A_{276}$. The pooled osteocalcin fraction is reduced to a volume of 10 mL by freeze-drying; dialyzed against deionized water at 4°C for four days with daily changes of water, and subsequently lyophilized to yield the pure osteocalcin. Appropriate precautions to avoid intersample contamination include use of separate columns for modern and fossil samples, extensive column washing, and isotopic and amino acid analysis of blank column eluent buffers.

The extraction of collagen in gelatin form is accomplished by the methods of DENIRO and EPSTEIN (1981), and SCHOENINGER and DENIRO (1984). Briefly, bone powder after TPIC washing is solubilized in 1 mM HCl for 10 hours at 90°C, filtered through a sintered filter, and lyophilized.

### Isotope analysis

Aliquots of osteocalcin and collagen were combusted using the methods of MINAGAWA et al. (1984), and the resulting nitrogen and $CO_2$ analyzed by dual collecting isotope ratio mass spectrometry for their $\delta^{15}N$ and $\delta^{13}C$, respectively. $^{14}C$ analysis was performed using the accelerator mass spectrometer at DSIR-INS, Radiocarbon Laboratory, Gracefield, New Zealand, and conventional scintillation counting at Institute of Geophysics and Planetary Physics, University of California, Los Angeles. Atomic C/N ratios were calculated from the manometrically determined volumes of $CO_2$ and nitrogen gases produced by combustion of weighed protein samples at 875°C (MINAGAWA et al., 1984; DENIRO, 1985).

Stable isotope ratios are reported in the $\delta$ per mil notation:

$$\delta^{13}C \text{ or } \delta^{15}N = [(R_{sample}/R_{standard}) - 1]1000 \qquad (1)$$

where $R = {}^{13}C/{}^{12}C$ for $\delta^{13}C$ and ${}^{15}N/{}^{14}N$ for $\delta^{15}N$, respectively. Standard deviation for replicate analysis is ±0.10‰ for both $\delta^{13}C$ and $\delta^{15}N$, respectively. Standard deviation for osteocalcin analysis obtained by the two methods of extraction and purification (EDTA vs. formic acid) is less than ±0.10 per mil for $\delta^{13}C$ and $\delta^{15}N$, respectively. $^{14}C$ dates are reported in years before present (BP) with a general precision of 1–1.5%.

### Amino acid analysis

Samples for amino acid analysis were hydrolyzed under vacuum in a nitrogen atmosphere for 18 hours in 6N HCl at 110°C. Derivatization with phenylisothiocyanate was performed before HPLC separation and identification of amino acids. Amino acid contents are expressed in amino acid residues/1000.

Gamma-carboxyglutamic acid (Gla) in bone protein samples was determined by high resolution amino acid analysis after alkaline hydrolysis (2 M KOH, 22 hr, 108°C) as previously described (HAUSCHKA, 1977). A modified procedure involved hydrolysis of 30 mg bone powder samples in 0.3 ml 2 M KOH in 1.5 ml polypropylene

Table 1. GLA analysis

| Sample | Residue GLA 1000 Residues GLU |
|--------|-------------------------------|
| HA-100 | 3.71 |
| HA-101 | 2.99 |
| HA-102 | 3.54 |
| HA-103 | 5.26 |
| HA-104 | 4.85 |
| HA-105 | 4.91 |
| HA-106 | 5.32 |
| Bovine* | 5.31 |
| Human rib† | 3.60 |

* Bovine samples reported in COLOMB et al. (unpublished result).
† HAUSCHKA (1977).

microfuge tubes, followed by perchloric acid ($HClO_4$) neutralization and analysis of the diluted hydrolyzate supernatants. Data are expressed as residues Gla/1000 residues Glu (glutamic acid). The Gla peak position in fossil bone samples was confirmed by spiking with an internal standard of authentic Gla.

*Radioimmunoassay (RIA) of osteocalcin*

A range of 30 to 200 mg samples of powdered bone were weighed into 1.5 ml microfuge tubes and extracted with 0.8 ml EPIC buffer (0.5 M ammonium EDTA, pH 6.1, containing proteinase inhibitors) by end-over-end mixing at 4°C for 18 hr (GUNDBERG et al., 1984). A previously described non-equilibrium radioimmunoassay was utilized for osteocalcin quantitation (HAUSCHKA et al., 1989), or the distantly related matrix Gla protein which also occurs in bone. Importantly, this assay detects only *intact* osteocalcin with high sensitivity (0.05 ng/tube) and specificity, but does not recognize proteolytic fragments of the native protein (GUNDBERG et al., 1984; HAUSCHKA et al., 1983). It exhibits equivalent crossreactivity with pure standards of human, monkey (*M. fascicularis*), and bovine osteocalcin which have a highly homologous 49 amino acid residue sequence (HAUSCHKA et al., 1989). The primary antiserum was rabbit anti-bovine osteocalcin, used at a final dilution of 12,600-fold. Bone extracts were serially diluted in assay buffer and assayed over a wide range corresponding to 0.05–2000 μg bone/tube. The competing tracer was freshly prepared $^{125}$I-monkey osteocalcin at 20,000 cpm/tube. Immuno-precipitation with goat anti-rabbit IgG second antibody was followed by centrifugation, washing of pellets, and gamma-counting. Data are expressed as the quotient $B/B_0$ as previously described (HAUSCHKA, 1977; GUNDBERG et al., 1984). Monkey osteocalcin standard gave a midpoint $B/B_0 = 0.5$ at 0.24 ng/tube, with an interassay variation of 10%. All fossil human bone samples gave parallel dilution curves, indicating strong identity of the ancient antigen to the modern osteocalcin standard. Osteocalcin contents were calculated by equating the μg bone-equivalent extract/tube required to produce $B/B_0 = 0.5$ with the corresponding value for the osteocalcin standard.

## RESULTS AND DISCUSSION

Analysis for Gla shows that it is present in the fossil bones at levels similar to the range present in modern bone (Table 1). Eighty percent of total Gla in modern bone is associated with osteocalcin with the remainder occurring in matrix Gla protein and traces of vitamin K-dependent coagulation factors (HAUSCHKA et al., 1989). RIA data, however, indicate that only a fraction of the normal osteocalcin is present (Table 2). Thus, a major fraction of the total measurable Gla is associated with non-immunoreactive fragments (polypeptides) of osteocalcin and matrix Gla protein which have been retained in the fossil materials. The overall RIA data of Table 2 do, however, demonstrate the presence of intact osteocalcin in the fossil bone samples. The fraction of the total original osteocalcin which remains intact, and thus detectable by RIA depends on the diagenetic conditions pertinent to each particular bone as long as mild laboratory extraction procedures are used. Further evidence that the extract isolated and identified as osteocalcin is truly osteocalcin and not collagen, or other high molecular weight proteins, is drawn from amino acid composition and from gel electrophoresis analyses. The amino acid composition of human fossil osteocalcin is similar to that of modern osteocalcin (Table 3), and collagen, or collagen peptide, contamination is precluded by the absence of hydroxyproline for the osteocalcin extract from the human samples. Additionally, to provide modern controls, Table 4 presents elemental and stable isotopes of carbon and nitrogen compositional data on collagen and osteocalcin extracts from a series of modern bones. Gel electrophoresis measurements performed on the fossil bone samples studied indicate the presence of only a low molecular weight protein in the size range of 6,000–17,000 daltons. The molecular size range obtained in this study by gel electrophoresis is similar for both modern and fossil osteocalcin and is also consistent with published results (TUROSS et al., 1989; GUNDBERG et al., 1984).

Unlike modern collagen, fossil and poorly preserved collagen shows mild to extreme variations in amino acid composition and elemental C/N ra-

Table 2. Comparison of intact osteocalcin in fossil bones to modern human, determined by radioimmunoassay

| Sample | Intact osteocalcin (% of modern human)* |
|--------|------------------------------------------|
| HA-100 | 3.3 |
| HA-101 | 2.6 |
| HA-102 | 5.2 |
| HA-103 | 5.1 |
| HA-104 | 17.4 |

* Modern human osteocalcin: 0.28 mg/g bone (HAUSCHKA, 1977).

Table 3. Amino acid residues/1000 of collagen and osteocalcin from bones that vary in age and state of preservation

| | Collagen | | | | | | | | | | | | | | |
|---|---|---|---|---|---|---|---|---|---|---|---|---|---|---|---|
| Sample no. | CGH-510 | CGH-511 | CGH-512 | HA-100 | HA-101 | HA-102 | HA-103 | HA-104 | HA-105 | HA-106 | HA-107 | HA-108 | HA-110 | HA-111 | HA-112 |
| Amino acid | | | | | | | | | | | | | | | |
| OH-PRO | 85 | 85 | 86 | 85 | 85 | 56 | 86 | 50 | 86 | 85 | 86 | 86 | 87 | 92 | 95 |
| OH-LYS | 2 | 2 | 2 | 2 | 2 | 1 | 2 | 1 | 2 | 2 | 2 | 2 | 1 | 2 | 2 |
| ASP | 48 | 48 | 48 | 48 | 48 | 66 | 47 | 55 | 47 | 48 | 47 | 48 | 42 | 45 | 47 |
| GLU | 73 | 73 | 73 | 73 | 73 | 91 | 74 | 83 | 74 | 73 | 73 | 73 | 73 | 76 | 77 |
| SER | 35 | 35 | 35 | 35 | 35 | 32 | 34 | 31 | 35 | 35 | 35 | 35 | 29 | 30 | 32 |
| GLY | 344 | 344 | 343 | 344 | 343 | 311 | 343 | 321 | 344 | 344 | 345 | 344 | 359 | 348 | 344 |
| HIS | 4 | 4 | 4 | 4 | 4 | 2 | 4 | 5 | 4 | 4 | 4 | 4 | 3 | 3 | 3 |
| ARG | 56 | 52 | 56 | 56 | 56 | 44 | 56 | 48 | 56 | 56 | 56 | 56 | 52 | 53 | 55 |
| THR | 19 | 19 | 18 | 18 | 18 | 14 | 18 | 17 | 22 | 23 | 23 | 22 | 15 | 15 | 15 |
| ALA | 111 | 111 | 110 | 111 | 111 | 141 | 112 | 130 | 106 | 105 | 106 | 106 | 113 | 115 | 117 |
| PRO | 118 | 118 | 118 | 118 | 118 | 101 | 119 | 121 | 120 | 120 | 121 | 120 | 125 | 126 | 122 |
| TYR | 3 | 3 | 3 | 3 | 3 | 5 | 3 | 3 | 2 | 2 | 2 | 2 | 2 | 2 | 2 |
| VAL | 24 | 24 | 24 | 24 | 24 | 28 | 24 | 20 | 23 | 23 | 23 | 23 | 25 | 26 | 27 |
| MET | 4 | 4 | 4 | 4 | 4 | 6 | 4 | 2 | 5 | 5 | 5 | 5 | 3 | 4 | 5 |
| ILE | 9 | 9 | 9 | 9 | 9 | 7 | 9 | 15 | 10 | 10 | 10 | 10 | 9 | 9 | 10 |
| LEU | 24 | 24 | 24 | 24 | 24 | 29 | 24 | 21 | 26 | 26 | 26 | 26 | 21 | 22 | 22 |
| PHE | 15 | 15 | 15 | 15 | 15 | 19 | 15 | 18 | 15 | 15 | 15 | 16 | 13 | 14 | 14 |
| LYS | 26 | 26 | 25 | 26 | 26 | 38 | 26 | 12 | 25 | 25 | 25 | 25 | 29 | 16 | 12 |
| CYS | 0 | 0 | 0 | 0 | 0 | 0 | 0 | 0 | 0 | 0 | 0 | 0 | 0 | 0 | 0 |

| | Osteocalcin | | | | | | | | | | | | | | | |
|---|---|---|---|---|---|---|---|---|---|---|---|---|---|---|---|---|
| Sample no. | CGH-510 | CGH-511 | CGH-512 | HA-100 | HA-101 | HA-102 | HA-103 | HA-104 | HA-105 | HA-106† | HA-107† | HA-108† | HA-110 | HA-111 | HA-112 | *Modern human |
| Amino acid | | | | | | | | | | | | | | | | |
| OH-PRO | 0 | 0 | 0 | 0 | 0 | 0 | 0 | 0 | 0 | 21 | 21 | 19 | 0 | 0 | 0 | 0 |
| OH-LYS | 0 | 0 | 0 | 0 | 0 | 0 | 0 | 0 | 0 | 0 | 0 | 0 | 0 | 0 | 0 | 0 |
| ASP | 102 | 102 | 102 | 102 | 101 | 102 | 103 | 102 | 100 | 120 | 121 | 122 | 104 | 104 | 103 | 102 |
| GLU | 102 | 102 | 104 | 103 | 101 | 100 | 102 | 103 | 104 | 81 | 82 | 80 | 147 | 150 | 151 | 143 |
| SER | 0 | 0 | 0 | 0 | 0 | 0 | 0 | 0 | 0 | 60 | 61 | 64 | 0 | 0 | 0 | 0 |
| GLY | 61 | 60 | 63 | 59 | 62 | 61 | 61 | 59 | 63 | 80 | 81 | 79 | 64 | 63 | 64 | 61 |
| HIS | 21 | 19 | 20 | 22 | 19 | 20 | 20 | 21 | 22 | 22 | 21 | 19 | 20 | 20 | 19 | 20 |
| ARG | 81 | 80 | 82 | 80 | 81 | 83 | 81 | 80 | 82 | 41 | 40 | 42 | 78 | 76 | 82 | 82 |
| THR | 0 | 0 | 0 | 0 | 0 | 0 | 0 | 0 | 0 | 41 | 40 | 40 | 0 | 0 | 0 | 0 |
| ALA | 60 | 62 | 61 | 61 | 63 | 62 | 62 | 61 | 60 | 101 | 103 | 101 | 80 | 86 | 80 | 61 |
| PRO | 143 | 140 | 141 | 142 | 142 | 139 | 140 | 139 | 143 | 80 | 81 | 80 | 137 | 149 | 137 | 143 |
| TYR | 102 | 100 | 101 | 101 | 102 | 100 | 102 | 103 | 103 | 60 | 63 | 61 | 104 | 96 | 104 | 102 |
| VAL | 60 | 63 | 63 | 61 | 61 | 62 | 60 | 62 | 61 | 41 | 40 | 42 | 45 | 47 | 43 | 61 |
| MET | 0 | 0 | 0 | 0 | 0 | 0 | 0 | 0 | 0 | 0 | 0 | 0 | 0 | 0 | 0 | 0 |
| ILE | 19 | 22 | 20 | 20 | 21 | 21 | 21 | 20 | 19 | 63 | 61 | 61 | 21 | 23 | 20 | 20 |
| LEU | 101 | 101 | 103 | 102 | 100 | 105 | 103 | 102 | 102 | 62 | 60 | 62 | 107 | 102 | 104 | 102 |
| PHE | 41 | 41 | 40 | 40 | 43 | 41 | 39 | 40 | 40 | 0 | 0 | 0 | 43 | 42 | 43 | 41 |
| LYS | 0 | 0 | 0 | 0 | 0 | 0 | 0 | 0 | 0 | 19 | 21 | 21 | 0 | 0 | 0 | 0 |
| CYS | 40 | 40 | 39 | 42 | 42 | 40 | 43 | 43 | 41 | 41 | 40 | 40 | 40 | 39 | 41 | 41 |

* Composition of modern human osteocalcin (POSER et al., 1980).
† Moa osteocalcin composition is not completely known (HUQ et al., 1990).

tios. Osteocalcin does not show such variations. The amino acid composition and elemental C/N ratios of osteocalcin from modern as well as from fossil (well-preserved, moderately preserved, and poorly preserved) bones are identical for the same species. Modern, unaltered collagen has an elemental C/N ratio averaging 3.2 for all vertebrates when bone collagen content >2%. Collagen from moderately to poorly preserved bones retaining their characteristic stable isotopic information has been shown to have elemental C/N ratios ranging from 2.9–3.6. Values outside this range suggest that the bone has

Table 4. Protein content, element C/N ratio, stable isotope ratio, $^{14}$C age, and other biogeochemical data of collagen and osteocalcin

| Lab # | Species | Collagen | | | | | | | Osteocalcin | | | | | $\Delta\delta^{13}C_{(O-C)}$* | $\Delta\delta^{15}N_{(C-O)}$* | $\Delta^{14}$C age[5] |
| | | OH-Pro[1] | Gly/Glu[2] | %wt[3] | C/N[4] | $\delta^{13}$C | $\delta^{15}$N | $^{14}$C age[5] | %wt[3] | C/N[4] | $\delta^{13}$C | $\delta^{15}$N | $^{14}$C age | | | |
| --- | --- | --- | --- | --- | --- | --- | --- | --- | --- | --- | --- | --- | --- | --- | --- | --- |
| | | | | | | | | Modern bone | | | | | | | | |
| HA-3 | dog | 86 | 4.7 | 19.9 | 3.4 | −14.5 | +6.8 | | .37 | 4.3 | −14.5 | +6.9 | | 0.0 | 0.1 | 10 |
| HA-4 | dog | 86 | 4.8 | 11.2 | 3.3 | −15.0 | +7.3 | | .38 | 4.3 | −14.5 | +7.5 | | 0.5 | 0.2 | 31 |
| HA-14 | deer | 86 | 4.6 | 14.3 | 3.2 | −20.5 | +6.9 | | .26 | 4.4 | −20.7 | +7.0 | | 0.2 | 0.1 | 1,540 |
| HA-15 | deer | 86 | 4.7 | 14.7 | 3.3 | −19.8 | +5.8 | | .30 | 4.0 | −20.1 | +5.8 | | 0.3 | 0.0 | 1,831 |
| CGH-510 | human | 85 | 4.7 | 7.5 | 3.1 | −20.9 | +10.3 | | .24 | 4.1 | −20.6 | +10.4 | | 0.3 | 0.1 | 10,647 |
| CGH-511 | human | 85 | 4.7 | 8.9 | 3.1 | −17.0 | +10.0 | | .20 | 4.2 | −17.1 | +10.3 | | 0.1 | 0.3 | 455 |
| CGH-512 | human | 86 | 4.7 | 19.9 | 3.3 | −19.6 | +10.3 | | .25 | 4.2 | −20.0 | +10.3 | | 0.4 | 0.0 | 560 |
| CGH-513 | human | 85 | 4.7 | 16.1 | 3.1 | −17.4 | +7.8 | | .26 | 4.2 | −17.7 | +7.9 | | 0.3 | 0.1 | 275 |
| CGH-514 | human | 85 | 4.7 | 12.9 | 3.2 | −18.6 | +8.4 | | .25 | 4.2 | −18.7 | +8.5 | | 0.1 | 0.1 | 130 |
| | | | | | | | | Fossil bone | | | | | | | | |
| HA-100 | human (Egyptian) | 85 | 4.7 | 11.9 | 3.1 | −18.8 | +12.1 | 3,845 ± 60† | .24 | 4.2 | −19.0 | +12.3 | 3,855 ± 93‡ | 0.2 | 0.2 | |
| HA-101 | human (Egyptian) | 85 | 4.7 | 4.4 | 3.1 | −18.3 | +12.4 | 3,630 ± 100† | .25 | 4.2 | −18.5 | +12.6 | 3,661 ± 100‡ | 0.2 | 0.2 | |
| HA-102 | human (Egyptian) | 56 | 3.4 | <0.2 | 11.1 | −17.1 | +6.1 | 1,720 ± 550† | .25 | 4.2 | −18.8 | +12.6 | 3,260 ± 120‡ | 1.7 | 6.5 | |
| HA-103 | human (Haverty) | 86 | 4.6 | 11.6 | 3.1 | −14.6 | +17.8 | 7,259 ± 89‡ | .25 | 4.3 | −14.5 | +17.8 | 9,090 ± 120‡ | 0.1 | 0.0 | |
| HA-104 | human (Haverty) | 50 | 3.8 | <0.8 | 18.3 | −24.9 | +9.1 | 5,253 ± 94‡ | .25 | 4.2 | −26.9 | +4.5 | 15,900 ± 250‡ | 2.0 | −4.6 | |
| HA-105 | moa | 86 | 4.6 | 2.2 | 5.7 | −22.0 | +3.9 | 24,510 ± 250‡ | .31 | 3.8 | +22.1 | +2.3 | 24,965 ± 220‡ | 0.1 | −1.6 | |
| HA-106 | moa | 85 | 4.7 | 9.9 | 3.4 | −22.8 | −0.6 | 10,490 ± 88‡ | .31 | 3.8 | −22.9 | −0.6 | 11,050 ± 110‡ | 0.1 | 0.0 | |
| HA-107 | moa | 86 | 4.7 | 11.0 | 3.4 | −21.6 | +1.1 | 15,000 ± 200‡ | .31 | 3.8 | −21.7 | +1.2 | 15,275 ± 230‡ | 0.1 | 0.1 | |
| HA-108 | moa | 86 | 4.7 | 10.5 | 3.4 | −22.8 | +2.2 | 18,650 ± 250‡ | .31 | 3.8 | −22.9 | +2.2 | 18,780 ± 260‡ | 0.1 | 0.1 | |
| HA-110 | human (Haverty) | 87 | 4.9 | 1.3 | 8.7 | −15.6 | +4.8 | 2,730 ± 90 | .26 | 4.1 | −16.6 | +11.5 | 4,630 ± 260 | 1.0 | −6.7 | 1,900 |
| HA-111 | human (Haverty) | 92 | 4.6 | 1.2 | 9.9 | −13.6 | +15.1 | 3,870 ± 350 | .25 | 4.2 | −17.2 | +14.1 | 12,600 ± 460 | 3.6 | 1.0 | 8,730 |
| HA-112 | human (Haverty) | 95 | 4.5 | 0.9 | 17.9 | −13.7 | +10.2 | 4,710 ± 190 | .25 | 4.2 | −17.4 | +16.6 | 11,960 ± 500 | 3.7 | 6.5 | 7,250 |

\* O = osteocalcin; C = collagen.
† Conventional decay counting (Isotope Laboratory, UCLA).
‡ AMS direct counting (DSIR, New Zealand).
[1] Hydroxyproline composition in residues/1000.
[2] Glycine/glutamic acid ratios.
[3] Protein content expressed as weight percent.
[4] Elemental carbon/nitrogen ratios.
[5] Carbon 14 ages are given in years.

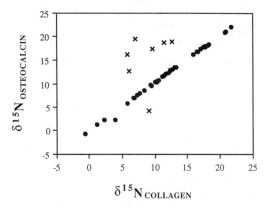

FIG. 1. Nitrogen isotope ratios of collagen vs. nitrogen isotope ratios of osteocalcin from 50 bone samples. Closed circles indicate bones with good collagen preservation. "x" indicates bones with poor collagen preservation.

undergone diagenetic modification, resulting in alteration of the collagen stable isotopic composition. Such bone materials have been shown to yield erroneous stable carbon and nitrogen isotope results (DeNiro, 1985). Most poorly preserved fossil bones fall into this category. Elemental C/N ratios of osteocalcin range from 3.6–4.4, depending on species. In individuals from the same species analyzed for this study, the elemental C/N ratio is constant irrespective of the state of preservation of the bone. The range of elemental C/N ratios in human bone osteocalcin is 4.18–4.33, yielding an average of 4.2.

Table 4 compares the protein content (expressed in weight percent), elemental carbon/nitrogen ratios, and stable isotope ratios of collagen and osteocalcin from a group of samples analyzed in this study. The samples selected cover the range from modern, well-preserved to poorly preserved fossil bones. It is apparent that whereas the protein content and elemental carbon/nitrogen ratios of collagen varied depending on the age and the preservation state of the bone, osteocalcin shows no such variations. Stable carbon and nitrogen isotope ratios of individual amino acids in collagen have been shown to be different from the bulk collagen. For example, glycine residues are often enriched in $^{13}$C relative to the total collagen (Tuross et al., 1988). The divergence in stable carbon and nitrogen isotope ratios between osteocalcin and collagen values observed in some cases may reflect a perturbation in the amino acid speciation observed in the collagen. Mild perturbation may suggest moderate diagenetic effects resulting from partial elimination of the most soluble amino acid residues from the polypeptide chains, thereby inducing the fractionation observed in the stable carbon and nitrogen

isotope ratios. Such mild perturbation may not affect the $^{14}$C content as long as no introduction of exogenous materials has occurred. For samples HA-102, 104, and 112, where the collagen is almost completely depleted, the carbon and nitrogen isotope ratios of collagen show a large deviation from their ratios in osteocalcin. The large stable carbon and nitrogen isotope ratio shifts measured in these collagen samples show a pattern consistent with terrestrial soil contaminants (Figs. 1 and 2), where $\delta^{13}$C and $\delta^{15}$N shift towards values typical of leached products from C$_3$ plants. By contrast, however, the amino acid compositions, concentrations, and elemental C/N ratios of osteocalcin from these same samples are relatively consistent with those for modern samples.

Table 4 also reports other biogeochemical data, as well as $^{14}$C data obtained from collagen and osteocalcin of fossil bone displaying various degrees of collagen preservation. Because of the generally small yields of organic extract, all but three of the $^{14}$C analyses were obtained by the AMS technique. For samples HA-100, HA-101, HA-105, HA-106, HA-107, and HA-108, the $^{14}$C ages of the collagen and osteocalcin fractions are essentially concordant. In those instances where the $^{14}$C ages of the collagen and osteocalcin are discordant, the collagen is extremely poorly preserved (<2% of the original content), and the residual collagen has experienced degradation and differential loss of peptide fragments as reflected in the depressed OH-Pro and Gly/Glu values. These collagen $^{14}$C ages are significantly younger than their osteocalcin values, suggesting contamination of the collagen components by younger carbon-containing substances.

Tables 3 and 4 provide stable isotopes of carbon

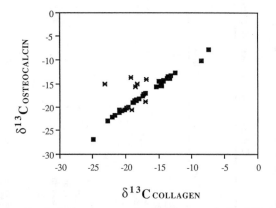

FIG. 2. Carbon isotope ratios of collagen vs. carbon isotope ratios of osteocalcin from 50 bone samples. Closed squares indicate bones with good collagen preservation. "x" indicates bones with poor collagen preservation.

and nitrogen, $^{14}$C, and amino acid compositional data on collagen and osteocalcin extracts from a series of bones from the Haverty location of southern California. The discordance in the collagen/osteocalcin values for HA-104, HA-110, HA-111, and HA-112 (Haverty location, southern California) is particularly interesting, as the archaeological and physical anthropological context of skeletons from this location has been extensively studied and, on the basis of anatomical evidence (BROOKS et al., 1991), it has been determined that the skeletons are genetically related and therefore they should have been buried at approximately the same historic period. However, previous $^{14}$C ages on collagen cover a range at about 5000–10,500 yr BP (ENNIS et al., 1986) for human skeletons from Haverty, whereas in this study a range of ages from 4630 to 15,900 were obtained from osteocalcin dating (Table 4). The significance of this is discussed in AJIE et al. (1990, 1991).

It is particularly interesting to note that for samples HA-104, HA-110, HA-111, and HA-112, there are large differences in $\delta^{13}$C and $\delta^{15}$N, pointing to possible source contamination. Sample HA-104 yielded a $\delta^{13}$C (−26.9 per mil) different from all other osteocalcin $\delta^{13}$C values in this series and may represent an experimentally contaminated sample. Unfortunately, insufficient sample was available to repeat the analysis.

### Ancient Egyptian chronology

Ancient Egyptian human remains are among the best preserved material available for radiocarbon dating. This is partly due to the process of mummification of dead humans in ancient Egypt and partly to the geographical location of burial.

Three bone samples (designated HA-100, HA-101, and HA-102) were part of the collection obtained from the British museum and generously donated by Dr. Rainer Berger, Radiocarbon Laboratory at UCLA. Collagen and osteocalcin were extracted from these samples and measured for their radiocarbon content. Because these bones derive from the IVth dynasty in Egyptian chronology, they should be about 3500 years old. Based on the concentration of the collagen from these samples, HA-102 is observed to have undergone a more severe diagenesis compared to the other two samples. Based on this observation, any anomaly in the radiocarbon ages is expected to be more prominent in this sample. Amino acid contents and elemental analyses for samples HA-100 and HA-101 are essentially similar to modern bone. The collagen and osteocalcin $^{14}$C ages for HA-100 and HA-101 are

essentially concordant, and also agree with the historical ages. However, in HA-102 (where the collagen is almost depleted but osteocalcin could be extracted), the $^{14}$C ages are disconcordant, with osteocalcin reflecting the presumed historical age, and the collagen measured by BERGER (1970) showing a much younger age (Table 4).

### Moa bones

This study also presents the biogeochemical characteristics, including $^{14}$C dates, from bones of the extinct moa birds. Moa is a name popularly applied to the gigantic struthious bird belonging to the Ratitae group. They are among the largest flightless birds that once inhabited New Zealand. Living members of this family include the ostrich of Africa and Arabia (Struthionidae); the rhea of South America (Rheidae) and the emu of Australia (Dromacus). The extinct prototypes are the Æpyornis of Madagascar; the Dromornis of Australia and the moa of New Zealand (Pachyornis elephantopus). Fossilized moa bones have been excavated from numerous locations in New Zealand, and some of these bones are associated with sediment/soil ranging from near-Recent to Pliocene ages. Based on $^{14}$C measured dates, it is widely believed that these birds underwent a process of extinction some time after New Zealand was settled by Polynesians (∼700 yrs BP) and before it was settled by Europeans (∼220 yrs BP). Because of the interest in Moa bones, several laboratories have undertaken numerous $^{14}$C measurements, especially at the Department of Scientific and Industrial Research (DSIR), New Zealand. Part of a well-preserved bone sample collection from the Canterbury Museum, Christchurch, New Zealand, used at DSIR was made available for this study by Dr. John Hulston, and these bones are designated HA-105–HA-108. As these bone samples had already been analyzed for their $^{14}$C content at the DSIR facility by $\beta$-counting using collagen (DSIR, unpubl. results), a comparative analysis of osteocalcin $^{14}$C content was undertaken. Both collagen and osteocalcin were isolated from these bones, and the measured data indicate that the bones were well preserved, as evidenced by the C/N ratios of the collagen, OHP of the collagen, and concentration of collagen. Amino acid compositions from these extracts were also obtained. Although the amino acid composition of moa osteocalcin is not well documented, efforts are underway to determine this composition. A partial amino acid sequence for moa bone osteocalcin has been obtained (HUQ et al., 1990). Interestingly, the presence of hydroxyproline in the moa bone osteocalcin was observed in this study (Table 3).

The result of the isotope analyses are presented in Table 4. All the collagen [14]C dates were obtained from the study at DSIR, whereas the osteocalcin [14]C dates were obtained in this study. Both sets of results are concordant, the greatest variation being ±300 years. The [14]C age agreement between osteocalcin and collagen provides evidence for the promising utility of osteocalcin for biogeochemical studies.

## SUMMARY

In this report, we have described the isolation of osteocalcin and collagen from bones of different organisms, different depositional environments, different degrees of preservation, and varying ages. In our comparative study, we find osteocalcin to be superior to collagen for stable carbon and nitrogen isotope studies and [14]C dating, especially for fossil and poorly preserved bones where collagen can give false results. Our observations demonstrate that when bone material is identifiable and the mineral phases are still present but collagen has largely disappeared, osteocalcin is more likely to be present and can be isolated and purified free of contaminant. The purified osteocalcin is observed to be present in two states: *viz.* intact protein and proteolytic polypeptides fragments. Based on the findings of this study, the use of osteocalcin is recommended for anthropogenic/paleoenvironmental reconstruction, where accurate chemical and isotopic information is desired from bones that have undergone extensive diagenesis.

*Acknowledgements*—We would like to thank Dr. R. Berger, Dr. G. Kennedy (University of California, Los Angeles), Dr. E. Taylor (University of California, Riverside), Dr. J. Hulston (DSIR, New Zealand), and Dr. P. V. Hauschka (Children's Hospital Medical Center, Boston) for generously donating samples and providing valuable criticism. We are also grateful to Drs. B. Runnegar (University of California, Los Angeles) and R. Hedges (Oxford University) for carefully reviewing our manuscript and for many useful suggestions.

## REFERENCES

AJIE H. O., KAPLAN I. R., SLOTA P. J. and TAYLOR R. E. (1990) AMS radiocarbon dating of bone osteocalcin. *Nucl. Instr. Meth. Phys. Res.* **B52**, 433–437.

AJIE H. O., HAUSCHKA P. V., KAPLAN I. R. and SOBEL H. (1991) Comparison of bone collagen and osteocalcin for determination of radiocarbon ages and paleodietary reconstruction. *Earth Planet. Sci. Lett.* (in press).

BENDER M. M. (1968) Mass spectrometric studies of carbon-13 variations in corn and other grasses. *Radiocarbon* **10**, 468–472.

BENDER M. M. (1971) Variations in the $^{13}C/^{12}C$ ratios of plants in relation to the pathway of photosynthetic carbon dioxide fixation. *Phytochemistry* **10**, 1239–1244.

BENDER M. M., ROUHANI I., VIONES H. M. and BLACK C. C., JR. (1973) $^{13}C/^{12}C$ ratio changes in Crassulacean acid metabolism plants. *Plant Physiol.* **52**, 427–430.

BERGER R. (1970) Ancient Egyptian radiocarbon chronology. *Phil. Trans. Roy. Soc. London* **269**, 23–36.

BROOKS S., BROOKS R. H., KENNEDY G. E., AUSTIN J., FIRBY J. R., PAYAN L. A., PRIOR C. A., SLOTA P. J., JR. and TAYLOR R. E. (1991) The Haverty human skeletons: Morphological, depositional, and geochronological characteristics. *J. Cal. Gt. Basin Anthropology* (in press).

CAPONE D. G. and CARPENTER E. J. (1982) Nitrogen fixation in the marine environment. *Science* **217**, 1140–1142.

CHISHOLM B. S., NELSON D. E. and SCHWARCZ H. P. (1982) Stable-carbon isotope ratios as a measure of marine versus terrestrial protein in ancient diets. *Science* **216**, 1131–1132.

CHISHOLM B. S., NELSON D. E. and SCHWARCZ H. P. (1983) Marine and terrestrial protein in the prehistoric diets on the British Columbia coast. *Current Anthropology* **24**, 396–398.

COLOMB E., SAINT MARTIN B., KING K., MITCHELL T. A. and HAUSCHKA P. V. (unpubl. result).

DENIRO M. J. (1985) Postmortem preservation and alteration of *in vivo* bone collagen isotope ratios in relation to paleodietary reconstruction. *Nature* **317**, 806–809.

DENIRO M. J. and EPSTEIN S. (1978) Influence of diet on the distribution of carbon isotopes in animals. *Geochim. Cosmochim. Acta* **42**, 495–506.

DENIRO M. J. and EPSTEIN S. (1981) Influence of diet on the distribution of nitrogen isotopes in animals. *Geochim. Cosmochim. Acta* **45**, 341–351.

ENNIS P., NOLTMANN E. A., HARE P. E., SLOTA P. J., JR., PAYAN L. A., PRIOR C. A. and TAYLOR R. E. (1986) *Radiocarbon* **28**, 539.

GUNDBERG C. M., HAUSCHKA P. V., LIAN J. B. and GALLOP P. M. (1984) Osteocalcin: Isolation, characterization and detection. *Meth. Enzym.* **107**, 516–544.

HAUSCHKA P. V. (1977) Quantitative determination of γ-carboxyglutamic acid in proteins. *Anal. Biochem.* **80**, 212–223.

HAUSCHKA P. V. and GALLOP P. M. (1977) Purification and calcium-binding properties of osteocalcin, the γ-carboxyglutamate-containing protein of bone. In *Calcium Binding Proteins and Calcium Functions* (eds. R. H. WASSERMAN *et al.*), pp. 338–544. Elsevier/North Holland, Amsterdam.

HAUSCHKA P. V., CARR S. A. and BIEMANN K. (1982) Primary structure of monkey osteocalcin. *Biochemistry* **21**, 638–642.

HAUSCHKA P. V., FRENKEL J., DEMUTH R. and GUNDBERG C. M. (1983) Presence of osteocalcin and related higher molecular weight γ-carboxyglutamic acid-containing proteins in developing bone. *J. Biol. Chem.* **258**, 176–182.

HAUSCHKA P. V., LIAN J. B., COLE D. E. C. and GUNDBERG C. M. (1989) Osteocalcin and matrix Gla protein: Vitamin K-dependent proteins in bone. *Physiol. Rev.* **69**, 990–1047.

HEDGES R. E. M. and LAW I. A. (1989) The radiocarbon dating of bone. *Appl. Geochem.* **4**, 249–253.

HUQ N. L., TSENG A. and CHAPMAN G. (1990) Partial amino acid sequence of osteocalcin from an extinct species of Ratite bird. *Biochem. Intl.* **21**, 491–496.

KEEGAN W. F. and DENIRO M. J. (1988) Stable carbon and nitrogen isotope ratios of bone collagen used to study coral reef and terrestrial components of prehistoric Bahamian diet. *Amer. Antiq.* **53,** 320–326.

MEIGHAN C. W. (1972) Midden remains and prehistoric food resources. *UCLA Archaeological Survey Annual Report 1972,* pp. 1–34.

MINAGAWA M., WINTER D. A. and KAPLAN I. R. (1984) Comparison of Kjeldahl and combustion methods for measurement of nitrogen isotope ratios in organic matter. *Anal. Chem.* **56,** 1859–1861.

MINAGAWA M., KARASAWA K. and KABAYA Y. (1986) Stable isotopes of carbon, nitrogen and hydrogen in the contemporary North America human food web. *Geochemistry* **20,** 79–170.

OSMOND C. B., ALLAWAY W. G., SUTTON B. G., TROUGHTON J. H., QUEROZ O., LÜTTGE U., and WINTER K. (1973) Carbon isotope discrimination in photosynthesis of CAM plants. *Nature* **246,** 41–42.

POSER J. W., ESCH F. S., LING N. C. and PRICE P. A. (1980) Isolation and sequence of the Vitamin K-dependent protein from human bone. *J. Biol. Chem.* **225,** 8685–8691.

PRICE P. A., OTSUKA A. S., POSER J. W., KRISTAPONIS J. and RAMAN N. (1976) Characterization of a γ-carboxyglutamic acid-containing protein from bone. *Proc. Natl. Acad. Sci. USA* **73,** 1447–1451.

SCHOENINGER M. J. (1985) Trophic level effects on $^{15}$N/$^{14}$N and $^{13}$C/$^{12}$C ratios in bone collagen and strontium levels in bone mineral. *J. Human Evolution* **14,** 515–525.

SCHOENINGER M. J. and DENIRO M. J. (1984) Nitrogen and carbon isotopic composition of bone collagen from marine and terrestrial animals. *Geochim. Cosmochim. Acta* **48,** 625–639.

SCHOENINGER M. J., DENIRO M. J. and TAUBER H. (1983) Stable nitrogen isotope ratios of bone collagen reflect marine and terrestrial components of prehistoric diet. *Science* **12,** 187–206.

SCHWARCZ H. P., MELBYE J., KATZENBERG M. A. and KNYF M. (1985) Stable isotopes in human skeletons of Southern Ontario: Reconstructing diet. *J. Archaeological Sci.* **12,** 187–206.

STAFFORD T. W., JULL A. J. T., BRENDEL K., DUHAMEL R. C. and DONAHUE D. (1987) Study of bone radiocarbon dating accuracy at the University of Arizona NSF Accelerator Facility for radioisotope analysis. *Radiocarbon* **29,** 24–44.

TAUBER H. (1981) $\delta^{13}$C evidence for dietary habits of prehistoric man in Denmark. *Nature* **292,** 332–335.

TREGANZA A. E. and COOKE S. F. (1948) The quantitative investigation of aboriginal sites: Complex excavation with physical and archaeological analysis of a single method. *Amer. Antiquity* **13,** 287–297.

TUROSS N., FOGEL M. L. and HARE P. (1988) Variability in the preservation of the isotopic composition of collagen from fossil bone. *Geochim. Cosmochim. Acta* **52,** 929–935.

TUROSS N., BEHRENSMEYER A. K., EANES E. D., FISHER L. W. and HARE P. E. (1989) Molecular preservation and crystallographic alteration in a weathering sequence of Wildebeest bone. *Appl. Geochem.* **4,** 261–270.

ULRICH M. M. W., PERIZONIUS W. R. K., SPOOR C. F., SANDBERG P. and VERMEER C. (1987) Extraction of osteocalcin from fossil bones and teeth. *Biochem. Biophys. Res. Comm.* **149,** 712–719.

VAN DER MERWE N. J. (1982) Carbon isotopes, photosynthesis and archaeology. *Amer. Scientist* **70,** 596–606.

VAN DER MERWE N. J. and VOGEL J. C. (1977) Isotopic evidence for early maize cultivation in New York state. *Amer. Antiquity* **42,** 238–242.

VIRGINIA R. A. and DELWICHE C. C. (1982) Natural $^{15}$N abundance of presumed $N_2$-fixing and non-$N_2$-fixing plants from selected ecosystems. *Oecologia* **54,** 317–325.

ZYTKOVICZ T. H. and NELSESTUEN G. L. (1976) γ-Carboxyglutamic acid distribution. *Biochim. Biophys. Acta* **444,** 344–348.

Stable Isotope Geochemistry: A Tribute to Samuel Epstein
© The Geochemical Society, Special Publication No. 3, 1991
Editors: H. P. Taylor, Jr., J. R. O'Neil and I. R. Kaplan

# The relationship between stable oxygen and hydrogen isotope ratios of water in astomatal plants

LEE W. COOPER,[1,*] MICHAEL J. DENIRO[1,†] and JON E. KEELEY[2]

[1]Department of Earth and Space Sciences, University of California, Los Angeles, CA 90024, U.S.A.
[2]Department of Biology, Occidental College, Los Angeles, CA 90041, U.S.A.

**Abstract**—Isotopic fractionation of leaf water during transpiration is influenced by both equilibrium and kinetic factors. Previous workers have predicted that the influence of each factor varies depending upon the path of water loss, whether centralized through stomata, or diffuse through the cuticle. We studied the relationship between the $\delta D$ and $\delta^{18}O$ values of leaf and stem waters of laurel sumac, *Rhus laurina* (Nutt.) T. & G., and its parasite, dodder, *Cuscuta subinclusa* D. & H., growing in the field. Stomatal transpiration, associated with more stagnant boundary layers, predominates in *R. laurina;* cuticular transpiration, associated with more turbulent boundary layers, is most important in the largely astomatal *C. subinclusa*. We also studied the diurnal variation in the $\delta D$ and $\delta^{18}O$ values of leaf waters of two astomatal plants, *Chiloschista lunifera* (Rchb. F.) J.J.S and *Stylites andicola* Amstutz, and two stomatal plants, *Tillandsia balbisiana* Schult. and *Lilaeopsis schaffneriana* (Schlecht.) C. & R., growing with them under the same conditions in the laboratory. Slopes, m, for the relation $\delta D = m\delta^{18}O + b$ were significantly higher for stem waters in *C. subinclusa* than for leaf waters in *R. laurina* (1.77), consistent with the difference in the boundary layers through which water was lost in the two species. The magnitude of diurnal heavy isotope enrichment of tissue water was smaller in *C. subinclusa* than in *R. laurina,* which is also consistent with predictions concerning evapotranspiration through different types of boundary layers. The slopes, m, in plant waters in the laboratory experiments, conducted at high humidity, were not different than those observed during evaporation of water from pans, regardless of plant anatomy. The observation suggests that cuticular transpiration is important in influencing isotopic fractionation of water only at low humidity. Our results indicate that the isotopic composition of water vapor released by plants in arid regions may be influenced by the relative proportions of stomatal versus cuticular transpiration.

## INTRODUCTION

LEAF WATER BECOMES enriched in the heavy isotopes of oxygen and hydrogen ($^{18}O$ and D) during evapotranspiration (GONFIANTINI *et al.,* 1965; WERSHAW *et al.,* 1970; DONGMANN *et al.,* 1974; ZUNDEL *et al.,* 1978; FARRIS and STRAIN, 1978; LEANEY *et al.,* 1985; STERNBERG *et al.,* 1986). This biologically mediated process influences the isotopic composition of oxygen and hydrogen that is incorporated into organic matter (STERNBERG, 1988). The isotopic composition of molecular oxygen, the carbon and oxygen isotope composition of atmospheric carbon dioxide, and the atmospheric concentrations of other trace and greenhouse gases are all affected by transpiration of water by plants (DOLE *et al.,* 1954; FRANCEY and TANS, 1987; MOONEY *et al.,* 1987; YAKIR *et al.,* 1989).

Two of the more important factors controlling enrichment of heavy isotopes in leaf water are equilibrium fractionations between liquid and vapor phases of water and kinetic fractionations that in-

fluence the rate at which different isotopic forms of water escape from the leaf surface (DONGMANN *et al.,* 1974). The relative importance of equilibrium versus kinetic isotope effects during leaf water evaporation can be studied by examining the relationship between the enrichment of D relative to $^{18}O$ in leaf water (ALLISON *et al.,* 1985; COOPER and DENIRO, 1989). Characteristically, this involves comparisons of the slope, *m,* for the following relation, obtained from analyses of leaf waters collected during diurnal cycles of evapotranspiration:

$$\delta D = m\delta^{18}O + b.$$

$\delta D$ and $\delta^{18}O$ are the isotopic compositions of leaf water, given in per mil in the conventional $\delta$ notation, where

$$\delta^{18}O \text{ or } \delta D = [(R_{sample}/R_{SMOW}) - 1] \times 1000.$$

$R$ is $^{18}O/^{16}O$ or D/H; SMOW is Standard Mean Ocean Water.

Kinetic fractionation effects are larger for $H_2^{18}O$ relative to $H_2^{16}O$ than for $DH^{16}O$ relative to $H_2^{16}O$ (DANSGAARD, 1964; MERLIVAT, 1978; GAT, 1980). As a result, *m,* the slope in the leaf water equation, $\delta D = m\delta^{18}O + b,$ will be lower in plants for which kinetic fractionation plays a larger role during

* *Corresponding author; current address:* Environmental Sciences Division, Oak Ridge National Laboratory, PO Box 2008, Oak Ridge, TN 37831-6038, U.S.A.

† *Current address:* Department of Earth Sciences, University of California, Santa Barbara, CA 93106, U.S.A.

evapotranspiration than in plants for which equilibrium processes dominate. Kinetic fractionation effects are influenced by the nature of the boundary layer through which water evaporates (DONGMANN et al., 1974; FARRIS and STRAIN, 1978; LEANEY et al., 1985; ALLISON et al., 1985). When stagnant boundary layer conditions exist, kinetic processes become more important. With more turbulent boundary layers, water molecules encounter less resistance to irreversible loss to the atmosphere, so that equilibrium-dominated processes involved in the evaporation of water become more significant. If the boundary layer adjacent to the leaf is more turbulent, evaporation will proceed faster, kinetic effects will be less important, and the slope, $m$, in the equation $\delta D = m\delta^{18}O + b$ will be higher. Hence, comparative studies of the slope, $m$, potentially can be used to characterize boundary layers associated with different plants. Unfortunately, several complications have precluded widespread application of this idea.

First, the possibility that different proportions of leaf water in various species are subject to evapotranspiration (LEANEY et al., 1985; YAKIR et al., 1989, 1990) could affect the slopes of the leaf water equations. As an example, consider two plants, both using the same source water, but with different proportions of leaf water subject to heavy isotope enrichments. Slopes for the leaf water lines in the two plants would be influenced by the relative abundances in the leaves of unfractionated source water, which lies on the meteoric water line, $\delta D = 8\delta^{18}O + 10$, and fractionated leaf water, for which slopes much lower than eight have been observed (BRICOUT et al., 1972; LESAINT et al., 1974; ALLISON et al., 1985; STERNBERG et al., 1986; COOPER and DeNIRO, 1989).

Nevertheless, a means for studying the influence of pools of fractionated versus unfractionated plant water on the slope, $m$, in the leaf water equation $\delta D = m\delta^{18}O + b$ can be found in the proposal that the fraction of leaf water subject to heavy isotope enrichment is proportional to the magnitude of daily heavy isotope enrichment observed in total leaf water (LEANEY et al., 1985). Two predictions follow from this proposal. First, plants with low daily ranges in leaf water isotopic composition should have higher slopes, $m$, because they contain a higher proportion of unfractionated (meteoric) source water. Second, the lines, $\delta D = m\delta^{18}O + b$, describing leaf water isotopic content in such plants during the daily cycle of heavy isotope enrichment should have a minimum point closer to meteoric source water. In a separate study of nine species (COOPER and DeNIRO, 1989), we observed that

plants with the smallest daily range of leaf water isotopic variability actually had the lowest, not the highest, slopes, although minima for the lines $\delta D = m\delta^{18}O + b$ were in fact closer to the meteoric source water for these plants. Thus only one of two predictions of LEANEY et al. (1985) was validated by our study.

A second complication in applying the relation $\delta D = m\delta^{18}O + b$ to studies of boundary-layer changes within stomata and adjacent to leaves is species-specific variability in the patterns of water utilization (COOPER and DeNIRO, 1989). Low humidity should increase the stagnant nature of leaf boundary layers (FARRIS and STRAIN, 1978; ALLISON et al., 1985) because of partial or complete stomatal closure, resulting in a longer path length before water molecules are irreversibly lost to the atmosphere. As an example, ALLISON et al. (1985) attributed a lower slope, $m$, observed in needle waters of Monterey pine, Pinus radiata, to more arid conditions during the summer relative to the winter. COOPER and DeNIRO (1989), however, observed that plants growing in more arid locations did not necessarily exhibit lower slopes in the equation $\delta D = m\delta^{18}O + b$. Rather, we observed that different species growing under the same environmental conditions showed different responses to the physical factors that are presumed to influence boundary layer characteristics associated with transpiration. COOPER and DeNIRO (1989) concluded that biological differences in water utilization among different species had an important influence on the relation $\delta D = m\delta^{18}O + b$. An association was found between the residence time of water within a plant and the slope, $m$: We proposed that this residence time may affect apparent or actual kinetic fractionation factors for D and $^{18}O$ (COOPER and DeNIRO, 1989).

A third complication that is pivotal to understanding biological effects upon enrichment of heavy isotopes in leaf waters is the role of stomatal versus cuticular transpiration. FARRIS and STRAIN (1978) proposed that loss of water through the cuticle, the wax-covered surface of leaves, is associated with more turbulent boundary conditions than loss of water through stomata, which are pores through which plants exchange gases with the atmosphere. This proposal was based on differences in topography between stomata, which are recessed into the leaf, and the cuticle, for which there is no physical barrier impeding air flow close to the surface of the leaf. Yet the analysis of the needle water line for Monterey pine (ALLISON et al., 1985) indicates that the cuticular-stomatal transpiration ratio, which would be greater under summer water-stressed conditions, is not as important as lowered humidity in determining the slope, $m$, in the relation $\delta D = m\delta^{18}O + b$. The interplay of species-specific effects with physical factors such as humidity has prevented an unambiguous test of the proposal of FARRIS and STRAIN (1978) regarding stomatal versus cuticular transpiration as it relates to changes in slope, $m$.

It was our intent in the present work to test the influence of diffusional boundary-layer conditions as they relate to stomatal versus cuticular transpiration. We studied the relationships between $\delta D$ and $\delta^{18}O$ values of waters in *Cuscuta subinclusa* D. & H., a largely non-photosynthetic parasite, and its host, *Rhus laurina* (Nutt.) T. & G., a common southern California chaparral shrub. The host-parasite relationship permits control of physical factors influencing leaf and tissue water enrichment because both plants are subject to the same humidity and temperature. To a large extent, this study also allowed control of stomatal distribution as it influences evapotranspiration, because the genus *Cuscuta* is characterized by an almost complete lack of stomata (MACLEOD, 1962). The mature parasite has no roots and is dependent upon the host plant for water and nutrients obtained through haustoria. Although it is not known what proportions of host water are derived from isotopically fractionated leaf water versus unfractionated source water, xylem to xylem water conduction exists between *Cuscuta* and its hosts (ASHTON, 1976). Xylem are the non-living water conduction vessels in vascular plants. Thus vegetative cells in *C. subinclusa* are likely to have similar sources of water as do vegetative cells in *R. laurina*. The major difference between the two plants is that water evaporating from *C. subinclusa* will be lost predominantly through the cuticle, while water lost from *R. laurina* will be evaporated primarily through stomata, with a much smaller loss through the cuticle.

We followed this work up with a laboratory study of the relationship between the $\delta D$ and $\delta^{18}O$ values of tissue waters of two additional astomatal plants, a largely leafless orchid, *Chiloschista lunifera* (Rchb. F.) J.J.S, and a specialized isoetid, or fern ally, *Stylites andicola* Amstutz. The latter has minimal gas exchange with the atmosphere and obtains inorganic carbon from the sediments through lacunae, which are air spaces within the stalk (KEELEY *et al.*, 1984; STERNBERG *et al.*, 1985). We also studied heavy isotope enrichment patterns during transpiration with two control, stoma-bearing plants growing under the same conditions, *Tillandsia balbisiana* Schult. and *Lilaeopsis schaffneriana* (Schlecht.) C. & R.

We expected the slope, $m$, in the equation $\delta D = m\delta^{18}O + b$ to be higher for the astomatal plants than for the stoma-bearing species. This hypothesized increase would be due to evaporation occurring through the plant surface in association with a more turbulent boundary layer in the astomatal plants than the less turbulent boundary layer associated with recessed stomata in the stoma-bearing plants. We tested for variability in slopes due to differing proportions of tissue water subject to enrichment of heavy isotopes by evaluating the total range of water isotopic variability over diurnal periods.

## MATERIALS AND METHODS

For the field experiment, samples consisted of 3 to 4 g of leaves from a single laurel sumac bush, *R. laurina*, and of leafless stems of dodder, *C. subinclusa*, growing on the same bush. Samples were collected and stored immediately in sealed tubes every 3 hours for 48 hours from 1400 local time, 24 September 1987 to 1400, 26 September 1987. The plants sampled were growing along the access road to the Pasadena, California, water supply in Arroyo Seco Canyon, adjacent to the Jet Propulsion Laboratory. Two samples of *C. subinclusa* were collected at each sampling time, one a sample of stems that were attached to the host and the second, stems that had been removed from the *Rhus laurina* bush at the beginning of the experiment. These detached stems were left in the general vicinity dangled from a dead branch of the sumac bush. The intention of detaching the parasitic stems was to gain some insight into the scope of oxygen and hydrogen isotope variability of water within the parasite that was distinct from variation in the host that was then transmuted to the attached parasitic stems. Air temperature and humidity were measured at the time of each collection.

For the laboratory experiments, *C. lunifera* was obtained from a retail orchid importer (Spencer Howard, Orchid Imports, North Hollywood, California), who obtained the plants from sources in Thailand. *S. andicola* and *L. schaffneriana* were taken from a collection at Occidental College, Los Angeles, that had been cultivated for over a year from plants collected in Peru and Columbia, respectively. The *T. balbisiana* used in the experiment was purchased from a local source.

Samples consisting of 1 g of roots (*C. lunifera*) and a 3 to 4 g whole leaf of *T. balbisiana* were collected every 4 hours for 24 hours during the first laboratory experiment, on April 13 and 14, 1988. Both species were growing in a covered glass case adjacent to a lighted window; artificial room lighting was turned off at night. (All of the plants except *L. schaffneriana* exhibit Crassulacean acid metabolism, in which $CO_2$ uptake and water loss can occur at night.) Since both *C. lunifera* and *T. balbisiana* obtain water from atmospheric vapor, two collections of the atmospheric vapor present in the glass case during the experiment were made for isotopic analyses of source water. Water vapor collections were made in the following manner. A glass trap, filled with molecular sieve pellets, size 5A (Linde, Tarrytown, New Jersey) was placed in Dewar flask containing liquid nitrogen. The inlet to the trap was connected through a flow meter to another trap containing Pyrex glass beads, which was also immersed in liquid ni-

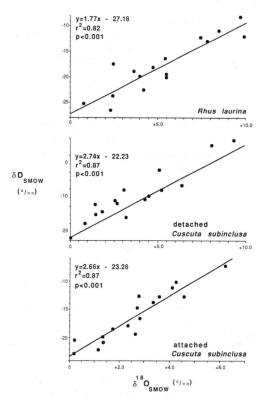

FIG. 1. Stable hydrogen and oxygen isotopic compositions plotted against one another and regression lines (of the form $\delta D = m\delta^{18}O + b$) for leaf waters from *R. laurina* (top), stem waters from *C. subinclusa* (detached from host at beginning of experiment) (middle), and for stem waters from *C. subinclusa* (attached to host) (bottom).

hours, purifying the equilibrated carbon dioxide cryogenically, analyzing the $CO_2$ mass spectrometrically, and using mass balance considerations to calculate the original oxygen isotope composition of the water (EPSTEIN and MAYEDA, 1953). For the laboratory experiments (for all plants except *T. balbisiana*, where 0.5 ml of water was analyzed as described above), because of the small size of the water samples, oxygen isotope ratios were determined by equilibrating 75 to 100 $\mu$L of water with approximately 500 $\mu$moles of carbon dioxide for 48 hours and then proceeding in the same manner as above. Hydrogen gas was extracted by passing approximately 10 $\mu$L of water over uranium metal heated to 700°C, which releases hydrogen gas that was collected using a uranium hydride pump prior to mass spectrometric analyses (FRIEDMAN and HARDCASTLE, 1970). Precision, based on repeated mass spectrometric determinations of secondary water standards analyzed concurrently with the samples, was found to be ±0.2 per mil for $\delta^{18}O$ values and ±2 per mil for $\delta D$ values. Accuracy of D/H ratios was evaluated by running the samples and SMOW directly against SMOW in the mass spectrometer. For small water volume (75 to 100 $\mu$L) determinations of $\delta^{18}O$ values, machine standards of $CO_2$ were prepared and used within the mass spectrometer by equilibration of $CO_2$ with a well-calibrated secondary water standard, matching the volumes used for each water sample. This served to correct small systematic errors resulting from high $CO_2/H_2O$ ratios used in small water volume equilibrations.

trogen. The inlet to the initial trap was connected through rubber tubing to a disposable Pasteur pipette, the tip of which was placed within 1 cm of plant surfaces within the terrarium. Air flow into the molecular sieve trap during two 40 minute periods, one during the day and one at night, resulted in water vapor being trapped on the Pyrex beads in the initial trap. The rate of air flow was variable, depending upon the amounts of oxygen and nitrogen condensed on the molecular sieve. After sufficient collection of atmospheric water vapor, the initial trap was then isolated, its water distilled and analyzed isotopically.

Conditions in the second laboratory experiment using *S. andicola* and *L. schaffneriana*, on July 26 and 27, 1988, were similar except for the following differences. Six collections in the 24 h period were made, rather than seven. All samples collected consisted of approximately 1 g of leaf material. The plants were growing together in a plastic container filled with water-logged sand. The container was placed in an ice-filled cooler, which was partially closed at night. Source water was sampled directly from the water-logged sand for isotopic analysis.

All plant samples were kept frozen in sealed tubes until water was extracted by quantitative freeze drying (STERNBERG *et al.*, 1986). For the field experiments, oxygen isotope ratios were determined by equilibrating 0.5 to 1.0 ml water samples with approximately 300 $\mu$moles of carbon dioxide for 48

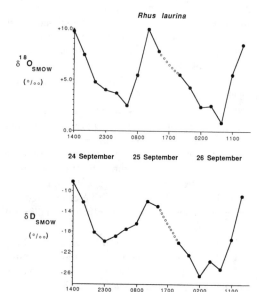

FIG. 2. Stable oxygen and hydrogen isotope ratios of leaf water of *R. laurina* over the course of the sampling period. Anamolous $\delta D$ and $\delta^{18}O$ values of water collected at 1700, 25 September, were excluded due to probable errors during collection or distillation. These data were also excluded from Fig. 1.

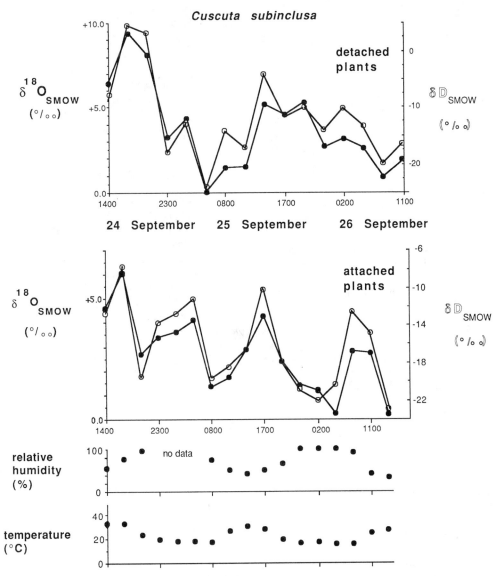

FIG. 3. Stable oxygen (darkened circles) and hydrogen isotope ratios (clear circles) of stem water of *C. subinclusa* (detached from host at beginning of experiment) (top) and stem water of *C. subinclusa* (attached to host) (bottom), over the course of the sampling period. Relative humidity and temperature at the time sampling are also indicated.

## RESULTS

### Field experiment

The slopes, $m$, in the relationship $\delta D = m\delta^{18}O + b$ for water of *R. laurina* leaves are 1.77 and 2.74 for *C. subinclusa* stems that had been detached from the host at the start of the experiment, and 2.66 for *C. subinclusa* stems that remained attached to *R. laurina*. These slopes were derived from regression analyses of $\delta D$ and $\delta^{18}O$ values for each of the three sets of plant samples (Fig. 1). Analysis of covariance (SACHS, 1984) indicated that slopes for the two types of *C. subinclusa* samples did not differ, but both were significantly higher than the slope for *R. laurina*. During the course of the experiment, both the detached *C. subinclusa* and *R. laurina* showed a regular diurnal fluctuation with heavy isotopic enrichment at a minimum at dawn and at a maximum in the late morning or the afternoon (Figs. 2 and 3). Heavy isotope enrichment in attached *C. sub-*

Table 1. Daily range of tissue water isotopic enrichment

| Sample | $\Delta \delta D$ (‰) | $\Delta \delta^{18}O$ (‰) |
|---|---|---|
| C. subinclusa (detached from host) | 29 | 9.3 |
| C. subinclusa (attached to host) | 15 | 6.0 |
| R. laurina | 18 | 9.8 |

inclusa did not follow a smooth diurnal pattern (Fig. 3), and the overall magnitudes of enrichment for D and $^{18}O$ were somewhat smaller than for either the detached C. subinclusa or R. laurina (Table 1).

The magnitudes of D- and $^{18}O$-enrichment for detached C. subinclusa and R. laurina were correlated with air temperature at a significant level ($p < 0.05$), but only R. laurina showed a significant negative correlation with relative air humidity. Heavy isotope enrichment in attached C. subinclusa was not correlated with either temperature or humidity (Table 2).

### Laboratory experiments

Overall variability in $\delta D$ and $\delta^{18}O$ values of tissue water in the four species grown in the laboratory

are shown in Figs. 4 and 5. A plot of tissue water $\delta D$ versus $\delta^{18}O$ values collected at each sampling time yields a regression line for each species, but the least-squares fit equation corresponding to S. andicola is not statistically significant (Table 3). The $\delta D$ and $\delta^{18}O$ values of water vapor in the first experiment were −98 and −12.6 (day) and −99 and −13.5 (night), respectively. The $\delta D$ and $\delta^{18}O$ values for source water in the second experiment were −90 and −11.3, respectively.

### DISCUSSION

The results of the field study are consistent with the proposal that the bulk of water transpiring from a largely astomatal plant, C. subinclusa, passes through a more turbulent boundary layer than the bulk of water transpiring from R. laurina. Slopes of leaf water, $m$, in the equation $\delta D = m\delta^{18}O + b$, for stem or leaf water were significantly higher for the parasite than for the host.

By contrast, in the laboratory experiment slopes, $m$, in the equation $\delta D = m\delta^{18}O + b$, observed for tissue water distilled from three of four species studied showed no clear pattern with respect to the

Table 2. Relationships between leaf and stem water isotopic ratios and air temperature ($T$) or relative humidity ($H$)

| Sample | $m$ | $b$ | $r^2$ | $p$ | $n$ |
|---|---|---|---|---|---|
| | | $T$ (°C) $= m\delta^{18}O + b$ | | | |
| C. subinclusa (detached from host) | 1.49 | 16.24 | 0.40 | $0.005 < p < 0.01$ | 16 |
| C. subinclusa (attached to host) | 1.76 | 17.54 | 0.21 | $0.05 < p < 0.10$ | 17 |
| R. laurina | 1.94 | 11.65 | 0.74 | $p < 0.0001$ | 16 |
| | | $T$ (°C) $= m\delta D + b$ | | | |
| C. subinclusa (detached from host) | 0.45 | 27.18 | 0.32 | $0.01 < p < 0.025$ | 16 |
| C. subinclusa (attached to host) | 0.44 | 29.32 | 0.11 | $0.10 < p < 0.25$ | 17 |
| R. laurina | 0.99 | 39.59 | 0.74 | $p < 0.0001$ | 16 |
| | | $H$ (%) $= m\delta^{18}O + b$ | | | |
| C. subinclusa (detached from host) | −0.30 | 73.68 | 0.001 | $p > 0.25$ | 14 |
| C. subinclusa (attached to host) | −2.54 | 75.83 | 0.03 | $p > 0.25$ | 14 |
| R. laurina | −6.74 | 109.68 | 0.59 | $0.001 < p < 0.005$ | 13 |
| | | $H$ (%) $= m\delta D + b$ | | | |
| C. subinclusa (detached from host) | 0.25 | 75.03 | 0.01 | $p > 0.25$ | 14 |
| C. subinclusa (attached to host) | −1.13 | 50.51 | 0.05 | $p > 0.25$ | 14 |
| R. laurina | −3.07 | 15.94 | 0.54 | $0.001 < p < 0.005$ | 13 |

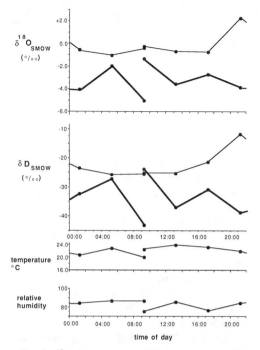

FIG. 4. $\delta^{18}O$ and $\delta D$ values of tissue water, air temperature and relative humidity (%) at the indicated time of day for *C. lunifera* (thickened lines) and *T. balbisiana* (narrow lines).

enrichment for the field and laboratory experiments. Unlike the field experiment, the ranges of $\delta D$ and $\delta^{18}O$ values observed for tissue water of plants studied in the laboratory were small. Over the 24 hour lab experiments, $\delta^{18}O$ values changed by little more than one per mil in *S. andicola,* with changes of only about two per mil in the remaining three species. These changes are comparatively small. We observed diurnal variability in leaf water $\delta^{18}O$ values up to ten per mil in the field; ranges as large as 30 per mil have been observed in desert plants (COOPER and DENIRO, 1989).

The high slopes, $m$, in the equation $\delta D = m\delta^{18}O + b$ determined for an astomatal plant, *C. lunifera,* and a stoma-bearing plant, *L. schaffneriana* grown with it, indicate that our original hypothesis, that astomatal plants will exhibit higher slopes than stoma-bearing plants, must be rejected at higher relative humidities. The laboratory study could not have been conducted under conditions of lower humidity, because such conditions would have interfered with basic metabolism in each of the plants. *T. balbisiana* and *C. lunifera* are epiphytes in moist tropical forests, and are specifically dependent on water vapor for photosynthesis. *L. schaffneriana* and *S. andicola* are wetland species that grow in

presence or absence of stomata (Table 1). Evaporation from surface bodies of water in mid-continental humid regions results in slopes, $m$, ranging from 4 to 6 (ALLISON *et al.,* 1985), within the range we observed for these plants. Heavy isotope enrichment, as it affects the slope, $m$, is apparently little different in at least three of the four species studied from that which occurs during water evaporation from surface bodies of water. No conclusions can be drawn concerning the fourth species, *S. andicola,* because the least-squares fit regression line generated by plotting leaf water $\delta D$ and $\delta^{18}O$ values (Fig. 2; Table 2) is not statistically significant. It should also be noted that the relation $\delta D = m\delta^{18}O + b$ for the stoma-bearing bromeliad *T. balbisiana* is somewhat tenuous because it is highly dependent on $^{18}O$- and D-enriched water collected from a leaf sampled at 20:00 (Fig. 4). All other individual *T. balbisiana* leaves sampled during the experiment showed small variations in $^{18}O$ and D content.

A major difference between the field and laboratory experiments was the high relative humidity in the laboratory growth chambers. The role that low relative humidity plays in driving the leaf water isotope enrichment process (FARRIS and STRAIN, 1978) was apparent in the magnitude of isotopic

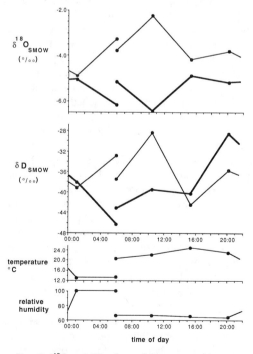

FIG. 5. $\delta^{18}O$ and $\delta D$ values of tissue water, air temperature and relative humidity (%) at the indicated time of day for *S. andicola* (thickened lines) and *L. schaffneriana* (narrow lines).

Table 3. Regression equations of the form $\delta D = m\delta^{18}O + b$ for tissue water: laboratory experiments

| Species (Anatomy) | $m$ (±SE) | $b$ | $r^2$ | $n$ | $p$ |
|---|---|---|---|---|---|
| C. lunifera (no stomata) | 4.89 (±0.86) | −17.56 | 0.867 | 7 | $0.001 < p < 0.005$ |
| T. balbisiana (stomata) | 4.15 (±0.80) | −21.75 | 0.843 | 7 | $0.001 < p < 0.005$ |
| S. andicola (no stomata) | 3.27 (±4.31) | −21.46 | 0.126 | 6 | $p > 0.25$ |
| L. schaffneriana (stomata) | 4.94 (±1.29) | −17.77 | 0.787 | 6 | $0.01 < p < 0.025$ |

bog ecosystems. This illustrates a fundamental problem with studies of the tissue water isotope composition of astomatal plants. Most astomatal vascular plants, and most stoma-bearing plants that appear suitable as control species, grow under humid conditions. Leaf water enrichment of $^{18}O$ and D is low under these conditions, and the enrichment that does occur appears to proceed much as it does in open-water evaporation processes; i.e., the slope, $m$, in the equation $\delta D = m\delta^{18}O + b$ is greater than four. Thus, under conditions of high humidity, the presence of stomata and the boundary layer characteristics of stoma-bearing leaves do not affect the heavy isotope enrichments that occur during evaporation.

Our results are also consistent with a separate study (COOPER and DENIRO, 1989) that indicates that variable inputs of unfractionated meteoric water do not significantly influence the slope, $m$. Using the reasoning of LEANEY et al. (1985) discussed in the introduction, we might have expected plants with larger diurnal ranges of leaf water isotope composition to have lower slopes, $m$, signifying a smaller contribution of unfractionated meteoric water. Compared with the attached parasites used in the field experiment, the detached parasites removed from the host plant at the beginning of the experiment no doubt had a higher proportion of tissue water subject to heavy isotope evaporation enrichments, and this is reflected in both the larger $\delta^{18}O$ and $\delta D$ ranges for the detached parasites (Table 1). Nevertheless, the slope, $m$, does not differ significantly between the detached and attached parasites. The different evaporative ranges in detached and attached C. subinclusa are no doubt in part due to unavoidable injuries in detaching the stems at the beginning of the experiment. Nevertheless, it is remarkable what little difference there is between the tissue water relationships for the detached ($\delta D = 2.74\delta^{18}O − 22.2$) and attached parasites ($\delta D = 2.66\delta^{18}O − 23.3$). These relationships held for at least 48 hours despite the obvious differences in water stress and the certainty that water loss occurred through broken stems in the detached plants.

Despite predominant cuticular transpiration that is presumably associated with a well-mixed bound-

ary layer, C. subinclusa probably does not lose much water over the course of a day compared to R. laurina, and hence the isotopic composition of its stem water does not respond to humidity and temperature changes as does leaf water in R. laurina. The same explanation accounts for the smaller heavy isotope enrichment ranges in attached C. subinclusa compared to R. laurina. The occurrence of significant correlations between temperature and stem water heavy isotope enrichments in the detached C. subinclusa suggests that this insulating physiology and anatomy may have been disturbed when the parasite was removed at the start of the experiment. Our experimental results support the proposal that water evaporation through the cuticle proceeds through a more turbulent boundary layer than that associated with stomatal transpiration (FARRIS and STRAIN, 1978), but that this evapotranspiration is only important under the conditions of lower humidity that increase the magnitude of leaf water heavy isotope enrichment. The relative importance of cuticular versus stomatal transpiration, particularly under arid conditions, could thus affect the relationship between the D and $^{18}O$ content of atmospheric water vapor. Recently, efforts have been undertaken to use the isotopic variability of atmospheric water vapor as an element in global circulation models (JOUZEL et al., 1989). Isotopic fractionation during the hydrological cycle in the soil-plant-atmosphere continuum could be altered by the ratios of cuticular to stomatal transpiration in different vegetation types. Changes in vegetation type have been shown to alter regional rates of evapotranspiration (MOONEY et al., 1987). Increasing desertification, together with vegetation and climate changes associated with human activity, can no doubt cause changes in the global hydrological cycle. Unfortunately, the isotopic fractionation processes in plants that could help provide information on the magnitude of elements of the global hydrological cycle and the fluxes of other gases exchanged by vegetation have been studied only in a preliminary way.

*Acknowledgements*—We thank Dave Winter for performing the mass spectrometric analyses. Supported by

NSF grants DMB 84-05003 and DCB 88-96201 and by DOE grant DE-87ER60615. Ian Kaplan provided comments that helped improve the manuscript.

## REFERENCES

ALLISON G. B., GAT J. R. and LEANEY F. W. J. (1985) The relationship between deuterium and oxygen-18 delta values in leaf water. *Isotope Geosci.* **58**, 145–156.

ASHTON F. M. (1976) *Cuscuta* spp. (Dodder): A literature review of its biology and control. *Div. of Agri. Sci. Bull. 1880*, University of California, Davis.

BRICOUT J., FONTES J.-CH. and MERLIVAT L. (1972) Sur la composition en isotopes stables de l'eau des jus d'oranges. *C. R. Seances Acad. Sci. (Paris), Sér. D.* **274**, 1803–1806.

COOPER L. W. and DENIRO M. J. (1989) Covariant stable oxygen and hydrogen isotope compositions of plant water: Species effects. *Ecology* **70**, 1619–1628.

CRAIG H. (1961) Isotopic variations in meteoric waters. *Science* **133**, 1702–1703.

DANSGAARD W. (1964) Stable isotopes in precipitation. *Tellus* **16**, 436–468.

DOLE M., LANE G. A., RUDD D. P. and ZAUKELIES D. A. (1954) Isotopic composition of atmospheric oxygen and nitrogen. *Geochim. Cosmochim. Acta* **6**, 65–78.

DONGMANN G., NURNBERG H. W., FORSTEL H. and WAGENER K. (1974) On the enrichment of $H_2^{18}O$ in the leaves of transpiring plants. *Rad. Environ. Biophys.* **11**, 41–52.

EPSTEIN S. and MAYEDA T. (1953) Variations of $^{18}O$ content of water from natural sources. *Geochim. Cosmochim. Acta* **4**, 213–224.

FARRIS F. and STRAIN B. R. (1978) The effects of water-stress on leaf $H_2^{18}O$ enrichment. *Rad. Environ. Biophys.* **15**, 167–202.

FRANCEY R. J. and TANS P. P. (1987) Latitudinal variation in oxygen-18 of atmospheric $CO_2$. *Nature* **327**, 495–497.

FRIEDMAN I. and HARDCASTLE K. (1970) A new technique for pumping hydrogen gas. *Geochim. Cosmochim. Acta* **34**, 125–126.

GAT J. R. (1980) The isotopes of hydrogen and oxygen in precipitation. In *Handbook of Environmental Isotope Geochemistry* (eds. P. FRITZ and J. CH. FONTES), Vol. 1, Chap. 1, pp. 24–48.

GONFIANTINI R., GRATSIU S. and TONGIORGI E. (1965) Oxygen isotopic composition of water in leaves. In *Use of Isotopes and Radiation in Soil-Plant Nutrition Studies*, pp. 405–410. International Atomic Energy Agency.

JOUZEL J., SUOZZO R. J., KOSTER R. D., RUSSELL G. L., WHITE J. W. C. and BROECKER W. S. (1989) Water isotope tracers in GISS GCM: Sensitivity Experiments. *Eos* **70**, 1016.

KEELEY J. E., OSMOND C. B. and RAVEN J. A. (1984) *Stylites*, a vascular plant without stomata, absorbs $CO_2$ via its roots. *Nature* **310**, 694–695.

LEANEY G. W., OSMOND C. B., ALLISON G. B. and ZIEGLER H. (1985). Hydrogen-isotope composition of leaf water in $C_3$ and $C_4$ plants: Its relationship to the hydrogen-isotope composition of dry matter. *Planta* **164**, 215–220.

LESAINT C., MERLIVAT L., BRICOUT J., FONTES J. C. and GAUTHERET R. (1974) Sur la composition en isotopes stables de l'eau de la tomate et de Mais. *C. R. Acad. Sci. Paris* **278**, 2925–2930.

MACLEOD D. G. (1962) Some anatomical and physiological observations on two species of *Cuscuta*. *Trans. Proc. Bot. Soc. Edinburgh* **39**, 302–315.

MERLIVAT L. (1978) Molecular diffusivities of $H_2^{16}O$, $HD^{16}O$, and $H_2^{18}O$ in gases. *J. Chem. Physics* **69**, 2864–2871.

MOONEY H. A., VITOUSEK P. M. and MATSON P. A. (1987) Exchange of materials between terrestrial ecosystems and the atmosphere. *Science* **238**, 926–932.

SACHS L. (1984) *Applied Statistics: A Handbook of Techniques.* Springer-Verlag, New York.

STERNBERG L. (1988) Oxygen and hydrogen isotope ratios in plant cellulose: Mechanisms and applications. In *Stable Isotopes in Ecological Research* (eds. P. W. RUNDEL, J. R. EHLERINGER and K. A. NAGY), Chap. 9, pp. 124–141. Springer-Verlag.

STERNBERG L. DA S. L., DENIRO M. J., MCJUNKIN D., BERGER R. and KEELEY J. E. (1985) Carbon, oxygen and hydrogen isotope abundances of *Stylites* reflect its unique physiology. *Oecologia* **67**, 598–600.

STERNBERG L. DA S. L., DENIRO M. J. and JOHNSON H. B. (1986) Oxygen and hydrogen isotope ratios of water from photosynthetic tissues of CAM and $C_3$ plants. *Plant Physiol.* **82**, 428–431.

WERSHAW R. L., FRIEDMAN I., HELLER S. J. and FRANK P. A. (1970) Hydrogen isotopic fractionation of water passing through trees. In *Advances in Organic Geochemistry* (ed. G. D. HOBSON), pp. 55–67. Pergamon Press.

YAKIR D., DENIRO M. J. and RUNDEL P. W. (1989) Isotopic inhomogeneity of leaf water: Evidence and implication for the use of isotopic signals transduced by plants. *Geochim. Cosmochim. Acta* **53**, 2769–2773.

YAKIR D., DENIRO M. J., and GAT J. R. (1990) Natural deuterium and oxygen-18 enrichment in leaf water of cotton plants grown under wet and dry conditions: Evidence for water compartmentation and its dynamics. *Plant, Cell Environ.* **13**, 49–56.

ZUNDEL G., MIEKELEY W., GRISI B. M. and FORSTEL H. (1978) The $H_2^{18}O$ enrichment of leaf water of tropic trees: Comparison of species from the tropical rain forest and the semi-arid region in Brazil. *Rad. Environ. Biophys.* **15**, 203–212.

Stable Isotope Geochemistry: A Tribute to Samuel Epstein
© The Geochemical Society, Special Publication No. 3, 1991
Editors: H. P. Taylor, Jr., J. R. O'Neil and I. R. Kaplan

# $^{13}C/^{12}C$ ratios of the Fe(III) carbonate component in natural goethites

CRAYTON J. YAPP and HARALD POTHS

Department of Geology, University of New Mexico, Albuquerque, NM 87131, U.S.A.

**Abstract**—Small amounts of $CO_2$ are evolved during incremental vacuum dehydration of natural goethites at *ca.* 230°C. Much of the $CO_2$ appears to originate in a minor Fe(III) carbonate component in goethite. The amounts of the putative Fe(III) carbonate (also referred to as trapped $CO_2$) in the samples of this study range from 0.041 to 0.14 $\mu$moles of $CO_2$ per milligram of goethite. The $\delta^{13}C$ values of this trapped $CO_2$ range from $-17.1$ to $+2.9$ per mil. While temperatures and pH may affect the $\delta^{13}C$ values of the Fe(III) carbonate component in goethites, differences in the $\delta^{13}C$ values of the ambient aqueous carbonate systems probably account for much of the observed $\delta^{13}C$ range of about 20 per mil.

## INTRODUCTION

THE SOLID-STATE phase transformation of natural goethite to hematite in vacuum at temperatures of *ca.* 230°C is accompanied by the release of $CO_2$ (YAPP, 1983, 1987a; YAPP and POTHS, 1986). YAPP and POTHS (1986) used isotopic and material-balance results to demonstrate that this evolved $CO_2$ originated predominantly from two sources: (1) organic matter and (2) an inorganic $CO_2$-bearing component "trapped" within the goethite structure. Discrete admixed carbonate phases such as siderite, calcite, dolomite, etc. were experimentally ruled out as probable sources of the inorganically derived $CO_2$, because these minerals do not decarbonate at 200 to 300°C in vacuum on the time scales of the goethite dehydration experiments. YAPP and POTHS (1986) were able to calculate the $\delta^{13}C$ values of the organic matter associated with some of the goethites by measuring total carbon abundances and $\delta^{13}C$ values before and after treatment with concentrated hydrogen peroxide solution at room temperature. However, their experiments could not provide information on the $\delta^{13}C$ value of the $CO_2$ evolved from the inorganic source within the goethite.

YAPP (1987a) hypothesized that the inorganically derived $CO_2$ ("trapped" $CO_2$) might originate from an Fe(III) carbonate component in solid solution in goethite. YAPP and POTHS (1990) presented infrared spectral evidence for a distorted carbonate molecule in natural goethites. The wavenumbers of the carbonate absorption peaks were similar to those measured by DVORAK *et al.* (1969) for an unstable synthetic Fe(III) carbonate and support the idea of an Fe(III) carbonate component in the goethite crystal structure. The results of YAPP and POTHS (1986) and YAPP (1987a) indicate that, although unstable, the putative Fe(III) carbonate component in goethite will not decompose to release $CO_2$ unless the confining goethite structure also breaks down.

This behavior implies that the Fe(III) carbonate ("trapped $CO_2$") which was incorporated in the goethite at the time of goethite formation will likely remain a closed system until the goethite structure is disrupted. Experiments to measure the concentrations and $\delta^{13}C$ values of trapped $CO_2$ in natural goethites and the paleoenvironmental implications of the results are considered in this paper.

## EXPERIMENTAL METHODS

Samples of five natural goethites from diverse locales were selected for this study. The five were chosen because their total carbon $\delta^{13}C$ values before $H_2O_2$ treatment represent a relatively large range from $-26.5$ to $-8.1$ (see Table 1). The samples are labeled Paleo-X, OPWis-9, SConn-1, PPColo-1, and NMx-2. Paleo-X is a pseudomorph of goethite after pyrite from an occurrence in the Lucero Mountains of New Mexico. This sample was collected by S. Hayden. OPWis-9 is a sample of the Late Ordovician oolitic ironstone of the Neda Fm. collected by C. Yapp from the type locality in Wisconsin (PAULL, 1977). The remaining three goethite samples are described in YAPP and PEDLEY (1985). All five samples were ground to powders under reagent-grade acetone and sized by passage through brass sieves. Only the size fractions of less than 63 microns were employed in subsequent experiments (see YAPP and POTHS, 1986). Prior to grinding, the Neda Fm. sample (OPWis-9) was physically separated into ooliths and matrix. Only the ooliths from this deposit were used in this study. After grinding, all five samples were treated with 0.5 N HCl at room temperature for about 20 hours then thoroughly rinsed with deionized water. The dilute HCl treatment has no measurable effect on the goethite (YAPP, 1987b) and is employed to dissolve any calcite or aragonite that might be present in these samples as either an indigenous impurity or one introduced during handling. Any subsequent discussion of "untreated" samples refers to those powdered samples which have been subjected to only the dilute HCl rinse.

The results of YAPP and POTHS (1986) indicate that the removal of admixed organic matter will be necessary to facilitate straightforward determination of the $\delta^{13}C$ values of trapped $CO_2$ in goethites. These workers employed concentrated solutions of $H_2O_2$ (30%) to effect the removal of organic matter. For the present study the five afore-

Table 1. Total carbon yield and $\delta^{13}C$ values before and after $H_2O_2$ treatment. Trapped $CO_2$ yield before and after $H_2O_2$ treatment

| Sample | Total Carbon | | | | | Trapped $CO_2$ yield | |
| | Untreated | | $H_2O_2$ treated | | | | |
| | Yield | $\delta^{13}C$ | Yield | $\delta^{13}C$ | $W$ | Untreated | $H_2O_2$ treated |
|---|---|---|---|---|---|---|---|
| Paleo-X | 0.13 | −17.5 | 0.073 | −10.0 | 0.44 | 0.045 | 0.041 |
| OPWis-9 | 0.082 | −19.8 | 0.052 | −16.5 | 0.37 | 0.055 | 0.050 |
| SConn-1 | 0.39* | −26.5* | 0.081 | −12.0 | 0.79 | 0.070* | 0.055 |
| PPColo-1 | 0.27* | −8.1* | 0.19 | +2.3 | 0.30 | 0.15* | 0.14 |
| NMx-2 | 0.45* | −19.5* | 0.15 | −3.1 | 0.67 | 0.13* | 0.12 |

Yield reported as ($\mu$moles C/mg sample).
$W$ = fraction of total carbon removed by $H_2O_2$.
* Data from YAPP and POTHS (1986).

mentioned samples were subjected to room temperature treatments with concentrated $H_2O_2$ solutions for times ranging from 20 to 86 days using the approach of YAPP and POTHS (1986). In all cases the concentration of total carbon in the goethite was lower after $H_2O_2$ treatment, while the total carbon $\delta^{13}C$ value was more positive. Similar results were reported by YAPP and POTHS (1986) for three of these samples (SConn-1, PPColo-1, and NMx-2). All results on peroxide-treated samples reported in the current work were obtained on aliquots of these samples which were newly treated in quantities sufficient to permit incremental dehydration experiments.

The dehydration-decarbonation experiments were performed (after outgassing the sample at 100°C for one hour) under open system conditions in vacuum at temperatures ranging from 200 to 300°C. A sample was introduced into the furnace at a specified temperature for a predetermined amount of time. During this time the evolved $CO_2$ and $H_2O$ were continuously recovered by freezing into a cold trap at liquid nitrogen temperatures. At the end of the specified time the mineral sample was removed from the furnace (while still under vacuum). The sample was kept in the room temperature portion of the evacuated dehydration chamber while the evolved $CO_2$ and water were separated and recovered for yield and isotopic measurements. After completion of the processing of this $CO_2$ and $H_2O$, the sample was reintroduced to the furnace (still under vacuum) for another specified time interval, and the evolved $CO_2$ and water were continuously collected in the liquid nitrogen-cooled cold trap. This procedure of incremental vacuum dehydration of an aliquot of goethite continued until there was little additional recovery of $CO_2$ or $H_2O$. Carbon and hydrogen which remained in the mineral after these incremental dehydration steps at "low" temperature were removed by dehydration at 850°C in about 0.16 bar of pure oxygen and recovered for measurement. Details of the dehydration-decarbonation vacuum system are given in YAPP (1983).

A small modification to the preceding procedure was introduced in experiments MHD-1087 and MHD-1090 (Tables 2 and 3). In these experiments the first dehydration step (after the outgassing at 100°C) was performed under closed-system conditions in 0.16 bar of pure $O_2$. YAPP (1983) observed that these kinds of closed-system conditions retarded the goethite dehydration. Consequently, it was felt that this low temperature combustion in the first dehydration step might result in removal of additional

organic matter (perhaps remaining after the $H_2O_2$ treatment) without causing significant breakdown of the goethite.

Yields of incrementally evolved $CO_2$ were measured manometrically. The carbon isotope ratios of the $CO_2$ were measured on a Finnigan MAT Delta E isotope ratio mass spectrometer and are reported in the usual $\delta$ notation:

$$\delta^{13}C = \left[ \frac{R(\text{sample})}{R(\text{standard})} - 1 \right] \times 1000$$

where $R = {}^{13}C/{}^{12}C$ and the standard is PDB (CRAIG, 1957). The evolved water was quantitatively converted to hydrogen gas over uranium metal at 750°C and the hydrogen yield was measured manometrically. $CO_2$ yields were measured with a precision of about ±0.15 $\mu$moles, while hydrogen yields were measured with a precision of about ±1 $\mu$mole. For $CO_2$ samples on the order of 1 $\mu$mole, the analytical error of $\delta^{13}C$ measurements is about ±0.3 per mil.

## RESULTS AND DISCUSSION

### The Fe(III) carbonate model for evolved $CO_2$

The results of the various dehydration-decarbonation experiments performed for this study are listed in Tables 2 and 3. With the exception of the untreated Paleo-X sample in Table 2, all the experiments of Tables 2 and 3 were performed as incremental dehydrations on a single aliquot of the sample in question. For the untreated Paleo-X material, each experiment involved only a single 230°C step followed by the 850°C combustion. Experiments of this type were run on four different aliquots of untreated Paleo-X to obtain information on the patterns of $CO_2$ and $H_2O$ release and the $\delta^{13}C$ values of the evolved $CO_2$. Untreated Paleo-X was analyzed in this fashion, because at the time these experiments were run we were unable to accommodate the larger sample sizes required to perform incremental vacuum dehydrations on a single aliquot.

Table 2. Results from incremental dehydration-decarbonation experiments on natural goethites

| MHD# | Time (min) | T (°C) | CO$_2$ µmoles | δ$^{13}$C | H$_2$ µmoles | MHD# | Time (min) | T (°C) | CO$_2$ µmoles | δ$^{13}$C | H$_2$ µmoles |
|---|---|---|---|---|---|---|---|---|---|---|---|
| OPWis-9 (oolites) untreated | | | | | | Paleo-X H$_2$O$_2$-treated | | | | | |
| 1067 | 15 | 230 | 1.25 | −13.0 | 150 | 1073 | 15 | 230 | 2.0 | −6.2 | 201 |
| 1067 | 60 | 230 | 1.5 | −16.1 | 260 | 1073 | 60 | 230 | 4.5 | −5.3 | 595 |
| 1067 | 60 | 240 | 3.5 | −17.6 | 322 | 1073 | 60 | 230 | 2.0 | — | 319 |
| 1067 | 60 | 250 | 7.5 | −17.4 | 649 | 1073 | 60 | 230 | 0.75 | −5.3 | 139 |
| 1067 | 60 | 250 | 1.75 | −17.4 | 193 | 1073 | 60 | 230 | 0.75 | −6.5 | 129 |
| 1067 | 60 | 260 | 1.0 | −19.2 | 122 | 1073 | 60 | 230 | 0.5 | −6.5 | 55 |
| 1067 | 30* | 850* | 11.75 | −23.5 | 188 | 1073 | 30* | 850* | 9.5 | −14.8 | 330 |
| sample mass (after 100°C) = 344 mg | | | | | | sample mass (after 100°C) = 326 mg | | | | | |
| OPWis-9 (oolites) H$_2$O$_2$-treated | | | | | | SConn-1 H$_2$O$_2$-treated | | | | | |
| 1059 | 15 | 230 | 1.25 | −12.4 | 82 | 1075 | 10 | 220 | 2.25 | −11.1 | 307 |
| 1059 | 60 | 230 | 0.25 | — | 76 | 1075 | 30 | 220 | 2.5 | −11.1 | 319 |
| 1059 | 60 | 240 | 1.5 | −16.7 | 189 | 1075 | 30 | 220 | 2.35 | −10.5 | 260 |
| 1059 | 60 | 250 | 2.0 | −16.9 | 193 | 1075 | 30 | 220 | 1.65 | −11.3 | 171 |
| 1059 | 60 | 250 | 1.35 | −16.9 | 143 | 1075 | 60 | 220 | 1.5 | −12.3 | 163 |
| 1059 | 60 | 250 | 1.0 | −16.4 | 102 | 1075 | 60 | 220 | 1.25 | −14.3 | 96 |
| 1059 | 30* | 850* | 2.0 | −18.8 | 203 | 1075 | 960 | 220 | 3.25 | −21.5 | 114 |
| sample mass (after 100°C) = 179 mg | | | | | | 1075 | 30* | 850* | 5.5 | −14.5 | 102 |
| | | | | | | sample mass (after 100°C) = 250 mg | | | | | |
| OPWis-9 (oolites) H$_2$O$_2$-treated | | | | | | | | | | | |
| 1090 | 60* | 230* | 1.6 | −15.7 | 81 | PPColo-1 H$_2$O$_2$-treated | | | | | |
| 1090 | 30 | 230 | 0.9 | −17.0 | 159 | 1060 | 45 | 200 | 4.25 | −2.5 | 384 |
| 1090 | 30 | 230 | 1.25 | −17.7 | 123 | 1060 | 60 | 200 | 2.25 | +1.4 | 199 |
| 1090 | 45 | 230 | 2.8 | −17.6 | 246 | 1060 | 60 | 200 | 2.75 | +2.6 | 162 |
| 1090 | 60 | 230 | 2.8 | −17.4 | 246 | 1060 | 60 | 200 | 1.75 | +2.6 | 96 |
| 1090 | 60 | 230 | 1.25 | −16.9 | 123 | 1060 | 60 | 200 | 2.75 | +2.9 | 120 |
| 1090 | 120 | 230 | 0.3 | — | 41 | 1060 | 60 | 200 | 2.0 | +3.0 | 85 |
| 1090 | 1080 | 230 | ~0.15 | — | 13 | 1060 | 90 | 200 | 2.5 | +3.2 | 85 |
| 1090 | 30* | 850* | 1.25 | −18.9 | 114 | 1060 | 180 | 200 | 2.75 | +3.0 | 86 |
| sample mass (after 100°C) = 213 mg | | | | | | 1060 | 3900 | 200 | 12.5 | +3.4 | 368 |
| | | | | | | 1060 | 60 | 270 | 2.0 | +1.1 | 42 |
| Paleo-X untreated | | | | | | 1060 | 60 | 300 | 0.75 | +2.6 | 19 |
| 934 | 20 | 230 | 1.25 | −6.8 | 139 | 1060 | 30* | 850* | 19.0 | +2.8 | 115 |
| 934 | 30* | 850* | 11.75 | −18.4 | 390 | sample mass (after 100°C) = 281 mg | | | | | |
| 935 | 30 | 230 | 1.25 | −7.0 | 139 | | | | | | |
| 935 | 30* | 850* | 9.75 | −19.2 | 286 | | | | | | |
| 936 | 60 | 230 | 1.5 | −6.5 | 193 | | | | | | |
| 936 | 30* | 850* | 9.0 | −19.5 | 262 | | | | | | |
| 937 | 180 | 230 | 2.8 | −7.2 | 408 | | | | | | |
| 937 | 30* | 850* | 9.75 | −20.3 | 123 | | | | | | |

* Indicates closed-system dehydration in about 0.16 bar of pure O$_2$.

Samples reported in YAPP and POTHS (1986) were also analyzed in the manner just discussed for untreated Paleo-X.

The model for an Fe(III) carbonate component in solid solution in goethite leads to some testable predictions under the following set of assumptions: (1) at temperatures of *ca.* 230°C the Fe(III) carbonate will break down to release CO$_2$ only when the local confining goethite structure breaks down; (2) the loss of structural hydrogen can be taken as a measure of the fraction of the goethite structure which has broken down to hematite; (3) the concentration of the Fe(III) carbonate component (trapped CO$_2$) is uniform throughout the goethite sample of interest; (4) the δ$^{13}$C value of the Fe(III) carbonate is uniform throughout the goethite sample of interest. If the trapped CO$_2$ is lost from lattice "compartments" during the thermal breakdown of goethite to hematite as suggested above, then in combination with the other assumptions it is ex-

Table 3. Dehydration-decarbonation experiments on NMx-2 goethite

| MHD# | Time (min) | $T$ (°C) | CO₂ μmoles | CO₂ $\delta^{13}C$ | H₂ μmoles |
|------|------|------|------|------|------|
| 1082 | 15 | 200 | 0.9 | −8.5 | 123 |
| 1082 | 60 | 200 | 4.9 | −2.7 | 414 |
| 1082 | 60 | 200 | 6.7 | −0.5 | 320 |
| 1082 | 60 | 200 | 2.0 | −0.1 | 71 |
| 1082 | 120 | 200 | 3.5 | 0.0 | 114 |
| 1082 | 120 | 200 | 0.8 | −0.9 | 24 |
| 1082 | 1080 | 200 | 0.8 | −8.1 | 28 |
| 1082 | 30* | 850* | 11.4 | −5.5 | 100 |

sample mass after (100°C) = 197 mg

NMx-2 H₂O₂-treated

| MHD# | Time (min) | $T$ (°C) | CO₂ μmoles | CO₂ $\delta^{13}C$ | H₂ μmoles |
|------|------|------|------|------|------|
| 1087 | 60* | 200* | 3.2 | −13.6 | 182 |
| 1087 | 15 | 200 | 0.0 | — | 58 |
| 1087 | 60 | 200 | 3.75 | −0.9 | 396 |
| 1087 | 60 | 200 | 1.9 | −0.2 | 106 |
| 1087 | 120 | 200 | 6.7 | 0.0 | 314 |
| 1087 | 120 | 200 | 5.4 | 0.0 | 216 |
| 1087 | 120 | 200 | 1.1 | −0.3 | 45 |
| 1087 | 240 | 200 | 1.1 | −0.3 | 41 |
| 1087 | 1200 | 200 | 1.6 | −7.5 | 51 |
| 1087 | 30* | 850* | 14.9 | −3.6 | 131 |

sample mass (after 100°C) = 256 mg

* Indicates closed-system dehydration in about 0.16 bar of pure O₂.

pected that the CO₂ and H₂O would be evolved in constant proportions. Thus,

$$\frac{n(CO_2)}{n(H_2O)} = m \quad (1)$$

where

$n(CO_2)$ = μmoles of CO₂ evolved over an increment of vacuum dehydration-decarbonation,

$n(H_2O)$ = μmoles of H₂O evolved over that same increment, and

$m$ = constant.

Equation (1) implies the following linear relation during dehydration-decarbonation of goethite:

$$X_s(CO_2) = [1 - X_s(CO_2)^*]X_s(H_2) + X_s(CO_2)^* \quad (2)$$

where

$X_s(CO_2)$ = mole fraction of the initial total carbon that remains in the mineral after some interval of dehydration-decarbonation,

$X_s(H_2)$ = mole fraction of the initial total hydrogen that remains in the mineral after that same interval, and

$X_s(CO_2)^*$ = value of $X_s(CO_2)$ when $X_s(H_2) = 0$.

Also, because the model assumes that the Fe(III) carbonate is locally confined within the goethite lattice and breaks down only when the local lattice breaks down, the carbonate molecules should be incapable of exchanging carbon isotopes with one another or of being selectively removed because of different decomposition rates of the carbonate isotopic molecules. Thus, the $\delta^{13}C$ values of increments of "trapped" CO₂ evolved at *ca.* 230°C should be constant during the transformation of goethite to hematite. Figure 1 depicts representative predicted patterns of (a) evolved incremental CO₂ $\delta^{13}C$ values *vs.* $X_v(CO_2)$ and (b) $X_s(CO_2)$ *vs.* $X_s(H_2)$. $X_v(CO_2)$ is the cumulative sum of evolved CO₂ as a mole fraction of the total initial carbon in the sample. As shown in Fig. 1b and Eqn. (2), the slope and intercept of the linear $X_s(CO_2)$ *vs.* $X_s(H_2)$ curves depend

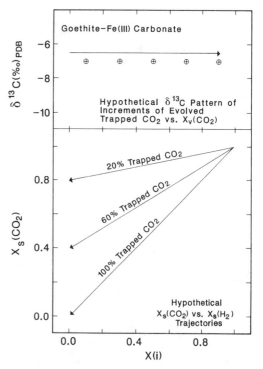

FIG. 1. Diagram at the top illustrates the constant $\delta^{13}C$ values expected for increments of CO₂ evolved from the Fe(III) carbonate component (trapped CO₂) in goethites as a function of fraction of total carbon removed [$X_v(CO_2)$]. The bottom graph depicts the pattern of $X_s(CO_2)$ *vs.* $X_s(H_2)$ expected during vacuum dehydration-decarbonation of H₂O₂-treated goethite. The percentage of the total carbon represented by trapped CO₂ (Fe(III) carbonate) determines the slope and intercept of the $X_s(CO_2)$ *vs.* $X_s(H_2)$ array. $X_s(H_2)$ is the fraction of total goethite hydrogen remaining in the mineral after some interval of dehydration. $X_s(CO_2)$ is the corresponding fraction of total carbon remaining in the mineral. See text for discussion of the model upon which these curves are based.

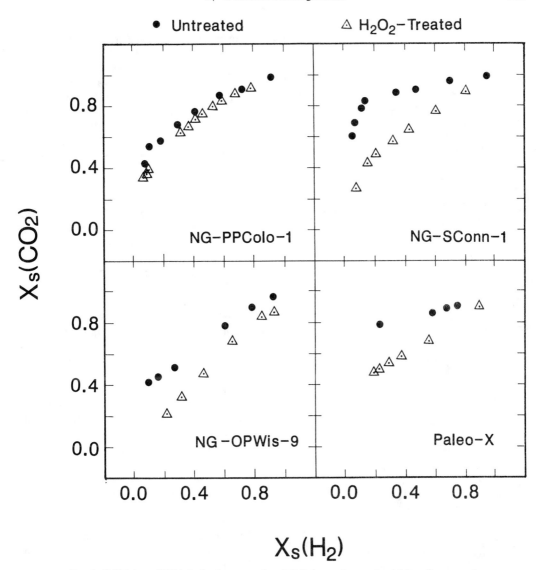

FIG. 2. $X_s(CO_2)$ vs. $X_s(H_2)$ for both untreated and $H_2O_2$-treated natural goethites. By comparison with Fig. 1 it is evident that the percentage of total carbon represented by trapped $CO_2$ (Fe(III) carbonate) is higher for an $H_2O_2$-treated sample aliquot than for a corresponding untreated aliquot. This is a consequence of removal of organic carbon in the $H_2O_2$-treated aliquots. The abrupt change in slope for the untreated SConn-1 data is discussed in the text.

upon how much refractory carbon $[X_s(CO_2)]^*$ is present in the goethite (e.g., as admixed discrete carbonate phases). The amount of trapped $CO_2$ in a goethite sample as a mole fraction of the total carbon in the sample could be obtained by extrapolating a linear array of $X_s(CO_2)$ vs. $X_s(H_2)$ data points to the condition of complete removal of hydrogen. The mole fraction of trapped $CO_2$ would be equal to $[1 - X_s(CO_2)^*]$, which is also the slope of the line (Eqn. 2).

Plots of $X_s(CO_2)$ vs. $X_s(H_2)$ as calculated from the data of Tables 2 and 3 are shown in Figs. 2 and

3. The data for the untreated samples PPColo-1, SConn-1, and NMx-2 in Figs. 2 and 3 were taken from YAPP and POTHS (1986). It is evident from the data arrays in Figs. 2 and 3 that the removal of organic matter by treatment of the goethite samples with concentrated $H_2O_2$ solution has a significant effect on the patterns of release of $CO_2$ and $H_2O$. The effects are most pronounced in samples for which the initial amount of total carbon was high and removal of organic carbon by $H_2O_2$ was most extensive (SConn-1, 79% of carbon removed; and NMx-2, 67% removed, see Table 1). In the cases of

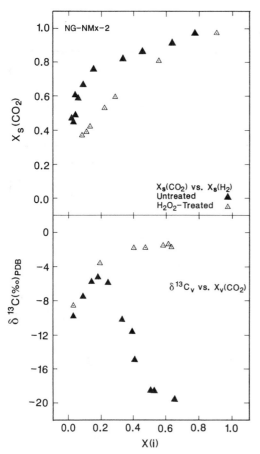

FIG. 3. Upper plot depicts $X_s(CO_2)$ vs. $X_s(H_2)$ for untreated and $H_2O_2$-treated NMx-2. The lower plot shows the variation of $\delta^{13}C_v$ with $X_v(CO_2)$. $\delta^{13}C_v$ is the $\delta^{13}C$ of the cumulative sum of $CO_2$ evolved at different extents of vacuum dehydration-decarbonation of goethite. $X_v(CO_2)$ is the cumulative sum of evolved $CO_2$ as a mole fraction of the total carbon in goethite. The contrasting patterns of $\delta^{13}C_v$ values for untreated and $H_2O_2$-treated NMx-2 reflect the increasing contribution of $^{13}C$-depleted $CO_2$ slowly evolved from organic matter in the latter stages of the untreated goethite dehydration (see text for discussion).

untreated SConn-1 (Fig. 2) and untreated NMx-2 (Fig. 3) the plots of $X_s(CO_2)$ vs. $X_s(H_2)$ exhibit abrupt changes in slope at $X_s(H_2)$ values of about 0.18. As open-system goethite dehydration-decarbonation in vacuum at ca. 230°C progresses to $X_s(H_2)$ values less than about 0.20, the rate of further goethite breakdown decreases rapidly (YAPP, 1983). Experiments must be run for much longer times to achieve any further significant recovery of $CO_2$ and $H_2O$. As discussed by YAPP and POTHS (1986), the steeper slope of $X_s(CO_2)$ vs. $X_s(H_2)$ data arrays when $X_s(H_2)$ values are less than about 0.20 implies that a second source of carbon has begun to dominate

the evolved $CO_2$ as trapped $CO_2$ becomes less important with the reduction in the rate of breakdown of goethite. YAPP and POTHS (1986) concluded that the second source of this slowly evolved $CO_2$ was organic matter. Because this organic-derived $CO_2$ is so slowly evolved, it should not be a major component of the $CO_2$ evolved early in the dehydration when the breakdown of goethite is rapid and the trapped $CO_2$ constitutes most of the recovered $CO_2$. Removal of most of the organic matter prior to dehydration-decarbonation of goethite should eliminate much of the abrupt change of slope in the $X_s(CO_2)$ vs. $X_s(H_2)$ arrays of untreated SConn-1 and NMx-2 in Figs. 2 and 3. The patterns of $X_s(CO_2)$ vs. $X_s(H_2)$ for $H_2O_2$-treated SConn-1 and NMx-2 are consistent with this expectation (see Figs. 2 and 3).

The proportions of trapped $CO_2$ in the total carbon of the samples of Figs. 2 and 3 were determined by extrapolation of these arrays to $X_s(H_2) = 0$. For untreated samples only the early portions of the arrays ($X_s(H_2) > 0.20$) were employed. These trapped $CO_2$ proportions and the measured concentrations of total carbon in the goethite were used to calculate the mineral-normalized concentrations of trapped $CO_2$ in the goethites. The trapped $CO_2$ concentrations for corresponding untreated and $H_2O_2$-treated goethite samples are listed in Table 1. Also listed in Table 1 are the concentrations of total carbon in corresponding untreated and $H_2O_2$-treated samples. The rather large differences between *total* carbon concentration before and after treatment with $H_2O_2$ are in sharp contrast to the generally unchanged values of *trapped* $CO_2$ concentrations before and after $H_2O_2$ treatment. The slightly higher calculated values for trapped $CO_2$ in untreated samples might reflect small contributions of $CO_2$ from organic matter. However, the good overall agreement between trapped $CO_2$ concentrations for corresponding untreated and $H_2O_2$-treated samples suggests that the peroxide treatment has had no measurable effect on the Fe(III) carbonate component in goethite.

The $\delta^{13}C$ values of $CO_2$ evolved from both untreated and $H_2O_2$-treated goethite samples are plotted in Figs. 3 and 4 against $X_v(CO_2)$. $\delta^{13}C_v$ is the $\delta^{13}C$ value of the cumulative sum of $CO_2$ evolved at a given value of $X_v(CO_2)$. The $\delta^{13}C_v$ values plotted in Figs. 3 and 4 were calculated from the incremental data in Tables 2 and 3 with the exception of untreated Paleo-X which was evolved in a manner that produced a directly measured $\delta^{13}C_v$ value for the single 230°C step of each of the four experiments (see Table 2). The $\delta^{13}C_v$ data for untreated NMx-2, SConn-1, and PPColo-1 were taken from

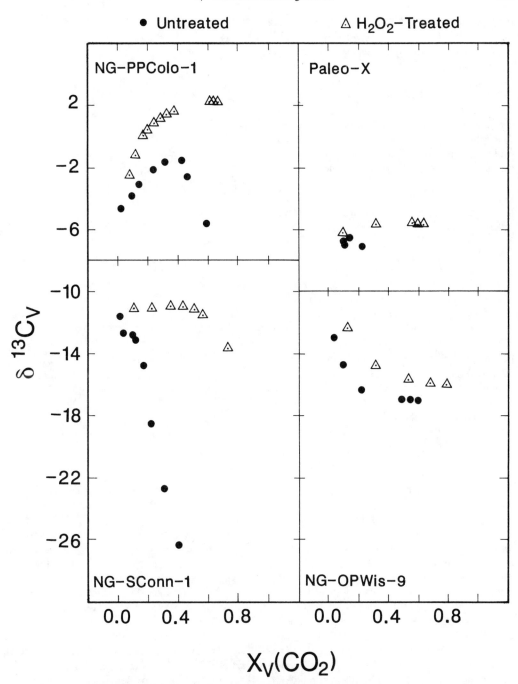

FIG. 4. $\delta^{13}C_v$ *vs.* $X_v(CO_2)$ for untreated and $H_2O_2$-treated aliquots of four different goethite samples. Note that the $\delta^{13}C_v$ values of the untreated aliquots are more negative than those of the corresponding $H_2O_2$-treated aliquots reflecting a contribution of ¹³C-depleted $CO_2$ from organic matter in the untreated samples.

YAPP and POTHS (1986). The $\delta^{13}C_v$ parameter is employed here rather than the $\delta^{13}C$ values of non-cumulative, discrete increments of evolved $CO_2$, because the data of YAPP and POTHS (1986), which are used for comparison, were directly determined as $\delta^{13}C_v$. The plots in Figs. 3 and 4 reveal distinct isotopic differences between $CO_2$ evolved from untreated and $H_2O_2$-treated goethites. In all five cases the $\delta^{13}C_v$ values of the $H_2O_2$-treated samples are more positive than those of the untreated samples. This isotopic distinction suggests that small amounts of organic-derived $CO_2$ contribute to the evolved $CO_2$ from untreated goethites even very early in the dehydration-decarbonation reaction. The two untreated samples with the largest concentrations of organic matter (NMx-2) and (SConn-1) exhibit the largest isotopic differences between evolved $CO_2$ from untreated and $H_2O_2$-treated samples as the reactions progress. The differences between treated and untreated $\delta^{13}C_v$ values can be as large as 17 per mil for NMx-2 (Fig. 3) and 14 per mil for SConn-1 (Fig. 4). These kinds of isotopic differences emphasize the importance of removal of organic matter before attempting to determine the carbon isotope composition of the Fe(III) carbonate (trapped $CO_2$) in goethites.

There are indications in the data for the $H_2O_2$-treated goethites of Figs. 3 and 4 that the $\delta^{13}C_v$ values may reach relatively constant or "plateau" values. However, $\delta^{13}C_v$ values representing later portions of the dehydration-decarbonation reactions contain isotopic "memories" of the earlier evolved $CO_2$, because the $\delta^{13}C_v$ value represents the $\delta^{13}C$ value of the cumulative sum of the $CO_2$ evolved to that point in an experiment. The $\delta^{13}C$ values of noncumulative, discrete increments of evolved $CO_2$ are preferable, because they provide the kind of information required for discussions of the model predictions represented by Eqns. (1) and (2) and Fig. 1. All of the data for $H_2O_2$-treated samples in Tables 2 and 3 are the noncumulative, incremental type. Subsequent discussions of both yield and isotope data employ these incremental results.

One test for linearity of the $X_s(CO_2)$ vs. $X_s(H_2)$ arrays of Figs. 2 and 3 is an examination of the value of the instantaneous slope of an array as a function of reaction progress measured by $X_v(CO_2)$. Values of the slopes of these arrays over finite increments were calculated as the ratios of $n(CO_2)$ to $n(H_2O)$. Values of $n(CO_2)$ and the corresponding $n(H_2O)$ are listed in Tables 2 and 3. Plots of incremental $n(CO_2)/n(H_2O)$ ratios vs. $X_v(CO_2)$ for the five different peroxide-treated samples are found in Figs. 5 and 6. The data for NMx-2 were plotted in Fig. 6 to minimize the clutter in Fig. 5. Samples OPWis-9 and Paleo-X exhibit relatively small variations in their $n(CO_2)/n(H_2O)$ ratios as the dehydration-decarbonation progresses (Fig. 5). The $n(CO_2)/n(H_2O)$ ratios for SConn-1 are also relatively constant for $X_v(CO_2)$ values up to about 0.50. Thus, given the analytical error associated with measurements of such small amounts of $CO_2$, the model prediction of a linear correlation between $X_s(CO_2)$

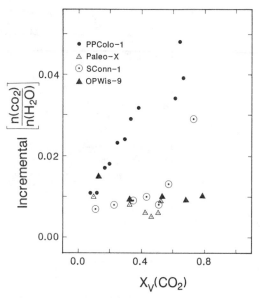

FIG. 5. A plot of the $n(CO_2)/n(H_2O)$ ratio for corresponding $CO_2$ and water increments evolved during vacuum dehydration-decarbonation of $H_2O_2$-treated goethite vs. $X_v(CO_2)$. Samples for which the loss of $CO_2$ is linearly correlated with loss of $H_2O$ should yield horizontal data arrays in the diagram above. Three of the four samples exhibit intervals of very little change in the value of the $[n(CO_2)/n(H_2O)]$ ratio as a function of extent of reaction $[X_v(CO_2)]$. PPColo-1 has a continuously increasing ratio and SConn-1 exhibits an abrupt increase in the $n(CO_2)/n(H_2O)$ ratio at $X_v(CO_2)$ values greater than about 0.50 (see text for discussion).

and $X_s(H_2)$ (i.e. constant slope) is largely realized by samples OPWis-9, Paleo-X, and SConn-1. The change in slope of the $X_s(CO_2)$ vs. $X_s(H_2)$ data for peroxide-treated SConn-1 that is indicated by the large increase in $n(CO_2)/n(H_2O)$ at $X_v(CO_2)$ values greater than 0.50 (Fig. 5) is reminiscent of the more abrupt change in slope noted for untreated SConn-1 (see Fig. 2). This suggests that not all of the organic matter was removed by the $H_2O_2$ treatment of SConn-1. Carbon isotope results to be discussed below are consistent with this suggestion.

As indicated by the $n(CO_2)/n(H_2O)$ vs. $X_v(CO_2)$ data of Figs. 5 and 6, the slopes of the $X_s(CO_2)$ vs. $X_s(H_2)$ arrays of peroxide-treated PPColo-1 and NMx-2 increase continuously as the dehydration-decarbonation reaction progresses. Consequently, the $X_s(CO_2)$ vs. $X_s(H_2)$ arrays are curvilinear for these samples. To determine if residual organic matter not removed by the $H_2O_2$ was contributing to the nonlinear behavior, a second aliquot of NMx-2 was subjected to vacuum dehydration-decarbonation (see experiment 1087 in Table 3). In this experiment the first step (after outgassing at 100°C)

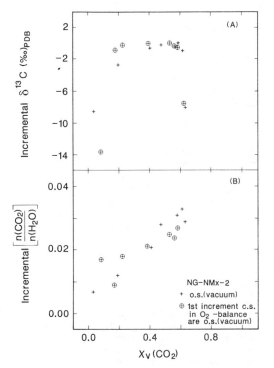

FIG. 6. The upper plot (A) shows the $\delta^{13}C$ values of increments of $CO_2$ evolved during dehydration-decarbonation of $H_2O_2$-treated NMx-2 vs. $X_v(CO_2)$. "O.S." refers to open-system vacuum dehydration conditions, while "C.S." refers to closed-system conditions. A "plateau" of $\delta^{13}C$ values near −0.2 per mil is evident in the $X_v(CO_2)$ range from about 0.10 to 0.50, particularly for the experiment for which the first $CO_2$ increment was recovered after closed-system dehydration in oxygen. Subsequent increments of $CO_2$ from this experiment were recovered during open-system dehydration in vacuum (see text for discussion). Plot (B) shows that the slope of the correlated loss of $CO_2$ and $H_2O$ in $H_2O_2$-treated NMx-2 generally increases as the dehydration of the goethite progresses. The principal exception to this general trend is the first increment in the population represented by the circled crosses. This increment was obtained under closed-system conditions in $O_2$ (see Table 3) which facilitated oxidation of some of the small amounts of organic matter remaining after $H_2O_2$ treatment and thus increased its $n(CO_2)/n(H_2O)$ ratio.

involved a 200°C closed-system extraction in 0.16 bar of pure $O_2$ for one hour. As can be seen in Table 3, the amount of hydrogen extracted by the closed-system step was not much greater than that extracted by the first open-system step of experiment 1082. Yet, the $n(CO_2)/n(H_2O)$ ratio of the closed-system step in $O_2$ at 200°C (experiment MHD 1087) is larger than that in the first open-system step of experiment 1082 (see Fig. 6B). The larger value of the $n(CO_2)/n(H_2O)$ ratio for the oxidative closed-system step of MHD 1087 suggests that there was

some organic matter remaining in this sample after $H_2O_2$ treatment. The $\delta^{13}C$ value of the $CO_2$ from the oxidative 200°C closed-system step of 1087 is more negative than that of the first open-system in vacuo step of 1082 (see Fig. 6A). The more negative $\delta^{13}C$ value of the closed-system $CO_2$ is consistent with the idea that the higher $n(CO_2)/n(H_2O)$ ratio of this step is a result of oxidation of a small amount of organic matter remaining in the sample. However, this residual organic matter is apparently not responsible for the nonlinear character of the $X_s(CO_2)$ vs. $X_s(H_2)$ data array of $H_2O_2$-treated NMx-2, because subsequent 200°C steps in experiment 1087 were run under open-system conditions in vacuum and the pattern of increasing $n(CO_2)/n(H_2O)$ ratios with increasing $X_v(CO_2)$ mimics that for experiment 1082 (see Fig. 6B). A similar experiment (unpublished) on a second aliquot of $H_2O_2$-treated PPColo-1 yielded the same type of pattern as that shown in Fig. 5 for PPColo-1. Therefore, it appears that the nonlinear $X_s(CO_2)$ vs. $X_s(H_2)$ arrays observed for peroxide-treated samples of PPColo-1 and NMx-2 are reproducible and are not related to the presence of small amounts of organic matter that were not removed by $H_2O_2$.

The assumptions adopted earlier for the model of Fe(III) carbonate in solid solution in goethite do not lead to a prediction of curvilinear behavior in $X_s(CO_2)$ vs. $X_s(H_2)$ plots. Although this curvilinear behavior seems to weaken support for the model, it is apparent from the carbon isotope data to be discussed later that the model of Fe(III) carbonate in goethite can explain all of the data obtained thus far, including those for the curvilinear $X_s(CO_2)$ vs. $X_s(H_2)$ arrays.

Figure 6A contains a plot of the $\delta^{13}C$ values of increments of evolved $CO_2$ vs. the cumulative progress variable $X_v(CO_2)$ for $H_2O_2$-treated NMx-2 (experiments 1082 and 1087). For both experiments the $\delta^{13}C$ values of the increments of evolved $CO_2$ are initially relatively negative then rapidly increase to a "plateau" of values near −0.2. In both experiments the final 200°C open-system vacuum dehydration steps were run for times in excess of 1000 minutes (see Table 3). The $\delta^{13}C$ of the $CO_2$ from this final long-term 200°C step was shifted to much more negative values in both experiments. Such negative $\delta^{13}C$ shifts in $CO_2$ evolved during a long-term vacuum dehydration step near the end of the reaction indicate that some of the evolved $CO_2$ originated from a small amount of organic matter which was only slowly oxidized to $CO_2$ (perhaps by reaction with the ferric oxide in the solid state at 200°C). With the small amounts of evolved $CO_2$ generated in these long duration final 200°C steps (*ca.* 1 μmole, see Table 3), organically derived $CO_2$ could constitute 15 to 20% of the $CO_2$ sample and not have a measurable effect on the yield, because the analytical precision of the manometric measurements is only about ±0.15 μmole. Addition of as little as 0.2 to 0.3 μmole of organically derived $CO_2$ with a $\delta^{13}C$ value of *ca.* −35 (see YAPP and POTHS, 1986) to *ca.* 1 μmole of evolved trapped $CO_2$ with a $\delta^{13}C$ value of −0.2 would yield a composite evolved $CO_2$ sample with a $\delta^{13}C$ of less than −7.0. Note that the initial 200°C closed-system oxidation step of 1087 had no significant effect on the organic matter hypothesized to explain the isotopic shifts in the terminal 200°C steps. However, the $\delta^{13}C$ values of $CO_2$ evolved under vacuum at 200°C in steps subsequent to the initial oxidative closed-system step of 1087 almost immediately attained the "plateau" values near −0.2 (see Fig. 6A). This suggests that a small amount of easily oxidizable organic matter which interfered with the approach to plateau $\delta^{13}C$ values early in experiment 1082 was largely removed by the initial oxidative closed-system 200°C step of experiment 1087. The constancy of evolved $CO_2$ $\delta^{13}C$ values manifested in the isotopic plateau of Fig. 6A is consistent with the prediction of the Fe(III) carbonate model.

Samples of goethite which fulfill all of the stated predictions of the Fe(III) carbonate model would produce a characteristic data array on a plot of incrementally evolved trapped $CO_2$ $\delta^{13}C$ values *vs.* the corresponding $n(CO_2)/n(H_2O)$ ratios. If the trapped $CO_2$ $\delta^{13}C$ values and the $n(CO_2)/n(H_2O)$ ratios are each constant (as predicted) during the dehydration-decarbonation reaction of a goethite, all of the data for that goethite should be superposed on a single point in such a plot. The existence of analytical error suggests that a more realistic expectation would be for a relatively tight cluster of data points on such a diagram.

The $\delta^{13}C$ values of incrementally evolved $CO_2$ are plotted in Fig. 7 against the corresponding $n(CO_2)/n(H_2O)$ ratios for $H_2O_2$-treated samples PPColo-1, Paleo-X, SConn-1, and OPWis-9 (data are listed in Table 2). Paleo-X, SConn-1, and OPWis-9 all exhibit small domains of data points which reflect the relative constancy of the evolved $CO_2$ $\delta^{13}C$ values and the linearity of their $X_s(CO_2)$ *vs.* $X_s(H_2)$ slopes over most of the extent of goethite dehydration. The first $CO_2$ increment from OPWis-9 (experiment 1059, Table 2) has a higher $n(CO_2)/n(H_2O)$ ratio and a more positive $\delta^{13}C$ value than subsequent evolved $CO_2$ increments (Fig. 7). The tight cluster of the subsequent OPWis-9 data (Fig. 7) implies that the initial point in 1059 contains a $CO_2$ component that did not originate as trapped

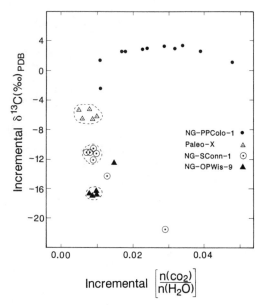

FIG. 7. Incremental $\delta^{13}C$ values *vs.* corresponding incremental $n(CO_2)/n(H_2O)$ ratios for $H_2O_2$-treated goethites. The model for Fe(III) carbonate in goethite that is discussed in the text predicts that in this type of plot all the data from a single goethite sample will plot on a common point. The enclosed data clusters in the diagram represent an approximate realization of the prediction. The data for PPColo-1 and three other apparently aberrant points are discussed in the text. All four of the samples in this figure exhibit "plateaus" of evolved $CO_2$ $\delta^{13}C$ values.

$CO_2$ in the goethite. This extra $CO_2$ in the initial 230°C step of OPWis-9 (1059) may contain a significant proportion of surface-adsorbed $CO_2$. Comparison of experiment 1059 with 1090 suggests that an initial closed-system oxidative step (1090) removes more of the extra "$^{13}C$-rich" $CO_2$, because subsequent trapped $CO_2$ $\delta^{13}C$ values in 1090 are more negative than in 1059. SConn-1 has five tightly grouped data points in Fig. 7 and two which display progressively larger $n(CO_2)/n(H_2O)$ ratios and more negative $\delta^{13}C$ values. The latter two points represent the two final 200°C *in vacuo* steps (see Table 2 and Fig. 5). In particular the SConn-1 data point with the largest $n(CO_2)/n(H_2O)$ ratio and the most negative $\delta^{13}C$ value represents the terminal 200°C *in vacuo* step which was run for 960 minutes. As was discussed earlier, the $CO_2$ from this step probably contains a portion of $CO_2$ that derived from the slow oxidation (by the ferric oxide?) of a small amount of organic matter which was not removed by the room temperature $H_2O_2$ treatment. The $\delta^{13}C$ value of −21.5 for the $CO_2$ evolved in this step is consistent with this suggestion. The enclosed domains of data for samples Paleo-X, SConn-1, and

OPWis-9 in Fig. 7 are assumed to represent the trapped $CO_2$(Fe(III) carbonate) in these samples, because these data represent a pattern of behavior predicted by the Fe(III) carbonate model.

The PPColo-1 data of Fig. 7 exhibit a "plateau" of $\delta^{13}C$ values which is close to +3 per mil. The initial 200°C step produced the $CO_2$ which is isotopically farthest removed from the plateau $\delta^{13}C$ values. The source for some of this initial $CO_2$ is unknown but may be surface-adsorbed $CO_2$ which was not outgassed at 100°C. The existence of relatively constant $\delta^{13}C$ values for the incrementally evolved $CO_2$ from both PPColo-1 (Fig. 7) and NMx-2 (Fig. 6A) is consistent with the origin of this $CO_2$ from a minor Fe(III) carbonate component in goethite in spite of the inconstancy of the $n(CO_2)/n(H_2O)$ ratio for each of these $H_2O_2$-treated samples. An Fe(III) carbonate origin for this $CO_2$ is supported by the infrared spectra of these same two samples (YAPP and POTHS, 1990).

We do not yet have an experimentally supported explanation for the nearly continuous increase of $n(CO_2)/n(H_2O)$ ratios during the course of dehydration-decarbonation experiments performed on $H_2O_2$-treated NMx-2 and PPColo-1. However, one speculation centers on the fact that these samples contain nonstoichiometric water which persists in the sample even after outgassing at 100°C (YAPP and PEDLEY, 1985). If this nonstoichiometric water were released at $ca.$ 230°C in vacuum at a somewhat higher rate than the structural hydroxyl hydrogen (and trapped $CO_2$), the $n(CO_2)/n(H_2O)$ ratios early in the vacuum dehydration would be smaller. As the dehydration progressed this ratio would become progressively larger, because the proportion of nonstoichiometric water would diminish relative to structural water. Furthermore, the release of extraneous nonstoichiometric water should not affect the constancy of $\delta^{13}C$ values of $CO_2$ incrementally evolved from Fe(III) carbonate. Such behavior would explain the relatively constant trapped $CO_2$ $\delta^{13}C$ values over the range of $n(CO_2)/n(H_2O)$ values observed for NMx-2 and PPColo-1 (Figs. 6 and 7).

The preceding results and discussion indicate that the $\delta^{13}C$ values of the putative Fe(III) carbonate component in natural goethites can be measured and that the predictions of the Fe(III) carbonate model concerning goethite vacuum dehydration-decarbonation experiments are generally realized. The averaged "plateau" $\delta^{13}C$ values of the Fe(III) carbonates (trapped $CO_2$) in the five goethites of Tables 2 and 3 are as follows: OPWis-9 (−17.1); SConn-1 (−11.2); Paleo-X (−5.7); PPColo-1 (+2.9); NMx-2 (−0.2). This $\delta^{13}C$ range of about 20 per mil

among these five samples suggests that information on the different environments of formation may be preserved in the Fe(III) carbonate in goethite.

## Fe(III) carbonate $\delta^{13}C$ values and paleoenvironment

Figure 8 depicts the approximate $\delta^{13}C$ ranges of a number of low temperature carbon reservoirs. The 20 per mil range of $\delta^{13}C$ values measured for the Fe(III) carbonate component in the five natural goethites of the current study is comparable to the $\delta^{13}C$ range for "freshwater" carbonates. All five of the goethite samples of Table 1 have hydrogen and oxygen isotope ratios which indicate formation in the presence of meteoric ("fresh") waters (YAPP, 1987b; also, unpubl. results). Sedimentary calcite which had precipitated from an aqueous system in isotopic equilibrium with atmospheric $CO_2$ ($\delta^{13}C$ of −7) would be expected to have $\delta^{13}C$ values of about +3 or +4 (FRIEDMAN and O'NEIL, 1977). Because the $\delta^{13}C$ values of freshwater calcium carbonates of diverse origins appear to be controlled by the $\delta^{13}C$ values of the ambient aqueous carbonate + $CO_2$ system (FRITZ and POPLAWSKI, 1974; QUADE et al., 1989), freshwater carbonates with $\delta^{13}C$ values significantly more negative then $ca.$ +3 were probably precipitated from waters in which oxidized organic matter lowered the $\delta^{13}C$ value of the aqueous carbonate (Fig. 8). However, the possible role of other environmental parameters in controlling carbonate $\delta^{13}C$ values needs to be evaluated to determine how directly the different $\delta^{13}C$ values of solid carbonates reflect differences in the $\delta^{13}C$ values of the ambient aqueous carbonate systems.

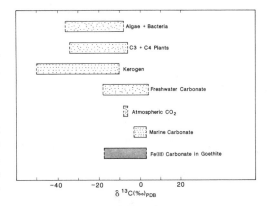

FIG. 8. Approximate ranges of $\delta^{13}C$ values for a number of surficial carbon reservoirs. Ranges were taken from HOEFS (1987) and SCHIDLOWSKI et al. (1983). The range of $\delta^{13}C$ values exhibited by the putative Fe(III) carbonate (trapped $CO_2$) in the goethite samples of the current study is shown for comparison.

The carbon isotope fractionation factor for Fe(III) carbonate $vs.$ $CO_2$ is not yet known. However, CAROTHERS et al. (1988) experimentally determined the $\alpha$ for $^{13}C/^{12}C$ partitioning between siderite and $CO_2$. Comparison of the siderite-$CO_2$ fractionation at the lowest experimental temperature (33°C) reported by CAROTHERS et al. (1988) with the calcite-$CO_2$ fractionation at 33°C (FRIEDMAN and O'NEIL, 1977) reveals that siderite would be enriched in $^{13}C$ by about 2.6 per mil relative to calcite. Over the range of sedimentary and early diagenetic temperatures (<100°C) it appears as if the carbon isotope fractionation between siderite and calcite does not vary greatly with temperature. By analogy it will be assumed as a first approximation that the carbon isotope fractionation between Fe(III) carbonate and calcite is independent of temperature and that the temperature dependence which applies to the calcite-$CO_2$ $\alpha$ also applies, with a constant correction, to $^{13}\alpha$ for Fe(III) carbonate $vs.$ $CO_2$.

OHMOTO (1972) pointed out the influence of pH on the $\delta^{13}C$ values of different aqueous carbonate species in hydrothermal systems. pH in low temperature carbonate systems is not often considered as a variable of isotopic importance, because sedimentary calcite precipitation commonly occurs in systems with pH values of about 7 to 8.5 (e.g., WHITE et al., 1963; HOLLAND, 1978). CRERAR et al. (1979) have studied the bog iron of the New Jersey pine barrens. The ferric hydroxides (including goethite) which make up these deposits seem to have been precipitated from water with pH values ranging from about 4.1 to 5.7. Tropical lateritic soils in which goethite is abundant commonly have pH values around 4 or 5 (SOIL SURVEY STAFF, 1975). In addition, goethites which are pseudomorphs after pyrite or siderite can be expected to have formed in low pH environments because of the formation of sulfuric acid and carbonic acid, respectively, during goethite formation. Thus, the carbon isotope fractionation between the minor Fe(III) carbonate component in goethite and the total aqueous carbonate system may originate in relatively low pH environments. Inspection of the temperature dependence of the carbon isotope fractionation factors for calcite-$CO_2$ and aqueous carbonate-$CO_2$ (FRIEDMAN and O'NEIL, 1977) suggests, by analogy, that the extent to which variations in temperature will cause variations in Fe(III) carbonate $\delta^{13}C$ values should be related to the pH of the environment.

The following closed-system equation represents the equilibrium carbon isotope fractionation ($\phi$) between calcite and total aqueous carbonate as a function of hydrogen ion activity and temperature.

The temperature dependence of $\phi$ arises through the temperature dependence of $\alpha$(a-b), $\alpha$(cc-b), $K_1$ and $K_2$:

$$\phi = \frac{R_{cc}}{R_{tot}} = \frac{\alpha(cc\text{-}b)}{A + B + C} \qquad (3)$$

where

$$A = \frac{\alpha(a\text{-}b)}{1 + \dfrac{K_1}{a_H} + \dfrac{K_1 K_2}{a_H^2}}$$

$$B = \frac{1}{\dfrac{a_H}{K_1} + 1 + \dfrac{K_2}{a_H}}$$

$$C = \frac{\alpha(c\text{-}b)}{\dfrac{a_H^2}{K_1 K_2} + \dfrac{a_H}{K_2} + 1}$$

$R_{cc} = {}^{13}C/{}^{12}C$ of calcite
$R_{tot} = {}^{13}C/{}^{12}C$ of total dissolved carbonate ($CO_2$ + $HCO_3^-$ + $CO_3^=$)
$\alpha$(cc-b) = $\alpha$ for carbon isotope fractionation between calcite and dissolved bicarbonate
$\alpha$(c-b) = $^{13}\alpha$ for dissolved carbonate $vs.$ bicarbonate
$\alpha$(a-b) = $^{13}\alpha$ for neutral aqueous $CO_2$ $vs.$ bicarbonate
$a_H$ = hydrogen ion activity
$K_1$ = first acid dissociation constant of $H_2CO_3$
$K_2$ = second acid dissociation constant of $H_2CO_3$

Dilute solution conditions were assumed. It was also assumed that $\alpha$(c-b) did not vary with temperature. Over the temperature range employed in these calculations, the latter assumption appears to be reasonable (FRIEDMAN and O'NEIL, 1977). The temperature dependence of $K_1$ and $K_2$ was determined from tabulations in DREVER (1982). The temperature dependence of $\alpha$(cc-b) and $\alpha$(a-b) was determined from graphs in FRIEDMAN and O'NEIL (1977).

A plot of $1000 \ln \phi$ $vs.$ $T$ (°C) at two different pH values is given in Fig. 9. As can be seen in Fig. 9, the temperature dependence of $\phi$ is greater at pH 4 than at pH 8. Furthermore, at a particular temperature, $\phi$ is larger at pH 4 than at 8. The temperature of formation for the goethites of Table 1 might range from about 10 to 30°C as determined with hydrogen and oxygen isotopes (YAPP, 1987b and unpubl. results). At pH 4 and treating variations of $\phi$ as a proxy for variations of Fe(III) carbonate,

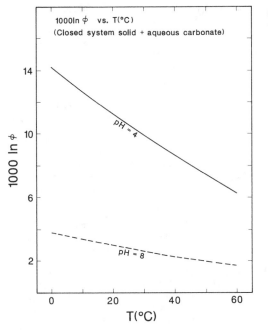

FIG. 9. 1000 ln $\phi$ vs. $T$ (°C) calculated at pH values of 4 and 8. $\phi$ is the equilibrium ratio of $^{13}C/^{12}C$ in calcite to $^{13}C/^{12}C$ in total aqueous carbonate under closed-system conditions. Note that the temperature dependence of $\phi$ is greater at low pH than at high pH.

Fig. 9 suggests that a temperature-controlled $\delta^{13}C$ range of about 2.7 per mil could result if the aqueous total carbonate $\delta^{13}C$ value were constant. Therefore, only about 14% of the observed 20 per mil range of goethite trapped $CO_2$ $\delta^{13}C$ values might be explained by differences in temperatures of formation.

As a further illustration of the effect of pH, it is assumed that Fe(III) carbonate carbon isotope systematics are the same as those of siderite. Figure 10 contains curves which depict the closed-system variation of Fe(III) carbonate (trapped $CO_2$) $\delta^{13}C$ values as a function of pH at 30°C. Curve A assumes that the total aqueous carbonate has a $\delta^{13}C$ value of −24 per mil, while curve B assumes a $\delta^{13}C$ value of −29 per mil. As can be seen in Fig. 10, the Fe(III) carbonate $\delta^{13}C$ values are insensitive to variations in pH at values less than about 5 and greater than about 7.5. Although shifts in pH over the range from 5 to 7.5 could produce about a six per mil shift in the goethite trapped $CO_2$ $\delta^{13}C$ value at 30°C in a closed system, pH-induced shifts of this magnitude are too small to explain the 20 per mil range observed in the Fe(III) carbonates of diverse goethites. Thus, although temperature and pH need to be considered, much of the Fe(III) carbonate $\delta^{13}C$ range of the goethites of Table 1 is probably a con-

sequence of the original environmental $CO_2$ $\delta^{13}C$ values.

## CONCLUSIONS

The dominant component in the small amounts of carbon dioxide evolved from $H_2O_2$-treated natural goethites during dehydration experiments in vacuum at *ca.* 230°C appears to be "trapped" $CO_2$ from a minor Fe(III) carbonate component apparently in solid solution in the goethites. Patterns of coupled $CO_2$-$H_2O$ release and incremental $CO_2$ $\delta^{13}C$ values are largely those expected for the hypothesized Fe(III) carbonate. The $\delta^{13}C$ range of about 20 per mil observed for trapped $CO_2$ from the different samples analyzed in this study indicates that information about the respective environments of formation is preserved in the carbon isotope ratios of Fe(III) carbonate in goethite. Temperature and pH may affect the $\delta^{13}C$ value of Fe(III) carbonate, but much of the observed $\delta^{13}C$ range of 20 per mil among diverse goethites is probably due to differences in the $\delta^{13}C$ values of ambient aqueous carbonate in the various environments of goethite for-

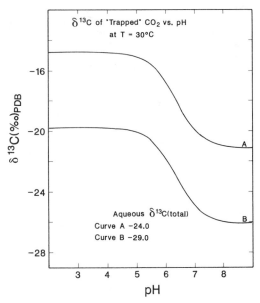

FIG. 10. $\delta^{13}C$ of Fe(III) carbonate (trapped $CO_2$) in goethite as a function of pH at 30°C for two different total aqueous carbonate $\delta^{13}C$ values. Closed-system conditions and Fe(III) carbonate ≪ total aqueous carbonate were two of the assumptions employed to calculate these curves. At this temperature pH changes alone are capable of producing a trapped $CO_2$ $\delta^{13}C$ range of about six per mil. However, most of this pH dependency occurs in the pH range from about 5.0 to 7.5. Above and below these pH values, the $\delta^{13}C$ value is insensitive to pH changes.

mation. Consequently, goethite-trapped $CO_2$ $\delta^{13}C$ values represent a new indicator of variation in ancient near-surface environmental conditions.

*Acknowledgements*—It is difficult to properly acknowledge someone who was such an outstanding mentor, but one of your former graduate students says, "Thanks, Sam." Dag Lopez drafted the figures, and this manuscript was typed by Marie Tenorio, Mary Sherman, and Mabel T. Chavez. This research was supported by NSF grants EAR-8719070 and EAR-9003108.

## REFERENCES

CAROTHERS W. W., ADAMI L. H. and ROSENBAUER R. J. (1988) Experimental oxygen isotope fractionation between siderite-water and phosphoric acid liberated $CO_2$-siderite. *Geochim. Cosmochim. Acta* **52**, 2445–2450.

CRAIG H. (1957) Isotopic standards for carbon and oxygen and correction factors for mass-spectrometric analysis of carbon dioxide. *Geochim. Cosmochim. Acta* **12**, 133–149.

CRERAR D. A., KNOX G. W. and MEANS J. L. (1979) Biogeochemistry of bog iron in the New Jersey pine barrens. *Chem. Geol.* **24**, 111–135.

DREVER J. I. (1982) *The Geochemistry of Natural Waters.* Prentice-Hall.

DVORAK V., FEITKNECHT W. and GEORGES P. (1969) Sur les carbonates basiques de fer (III): I. Carbonate basique de fer (III) amorphe. *Helv. Chim. Acta* **52**, 501–515.

FRIEDMAN I. and O'NEIL J. R. (1977) Compilation of stable isotope fractionation factors of geochemical interest. *U.S. Geol. Surv. Prof. Pap.* 440-K; *Data of Geochemistry*, 6th ed.

FRITZ P. and POPLAWSKI S. (1974) $^{18}O$ and $^{13}C$ in the shells of freshwater molluscs and their environments. *Earth Planet. Sci. Lett.* **24**, 91–98.

HOEFS J. (1987) *Stable Isotope Geochemistry*, 3rd ed. Springer-Verlag, Berlin.

HOLLAND H. D. (1978) *The Chemistry of the Atmosphere and Oceans.* J. Wiley & Sons.

OHMOTO H. (1972) Systematics of sulfur and carbon isotopes in hydrothermal ore deposits. *Econ. Geol.* **67**, 551–578.

PAULL R. A. (1977) The Upper Ordovician Neda Formation of Eastern Wisconsin. In *Geology of Southern Wisconsin* (ed. K. G. NELSON); *A Guidebook for the 41st Annual Tri-State Field Conference, Wisconsin Geol. Nat. Hist. Surv.*, pp. C-1 to C-18.

QUADE J., CERLING T. E. and BOWMAN J. R. (1989) Systematic variations in the carbon and oxygen isotopic composition of pedogenic carbonate along elevation transects in the southern Great Basin, United States. *Geol. Soc. Amer. Bull.* **101**, 464–475.

SCHIDLOWSKI M., HAYES J. M. and KAPLAN I. R. (1983) Isotopic inferences of ancient biochemistries: Carbon, sulfur, hydrogen and nitrogen. *In Earth's Earliest Biosphere Its Origin and Evolution* (ed. J. W. SCHOPF), pp. 149–186. Princeton University Press.

SOIL SURVEY STAFF (1975) *Soil Taxonomy.* U.S. Dept. of Agriculture and U.S. Government Printing Office, *Agriculture Handbook 436,* Washington, D.C.

WHITE D. E., HEM J. D. and WARING G. A. (1963) Chemical composition of subsurface waters, In *Data of Geochemistry; U.S. Geol. Surv. Prof. Pap.* 440-f, 6th ed.

YAPP C. J. (1983) Stable hydrogen isotopes in iron oxides-isotope effects associated with the dehydration of a natural goethite. *Geochim. Cosmochim. Acta* **47**, 1277–1287.

YAPP C. J. (1987a) A possible goethite-iron (III) carbonate solid solution and the determination of $CO_2$ partial pressures in low temperature geologic system. *Chem. Geol.* **64**, 259–268.

YAPP C. J. (1987b) Oxygen and hydrogen isotope variations among goethites ($\alpha$-FeOOH) and the determination of paleotemperatures. *Geochim. Cosmochim. Acta* **51**, 355–364.

YAPP C. J. and PEDLEY M. D. (1985) Stable hydrogen isotopes in iron oxides—II. D/H variations among natural goethites. *Geochim. Cosmochim. Acta* **49**, 487–495.

YAPP C. J. and POTHS H. (1986) Carbon in natural goethites. *Geochim. Cosmochim. Acta* **50**, 1213–1220.

YAPP C. J. and POTHS H. (1990) Infrared spectral evidence for a minor Fe(III) carbonate-bearing component in natural goethite. *Clays Clay Mineral.* **38**, 442–444.

Stable Isotope Geochemistry: A Tribute to Samuel Epstein
© The Geochemical Society, Special Publication No. 3, 1991
Editors: H. P. Taylor, Jr., J. R. O'Neil and I. R. Kaplan

# Oxygen isotope studies of zeolites: Stilbite, analcime, heulandite, and clinoptilolite—I. Analytical technique*

XIAHONG FENG† and SAMUEL M. SAVIN

Department of Geological Sciences, Case Western Reserve University, Cleveland, OH 44106, U.S.A.

**Abstract**—An analytical technique for measuring $\delta^{18}O$ values of the zeolites stilbite, analcime, heulandite, and clinoptilolite has been developed and tested. The framework oxygen of these minerals can be isotopically analyzed with a good precision using a standard dehydration procedure developed in this study. The analytical accuracy, however, is impaired by isotopic exchange between the framework oxygen and channel water, which is unavoidable during the process of dehydration. The errors thus introduced into the isotopic analyses can be corrected empirically using a calibration curve generated by controlled experiments.

## INTRODUCTION

THE OXYGEN ISOTOPIC composition of a mineral is a function of both the $^{18}O/^{16}O$ ratio of the ambient fluid and the temperature of the environment in which it formed. If the mineral is not in equilibrium with its environment, its isotopic composition is also affected by the extent to which it exchanged with the environment prior to the time it was collected. Therefore, the isotopic composition of a mineral may carry some information both about the environment in which it formed and about its subsequent history. These concepts have been the basis for numerous studies of paleoenvironment and of diagenesis and other low temperature processes.

In isotopic studies of diagenesis, $\delta^{18}O$ values of quartz, feldspars, carbonates, and clays are commonly measured (ESLINGER and SAVIN, 1973; YEH and SAVIN, 1977; LAND, 1984; DUTTON and LAND, 1985; LONGSTAFFE, 1986; LAND and FISHER, 1987; AYALON and LONGSTAFFE, 1988; LEE et al., 1989; GIRARD et al., 1989; and many others). Zeolite minerals are common products of low-grade metamorphism and diagenesis, particularly in volcanogenic sediments. Knowledge of the conditions of their formation is important not only to an understanding of problems directly related to the characteristics (e.g., porosity and permeability) of reservoirs in clastic rocks, but also to an understanding of high-grade diagenetic and low-grade metamorphic processes. However, stable isotope methods have only rarely been applied to the study of zeolites.

There are two main reasons for the paucity of isotopic analyses of zeolites. The first is the difficulty of performing isotopic analyses of zeolites. The $\delta^{18}O$ value of the framework (i.e., aluminosilicate) oxygen of a zeolite can be measured only after the removal of channel water. Second, the occurrence of labile channel water within the open framework structure of zeolites raised suspicions that the framework oxygen of these minerals might be susceptible to post-formational isotopic exchange. If so, their isotopic compositions would be of limited usefulness in studies of diagenesis and metamorphism. This paper is a report of the development and testing of a technique for precise, accurate measurement of $\delta^{18}O$ values of zeolites. The preservation of isotopic records in naturally occurring zeolites will be discussed in another paper (FENG and SAVIN, in prep.).

## PREVIOUS WORK

SAVIN and EPSTEIN (1970) analyzed three authigenic phillipsite samples, separated from ocean floor sediments. Samples were treated by drying at room temperature in a dry box for between 24 and 72 hours prior to loading in the Ni reaction vessels. The results of drying aliquots of the same sample for differing lengths of time pointed out the complexity of the dehydration behavior of phillipsite and the difficulty of measuring its $^{18}O/^{16}O$ ratio accurately. SAVIN and EPSTEIN (1970) estimated a value of 1.034 for $\alpha_{phillipsite-water}$ at 0°C.

FENG (1985) analyzed phillipsite that had been hand-picked from within a manganese nodule collected in the central North Pacific Ocean. This analysis also indicated a fractionation factor of about 1.034 at ocean bottom temperature. BOHLKE et al. (1984) reported $\delta^{18}O$ values of a phillipsite from Deep Sea Drilling Project (DSDP) Hole 396B and of a number of bulk rock samples containing zeolite minerals from the same core and from DSDP Holes 417A and 417D. They studied alteration of deep-sea basalts by correlating the $\delta^{18}O$ values of minerals and bulk rocks in those cores with the $H_2O^+$ contents. HAY et al. (1991) studied clay mineral diagenesis in core KM-3 from Searles Lake, California. They used $\delta^{18}O$ values of a number of minerals, including phillipsite, as the basis for conclusions about the water chemistry of the lake dur-

---

* Contribution No. 183, Department of Geological Sciences, Case Western Reserve University.

† Present address: Division of Geological and Planetary Sciences, California Institute of Technology, Pasadena, CA 91125, U.S.A.

ing diagenesis. Both BOHLKE *et al.* (1984) and KITA and HONDA (1987) used $\delta^{18}O$ values of mordenite and clinoptilolite, as well as quartz, cristobalite, kaolinite, and other minerals to distinguish hydrothermally altered rocks from those of diagenetic origin.

In all of the studies mentioned above except that of SAVIN and EPSTEIN (1970), zeolites were dehydrated in the Ni reaction vessels of the fluorination line prior to reaction with $BrF_5$ according to the technique of CLAYTON and MAYEDA (1963). Because the reaction vessels become lined with hygroscopic fluorine compounds, the water liberated from the zeolites may be absorbed on the sides of the vessels. If this occurs, the oxygen of the absorbed water will be liberated during fluorination of the minerals, resulting in erroneous measurements.

STALLARD and BOLES (1989) reported $\delta^{18}O$ values of laumontite, stilbite, and heulandite from zeolite-facies metavolcanic rocks of the Hokonui Hills, New Zealand. They pointed out that incompleteness of dehydration of the zeolites significantly affects the reproducibility of the isotopic analysis, and showed large isotopic effects of dehydrating at different temperatures and for different lengths of time. In their geological interpretations, they used the data obtained using those dehydration conditions that gave the best precision.

Recently, KARLSSON and CLAYTON (1990) reported $\delta^{18}O$ values of both framework oxygen and channel water of analcime, chabazite, clinoptilolite, laumontite, mordenite, and natrolite. They dehydrated their samples outside of the fluorination line by heating under high vacuum to 450°C prior to analysis of framework oxygen. They qualitatively examined the possibility of isotope exchange between framework oxygen and channel water during dehydration by varying the conditions of dehydration and by exchanging the channel water with a water of different isotopic composition. They concluded that the $\delta^{18}O$ values of dehydrated analcime and mordenite are not affected significantly by changing the procedures of dehydration, and argued that this indicated that the measurements were accurate. However, their treatments affected the $\delta^{18}O$ values of chabazite and laumontite by as much as 2 per mil, leading KARLSSON and CLAYTON (1990) to conclude that the $^{18}O/^{16}O$ ratios of those minerals should be interpreted with caution.

In this paper we show that the dehydration conditions used by STALLARD and BOLES (1989) may not have been appropriate to yield $\delta^{18}O$ values representative of the framework oxygen of stilbite. In addition, we show that dehydration conditions which yield high precision do not necessarily yield accurate $\delta^{18}O$ values.

## EXPERIMENTAL

### Sample selection and preparation

Stilbite, analcime, heulandite, and clinoptilolite were used in our experimental studies. Purity was the main consideration in the selection of large clean crystals of stilbite (Lonavla, India), analcime (Mont St. Hilaire, Quebec, Canada) and heulandite (Nasik, India). The crystals were crushed, ground, and sieved into two size fractions, 100–200 mesh (74–149 $\mu m$) and <200 mesh (<74 $\mu m$). Most isotope analyses were made with the 100–200 size fraction. Dehydration experiments and X-ray diffraction analyses (XRD) were mainly done with the finer than 200 mesh fraction. Clinoptilolite, which has a framework structure similar to that of heulandite, but which does not undergo

a phase transformation during dehydration, was selected later in the study for comparison with heulandite. Two clinoptilolite samples were used. One (denoted as Clinoptilolite-1) was donated by Giday WoldeGabriel of Los Alamos National Laboratory. He separated the mineral from a bulk rock sample (Yucca Mountain Nuclear Waste Repository Site, bore hole G1) by particle size separation. The 1 to 3 $\mu m$ fraction used in this study was more than 90% pure clinoptilolite. A second clinoptilolite (Castle Creek, Owyhee Co, Idaho) was obtained from Miriam Kastner of Scripps Institution of Oceanography. XRD and TGA analyses indicated that this sample was greater than 95% clinoptilolite. This clinoptilolite sample will be referred to as Clinoptilolite-2.

### Thermogravimetric analysis (TGA)

Thermogravimetric analyses or dehydration studies of the zeolites were undertaken using two methods. In the first method, a Tem-Pres Research TG-716 Thermogravimetric Analyzer was used to obtain curves of weight loss *vs.* temperature while the temperature was raised at a controlled rate. With this instrument the sample can be heated either in the atmosphere or under vacuum ($\approx 10^{-3}$ torr). Weight can be measured with a relative error of less than 5%, and temperature with a relative error of 2%.

In the second method, a McBain-Bakr balance was used to measure the weight loss of the sample during dehydration. The McBain-Bakr balance (Fig. 1) consists of a quartz spring with a hook at either end. The spring is suspended from one hook and a sample cup hangs from a wire about 20 cm long attached to the other. The spring stretches or contracts in proportion to the change in weight of the material in the sample cup. The sample and the balance were enclosed in a 25 mm O.D. quartz tube, sealed at the bottom and connected to a vacuum system at the top. A furnace operated by a temperature controller was placed around the quartz tube. The length of the spring (and hence the sample weight) is measured with a cathetometer. The precision of the cathetometer is 0.005 cm, corresponding to a weight change of 0.05 mg. The amount of sample used for each dehydration experiment was greater than 100 mg, and thus the relative error introduced by the cathetometer reading is smaller than 0.1%.

The apparatus was designed to permit collection of the water liberated upon dehydration. In some experiments, water vapor was introduced into the system by evaporation from a water reservoir held at a constant temperature. The reservoir temperature was always kept lower than room temperature in order to prevent water from condensing on the inner surfaces of the system. The vapor pressure inside the system is determined solely by the temperature of the reservoir.

### Oxygen isotope analysis

In preparation for oxygen isotopic analysis, zeolites were partially or completely dehydrated outside of the fluorination line, using the methods described below. To prevent rehydration, samples were exposed only to vacuum or to dry air after dehydration. Oxygen was extracted from the partially or completely dehydrated material using the $BrF_5$ method of CLAYTON and MAYEDA (1963). Oxygen was converted to $CO_2$ by a reaction with a hot carbon rod, and then analyzed on a mass spectrometer.

Oxygen was liberated from water samples extracted from

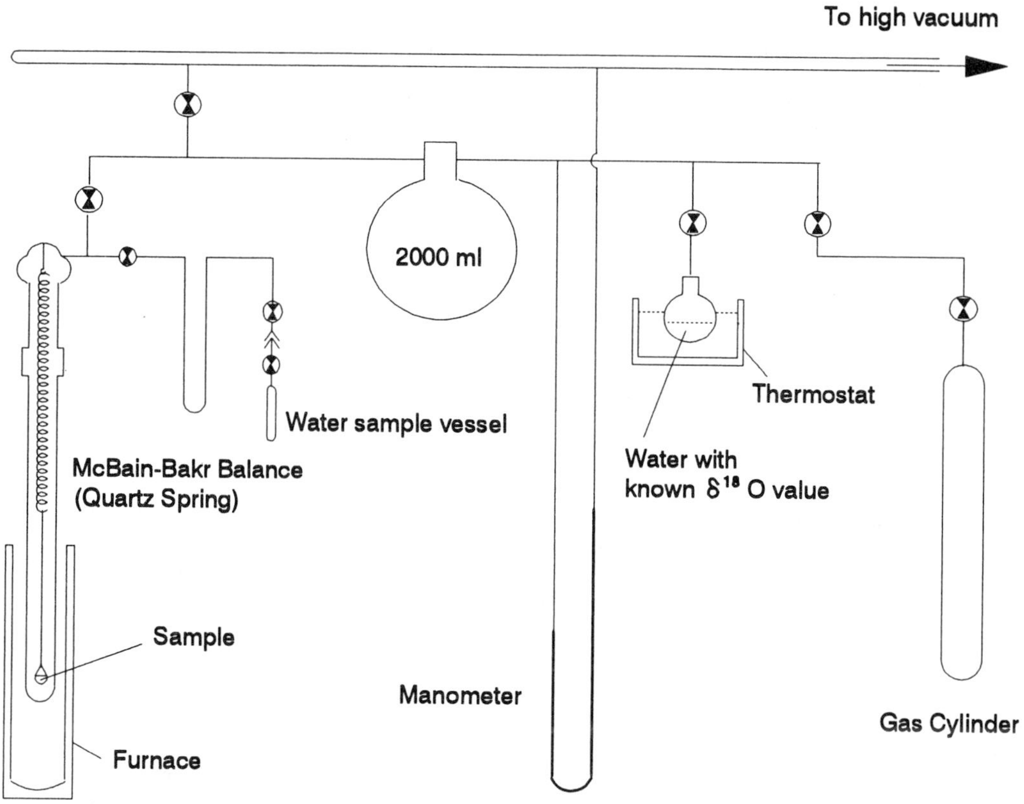

FIG. 1. McBain-Bakr balance used for thermogravimetric studies of zeolites at controlled temperature and $P_{H_2O}$, studies of gas absorption by zeolites, and extraction of channel water from zeolites.

zeolites by reaction with $BrF_5$ at 300°C using the method of O'NEIL and EPSTEIN (1966).

Oxygen isotope ratios are expressed in $\delta$ notation as deviation in per mil from SMOW (Standard Mean Ocean Water). The $\delta^{18}O$ values of water samples were directly calculated using the $\delta^{18}O$ value of V-SMOW (Vienna SMOW provided by the International Atomic Energy Agency) relative to the mass spectrometer reference gas. The calculated $\delta^{18}O$ values were then normalized using a scale in which the $\delta^{18}O$ value of SLAP (Standard Light Antarctic Precipitation) is defined as $-55.5$ relative to V-SMOW (COPLEN et al., 1983). The $\delta^{18}O$ value of NBS-28, the isotopic reference material for silicates, was also determined in this fashion. The $\delta^{18}O$ value of NBS-28 was $+9.66$ with respect to V-SMOW after normalization, and this value was used in the calculations of $\delta^{18}O$ of the framework oxygen of the zeolites.

## DEHYDRATION BEHAVIOR OF ZEOLITES

Zeolites contain oxygen in at least two distinct structural positions, the oxygen of the aluminosilicate framework and the oxygen of the channel water. The channel water of most zeolites exchanges with the environment very rapidly (KARLSSON, 1988), and, consequently, it does not preserve geo-

logical information about the formation of the mineral. In isotopic analysis of the framework oxygen of zeolites, therefore, two things are important: (1) that the channel water be completely eliminated from the zeolite structure and (2) that the dehydration be done in such a way that isotopic exchange between the framework oxygen and the zeolitic water is minimized.

The dehydration behavior of zeolites has been well documented by GOTTARDI and GALLI (1985). Data are mostly in the form of thermogravimetric analysis (TGA) and differential thermal analysis (DTA). Most published data were collected while the zeolite minerals were heated in air at a constant heating rate (typically, 20°C/min). These data are not sufficient for our needs. In order to determine the optimal dehydration condition for isotope analysis of a zeolite it is necessary to investigate carefully its dehydration behavior as a function of temperature, time, and $P_{H_2O}$. The results of our investigations of the dehydration of analcime, stilbite, clinoptilolite, and heulandite are summarized below. Details can be found in FENG (1991).

1) The dehydration state of each of the four minerals studied is a function of temperature, $P_{H_2O}$, and, until equilibrium with the surroundings is established, the time the sample is held at a particular temperature and $P_{H_2O}$.

2) Clinoptilolite, heulandite, and stilbite lose approximately half of their total channel water during evacuation overnight at room temperature. Analcime, on the other hand, does not lose any measurable weight, *in vacuo,* at room temperature.

3) At every temperature, the dehydration of the zeolites is rapid at first and decreases with increasing time.

4) Stilbite undergoes a phase transformation to metastilbite between 100 and 150°C. If the maximum temperature to which the stilbite was heated is less than 250°C, the mineral returns to its original structure when cooled to room temperature and returns to its original hydration state if water vapor is present at room temperature. Heulandite is irreversibly transformed to metaheulandite (heulandite B) when heated to 250 to 300°C. When heated to temperatures lower than 250°C it undergoes no phase transformation, and when cooled to room temperature it regains its original water content.

5) Clinoptilolite, heulandite, and stilbite all undergo structural collapse when completely dehydrated. Collapse of heulandite and stilbite occurs at about 450 to 500°C. Collapse of clinoptilolite occurs between 700 and 800°C. The crystal structure of analcime is not altered at temperatures at least as high as 800°C.

6) Reversible or nearly reversible rehydration is possible for all the zeolites except zeolite analcime if they are not heated above a critical temperature (250°C for the heulandite and stilbite and 450°C for clinoptilolite).

## ISOTOPIC ANALYSIS OF ZEOLITES

### Dehydration procedure

The dehydration behavior of the zeolites studied suggests that the optimal dehydration procedure preceding the isotopic analysis of the framework oxygen ought to consist of evacuation at room temperature followed by stepwise thermal dehydration. This procedure is based on the assumption that if isotope exchange between framework oxygen and channel water occurs during dehydration it would occur to the greatest extent at higher temperatures. The procedure was therefore designed to remove as much channel water as possible at low temperatures.

Heulandite, stilbite, and clinoptilolite samples are held under vacuum for exactly 14 hours. This time is sufficient to remove 50% of the channel water from the structure of those zeolites. Because analcime does not lose weight at room temperature (FENG, 1991), it may be evacuated for a shorter interval.

Stepwise thermal dehydration *in vacuo* is done using a 50°C interval between steps. Below 300°C, the system is held at each temperature for 1.5 hours. Since constant weight is approached much more rapidly at higher temperatures, the time of evacuation often can be reduced to one hour or even less at temperatures of 300°C and above. In the following context, we shall call this two-stage, stepwise dehydration procedure the *Standard Procedure.*

### Analytical precision

Aliquots of each of our samples were dehydrated using the standard procedure. These were all treated identically except for the ultimate dehydration temperature, which varied from room temperature to 700°C.

The results of these experiments are contained in Table 1. Figures 2 to 5 show the relationships between $\delta^{18}O$ and the ultimate dehydration temperature for each zeolite.

When the ultimate dehydration temperature is below 150°C, the $\delta^{18}O$ values of dehydration residues of stilbite are low and increase with increasing temperature (Fig. 2). Above 150°C the curve levels off. The shape of the curve through the data points is very similar to the curve of weight loss of stilbite as a function of temperature (FENG, 1991). The low $\delta^{18}O$ values obtained in experiments with ultimate dehydration temperatures lower than 150°C probably reflects the analysis of mixtures of framework oxygen and residual $^{18}O$-depleted channel water. At temperatures between 150 and 650°C, the total range of variation of $\delta^{18}O$ values is only 0.56 per mil. The average $\delta^{18}O$ value is 24.18 ± 0.16 (one standard deviation). This standard deviation is similar to those we typically obtain in our laboratory for oxygen isotope analyses of quartz.

Similar results were obtained for analcime (Fig. 3). The $\delta^{18}O$ values increase slightly with temperature up to 250°C. They then increase sharply with temperature between 250 and 400°C, the interval in which the greatest loss of channel water occurs (FENG, 1991). The curve levels off above 400°C. The average of the seven $\delta^{18}O$ analyses with ultimate dehydration temperatures of 400°C and above is 13.36 ± 0.12.

The data obtained for heulandite do not indicate any plateau temperature above which the measured $\delta^{18}O$ values of the framework oxygen remain es-

Table 1. Oxygen isotope analyses of stilbite, analcime, heulandite, and clinoptilolite: Effect of dehydration on $\delta^{18}O$ value and analytical precision.

| Mineral | Ultimate dehydration temperature (°C)* | $\delta^{18}O$ (per mil) | Statistics |
|---------|------------------|-----------|------------|
| Stilbite | 28 | 22.20 | For ten samples dehydrated up to 150°C |
| | 50 | 22.71 | and higher temperatures: |
| | 100 | 23.36 | Mean: 24.18 |
| | 150 | 24.29 | Standard Deviation: 0.16 |
| | 230 | 24.09 | $n$: 10 |
| | 250 | 24.11 | |
| | 300 | 24.29 | |
| | 320 | 23.95 | |
| | 340 | 23.87 | |
| | 400 | 24.22 | |
| | 521 | 24.43 | |
| | 600 | 24.20 | |
| | 653 | 24.32 | |
| Analcime | 24 | 9.11 | For seven samples dehydrated up to |
| | 100 | 9.33 | 400°C or higher temperatures: |
| | 150 | 9.35 | Mean: 13.36 |
| | 200 | 9.51 | Standard Deviation: 0.12 |
| | 250 | 9.79 | $n$: 7 |
| | 300 | 10.28 | |
| | 350 | 11.76 | |
| | 400 | 13.16 | |
| | 450 | 13.31 | |
| | 500 | 13.28 | |
| | 550 | 13.38 | |
| | 600 | 13.59 | |
| | 650 | 13.38 | |
| | 700 | 13.39 | |
| Heulandite | 24 | 20.74 | For eight samples dehydrated up to |
| | 50 | 21.54 | 350°C or higher temperatures: |
| | 100 | 22.38 | Mean: 25.45 |
| | 150 | 23.59 | Standard Deviation: 0.27 |
| | 200 | 24.02 | $n$: 8 |
| | 250 | 23.94 | |
| | 300 | 24.34 | |
| | 350 | 25.16 | |
| | 400 | 25.10 | |
| | 450 | 25.26 | |
| | 500 | 25.34 | |
| | 550 | 25.44 | |
| | 600 | 25.72 | |
| | 650 | 25.87 | |
| | 700 | 25.72 | |
| Clinoptilolite-1 | 24 | 18.15 | For seven samples dehydrated up to |
| | 50 | 17.69 | 150°C or higher temperatures: |
| | 100 | 17.54 | Mean: 17.03 |
| | 150 | 17.09 | Standard Deviation: 0.10 |
| | 200 | 17.24 | $n$: 7 |
| | 250 | 17.01 | |
| | 300 | 16.94 | |
| | 350 | 17.08 | |
| | 400 | 16.92 | |
| | 450 | 16.95 | |

* Ultimate dehydratation temperature: Samples were dehydrated stepwise to these temperatures using the Standard Procedure as defined in the text.

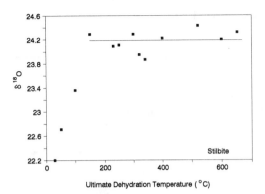

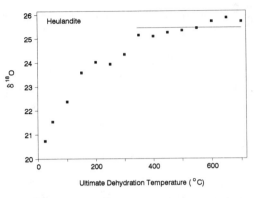

FIG. 2. Measured $\delta^{18}O$ value of stilbite following stepwise dehydration according to the standard procedure at a range of ultimate dehydration temperatures. Each point represents a different aliquot of stilbite. The horizontal line shows the average $\delta^{18}O$ value, 24.18 ± .16 (one standard deviation), of the aliquots dehydrated to ultimate dehydration temperatures between 150 and 650°C.

FIG. 4. Measured $\delta^{18}O$ value of heulandite following stepwise dehydration according to the standard procedure at a range of ultimate dehydration temperatures. Each point represents a different aliquot of the heulandite. The horizontal line shows the average $\delta^{18}O$ value, 25.45 ± .27, of aliquots dehydrated to ultimate dehydration temperatures between 350 and 700°C.

sentially constant (Fig. 4). Weight loss measurements done under the same dehydration conditions (FENG, 1991) show that heulandite continues to lose weight up to at least 850°C, with no obvious sign of becoming completely dehydrated. The eight analyses with ultimate dehydration temperatures between 350 and 700°C give a range of $\delta^{18}O$ values between 25.10 and 25.87, with an average of 25.45 ± 0.27. The standard deviation (which includes variation other than random errors) is slightly greater than those obtained for stilbite and analcime.

Unlike the other three minerals, the $\delta^{18}O$ value of clinoptilolite decreases with increasing temper-

ature at temperatures below 150°C (Fig. 5). Consistent analyses were obtained for those aliquots that were heated to 150°C or higher (mean $\delta^{18}O$ = 17.03 ± 0.10). The residual channel water in aliquots with ultimate dehydration temperatures less than 150°C must have been enriched in $^{18}O$ relative to the framework oxygen in order to yield the results shown in Fig. 5. In a later section we show that when the channel water of a zeolite is removed from the mineral structure, there is an isotopic fractionation between the evolved and the residual channel water, in which the water removed is preferentially enriched in $H_2^{16}O$. The clinoptilolite data can be

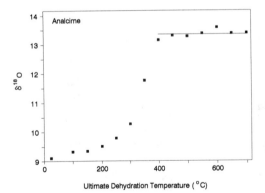

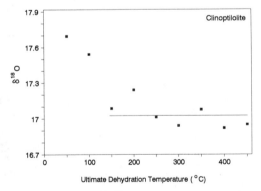

FIG. 3. Measured $\delta^{18}O$ value of analcime following stepwise dehydration according to the standard procedure at a range of ultimate dehydration temperatures. Each point represents a different aliquot of analcime. The horizontal line shows the average $\delta^{18}O$ value, 13.36 ± .12, of aliquots dehydrated to ultimate dehydration temperatures between 400 and 700°C.

FIG. 5. Measured $\delta^{18}O$ value of clinoptilolite following stepwise dehydration according to the standard procedure at a range of ultimate dehydration temperatures. Each point represents a different aliquot of the clinoptilolite. The horizontal line shows the average $\delta^{18}O$ value, 17.03 ± .10, of aliquots dehydrated to ultimate dehydration temperatures between 150 and 450°C.

interpreted as resulting from an isotopic fractionation between the evolved and the residual channel
water so large that the $\delta^{18}O$ value of the residual
channel water at room temperature became higher
than that of the framework oxygen.

In summary, consistent $\delta^{18}O$ values can be obtained when analcime, clinoptilolite, stilbite, and
possibly heulandite are analyzed using the standard
stepwise dehydration procedure.

*Oxygen isotope exchange between zeolite*
*framework and channel water during dehydration*

The good precision obtained in the isotopic analysis of the four zeolite minerals suggests two alternative interpretations: (1) there is no isotopic exchange between the framework oxygen and channel
water during dehydration, so that the mean of the
$\delta^{18}O$ values (obtained at ultimate dehydration temperatures in the plateau temperature range) represents the true isotopic composition of the framework oxygen; (2) alternatively, isotopic exchange
between the framework oxygen and channel water
does occur, but the amount of exchange is equal
for those aliquots that give the same $\delta^{18}O$ values. If
the latter possibility is true the measured $\delta^{18}O$ values
may be inaccurate. To test whether isotopic exchange between channel water and framework oxygen occurs during dehydration, a set of experiments was conducted using the procedure described
below.

Aliquots of stilbite, heulandite, and clinoptilolite
were partially dehydrated, following the standard
procedure, up to a desired ultimate temperature,
230°C for stilbite and 250°C for heulandite and
clinoptilolite. (This partial dehydration procedure
will be referred to as *Dehydration Procedure-I.*)
Samples were then isolated from the vacuum pump
and allowed to cool to room temperature. Water
vapor (evaporated, *in vacuo,* at a constant temperature, usually 23.5°C, from a water reservoir with
a $\delta^{18}O$ of +102.3) was then introduced into the system. The temperature determines both the $\delta^{18}O$
value of the vapor ($\approx$ +93) and the $P_{H_2O}$ (about 21
torr). The zeolites were exposed to the vapor for no
less than 30 min in order to become largely rehydrated. Following rehydration the samples were
disconnected from the water reservoir and dehydrated for a second time, following the standard
procedure to various ultimate dehydration temperatures. (This step will be called *Dehydration Procedure-II.*) The $\delta^{18}O$ values of the dehydration residues were measured, and the analytical results are
listed in Table 2.

A plot of the $\delta^{18}O$ value of stilbite *vs.* ultimate

heating temperature of Dehydration Procedure-II
is shown in Fig. 6. The original $\delta^{18}O$ value of the
material before rehydration with $^{18}O$-enriched water
vapor is also shown.

The $\delta^{18}O$ values decrease sharply with increasing
ultimate dehydration temperature up to approximately 200°C. Most of this decrease in $\delta^{18}O$ must
reflect progressive loss of the $^{18}O$-enriched channel
water that was introduced into the mineral. While
measurements of oxygen yields obtained from these
partially hydrated residues are not particularly accurate, the samples with dramatically high $^{18}O/^{16}O$
ratios definitely yield more oxygen upon fluorination than the stoichiometric amount of framework
oxygen. As the ultimate dehydration temperature
increases above 250°C, the $\delta^{18}O$ value, as expected,
approaches a constant value (28.16 ± 0.35 and a
total range of values of 0.84). This value is about 4
per mil higher than the $\delta^{18}O$ value obtained by
analysis of the original stilbite (24.14 ± 0.16). This
clearly indicates that the aluminosilicate structure
of the stilbite was isotopically altered during the
treatments following Dehydration Procedure-I (*i.e.,*
during rehydration at room temperature and/or
during Dehydration Procedure-II). Isotopic exchange between framework oxygen and channel
water at room temperature is slow (FENG, 1991),
suggesting that most of the observed isotopic exchange occurs during Dehydration Procedure-II. It
is possible that some additional exchange may also
occur during rehydration (FENG, 1991). Although
analytical precision was poorer by about 0.2 per
mil following Dehydration Procedure-II, this would
nevertheless be satisfactory for many geological applications. It is clear from the results, however, that
the precision of the analyses is in no way an indicator of their accuracy.

The results for heulandite and clinoptilolite are
illustrated in Figs. 7 and 8. Although quantitatively
different, these two curves are similar in shape to
the one for stilbite (Fig. 6). Below an ultimate dehydration temperature of 150°C, $\delta^{18}O$ values and
oxygen yields both decrease progressively with increasing temperature. This indicates that the dehydration residues contain $^{18}O$-rich remnant channel water. At higher ultimate dehydration temperatures the $\delta^{18}O$ value of each mineral approaches a
constant value, which is significantly higher than
the $\delta^{18}O$ values measured for the original framework
oxygen (6 per mil higher for heulandite and 1.5 per
mil higher for clinoptilolite). For each of those
minerals the standard deviation of the measurements is comparable to that obtained before rehydration and is much smaller than the shift in $\delta^{18}O$
values. This indicates that, as with stilbite, isotope

Table 2. Oxygen isotope analyses of zeolites after dehydration and rehydration with $^{18}O$-enriched water.

| Sample | Ultimate dehydration temperature (°C) | Oxygen yield (percent) | $\delta^{18}O$ (per mil) | Statistics |
|---|---|---|---|---|
| Stilbite | 25 | 115 | 44.64 | Temperature Range: 250–600°C |
| | 60 | 109.5 | 42.24 | Mean: 28.16 |
| | 90 | 102.3 | 40.22 | Standard Deviation: 0.35 |
| | 125 | 90.2 | 36.04 | $n$: 5 |
| | 175 | 96.3 | 34.02 | |
| | 230 | 75.6 | 29.86 | |
| | 250 | 94.1 | 28.55 | |
| | 300 | 93.6 | 27.88 | |
| | 400 | 94.3 | 27.78 | |
| | 500 | 95.8 | 28.62 | |
| | 600 | 93 | 27.99 | |
| Heulandite | 24 | 118.4 | 36.35 | Temperature Range: 150–700°C |
| | 100 | 114.1 | 33.94 | Mean: 31.45 |
| | 150 | 106 | 31.53 | Standard Deviation: 0.34 |
| | 200 | 106 | 31.49 | $n$: 7 |
| | 300 | 103.9 | 30.94 | |
| | 400 | 101.3 | 31.25 | |
| | 500 | 96.8 | 31.84 | |
| | 600 | 96.8 | 31.95 | |
| | 700 | 90.6 | 31.15 | |
| Clinoptilolite-1 | 24 | 106.8 | 22.36 | Temperature Range: 150–450°C |
| | 50 | 103.3 | 21.59 | Mean: 18.56 |
| | 100 | 98 | 19.43 | Standard Deviation: 0.18 |
| | 150 | 96.9 | 18.63 | $n$: 7 |
| | 200 | 95.3 | 18.46 | |
| | 250 | 91.2 | 18.31 | |
| | 300 | 91.3 | 18.38 | |
| | 350 | 92.1 | 18.59 | |
| | 400 | 92.4 | 18.87 | |
| | 450 | 87 | 18.68 | |

\* Ultimate dehydration temperature: samples were dehydrated using Dehydration Procedure-I (see text), then cooled to room temperature. Water vapor with $\delta^{18}O$ value of about +93 was introduced. After the zeolites were completely rehydrated, they were again dehydrated, using Dehydration Procedure-II and heating to the indicated temperature.

exchange takes place between the channel water and the framework oxygen during Dehydration Procedure-II.

Additional evidence that isotope exchange between channel water and framework oxygen occurs during dehydration comes from the isotopic analyses of the fractions of channel water extracted during dehydration (Table 3). In Fig. 9a the $\delta^{18}O$ value of each fraction of channel water is plotted against the temperature at which it was extracted. The lower curve is drawn through the data points obtained by stepwise dehydration of the original stilbite, and the upper curve is drawn through the data points obtained from the stilbite rehydrated with $^{18}O$-enriched water. In each case, at low temperatures the $\delta^{18}O$ values of the water fractions increase sharply with extraction temperature. This indicates that during evolution of channel water from the zeolite

structure $H_2^{16}O$ molecules are lost preferentially to $H_2^{18}O$, leaving the residual channel water increasingly enriched in $^{18}O$. This progressive isotopic enrichment of the residual water terminates at around 200°C and the trend then reverses; in the latter part of the dehydration process channel water becomes progressively enriched in $^{16}O$ as the ultimate dehydration temperature increases. This reversal is especially striking in the dehydration of stilbite rehydrated with $^{18}O$-rich water. It is also clear, and is shown in Fig. 9b, that the difference between the $\delta^{18}O$ values of the water fractions in the two sets of experiments decreases sharply with temperature at temperatures above 100°C.

Because the liberated water was immediately removed from the system and $P_{H_2O}$ was very low, back exchange between water vapor and channel water was limited. If the only mechanism affecting

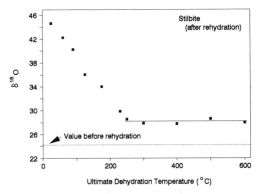

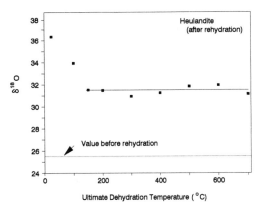

FIG. 6. Measured $\delta^{18}O$ values of the framework oxygen of stilbite analyzed after partial dehydration using the Dehydration Procedure-I and rehydration at room temperature with $^{18}O$-enriched water vapor ($\delta^{18}O_{vapor} \approx +93$). The second dehydration was done using Dehydration Procedure-II. The dashed line shows the average $\delta^{18}O$ value before the water vapor was introduced (from Fig. 2). The solid line is the average $\delta^{18}O$ value ($28.16 \pm .35$) obtained from the aliquots which were heated to ultimate temperatures between 250 and 600°C during Dehydration Procedure-II.

FIG. 7. Measured $\delta^{18}O$ values of the framework oxygen of heulandite analyzed after partial dehydration using the Dehydration Procedure-I and rehydration at room temperatures with $^{18}O$-enriched water vapor ($\delta^{18}O_{vapor} \approx +93$). Details are described in caption to Fig. 6. The solid line is the average $\delta^{18}O$ value ($31.45 \pm .34$) obtained from the aliquots which were heated to ultimate temperatures between 150 and 700°C during Dehydration Procedure-II.

the isotopic compositions of the water fractions in the two experiments was the fractionation which occurs during the evolution of channel water, the two curves of Fig. 9a would be almost parallel and the difference between them (Fig. 9b) would be almost constant. Thus, an additional mechanism must be affecting the isotopic composition of the channel water. As suggested by the analysis of the zeolite residues following Dehydration Procedure-II and confirmed here, this mechanism is isotopic exchange between channel water and the framework oxygen of stilbite. Both mechanisms, isotope fractionation during evolution of channel water and isotopic exchange between framework oxygen and channel water, must occur throughout the entire process of dehydration. At low temperatures, at which the rate of exchange is low and the amount of channel water is large, the $\delta^{18}O$ value of the evolved water is largely controlled by the fractionation that accompanies its evolution. As the temperature is raised and the ratio of channel water to framework oxygen decreases, isotope exchange between the channel water and the framework oxygen becomes progressively more important. In the case of stilbite, this exchange is measurable at temperatures as low as 100°C. In the extreme, at high temperatures the isotopic composition of the evolved water is controlled almost completely by exchange between the channel water and the framework oxygen, as witnessed by the convergence of the two curves in Fig. 9a.

The isotopic exchange of the framework oxygen of stilbite, heulandite, and clinoptilolite with channel water during dehydration clearly impairs the accuracy of analysis of these zeolites. In the following section we discuss an approach for determining the effect on the measured $\delta^{18}O$ value of this isotopic exchange and present a method for correcting the analytical data to obtain $\delta^{18}O$ values that are accurate as well as precise.

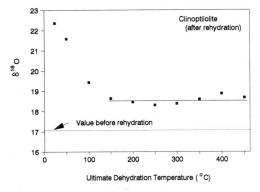

FIG. 8. Measured $\delta^{18}O$ values of the framework oxygen of clinoptilolite analyzed after partial dehydration using the Dehydration Procedure-I and rehydration at room temperature with $^{18}O$-enriched water vapor ($\delta^{18}O_{vapor} \approx +93$). Details are described in caption to Fig. 6. The solid line is the average $\delta^{18}O$ value ($18.56 \pm .18$) obtained from the aliquots which were heated to ultimate temperatures between 150 and 450°C during Dehydration Procedure-II.

Table 3. Oxygen isotope ratios of channel water fractions extracted during dehydration of stilbite.

| Channel water | Extraction temperature (°C) | Water amount (μl) | Oxygen yield (percent) | $\delta^{18}O$ (per mil) |
|---|---|---|---|---|
| Original* | 23 | 0.95 | 98.5 | −27.47 |
| | 23 | 3.45 | 99.2 | −44.89 |
| | 23 | 3.00 | 93 | −46.2 |
| | 23 | 2.55 | 88.3 | −39.43 |
| | 60 | 1.87 | 80.9 | −28.69 |
| | 90 | 2.97 | 94.5 | −18.55 |
| | 125 | 1.37 | 94.5 | 7.23 |
| | 175 | 2.76 | 90 | 27.62 |
| | 230 | 2.10 | 87.4 | 29.12 |
| | 330 | 1.50 | 78 | 11.94 |
| | 500 | 0.76 | 66.3 | 1.54 |
| $^{18}O$ rich** | 25 | 1.90 | 108 | 66.06 |
| | 25 | 3.25 | 97 | 54.88 |
| | 25 | 3.16 | 99.7 | 56.22 |
| | 25 | 1.99 | 103 | 57.48 |
| | 60 | 1.76 | 102.4 | 68.58 |
| | 90 | 2.10 | 97.6 | 79.48 |
| | 125 | 2.49 | 102.6 | 94.21 |
| | 175 | 1.61 | 91.7 | 102.88 |
| | 175 | 1.37 | 92 | 94.24 |
| | 230 | 2.21 | 88 | 94.31 |
| | 330 | 1.25 | 93.6 | 47.25 |
| | 500 | 0.78 | 87.6 | 7.95 |

  * Original channel water is the water which existed in the stilbite channels prior to any treatment in our laboratory. Fractions of water were collected at the indicated extraction temperatures.

  ** $^{18}O$ rich water was extracted from stilbite that had been dehydrated and then rehydrated with water vapor that had a $\delta^{18}O \approx +93$.

## Analytical accuracy

The results of stepwise dehydration experiments such as those shown for stilbite in Fig. 2 and for heulandite in Fig. 4 suggest an empirical approach to determine the $\delta^{18}O$ value of a zeolite. For each zeolite studied there is an ultimate dehydration temperature (e.g., 150°C in the case of stilbite) above which (1) the measured $\delta^{18}O$ value is approximately constant and (2) it is possible to rehydrate the partially dehydrated mineral almost completely. It is thus possible to create in the laboratory a zeolite with framework oxygen of known $\delta^{18}O$ value. This dehydrated zeolite can be rehydrated in a water vapor atmosphere of known $\delta^{18}O$. The measured $\delta^{18}O$ value of this rehydrated zeolite is, in general, different from that of the before rehydration. The magnitude of the shift in the measured $\delta^{18}O$ value can be determined as a function of the $^{18}O/^{16}O$ ratio of the introduced water vapor. The relationship obtained can be used as a calibra-

tion curve to correct the measured $\delta^{18}O$ value of the framework oxygen.

In practice, the calibration curve is generated as follows: Several aliquots of a zeolite are treated according to Dehydration Procedure-I. One aliquot is analyzed directly and the others are subject to rehydration in water vapor atmospheres of different isotopic compositions. This is followed by Dehydration Procedure-II and, then, isotopic analysis of each residue.

The ultimate heating temperature of Dehydration Procedure-II was uniformly 600°C for each aliquot of stilbite and heulandite. Several duplicates were run to improve statistical significance. The results of these experiments are included in Table 4 and are plotted in Figs. 10 and 11. In these figures and in the discussion below,

$$\Delta_{ff\text{-}wv} = 10^3 \ln \alpha_{ff\text{-}wv}, \quad \text{and}$$

$$\Delta_{ff\text{-}of} = 10^3 \ln \alpha_{ff\text{-}of}$$

where $ff$ designates the final framework oxygen after

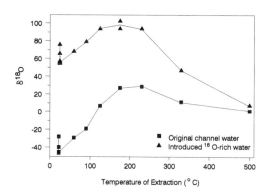

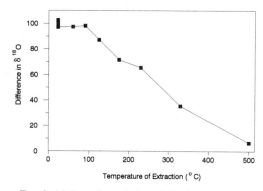

FIG. 9. (a) Isotopic evolution of fractions of channel water extracted from the original stilbite (squares) and stilbite rehydrated with $^{18}O$-rich water vapor (triangles). (b) Arithmetic difference between $\delta^{18}O$ values of fractions of channel water fractions extracted, under the same experimental conditions, from the original stilbite and the stilbite rehydrated with $^{18}O$ rich water vapor.

Table 4. Effect of $\delta^{18}O$ value of channel water on the measured $\delta^{18}O$ value of framework oxygen of stilbite and heulandite.

| Mineral | $\delta^{18}O_{of}$* | $\delta^{18}O_{wv}$* | $\delta^{18}O_{ff}$* | $\Delta_{ff\text{-}wv}$† | $\Delta_{ff\text{-}of}$‡ |
|---|---|---|---|---|---|
| Stilbite | 24.18 | −32.31 | 24.22 | 56.77 | 0.05 |
| | 24.18 | −32.31 | 24.04 | 56.60 | −0.12 |
| | 24.18 | −8.52 | 24.73 | 32.98 | 0.54 |
| | 24.18 | −8.52 | 24.51 | 32.77 | 0.33 |
| | 24.18 | 16.79 | 24.93 | 7.98 | 0.74 |
| | 24.18 | 16.79 | 25.49 | 8.52 | 1.29 |
| | 24.18 | 46.23 | 26.27 | −19.26 | 2.05 |
| | 24.18 | 91.92 | 27.99 | −60.34 | 3.72 |
| Heulandite | 25.45 | −32.31 | 26.66 | 59.15 | 1.17 |
| | 25.45 | −32.31 | 26.91 | 59.40 | 1.43 |
| | 25.45 | −8.52 | 28.84 | 36.99 | 3.30 |
| | 25.45 | −8.52 | 28.87 | 37.02 | 3.33 |
| | 25.45 | 16.79 | 29.70 | 12.61 | 4.13 |
| | 25.45 | 16.79 | 29.99 | 12.90 | 4.42 |
| | 25.45 | 46.23 | 30.53 | −15.12 | 4.94 |
| | 25.45 | 46.23 | 30.79 | −14.87 | 5.20 |
| | 25.45 | 91.92 | 31.95 | −56.49 | 6.32 |
| | 25.45 | 91.92 | 31.15 | −57.27 | 5.54 |

* $\delta^{18}O_{of}$ (*of* denotes original framework oxygen) is the $\delta^{18}O$ value of the mineral prior to rehydration (*i.e.*, the true $\delta^{18}O$ value of the framework oxygen at the start of the experiment). $\delta^{18}O_{wv}$ (*wv* denotes the water vapor) is the $\delta^{18}O$ value of the vapor used to rehydrate the mineral after Dehydration Procedure-I. $\delta^{18}O_{ff}$ (*ff* denotes the final framework oxygen) is the measured $\delta^{18}O$ of the framework oxygen following rehydration with isotopically labeled vapor and dehydration according to Dehydration Procedure-II.

† $\Delta_{ff\text{-}wv} = 10^3 \ln \alpha_{ff\text{-}wv}$, where *ff* denotes the final framework oxygen and *wv* denotes the water vapor.

‡ $\Delta_{ff\text{-}of} = 10^3 \ln \alpha_{ff\text{-}of}$, where *of* denotes original framework oxygen.

Dehydration Procedure-II, *of* designates the original framework oxygen after Dehydration Procedure-I, and *wv* designates water vapor (note that $\delta^{18}O_{of}$ for all of the runs using Dehydration Procedure-II is equivalent to $\delta^{18}O_{true}$ for those runs). In the experiment design used, $\delta^{18}O_{wv}$ may be taken to be constant for the duration of any single rehydration experiment.

Figure 10 is a plot of $\Delta_{ff\text{-}of}$ *vs.* $\Delta_{ff\text{-}wv}$ for stilbite, and Fig. 11 is a similar plot for heulandite. Polynomial regressions through the data points are also plotted on the figures. A quadratic fit of the stilbite data gives the following equation:

$$\Delta_{ff\text{-}of}^{\text{stilbite}} = 1.312 - 0.0317\Delta_{ff\text{-}wv}^{\text{stilbite}}$$

$$+ 1.4 \times 10^{-4}(\Delta_{ff\text{-}wv}^{\text{stilbite}})^2. \quad (1)$$

The regression is statistically significant and the standard error of $\Delta_{ff\text{-}of}^{\text{stilbite}}$ estimate is 0.20 per mil. This error is comparable to the analytical precision.

Both quadratic and a cubic fits through the heulandite data are statistically significant, but a smaller standard error (0.28) comparable to the analytical precision is obtained with the cubic fit, which has the equation (where *heul* denotes heulandite)

$$\Delta_{ff\text{-}of}^{\text{heul}} = 4.732 - 0.0232\Delta_{ff\text{-}wv}^{\text{heul}} - 3.02$$

$$\times 10^{-4}(\Delta_{ff\text{-}wv}^{\text{heul}})^2 - 4.647 \times 10^{-6}(\Delta_{ff\text{-}wv}^{\text{heul}})^3. \quad (2)$$

If several assumptions and conditions are satisfied

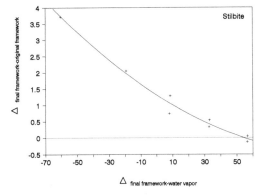

FIG. 10. Calibration curve for correction of isotopic analyses of stilbite. The curve is the quadratic fit to the experimental data and is given by the equation

$$\Delta_{ff\text{-}of}^{\text{stilbite}} = 1.312 - 0.0317\Delta_{ff\text{-}wv}^{\text{stilbite}} + 1.4 \times 10^{-4}(\Delta_{ff\text{-}wv}^{\text{stilbite}})^2.$$

When used for the purpose of correction of analyses, the final framework oxygen is equivalent to the measured framework oxygen and the original framework oxygen corresponds to the true framework oxygen of the natural stilbite.

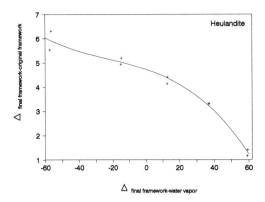

FIG. 11. Calibration curve for correction of isotopic analyses of heulandite. The curve is the quadratic fit to the experimental data and is given by the equation

$$\Delta^{heul}_{ff\text{-of}} = 4.732 - 0.0232\Delta^{heul}_{ff\text{-wv}} - 3.02$$
$$\times 10^{-4}(\Delta^{heul}_{ff\text{-wv}})^2 - 4.647 \times 10^{-6}(\Delta^{heul}_{ff\text{-wv}})^3.$$

When used for the purpose of correction of analyses, the final framework oxygen is equivalent to the measured framework oxygen and the original framework oxygen corresponds to the true framework oxygen of the natural heulandite.

we may use Figs. 10 and 11 to estimate $\delta^{18}O_{true}$ for stilbite and heulandite.

1) *The $\delta^{18}O$ value of water vapor in the environment of the zeolite prior to analysis must be known or estimated.* In the analysis of an unknown sample, this condition may be met if the $\delta^{18}O$ value of the water vapor in the natural environment is known or if the channel water in the sample has been completely exchanged with water vapor in the laboratory.

2) *The channel water of the stilbite or heulandite must be in isotopic equilibrium with this water vapor.* This condition is nearly valid for the samples and conditions used to generate the calibration curve in Fig. 10 (FENG, 1991). It is much harder to verify for natural zeolites. Because of the mobility of channel water and the relatively large size of the internal channels in stilbite and heulandite, we suspect that the channel water exchanges with the atmospheric water vapor fairly rapidly on the laboratory shelf. However, the details of the kinetics of this exchange require further study.

3) *Oxygen isotope exchange between the channel water and the framework oxygen of the stilbite or heulandite must occur in the same way and in the same rate in the unknown sample as in the stilbite and heulandite used in this study.* The calibration curves in Figs. 10 and 11 were

generated using one stilbite sample and one heulandite sample, each of uniform grain size. Further study is required to determine whether these curves are sensitive to grain size or to chemical or crystallographic variability of the zeolites.

The calibration curves for stilbite and heulandite may be used to estimate $\delta^{18}O_{true}$ of those minerals. In that application, $\delta^{18}O_{ff}$ is the measured $\delta^{18}O$ value of the mineral, $\delta^{18}O_{measured}$, and as in the calibration experiments, $\delta^{18}O_{of}$ is equivalent to $\delta^{18}O_{true}$. Use the calibration curve for stilbite as an example. Imagine that the channel water in a hypothetical stilbite has equilibrated, either in nature or in the laboratory, with a water vapor atmosphere with $\delta^{18}O$ of, say, −10 per mil, and that $\delta^{18}O_{measured}$ is +30 per mil. $\Delta_{measured\text{-}wv}$ is $10^3\ln[(1000 + 30)/(1000 - 10)]$, or 39.61. This corresponds to a value of 0.28 for $\Delta_{measured\text{-}true}$ using the curve in Fig. 10 or regression Eqn. (1). Thus, $\delta^{18}O_{true}$ is 29.72 per mil (30 − 0.28).

It is clear that precise but inaccurate results may be obtained if no correction is made for isotopic exchange between the framework oxygen and the channel water of at least some zeolites. Using extremes of natural ranges of variation of waters and silicates as a guide, one might expect errors as large as 1 or 2 per mil in the analysis of stilbite and 4 or 5 per mil in the analysis of heulandite, although in most cases the errors would be smaller. A few preliminary experiments suggest that the errors in the analysis of clinoptilolite would be smaller than those of stilbite, but those results require confirmation.

## CONCLUSIONS

The rather complex series of experiments described in this article were necessary for the development of analytical techniques for measuring $\delta^{18}O$ values of the framework oxygen of zeolites, and for the assessment of both the precision and accuracy of those techniques. A dehydration procedure (Standard Dehydration Procedure) was developed that yields $\delta^{18}O$ values that are precise. However, it quickly became clear that isotopic exchange occurs between the channel water and framework oxygen of stilbite, heulandite, and clinoptilolite during dehydration. This exchange causes some degree of analytical inaccuracy. A direct test of isotopic exchange between channel water and framework oxygen of analcime was not conducted because analcime does not rehydrate easily after partial dehydration. FENG (1991) analyzed two sets of analcime aliquots dehydrated with slightly different procedures and found a difference of more than 0.5 per mil between the mean $\delta^{18}O$ values of the two sets. This suggests that exchange between framework oxygen and channel water may also have occurred during a the dehydration of analcime at temperatures above 250–300°C (temperatures which must be achieved if analcime is to be completely dehydrated). This will be discussed further in a separate paper (FENG and SAVIN, in prep.).

The magnitude of the errors produced by isotopic exchange between channel water and framework oxygen can be estimated and the analytical results can be adjusted through an empirical calibration. However, further testing is required to determine the general applicability of the calibration curves generated from the single stilbite and heulandite samples used in this work to the isotopic analyses of other stilbite and heulandite samples with different chemical compositions, physical characteristics, and crystallographic properties.

*Acknowledgements*—Most importantly, we acknowledge Samuel Epstein for his role in laying the foundations for much of the work presented here, and for his tutelage, in person and by example, in the art and science of isotope geochemistry. Linda Abel assisted in all phases of this work. We thank Giday WoldeGabriel and Miriam Kastner for providing the clinoptilolite samples used in this study. Ray Teller and Sampath Iyengar made high temperature XRD equipment available to us at the BP Research Center. Peter McCall advised us on the use of statistics. Financial support was provided by the National Science Foundation under grant EAR-87-20387 to SMS.

## REFERENCES

AYALON A. and LONGSTAFFE F. (1988) Oxygen isotope studies of diagenesis in the western Canada sedimentary basin: Evidence from the upper Cretaceous basal Belly River Sandstone, Alberta. *J. Sediment. Petrol.* **58**, 489–505.

BOHLKE J. K., ALT J. C. and MUEHLENBACHS K. (1984) Oxygen isotope-water relations in altered deep-sea basalts: Low temperature mineralogical controls. *Canadian J. Earth Sci.* **21**, 67–77.

CLAYTON R. N. and MAYEDA T. K. (1963) The use of bromine pentafluoride in the extraction of oxygen from oxides and silicates for isotopic analysis. *Geochim. Cosmochim. Acta* **27**, 43–52.

COPLEN T. B., KENDALL C. and HOPPLE J. (1983) Comparison of stable isotope reference samples. *Nature* **302**, 236–238.

DUTTON S. and LAND L. (1985) Meteoric burial diagenesis of Pennsylvanian arkosic sandstones, Southwestern Anadarko Basin, Texas. *Amer. Assoc. Petrol. Geol. Bull.* **69**, 22–38.

ESLINGER E. and SAVIN S. M. (1973) Oxygen isotope geothermometry of the burial metamorphic rocks of the Precambrian Belt Supergroup, Glacier National Park, Montana. *Geol. Soc. Amer. Bull.* **84**, 2549–2560.

FENG X. (1985) Stable isotope studies of manganese nodules from central Northern Pacific Ocean. Masters thesis, Peking University, China.

FENG X. (1991) Oxygen isotope studies of zeolites: Stilbite, analcime, heulandite and clinoptilolite. Ph.D. thesis, Case Western Reserve University.

GIRARD J.-P., SAVIN S. and ARONSON J. L. (1989) Diagenesis of the lower Cretaceous arkoses of the Angola Margin: Petrologic, K/Ar dating and $^{18}O/^{16}O$ evidence. *J. Sediment. Petrol.* **59**, 519–538.

GOTTARDI G. and GALLI E. (1985) *Natural Zeolites.* Springer-Verlag.

HAY R. L., GULDMAN S. G., MATTHEWS J. C., LANDER R. H., DUFFIN M. E. and KYSER K. T. (1991) Clay mineral diagenesis in core KM-3 of Searles Lake, California. *Clays Clay Minerals* **39**, 84–96.

KARLSSON H. R. (1988) Oxygen and hydrogen isotope geochemistry of zeolites. Ph.D. thesis, The University of Chicago.

KARLSSON H. R. and CLAYTON R. N. (1990) Oxygen and hydrogen isotope geochemistry of zeolites. *Geochim. Cosmochim. Acta* **54**, 1369–1386.

KITA I. and HONDA S. (1987) Oxygen isotopic difference between hydrothermally and diagenetically altered rocks from the Tsugaru-Yunosawa area, Aomori, Japan. *Geochem. J.* **21**, 35–41.

LAND L. (1984) Frio sandstone diagenesis, Texas Gulf Coast: A regional isotopic study. In *Clastic Diagenesis* (eds. D. A. McDONALD and R. C. SURDAM); *Amer. Assoc. Petrol. Geol. Mem. 37*, pp. 47–62.

LAND L. and FISHER R. S. (1987) Wilcox sandstone diagenesis, Texas Gulf Coast: a regional isotopic comparison with the Frio Formation. In *Diagenesis of Sedimentary Sequences* (ed. J. D. MARSHALL); *Geol. Soc. Spec. Pub. 36*, pp. 219–235.

LEE M., ARONSON J. L. and SAVIN S. M. (1989) Timing and conditions of Permian Rotliegende sandstone diagenesis, southern North Sea: K/Ar and oxygen isotopic data. *Amer. Assoc. Petrol. Geol. Bull.* **73**, 195–215.

LONGSTAFFE F. J. (1986) Oxygen isotope studies of diagenesis in the basal Belly River Sandstone, Pembina I-pool, Alberta. *J. Sediment. Petrol.* **56**, 78–88.

O'NEIL J. R. and EPSTEIN S. (1966) A method for oxygen isotope analysis of milligram quantities of water and some of its applications. *J. Geophys. Res.* **71**, 4956–4961.

SAVIN S. M. and EPSTEIN S. (1970) The oxygen and hydrogen isotope geochemistry of ocean sediments and shales. *Geochim. Cosmochim. Acta* **34**, 43–63.

STALLARD M. and BOLES J. R. (1989) Oxygen isotope measurements of albite-quartz-zeolite mineral assemblages, Hokonui Hills, Southland, New Zealand. *Clays Clay Minerals* **37**, 409–418.

YEH H.-W. and SAVIN S. M. (1977) Mechanism of burial metamorphism of argillaceous sediments: 3. O-isotope evidence. *Geol. Soc. Amer. Bull.* **88**, 1321–1330.

Stable Isotope Geochemistry: A Tribute to Samuel Epstein
© The Geochemical Society, Special Publication No. 3, 1991
Editors: H. P. Taylor, Jr., J. R. O'Neil and I. R. Kaplan

# Eolian inputs of lead to the South Pacific via rain and dry deposition from industrial and natural sources

DOROTHY M. SETTLE and CLAIR C. PATTERSON

Division of Geological and Planetary Sciences, California Institute of Technology, Pasadena, CA 91125, U.S.A.

**Abstract**—Virtually all lead in air at American Samoa is industrial. About 63% of total lead in the air originated from industrially produced, lead-rich, carbonaceous-oxide aerosols. Another 30% of total lead in air originated from industrial lead recycled in sea spray salt, while about 6% originated from industrial lead-rich aerosols which had been deposited on plant leaf surfaces and reintroduced to the atmosphere as plant aerosols. Natural volcanic and soil dust lead in air each amounts to about 1% of the total. The net eolian input flux of lead to the ocean at Samoa was 1.61 ng $Pb/cm^2yr$ from rain after a 15% correction (0.28 ng/cm² yr) had been applied to the above flux for lead recycled in sea salt contained in rain. 73% of the net input of lead originated from industrially produced carbonaceous-oxide aerosols, while 25% originated from natural lead and 2% from industrial lead in soil dust. Natural lead in volcanic $SO_4$ amounts to about 1% of the net input. The bulk of the mass of dry deposition to the ocean consists of recycled sea salt. This recycled sea salt returns an amount of lead to the ocean by dry deposition that is equivalent to the net amount added by rain. This recycled lead in sea spray salt (1.6 ng/cm² yr) originated from lead contained in industrially produced aerosols that had been previously added to the ocean surface microlayer by rain. The maximum contribution of natural soil dust lead to the dry deposition flux is less than 1% of the total (<0.02 g/cm² yr). At this location four times as much sea salt is returned to the ocean by dry deposition (1900 μg/cm² yr) compared to that returned by rain (490 μg/cm² yr). Thirty times more dust is added to the ocean at this location by rain (60 μg/cm² yr) than is added by dry deposition (2 μg/cm² yr). $^{206}Pb/^{207}Pb$ ratios of atmospheric lead, when correlated with isotopic compositions of industrial lead emissions from various regional sources, suggest that lead in air collected during the summer came from industrial sources in New Zealand and Australia, and that lead in air collected during the winter was either from industrial sources in northern South America or was lead from North American sources that had been exported to the Southern Hemisphere and used there. These assignments are validated because they correlate well with isentropic air mass trajectories assigned to periods when the air was sampled.

## INTRODUCTION

IT HAS BEEN SHOWN (PATTERSON and SETTLE, 1987a) that during preindustrial times about half the lead in the troposphere came from soil dusts, while the remainder came from volcanic gases. Today the proportion of this natural lead in the atmosphere is overwhelmed by industrial lead emitted from smelters, automobile exhausts, and power plants. About 85% of industrial lead emissions to the global atmosphere are introduced into the Northern Hemisphere Westerlies from North America, Europe, and Japan, with most of the remainder being introduced into the Southern Hemisphere Westerlies from Brazil, South Africa, Australia, and New Zealand. This creates a negative north-south gradient in global atmospheric lead concentrations across boundaries between the northern hemisphere Westerlies and Easterlies meridional tropospheric circulation cells, as well as across the equatorial boundary between the northern and southern Easterlies cells, because their convergence barriers restrict latitudinal mixing and the residence time of lead-rich aerosols is about ten days. Atmospheric lead concentrations in a pole to pole strip across the central Pacific show declines within meridional cells on either side of the Westerlies, with the northern hemispheric set containing higher lead concentrations than the corresponding southern hemispheric set, and with the Antarctic polar cap being the least lead polluted tropospheric cell within the Earth's atmosphere.

Eolian anthropogenic lead inputs added to the oceans during the past century were discovered to far outweigh ancient natural riverine inputs (CHOW and PATTERSON, 1962). Later work showed that these industrial inputs now account for about 90% of the total marine lead reservoir (SCHAULE and PATTERSON, 1981, 1983; SHEN and BOYLE, 1987). Present-day riverine anthropogenic lead inputs are sequestered on shelf deposits before that lead enters the open oceans (SCHAULE and PATTERSON, 1981; NG and PATTERSON, 1982; FLEGAL et al., 1986; TREFREY and PRESLEY, 1976). Most of this lead is stored in the thermocline above 1000 m, creating steep negative concentration gradients with depth down to the base of the thermocline where magnitudes of concentration changes with depth are highest in the North Atlantic region, intermediate in the North Pacific region, and lowest in the South Pacific (CHOW and PATTERSON, 1962; FLEGAL and PATTERSON, 1983; FLEGAL et al., 1986; SCHAULE and PATTERSON, 1981, 1983). Such regional differences exist because of the slowness of horizontal mixing at depth on a time scale of centuries. Lead isotopic compositions of marine leads can be used for identification of regional origins of industrial lead to oceanic lead reservoirs at various locations (FLEGAL and PATTERSON, 1983; FLEGAL et al., 1984, 1986; MARING et al., 1987, 1990).

The aims of this investigation were (1) to establish separate *net* eolian input fluxes of natural soil dust lead, volcanic lead, and industrial lead to the oceans; and (2) to quantitatively evaluate fluxes via rain and dry deposition, together with the separate eolian input fluxes of lead, salt, and dust recycled in sea spray aerosols through rain and dry deposition. It was also our purpose to identify regional sources of inputs of industrial lead by use of isotope tracers.

## SAMPLE COLLECTION

The sample collection site was located in the South Pacific Easterlies on the eastern end of Tutuila Island (American Samoa 14°S, 170°W). Sampling devices were mounted on the top of an 18 m tower located at the edge of a 30 m cliff on the coast. Air was monitored continuously by meteorological recording devices, and decisions to collect samples were made manually on the basis of both local and antecedent wind trajectory characteristics, selecting only parcels of air believed to represent large regional character not contaminated by local emissions of anthropogenic lead. This experiment was part of the NSF SEAREX Program operation carried out at American Samoa in 1981. Descriptions of the program, site, and relation to other major wind systems are given in DUCE (1981) and ARIMOTO et al. (1987).

Samples of sea salts, soil dusts, volcanic and industrial fume aerosols in South Pacific Easterlies boundary layer air were collected on total air filters, cascade air impactors, and dry deposition plates at various times during winter and summer seasons. Seawater was collected by dipping bottles attached to long poles from the bow of a small U.S. Coast Guard boat as the boat moved slowly forward. Samples of rain formed at high altitudes were collected in the boundary layer near the ocean surface during these periods, together with surface seawater samples that were collected at distances of 20 to 30 miles from the shore site of rain collection. Ultra-clean *manual* collection procedures together with ultra-clean sampling equipment and analytical techniques were used for all samples. Actual sampling times for air, rain, and dry deposition were severely restricted to small windows within the total site occupation time because of interference from local atmospheric emissions. Pathway sources of sampled air were continuously monitored by meteorological recording devices and meteorological network information input. These data were continuously evaluated and used to make decisions over short time intervals whether to collect or not collect air, impactor, dry deposition, and rain samples. Only those air parcels believed not to be contaminated by local emissions of an-

thropogenic lead were accepted. Some of these constraint evaluation techniques have been described in ARIMOTO et al. (1987).

Descriptions of the rain and air collection apparatus are given in MARING et al. (1989). The dry deposition collector was a 40-cm diameter rimless 1-cm thick polyethylene disk supported from the bottom center. Deposits were removed by sweeping (by means of an ultra-pure quartz rod) a 1 cm$^3$ drop of dilute HCl over the entire surface, twice. Crucial aspects of control of contamination in cleaning apparatus and containers and in handling, transport and storage of samples are outlined in MARING et al. (1989).

## ANALYTICAL METHODS

Sizes of samples were: air ~250 m$^3$; rain 0.2 to 2 liters; dry deposition 30 to 140 hrs; and seawater ~2 liters. Concentrations of Pb, Ca, Sr, Ba, K, and Rb, together with isotopic compositions of lead, were determined in the samples by thermal ionization high-resolution magnetic scanning isotope dilution mass spectrometry under ultra-low level lead contamination control in the ultra-clean biogeochemical laboratory of the Geology Division at the California Institute of Technology. Descriptions of the methods have been given elsewhere (PATTERSON and SETTLE, 1976, 1977; PATTERSON et al., 1976; EVERSON and PATTERSON, 1980; SETTLE and PATTERSON, 1980; BOUTRON and PATTERSON, 1983). A known amount of stable $^{208}$Pb isotope spike was added to all samples being analyzed for lead. This mixture of spike and sample was dissolved in HNO$_3$/HClO$_4$ in an ultra-pure quartz dish and taken to dryness. The redissolved residue was complexed with citrate and cyanide and extracted with dithizone in CHCl$_3$ to isolate mixtures of intrinsic $^{207}$Pb and spike $^{208}$Pb isotopes free from other metals. Isolated lead samples were evaporated on rhenium filaments and the $^{208}$Pb/$^{207}$Pb ratios in them were measured in the mass spectrometer.

Contamination introduced from each container and reagent was determined separately and then summed as 11 separate additions which varied slightly for each analysis, yielding a total of about 340 pg with an uncertainty of about 20 pg. Amounts of sample lead ranged from 1 to 10 ng, with an uncertainty of ±0.5% in reported concentrations. Calcium and barium were determined by IDMS by adding stable $^{42}$Ca and $^{136}$Ba isotope tracers to aliquots of acid solutions of some of the dissolved samples being analyzed for lead. These mixtures of sample and tracer isotopes of calcium and barium were evaporated on oxidized tantalum filaments and inserted into the source of the mass spectrometer for isotopic analysis. Leads were separately isolated from unspiked samples to measure $^{206}$Pb/$^{207}$Pb ratios of lead intrinsic within the samples. Representative contamination values from various sources introduced during collection and analyses are reported in MARING et al. (1989).

## RESULTS

Eolian input fluxes from rain and dry deposition of lead, salt, and dust to the ocean determined from these concentrations are listed in Table 2. Characteristic isotopic compositions of lead measured in the fluxes are also listed.

Table 1. Summary of observed concentrations of lead, salt, and dust, distributions of industrial and natural lead among different types of aerosols, and isotopic compositions of lead in air and rain collected at American Samoa during 1981. Concentrations and isotopic concentrations of lead in seawater collected at the time and place are also listed

| Type of sample | Date (1981) | Sea salt | Soil dust | Total lead | Distribution of total lead | | | | | | | Pb isotopic composition | | |
|---|---|---|---|---|---|---|---|---|---|---|---|---|---|---|
| | | | | | Soil dust | | Sea salt | | Indust. from plant leaves | Indust. aerosols | Volcanic aerosols | 6/7 | 6/8 | 6/4 |
| | | | | | Nat. | Ind. | Nat. | Ind. | | | | | | |
| **Air** | | $\mu g/m^3$ | $ng/m^3$ | $pg/m^3$ | | | | | $pg/m^3$ | | | | | |
| Summer | 1/14–2/27 | 5.5 | 12 | 40 | 0.08 | 0 | — | 14 | 2.1 | 24 | 0.3 | 1.1948 | 0.4911 | 18.31 |
| Winter | 7/04–7/21 | 13 | 48 | 22 | 0.32 | 0 | — | 4.0 | 1.4 | 16 | 0.3 | 1.1766 | 0.4872 | 18.31 |
| Mean air | | 9 | 30 | 31 | 0.2 | 0 | | 9 | 1.8 | 20 | 0.3 | | | |
| **Rain** | | $\mu g/m^3$ | $ng/m^3$ | $pg/m^3$ | | | | | $ng/kg$ | | | | | |
| Summer | 1/19 | 0.6 | 0.3 | 12.6 | 2.1 | 0.15 | — | 1.5 | — | 8.8 | 0.1 | — | — | — |
| Summer | 2/3 | 2.7 | 1.0 | 9.0 | 7.0 | .5 | — | 4.3 | — | 0 | .06 | 1.2240 | 0.4998 | 19.12 |
| Winter | 7/25 | 2.1 | 0.05 | 24.8 | 0.35 | 0.02 | — | 0.6 | — | 23.9 | 0.1 | — | — | — |
| Winter | 7/26 | 6.9 | 0.13 | 0.9 | 0.9 | 0.06 | — | 0.6 | — | 0 | .03 | — | — | — |
| Mean rain | | 3.1 | 0.6 | 12 | 2.6 | 0.18 | | 1.7 | | 7.5 | 0.07 | | | |
| **Sea Water** | | | $ng/kg$ | | | | | | | | | | | |
| Summer | 1/27 | | 3.5 | | | | | | | | | 1.1820 | 0.4830 | 18.36 |
| Winter | 7/28 | | 4.3 | | | | | | | | | 1.1799 | 0.4833 | 18.26 |

Table 2. Summary of eolian inputs and dry deposition fluxes of lead, salt, and dust to the ocean, together with the isotopic compositions of the flux leads at American Samoa during 1981

| Type of flux | Date (1981) | Sea salt | Soil dust | Total lead | Recycled Pb in sea salt | Net input Pb flux | Pb isotopic composition | | |
|---|---|---|---|---|---|---|---|---|---|
| | | | | | | | 6/7 | 6/8 | 6/4 |
| Via Rain* | | $\mu g/cm^2$ yr | $\mu g/cm^2$ yr | $ng/cm^2$ yr | $ng/cm^2$ yr | $ng/cm^2$ yr | | | |
| Summer | 1/19 | 96 | 48 | 2.01 | 0.25 | 1.76 | — | — | — |
| Summer | 2/3 | 440 | 160 | 1.44 | 0.69 | 0.75 | 1.2240 | 0.4998 | 19.12 |
| Winter | 7/25 | 340 | 8 | 3.96 | 0.10 | 3.86 | | | |
| Winter | 7/26 | 1100 | 21 | 0.14 | 0.10 | 0.05 | | | |
| Mean Rain | | 490 | 60 | 1.89 | 0.28 | 1.61 | | | |
| Via Dry Dep.* | | | | | | | | | |
| Summer | 1/19–2/6 | 950 | 2.3 | 2.43 | 2.4 | 0 | 1.2291 | 0.4994 | 19.21 |
| Winter | 7/3–7/18 | 2800 | 2.7 | 0.83 | 0.83 | 0 | 1.2223 | 0.4992 | 19.07 |
| Mean Dry Dep. | | 1900 | 2.5 | 1.6 | 1.6 | 0 | | | |

* Seasonal fluxes converted to annual fluxes.

Observed concentrations of lead, salt, and dust and distributions of industrial and natural lead among different types of aerosols in air and rain and lead concentrations in seawater are summarized in Table 1. Soil dust concentrations in air and rain were determined from measured barium concentrations × 2500 (wt. ratio in silicate source rock) × 1.33 (correction applied for humus component, PATTERSON and SETTLE, 1987a). Sea salt concentrations in air and rain were determined from measured total calcium minus calcium contributed by dust × 86 (wt. ratio in sea salt) and/or from total measured potassium minus potassium contributed by dust × 91. Volcanic lead concentrations in rain were determined from measured average non-sea salt $SO_4$ concentrations in rain (reported by PSZENNY et al., 1982) × 0.1 (fraction that is volcanic, ZEHNDER and ZINDER, 1980) × S/SO₄ wt. ratio × Pb/S volcanic wt. ratio (PATTERSON and SETTLE, 1987a, 1988), yielding a mean for both season and year of 0.1 ng volcanic lead per 3 mg sea salt per kg rain. A mean concentration of volcanic lead in air was obtained from this value for volcanic lead in rain by multiplying it by three to yield a mean of 0.3 pg volcanic lead per 9 $\mu g$ sea salt per m³ air, for season and year. Concentrations of natural lead in soil dust contained in both air and rain were determined from measured dust concentrations × 7 ppm (concentration in total silicate fraction, PATTERSON and SETTLE, 1987a). Concentrations of industrial lead in contaminated humus of soil dust (in the Southern Hemisphere) were determined from measured dust concentrations × 0.5 ppm (PATTERSON and SETTLE, 1987a). Concentrations of lead contained in sea salt contained in both

rain and air (all of the lead was industrial—see below) were obtained from measured concentrations of sea salt in air and rain × Pb/salt in sea water × enrichment factors that were 2500 in winter and 25,000 in summer (see below). Concentrations of industrial lead in plant leaf aerosols contained in air were set equal to 8% of total industrial lead in <1.5 $\mu m$ aerosols (see below). Such lead was set equal to 0% in rain. The sum of leads in soil dust, sea salt, volcanic aerosols, and in plant leaf aerosols was subtracted from total lead in air to yield concentrations of lead in industrially produced lead-rich aerosols. Concentrations of net industrial lead in industrially produced lead-rich aerosols contained in rain were assigned to the net remaining after total lead was corrected for lead in sea salt, dust, and volcanic aerosols.

Uncertainties in measurements of metal concentrations in air are about 10%, determined mainly by an uncertainty of this magnitude in air volumes. Error in measurement of air volumes was reduced to about 10% through use of three calibration methods in the field at the time of collection: integrated rotameter flow, hot wire conductivity flow meter, and integrated bellows gas meter. Uncertainties of metal concentrations (except Ba) in rain ranged from <1% to 10% with smaller concentrations being less certain. Uncertainties for Ba concentrations ranged from 3 to 30%. Uncertainties for Pb concentrations in seawater were about 1%. These values were not determined from statistical considerations but were derived essentially from human interpretative knowledge, gained through measurement, of influences by errors in contamination control, which greatly exceeded instrumental errors and varied with sample type and element being studied. Measurement errors were about ±0.1% of the $^{206}Pb/^{207}Pb$ ratio, about ±0.2% of the $^{206}Pb/^{208}Pb$ ratio, and about ±0.5% of the $^{206}Pb/^{204}Pb$ ratio.

Other investigators determined the following constituents in samples related to those we studied: Cl, Br, I, Na, Mg, K, Ca, Al, Fe, Mn, V, Pb, Ag, Cd, Cu, Zn, Sc, Co, Hf, Rb, and Se by ARIMOTO et al., (1987); sea salts, $NO_3$, $SO_4$, pH by PSZENNY et al. (1982); Hg by FITZGERALD (1989); organic compounds by ATLAS and GIAM (1989) and by PELTZER and GAGOSIAN (1989); and $^{210}Pb$ by TUREKIAN et al. (1989).

Our salt and dust data were compatible with that determined by our colleagues R. Arimoto, R. Duce, P. Harder, B. Ray, and C. Unni at the University of Rhode Island. Investigators in the SEAREX group used our expertise and guidance in development of ultra-clean collection and analytical methods for their studies of trace metals by means of sharing of samples and collection apparatus.

## DISCUSSION

Lead in rain and dry deposition impacting the ocean's surface originates from four major types of lead-containing aerosols in marine air: soil dust, industrial smokes, volcanic sulfate, and sea salt. Net oceanic inputs of lead at various locations and times are determined by magnitudes of scavenging of the first three types of aerosols from air into rain. However, lead-rich industrial aerosols originating from the ocean surface microlayer (originating there, in turn, from such aerosols contained in rain impacting the surface) introduced into sea spray salt and scavenged by rain constitutes a major component of the gross flux which must be corrected out of the measured total in rain to obtain the true input. Net lead introduced to the oceans originates from two kinds of continental and island sources: natural and industrial. Natural lead is contained in soil dust silicates and volcanic sulfate aerosols, while industrial lead is contained in industrially contaminated soil dust humus, industrially contaminated plant leaf debris, and industrially produced lead-rich carbonaceous and oxide aerosols. Although the magnitude of dry deposition input of lead to the ocean's surface at Samoa is quite significant and equal to the net input via rain, the former consists virtually entirely of recycled industrially produced lead-rich aerosols contained in sea spray salt that had originated from the ocean surface microlayer. These data indicate that dry deposition of soil dust is not a significant pathway by which lead enters the oceans.

*Atmospheric occurrences*

As shown in Table 1, concentrations of salts and dusts were three to four times higher in winter air compared to summer air at Samoa, while concentrations of lead were twice as high in the summer. The mass of sea salt aerosols in air was about a thousand-fold greater than the mass of dust particles, which in turn exceeded by a thousand-fold the mass of aerosol lead. About 99% of the lead in Samoan air originated from industrial sources, with about two-thirds being net input occurring in industrially produced carbonaceous-oxide aerosols, about one-third being recycled industrial lead occurring in sea salt aerosols, and about one-fifteenth occurring in industrial lead-rich aerosols attached to larger plant-leaf aerosols. The remaining one percent of atmospheric lead originated from natural clay lead in soil dusts and from natural volcanic fume lead trapped in oxidized and hydrolyzed volcanic sulfur.

*Soil dusts.* Soil dust in air at Samoa was a net introduction and was not present as a recycled constituent of sea spray. Concentrations of natural clay lead in these dusts are about 7 ppm, showing that the average 30 ng dust/$m^3$ air contributes about 1% of total lead in air. This amount compares favorably with the estimated amount of volcanic lead in the air (see below). On the basis of relative global inputs to the atmosphere, dust and volcanic eolian deposition flues should be approximately the same.

Indications have been found suggesting that about one-third of the average total 11 ppm lead in the upper 3 cm of soil in non-urban, non-agricultural regions of the northern hemisphere (about 3.7 ppm) is industrial lead, contained in the humus fraction (from unpubl. data by G. KOLBASUK, R. ELIAS, Y. HIRAO, and C. PATTERSON; summary reported in PATTERSON and SETTLE, 1987a). Differences in tropospheric lead concentrations between the Northern and Southern Hemispheres suggest that soil humus in the Southern Hemisphere is contaminated about one-seventh of that in the Northern Hemisphere, so that it can be assumed that the concentration of industrial lead in soil dusts in the Southern Hemispheric troposphere is about 0.5 ppm. This indicates that industrial lead in soil dust is less than 0.1% of the total lead in air.

*Leaf particles.* Cascade impactor aerosol size studies also disclosed that a significant fraction of industrial atmospheric lead was contained in a new category of intermediate-sized (1 ↔ 1.5 $\mu m$) leaf wax particles. It is known that about two-thirds of the eolian input flux of industrial Pb to vegetated regions is introduced via momentum and diffusion impact collection of fine Pb-rich aerosols onto leaf surfaces (ELIAS et al., 1982). It had also been found that 1 ↔ 1.5 $\mu$m sized leaf wax particles are transported large distances over the oceans (PELTZER and GAGOSIAN, 1989). The cascade impactor findings (ROSMAN et al., 1990) showed that these leaf wax particles contain industrial lead deposits which amounted to about 8% of total lead contained in <1.5 $\mu$m particles in air and about 6% of total lead in air.

*Volcanic sulfate aerosols.* In preindustrial times the emission flux of volcanic lead to the troposphere was about the same as the emission flux of soil dust (PATTERSON and SETTLE, 1987b, 1988). Most volcanic lead is probably emitted in the form of molecular halides which become attached to sulfur aerosols within a few seconds after emission. This sulfur becomes oxidized, and then hydrolyzed, where it accounts today for about 10% of global non-sea salt sulfate in the atmosphere (PATTERSON and SETTLE, 1987b, 1988; ZEHNDER and ZINDER, 1980). It was assumed that the ratio of total non-sea salt $SO_4$ aerosols to sea salt in rain formed at high altitudes was similar to that in boundary layer air. This is an overestimate because the ratio is probably smaller in boundary layer air. If this ratio is assigned to the yearly mean of 9 $\mu$g sea salt/m$^3$ air, and volcanic lead is computed from it and the measured global mean volcanic Pb/S ratio (PATTERSON and SETTLE, 1987b, 1988), an average concentration of 0.3 pg volcanic lead/m$^3$ air is estimated, which amounts to about 1% of the total lead in air and at the same time compares favorably with the equal amount of natural dust lead measured in marine boundary layer air.

*Sea salt aerosols.* It is proved from lead isotopic tracers that lead in sea spray salt originates virtually entirely from industrial lead in the sea surface microlayer, and at concentrations in the salt aerosol that are greatly enriched over seawater concentrations (see *Dry Deposition* section below). The amount of recycled (non-net input) industrial lead (9 pg/m$^3$) in average 9 ug sea salt/m$^3$ air comprises 30% of total average lead in air.

*Industrially produced lead-rich aerosols.* Impactor aerosol size studies (ROSMAN et al., 1989) showed that lead in air not contained in sea salt or dust was divided: 8% on 1 ↔ 1.5 um plant leaf particles and 92% on <0.5 $\mu$m industrially produced carbonaceous-oxide aerosols. The proportions of air lead measured in salt and dust on the impactor were not reliable because of loss of the latter on entry surfaces before the air entered the impactor. Bulk air filter data obtained in this study show, reliably, that the net amount of industrial lead in <0.5 $\mu$m

aerosols, obtained by subtracting lead in soil dust, volcanic $SO_4$, sea salt, and plant leaf particles amounts to an average 20 pg/m$^3$ air, or 63% of total lead in air.

*Regional origins.* $^{206}Pb/^{207}Pb$ ratios of atmospheric lead in boundary-layer air below 1000 m, when correlated with isotopic compositions of industrial lead emissions from various regional sources, show that: (1) lead in such air collected at American Samoa within the Easterlies meridional cell in the Southern Hemisphere during a specific meteorological regime in the winter (ratio = 1.1766) came from industrial sources in New Zealand and Australia, because the values of the ratio of leads emitted from those regions were low; and (2) lead in air collected during a specific meteorological regime in the summer (ratio = 1.1948) came from industrial sources in northern South America, because the values of the ratio of leads emitted from that region were high (PATTERSON and SETTLE, 1987a). These assignments derived from isotopic tracers correlate well with specific isentropic air mass trajectories assigned to air (MERRILL, 1989) that was sampled at various periods. Such isotopic assignments serve, in this manner, to validate those isentropic trajectories.

Air masses, identified as originating from specific regions in the Southern Hemisphere by means of both isentropic trajectories and lead isotopic tracers, appear to contain lead with somewhat higher values of $^{206}Pb/^{207}Pb$ ratios than would be expected. An estimate of the mean value for this ratio in Australian lead alkyls would be about 1.135 for early 1980s (see *Global Context* section below), while alkyls made of Chilean lead should have had values for the ratio equal to about 1.18 for that time. The average value of $^{206}Pb/^{207}Pb$ in U.S. lead alkyls for 1980 was about 1.225 (MANEA-KRICHTEN et al., 1991). This suggests that lead alkyls containing leads from the U.S.A. were being exported to and used within the Southern Hemisphere, so that emissions of this lead within the Southern Hemisphere mixed with emissions of Australian and Chilean lead to elevate $^{206}Pb/^{207}Pb$ ratios of the latter.

## Occurrences in rain

The isotopic composition of lead in rain is quite unlike that in boundary-layer air, indicating that the collected rain had formed in high altitude air masses originating from a different meteorological regime than that responsible for the lower altitude air mass sampled close to the time the rain was collected. Isotopic tracers indicate that the high altitude lead in rain originated from industrial aerosols emitted from restricted regions of southern United States and northern Mexico, while the low altitude lead in air originated from mixtures of the above type of air mass with air that originated from northern swirls of Westerlies from Australia and New Zealand.

Proportions of dust relative to salt and industrially produced lead-rich aerosols scavenged from air by rain at high altitudes differ from those measured in air at lower boundary layer altitudes because (1) concentrations of salt decrease while concentrations of dust and lead-rich industrial aerosols increase with altitude, and (2) scavenging ratios (conc. in rain/conc. in air) for salt are greater than for dust while those for dust are greater than for lead-rich aerosols (MARING et al., 1989; CHURCH et al., 1991a,b). These factors account (aside from meteorological regime differences) for the greater proportion of dust lead in total lead in rain compared to its proportion of total lead in boundary-layer air (23% vs. 1%), the smaller proportion of sea salt lead in rain lead compared to air lead (15% vs. 30%), and the unchanged proportion of industrial lead-rich aerosols in both rain lead and air lead (64%). The average concentration of volcanic lead in rain was computed from the observed average non-sea salt concentration.

Sea salt is the only effective source of recycled lead in rain, amounting to 15% of the total, leaving a net input of 1.6 ng pb/cm$^2$ yr to the oceans from the Easterlies at Samoa (computed from an annual rainfall of 160 cm/cm$^2$, DORMAN and BOURKE, 1979). 73% of this net input lead originated from industrially produced carbonaceous-oxide aerosols, while 25% originated from natural lead and 2% from industrial lead in soil dust. Natural lead in volcanic $SO_4$ aerosols amounts to about 1% of the net input. The eolian input of sea spray salt returned to the oceans in rain is 490 $\mu$g/cm$^2$ yr. The eolian input of dust in rain is 60 $\mu$g/cm$^2$ yr.

*Occurrences in dry deposition*

The bulk of the mass of dry deposition to the ocean consists of recycled sea salt. This recycled sea salt returns an amount of lead to the ocean by dry deposition (1.6 ng/cm$^2$ yr) that is equivalent to the net amount added by rain. This recycled lead originated from lead contained in industrially produced aerosols that had been previously added to the ocean surface microlayer by rain. The maximum contribution of natural soil dust lead to the dry deposition flux is less than 1% of the total (<0.02 ng/cm$^2$ yr). The amount of sea spray salt returned to the ocean by dry deposition is 1900 $\mu$g/cm$^2$ yr, which is four

times that returned in rain. The sum of dust added by dry deposition of both pure dust aerosols and dust contained in recycled sea salt (1.7 $\mu$g/cm$^2$ yr) is only one-thirtieth of dust in such forms added to the oceans in rain (60 $\mu$g/cm$^2$ yr). The small amount of dust added to the ocean surface by dry deposition indicates that not much dust is sequestered in the sea surface microlayer, and dust is therefore probably not greatly enriched in sea spray. This means that lead/dust ratios are probably greatly increased in sea spray when lead-rich industrial aerosols are enriched in sea spray. It follows that most of the dust observed in dry deposition and in rain probably originates from pure dust aerosols.

There is no discernible amount of lead-rich industrial aerosols added in pure form by dry deposition to the ocean surface. $^{206}Pb/^{207}Pb$ ratios in rain and in large particles on the dry deposition plate were nearly identical, 1.2240 vs. 1.2223, but quite different from those ratios in bulk air filters (1.1766), and surface seawater (1.1799), all collected within the same brief time period. This proves that lead in sea spray originates from undissolved particles in rain which are sequestered in the sea surface microlayer and then incorporated in sea spray particles. Lead isotopic tracers force us to assign all of the dry-deposition lead to recycled sea salt, and the ratio of lead to salt in dry deposition compared to the ratio of lead to salt in nearby seawater gives a measurement of the enrichment factor for lead in sea spray salt. Such measured enrichment factors were 26,000 for summer sea spray and 2400 for winter sea spray. Our impactor studies indicated an enrichment factor of 1200 for winter sea spray salt deposited on the coarse particle sized stages. This measurement of the ratio in size separated particles (even though some of the salt and dust in air had been lost) concurred with and verified the measurement of the ratio in dry-deposition deposit mixtures of all-sized particles. This conclusion is based on the indication by isotopic tracers that contributions of lead from small-sized particles was insignificant.

It is not known now why the enrichment factor changes with season, but it is known from isotopic tracers that the enriched lead in sea spray salt aerosols originates from lead-rich industrial aerosols that are first scavenged from air by rain and collected by the oily ocean microlayer after the rain impacts on the ocean surface. The lead dissolves from the collected particles into seawater at a slow rate of about 50% per day (MARING, 1986) to provide added lead to seawater. It is during this short period before dissolution that the lead is added to sea spray, where its quantities greatly outweigh dissolved seawater lead in the spray. The isotopic compositions of lead in rain fluctuate with time at any given location, but the isotopic composition of lead in seawater is an average of both added and advected lead and changes only slowly with time. The global average value of the enrichment factor has been put at 5000, based on a number of similar type of measurements carried out at various locations (PATTERSON and SETTLE, 1987a).

## Global context

There is a clear demarkation between air concentrations and eolian input fluxes of lead to the mid-Pacific on either side of the equatorial boundary separating the Northern and Southern Easterlies. Concentrations in boundary layer air are 160 pg $Pb/m^3$ north of the Equator, and 31 ng $Pb/m^3$ south of the Equator, while net eolian input fluxes (corrected for recycled lead in sea salt) from these meridional cells are 6 and 1.6 ng $Pb/cm^2$ yr, respectively (northern Easterlies data from SETTLE and PATTERSON, 1982). About 7% of the larger amount of lead in rain north of the Equator originates from natural sources, compared to about 30% of the smaller amount of lead in rain south of the Equator. There is also a demarkation between air concentrations and eolian input fluxes of lead to the mid-Pacific on either side of the boundary separating the southern Easterlies and Westerlies. Lead concentrations in boundary layer air are 30 and 150 $pg/m^3$ and net lead fluxes are 1.6 and 10 ng/$cm^2$ yr in Easterlies and Westerlies, respectively (southern Westerlies data from SETTLE and PATTERSON, 1985).

Industrial lead enters the atmosphere of the Southern Hemisphere mostly by injection into the Westerlies meridional cell, so that eolian inputs to the Earth's surface from tropospheric meridional cells on either side of the southern Westerlies cell can be reliably expected to be smaller. However, eolian input fluxes from the Easterlies cell to the oceans should greatly exceed those from the Antarctic polar cap cell to the snow pack because lead concentrations in the latter atmosphere should be much smaller. The rationale for this is that the Antarctic circumpolar convergence provides a much stronger barrier to mixing from the Westerlies on its southern edge compared to effectiveness against mixing by the intertropical convergence on its northern edge. Furthermore, some industrial lead is injected directly into the Easterlies cell. Therefore, eolian input fluxes of lead to the snow surface of the Antarctic, being driven by much smaller atmospheric lead concentrations, must be consider-

ably smaller than those from the Easterlies, so values of eolian inputs to the oceans measured in this study have served as valuable restrictive guides to studies and measurements of eolian lead inputs to snow in the Antarctic (BOUTRON and PATTERSON, 1987).

The $^{206}Pb/^{207}Pb$ ratios of lead in surface seawater underlying the Antarctic meridional cell (avg. $\sim 1.160$) reported by (FLEGAL et al., 1991) are considerably higher than that observed underlying the Westerlies meridional cell by us in 1983 (1.1347, SETTLE and PATTERSON, 1985). These values for lead in water reflect sums of eolian contributions over a period of several years earlier than the dates of collection of the waters. The elevated values in the Antarctic cell may reflect the greater use of lead alkyls of U.S. origin within the Southern Hemisphere since 1980 (FLEGAL et al., 1991), because U.S. lead has possessed values for this ratio of about 1.225 since 1980 and about 1.230 since 1985 (MANEA-KRICHTEN et al., 1991), and much greater amounts of U.S. lead alkyls have been exported to the Southern Hemisphere during the last decade than was the case previously.

## Future work

Scavenging ratios of salts, dusts, and metals determined in this work are not true values because atmospheric concentrations were measured in boundary layer air and concentrations were measured in rain that had formed in high altitude air. There is a need to determine true values, and this can be done by collecting samples of both air and fog-water formed in that air at elevated altitudes and collected from an airplane or blimp before and after the fog formed. At the same time there is need for reliable enrichment factors for metals in sea salt spray determined directly from cascade impactor aerosol size-sorted samples. These data are required for reliable measurement of eolian input fluxes of metals corrected for recycled metals in sea salt spray.

*Acknowledgements*—This experiment was made possible by the cooperative effort of members of the interuniversity NSF SEAREX program, and their contributions of logistical support, field assistance, equipment exchange, and intercommunication of data made this experiment possible. We also thank members of the NOAA GMCC observatory at the American Samoa site for their generous assistance in field operations. This research was supported by NSF grants OCE 77-14520 and OCE 81-11893, A02. Contribution 5001 from the Division of Geological and Planetary Sciences, California Institute of Technology.

## REFERENCES

ARIMOTO R., DUCE R. A., RAY B. J., HEWITT A. D. and WILLIAMS J. (1987) Trace elements in the atmosphere of American Samoa: Concentrations and deposition to the tropical South Pacific. *J. Geophys. Res.* **92**, 8465–8479.

ATLAS E. and GIAM C. S. (1989) Sea-Air exchange of high molecular weight synthetic organic compounds: Results from the SEAREX Program. In *Chemical Oceanography* (eds. R. A. DUCE, J. P. RILEY and R. CHESTER), Vol. 10, pp. 339–378. Academic Press, London.

BOUTRON C. F. and PATTERSON C. C. (1983) The occurrence of lead in Antarctic recent snow, firn deposited over the last two centuries and prehistoric ice. *Geochim. Cosmochim. Acta* **47**, 1355–1368.

BOUTRON C. and PATTERSON C. C. (1987) Relative levels of natural and industrial lead in recent Antarctic snow. *J. Geophys. Res.* **92**, 8454–8465.

CHOW T. J. and PATTERSON C. C. (1962) The occurrence and significance of lead isotopes in pelagic sediments. *Geochim. Cosmochim. Acta* **26**, 263–308.

CHURCH T., VERON A., PATTERSON C. and SETTLE D. (1991a) Trace metal scavenging from the North Atlantic Troposphere. *Proc 5th Intl. Conf. Precipitation Scavenging and Atmospheric-Surface Exchange Processes* (in press).

CHURCH T. M., VERON A., PATTERSON C. C., SETTLE D., EREL Y., MARING H. R. and FLEGAL A. R. (1991b) Trace elements in the North Atlantic Troposphere: Shipboard results of precipitation and aerosols. *Global Biogeochemical Cycles* **4**, 431–443.

DORMAN C. E. and BOURKE R. H. (1979) Precipitation of the Pacific Ocean, 30°S to 60°N. *Monthly Weather Rev.* **107**, 896–910.

DUCE R. A. (1981) SEAREX: A multi-institutional investigation of the sea/air exchange of pollutants and natural substances. In *Marine Pollutant Transfer Processes* (eds. M. WALDICHUK, G. KULLENBERG and M. ORREN). Elsevier, NY.

ELIAS R. W., HIRAO Y. and PATTERSON C. C. (1982) The circumvention of natural biopurification of calcium along nutrient pathways by atmospheric inputs of industrial lead. *Geochim. Cosmochim. Acta* **46**, 2561–2580.

EVERSON J. and PATTERSON C. C. (1980) Ultra-clean isotope dilution/mass spectrometric analyses for lead in human blood plasma indicate that most reported values are artificially high. *Clin. Chem.* **26**, 1603–1607.

FITZGERALD W. F. (1989) Atmospheric and oceanic cycling of mercury. In *Chemical Oceanography* (eds. R. A. DUCE, J. P. RILEY and R. CHESTER), Vol. 10, pp. 151–186. Academic Press, London.

FLEGAL A. R. and PATTERSON C. C. (1983) Vertical concentration profiles of lead in the Central Pacific at 15 N and 20 S. *Earth Planet. Sci. Lett.* **64**, 19–32.

FLEGAL A. R., SCHAULE B. K. and PATTERSON C. C. (1984) Stable isotopic ratios of lead in surface waters of the Central Pacific. *Marine Chem.* **14**, 281–287.

FLEGAL A. R., ITOH K., PATTERSON C. C. and WONG C. S. (1986) Vertical profile of lead isotopic compositions in the Northeast Pacific. *Nature* **321**, 689–690.

FLEGAL A. R., PATTERSON C. C., MARING H. and NIEMEYER S. (1991) Anthropogenic lead in Antarctic surface waters implicates U.S. industrial lead export (in prep.).

MANEA-KRICHTEN M., PATTERSON C., MILLER G., SETTLE D. and EREL Y. (1991) Comparative increases of lead and barium with age in human tooth enamel, rib and ulna. *Sci. Total Env.* (in press).

MARING H. (1986) The impact of atmospheric aerosols on trace metal chemistry in open ocean surface sea water. Ph.D. thesis, University of Rhode Island.

MARING H., SETTLE D. M., BUAT-MÉNARD P., DULAC F. and PATTERSON C. C. (1987) Stable lead isotope tracers of air mass trajectories in the Mediterranean region. *Nature* **330**, 154–156.

MARING H., PATTERSON C. C. and SETTLE D. M. (1989) Atmospheric input fluxes of industrial and natural Pb from the westerlies to the Mid-North Pacific. In *Chemical Oceanography* (eds. R. A. DUCE, J. P. RILEY and R. CHESTER), Vol. 10, pp. 83–106. Academic Press, London.

MERRILL J. T. (1989) Atmospheric long-range transport to the Pacific Ocean. In *Chemical Oceanography* (eds. R. A. DUCE, J. P. RILEY and R. CHESTER), Vol. 10, pp. 15–50. Academic Press, London.

NG A. and PATTERSON C. C. (1982) Changes of lead and barium with time in California off-shore basin sediments. *Geochim. Cosmochim. Acta* **46**, 2307–2321.

PATTERSON C. C. and SETTLE D. M. (1976) The reduction of order of magnitude errors in lead analyses of biological materials and natural waters by evaluating and controlling the extent and sources of industrial lead contamination introduced during sample collecting, handling, and analysis. In *Accuracy in Trace Analysis: Sampling, Sample Handling, and Analysis* (ed. P. LaFLEUR); *Nat. Bur. Stand. Spec. Pub. 422,* pp. 321–351.

PATTERSON C. and SETTLE D. (1977) Comparative distributions of alkalies, alkaline earths and lead among major tissues of the tuna *Thunnus alalunga. Marine Biol.* **39**, 289–295.

PATTERSON C. C. and SETTLE D. M. (1987a) Review of data on eolian fluxes of industrial and natural lead to the lands and seas in remote regions on global scale. *Marine Chem.* **22**, 137–162.

PATTERSON C. C. and SETTLE D. M. (1987b) Magnitude of lead flux to the atmosphere from volcanoes. *Geochim. Cosmochim. Acta* **51**, 675–681.

PATTERSON C. C. and SETTLE D. M. (1988) Corrected values for global volcanic fluxes of Pb, Tl and Bi. *Geochim. Cosmochim. Acta* **52**, 245.

PATTERSON C. C., SETTLE D. M., SCHAULE B. K. and BURNETT M. W. (1976) Standardization of reference samples for certain trace metals: The first step in a multistage program designed to insure the reliability and significance of baseline data for trace metals. *Baseline Studies of Outer Continental Shelf, Southern California* **3**, Report 4.4, Bureau Land Management, U.S. Dept. Interior, Washington, DC.

PELTZER E. T. and GAGOSIAN R. B. (1989) Organic geochemistry of aerosols over the Pacific ocean. In *Chemical Oceanography* (eds. R. A. DUCE, J. P. RILEY and R. CHESTER), Vol. 10, pp. 281–338. Academic Press, London.

PSZENNY A. P., MACINTYRE F. and DUCE R. A. (1982) Sea-salt and the acidity of marine rain on the windward coast of Samoa. *Geophys. Res. Lett.* **9**, 751–754.

ROSMAN K. J. R., PATTERSON C. C. and SETTLE D. M. (1990) The distribution of lead between sea salt, dust, and lead-rich aerosols in the mid South Pacific Easterlies at American Samoa. *J. Geophys. Res.* **95**, 3687–3691.

SCHAULE B. K. and PATTERSON C. C. (1981) Lead concentrations in the northeast Pacific: evidence for global anthropogenic perturbations. *Earth Planet. Sci. Lett.* **54,** 97–116.

SCHAULE B. K. and PATTERSON C. C. (1983) Perturbations of the natural lead depth profile in the Sargasso Sea by industrial lead. In *Trace Metals in Sea Water, NATO Conference Series IV: Marine Sciences* (eds. C. S. WONG et al.), Vol. 9, pp. 487–503, Plenum Press, New York.

SETTLE D. M. and PATTERSON C. C. (1980) Lead in albacore: Guide to lead pollution in Americans. *Science* **207,** 1167–1176.

SETTLE D. M. and PATTERSON C. C. (1982) Magnitudes and sources of precipitation and dry deposition fluxes of industrial and natural leads to the North Pacific at Enewetak. *J. Geophys. Res.* **87,** 8857–8869.

SETTLE D. M. and PATTERSON C. C. (1985) New Zealand results. *SEAREX Newsletter* **8,** 10.

SHEN G. T. and BOYLE E. A. (1987) Lead in corals: Reconstruction of historic industrial fluxes to the surface ocean. *Earth Planet. Sci. Lett.* **326,** 278–280.

TREFREY J. H. and PRESLEY B. J. (1976) Heavy metal transport from the Mississippi River to the Gulf of Mexico. In *Marine Pollutant Transfer* (eds. H. L. WINDOM and R. A. DUCE), pp. 39–76. Heath and Co., Lexington.

TUREKIAN K. K., GRAUSTEIN W. C. and COCHRAN J. K. (1989) Lead-210 in the SEAREX Program: an aerosol tracer the Pacific. In *Chemical Oceangraphy* (eds. R. A. DUCE, J. P. RILEY and R. CHESTER), Vol. 10, pp. 51–81. Academic Press, London.

ZEHNDER A. J. B. and ZINDER S. H. (1980) Sulphur fluxes to the Atmosphere. In *Handbook of Environmental Chem.* (ed. O. HUNTZINGER), Vol. 1, pp. 105–145. Springer-Verlag, Berlin.

Stable Isotope Geochemistry: A Tribute to Samuel Epstein
© The Geochemical Society, Special Publication No. 3, 1991
Editors: H. P. Taylor, Jr., J. R. O'Neil and I. R. Kaplan

# Stable isotopes and the Roman marble trade—evidence from Scythopolis and Caesarea, Israel*

ZE'EV PEARL and MORDECKAI MAGARITZ

Department of Environmental Sciences and Energy Research, Weizmann Institute of Science, 76100 Rehovot, Israel

**Abstract**—Analysis of carbon and oxygen stable isotopes of antique white marbles at two Roman sites in Israel is used to study trade practices in the Roman Empire. The range and variance in $\delta^{18}O$ values for 30 out of 42 marble artifacts from the Scythopolis Theatre (1.33 per mil and 0.237 per mil, respectively) is significantly smaller than the respective range and variance for 17 out of 33 artifacts from the Scythopolis Monument (2.62 and 0.443, respectively). An $F$-test to compare these variances with the variance in $\delta^{18}O$ of the quarry indicates that the variance of the theatre artifacts is significantly different from that of the quarry ($P = 0.02$), whereas the variance for the monument artifacts is not ($P = 0.50$). A probable explanation is that marble for the theatre was purchased directly from the Marmara quarry, and possibly was quarried from a single outcrop. On the other hand, marble for the monument was purchased from a local stock yard which held a variety of marbles, including marble from different sections in Marmara. Similar patterns of variation are found for Corinthian Capitals from Caesarea. Sixteen capitals are similar in their decoration and isotopic composition. A range of 0.35 per mil in $\delta^{13}C$ and 1.1 per mil in $\delta^{18}O$ found for these capitals is smaller than the respective ranges that were found for the theatre and monument artifacts above. This indicates that these capitals are relatively more homogenous. An $F$-test to compare the variances in $\delta^{13}C$ and $\delta^{18}O$ between the capitals and the Marmara quarry indicates that the capitals differ significantly in their variances from the quarry ($P < 0.0001$ for both $\delta^{13}C$ and $\delta^{18}O$). This suggests that these capitals originated from a single outcrop in Marmara. A probable explanation to the similarity of the capitals in both decoration and isotopic composition is that they belong to a single monument. These capitals were found out of their archeological context, suggesting that stable isotope analysis can be used in reconstruction of artifacts to their original archeological context.

## INTRODUCTION

ANTIQUE WHITE MARBLE artifacts have been studied by a large number of analytical methods (see HERZ, 1985, for review). In particular, stable isotope analysis has been applied extensively to studies in this field. CRAIG and CRAIG (1972) demonstrated that the distinct isotopic signature of quarries is useful in determining the source quarry of marble artifacts. HERZ and WENNER (1978) suggested isotopic analysis as an objective tool to evaluate whether reconstruction of fragments on the basis of aesthetic criteria is correct. MARGOLIS (1989) used the stable isotope composition of the weathered crust of marbles to evaluate the authenticity of marble statues.

In the present study we discuss the application of stable isotope analysis to study trade practices in the Roman Empire. The degree of homogeneity in the stable isotope signature of groups of artifacts from the same archeological context (*e.g.* a known structure) are discussed. Isotopic exchange in most metamorphic terranes is channelized and thus is limited to the boundaries between marbles and other lithological units (see VALLEY, 1986, for re-

view). Therefore, the isotopic composition of marble samples from a single source is expected to be more homogenous than the isotopic composition of marble samples from several origins which were exposed to different metamorphic conditions. These variations can be related to purchase modes prevailing in the Roman Empire. WARD-PERKINS (1971, 1980) suggested that the Roman marble trade system changed completely during the first century AD. Before that time, marble was purchased directly from the quarry, and that was also the common practice in Classical Greece. The new trade system involved stock-piling in the importing cities, more efficient quarrying methods, standardization of sizes and partial prefabrication. Under this trade system most demands were met by the marble yards, and only exceptionally were direct quarry-customer relations involved. These two modes of marble purchase can be evaluated by the $\delta^{13}C$ and $\delta^{18}O$ values of a group of artifacts. It is expected that the range of isotopic values from artifacts purchased from a single quarry will be smaller than that found for artifacts purchased from a marble yard, as the latter will be more heterogeneous in their isotopic signature. Ranges mentioned in this study are used to describe the absolute difference between the maximum and minimum isotopic value determined for a group of artifacts.

---

* Contribution No. 33, Department of Environmental Sciences and Energy Research, The Weizmann Institute of Science, Rehovot, Israel.

Roman sites in Israel are most suitable for this type of study. Because there is no local source for marble, extensive marble should have been imported to Roman Palestine in one of these modes, from the Roman quarries around the Mediterranean (Fig. 1). Independent evidence (*e.g.* stone inscriptions) indicates that these quarries were indeed the Roman marble source quarries (see DWORA-KOWSKA, 1975, 1983, for review). In this study we apply a multi-method approach to determine the source of the marble artifacts. This approach includes the analysis of $\delta^{13}C$ and $\delta^{18}O$, Mn content and the determination of the calcite/dolomite ratio.

## SITES DESCRIPTION

Marble artifacts for this study were collected in the excavations of two Roman cities in Israel, Scythopolis and Caesarea (Fig. 1). These sites were selected because marble was extensively used as an ornamental stone for construction at both sites.

In Scythopois, we selected marble artifacts which are clearly related to one of two structures, the theatre and the so-called monument, where most of the marble artifacts used for construction in Roman Scythopolis were found. Marble artifacts in Scythopolis are found at or close to their original sites, as the city was destroyed by an earthquake during the eighth century AD, and subsequently a swamp developed in the area and preserved the archeological record. The theatre and the monument were constructed during the second century AD, a prosperous period for the city which was established in the third century BC incorporating the biblical Beth Shean. The theatre is a medium-sized Roman theatre of the "western" type. This type is common in Africa. Other theatres in the region, in Caesarea and Palmyra, are of the same type. The monument, of which only the lower part was preserved, was erected in the heart of Roman Scythopolis.

In Caesarea, we studied Corinthian Capitals of unknown archaeological context; *i.e.,* the structure they were part of is not known. Most artifacts from Caesarea are not found in their original archeological context since Caesarea remained an important city during the Byzantine and later periods. Consequently, Roman marble was reused for construc-

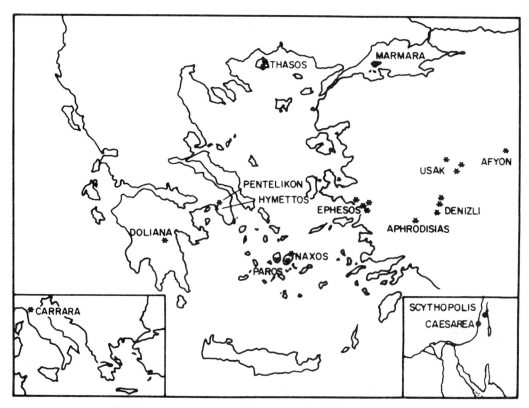

FIG. 1. Location map of the major marble source quarries in Turkey and Greece (center), and in Italy (lower left insert), which operated during the Roman period. Notice the convenient location off shore of the Marmara quarry. A location map of the studied sites in Israel is also given (lower right insert).

tion in later periods, and thus the archeological record is not well preserved. These capitals belong to six well-defined groups according to their artistic features, and are related to the second–third centuries AD (FISCHER, 1991). Caesarea was erected by King Herod the Great and became the seat of the prefecture in the year 6 AD. Throughout the Roman period it served as a major port in Roman Palestine.

## METHODS

In Scythopolis, marble samples were collected at the site. The theatre and monument artifacts were gathered nearby their place of excavation. In Caesarea, samples were collected in the site and from a local museum. Small portions of marble (a few $cm^3$) were removed from each artifact. All samples were taken from uncarved surfaces. The weathered surface was mechanically scraped to avoid analysis of the weathered marble crust.

The source of the marbles was determined by the multimethod approach described below. This approach used several geochemical, petrographical and architectural calibrations in order to specify the source quarry, and was adopted because some overlap exists in the ranges of $\delta^{13}C$ and $\delta^{18}O$ values between quarries (HERZ, 1987). Nevertheless, stable isotope analysis is of prime importance as it is the only technique for which an extensive data base is available (HERZ, 1987). The data base includes the stable isotope composition of marble samples from the 22 major white marble source quarries of the Classical World. For some samples the calcite/dolomite ratio was determined by X-ray diffraction (XRD). Data on the calcite/dolomite ratio of marble quarry samples were adopted from LLOYD et al. (1988). Mn contents were measured also by electron paramagnetic resonance (EPR). Data on the Mn contents of samples from 14 marble quarries were compiled from the data reported by HERZ and DEAN (1986), MOENS et al. (1988), GERMAN et al. (1988), and LLOYD et al. (1988). This compilation is presented in Fig. 2. A particular advantage of these techniques for analysis of valuable artifacts is the small sample size required. Furthermore, EPR is nondestructive.

Samples were crushed with a mortar and pestle to fine powder, and aliquots were taken for stable isotope, XRD, and EPR analyses. The carbon and oxygen isotopes in marble were measured using the conventional phosphoric acid method (McCREA, 1950). The $CO_2$ gas was analyzed in a Varian M250 mass spectrometer, and results are reported using the conventional $\delta$ notation relative to the PDB standard. Isotope values were calibrated using the NBS 19 Calcite standard ($\delta^{18}O = -2.20$; $\delta^{13}C = +1.96$). Reproducibility of duplicate samples is better than 0.1 per mil for $\delta^{13}C$ and 0.15 per mil for $\delta^{18}O$. An aliquot of the powder was analyzed by a standard X-ray diffraction (XRD) procedure with a fully computerized automatic Rigaku 505 diffractometer over the range $2\Theta = 26°-32°$ at a rate of one °/min. Weight percent dolomite/(dolomite + calcite) ratio was calculated using the areas under the peaks $2\Theta = 30.94$ and 29.44 based on the formula of WEBER and SMITH (1961). Mn contents were determined by EPR spectroscopy using a Varian E-12 spectrometer. The EPR spectrum of carbonates consists of six peaks. Quantification was done on the low magnetic field peak against the NBS 88 standard (LLOYD et al. 1988). A computerized system was used for spectrum collection, baseline

correction and double integration. Analytical error is about 10%.

The following rationale was followed in order to determine the marble source of each artifact and the homogeneity in the isotopic signature of groups of artifacts:

(1) The quarry isotopic fingerprint (Qi) was determined by a convex hull drawn through the extreme $\delta^{13}C$ and $\delta^{18}O$ values found for each quarry. These data were taken from the stable isotope data base of quarry samples (HERZ, 1987).

(2) The artifact's isotopic composition (Ai) was compared to the quarry's fingerprint to determine if Ai⊂Qi the marble of Ai originated from Qi.

(3) The Mn content of the artifact was compared with the Mn source quarries' data compilation (Fig. 2), and the calcite/dolomite ratios were compared with the data of LLOYD et al. (1988). These steps were performed for some artifacts to confirm the origin which was determined from their isotopic composition.

(4) A group of artifacts was defined to include all the artifacts which were imported from a common origin and belong to the same structure (theatre or monument) in Scythopolis, or to the same artistic type (Caesarea Capitals). To compare the relative homogeneity between groups, the ranges and variances in their $\delta^{13}C$ and $\delta^{18}O$ values were calculated.

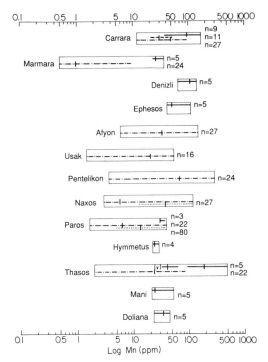

FIG. 2. Compilation of data on Mn contents in source quarry samples. Ranges are given by rectangles. Specific data sources are indicated as follows: – – – HERZ and DEAN (1986); ··· GERMANN et al. (1988); —— LLOYD et al. (1988); ·–·– MOENS et al. (1988). Data for Thasos are for Thasos Aliki (unmarked), and for Thasos Cape vathy (marked with a (v)). N denotes the number of samples. Medians are indicated by vertical bars.

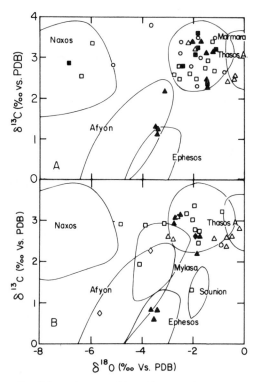

FIG. 3. Isotopic composition of Scythopolis (A) Theatre and (B) Monument artifacts and their possible source quarries. Quarry fields are within the drawn lines. They represent the fingerprint of each quarry as defined in the text. Symbols indicate the architectural function of the artifacts as follows: ♦ = pedestal; ◊ = shaft; ▲ = base; △ = capital; □ = cornice; ■ = architrave; ○ = entablature and unassigned fragments.

(5) An *F*-test (two tailed) was made to evaluate whether the variances in the isotopic signature of groups of artifacts are significantly different from that of the variance in the isotopic signature of their source quarry. A significant smaller variance for the artifacts indicates that their origin is from a restricted section in the quarry, whereas insignificant differences indicate that the artifacts could have originated from the entire quarry. This approach implicitly assumes that the (quarries) sample data base represents the stable isotope signature of the entire quarry.

## RESULTS AND DISCUSSION

### Scythopolis

Forty-two artifacts from the theatre, including bases, capitals, cornices and architraves, were examined. Their chemical and isotopic composition is listed in Table 1. On the $\delta^{13}C$-$\delta^{18}O$ plane (Fig. 3A) the theatre artifacts cluster into four groups as follows. (a) A group of 30 artifacts originated, according to their isotopic composition, from Marmara. This conclusion is supported by the low Mn

content of five samples from this group (2–16 ppm, Table 1). The range in the $\delta^{13}C$ and $\delta^{18}O$ values of these artifacts is 1.33 per mil and 1.95 per mil, respectively. This group includes artifacts of all architectural types. (b) A group of three capitals originated from Thasos Aliki (Fig. 3A). (c) Four bases originated from Afyon (Fig. 3A). Three bases (33–35, Table 1) are distinct also in their size; they have a larger diameter (*ca.* 1m) than all the other bases from the theatre (*ca.* 0.5 m). (d) The remaining five artifacts are depleted in $^{18}O$ relative to the main cluster. For two of them (9 and 20, Table 1) the

Table 1. Isotopic and chemical composition of marble artifacts from Scytopholis Theatre. Isotopic values are in per mil vs. PDB. Weight percent of dolomite is denoted by dd.

| Sample | Description | $\delta^{13}C$ | $\delta^{18}O$ | dd | Mn (ppm) |
|---|---|---|---|---|---|
| 1 | Cornice | 2.48 | −2.53 | 0 | |
| 2 | Cornice | 2.48 | −1.87 | 0 | |
| 3 | Cornice | 2.60 | −2.13 | 0 | |
| 4 | Cornice | 2.53 | −6.37 | 0 | 2 |
| 5 | Cornice | 2.79 | −2.55 | 0 | |
| 6 | Cornice | 3.43 | −1.24 | <5 | |
| 7 | Cornice | 2.93 | −1.44 | 12 | |
| 8 | Cornice | 2.76 | −1.52 | 0 | |
| 9 | Cornice | 3.35 | −5.96 | 83 | |
| 10 | Cornic | 2.59 | −2.74 | | |
| 11 | Cornic | 2.68 | −1.17 | 0 | |
| 12 | Architrave | 3.22 | −1.12 | 15 | |
| 13 | Architrave | 3.24 | −1.82 | 0 | |
| 14 | Architrave | 3.08 | −1.91 | | |
| 15 | Architrave | 2.35 | −1.45 | 0 | |
| 16 | Architrave | 2.78 | −2.40 | 0 | |
| 17 | Architrave | 2.85 | −6.86 | tr. | |
| 18 | Architrave | 3.60 | −1.82 | tr. | |
| 19 | Entablature | 3.50 | −1.13 | | |
| 20 | Entablature | 3.80 | −3.65 | 31 | |
| 21 | Entablature | 2.80 | −2.06 | 0 | 4 |
| 22 | Entablature | 3.01 | −1.72 | 0 | |
| 23 | Entablature | 2.81 | −5.16 | <5 | |
| 24 | Entablature | 2.66 | −0.79 | | |
| 25 | Entablature | 2.30 | −1.86 | | |
| 26 | Entablature | 3.50 | −1.81 | 36 | 3 |
| 27 | Entablature | 3.12 | −2.50 | <5 | |
| 28 | Capital | 2.55 | −0.38 | 0 | |
| 29 | Capital | 2.48 | −0.40 | | |
| 30 | Capital | 3.21 | −1.91 | tr. | |
| 31 | Capital | 3.36 | −2.18 | 0 | |
| 32 | Capital | 2.42 | −0.64 | 0 | |
| 33 | L. Base | 1.26 | −3.39 | 0 | 102 |
| 34 | L. Base | 1.34 | −3.45 | | |
| 35 | L. Base | 1.14 | −3.40 | 0 | |
| 36 | Base | 3.42 | −1.97 | <5 | 11 |
| 37 | Base | 3.12 | −1.47 | 0 | 16 |
| 38 | Base | 2.27 | −1.39 | | |
| 39 | Base | 3.16 | −1.23 | 0 | |
| 40 | Base | 2.18 | −3.12 | 0 | |
| 41 | Base | 2.48 | −1.48 | 0 | |
| 42 | Base | 3.40 | −1.68 | 0 | |

Table 2. Isotopic and chemical composition of marble artifacts from Scythopolis Monument. Isotopic values are in per mil vs. PDB. Weight percent of dolomite is denoted by dd.

| Sample | Description | $\delta^{13}C$ | $\delta^{18}O$ | dd | Mn (ppm) |
|--------|-------------|----------------|----------------|-----|----------|
| 1 | Cornice | 2.88 | −3.89 | 0 | 3 |
| 2 | Cornice | 3.17 | −2.27 | 0 | |
| 3 | Cornice | 3.36 | −1.94 | 0 | |
| 4 | Cornice | 3.02 | −2.02 | | |
| 5 | Cornice | 2.93 | −3.13 | 17 | |
| 6 | Cornice | 2.74 | −1.77 | 0 | 3 |
| 7 | Cornice | 2.91 | −4.85 | 0 | |
| 8 | Cornice | 2.46 | −1.79 | | |
| 9 | Cornice | 2.79 | −1.92 | | |
| 10 | Cornice | 1.32 | −2.06 | 9 | |
| 11 | Cornice | 2.74 | −1.94 | | |
| 12 | Cornice | 3.21 | −0.84 | | |
| 13 | Capital | 3.09 | −2.60 | 0 | |
| 14 | Capital | 2.59 | −0.68 | 0 | |
| 15 | Capital | 2.36 | −0.71 | 0 | |
| 16 | Capital | 2.61 | −2.98 | | |
| 17 | Capital | 2.56 | −1.17 | | |
| 18 | Capital | 2.82 | −0.16 | | |
| 19 | Capital | 2.54 | −2.78 | 0 | |
| 20 | Capital | 2.62 | −0.50 | 0 | |
| 21 | Shaft | 2.27 | −3.67 | 0 | |
| 22 | Shaft | 0.75 | −5.66 | 0 | |
| 23 | Base | 0.61 | −3.50 | 0 | 22 |
| 24 | Base | 0.81 | −3.37 | | |
| 25 | Base | 2.93 | −2.74 | | |
| 26 | Base | 3.15 | −2.48 | | |
| 27 | Base | 3.07 | −2.67 | | |
| 28 | Base | 0.85 | −3.65 | | |
| 29 | Base | 2.20 | −1.83 | 0 | |
| 30 | Base | 2.61 | −1.72 | 0 | |
| 31 | Other | 1.93 | −4.12 | | |
| 32 | Other | 2.40 | −0.88 | | |
| 33 | Pedestal | 2.64 | −1.87 | 0 | |

marble is partially dolomitic. Their depleted $^{18}O$ values relative to the main cluster can be explained by isotopic disequilibrium between the coexisting calcite and dolomite (SHEPPARD and SCHWARCZ, 1970). Therefore, these two cornices may not be different from the main group with regard to their origin. For the remaining three artifacts the deple-

tion in $^{18}O$ probably indicates a different origin, possibly from the island of Naxos (Fig. 3A).

Thirty-three artifacts from the monument were studied. These include bases, shafts, capitals, cornices, and a pedestal. Table 2 lists their isotopic and chemical composition. In general, the monument artifacts are more scattered in their $\delta^{13}C$ and $\delta^{18}O$ values than the theatre artifacts. These artifacts can be divided into four groups according to their isotopic composition. (a) Seventeen artifacts' $\delta^{13}C$ and $\delta^{18}O$ values match with that of Marmara. The range in the $\delta^{13}C$ and $\delta^{18}O$ values of these artifacts is 1.16 per mil and 2.62 per mil, respectively. All architectural functions except the shafts are present in this group. (b) A group of four capitals has an origin in Thasos Aliki. (c) Three bases are from Afyon. (d) Nine artifacts originated in other quarries (Fig. 3B).

The origins of the marbles used in the theatre and monument are mostly from Asia Minor. The quarry of Marmara is the largest source in both cases. From all the studied artifacts, a clear correlation between the isotopic composition and architectural role is found for several capitals from Thasos and for six bases from Afyon (Table 3). These similarities are found in the theatre and in the monument, suggesting that these artifacts might have been purchased at the same time for both structures.

There is a difference between the isotopic signature of the theatre and monument artifacts. (a) Since 30 out of 42 artifacts from the theatre originated in Marmara, but only 17 out of 33 artifacts from the monument originated from this quarry, the theatre artifacts are more homogenous in their isotopic composition. (b) For the theatre and monument artifacts that originated from Marmara a similar range in $\delta^{13}C$ values is found, but a larger range in $\delta^{18}O$ values is found for the monument artifacts (Table 4). (c) It is seen from Table 4 that the theatre artifacts have a significantly lower variance than the monument artifacts in their $\delta^{18}O$ and a similar variance for $\delta^{13}C$. The above three comparisons indicate that the theatre artifacts are iso-

Table 3. Isotopic means (per mil vs. PDB) and ranges for capitals that originated in Thasos Aliki and bases that originated from Afyon found in Scythopolis.

| Location | Description | $n$ | Mean $\delta^{13}C$ | Mean $\delta^{18}O$ | Range $\delta^{13}C$ | Range $\delta^{18}O$ |
|----------|-------------|-----|---------------------|---------------------|----------------------|----------------------|
| theatre | capitals | 3 | 2.48 | −0.47 | 0.13 | 0.26 |
| monument | capitals | 4 | 2.60 | −0.51 | 0.46 | 0.55 |
| theatre | bases | 3 | 1.25 | −3.41 | 0.20 | 0.06 |
| monument | bases | 3 | 0.76 | −3.51 | 0.24 | 0.28 |

Table 4. Ranges, variances and F-values for groups of artifacts originated in Marmara and the quarry fingerprint. See text for discussion. F-values denote the ratio between the quarry and the respective group variances. F-values are used to calculate the probabilities for difference of in variances (P).

| Samples | n | Range | | Variance | | F-values | |
|---|---|---|---|---|---|---|---|
| | | $\delta^{13}C$ | $\delta^{18}O$ | $^{13}C$ | $^{18}C$ | $^{13}C$ | $^{18}O$ |
| quarry | 41 | 2.40 | 3.42 | 0.2888 | 0.5874 | | |
| theatre | 30 | 1.33 | 1.92 | 0.1595 | 0.2368 | 1.81 | 2.48 |
| monument | 17 | 1.16 | 2.62 | 0.0998 | 0.4427 | 2.89 | 1.33 |
| capitals | 16 | 0.35 | 1.40 | 0.0110 | 0.0898 | 26.25 | 6.54 |

topically more homogenous than the monument artifacts.

The degree of homogeneity in the isotopic composition relative to the quarry samples is evaluated by the F-test (two tailed). The probability that the variance in $\delta^{18}O$ of the theatre artifacts is significantly different from the variance of the Marmara quarry is high ($P = 0.02$), whereas the variance in $\delta^{18}O$ for the monument artifacts is not significantly different from that of the quarry ($P = 0.50$). This suggests that the theatre artifacts were quarried from a limited part of the quarry, possibly from a single outcrop. On the other hand the range and variance in $\delta^{18}O$ of the monument artifacts suggest that they were quarried from several sections in Marmara.

From these comparisons we infer that marble for the theatre was shipped to Scythopolis directly from one quarry and was not purchased through a marble yard which held stocks of several marble sources. Direct customer-quarry relations are an exception under the Roman trade system (WARD-PERKINS, 1980). The remaining artifacts from the theatre could have been added later to the structure, or possibly replaced damaged blocks from the initial shipment. The isotopically heterogeneous artifacts from the monument reflect a marble purchase from a stock-yard which probably held a variety of marble of different quality, including blocks from different regions in Marmara.

A possible explanation for the difference in the purchase mode between the theatre and the monument materials may lie in the larger amount of marble used for the theatre construction. Marble for the theatre was ordered directly from the quarries because local marble yards could not meet the quantity required for its construction, whereas the smaller quantity required for the monument was available from a local yard supplier. An alternative explanation might lie in the actual construction time of these two structures. If the theatre was erected during a period when large construction projects were under way in Scythopolis and elsewhere, local marble yards' stocks may have become depleted,

so constructors would have been forced to "rush" material from the large quarries of Marmara. The existence of these two modes of distribution side by side, as interpreted from the data obtained by isotopic analysis, exemplifies the full development of the advanced Roman marble trade system.

### Caesarea

Fifty-eight Corinthian capitals from Caesarea were studied. They form six groups based on their decoration (I–IV, VI–VII). These groups are subdivided according to specific decorative motifs (A–E, $\lambda$). Table 5 presents the isotopic and chemical composition and their inferred origin. A large scatter is found in the isotopic signature of 40 capitals of five types (I, II, IV, VI, and VII, Fig. 4). This reflects the multiple origin of these capitals. Eighteen capitals belonging to type IIID and IIIDE were studied. Sixteen capitals cluster into one group. A range of 0.35 per mil and 1.1 per mil is found in their $\delta^{13}C$ and $\delta^{18}O$ values, respectively. These capitals originated from Marmara, as indicated by their isotopic composition (Fig. 4). The Mn content of these capitals (7–16 ppm) support this conclusion (Fig. 2). Two capitals are enriched in $^{13}C$ and differ in their $^{18}O$ relative to the main group. Note also that other capitals of group III also differ from the main IIID–IIIDE group with respect to their isotopic signature and thus indicate a different origin.

As the Corinthian capitals originated from an unknown number of structures, tracing the mode by which their marble reached Caesarea is more complicated. The multiple origin of the 40 capitals of scattered isotopic signature might reflect either the large number of constructions that they were originally part of, or a purchase mode similar to that found for the monument (i.e., from a local marble stock yard), or more likely both. For the 16 capitals of type III we follow the same rationale that was used to evaluate the homogeneity of the theatre and monuments artifacts from Marmara. The ranges and variances of the 16 capitals are smaller

Table 5. Isotopic and chemical composition of Corinthian capitals from Caesarea. The artistic type and the probable origin is also given. Weight per cent of dolomite content is denoted by dd. Isotope values are in per mil.

| Sample | Type | $\delta^{13}C$ | $\delta^{18}O$ | dd | Mn (ppm) | Origin |
|---|---|---|---|---|---|---|
| 1 | I | 2.66 | −2.32 | 0 | 3 | Marmara |
| 2 | I | 2.96 | −5.63 | 0 | 3 | Naxos |
| 3 | I | 3.28 | −1.84 | | | Marmara |
| 4 | I | 2.94 | −1.02 | | 3 | Marmara |
| 5 | IB | 2.82 | −2.41 | 0 | 9 | Marmara |
| 6 | IBD | 3.83 | −3.66 | tr. | | Paros |
| 7 | IE | 2.26 | −2.96 | tr. | | Afyon/Aph. |
| 8 | II | 3.39 | −1.68 | | | Marmara |
| 9 | IIA | 2.48 | −1.78 | | | Marmara |
| 10 | IIB | 1.68 | −2.92 | 0 | | Afyon/Aph. |
| 11 | IIC | 2.24 | −2.72 | | 34 | Afyon/Aph. |
| 12 | IID | 1.53 | −3.72 | | 26 | Afyon/Aph. |
| 13 | IID | 3.47 | −2.14 | 0 | 35 | Denizli? |
| 14 | IIE | 2.34 | −1.58 | | | Marmara |
| 15 | IIIAc | 3.32 | −2.59 | 0 | | Marmara |
| 16 | IIIA | 2.02 | −4.02 | | | Afyon/Aph. |
| 17 | IIIA | 1.43 | −3.65 | | 36 | Afyon/Aph. |
| 18 | IIIB | 3.78 | −5.99 | 0 | 195 | Sardis |
| 19 | IIIDc | 3.19 | −1.88 | | | Marmara |
| 20 | IIIDc | 3.75 | −3.88 | tr. | | Paros |
| 21 | IIIDc | 3.87 | −0.77 | <5 | | Marmara |
| 22 | IIIDc | 3.49 | −1.75 | tr. | | Marmara |
| 23 | IIIDc | 3.26 | −1.92 | 0 | | Marmara |
| 24 | IIIDc | 3.50 | −1.82 | 0 | 13 | Marmara |
| 25 | IIIDc | 3.15 | −2.64 | | | Marmara |
| 26 | IIIDc | 3.24 | −1.86 | 0 | 7 | Marmara |
| 27 | IIIDc | 3.33 | −2.18 | | | Marmara |
| 28 | IIIDc | 3.23 | −2.01 | 0 | | Marmara |
| 29 | IIIDc | 3.23 | −2.15 | | | Marmara |
| 30 | IIIED | 3.41 | −2.00 | | | Marmara |
| 31 | IIIED | 3.36 | −1.92 | | | Marmara |
| 32 | IIIED | 3.37 | −2.31 | 0 | 13 | Marmara |
| 33 | IIIED | 3.32 | −1.75 | | | Marmara |
| 34 | IIIED | 3.45 | −1.83 | tr. | 14 | Marmara |
| 35 | IIIED | 3.36 | −1.24 | | | Marmara |
| 36 | IIIED | 3.37 | −1.84 | 0 | 16 | Marmara |
| 37 | IVA | 3.86 | −1.63 | 0 | <1 | Marmara |
| 38 | IVB | 2.26 | −2.69 | | 25 | Marmara/Mylasa |
| 39 | IVB | 1.87 | −2.84 | | 22 | Afyon/Aph. |
| 40 | IVB | 2.41 | −4.00 | 0 | | Afyon/Mylasa |
| 41 | IVB | 2.26 | −4.50 | 0 | | Afyon |
| 42 | IVB | 1.08 | −2.78 | | | Aph./Ephesos |
| 43 | IVC | 1.42 | −3.83 | 0 | 26 | Afyon |
| 44 | IVC | 2.53 | −2.86 | | 6 | Marmara/Mylasa |
| 45 | IVC | 2.81 | −3.86 | 0 | 2 | Mylasa |
| 46 | IVC | 0.51 | −3.62 | 0 | | Aph./Ephesos |
| 47 | IVC | 2.12 | −4.12 | 0 | | Afyon/Aph. |
| 48 | IVC | 2.00 | −1.98 | 0 | | Marmara |
| 49 | VIE | 2.06 | −7.46 | 0 | 18 | Naxos |
| 50 | VIE | 2.56 | −0.51 | | 15 | Marmara |
| 51 | VIE | 2.79 | −1.21 | 0 | | Marmara |
| 52 | VII | 2.63 | −1.40 | 0 | 5 | Marmara |
| 53 | VII | 2.01 | −0.93 | 0 | 5 | Marmara/Iasos |
| 54 | VII | 2.73 | −2.75 | | 6 | Marmara |
| 55 | VII | 2.58 | −1.24 | | 3 | Marmara |
| 56 | VII | 3.15 | −2.84 | 0 | | Marmara |
| 57 | VII | 2.66 | −2.37 | | | Marmara |
| 58 | VII | 1.91 | −1.71 | | | Marmara/Iasos |

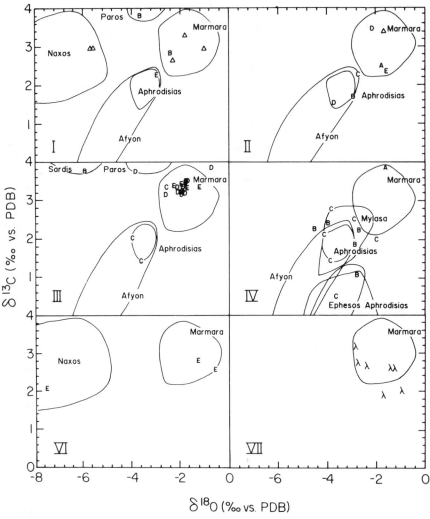

FIG. 4. Isotopic composition and possible source quarries for the Caesarea Corinthian capitals. Quarry fields are as in Fig. 3. Capitals are plotted according to their artistic type (I–VII) and artistic features (A–E; λ). See text for discussion on artistic classification. Triangles represent capitals of which an exact artistic character could not be determined. The determined isotopic composition is given by the center of each letter.

than the respective ranges and variances found for Scythopolis Theatre and Monument in both $\delta^{13}C$ and $\delta^{18}O$ values (Table 4). Further, applying an F-test to compare the variances in the isotopic signature of these capitals to that of their source quarry, Marmara, indicates that the probability that these capitals are different in their variances from the quarry fingerprint is very high ($P < 0.0001$ for both $\delta^{13}C$ and $\delta^{18}O$). This indicates that these capitals were quarried from a single outcrop in Marmara. The similarities in style and isotopic composition suggest that these capitals were part of a single monument in Caesarea. These similarities might

imply also a marble purchase mode similar to that proposed for the Scythopolis Theatre.

## CONCLUSIONS

Methods which were developed for understanding geological systematics can be applied to other fields of sciences and arts. Professor S. Epstein, who pioneered the field of stable isotopes in geochemistry, was the first to notice their potential use in other fields such as meteorology, oceanography, biology, and medicine. The natural variability of stable isotope composition assists in answering important questions in the relevant field. In this study we have shown that the stable isotope signature of assemblages of artifacts can provide important archeological information. The mode of marble purchase can be estimated provided that all artifacts are related to a single structure. If this approach is applied to other Roman monuments, a more complete understanding of the Roman marble trade system may be reached. A second outcome of this study is the possible use of stable isotopes to relate marble artifacts from an unknown monument together and perhaps to their original monument. In Roman sites like Caesarea, where most of the artifacts are found out of their original context, this is of great importance to historical reconstruction. These and the previously suggested applications of stable isotope analysis to this field (provenance, fragment reconstruction, authenticity) can lead to a better understanding of antique white marble finds.

*Acknowledgements*—The authors would like to thank Professor Norman Herz for providing a detailed copy of the Classical quarries samples stable isotope data base. Reviews by Dr. A. Shemesh, Dr. G. Goodfriend, Dr. D. Ronen and Prof. I. R. Kaplan greatly improved this text. The assistance of Mrs. R. Silanikov in stable isotope measurements and B. Khadmi in XRD measurements is appreciated. We wish to thank Dr. G. Foerster and Dr. M. Fischer who introduced us to the archeological finds. We acknowledge the permission of the Israel Antiquity Authority to examine the studied artifacts.

## REFERENCES

CRAIG H. and CRAIG V. (1972) Greek marbles: determination of provenance by isotopic analysis. *Science* **176,** 401–403.

DWORAKOWSKA A. (1975) *Quarries in Ancient Greece; Bibliotheca Antiqua 14.* Polish Academy of Science.

DWORAKOWSKA A. (1983) *Quarries in the Roman Provinces; Bibliotheca Antiqua 16.* Polish Academy of Science.

FISCHER M. (1991) *Das korinthische kapitall im alten Israel in der hellenistischen und romischen periode—studien zur freschichle der bandekoration in nahen osten.* Verlag Phillip Von Zabern (in press).

GERMANN K., GRUBEN G., KNOLI H., VALIS V. and WINKLER F. J. (1988) Provenance characteristics of Cycladic (Paros and Naxos) marbles—A multivariate geological approach. In *Classical Marble: Geochemistry, Technology, Trade* (eds. N. HERZ and M. WAELKENS), vol. 153, Chap. 28, pp. 251–262. NATO ASI series, Kluwer Academic Publishers.

HERZ N. (1985) Isotopic analysis of marble. In *Archaeological Geology* (ed. G. RAPP), Chap. 13, pp. 313–335. Wiley.

HERZ N. (1987) Carbon and oxygen isotopic ratios: a data base for classical Greek and Roman marble. *Archaeometry* **29,** 35–43.

HERZ N. and DEAN N. (1986) Stable isotopes and archaeological geology: the Carrara marble, northern Italy. *Appl. Geochem.* **1,** 139–151.

HERZ N. and WENNER D. B. (1978) Assembly of Greek marble inscriptions by isotopic method. *Science* **199,** 1070–1072.

LLOYD R. V., TRANH A., PEARCE S., CHEESEMAN M. and LUMSDEN D. N. (1988) ESR spectroscopy and X-ray powder diffractometry for marble provenance determination. In *Classical Marble: Geochemistry, Technology, Trade* (eds. N. HERZ and M. WAELKENS), Vol. 153, Chap. 28, pp. 251–262. NATO ASI series, Kluwer Academic Publishers.

MARGOLIS S. V. (1989) Authenticating ancient marble sculptures. *Sci. Amer.* **264,** 78–85.

McCREA J. M. (1950) On the isotopic chemistry of carbonates and a paleotemperature scale. *J. Chem. Phys.* **18,** 849–857.

MOENS L., ROOS P., DE RUDDER J., DE PAEPE P., VAN HENDE J. and WAELKENS M. (1988) A multi-method approach to the identification of white marbles used in antique artifacts. In *Classical Marble: Geochemistry, Technology, Trade* (eds. N. HERZ and M. WAELKENS), Vol. 153, Chap. 28, pp. 251–262. NATO ASI series, Kluwer Academic Publishers.

SHEPPARD S. M. F. and SCHWARCZ H. P. (1970) Fractionation of carbon and oxygen isotopes between coexisting metamorphic calcite and dolomite. *Contrib. Mineral. Petrol.* **26,** 161–198.

VALLEY J. W. (1986) Stable isotope geochemistry of metamorphic rocks. In *Reviews in Mineralogy* (eds. J. W. VALLEY, H. P. TAYLOR JR. and J. R. O'NEIL), Vol. 16, Chap. 13, pp. 445–489. Mineralogical Society of America.

WARD-PERKINS J. B. (1971) Quarrying in antiquity technology, tradition and social change. *Proc. British Acad.* **57,** 2–24.

WARD-PERKINS J. B. (1980) Nicomedia and the marble trade. *Proc. British School in Rome* **48,** 23–69.

WEBER J. N. and SMITH F. G. (1961) Rapid determination of calcite dolomite ratios in sedimentary rocks. *J. Sediment. Petrol.* **31,** 130–132.

# Part E.
# Igneous and Metamorphic
# Geochemistry

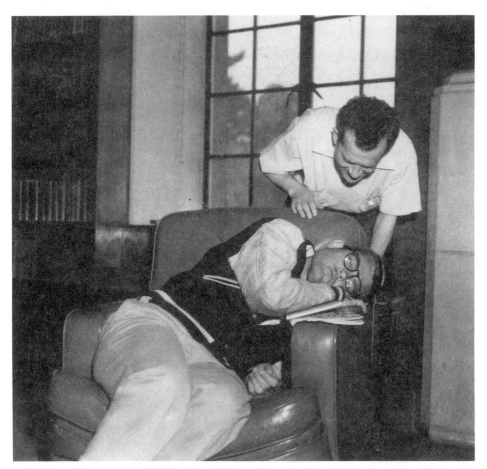

Sam watching over one of his hard-working graduate students (Hugh Taylor) in the Geology Library at Caltech in 1957. Photograph by Professor Richard H. Jahns.

Stable Isotope Geochemistry: A Tribute to Samuel Epstein
© The Geochemical Society, Special Publication No. 3, 1991
Editors: H. P. Taylor, Jr., J. R. O'Neil and I. R. Kaplan

# Comparisons of $^{18}O/^{16}O$ and $^{87}Sr/^{86}Sr$ in volcanic rocks from the Pontine Islands, M. Ernici, and Campania with other areas in Italy*

B. Turi,[1] H. P. Taylor, Jr.[2] and G. Ferrara[3]

[1]Dipartimento Di Scienze Della Terra, Universita' La Sapienza, P.le A. Moro-00100 Roma, Italy
[2]Division of Geological and Planetary Sciences, California Institute of Technology, Pasadena, CA 91125, U.S.A.
[3]Istituto Di Geocronologia e Geochimica Isotopica, C.N.R., V. Cardinale Maffi 36, 56100 Pisa, Italy

**Abstract**—New $^{18}O/^{16}O$ and $^{87}Sr/^{86}Sr$ data dramatically confirm and extend the systematic regional isotopic and geographic correlations observed in Quaternary volcanic rocks from Italy: (1) The High-K Series (HKS) and Low-K Series (LKS) potassic magma source regions are isotopically distinct; the relatively rare, *primitive* (high-Ca) parent magmas of both suites have $\delta^{18}O = +5.5$ to $+7.5$, but the LKS parent has a much lower $^{85}Sr/^{86}Sr$ and slightly lower $\delta^{18}O$ than the HKS parent. (2) The more abundant *evolved* (fractionated) magmas of both suites have a wide range of $\delta^{18}O$ (+6.0 to +13.0), but in the offshore island centers (Ischia, Pontine Is., Procida) these magmas are all much lower in $\delta^{18}O$ (< +8.0) than those from the Italian mainland, as a result of the absence of involvement of high-$^{18}O$ continental crust. (3) At a given center, the $^{18}O$-enrichments correlate with major-element changes (*i.e.*, CaO depletion and $K_2O$ and $SiO_2$ enrichment) attributable to fractional crystallization in *crustal* magma chambers (4 to 13 km depth?); because such $^{18}O$ enrichments cannot be produced in a closed system, these correlations imply that AFC processes were important, particularly north of Rome where they are enhanced by an increase in the temperature of the crust (due to igneous activity associated with the 0–7 Ma Tuscan anatectic event). Thus, the high $\delta^{18}O$ values of the potassic magmas of Italy should not be used as evidence in support of genetic models invoking recent subduction of sedimentary rocks into the source regions of these magmas. (4) On $\delta^{18}O$ vs. $^{87}Sr/^{86}Sr$ diagrams, the LKS and HKS magmas at each volcanic center display separate, steep positive trends indicating mixing with high-$^{18}O$ continental crustal material; this type of mixing had little effect on $^{87}Sr/^{86}Sr$ in these Sr-rich magmas, but it had a dramatic effect on the $\delta^{18}O$ values. (5) Two distinctly different groups of rhyolites and quartz-normative trachytes are observed in the northernmost Pontine Islands, a high-$^{18}O$ group similar to the anatectic Tuscan rhyolites ($\delta^{18}O > +10$) and a low-$^{18}O$ group similar to the rhyolites of the Aeolian Islands ($\delta^{18}O = +7$ to $+7.5$). (6) All of the magmas produced in and around Italy during the past five million years can be derived by mixing of (i) a $SiO_2$-rich continental crustal end member, having $^{87}Sr/^{86}Sr \sim 0.715$ to $0.735$ and $\delta^{18}O \sim +10$ to $+20$, with three distinct mantle end members: (ii) a relatively low-K (LKS), moderate-Sr parent with $^{87}Sr/^{86}Sr \sim 0.706$ and $\delta^{18}O \sim +6$, dominant to the south of Rome and perhaps related to an upper mantle source modified by a recent subduction event; (iii) a high-K (HKS), high-Sr parent with $^{87}Sr/^{86}Sr \sim 0.711$ and $\delta^{18}O \sim +7$ dominant in the vicinity of Rome and farther north, and possibly related to older subcontinental mantle modified by a recent metasomatic event; and (iv) a very low-K, low-Sr Tyrrhenian Sea MORB-type parent with $^{87}Sr/^{86}Sr \sim 0.7025$ and $\delta^{18}O \sim +5.7$.

## INTRODUCTION

IN THIS PAPER, we compare $^{18}O/^{16}O$ and $^{87}Sr/^{86}Sr$ data on potassic rocks from volcanic centers south and southeast of Rome with earlier studies on the Pleistocene and Holocene potassic volcanic rocks of Italy: FORNASERI and TURI (1969), BARBIERI *et al.* (1975), TURI and TAYLOR (1976), TAYLOR and TURI (1976), TAYLOR *et al.* (1979, 1984, 1987), VOLLMER (1976), HURLEY *et al.* (1966), COX *et al.* (1976), HOLM and MUNKSGAARD (1982); CIVETTA *et al.* (1981), FERRARA *et al.* (1985, 1986), CORTINI and HERMES (1981), ROGERS *et al.* (1985), and HAWKESWORTH and VOLLMER (1979), and other references quoted in the above papers.

The new samples analyzed in the present work are mainly from M. Ernici and from the islands off the western coast of Italy—Ischia, Procida, and the Pontinian Archipelago (Fig. 1). However, a few samples were also analyzed from on-shore centers (Roccamonfina, Phlegrean Fields, and Vesuvius), as well as single samples from some more distant centers (Table 1).

## REGIONAL PETROLOGICAL AND GEOLOGICAL RELATIONSHIPS

### General statement

APPLETON (1972) used $K_2O$-$SiO_2$ diagrams to delineate a High-K Series (HKS) and a Low-K Series (LKS, also simply termed Potassic Series, or KS, by some workers) among the potassic volcanic rocks of Italy. HKS rocks include strongly $SiO_2$-

* Contribution No. 3144, Division of Geological and Planetary Sciences, California Institute of Technology, Pasadena, CA 91125, U.S.A.

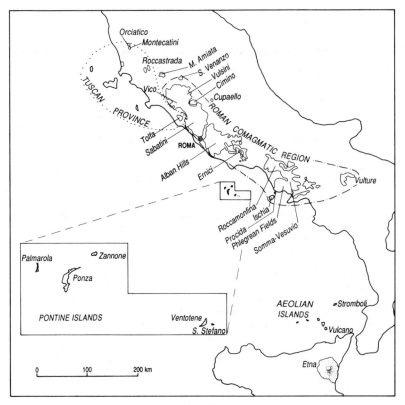

FIG. 1. Map of central Italy, showing the localities referred to in the text. The Pontine Islands are shown at a larger scale on the inset.

undersaturated leucitite, leucite tephrite, and leucite phonolite, with $K_2O$ = 4 to 11 wt.%, $K_2O/Na_2O$ = 3 to 5, and $Al_2O_3$ = 16 to 20 wt.%. LKS rocks include trachybasalt, latite, and trachyte just slightly over- or just slightly undersaturated with respect to $SiO_2$. They typically have $K_2O$ = 1 to 3 wt.% and $K_2O/Na_2O$ = 0.5 to 1.5.

HKS and LKS volcanic rocks occur together in close association at Ernici and Roccamonfina, and in the Somma-Vesuvius-Phlegrean Fields area (Fig. 1), as well as farther north at M. Vulsini (although at Vulsini the HKS is *much* more abundant than LKS rocks). South of the Alban Hills, the LKS is predominant over the HKS, particularly in the islands of southern Italy (Pontine Islands, Stromboli, and Vulcano). LKS rocks occur only sporadically to the north of M. Ernici. For example, the Alban Hills, M. Sabatini, and most of Vico seem to be composed exclusively of HKS lavas and pyroclastics. However, LKS volcanic rocks do occur at Radicofani in southern Tuscany, situated just a few km NE of M. Vulsini, as well as at Capraia, the northernmost island of the Tuscan Archipelago; both of these centers belong to the Plio-Pleistocene Tuscan Magmatic Province (Fig. 1; see TAYLOR *et al.*, 1991).

*Pontine Islands*

The Pontine Islands (Fig. 1) lie between the northern and southern basins of the Tyrrhenian Sea on the edge of a 20 to 25 km-thick continental platform that borders the western coast of the Italian peninsula. They are divided into two geologically and geographically distinct groups, a northwestern group (Ponza, Palmarola, and Zannone) and a southeastern group (Ventotene and S. Stefano).

In the southeastern Pontine Islands, volcanic activity was dominantly subaerial, producing trachybasaltic pyroclastics and lavas (at Ventotene) to phonolitic lava flows and pyroclastics (at S. Stefano). Two volcanic series are identified on Ponza: an older rhyolitic group and a younger group of $SiO_2$-undersaturated trachytic rocks. The early rhyolites and rhyodacites on Ponza were emplaced in a submarine environment (CARMASSI *et al.*, 1987), but the youngest volcanics are trachytic and subaerial (*e.g.*, the M. La Guardia trachytic dome, with a K/Ar age of 1.1 to 1.2 Ma, BARBERI *et al.*, 1967).

Table 1. Oxygen isotope, strontium isotope, and chemical compositions of samples of volcanic rocks from central and southern Italy (south of Rome)

| Sample[a] | Rock[b] type | $\delta^{18}O$ W.R. (meas.) | $\delta^{18}O$[c] W.R. (calc.) | $\delta^{18}O$ Mineral | $\delta^{18}O$[d] "corrected" (W.R.) | $^{87}Sr/^{86}Sr$[e] $\pm 1\sigma$ (W.R.) $(^{87}Sr/^{86}Sr)_0$ | Sr (ppm) | SiO₂ | Al₂O₃ | CaO | K₂O | H₂O |
|---|---|---|---|---|---|---|---|---|---|---|---|---|
| **Ponza** | | | | | | | | | | | | |
| PO-401 (=P30[9]) | Tr | 8.05 | 7.03 | 7.33 ± 0.15 kf | 7.73 | 0.7086 ± 6 (0.7086)° | 527 | 58.01[9] | 18.94 | 3.52 | 6.72 | 0.86+ |
| PO-402 (=P4[9]) | R | 17.40 | 11.11 | 10.91 ± 0.12 plag | 11.11 | 0.71098 ± 6 (0.71055)° | 156 | 72.85[9] | 14.11 | 1.54 | 4.92 | 4.43+ |
| PO-403 (=P1[9]) | R (dike) | 10.57 | 10.40 | 10.20 ± 0.07 kf | 10.08 | 0.7111 ± 4 (0.7106)° | 100 | 75.01[9] | 13.18 | 1.12 | 5.45 | 1.06+ |
| PO-101 (=101[9]) | sR (dike) | 7.93 | — | — | 6.55 | 0.71010 ± 3 [age not known] | 40 | 69.05[9] | 13.14 | 0.61 | 4.74 | 2.14+ |
| **Palmarola[17]** | | | | | | | | | | | | |
| PAL-1 | R | 7.06 ± 0.10 | — | — | — | 0.7146 ± 4 (0.7108)° | 8 | — | — | — | — | — |
| 156-A[9] | R | 7.41 ± 0.07 | — | — | 7.04 | 0.7130 ± 4 (0.7084)° | 7 | 73.72[9] | 13.77 | 0.62 | 4.97 | 0.95+ |
| **Ventotene** | | | | | | | | | | | | |
| VT-451 | TrB | 6.89 ± 0.03 | — | — | 6.89 | 0.7072 ± 3 | 697 | 49.12 | 17.68 | 10.75 | 2.19 | 0.13+ |
| VT-453 | TrB | 6.83 | — | — | 6.35 | 0.70760 ±10 | 829 | 49.28 | 18.20 | 10.43 | 2.88 | 1.08+ |
| V-58[9] | TrB | 6.66 ± 0.17 | — | — | 5.95 | 0.70782 ± 4 | 873 | 48.96[9] | 18.52 | 10.64 | 2.95 | 1.34+ |
| **S. Stefano** | | | | | | | | | | | | |
| ST-533 (=76[9]) | P | 8.02 ± 0.19 | — | — | 7.62 | 0.7102 ± 5 | 16 | 57.83[9] | 21.47 | 1.37 | 7.49 | 0.94+ |
| **Procida** | | | | | | | | | | | | |
| PP-2[10] | Tr | 8.84 | 7.80 kf<br>7.53 px | 8.10 ± 0.13 kf<br>7.08 ± 0.08 px | — | 0.7069 ± 4 | 354 | 59.81[10] | 18.77 | 2.80 | 8.00 | 0.33+ |
| PL-11 | La | 7.46 ± 0.09 | 7.76 | 7.31 ± 0.05 px | 7.00 | 0.7078 ± 2 | 308 | 55.87 | 17.68 | 7.41 | 4.08 | 1.06+ |
| PS-9 | TrB | 6.49 g | 6.21 | 5.76 ± 0.02 px | — | 0.7053 ± 5 | 473 | 48.12 | 15.53 | 12.00 | 1.49 | — |
| PS-11 | TrB | 6.60 ± 0.10 | — | — | 6.60 | 0.70594 ± 7 | 705 | 48.01 | 17.66 | 11.51 | 2.78 | 0.43+ |
| PS-12 | TrB | 6.12 ± 0.40 | 5.98 | 5.53 ± 0.03 px | 5.75 | 0.70593 ± 2 | 738 | 48.50 | 17.32 | 11.72 | 2.65 | 1.10+ |
| **Ischia** | | | | | | | | | | | | |
| IS-1 (=35 y[21]) | Tr | — | 6.44 | 6.74 kf | — | 0.70763 ± 5[1] | — | 63.60 | 18.32 | 1.24 | 6.37 | 0.55* |
| IS-4 (=RE-17[1]) | SP | 6.65 | 6.24 | 6.54 ± 0.01 kf | 5.85 | 0.70703 ± 6[1] | 30[1] | 60.26[8] | 18.11 | 1.48 | 7.52 | 1.36+ |
| IS-5 (=Mt. S. Angelo[1]) | SP | — | 6.58 | 6.88 ± 0.08 kf | — | 0.70638 ± 4 g[2] | 13[1] | 63.15 | 18.74 | 0.98 | 5.91 | 1.03* |
| IS-2 (=11[2]) | La | 6.35 ± 0.01 | 6.30 kf<br>6.26 px | 6.60 ± 0.09 kf<br>5.81 ± 0.06 px | 6.35 | | 551 g[2] | 55.30 | 19.14 | 5.88 | 5.29 | 0.32* |
| IS-3 (=RE-12[1]) | TPTr | 7.02 | 6.54 kf<br>5.91 px | 6.84 ± 0.09 kf<br>5.46 ± 0.10 px | 7.02 | 0.70607 ± 3[1] | 54[1] | 62.88 | 18.64 | 1.47 | 6.80 | 0.42* |
| IS-7 (=27[21]) | ATr | — | 6.40 | 6.70 ± 0.11 kf | — | — | — | 62.10[8] | 18.13 | 1.15 | 6.74 | 0.37## |
| IS-8 (=35 La[21]) | ATr | — | 6.37 | 6.67 ± 0.13 kf | — | — | — | 61.58[8] | 18.62 | 2.29 | 6.36 | 0.50## |

Table 1. (Continued)

| Sample[a] | Rock[b] type | δ18O W.R. (meas.) | δ18O[c] W.R. (calc.) | δ18O Mineral | δ18O[d] "corrected" (W.R.) | 87Sr/86Sr[e] ±1σ (W.R.) (87Sr/86Sr)₀ | Sr (ppm) | Oxide (wt.%)[f] | | | | |
|---|---|---|---|---|---|---|---|---|---|---|---|---|
| | | | | | | | | $SiO_2$ | $Al_2O_3$ | CaO | $K_2O$ | $H_2O$ |
| IS-6 (=1146[21]) | ATr (tuff) | 13.10 ± 0.06 | 7.45 | 7.75 ± 0.13 kf | — | — | — | 62.92 | 18.00 | 0.82 | 7.78 | 7.15* |
| I-109[1] | TrB | 6.14 | — | — | 5.28 | 0.70617 ± 4[1] | 600[1] | 54.54 | 18.50 | 8.42 | 2.98 | 1.52+ |
| Re-9[1,7] (Arso flow) | Tr | 6.86 ± 0.03 | — | — | 6.86 | 0.70661 ± 3[1] | 533[1] | 53.18[7] | 18.38 | 6.86 | 4.33 | 0.44+ |
| 5103e[3] | Tr | 6.74 ± 0.25 | — | — | — | 0.7068[3] | 77[3] | — | — | — | — | — |
| **Phlegrean Fields** | | | | | | | | | | | | |
| Cf-1[10] | ATr | — | 8.06 | 8.36 kf | — | — | — | 58.64[10] | 19.09 | 3.90 | 8.18 | 0.23+ |
| CF-3[10] | SP | — | 8.08 | 8.38 ± 0.09 kf | — | 0.70769 ± 3[1] | 12[1] | 59.48[10] | 19.30 | 2.00 | 6.61 | 0.33+ |
| CF-231 | TrB | — | 7.90 | 7.45 ± 0.16 px | — | — | — | 52.36 | 16.74 | 10.44 | 3.16 | 1.01+ |
| 5106[3] | Tr | 7.09 ± 0.12 | — | — | — | 0.7077[3] | 700[3] | — | — | — | — | — |
| 5107[3] | Tr | 7.68 ± 0.03 | — | — | 6.97 | 0.7082[3] | 1114[3] | 59.73[11] | 20.24 | 1.74 | 6.86 | 1.36* |
| **Parete#** | | | | | | | | | | | | |
| PAR-2 (−1800m) | BAnd | 9.26 ± 0.24 | — | 9.73 plag | — | 0.70776 ± 3[4] | 587[4] | 54.13[4] | 18.20 | 10.01 | 2.26 | 1.00+ |
| PAR-2 (−1203m) | BAnd | — | — | — | — | 0.70776 ± 3[4] | 579[4] | 51.53 | 19.64 | 11.25 | 1.67 | 3.06+ |
| **Somma** | | | | | | | | | | | | |
| Cast. di Cisterna[1] | PLT | 7.33 | — | — | — | 0.70761 ± 4[1] | 737[1] | 50.55[1] | — | — | 5.76 | — |
| PFSV-16[1] | Tr (block) | 8.77 | — | — | 6.98 | 0.70734 ± 4[1] | — | 59.94[12] | 20.56 | 2.66 | 8.96 | 2.72* |
| **Vesuvius****** | | | | | | | | | | | | |
| 02717 (1858 flow)[1] | PLT | 9.17 ± 0.02 | — | — | 9.17 | 0.70740 ± 3[1] | 977[1] | 47.67[1] | — | — | 8.00 | 0.28* |
| 02718 (1872 flow)[1] | L | 7.72 | — | — | 7.72 | 0.70722 ± 3[1] | 1031[1] | 48.11[11] | — | — | 7.98 | 0.41* |
| PFSV-36 (1906 flow)[1] | LT | 7.89 | — | — | 7.87 | 0.70737 ± 2[1] | 1066[1] | 47.77[12] | 19.66 | 8.04 | 7.89 | 0.54* |
| VES-3 | | 7.22 ± 0.13 | — | — | — | — | — | — | — | — | — | — |
| 5098[3] | | 7.10 ± 0.20 | — | — | — | 0.7096[3] | 977[3] | — | — | — | — | — |
| 5099 (1861 flow?)[3] | LT | 7.68 ± 0.01 | — | — | — | 0.7079[3] | 905[3] | — | — | — | — | — |
| 5100 (1804 flow?)[3] | LT | 8.13 ± 0.16 | — | — | — | 0.7098[3] | 974[3] | — | — | — | — | — |
| VES-1 (1858 flow) | L | 7.72 ± 0.16 | — | — | — | 0.70739 ± 3[1] | 1033[1] | 47.38 | 18.40 | 9.10 | 8.28 | — |
| VES-2 (1944 flow) | LT | 8.02 | 8.13 | 7.93 ± 0.15 leucite | — | 0.70721 ± 3[1] | — | 48.6 | 18.90 | 8.60 | 7.50 | — |
| **Roccamonfina** | | | | | | | | | | | | |
| 36R (>1.0 Ma) | LBs | 6.69 ± 0.11 | — | — | 6.69 | 0.70799 ± 3 | 1116 | 46.39 | 17.32 | 13.64 | 1.92 | 0.25* |
| 41R (.616 Ma) | LP | 8.68 ± 0.15 | — | — | 8.68 | 0.70947 ± 2 | 146 | 60.09 | 20.68 | 1.75 | 9.60 | 0.47* |
| 46R (.695 Ma) | LT | 7.28 ± 0.06 | — | — | 7.08 | 0.70947 ± 5 | 2027 | 50.36 | 19.02 | 8.58 | 7.51 | 0.83* |
| 53R (.053 Ma) | MgL | 6.46 ± 0.05 | — | — | 6.20 | 0.70989 ± 4 | 1858 | 46.12 | 15.95 | 12.27 | 6.98 | 0.93* |
| 56R (.656 Ma) | ShB | 10.96 ± 0.04 | — | — | 10.96 | 0.70850 ± 4 | 656 | — | — | — | — | — |
| 58R (.096 Ma) | LaTr | 7.93 ± 0.06 | — | — | — | 0.70712 ± 2 | — | — | — | — | — | 0.27* |
| **M. Ernici** | | | | | | | | | | | | |
| M-1 | PL | 6.69 ± 0.02 | — | — | 5.80 | 0.71121 ± 3[5] | 1815[5] | 46.99 | 17.24 | 9.85 | 9.01 | 1.83*[5] |
| Ern-1N (=ERN5[5]) | TL | 7.98 ± 0.10 | — | — | 7.80 | 0.70967 ± 7[5] | 1538[5] | 47.68[6] | 17.21 | 10.96 | 8.13 | 0.77+ |
| Ern-1B (=ERN5[5]) | TL | 8.38 ± 0.23 | — | — | 8.16 | 0.70967 ± 7[5] | 1538[5] | 47.52 | 17.37 | 11.12 | 6.80 | 0.84+ |
| Ern-3 | TL | 8.63 ± 0.21 | — | — | 8.10 | 0.70928 ± 4 | 1397 | 47.88 | 17.14 | 10.90 | 7.14 | 1.35+ |
| Ern-4 | PL | 8.85 ± 0.11 | — | — | 8.45 | 0.71078 ± 2 | 1419 | 46.85 | 17.40 | 9.93 | 9.79 | 1.09+ |
| Ern-5 | TL | 8.18 ± 0.11 | — | — | 7.80 | 0.70989 ± 2 | 1505 | 46.92 | 17.11 | 11.30 | 7.23 | 1.06+ |
| VL-6A | | 8.15 | — | — | — | 0.70951 ± 4 | 1515 | 47.48 | 18.25 | 10.23 | 7.27 | — |

Table 1. (Continued)

| Sample[a] | Rock[b] type | δ18O W.R. (meas.) | δ18O W.R. (calc.)[c] | δ18O Mineral | δ18O "corrected" (W.R.)[d] | $^{87}Sr/^{86}Sr$[e] ± 1σ (W.R.) $(^{87}Sr/^{86}Sr)_0$ | Sr (ppm) | Oxide (wt.%)[f] | | | | |
|---|---|---|---|---|---|---|---|---|---|---|---|---|
| | | | | | | | | SiO2 | Al2O3 | CaO | K2O | H2O |
| Mt. Vulture | | | | | | | | | | | | |
| VU-342[13] | Hf | 6.72 ± 0.14 | — | — | 6.00 | 0.70594 ± 7[13] | 5703[13] | 40.24[14] | 18.29 | 13.17 | 4.70 | 1.54+ |
| Vulcano | | | | | | | | | | | | |
| VOL-2 (=VO24, IV14)[15] (=Vulc 72)[18] | LT | 6.95 | — | — | — | 0.7046[18] | 1233 | 53.23[15] | 16.67 | 7.60 | 4.95 | 0.50+ |
| Etna (1971 lava flow) | | | | | | | | | | | | |
| E-1 (=EC3[16]) | AB | 5.96 | — | — | — | 0.70350[22] | 1119[22] | 46.82[16] | 16.94 | 10.99 | 1.73 | 0.61+ |
| E-2 (=VC11[16]) | AB | 5.89 ± 0.09 | — | — | — | 0.70349[22] | 1150[22] | 47.56[16] | 16.73 | 10.97 | 1.59 | 0.54+ |
| E-3 (=VC13a[16]) | AB | 6.12 ± 0.01 | — | — | — | 0.70357[22] | 1040[22] | 48.15[16] | 17.06 | 10.46 | 1.77 | 0.65+ |
| P. Pietre Nere | | | | | | | | | | | | |
| PDPN | Msy | 8.57 ± 0.00 | — | — | — | 0.70370[19] | 1102[19] | 40.62[20] | 16.14 | 13.08 | 4.01 | — |

[a] Sample numbers either refer to new samples collected by us (no superscript), or to the exact specimens previously collected and studied by other authors (indicated by superscript). In some cases, in parentheses, we indicate equivalent samples from the same outcrop localities from the references cited in the footnote. Exact locations of the samples are available from the authors on request.

[b] LT = leucite tephrite; TL = tephritic leucitite; Tr = trachyte; BAnd = basaltic andesite; ShB = shoshonitic basalt; R = rhyolite; sR = sodic rhyolite; TrB = trachybasalt; P = phonolite; La = latite; SP = sodalite phonolite; TPTr = tephritic phonolite trachyte; ATr = alkali trachyte; PLT = phonolitic leucite tephrite; L = leucitite; LBs = leucite basanite; LP = leucite phonolite; MgL = magnesian leucitite; LaTr = latitic trachyte; PL = phonolitic leucitite; Hs = haüynophir; AB = alkali basalt.

[c] The whole-rock (calc.) values are calculated from the δ18O values of the phenocryst minerals, pyroxene (px) and K feldspar (kf): Δ(W.R.-px) = +0.45; and Δ(W.R.-kf) = −0.30, except for the rhyolites, where Δ(W.R.-kf) = +0.20. The δ18O values were measured by conventional mass spectrometric techniques, using the fluorine method (e.g., see TAYLOR, 1968). NBS-28 has a δ18O = +9.60 in our laboratories. The ± indicates average deviation from the mean when two or more analyses were carried out.

[d] The "corrected" whole-rock δ18O values are calculated from the δ18O (meas.)-H2O plot shown in Fig. 3 in TURI et al. (1991).

[e] The $^{87}Sr/^{86}Sr$ ratios are either from the indicated literature references, or they were obtained using a Varian MAT THS mass spectrometer (4 decimal places) or a VG Micromass 54E mass spectrometer (5 decimal places) on line with a computer for data collection and evaluation, normalized to a $^{86}Sr/^{88}Sr$ value of 0.1194. Determinations of Eimer and Amend SrCO3 standard gave either $^{87}Sr/^{86}Sr$ = 0.7081 ± 0.0002 (1σ) or 0.70805 ± 0.00002 (1σ), respectively. Sr and Rb concentrations were determined by isotope dilution, spiked during dissolution with a mixed $^{84}Sr$ and $^{87}Rb$ spike.

[f] SiO2, Al2O3, CaO, and K2O values recalculated on an anhydrous basis. A superscript on an SiO2 analysis indicates that all of the major element chemical values are from the indicated reference. H2O is given either as L.O.I., H2O+, or H2O (total).

Superscripts: * = L.O.I.; ## = H2O+; + = H2OTOT; ° = H2O+; ° = corrected for age; g = groundmass; ** GARLICK (1966) reports δ18O values of leucite from the 1906 flow (+7.71) and clinopyroxene from the 1760 flow (+6.9), which would give calculated δ18O whole-rock values of +7.9 and +7.35, respectively. #The Parete samples are the same specimens described in BARBIERI et al. (1975), ALBINI et al. (1980), and DI GIROLAMO et al. (1976); these hydrothermally altered samples were collected from PAR-2 drill hole at the indicated depths in meters. (1) CORTINI and HERMES (1981); (2) VOLLMER et al. (1981); (3) HURLEY et al. (1966); (4) BARBIERI et al. (1979); (5) DEGENNARO and FRANCO (1971); (7) GHIARA et al. (1979); (8) RITTMANN, pers. comm. (1977); (9) BARBIERI et al. (1967); (10) DIGIROLAMO and STANZIONE (1973); (11) DIGIROLAMO et al. unpub. anal.; (12) Dept. of Earth Science, Univ. Pisa, unpub. anal.; (13) HAWKESWORTH and VOLLMER (1979); (14) HIEKE-MERLIN (1967); (15) Two different specimens from KELLER (1974) and PECCERILLO and MANETTI (1985); (16) CAGNETTI et al. (1973); (17) Note that GALE (1981) made two other analyses of Palmarola obsidian: $^{87}Sr/^{86}Sr$ = 0.71317 ± 6 (Sr = 7 ppm); 0.71375 ± 11 (Sr = 6.9 ppm); (18) BURRI (1959); (20) VOLLMER (1976); (21) VEZZOLI (1988); (22) BARBIERI and TADDEUCCI (pers. comm., 1987).

Zannone is dominantly made up of rhyolite. This is the only Pontine Island that contains metamorphic rocks ("schistes lustrés") and sedimentary rocks (ranging from Triassic dolomites and limestones to late Tertiary flysch), tentatively correlated with the basement rocks in Tuscany by PAROTTO and PRATURLON (1975).

## Ischia

The Island of Ischia (Fig. 1) is essentially a volcano-tectonic horst made up of >150,000-year-old latitic and trachytic lavas and pyroclastics intruded by younger lava domes, which are in turn overlain by a major (about 1000 m thick) alkali-trachyte pyroclastic flow (the "Mt. Epomeo Green Tuff"); the latter was erupted subaerially about 55,000 years ago. The chemical compositions of the volcanic products at Ischia range from olivine latite to alkali trachyte, these latter being dominant (CAPALDI et al., 1985; VEZZOLI, 1988). The latest eruption was in 1302 A.D. (Arso flow).

## Procida

Although geographically and geologically linked to Ischia on the west and the Phlegrean Fields to the northeast by a NE-trending, deep-seated fault system (Fig. 1), the Island of Procida is petrographically distinct from these adjacent centers (see ALBINI et al., 1977, 1980, and refs. therein). The dominant lavas on Procida and in the Ischia Channel are trachybasalt.

## Mts. Ernici

The Mts. Ernici or Media Valle Latina district is located about 50 km ESE of the Alban Hills and 70 km NW of Roccamonfina (Fig. 1). It comprises numerous small eruptive centers spread over about 100 km². The volcanic activity was mainly explosive, producing both HKS and LKS pyroclastics and subordinate lava flows between about 700 ± 20 to 80 ± 40 Ka. The HKS products have K/Ar ages from about 700 to 200 Ka, and thus appear to be typically older than the LKS lavas, which have K/Ar ages between about 200 and 100 Ka (BASILONE and CIVETTA, 1975; CIVETTA et al., 1981).

## EXPERIMENTAL PROCEDURES

Measurements of strontium isotope ratios and concentrations were obtained by conventional techniques, as indicated in Table 1. Oxygen was liberated from the silicate samples by reaction with fluorine gas (TAYLOR and EPSTEIN, 1962). The $^{18}O/^{16}O$ data obtained on these samples are reported in Table 1 in the familiar $\delta$ notation; the reference standard is Standard Mean Ocean Water (SMOW) and NBS-28 has a $\delta^{18}O = +9.60$ on this scale. The mineral separates were obtained by conventional techniques, and their purity, checked by XRD, was found to be generally better than 95%.

Essentially all measured whole-rock $\delta^{18}O$ values of old volcanic rocks on Earth have been increased by hydration and water/rock exchange during low-temperature weathering and diagenesis (even in some rocks only a couple of thousand years old). The $^{18}O/^{16}O$ ratios of all such rocks are therefore suspect and cannot be assumed to reflect the $\delta^{18}O$ of the original magmas (TAYLOR, 1968; TAYLOR et al., 1984). This particularly applies to tuffs, pyroclastics, and ignimbrites, but it is also true of lavas. Therefore, except for such recently erupted lavas as those from Vesuvius and Etna, which are very fresh, we have followed two different procedures used previously by us and by other workers (e.g., FERRARA et al., 1985, 1986; MUEHLENBACHS and BYERLY, 1982; MUEHLENBACHS and CLAYTON, 1972) to calculate the primary $\delta^{18}O$ values of the lavas: (1) calculation of whole-rock $\delta^{18}O$ by measuring the $\delta^{18}O$ of coexisting phenocrysts, and then assuming an appropriate equilibrium $^{18}O/^{16}O$ fractionation between mineral and melt (Table 1); (2) "correcting" the whole-rock $\delta^{18}O$ in a crude way simply from the correlation between the measured $H_2O$ content (or L.O.I.) and the $^{18}O$ increase due to hydration.

The "correction" procedure in this paper follows that utilized by FERRARA et al. (1985, 1986) for similar rock types from the Alban Hills and M. Vulsini (see TURI et al., 1991). For two extremely hydrated samples from Ischia and Ponza (IS-6 and PO-402), we made direct measurements of phenocrysts and hydrated lava; the "correction" lines determined in this way for IS-6 and particularly for PO-402 are even steeper than the one obtained for the Alban Hills lavas by FERRARA et al. (1985). Therefore, we have conservatively utilized the original Alban Hills trend-line for all the samples from the Italian mainland and used the slightly steeper Ischia (IS-6) trend line only for samples from the offshore islands and the directly adjacent localities of Somma-Vesuvius and the Phlegrean Fields. In all cases, the lowering of the measured $\delta^{18}O$ value is less than 0.8 per mil, with the exception of one sample from Somma (PFSV-16), one from Ponza (PO-101), and the aforementioned samples PO-402 and IS-6; in most cases the "corrections" are only 0.0 to 0.4 per mil (Table 1; also see TURI et al., 1991). Even though these corrections are small, they must be made, otherwise, the $^{18}O/^{16}O$ data cannot be plotted in graphs or discussed as if they represented true magmatic values. Fortunately, for comparative purposes, these hydration corrections are always unidirectional (i.e., they always give results that are lower than the measured $\delta^{18}O$ value).

## CORRELATIONS BETWEEN CHEMICAL AND ISOTOPIC COMPOSITIONS

### $K_2O$ vs. $SiO_2$

Our new data from Table 1 are plotted on Fig. 2, where they are compared with samples from other volcanic centers south of Rome (Alban Hills—FERRARA et al., 1985; Roccamonfina—TAYLOR et al., 1979; HAWKESWORTH and VOLLMER, 1979). Linear trends upward and to the right on such dia-

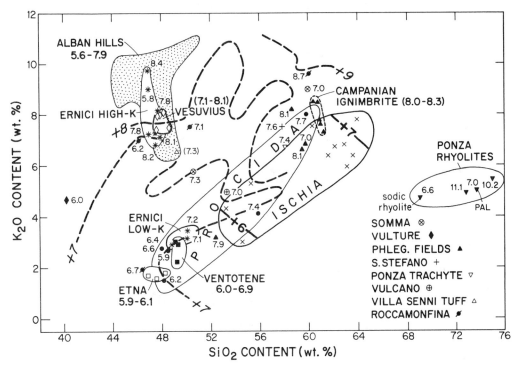

FIG. 2. Plot of $K_2O$ vs. $SiO_2$ for the samples studied in this work, showing that the $\delta^{18}O$ values are related to the major-element chemistry. The positions of the Alban Hills and Roccamonfina volcanic rocks are also indicated (see text).

grams were interpreted by APPLETON (1972) to represent fractional crystallization of alkali-rich, mantle-derived primary magmas with $SiO_2$ contents of about 44–47 wt.% and *variable* $K_2O$ contents (as low as 1–2 wt.% in the LKS lavas and as high as 8–10 wt.% $K_2O$ for the HKS). These trends were later ascribed to processes of *combined* assimilation-fractional crystallization (AFC) in crustal magma chambers (TAYLOR *et al.*, 1979; TAYLOR, 1980).

Our new data plot in three well-defined $K_2O$-$SiO_2$ groupings on Fig. 2, two of which show a clear correspondence with the HKS and LKS trends of APPLETON (1972); the third corresponds closely with the high-$^{18}O$ rhyolites of the Tuscan Province (Ponza and Palmarola rhyolites). The Ischia, Procida, Ventotene, S. Stefano, Vulcano, and Phlegrean Fields samples, as well as the Ponza trachyte, all fit well with the trend of Appleton's Low-K Series. The strongly differentiated Campanian Ignimbrite (Campanian Grey Tuff), erupted from the northern part of the Phlegrean Fields 33,000 years ago, also belongs to the LKS. The only new lavas studied in this work that belong to the High-K Series are the three samples from Roccamonfina, the Ernici HKS, and the Somma-Vesuvius samples.

The $^{18}O/^{16}O$ variations on Fig. 2 are indicated in

different ways, either with the $\delta^{18}O$ value lettered alongside a single data point, or giving the range of $\delta^{18}O$ for an entire group of samples. In addition, the dashed contours at $\delta^{18}O = +7$, $+8$, and $+9$ show how the $\delta^{18}O$ values of the Roccamonfina samples change with chemical composition (it is satisfying to note that the plotting of our new samples did not require any modification of the systematic $\delta^{18}O$-$K_2O$-$SiO_2$ patterns originally delineated by TAYLOR *et al.*, 1979). Note that the lowest-$^{18}O$ Roccamonfina sample (53R) is among the *youngest* of the products of this volcano (only 53,000 years old; RADICATI DI BROZOLO *et al.*, 1988).

Trachybasalts with $SiO_2 < 50$ wt.% are the most primitive LKS lavas analyzed in this study, and together with the Mt. Etna alkali basalts, these samples plot at the low-$SiO_2$, low-$K_2O$ end of the Roccamonfina LKS field (Fig. 2). This grouping includes three Procida samples, one Ernici sample, and all three Ventotene rocks; *all* of these samples are very low in $\delta^{18}O$ (+5.9 to +6.9), in keeping with their other primitive chemical characteristics. Moving upward and to the right on the $K_2O$-$SiO_2$ plot, the $\delta^{18}O$ values increase slightly to +7.1 to +7.2 for the Ernici trachybasalts with $SiO_2 > 50$ wt.%, and to +7.4 and +7.7 for the Procida latite and trachyte.

The S. Stefano phonolite ($\delta^{18}O = +7.6$) is geographically related to the Ventotene volcanic center (Fig. 1), and together the Ventotene and S. Stefano samples also define a trend of slight $^{18}O$-enrichment with increasing $K_2O$ and $SiO_2$.

The Ischia samples overlap the trends described above, but they are overall shifted downward and to the right on Fig. 2 (note that this shift is not because they are less rich in *total* alkalis; the lower $K_2O$ concentrations of the Ischia rocks at a given $SiO_2$ content go hand-in-hand with the fact that their Na/K ratios are considerably higher than those of equivalent lavas on the Italian mainland). Like the Procida and Roccamonfina samples, the $\delta^{18}O$ values at Ischia also show a slight increase upward and to the right on Fig. 2, but the most important feature of the data is that, compared with other samples having similarly high $SiO_2$ contents (54–64 wt.%), these Ischia samples have the lowest $\delta^{18}O$ values of *any* Quaternary volcanic rocks so far analyzed from Italy.

The four Ponza samples and the geographically closely associated rocks from Palmarola are chemically and isotopically heterogeneous; however, the Ponza group can be subdivided into (1) a couple of very high-$SiO_2$ rhyolites (73–75 wt.% $SiO_2$) that have *very* high $\delta^{18}O$ values (+10.2 to +11.1), and (2) a couple of lower-$^{18}O$, lower-$SiO_2$, alkalic rocks (a trachyte and a sodic rhyolite dike with $\delta^{18}O = +7.0$ to +7.4). The high-$^{18}O$ sub-group is analogous to the anatectic rhyolites of the Tuscan Magmatic Province on the mainland, compatible with the nearby occurrence of Tuscan metamorphic basement rocks on the island of Zannone. The adjacent Palmarola rhyolites are isotopically very similar to the second, or low-$^{18}O$ sub-group of Ponza samples. It is remarkable that rhyolitic rocks from such a small geographic area (Fig. 1) display such a large range in $\delta^{18}O$. The only other localities in Italy where such low-$^{18}O$ Quaternary rhyolites are known are in the Aeolian Islands (M. JAVOY, pers. comm.).

The M. Ernici HKS samples are coincident with the Alban Hills field on Fig. 2, and both geochemically and geographically, these are also the lavas closest to the Alban Hills volcanic rocks (Fig. 1). They also display a similar range of $\delta^{18}O$ (+5.8 to +8.5 at Ernici vs. +5.6 to +7.9 at the Alban Hills). Much of the general discussion and interpretation by FERRARA *et al.* (1985) concerning the origin and evolution of the Alban Hills volcanic rocks thus probably applies to the Ernici HKS lavas, as well.

*CaO vs. $\delta^{18}O$*

On Fig. 3 we present a schematic diagram that shows the kinds of changes expected in CaO and

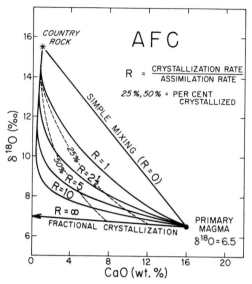

FIG. 3. Plot of CaO vs. $\delta^{18}O$, showing schematically how these parameters change during closed-system differentiation, simple mixing, and combined assimilation-fractional crystallization.

$\delta^{18}O$ during closed-system fractional crystallization, combined assimilation-fractional crystallization (AFC), and simple mixing. APPLETON (1972) and most subsequent workers (*e.g.*, HOLM and MUNKSGAARD, 1982; FERRARA *et al.*, 1986) attributed great importance to the most Ca-rich and $SiO_2$-depleted lavas in the volcanic series of Italy, because these are the best candidates for primary magmas. Contrary to the opinions of VOLLMER (1989), essentially all other studies of the petrology of the potassic Roman Province have concluded that if there are *any* primitive, uncontaminated magmas represented among the eruptive products of these volcanic centers, *they must be these Ca-rich lavas*. Although fractional crystallization of olivine and clinopyroxene will drive such magmas toward higher $SiO_2$ and $K_2O$ (APPLETON, 1972), thereby explaining much of the major-element variation in these K-rich lavas (Fig. 2), this process cannot account for the $^{18}O/$ $^{16}O$ variations (TAYLOR *et al.*, 1979; FERRARA *et al.*, 1985, 1986).

On a CaO-$\delta^{18}O$ plot (Fig. 3), the above-described fractional crystallization process drives the evolved magmas horizontally to the left toward lower CaO contents. As shown by GARLICK (1966), TAYLOR (1968), MATSUHISA (1979), MUEHLENBACHS and BYERLY (1982), CHIVAS *et al.* (1982), SHEPPARD and HARRIS (1985), and TAYLOR and SHEPPARD (1986), there is probably a slight enrichment of $\delta^{18}O$ during such a closed-system process, but it will be very small for such high-temperature magmas, certainly no more than one per mil. Thus, a diagram like Fig. 3 can provide a sensitive test of closed-system fractional crystallization (HOLM and MUNKSGAARD, 1982; FERRARA *et al.*, 1986).

Simple mixing curves are nearly straight lines on diagrams like Fig. 3 because the oxygen contents of most rocks and magmas are similar. For a specific pair of end members, processes of combined assimilation-fractional crystallization (AFC, see TAYLOR, 1980) also start off as approximately straight lines at a given $R$ value (ratio of cumulates to assimilated rock, see TAYLOR and SHEPPARD, 1986), before beginning to curve sharply as the assimilation process starts to dominate. The various AFC curves thus lie at intermediate positions between a closed-system fractional crystallization "line" and a simple mixing line. Even for relatively low degrees of fractional crystallization (25 to 50%), the <sup>18</sup>O enrichments of the magmas should be apparent, especially if the $R$ values are as low as two to five (Fig. 3).

On Fig. 4 we show how the $\delta^{18}O$ values of lavas from previously studied potassic volcanic centers on the Italian mainland change with CaO concentration. The two best-studied volcanic centers that also have erupted significant quantities of lavas with "primitive" CaO contents are M. Vulsini and Roccamonfina (FERRARA *et al.*, 1986; ROGERS *et al.*, 1985; HOLM and MUNKSGAARD, 1982; TAYLOR *et al.*, 1979; APPLETON, 1972). The most Ca-rich samples from both Roccamonfina and Vulsini have relatively low $\delta^{18}O$; however, with decreasing CaO the lavas of both volcanoes, but particularly those from M. Vulsini, display a sharp $\delta^{18}O$ increase. The *only* way these <sup>18</sup>O/<sup>16</sup>O data can be reconciled with the strong consensus that the trend of decreasing CaO is a result of low-pressure fractional crystallization is to combine that process with a simultaneous and concurrent enrichment in <sup>18</sup>O due to assimilation of high-<sup>18</sup>O country rocks (*i.e.*, AFC).

There are significant geographic differences in Italy in the magnitudes of the <sup>18</sup>O/<sup>16</sup>O effects attributable to AFC processes. For example, although the most Ca-rich lavas at both Vulsini and Roccamonfina display low $\delta^{18}O$ values, the more evolved Ca-poor magmas are *much* richer in <sup>18</sup>O at Vulsini (Fig. 4). Therefore, the AFC processes at Vulsini for some reason produced much greater <sup>18</sup>O enrichments. TURI and TAYLOR (1976) and TAYLOR and TURI (1976) explained these geographic differences in Italy as resulting from the fact that the M. Vulsini volcano erupted upward through a thick section of continental crust that had been heated on a *regional* scale during the previous million or so years; this event was sufficiently intense

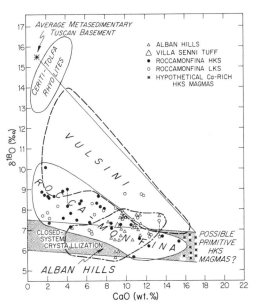

FIG. 4. Plot of CaO vs. $\delta^{18}O$ for volcanic rocks from various localities referred to in the text. For Vulsini, only the generalized data envelope is shown. Note that the Villa Senni Tuff represents the most voluminous eruption at the Alban Hills, and that the Ceriti-Tolfa rhyolites are anatectic magmas from the southern part of the Tuscan Province (see Fig. 1).

that widespread melting of the continental crust occurred, producing the characteristic high-<sup>18</sup>O Tuscan granites and rhyolites. The Tuscan rhyolites that are geographically closest to the Pontine Islands are also plotted on Fig. 4, namely those from the Ceriti-Tolfa center (TAYLOR *et al.*, 1991). Mixing between these crustal-anatectic Tuscan magmas and the mantle-derived Roman magmas appears to have been fairly widespread, particularly at the <sup>18</sup>O-rich, hybrid M. Cimini center that lies just southeast of, and is partially covered by, the products of the M. Vulsini center (TAYLOR and TURI, 1976; TAYLOR *et al.*, 1991; BARTON *et al.*, 1982).

Because of heat-balance considerations, the isotopic effects produced by AFC processes will be enhanced dramatically if the country-rock temperatures are raised significantly above those characteristic of a normal geothermal gradient (TAYLOR, 1980; DE PAOLO, 1981). Although R values of seven to nine might be appropriate for "cold" wall rocks, R values as low as one to three might be expected for magma chambers emplaced into country rocks that have been strongly heated. North of Rome, we *know* that the continental crust was strongly heated and locally partially melted during the past four million years by the Tuscan magmatic episode, and the surface rocks are locally still very hot (*e.g.*, at

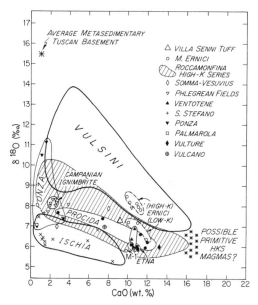

FIG. 5. Plot of CaO vs. $\delta^{18}O$ comparing new data from the offshore islands of Ischia, Procida, and the Pontine Islands with other localities referred to in the text.

at the margin or outboard of the high-$^{18}O$ continental crust of the Italian peninsula. For example, can it be a coincidence that the sequence of increasing $\delta^{18}O$ in the Quaternary lavas erupted within a relatively small area in the vicinity of the Gulf of Naples is Ischia—Procida—Phlegrean Fields? This geochemical transition takes place over a lateral distance of only 30 km (Fig. 1) and is identical to the geographic sequence from southwest to northeast, going from low-$^{18}O$ oceanic crust toward high-$^{18}O$ continental crust.

## $^{87}Sr/^{86}Sr$ vs. $\delta^{18}O$

On Fig. 6, the initial $^{87}Sr/^{86}Sr$ ratios of the new samples from this study are plotted against $\delta^{18}O$. Also included are all available data from Roccamonfina (TAYLOR et al., 1979; HAWKESWORTH and VOLLMER, 1979). Two important features are indicated on Fig. 6, both of which were previously pointed out at Roccamonfina by TAYLOR et al. (1979): (1) There is a steep positive correlation between $\delta^{18}O$ and $^{87}Sr/^{86}Sr$ at each volcanic center. (2) At a given locality, the Low-K Series and High-K Series samples each form separate groupings, with the HKS exhibiting a much higher $^{87}Sr/^{86}Sr$ than the LKS.

The steep trends shown on Fig. 6 clearly require some type of mixing process between a high-$^{18}O$, $^{87}Sr$-rich end member(s) and a low-$^{18}O$, $^{87}Sr$-poor end member(s); this mixing is a local phenomenon that occurred separately beneath each volcanic center. On Fig. 7, the data from Fig. 6 are compared with data from some other Italian volcanic centers, confirming and amplifying the above conclusions.

M. Amiata and Larderello); however, south of Rome such heating prior to the late Quaternary potassic volcanism was minor or non-existent. On a regional scale these lateral gradients in temperature at a given depth within the Italian continental crust (i.e., country-rock temperatures decreasing to the south) seem adequate to explain the observed $\delta^{18}O$ differences between the Vulsini and Roccamonfina magmas on Fig. 4 (compare with Fig. 3).

With the above discussion as background, on Fig. 5 we plot the CaO-$\delta^{18}O$ relationships observed for the other samples from the present study. This diagram elaborates on certain features in the $K_2O$-$SiO_2$ plot (Fig. 2), including the correspondence between the Procida and the Ventotene-S. Stefano trends and the fact that on a CaO-$\delta^{18}O$ plot the lavas from these islands plot between the Ischia field and the main portion of the Roccamonfina HKS field, and at much lower $\delta^{18}O$ values than the Vulsini samples. All of these trends project toward a possible primitive parent magma having a $\delta^{18}O$ somewhere in the range +5.5 to +7.5 and a CaO content of about 14 to 17 wt.%. Interestingly, the lowest $^{18}O$ samples that have yet been found among the highly differentiated lavas of Italy (i.e., those with CaO < 2 wt.%) are all from the offshore islands, namely the Ischia trachytes and phonolites, some of the Ponza-Palmarola rhyolites, and the rhyolites from the Aeolian Islands (M. JAVOY, pers. comm.). This may be correlated with the fact that these centers are located

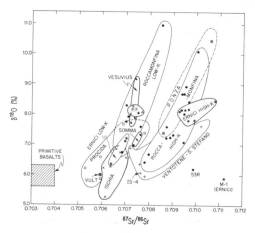

FIG. 6. Plot of $\delta^{18}O$ vs. $^{87}Sr/^{86}Sr$ for various localities referred to in the text (see Fig. 1). P.F. indicates Phlegrean Fields.

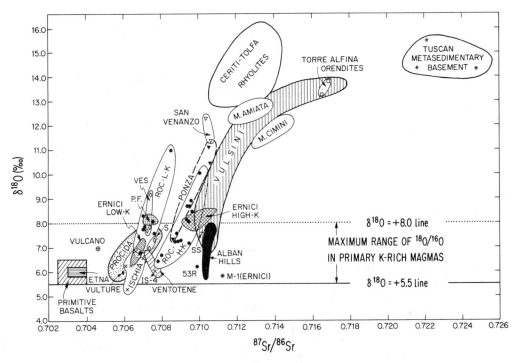

FIG. 7. Plot of $\delta^{18}O$ vs. $^{87}Sr/^{86}Sr$ comparing the data from Fig. 6 with data from other localities referred to in the text, including the Tuscan Igneous Province (compare with Fig. 1).

At each center, the data-point envelope exhibits a steep, positive slope that projects downward toward a low-$^{18}O$, low-$^{87}Sr$ end member; these low-$^{18}O$ end members all have a primitive $\delta^{18}O = +5.5$ to $+7.5$, but distinctly different $^{87}Sr/^{86}Sr$ (ranging from 0.706 to 0.710). The $^{87}Sr/^{86}Sr$ of the low-$^{18}O$ end member(s) changes systematically from lower values in the Low-K Series and/or in samples from the southern part of the Roman Province to higher $^{87}Sr/^{86}Sr$ in the High-K Series and/or in the northern part of the province. The highest $^{87}Sr/^{86}Sr$ values of the low-$^{18}O$ end member(s) are observed in the HKS lavas, as typified by the Alban Hills and M. Vulsini. Based on limited data from the Vico and M. Sabatini volcanoes, which lie geographically between M. Vulsini and the Alban Hills, similar isotopic effects appear to be characteristic of all HKS samples within this entire region to the north of Rome (see TAYLOR et al., 1991).

The high-$^{18}O$, high-$^{87}Sr/^{86}Sr$ end member(s) can be identified with the characteristic Tuscan metasedimentary basement rocks of central Italy (TAYLOR and TURI, 1976; TAYLOR et al., 1991; VAREKAMP and KALAMARIDES, 1989). Hyperbolic mixing curves between various low-$^{18}O$, variable-$^{87}Sr$ end member(s) and these metasedimentary basement rocks can explain all the convex-upward,

curved trajectories exhibited by the various data-point envelopes on Figs. 6 and 7 (compare with Fig. 9 of FERRARA et al., 1986, or Fig. 21 of TAYLOR and SHEPPARD, 1986). Because of the extremely high Sr contents of the low-$^{18}O$ end members (typically 1000–2000 ppm Sr, or more; Table 1), these trajectories always start out with a near-vertical slope. Because the trends are very steep, there is virtually no ambiguity about the $^{87}Sr/^{86}Sr$ ratio of the low-$^{18}O$ end member at each center (for example, at the Alban Hills, the HKS end member must have a remarkably uniform $^{87}Sr/^{86}Sr$ between 0.7100 and 0.7104 (FERRARA et al., 1985). The strongly quartz-normative Tuscan rhyolites at Ceriti-Tolfa, San Vincenzo, and Roccastrada (TAYLOR et al., 1991) plot very close to the field of Tuscan basement rocks, compatible with their anatectic origin from these rocks (Fig. 7). Also, the hybrid trachytic and latitic magmas at M. Amiata and M. Cimini were apparently formed by some type of mixing between these Tuscan anatectic magmas and potassic magmas analogous to those of the Roman Province, confirming the conclusions of TAYLOR and TURI (1976).

Some of the rhyolites from the Pontine Islands have markedly different isotopic compositions than the characteristic Tuscan rhyolites (Roccastrada,

San Vincenzo, Tolfa-Ceriti) and granites (Elba, Montecristo, Giglio). The Palmarola rhyolites are not plotted on Fig. 7 because the initial $^{87}Sr/^{86}Sr$ ratios of samples with such extremely low Sr concentrations (7 ppm) cannot be calculated unless the age of crystallization is *exactly* known; however, their initial $^{87}Sr/^{86}Sr$ ratios can be roughly estimated at about 0.708–0.710 (Table 1), and together with their $\delta^{18}O$ values of +7.0 to +7.1, we see that the Palmarola rhyolites approximately overlap with the most primitive Roccamonfina HKS and Alban Hills HKS samples on Fig. 7, even though they are chemically *much* different rock types.

None of these relatively low-$^{18}O$ rhyolites and trachytes from the off-shore islands of Ponza and Palmarola can be derived from melting of sedimentary or metasedimentary rocks of the type that make up the continental crust of Italy. Because they display isotopic compositions similar to those found in most other ocean islands, they could have been derived in a similar fashion as the typical trachytes and rhyolites from such islands (*e.g.*, Easter Island, Ascension, and Tristan de Cunha; see review by SHEPPARD, 1986). The two high-$^{18}O$ Ponza rhyolites (P0402,403) however, definitely require the admixture of a metasedimentary component, and some type of mixing between such a component and a Palmarola-type magma would be an adequate way to form such magmas. Such metasedimentary rocks do in fact occur nearby on the island of Zannone.

## CONCLUSIONS

Although crustal assimilation (AFC) effects are readily apparent in the $^{18}O/^{16}O$ results, they are obscured in the Sr and Nd isotope data because of the extremely high Sr and rare earth concentrations in these potassic magmas. This is particularly true for the more fractionated lavas, and especially to the north of Rome where the potassic magmas were erupted upward through thick continental crust where the geothermal gradient was much higher than normal. Hence, in this situation the radiogenic isotopes are a sensitive monitor of the mantle source-region characteristics of these magmas, whereas the $^{18}O/^{16}O$ signatures are much more sensitive to continental crustal assimilation effects. The *major* Sr isotope variations in the volcanic rocks of the Roman Province are clearly a result of fairly recent mixing processes (*e.g.*, HURLEY *et al.*, 1966) in the upper mantle source regions of these magmas, as typified by the Continental Mantle Mixing Line (CMML) of FERRARA *et al.* (1985), shown in Figs. 8 and 9.

Except for the emphasis on AFC processes instead of simple closed-system fractional crystallization,

our new data fit nicely with most earlier conclusions by APPLETON (1972), CORTINI and HERMES (1981), and by HAWKESWORTH and VOLLMER (1979) concerning the origin of these magmas; the new data are also in thorough agreement with our previous results from other areas of the Roman Province (FERRARA *et al.*, 1985, 1986; TAYLOR *et al.*, 1987; TURI *et al.*, 1986). Our conclusions are, however, incompatible with certain conclusions of HOLM and MUNKSGAARD (1982), PECCERILLO (1985), PECCERILLO and MANETTI (1985), and VOLLMER (1989), as follows:

(1) We believe that the $\delta^{18}O$ values of the *primitive* HKS and LKS parent magmas at each volcanic center in Italy are quite low, typically +5.5 to +7.0. Although some of these magmas may begin the ascent from their mantle source regions with a $\delta^{18}O$ as high as +7.5 ± 0.3, we can pretty well rule out the existence of *any* primary HKS or LKS magmas with $\delta^{18}O > +8.0$.

(2) In contrast to the *primitive* HKS and LKS magmas, which are actually quite rare as erupted products in Italy, the $\delta^{18}O$ values of the much more abundant, *evolved* (i.e., fractionated) HKS and LKS magmas *commonly* have $\delta^{18}O$ values higher than +7.0, locally going up to +12.0 in the northernmost centers. These $^{18}O$-enrichments correlate with major-element changes (*i.e.*, CaO depletion and $K_2O$ and $SiO_2$ enrichment) which essentially all workers except VOLLMER (1989) agree must have been produced by fractional crystallization in *crustal* magma chambers (perhaps at about 4 to 13 km depth, based on fluid inclusion data at Somma-Vesuvius; BELKIN *et al.*, 1985). In some cases, fragments torn loose from the crystallized margins of these crustal magma chambers and erupted in pyroclastic deposits have extremely high $\delta^{18}O$ values (+9 to +11 at Roccamonfina, TAYLOR *et al.*, 1979; +12.6 for clinopyroxene from a biotite-pyroxenite nodule at the Alban Hills, BARBIERI *et al.*, 1975). Inasmuch as the $^{18}O$ enrichments in these nodules and in the fractionated lavas *cannot* be produced by closed-system magma processes, all of these chemical and isotopic changes must be a result of some type of AFC process such as was modelled by TAYLOR *et al.* (1979) and TAYLOR (1980), or to mixing with crustally derived anatectic magmas (*e.g.*, TAYLOR and TURI, 1976).

(3) The alkali-rich, *evolved* LKS magmas from the southwestern-most volcanic centers (Ischia, Pontine Islands) typically have much lower $\delta^{18}O$ values and higher Na/K ratios than the petrologically analogous magmas found onshore in central

Italy. This correlates with the fact that these centers are all on islands located off the Italian coast, away from the continental crust. However, in the northernmost Pontine Islands, where continental basement *is* locally exposed, we encounter some high-$^{18}O$ rhyolites analogous to those of the Tuscan Province.

(4) The oxygen-isotopic systematics delineated in Italy prove that there has been a grand-scale mixing between the low-$^{18}O$, low-$SiO_2$, mantle-derived primitive potassic magmas and a high-$^{18}O$ reservoir that may be readily identified as the continental crust of peninsular Italy. This identification is based on the geographic relationship described above (Fig. 9), and on the fact that the mixing process that increased the $\delta^{18}O$ values of these evolved magmas occurred during fractional crystallization within the crust, not in the upper mantle. Because the continental basement rocks have $^{87}Sr/^{86}Sr$ even higher than the HKS end member (*i.e.*, >0.725, see Figs. 7 and 8), the $^{87}Sr/^{86}Sr$ signatures also permit a similar interpretation, particularly to the north of Rome, and particularly for the LKS magmas (FERRARA *et al.*, 1986; ROGERS *et al.*, 1985) as these tend to have lower $^{87}Sr/^{86}Sr$ and lower ppm Sr contents than the HKS magmas. The isotopic signature of this high-$^{18}O$, high-$^{87}Sr$ component becomes much less apparent to the south along the Italian peninsula, and southwestward from the coast, presumably because of a lower $\delta^{18}O$ and lower $^{87}Sr/^{86}Sr$ in the offshore transitional crust, as well as because of systematic changes to the south and to the west in the average temperature and/or the thickness of the Italian continental crust. In this connection, we note that crustal thinning, oceanization, and uplift of the isogeotherms apparently took place in areas adjacent to the Tyrrhenian abyssal plain since Miocene time (SCANDONE, 1979). It is well known that crustal assimilation and AFC processes are greatly enhanced by an increase in either the temperature or the thickness of the crust (TAYLOR *et al.*, 1979; TAYLOR, 1980; DE PAOLO, 1981; TAYLOR and SHEPPARD, 1986).

(5) We agree in general with APPLETON (1972) and CUNDARI (1980) that the geochemical differences between the primitive HKS and LKS magmas are very likely a result of different degrees of potassium metasomatism combined with a low percent of partial melting of the upper mantle source rocks of these magmas. However, two distinct mantle source regions are required, and the LKS source region in particular may be related to a unique, recent subduction event (see below). The metasomatic fluids that produced the HKS source region were remarkably rich in K, Ba, Sr, rare earths,

and other incompatible elements, as well as in $H_2O$ and other volatile constituents such as $CO_2$, F, etc.; they also came from a time-integrated, Rb-enriched source region, and thus had high $^{87}Sr/^{86}Sr$ ratios that show a positive correlation with the level of K and Sr enrichment. These HKS $^{87}Sr/^{86}Sr$ ratios were homogenized at an astonishingly uniform value of 0.710 to 0.711 over a wide area northwest from M. Ernici and the Alban Hills for at least 120 km, all the way to M. Vulsini. In agreement with CORTINI and HERMES (1981) and HAWKESWORTH and VOLLMER (1979), we have argued that this $^{87}Sr$ enrichment event was a fairly recent phenomenon (FERRARA *et al.*, 1985, 1986; TAYLOR *et al.*, 1987). By lowering the melting points of the mantle rocks, the event that introduced the $H_2O$-rich and $CO_2$-rich metasomatic fluids may have been the "trigger" that initiated widespread melting in the upper mantle beneath Italy during the past million or so years.

(6) Prior to or during mantle metasomatism, both K-rich source regions in the upper mantle became slightly $^{18}O$-enriched relative to MORB-type ($\delta^{18}O$ = +5.5 to +5.9) source regions. Whether or not these slight $^{18}O$ enrichments are attributable to the metasomatic event, we cannot say, but the primary HKS magmas in Italy are locally as $^{18}O$-enriched (up to +7.5 or +8.0?) as any that can be *proven* to be derived from ultramafic mantle anywhere in the world. Similar levels of metasomatic $^{18}O$-enrichments have actually been observed in mantle nodules brought up in kimberlites and other alkalic volcanic rocks (KYSER *et al.*, 1982; GREGORY and TAYLOR, 1986a,b), and it is now well established that alkali-rich basaltic magmas in general are *slightly* enriched in $^{18}O$ (*e.g.*, +6.0 to +6.5, see KYSER, 1986). A *slight* degree of enrichment in $^{18}O$ seems to be a common characteristic that goes hand-in-hand with alkali enrichment in mafic igneous rocks, including most ultrapotassic volcanic rocks (TAYLOR *et al.*, 1984). Although it is difficult to look backward through all of the other $^{18}O$-enrichment and fractionation events that have later been superimposed upon most of these potassic magmas, the $^{18}O/^{16}O$ ratio of the primitive LKS end member ($\delta^{18}O \sim$ +6?) is almost certainly a little lower than that of the HKS end member ($\delta^{18}O \sim$ +7?). For example, this difference can be observed directly in the positions of the Ernici LKS and HKS fields on Fig. 7. Also, some of the most Ca-rich M. Vulsini and Alban Hills HKS lavas have $\delta^{18}O \geq$ +7 (FERRARA *et al.*, 1985, 1986), and the level of $^{18}O$ enrichment in the LKS samples at Ischia and Procida (Fig. 7) is distinctly lower than in the nearby HKS samples at Vesuvius. Thus, the HKS end member

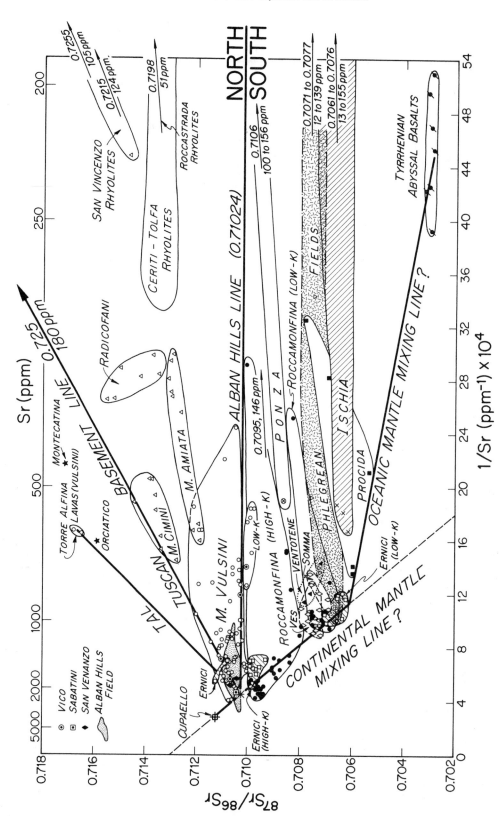

FIG. 8. Plot of $^{87}Sr/^{86}Sr$ vs. $1/Sr$ (ppm$^{-1}$ × 10$^4$) comparing data for samples analyzed in this work with previous data from other localities in Italy (for definitions of the major boundaries shown, and an indication of the $^{18}O/^{16}O$ variations in these same samples, see Fig. 9). The isotopic data plotted above are from the present work, from our own unpublished work, from Ferrara *et al.* (1985, 1986), and from a variety of other studies given in the list of references.

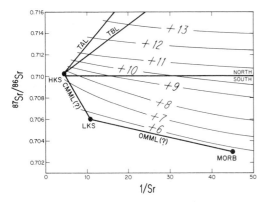

FIG. 9. Schematic plot of $^{87}Sr/^{86}Sr$ vs. 1/Sr (ppm$^{-1}$ × 10$^4$) showing the major boundaries described in Fig. 8, together with generalized whole-rock $\delta^{18}O$ contours for the volcanic rocks of Italy. The major boundaries shown by the heavy lines are defined as follows: (1) the horizontal line at 0.71024 separates the HKS-dominated lavas and pyroclastics north of and including the Alban Hills from the LKS-dominated volcanics to the south; (2) the CMML is the continental mantle mixing line defined by Ferrara *et al.* (1985), and connects the primitive HKS and LKS end members; (3) the upper diagonal lines connect the HKS end member with two types of typical Tuscan basement (TAL, Torre Alfina Line; TBL, Tuscan Basement Line); (4) the lowermost diagonal line (OMML) is an oceanic mantle mixing line connecting the LKS primitive end member with the MORB-type basalts of the Tyrrhenian Sea.

is much higher in $^{87}Sr/^{86}Sr$, but only slightly higher in $\delta^{18}O$, than the LKS end member; *both* are strongly enriched in $^{87}Sr/^{86}Sr$ and slightly enriched in $^{18}O$ compared to typical MORB samples.

(7) All of the magmas produced in Italy during the past five million years can be explained by mixing between the HKS and LKS parental end members and two other components: a continental metasedimentary basement end member and a MORB(?)-type end member similar to the source of the abyssal lavas of the Tyrrhenian Sea. Each of the volcanic centers in Italy occupies a well-defined position on a $^{87}Sr/^{86}Sr$ versus 1/Sr diagram (Fig. 8), lying within a quadrilateral bounded by the CMML, an LKS-MORB line, and a line between the HKS end member and the average Tuscan basement; these boundaries are also shown in Fig. 9, along with generalized $\delta^{18}O$ contours. The fourth side of the quadrilateral is represented by the limit of very low ppm Sr values in the most fractionated lavas at each center. A horizontal line at $^{87}Sr/^{86}Sr$ = 0.71024 (Figs. 8 and 9) neatly divides the low-$^{18}O$, low-$^{87}Sr/^{86}Sr$ centers south of the Alban Hills (which are dominated by LKS magmas) from the higher-$^{18}O$, higher $^{87}Sr/^{86}Sr$ centers to the north (which are dominated by HKS magmas).

(8) We now turn to the subducted-sediment theory of origin of the potassic Roman magmas (*e.g.,* BECCALUVA *et al.* 1991; PECCERILLO, 1985; ROGERS *et al.,* 1985; ELLAM *et al.,* 1989). One of the earliest formulations of this concept (THOMPSON, 1977) was based on the combined high $\delta^{18}O$ and high $^{87}Sr/^{86}Sr$ values discovered in the Roman magmas by TURI and TAYLOR (1976). Although the high $\delta^{18}O$ signatures indicate beyond doubt that sedimentary or metasedimentary rocks were *somehow* involved in the genesis of these magmas, we believe we have demonstrated conclusively that the *major* $^{18}O$ enrichments were produced within the continental crust, not in the upper mantle; thus, these $\delta^{18}O$ effects are not attributable to *subducted* sediments (unless that subduction process was a shallow one that simply involved a doubling of the continental crust, as has been suggested for central-southern Italy by SCANDONE, 1979). Interactions between mantle-derived magmas and such a tectonically thickened crust are a perfectly feasible way to explain most of our isotopic data, but it is clear that most of the workers who favor involvement of subducted sediments are not referring to such a process.

Although the mantle-derived, primary HKS and LKS magmas in Italy are slightly enriched in $^{18}O$ and markedly enriched in $^{87}Sr/^{86}Sr$ relative to MORB, they are *not* markedly enriched in either $^{18}O$ or $^{87}Sr/^{86}Sr$ relative to other potassic magmas throughout the world (VOLLMER and NORRY, 1983; COLLERSON and McCULLOCH, 1983; TAYLOR *et al.* 1984; NELSON *et al.,* 1986; GARLICK, 1966; KYSER, 1986; KYSER *et al.,* 1982). The new data from the off-shore islands of Ischia, Ventotene, and Vulcano are particularly compelling in this regard. Therefore, based simply on the *isotopic* data, there is no more reason to invoke subducted sediments in the *source* regions of the potassic magmas beneath Italy than in any other areas of potassic volcanism. The enrichment of both $^{18}O$ and $^{87}Sr$ that is observed in virtually all potassic magmas on Earth may be (probably is?) related to ancient subduction events that recycled high-$^{18}O$, LIL-enriched material into the upper mantle and changed the fundamental geochemical characteristics of the sub-continental lithosphere. However, this need have nothing to do with any *recent* subduction event, as favored by PECCERILLO (1985), ROGERS *et al.* (1985), and HOLM and MUNKSGAARD (1982). If there is sufficient evidence of another kind to require it, we would not quarrel with such an interpretation, but the very high $\delta^{18}O$ values of the Italian volcanic rocks should not be used as *evidence* for a recent subduction event. In fact, we believe that the astonishingly uniform and elevated $^{87}Sr/^{86}Sr$ ratios of 0.7100 to 0.7110 exhibited by the HKS end member over a wide area in Italy are difficult to reconcile with a recent subduction event, which would probably be associated with much more heterogeneous and lower $^{87}Sr/^{86}Sr$ values. It is perhaps more plausible to relate just the LKS end member to the recent subduction event, although fluids derived from dehydration of the subducted material conceivably might also have contributed to the required metasomatic homogenization of the HKS source.

It seems to us that the primitive potassic magmas of Italy probably formed in an extensional tectonic environment more-or-less analogous to the way other potassic volcanic rocks on Earth seem to have formed. However, superimposed on these tectonic events (recent subduction? back-arc spreading? local pull-apart basins?) are a large number of complexities unique to the late Tertiary and Quaternary geology and geography of Italy. These produced two distinct "enriched" upper mantle reservoirs with unusual trace-element and radiogenic isotope patterns, in close proximity to the MORB-type reservoir that produced the basalts of the Tyrrhenian Sea. Subsequently, interactions between the continental crust and potassic magmas derived from the two different sub-continental reservoirs locally produced higher $\delta^{18}O$ values in the *evolved* potassic magmas than those seen anywhere else on Earth.

*Acknowledgements*—We are indebted to M. Preite-Martinez and C. Trudu in Rome and to S. Tonarini in Pisa for their efforts in obtaining the O-isotope, Sr-isotope, and chemical analyses. We thank S. Epstein and J. Goris for their help in the laboratory work carried out at Caltech. The Sr-isotope analyses of some samples from M. Ernici were kindly made by M. Barbieri. Thanks are also due to P. Di Girolamo for discussions and assistance, and to R. Vollmer and M. Cortini for supplying several samples. M. Barbieri and A. Taddeucci permitted us to report unpublished data on the 1971 Etna lava flow. Funding for Taylor was provided by the United States National Science Foundation, Grant No. 83-13106 and Grant No. 88-16413. Funding for Turi was provided by the Consiglio Nazionale delle Ricerche through the Centro Studi per la Geochimica Applicata alla Stratigrafia Recente and the Cooperative U.S.-Italy Program, C.N.R. Grant No. 86.00709.05, and by the Ministero della Pubblica Istruzione.

## REFERENCES

ALBINI A., CRISTOFOLINI R., DI GIROLAMO P., NARDI G., ROLANDI G. and STANZIONE D. (1977) Rare earth element and thorium distribution in volcanic rocks of the potassic kindred from Procida Island and Phlegraean Fields, southern Italy. *Acc. Naz. Lincei Red. Cl. Sci. Fis. Mat. Nat.* **63**(5), 416–429.

ALBINI A., CRISTOFOLINI R., DI GIROLAMO P. and STANZIONE D. (1980) Rare earth and other trace-element distribution in the calc-alkaline volcanic rocks from deep boreholes in the Phlegraean Fields, Campania (South Italy). *Chem. Geol.* **28**, 123–133.

APPLETON J. D. (1972) Petrogenesis of potassium-rich lavas from the Roccamonfina Volcano, Roman Region, Italy. *J. Petrol.* **13**, 425–456.

BARBERI F., BORSI S., FERRARA G. and INNOCENTI F. (1967) Contributo alla conoscenza vulcanologica e magmatolgica delle isole dell' Arcipelago Pontino. *Mem. Soc. Geol. Ital.* **6**, 581–606.

BARBIERI M., PENTA A. and TURI B. (1975) Oxygen and strontium isotope ratios in some ejecta from the Alban Hills volcanic area, Roman Comagmatic Region. *Contrib. Mineral. Petrol.* **51**, 127–133.

BARBIERI M., PECCERILLO A., POLI G. and TOLOMEO L. (1988) Major, trace element, and Sr isotopic composition of lavas from Vico volcano (Central Italy) and their evolution in an open system. *Contrib. Mineral. Petrol.* **99**, 485–497.

BARTON M., VAREKAMP J. C. and VANBERGEN M. J. (1982) Complex zoning of clinopyroxenes in the lavas of Vulsini, Latium, Italy: Evidence for magma mixing. *J. Volcanol. Geotherm. Res.* **14**, 361–388.

BASILONE P. and CIVETTA L. (1975) Datazione K/Ar dell' attivita vulcanica dei Monti Ernici (Latina). *Rend. Soc. Ital. Mineral. Petrol.* **31**, 175–179.

BECCALUVA L., DI GIROLAMO P. and SERRI G. (1991) Petrogenesis and tectonic setting of the Roman Volcanic Province, Italy. *Lithos* **26**, 191–221.

BELKIN H. E., DE VIVO B., ROEDDER E. and CORTINI M. (1985) Fluid inclusion geobarometry from ejected Mt. Somma-Vesuvius nodules. *Amer. Mineral.* **70**, 288–303.

CAPALDI G., CIVETTA L. and GILLOT P. Y. (1985) Geochronology of Plio-Pleistocene volcanic rocks from southern Italy. *Rend. Soc. Ital. Mineral. Petrol.* **40**, 25–44.

CARMASSI M., DE RITA D., DE FILIPPO M., FUNICELLO R. and SHERIDAN M. F. (1987) Geology and volcanic evolution of the island of Ponza, Italy (unpubl. ms.).

CHIVAS A. R., ANDREW A. S., SINHA A. K. and O'NEIL J. R. (1982) Geochemistry of a Pliocene-Pleistocene oceanic-arc plutonic complex, Guadalcanal. *Nature* **300**, 139–143.

CIVETTA L., INNOCENTI F., MANETTI P., PECCERILLO A. and POLI G. (1981) Geochemical characteristics of potassic volcanics from Mts. Ernici (Southern Latium, Italy). *Contrib. Mineral. Petrol.* **78**, 37–47.

COLLERSON K. D. and McCULLOCH M. T. (1983) Nd and Sr isotope geochemistry of leucite-bearing lavas from Gaussberg, East Antarctica. *Proc. 4th Symp. Antarctic Earth Sci.,* 676–680.

CORTINI M. and HERMES O. D. (1981) Sr isotopic evidence for a multi-source origin of the potassic magmas in the Neapolitan area (S. Italy). *Contrib. Mineral. Petrol.* **77**, 47–55.

COX K. G., HAWKESWORTH C. J., O'NIONS R. K. and APPLETON J. D. (1976) Isotopic evidence for the derivation of some Roman region volcanics from anomalously enriched mantle. *Contrib. Mineral. Petrol.* **56**, 173–180.

CUNDARI A. (1980) Role of subduction in the genesis of leucite-bearing rocks, facts or fashion? Reply to A. D. EDGAR's discussion paper. *Contrib. Mineral. Petrol.* **73**, 432–434.

DE PAOLO D. J. (1981) Trace element and isotopic effects

of combined wall rock assimilation and fractional crystallization. *Earth Planet. Sci. Lett.* **53**, 189–202.

ELLAM R. M., HAWKESWORTH C. J., MENZIES M. A. and ROGERS N. W. (1989) The volcanism of southern Italy: role of subduction and the relationship between potassic and sodic alkaline magmatism. *J. Geophys. Res.* **94**, 4589–4601.

FERRARA G., LAURENZI M. A., TAYLOR H. P., JR., TONARINI S. and TURI B. (1985) Oxygen and strontium isotope studies of K-rich volcanic rocks from the Alban Hills, Italy. *Earth Planet. Sci. Lett.* **75**, 13–28.

FERRARA G., PREITE-MARTINEZ M., TAYLOR H. P., JR., TONARINI S. and TURI B. (1986) Evidence for crustal assimilation, mixing of magmas, and a $^{87}Sr$-rich upper mantle: An oxygen and strontium isotope study of the M. Vulsini volcanic area, Central Italy. *Contrib. Mineral. Petrol.* **92**, 269–280.

FORNASERI M. and TURI B. (1969) Carbon and oxygen isotopic composition of carbonates in lavas and ejectites from the Alban Hills, Italy. *Contrib. Mineral. Petrol.* **23**, 224–256.

GARLICK G. D. (1966) Oxygen isotope fractionation in igneous rocks. *Earth Planet. Sci. Lett.* **1**, 361–368.

GREGORY R. T. and TAYLOR H. P., JR. (1986a) Non-equilibrium, metasomatic $^{18}O/^{16}O$ effects in upper mantle mineral assemblages. *Contrib. Mineral. Petrol.* **93**, 124–135.

GREGORY R. T. and TAYLOR H. P., JR. (1986b) Possible non-equilibrium $^{18}O/^{16}O$ effects in mantle nodules, an alternative to the Kyser-O'Neil-Carmichael $^{18}O/^{16}O$ geothermometer. *Contrib. Mineral. Petrol.* **93**, 114–119.

HAWKESWORTH C. J. and VOLLMER R. (1979) Crustal contamination versus enriched mantle: $^{143}Nd/^{144}Nd$ and $^{87}Sr/^{86}Sr$ evidence from Italian volcanics. *Contrib. Mineral. Petrol.* **69**, 151–165.

HOLM P. M. and MUNKSGAARD N. C. (1982) Evidence for mantle metasomatism: An oxygen and strontium isotope study of the Vulsinian District, central Italy. *Earth Planet. Sci. Lett.* **60**, 376–388.

HURLEY P. M., FAIRBAIRN H. W. and PINSON W. H. (1966) Rb-Sr isotopic evidence on the origin of potash-rich lavas of western Italy. *Earth Planet. Sci. Lett.* **1**, 301–306.

KYSER T. K. (1986) Stable isotope variations in the mantle. In *Stable Isotopes in High-Temperature Geological Processes* (eds. J. W. VALLEY, H. P. TAYLOR JR. and J. R. O'NEIL); *Reviews in Mineralogy 16*, pp. 141–164. Mineralogical Society of America.

KYSER T. K., O'NEIL J. R. and CARMICHAEL I. S. E. (1982) Genetic relations among basic lavas and ultramafic nodules: evidence from oxygen isotope compositions. *Contrib. Mineral. Petrol.* **81**, 88–102.

MATSUHISA Y. (1979) Oxygen isotopic compositions of volcanic rocks from the East Japan island arcs and their bearing on petrogenesis. *J. Volcanol. Geotherm. Res.* **5**, 271–296.

MUEHLENBACHS K. and BYERLY G. (1982) $^{18}O$-enrichment of silicic magmas caused by crystal fractionation at the Galapagos spreading center. *Contrib. Mineral. Petrol.* **79**, 76–79.

MUEHLENBACHS K. and CLAYTON R. N. (1972) Oxygen isotope studies of fresh and weathered submarine basalts. *Canadian J. Earth Sci.* **9**, 172–184.

NELSON D. R., McCULLOCH M. T. and SUN S. S. (1986) The origins of ultrapotassic rocks as inferred from Sr, Nd, and Pb isotopes. *Geochim. Cosmochim. Acta.* **50**, 231–245.

PAROTTO M. and PRATURLON A. (1975) Geological summary of the Central Appennines. In *Structural Model of Italy* (eds. L. OGNIBEN, M. PAROTTO and A. PRATURLON); *C. N. R. Quaderni de "La Ricerca Scientifica" 90*, pp. 257–311.

PECCERILLO A. (1985) Roman comagmatic province (Central Italy): Evidence for subduction-related magma genesis. *Geology* **13**, 103–106.

PECCERILLO A. and MANETTI P. (1985) The potassium-alkaline volcanism of central-southern Italy: A review of the data relevant to petrogenesis and geodynamic significance. *Trans. Geol. Soc. S. Africa* **88**, 379–394.

RADICATI DI BROZOLO F., DI GIROLAMO P., TURI B. and ODDONE M. (1988) $^{40}Ar/^{39}Ar$ and K-Ar dating of the K-rich volcanic rocks from the Roccamonfina volcano, Roman Comagmatic Region, Italy. *Geochim. Cosmochim. Acta.* **52**, 1435–1441.

ROGERS N. W., HAWKESWORTH C. J., PARKER R. J. and MARSH J. S. (1985) The geochemistry of potassic lavas from Vulsini, central Italy and implications for mantle enrichment processes beneath the Roman region. *Contrib. Mineral. Petrol.* **90**, 244–257.

SCANDONE P. (1979) Origin of the Tyrrhenian Sea and Calabrian arc. *Boll. Soc. Geol. Ital.* **98**, 27–34.

SHEPPARD S. M. F. (1986) Igneous rocks: III. Isotopic case studies of magmatism in Africa, Eurasia, and oceanic islands. In *Stable Isotopes in High-Temperature Geological Processes* (eds. J. W. VALLEY, H. P. TAYLOR JR. and J. R. O'NEIL); *Reviews in Mineralogy 16*, pp. 319–371. Mineralogical Society of America.

SHEPPARD S. M. F. and HARRIS C. (1985) Hydrogen and oxygen isotope geochemistry of Ascension Island lavas and granites: Variations with crystal fractionation and interaction with sea water. *Contrib. Mineral. Petrol.* **91**, 74–81.

TAYLOR H. P., JR. (1968) The oxygen isotope geochemistry of igneous rocks. *Contrib. Mineral. Petrol.* **19**, 1–71.

TAYLOR H. P., JR. (1980) The effects of assimilation of country rocks by magmas on $^{18}O/^{16}O$ and $^{87}Sr/^{86}Sr$ systematics in igneous rocks. *Earth Planet. Sci. Lett.* **47**, 243–254.

TAYLOR H. P., JR. and EPSTEIN S. (1962) Relationship between $^{18}O/^{16}O$ ratios in coexisting minerals of igneous and metamorphic rocks. Part I: Principles and experimental results. *Bull. Geol. Soc. Amer.* **73**, 461–480.

TAYLOR H. P., JR. and SHEPPARD S. M. F. (1986) Igneous rocks: I. Processes of isotopic fractionation and isotope systematics. In *Stable Isotopes in High-Temperature Geological Processes* (eds. J. W. VALLEY, H. P. TAYLOR JR. and J. R. O'NEIL); *Reviews in Mineralogy 16*, pp. 227–271. Mineralogical Society of America.

TAYLOR H. P., JR. and TURI B. (1976) High-$^{18}O$ igneous rocks from the Tuscan magmatic province, Italy. *Contrib. Mineral. Petrol.* **55**, 33–54.

TAYLOR H. P., JR., GIANNETTI B. and TURI B. (1979) Oxygen isotope geochemistry of the potassic igneous rocks from the Roccamonfina volcano, Roman Comagmatic region, Italy. *Earth Planet. Sci. Lett.* **46**, 81–106.

TAYLOR H. P., JR., TURI B. and CUNDARI A. (1984) $^{18}O/^{16}O$ relationships in leucite-bearing volcanic rocks from New South Wales, Australia, Birunga, Africa, and San Venanzo-Cupaello, Italy. *Earth Planet. Sci. Lett.* **69**, 263–275.

TAYLOR H. P., JR., GREGORY R. T. and TURI B. (1987) $^{18}O/^{16}O$ evidence for fluid-rock interaction in the upper mantle: Data from ultramafic nodules and K-rich volcanic rocks in Italy. In *Chemical Transport in Metasomatic Processes* (ed. H. C. HELGESON); *NATO ASI Series C 218,* pp. 1–37. D. Reidel.

TAYLOR H. P., JR., FERRARA G., TURI B. and TONARINI S. (1991) Comparisons of $^{18}O/^{16}O$ and $^{87}Sr/^{86}Sr$ in volcanic rocks from the Tuscan Igneous Province with other areas in Italy (in prep).

THOMPSON R. N. (1977) Primary basalts and magma genesis. III. Alban Hills, Roman comagmatic province, Central Italy. *Contrib. Mineral. Petrol.* **50,** 91–108.

TURI B. and TAYLOR H. P., JR. (1976) Oxygen isotope studies of potassic volcanic rocks of the Roman Province, Central Italy. *Contrib. Mineral. Petrol.* **55,** 1–31.

TURI B., TAYLOR H. P., JR. and FERRARA G. (1986) A criticism of the Holm-Munksgaard oxygen and strontium isotope study of the Vulsinian District, Central Italy. *Earth Planet. Sci. Lett.* **69,** 447–453.

TURI B., TAYLOR H. P., JR., FERRARA G., MARTINEZ M. P., TONARINI S. and DI GIROLAMO P. (1991) $^{18}O/^{16}O$ and $^{87}Sr/^{86}Sr$ Ratios in volcanic rocks from the Pontine Islands, M. Ernici, and Campania, Italy. *Lithos* (in press).

VAREKAMP J. C. and KALAMARIDES R. I. (1989) Hybridization processes in leucite tephrites from Vulsini, Italy, and the evolution of the Italian potassic units. *J. Geophys. Res.* **94,** 4603–4618.

VEZZOLI L. (1988) Island of Ischia. *Quaderni de "La Ricerca Scientifica." Progetto Finalizzeto Geodinamica, Monografie Finali* **10,** 133 pp. C.N.R., Roma.

VOLLMER R. (1976) Rb-Sr and U-Th-Pb systematics of alkaline rocks: The alkaline rocks from Italy. *Geochim. Cosmochim. Acta* **40,** 283–295.

VOLLMER R. (1989) On the origin of the Italian potassic magmas 1. A discussion contribution. *Chem. Geol.* **74,** 229–239.

VOLLMER R. and NORRY M. J. (1983) Possible origin of K-rich volcanic rocks from Virunga, East Africa, by metasomatism of continental crustal material: Pb, Nd and Sr isotopic evidence. *Earth Planet. Sci. Lett.* **64,** 374–386.

Stable Isotope Geochemistry: A Tribute to Samuel Epstein
© The Geochemical Society, Special Publication No. 3, 1991
Editors: H. P. Taylor, Jr., J. R. O'Neil and I. R. Kaplan

# Hydrogen, sulphur and neodymium isotope variations in the mantle beneath the EPR at 12°50′N

MARC CHAUSSIDON, SIMON M. F. SHEPPARD and ANNIE MICHARD

Centre de Recherches Pétrographiques et Géochimiques, C.N.R.S., B.P. 20, F54501 Vandoeuvre-lès-Nancy, France

**Abstract**—Eight ridge and seamount glasses, from the East Pacific Rise near 13°N, have been analysed for $\delta D$, $\delta^{18}O$, $\delta^{34}S$, $^{143}Nd/^{144}Nd$, and $^{87}Sr/^{88}Sr$ of whole rocks, $\delta^{13}C$ and $\delta^{18}O$ of the dissolved carbonates, and for major and trace (Nd, Sr, $H_2O^+$, . . .) elements. The results from this restricted area span nearly the entire field of variations previously reported for MORB compositions: $-88 < \delta D < -54$, $-10.7 < \delta^{13}C_{carb} < -7.4$, $+23.6 < \delta^{18}O_{carb} < +26.9$, $+5.7 < \delta^{18}O < +6.1$, $+0.0 < \delta^{34}S < +1.3$, $0.702616 < ^{87}Sr/^{88}Sr < 0.702981$, $0.513038 < ^{143}Nd/^{144}Nd < 0.513180$, $0.09 < wt\% \ H_2O^+ < 0.49$, $218 < \Sigma C < 545$ ppm, $9 < \Sigma C_{carb} < 129$ ppm, and $877 < \Sigma S < 1104$ ppm.

Systematic chemical and isotopic variations are observed among the glasses, from those with low concentrations in incompatible elements (*e.g.* $H_2O^+$, $TiO_2$, Nd) and with low $\delta D$ ($\approx -84$) and low $^{143}Nd/^{144}Nd$ ($\approx 0.513069$), to glasses with high concentrations in incompatible elements, high $\delta D$ ($\approx -55$), and high $^{143}Nd/^{144}Nd$ ($\approx 0.513173$). These chemical and isotopic variations are principally reflecting within-mantle magmatic variations with effects due to degassing and/or high level contamination processes of the magma being minor. At least three mantle sources are involved as well as magma-mixing processes. The different end members may represent regions in the mantle which underwent incompatible element depletion in the past to varying extent, with the least depleted one having $\delta D \approx -80$. The $H_2O^+$ content of the MORB source is estimated to be 0.01–0.06 wt%, assuming 10–20% partial melting. Different degrees of partial melting, accompanied or followed by mixing, produced the observed relations among the incompatible element concentrations and isotopic ratios.

## INTRODUCTION

STUDIES OF THE noble gas, Sr, Nd, and Pb isotopic compositions of MORB (Mid Ocean Ridge Basalts) have identified the existence of several reservoirs in the upper mantle. Mixing between these reservoirs can explain the major part of the observed Sr, Nd, and Pb isotopic variations and, at least in part, the noble gas variations (*e.g.* DUPRÉ and ALLÈGRE, 1983; MARTY and OZIMA, 1986; ZINDLER *et al.*, 1984; ITO *et al.*, 1987; STAUDACHER and ALLÈGRE, 1988; HART, 1988). Some of the noble gas isotopic variations, however, have been shown to be associated with phenomena occurring during the evolution of the magma chamber under ridges and eruption on the sea floor, such as interaction with seawater (*e.g.* SARDA *et al.*, 1985). At the East Pacific Rise (EPR) in particular, ZINDLER *et al.* (1984) have shown the presence of large magnitude small-scale heterogeneities which demonstrate that the source materials are intermixed on a scale ranging from ten cm to one km. Despite the large number of isotopic analyses of Nd, Sr, and Pb, relatively few analyses of light stable isotopes such as H, C, and S have been carried out on MORB samples. Contrary to Sr, Nd, or Pb isotopic compositions, initial or primary $\delta D$, $\delta^{13}C$, and/or $\delta^{34}S$ values can be more readily modified by late-magmatic or post-magmatic processes such as degassing, interaction with the oceanic crust, or even interaction with seawater.

Therefore, $\delta D$, $\delta^{13}C$, or $\delta^{34}S$ variations found in MORB are thought to be related in part to such secondary processes (*e.g.* KYSER and O'NEIL, 1984; SAKAI *et al.*, 1984; PINEAU and JAVOY, 1983; MATTEY *et al.*, 1984).

A well-characterized set of samples were studied from a restricted area of the EPR at 12°50′N. The aims of the work were (1) to determine the range of variations of $\delta D$ and $\delta^{34}S$ values at the EPR, and (2) to try to link these values ($\delta D$, $\delta^{34}S$) using constraints from both trace element contents and O, Sr, Nd isotope ratios to variations in magma source compositions. For this purpose eight samples of glass from pillow lavas have been analyzed for their $H_2O^+$, total and carbonate carbon, sulphur, neodymium and strontium contents, as well as for their $\delta D$, $\delta^{13}C$, $\delta^{18}O$, $\delta^{34}S$, $^{143}Nd/^{144}Nd$, and $^{87}Sr/^{86}Sr$ ratios.

## LOCATION AND DESCRIPTION OF THE SAMPLES

The samples come from the EPR near 12°50 N (Fig. 1). The depths of collection (Table 1) range from 2163 m for the Clipperton seamount to 2600 m for samples from the axial graben (HEKINIAN and FOUQUET, 1985). Samples labelled V correspond to the external few millimetres of glassy rim of the pillow, which were handpicked from the whole sample. The maximum ages of the samples,

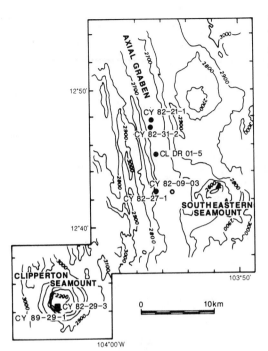

FIG. 1. Map of the East Pacific Rise at 12°50'N, with the location of the samples. CLDR samples were dredged and CY were collected by manned submersible (Cyana) (HEKINIAN and FOUQUET, 1985).

estimated from a maximum total spreading velocity of 12 cm/year (HEKINIAN and FOUQUET, 1985) and the $^{210}Pb/Pb$ ages on the smokers associated with the ridge (LALOU et al., 1985), are less than 100 years for the axial graben and $\approx 2000$ years for sample CY82-09-03V.

The petrology, mineralogy, and general geochemistry of the samples have been presented by HEKINIAN and FOUQUET (1985). The glasses contain between 5 and 15% phenocrysts and appear to be essentially free of microscopically visible vesicles. A vesicularity of 0.5 vol% has been reported for CY82-31-2V: this is typical of EPR glasses in general (MARTY and OZIMA, 1986). Sample CY82-21-1V also contains a few percent of microcrystalline aggregates and is therefore transitional towards the microcrystalline pillow core. The samples (Table 1, Fig. 2) include: (1) tholeiitic basalts with low $TiO_2$, $K_2O$, and $FeO^T/MgO$ (CY82-29-3V, CY82-29-1V, and CY82-21-1V from the Clipperton seamount and axial graben, respectively) which represent the least differentiated basalts in the area; (2) $TiO_2$-$K_2O$ depleted tholeiitic basalts (CY82-31-2V, CLDR01-5V, and CY82-10-02V from the axial graben zone) which are similar to basalts at 21°N; (3) a high $TiO_2$-$K_2O$ alkali-enriched basalt with a composition in-

termediate between a typical alkali and a silica saturated tholeiitic basalt (CY82-09-03V from the southeastern constructional margin of the graben); and (4) a sample (CY82-27-1V from the axial graben) of the Ti-FeO/MgO enriched tholeiite group of HEKINIAN and FOUQUET (1985). These authors suggest that at least two different parent magmas were involved at the EPR 13°N, plus superposition of variable degrees of fractional crystallization and magma mixing (see Fig. 2).

## ANALYTICAL PROCEDURES

Initially, one glass was tested for the presence of surface contaminants such as carbonates and sulphates. Several grams of sample (CLDR01-5V) were crushed to 4 mm and attacked by 1 N oxalic acid at 25°C for 12 hours. No measurable difference was observed for the sulphur and carbonate contents of this glass before and after the oxalic acid treatment.

Hydrogen was extracted by fusion of the sample, after pre-heating at either 160°C for two hours under vacuum or 120°C overnight, the water produced being reduced to $H_2$ by uranium at about 750°C (BIGELEISEN et al., 1952). Oxygen was liberated from silicates using $BrF_5$ (CLAYTON and MAYEDA, 1963), and carbon and oxygen from carbonates using the 100% $H_3PO_4$ method (MACCREA, 1950) followed by $Ag_3PO_4$ purification to remove sulphur contaminants (CHAREF and SHEPPARD, 1984). Yields were measured manometrically and are accurate to ±5%. Isotopic ratios were determined with a VG602D mass spectrometer and are reported in per mil in $\delta$ notation against SMOW for H (±2 per mil), and O (±0.2 per mil) and PDB for C (±0.2 per mil) (Table 2). NBS 28 has $\delta^{18}O = +9.6$ in our laboratory.

The extraction line and procedures used for the Kiba technique (extraction of sulphur and carbonate carbon) were similar to those described by UEDA and SAKAI (1983) except that reduced and oxidized sulphur were not routinely separated. Between 0.8 and 3 g of powdered rock were reacted under vacuum at 280°C in a quartz vessel with 50 ml of Kiba solution. Kiba reagent is obtained by adding $SnCl_2$ to $H_3PO_4$ (>85%, $d = 1.7$ and pre-purified by heating to 250°C for one hour) in the proportion of 1.85 g of $SnCl_2$ for 100 ml of $H_3PO_4$ followed by heating the mixture up to 280°C (UEDA and SAKAI, 1983). The mean of the sulphur extractions is 92% while measured $\delta^{34}S$ values were constant to within ±0.3 per mil, for yields greater than 75%. Sulphur isotopic measurements are given in $\delta$ notation against CDT (±0.3 per mil).

Total sulphur, total carbon, and carbonate carbon contents were additionally determined by another technique: fusion of the sample under a stream of oxygen followed by a coulometric titration (Mr Vernet analyst, CRPG). These values were used to control the yields of the isotopic extractions. The C and S contents agree well with the Kiba technique for high contents, but for low contents (<100 ppm) the agreement was only within ±20%, especially for C. The C and S contents given in Table 2 are the mean of these different techniques.

Sr and Nd analytical procedures are those described by ALIBERT et al. (1983) and MICHARD et al. (1985). Measurements of standards are listed in Table 4.

Table 1. Chemical analyses of basalt glasses from the EPR 12°50'N.

| Sample Location | CLDR01-5V Axial zone | CY82-31-2V* Axial zone | CY82-21-1V†* Axial zone | CY82-27-1V* Axial zone | CY82-10-02V Axial zone | CY82-09-03V* Constructional high | CY82-29-3V* Clipperton seamount | CY82-29-1V* Clipperton seamount |
|---|---|---|---|---|---|---|---|---|
| Depths (m) | — | 2596 | 2586 | — | — | 2623 | 2173 | 2180 |
| $SiO_2$ | 50.43 | 49.06 | 49.12 | 50.67 | 51.50 | 50.33 | 49.27 | 49.52 |
| $Al_2O_3$ | 15.83 | 16.90 | 16.21 | 15.39 | 14.53 | 17.10 | 16.11 | 16.36 |
| $FeO^T$ | 8.80 | 7.54 | 8.49 | 9.22 | 8.72 | 8.40 | 8.37 | 8.56 |
| $MgO$ | 8.43 | 9.28 | 9.60 | 7.70 | 7.68 | 7.55 | 9.56 | 9.60 |
| $MnO$ | 0.14 | 0.09 | 0.05 | n.d. | 0.15 | 0.02 | 0.10 | 0.21 |
| $CaO$ | 12.10 | 12.06 | 12.93 | 11.52 | 12.20 | 11.51 | 12.54 | 12.50 |
| $Na_2O$ | 2.92 | 2.63 | 2.14 | 3.08 | 2.73 | 3.15 | 2.12 | 2.22 |
| $K_2O$ | 0.05 | 0.11 | 0.11 | 0.26 | 0.06 | 0.45 | 0.03 | 0.04 |
| $TiO_2$ | 1.19 | 1.16 | 0.90 | 1.64 | 1.39 | 1.81 | 0.84 | 0.96 |
| Total | 99.89 | 98.83 | 99.55 | n.d. | 98.96 | 100.32 | 98.94 | 99.97 |
| $H_2O^+$ | 0.16 | 0.17 | 0.21 | 0.32 | 0.27 | 0.49 | 0.19 | 0.09 |
| S (ppm) | 957 | 877 | 1056 | 1104 | n.d. | 1073 | 1011 | n.d. |
| C (ppm) | 273 | 300 | 327 | 218 | n.d. | 545 | 409 | n.d. |

\* Data (major elements) from HEKINIAN and FOUQUET (1985).
† Contains a few percent of crystalline interior.
n.d.: not determined.

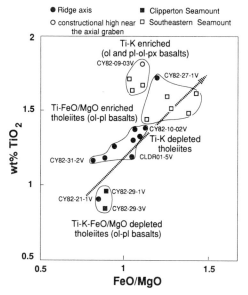

FIG. 2. Wt% $TiO_2$ versus FeO/MgO ratios for all available samples from the EPR 13°N (data from HEKINIAN and FOUQUET, 1985; and Table 1). The trend for differentiation predicted by HEKINIAN and FOUQUET (1985) and their four different chemical groups are represented. Note the large range of chemical variations of these basalt glasses collected in a restricted area of the EPR, and the absence of correlation between the chemistry and the location.

## RESULTS

### Water contents and hydrogen isotopes

Water contents show a large variation between 0.09 and 0.49 wt% $H_2O^+$ (Table 1), with a mean value of 0.24 wt%. They are not correlated with the depth of eruption. Similar to other localities, 13°N basalts are undersaturated in $H_2O^+$ (DELANEY et al., 1978; BYERS et al., 1983); saturation occurs around 1.5 wt% $H_2O^+$ for a pressure of 300 bars (extrapolated from HAMILTON et al., 1964). δD values range from −88 to −54 and no direct correlation is observed with the $H_2O^+$ contents (Fig. 3a, Table 2). Sample CY-82-21-1V, which has the lowest δD value (−88) contains ≈10% of micro-crystalline aggregates which were impossible to separate. This could explain a shift of δD towards more negative values by a few per mil, as the crystalline inner parts of this pillow have more negative δD values down to −103 (CHAUSSIDON, 1988). On all figures which include this sample, the tip of the arrow represents the estimated δD value of the pure glass after correction for ≈10% content of micro-crystalline basalt.

Step heating experiments have been performed with samples CLDR01-5V and CY82-09-03V (glass chips of several mm to 1 cm or powdered to <74 μm) to examine the effect of grain size on the water release pattern. The ground glass (CY82-09-03V) lost 80% of its water between 160 and 650°C and 20% between 650 and 800°C, whilst the chips of glass (CLDR01-5V) lost ≈100% of water between 850 and 1200°C (Table 3). Although the hydrogen release pattern and the δD of the successive fractions are related to the grain size, no difference in total δD or $H_2O^+$ was seen before or after crushing (sample CLDR01-5V, Table 3). Similar results were previously observed on MORB glasses (KYSER and O'NEIL, 1984), probably indicating differences in the kinetics of diffusion of H and D in the glasses at high temperatures due to variation in grain sizes. The reproducibility of the results also implies that the pre-heating process effectively removed adsorbed water.

### Oxygen

The $\delta^{18}O$ values of five glasses were determined (Table 2). They all fall in the range +5.7 to +6.1, and are similar to values of other EPR basalts (KYSER et al., 1982). This range corresponds to the upper part of the $\delta^{18}O$ range of MORB (e.g. KYSER, 1986).

### Carbonates

The total carbon contents range from 218 to 545 ppm and carbonate or acid extractable carbon range from 9 to 129 ppm (Table 2). The ratio of carbonate carbon to total carbon is about 0.3 ± 0.1 for four of the glasses, but for the two samples with the highest concentrations it is very low (0.08 and 0.02) (Table 2). This difference cannot be explained by the presence of carbonates as contaminants either at the surface of the glass chips or in the many little cracks which developed in the pillows during cooling. An attempt was made to extract $CO_2$ by reacting with $H_3PO_4$ 15 to 20 g sample of glass (CLDR01-5V) ground to six mesh (>3.36 mm). Less than one μmole of gas was recovered. These experiments, combined with the fact that we needed finely ground powder (200 mesh ≈ 74 μm) to obtain reproducible yields for $CO_2$, suggest that the carbonates are present in the rock as "internal" components such as carbonate species as identified by FINE and STOLPER (1986). Bubbles were not observed in the glasses in thin section, and no gas could be recovered during vacuum crushing (<1 μmol/15 g).

The $\delta^{13}C$ of the carbonates range from −10.7 to −7.4 and their $\delta^{18}O$ from +23.6 to +26.9. There is

Table 2. H, C, O, S quantitative and isotopic analyses.

| Samples | Hydrogen | | | Carbonates | | | | Oxygen | Sulphur | |
|---------|----------|----|----|--------------|----|----|----|--------|---------|----|
| | wt% $H_2O^+$ | $\delta D$ | ppm $C_{(tot)}$ | ppm $C_{(CO_3)}$[(a)] | $\delta^{13}C_{(CO_3)}$[(b)] | $\delta^{18}O_{(CO_3)}$ | $\delta^{18}O_{(tot)}$ | ppm $S$[(c)] | $\delta^{34}S$ |
| Ridge axis: | | | | | | | | | | |
| CLDR01-5V | 0.16 | −57 | 273 | 92 | −9.9* | n.d. | 6.1 | 957 | 0.0 |
| CY82-31-2V | 0.17 | −54 | 300 | 107 | −8.0 | 23.6 | 5.7 | 877 | 1.3 |
| CY82-21-1V† | 0.21 | −88 | 327 | 129 | −10.7 | 24.3 | n.d. | 1056 | 1.0 |
| CY82-27-1V | 0.37 | −66 | 218 | 45 | −7.4 | 26.9 | 6.0 | 1104 | 0.8 |
| CY82-10-02V | 0.27 | −66 | n.d. | n.d. | n.d. | n.d. | n.d. | n.d. | n.d. |
| CY82-09-03V | 0.49 | −58 | 545 | 45 | n.d. | n.d. | 5.9 | 1073 | 1.1 |
| Clipperton seamount: | | | | | | | | | | |
| CY82-29-3V | 0.19 | −80 | 409 | 9 | n.d. | n.d. | 6.1 | 1011 | 0.4 |
| CY82-29-1V | 0.09 | −67 | n.d. | n.d. | n.d. | n.d. | n.d. | n.d. | n.d. |

n.d.: not determined.
* $\delta^{13}C$ obtained by the Kiba method only.
† Contains a few percent of crystalline interior.
(a) carbonate contents are for most samples a mean between coulometric, phosphoric acid, and Kiba techniques.
(b) mean between phosphoric acid and Kiba techniques.
(c) mean between coulometric and Kiba techniques.

no correlation between $\delta^{18}O$ and $\delta^{13}C$. The $\delta^{13}C$ values, however, tend to increase with an increase in $TiO_2$ (or Nd) and a decrease in $CO_3$ (Tables 1, 2, and 3). These $\delta^{13}C$ values are only slightly lower than those of most diamonds ($\approx$ −5 and −8; DEINES, 1980) or of $CO_2$ released from vesicles or carbon liberated during high temperature (>600°C) combustion of MORB (PINEAU and JAVOY, 1983; MATTEY et al., 1984; JAVOY et al., 1986). However, they are very different from the very light MORB $\delta^{13}C$ values ($\approx$ −20 to −25) which are interpreted either as traces of organic carbon contaminant or of important degassing of $CO_2$ of the upper mantle (e.g. MATTEY et al., 1984; JAVOY et al., 1986). The $\delta^{18}O$ values of the carbonates are within the range reported by PINEAU and JAVOY (1983) for MORB from the MAR and the EPR.

## Sulphur

The glasses have sulphur contents of 1000 ± 90 ppm. Based on 35 fresh MORB glasses (MATHEZ, 1976), sulphur solubility in basaltic magmas has been shown to be principally related to Fe content. Using these data and the mean Fe content of our EPR glasses (6.6 wt%; Table 1), the value for sulphur saturation can be estimated to be about 1020 ppm. Taking into account the volume of phenocrysts present in the glasses ($\approx$2.5 to 10% by volume olivine and $\approx$2.5 to 10% by volume plagioclase; HEKINIAN and FOUQUET, 1985) the actual sulphur

contents of the glass are probably from 3 to 14% higher than the measured ones (Table 2). However, this correction is imprecise. Gas inclusions ($SO_2$ or $H_2S$) were not observed, but small magmatic sulphide globules (micron size) have been detected in one glass (CY82-21-1V) in accordance with saturation of the glass with sulphur. All the glasses from 13°N (except possibly CY82-31-2V) can be considered to be sulphur saturated.

The range of $\delta^{34}S$ values of the glasses is 0.0 to +1.3 with a mean of +0.8 ± 0.5 (Fig. 3b). These $\delta^{34}S$ values represent nearly the whole range of $\delta^{34}S$ already found for MORB (SAKAI et al., 1984). No systematic differences are noted between samples from the ridge and the Clipperton seamount (Table 2). The "magmatic value" of $\delta^{34}S$ = +0.8 ± 0.5 for 13°N sulphur saturated glasses is a little higher than that estimated from other ridges (+0.3 ± 0.5; SAKAI et al., 1984). However, data from SAKAI et al. (1982, 1984) show clearly that $\delta^{34}S$ values of +1.0 can be found for basaltic glasses. They have related these values to the sulphate/sulphide ratio in the rock, itself related to the water content.

## Strontium and neodymium

$^{143}Nd/^{144}Nd$ and $^{87}Sr/^{86}Sr$ ratios as well as Sr and Nd contents are given in Table 4. The total spread of the isotope data from 0.513038 to 0.513180 for Nd isotope ratios and from 0.702616 to 0.702981 for Sr isotope ratios is outside the analytical uncer-

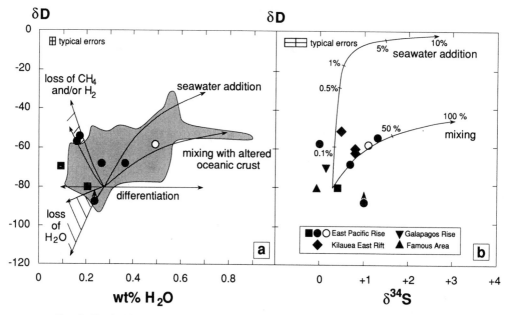

FIG. 3. δD of 13°N EPR glasses versus their water contents (Fig. 3a) and their δ³⁴S values (Fig. 3b). Data are from CRAIG and LUPTON (1976), KYSER and O'NEIL (1984), POREDA *et al.* (1986) (grey field), SAKAI *et al.* (1984), and from this study: solid square for the Clipperton seamount, solid circles for the ridge axis, and open circle for the constructional high near the axial graben, as in Figs. 1 and 2. In Fig. 3a trends are shown for loss of $H_2O$, loss of $CH_4$ or $H_2$, mixing with altered oceanic crust, direct seawater addition, and differentiation, for an arbitrary starting point corresponding to the mean of all the data with δD < −70 (δD = −80 ± 10 and wt% $H_2O^+$ = 0.27). In Fig. 3b mixing lines are represented between a magmatic end member (0.27 wt% $H_2O^+$, δD = −80, 800 ppm S, δ³⁴S = +0.3) and either seawater (δD = 0, 28.6 mM $SO_4^{2-}$/kg, δ³⁴S = +21) or another magmatic pole (1 wt% $H_2O$, δD = −45, 800 ppm S, δ³⁴S = +3).

tainties, and therefore reflects real sample variations at the EPR 13°N. The same range of variations has already been found for the EPR (MACDOUGALL and LUGMAIR, 1986), although their four samples from the EPR near 13°N have $^{143}Nd/^{144}Nd$ and $^{87}Sr/^{86}Sr$ ratios restricted to 0.513133 ± 7 and 0.702591 ± 19, respectively. Since the submission of the present work, PRINZHOFER *et al.* (1989) published Sr and Nd isotope analyses on some of the samples ana-

lyzed here. Their results show the same ranges of variations as those found in this study and confirm the fact that the isotopic heterogeneity is present at a very small scale, down to the sample scale. This outlines the interest of the present work which gives H, S, Sr, and Nd isotopic measurements on the same chip of sample. In a diagram of $^{143}Nd/^{144}Nd$ versus $^{87}Sr/^{86}Sr$ our data plot within the "mantle array" like all other samples from the ridge or seamounts

Table 3. $H_2O$ step heating extractions.

| T (°C) | 160†–650 | 650–800 | 800–1400 | Mean | Duplicate* |
|---|---|---|---|---|---|
| **CY82-09-03V (powdered)** | | | | | |
| wt% $H_2O$ | 0.42 | 0.1 | <0.01 | 0.52 | 0.49 |
| δD ‰ | −58 | −46 | — | −56 | −58 |
| **CLDR01-5V (chips)** | | | | | |
| wt% $H_2O$ | — | — | 0.16 | 0.16 | 0.16 |
| δD ‰ | — | — | −57 | −57 | −58 |

† $H_2O^-$ was removed by heating under vacuum at 160°C for 2 hours.
* Duplicate obtained on powdered samples.

of the EPR (MACDOUGALL and LUGMAIR, 1986; ZINDLER *et al.*, 1984; ITO *et al.*, 1987). No correlation is observed between the $^{143}Nd/^{144}Nd$ and $^{87}Sr/^{86}Sr$ ratios. This is not surprising on a restricted set of samples, because at the EPR one finds a large range of variations of Nd isotope ratios for a given Sr ratio, as well as the contrary (MACDOUGALL and LUGMAIR, 1986). However, our samples define a positive correlation between the Nd and Sr contents (Table 4), which is not clear in previous data.

## DISCUSSION

The H and S isotope compositions of MORB glasses can be a function of both the source region of the magma and high-level late magmatic and post-magmatic processes. The relative importance of these different possibilities can be assessed by examining the nature of the relationships between $\delta D$ or $\delta^{34}S$ and those parameters which directly reflect characteristics of the source regions, such as the $^{143}Nd/^{144}Nd$ ratio and certain chemical constituents. Thus, this section first considers such relationships.

### Relations among $\delta D$, $^{143}Nd/^{144}Nd$, and chemistry

The data for $\delta D$, $^{143}Nd/^{144}Nd$, Nd, $H_2O^+$, and $TiO_2$ contents are plotted on Figs. 4 and 5. Parameters such as Nd, $TiO_2$, and $^{143}Nd/^{144}Nd$ are not readily modified by late- and post-magmatic processes. For example, we do not expect any variation from a mantle $^{143}Nd/^{144}Nd$ ratio or any change in the Nd content of the magma during either the direct contamination of the magma by seawater or during assimilation of seawater hydrothermally al-

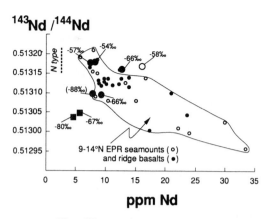

FIG. 4. $^{143}Nd/^{144}Nd$ of the EPR ridge and seamount basalts versus their Nd contents (data from ZINDLER *et al.*, 1984; PRINZHOFER *et al.*, 1989; and this work). $\delta D$ values for the EPR 13°N are given for each sample. Symbols for the EPR 13°N are the same as in Figs. 1, 2, and 3. Note that the samples from this study do not plot entirely within the field of previous data and that a rough trend of increasing $^{143}Nd/^{144}Nd$ with increase of Nd contents is observed. This is best interpreted in terms of mixing between different and variably depleted sources. Most depleted N-type MORB samples typically have the highest $\delta D$ values.

tered oceanic crust, because the concentrations of Sm and Nd in seawater are very low, $0.545 \pm 0.04$ $10^{-6}$ ppm and $2.58 \pm 0.23$ $10^{-6}$ ppm, respectively (PIEPGRAS and WASSERBURG, 1982). The Nd and $^{143}Nd/^{144}Nd$ ratio variations (Figs. 4 and 5a) therefore support the interpretations of HEKINIAN and FOUQUET (1985) that at least two magmas were involved at EPR 13°N. In fact, comparison of our data with those from the ridge basalts and sea-

Table 4. Strontium and neodymium measurements of EPR (12°50N) MORB glasses.

| Sample | Sr | $^{87}Sr/^{86}Sr$ | Nd | $^{143}Nd/^{144}Nd$ |
|---|---|---|---|---|
| Ridge axis | | | | |
| CLDR01-5V | 93 | $0.702616 \pm 31$ | 7.45 | $0.513178 \pm 28$ |
| CY82-31-2V | 116 | $0.702617 \pm 28$ | 8.15 | $0.513180 \pm 27$ |
| CY82-21-1V | 109 | $0.702617 \pm 31$ | 7.83 | $0.513099 \pm 24$ |
| CY82-27-1V | 159 | $0.702981 \pm 35$ | 12.75 | $0.513162 \pm 29$ |
| CY82-10-02V | 118 | $0.702623 \pm 40$ | 9.21 | $0.513096 \pm 22$ |
| CY82-09-03V | 219 | $0.702670 \pm 30$ | 16.00 | $0.513170 \pm 29$ |
| | | | | |
| Clipperton seamount | | | | |
| CY82-29-03V | 79 | $0.702666 \pm 31$ | 4.60 | $0.513038 \pm 28$ |
| CY82-29-01V | 88 | $0.702719 \pm 31$ | 5.63 | $0.513048 \pm 21$ |

Sr and Nd contents are given in ppm.
Measured values for the Eimer and Amend standard and the La Jolla standard are respectively. $^{87}Sr/^{86}Sr = 0.708030$ ($\pm 38$) and $^{143}Nd/^{144}Nd = 0.511841$ ($\pm 25$). $^{87}Sr/^{86}Sr$ normalized to $^{86}Sr/^{88}Sr = 0.1194$, $^{143}Nd/^{144}Nd$ to $^{146}Nd/^{144}Nd = 0.7219$. Data obtained on a Cameca 206S, single collector.

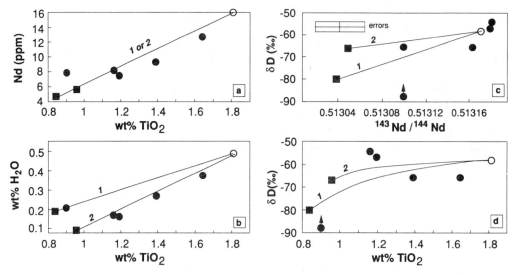

FIG. 5. Variations of the Nd (Fig. 5a), water (Fig. 5b) contents, and $\delta D$ values (Fig. 5d) versus the TiO$_2$ contents for all the glasses from the EPR and of the $\delta D$ values versus the $^{143}$Nd/$^{144}$Nd ratios (Fig. 5c). Symbols are the same as in Figs. 1, 2, and 3. Mixing lines between samples with extreme Nd contents (CY82-29-3V, CY82-29-1V, and CY82-09-03V) are presented (see text). In Fig. 5c high $\delta D$ values ($-55 \pm 5$) appear to be systematically associated with high $^{143}$Nd/$^{144}$Nd ratios (>0.513160), corresponding to N-type MORB.

mounts between 9° and 14°N (EPR) on Fig. 4 show that they scatter about a trend which is nearly opposite to that observed by ZINDLER *et al.* (1984) and that therefore three or more mantle sources are involved at 13°N.

On a Nd versus TiO$_2$ diagram any mixing between two end members gives a straight line. The line labelled 1 or 2 on Fig. 5a is such a mixing line between samples having the lowest and the highest Nd contents. The reasonable correlation shown between Nd and TiO$_2$ indicates that, to a first approximation, most of the Nd and TiO$_2$ variations can be explained by a two end-member mixing model. A similarly reasonable correlation is observed with FeO/MgO (Fig. 2), K$_2$O, Sr, and Nd (Tables 1 and 4). If, as suggested by HEKINIAN and FOUQUET (1985), part of the variation in TiO$_2$ and FeO/MgO can be explained by a fractional crystallization process, this might also explain part of the H$_2$O$^+$ variation (Fig. 5b), because water in MORB melts behaves like an incompatible element. Measurements of H$_2$O$^+$ contents in Juan de Fuca ridge basalt glasses have shown that water has a bulk distribution coefficient of $\approx 0.01$ similar to that of La during partial melting (DIXON *et al.,* 1988). However, for TiO$_2$, Nd, K$_2$O, H$_2$O, etc., this would require more than 50% fractional crystallization, which is unrealistic. Noting that the various melt-mineral partition coefficients for all these elements are not similar to each other (*e.g.* COX, 1983), these

correlations exclude fractional crystallization as the principal cause of the elemental variations.

The water content increases with increase in TiO$_2$ content (Fig. 5b) but the correlation is not so good as in Fig. 5a. Two mixing curves are shown, because of the large variations in H$_2$O$^+$ at very low TiO$_2$ values. These two curves are indistinguishable on Fig. 5a. The H$_2$O$^+$ contents of the different glasses can also be interpreted to be dominantly controlled by magma-magma mixing processes or other magmatic processes taking place in the upper mantle. Although two low-TiO$_2$ end members are necessary to account for the observed relations, note that sample CY82-21-1V on mixing curve 1 plots above the curve labelled 1 or 2 on Fig. 5a.

Figures 5c and d present the $\delta D$ data as a function of $^{143}$Nd/$^{144}$Nd and TiO$_2$ content. The mixing curves 1 and 2 are from Figs. 5a and b. Although there is no *a priori* reason why $\delta D$ should be coupled to $^{143}$Nd/$^{144}$Nd or TiO$_2$, some trends are observed. The most deuterium-depleted glasses ($\delta D \approx -80$) have $^{143}$Nd/$^{144}$Nd lower than 0.51310 and low TiO$_2$ (<1 wt%), whilst the most D-enriched samples ($\delta D > -60$) have higher $^{143}$Nd/$^{144}$Nd (>0.51316) and higher TiO$_2$. These relations, together with the trend of increasing H$_2$O$^+$ with an increase in TiO$_2$, imply that at least a major part of the $\delta D$ variation must also be inherited from the mantle source regions.

Such correlations involving $\delta D$ have rarely been found in MORB except for the oceanic ridges near

Iceland where PoREDA *et al.* (1986) reported correlations between $\delta D$, $H_2O^+$, La/Sm, and $^{87}Sr/^{86}Sr$. For these ridges several local variations over a few degrees of latitude were found to be opposite to the general trend followed by samples collected over 20° of latitude. Additionally, for seamount glasses from the EPR 21°N and 12–14°N, AGGREY *et al.* (1988) reported correlations between the water contents and both the La/Sm and $^{87}Sr/^{86}Sr$ ratios. They interpreted these in terms of magma mixing between at least two different sources.

Viewing all of these relationships as a whole (Figs. 2 to 5) indicates that most of the chemical and isotopic variations in all of our glasses record within-mantle magmatic processes. At least three sources are required plus magma mixing. These conclusions specifically apply to $H_2O^+$ and $\delta D$. The scatter about the mixing curves on diagrams such as $\delta D$ versus $^{143}Nd/^{144}Nd$ reflects the absence of perfect coupling between these parameters. However, good coupling between $\delta D$ and $H_2O^+$ is to be expected if late magmatic processes such as degassing or interaction with seawater were dominant processes (Fig. 3). Contamination by (1) assimilation of seawater hydrothermally altered oceanic crust, which is estimated to have $\delta D = -45 \pm 10$ and $H_2O^+ = 1.5$ wt%, based on data from the Troodos ophiolite (HEATON and SHEPPARD, 1977; SHEPPARD, 1980), or (2) mixing with magmas produced by partial melting of the seawater hydrothermally altered roof rocks above the high-level magma chamber (HEATON and SHEPPARD, 1977; TAYLOR, 1977, 1980), which could have compositions comparable to plagiogranite (COLEMAN, 1977) and $\delta D$ values of about −50 (HEATON and SHEPPARD, 1977) can also be excluded as dominant processes. Such processes cannot be totally excluded, but they have not contributed to the overall general trends and variations. Similarly, it is considered very improbable that the different sources had similar $\delta D$ values and that processes such as degassing or direct or indirect addition of seawater (Fig. 3a) have been effective selectively for each glass.

### Sulphur and carbon isotope heterogeneities

All the MORB samples (glassy rims of pillows only) yet analyzed both for $\delta D$ and $\delta^{34}S$ are plotted in Fig. 3b, together with the samples from this study. The data are scattered with no well-defined trend, although samples with high $\delta D$ values more often have high $\delta^{34}S$ values. This diagram emphasizes, however, that seawater addition can only be a minor process in controlling the $\delta^{34}S$ of the ridge and seamount glasses, because it would drastically increase

the $\delta D$ value before increasing the $\delta^{34}S$ value. A mixing line is presented in Fig. 3b between one end member with $\delta D = -80$ (0.27 wt% $H_2O^+$) and $\delta^{34}S = +0.3$ (800 ppm S) and another with $\delta D = -45$ (1 wt% $H_2O^+$) and $\delta^{34}S = +3$ (800 ppm S). The values chosen for the former correspond to the mean of all the available $\delta D$-$H_2O^+$ data on MORB samples having $\delta D < -70‰$ (data from CRAIG and LUPTON, 1976; KYSER and O'NEIL, 1984; POREDA *et al.,* 1986; and this study) and for sulphur to the mean of all MORB samples (data from SAKAI *et al.,* 1984; and this study). The latter end member represents parts of the mantle which could have high $\delta D$ and $\delta^{34}S$ values. Ion microprobe $\delta^{34}S$ measurements have shown that unaltered immiscible mantle sulphides can have $\delta^{34}S$ values of +3 (CHAUSSIDON *et al.,* 1989). Furthermore, amphibole pyroxenite layers from orogenic spinel lherzolite massifs from Ariège (Northeastern Pyrénées, France) contain sulphides having a mean $\delta^{34}S$ value of +3 (CHAUSSIDON and LORAND, 1990), and such massifs can contain amphiboles having high $\delta D$ values (up to −47; JAVOY, 1980). The origin of these variations of $\delta D$ and $\delta^{34}S$ in the mantle will be addressed below, but it is striking to note that altered oceanic crust (subducted or not) is known to have such high $\delta D$ and $\delta^{34}S$ values (*e.g.* HEATON and SHEPPARD, 1977; SHEPPARD, 1980; ALT *et al.,* 1989).

Despite the limited $\delta^{13}C$ data on carbonate species in glasses, the observed trends between $\delta^{13}C$ and $TiO_2$ or Nd, etc., imply that the $\delta^{13}C$ values are also predominantly reflecting within-mantle magmatic processes. These trends can similarly be due in part to magma-mixing processes. Degassing of $CO_2$ may not have been very important in so far as the trend of increasing $\delta^{13}C$ with decreasing $CO_3$ content is not in the expected sense (TAYLOR, 1986). The $\delta^{18}O$ values are not understood, as they are too $^{18}O$-enriched to be in equilibrium with silicate magma and there is no other evidence to invoke low temperature exchange processes (30–60°C if in equilibrium with seawater) or mixing with marine carbonate. We note, however, that such values have also been reported from the MAR and the EPR (PINEAU and JAVOY, 1983).

### $\delta D$ variations in the mantle

The range of $\delta D$ values from MORB and seamount glasses, $-90 < \delta D < -40$ (CRAIG and LUPTON, 1976; KYSER and O'NEIL, 1984; POREDA *et al.,* 1986; this study), is indistinguishable from that reported on phlogopites, kaersutitic, and pargasitic amphiboles from kimberlites, peridotites, and alkali intrusions (SHEPPARD and EPSTEIN, 1970; SHEPPARD and DAWSON, 1975; SHEPPARD et al., 1977; BOETTCHER and O'NEIL, 1980; JAVOY, 1980). For all these types of samples, interpretations have fallen into two main categories. Firstly, the isotopic variations are principally related to mantle heterogeneities. Secondly, the initial δD value of the mantle is inferred to be about −70 ± 10, and the higher δD values are assumed to be a product of late-stage magmatic or post-magmatic processes acting in the continental or oceanic crustal environment. However, concerning the latter hypothesis no generally applicable arguments have been presented to exclude the possibility that some parts of the mantle have δD > −60. This study supports the original proposition of SHEPPARD and EPSTEIN (1970) that the D/H ratio of the mantle is quite variable. Moreover, D/H ratios of certain amphiboles from mantle-derived lherzolite xenoliths have recently been shown (DELOULE et al., 1991) to be variable on a sub-millimetric scale, using ion microprobe techniques.

The scale of δD variations at the EPR 13°N is on the order of 100 m from our sampling, and no general relationship can be discerned between δD and the occurrence of the basalt (ridge or seamount). This suggests, as proposed by ZINDLER et al. (1984) for Nd and Sr, that the scale of δD heterogeneity in the mantle beneath the EPR is also very small.

The high $^{143}Nd/^{144}Nd$ ratios of normal MORB (0.513170 ± 20 for the N-type MORB of the EPR; ZINDLER et al., 1984) are generally interpreted as reflecting a long-term depletion history of their mantle source. Similarly high δD values of −55 ± 2 associated with these high $^{143}Nd/^{144}Nd$ ratios (Fig. 4) are likely to be a characteristic of the "depleted mantle" source of the N-type MORB. ZINDLER et al. (1984) propose to explain lower $^{143}Nd/^{144}Nd$ ratios by mixing between a "normal depleted peridotite source" with either (1) subducted oceanic crust, (2) old segregation of basaltic melts, or (3) metasomatized peridotite. Such multiple hypotheses provide good explanations for the Nd contents and isotopic compositions of the samples within the field of Fig. 4 (after ZINDLER et al., 1984). However, these three end members are likely to be enriched in incompatible elements relative to normal depleted peridotites, particularly in $H_2O^+$. Therefore, they could hardly explain our two samples from the Clipperton seamount, which have the lowest incompatible elements contents (Nd, Sr, $K_2O$, $TiO_2$, $H_2O^+$, . . .) as well as δD and low $^{143}Nd/^{144}Nd$ ratios. Since, as discussed previously, these two latter samples could not be related to the other ones from the EPR 13°N by either partial melting or fractional crystallization processes operating differentially, we propose that they represent a different end member in the mantle. This end member is characterized by low contents in incompatible elements, low δD values (≈ −80), and low $^{143}Nd/^{144}Nd$ ratios (0.51304), and could correspond to a more primary part of the upper mantle in which metasomatism and/or addition of external components has been limited.

In this latter hypothesis the typical N-type source of MORB, depleted in the past, would yield basalts with δD values around −55. On the other hand, a source less depleted in the past according to its $^{143}Nd/^{144}Nd$ ratios, but probably impoverished in incompatible elements in general more recently, according to its incompatible element contents, would yield more negative δD values (down to −80). Therefore, δD values of −80 ± 5 for the upper mantle seem to be the most primitive ones which can be deduced from MORB studies. This range of δD corresponds to the lowest δD values of all MORB (Fig. 3a), of unmetasomatized or unaltered alkali basalts and peridotites (SHEPPARD et al., 1977; KYSER, 1986; TAYLOR, 1986; TAYLOR and SHEPPARD, 1986), and to δD values of water from glass inclusions in olivine nodules from Japanese alkali basalts and peridotites (KURODA et al., 1977). Unfortunately, this cannot be more tightly constrained by δD systematics because the primordial D/H ratio of the Earth is unknown (see TAYLOR and SHEPPARD, 1986, p. 231). Meteorites with their enormous range of δD values (from −500 to +9000; YANG and EPSTEIN, 1983) cannot be used to constrain the problem. However, when considering the available MORB samples analyzed for δD and $δ^{34}S$ (Fig. 3b), δD values of −80 ± 5 seem to be more typically associated with $δ^{34}S$ values of 0 ± 0.5, which correspond to the range of $δ^{34}S$ values of meteorites (THODE et al., 1961). Assuming a distribution coefficient $D ≈ 0.01$ for water between residual mantle and melt during partial melting (DIXON et al., 1988) and 10 to 20% partial melting, a $H_2O^+$ content ranging between 0.01 and 0.02 wt% is calculated for the case of a simple batch melting model for our MORB samples having δD = −80 and $H_2O^+ = 0.1$ wt%. This water content probably represents an upper estimate for the least modified or most "primary" upper mantle.

Two principal hypotheses, subduction and degassing, can explain the origin of the variations in δD observed in the mantle. First, as suggested by the mixing line in Fig. 3b, the range of δD and $δ^{34}S$ values observed in MORB can be attributed to addition of altered oceanic crust with δD ≈ −45 and $δ^{34}S ≈ +3$ to a "primary" mantle. Second, the observed $\delta D$ and $\delta^{34}S$ variations can be explained by degassing of $H_2O$ and $H_2S$ from parts of the mantle. This second hypothesis seems the least likely, at least for hydrogen, because mass-balance considerations suggest that degassing of the Earth, which presumably created the seawater reservoir with $\delta D \approx 0$, should have decreased the $\delta D$ of the remaining water in the mantle. However, this argument is not definitive, because the initial $\delta D$ of the whole system is perhaps very different from $-80$, particularly if the mass of protium lost to space via the atmosphere is significant during the total evolution of the Earth (HUNTEN and DONAHUE, 1976). Finally, all the processes which created variations in $\delta D$, $\delta^{34}S$, and $^{143}Nd/^{144}Nd$ may have operated within the mantle but probably selectively, which explains the lack of perfect correlation between these parameters.

## CONCLUSIONS

The combined use of incompatible element concentrations and both light and heavy stable isotope ratios of glasses indicates mixing of three or more sources occurring along and near a 25 km ridge length at EPR 13°N. A major part of the total range of isotopic variations in MORB glasses is observed in this small area. Good circumstantial evidence suggests that the isotopic variations of elements such as H, C, and S, which are sensitive to near seafloor late-magmatic and post-magmatic processes, are dominantly of mantle origin. Although such later stage processes may well have contributed to the scatter in the data, it is difficult to envisage that these processes could have been dominant whilst preserving the overall consistency among all of the chemical and isotopic variations, and in particular $H_2O^+$ versus $TiO_2$ or Nd (Figs. 5a and b).

Previous H-isotope studies of MORB glasses have considered that normal values are around $-75 \pm 5$ (KYSER and O'NEIL, 1984; POREDA et al., 1986). Reexamination of their data in the light of our results reveals no compelling arguments that most of the large number of MORB glasses with $-70 < \delta D < -50$ are predominantly of secondary origin (i.e. due to degassing or to direct or indirect interaction with seawater). The mantle is thus considered to have variable D/H as well as $^{13}C/^{12}C$ and $^{34}S/^{32}S$ values. Based principally on the Nd and $^{143}Nd/^{144}Nd$ ratio data, the several identified mantle sources are considered to have had variable partial melting histories in time and in extent. The isotopic variations reflect these differences. The least modified or most "primary" source has $\delta D \approx -80$ and $\delta^{34}S \approx 0$. The importance of subducted oceanic crust in contributing to these variations is difficult to quantify from our results and absence of experimental isotopic fractionation data.

Water contents are relatively homogeneous with the great majority of MORB samples containing $0.2 \pm 0.1$ wt% $H_2O^+$. This implies that the $H_2O^+$ content of the MORB sources is around 0.01 to 0.06 wt%, assuming 10 to 20% partial melting.

*Acknowledgements*—We are grateful to R. Hekinian for having provided all the samples from the EPR 12°50'N, to P. Coget and B. Jacquier for their help in the isotopic analyses, to M. Vernet for all the coulometry measurements, and to C. Devey for fruitful discussions and review. This is contribution CRPG no. 879.

## REFERENCES

AGGREY K. E., MUENOV D. W. and BATIZA R. (1988) Volatile abundances in basaltic glasses from seamounts flanking the East Pacific Rise at 21°N and 12–14°N. *Geochim. Cosmochim. Acta* **52**, 2115–2119.

ALIBERT C., MICHARD A. and ALBAREDE F. (1983) The transition from alkali basalts to kimberlites: isotope and trace elements from melilites. *Contrib. Mineral. Petrol.* **82**, 176–186.

ALT J. C., ANDERSON T. F. and BONNEL L. (1989) The geochemistry of sulfur in a 1.3 km section of hydrothermally altered oceanic crust, DSDP hole 504B. *Geochim. Cosmochim. Acta* **53**, 1011–1023.

BIGELEISEN J., PEARLMAN M. L. and PROSSER H. C. (1952) Conversion of hydrogenic materials to hydrogen for isotopic analyses. *Anal. Chem.* **24**, 1356–1357.

BOETTCHER A. L. and O'NEIL J. R. (1980) Stable isotope, chemical and petrographic studies of high pressure amphiboles and micas: evidence for metasomatism in the mantle source regions of alkali basalts and kimberlites. *Amer. J. Sci.* **280A**, 594–621.

BYERS C. D., MUENOV D. W. and GARCIA M. O. (1983) Volatiles in basalts and andesites from the Galapagos Spreading Center, 85° to 86°W. *Geochim. Cosmochim. Acta* **47**, 1551–1558.

CHAREF A. and SHEPPARD S. M. F. (1984) Carbon and oxygen isotope analysis of calcite or dolomite associated with organic matter. *Isotope Geosci.* **2**, 325–333.

CHAUSSIDON M. (1988) Géochimie du soufre dans le manteau et la croûte océanique: apports de l'analyse isotopique in situ par sonde ionique. Thèse de l'INPL.

CHAUSSIDON M. and LORAND J. P. (1990) Sulphur isotope composition of orogenic spinel lherzolite massifs from Ariège (North Eastern Pyrénées, France): an ion microprobe study. *Geochim. Cosmochim. Acta* **54**, 2835–2846.

CHAUSSIDON M., ALBARÈDE F. and SHEPPARD S. M. F. (1989) Sulphur isotope variations in the mantle from ion microprobe analyses of micro-sulphide inclusions. *Earth Planet. Sci. Lett.* **92**, 144–156.

CLAYTON R. N. and MAYEDA T. D. (1963) The use of bromine pentafluoride in the extraction of oxygen from oxides and silicates for isotopic analyses. *Geochim. Cosmochim. Acta* **27**, 43–52.

COLEMAN R. G. (1977) *Ophiolites*. Springer-Verlag. Berlin, Heidelberg, New York.

COX K. G. (1983) The Karroo province of southern Africa: origin of trace elements enrichment patterns. In *Con-*

*tinental Basalts and Mantle Xenoliths* (eds. C. J. HAWKESWORTH and M. J. NORRY), pp. 139–157. Shiva Publishing Limited.

CRAIG H. and LUPTON J. E. (1976) Primordial neon, helium and hydrogen in oceanic basalts. *Earth Planet. Sci. Lett.* **31**, 369–385.

DEINES P. (1980) The carbon isotopic composition of diamonds: relationship to shape, color, occurrence and vapor composition. *Geochim. Cosmochim. Acta* **44**, 943–961.

DELANEY J. R., MUENOV D. W. and GRAHAM D. G. (1978) Abundance and distribution of water, carbon and sulphur in glassy rims of submarine pillow basalts. *Geochim. Cosmochim. Acta* **42**, 581–594.

DELOULE E., ALBAREDE F. and SHEPPARD S. M. F. (1991) Hydrogen isotope heterogeneities in the mantle from ion probe analysis of amphiboles from ultramafic rocks. *Earth Planet. Sci. Lett.* (in press).

DIXON J. E., STOLPER E. and DELANEY J. R. (1988) Infrared spectroscopic measurements of $CO_2$ and $H_2O$ in Juan de Fuca Ridge basaltic glasses. *Earth Planet. Sci. Lett.* **90**, 87–104.

DUPRÉ B. and ALLÈGRE C. J. (1983) Pb-Sr isotope variation in Indian ocean basalts and mixing phenomena. *Nature* **303**, 142–146.

FINE G. and STOLPER E. (1986) Carbon dioxide in basaltic glasses: concentrations and speciation. *Earth Planet. Sci. Lett.* **76**, 263–278.

HAMILTON D. C., BURNHAM C. W. and OSBORN E. F. (1964) The solubility of water and effects of oxygen fugacity and water content on crystallization in mafic magmas. *J. Petrol.* **5**, 21–29.

HART S. R. (1988) Heterogeneous mantle domains: signatures, genesis and mixing chronologies. *Earth Planet. Sci. Lett.* **90**, 273–296.

HEATON T. H. E. and SHEPPARD S. M. F. (1977) Hydrogen and oxygen isotope evidence for seawater hydrothermal alteration and ore deposition, Troodos Complex, Cyprus. In *Volcanic Processes in Ore Genesis; Geol. Soc. Lond. Spec. Paper 7*, pp. 42–57.

HEKINIAN R. and FOUQUET Y. (1985) Volcanism and metallogenesis of axial and off axial structures on the East Pacific Rise near 13°N. *Econ. Geol.* **80**, 221–249.

HUNTEN D. M. and DONAHUE T. M. (1976) Hydrogen loss from the terrestrial planets. *Ann. Rev. Earth Planet. Sci.* **4**, 265–293.

ITO E., WHITE W. M. and GOPEL C. (1987) The O, Sr, Nd and Pb isotope geochemistry of MORB. *Chem. Geol.* **62**, 157–176.

JAVOY M. (1980) $^{18}O/^{16}O$ and D/H ratios in high temperature peridotites. In *Basic Ultramafic Association in Orogenic Belts; Intl. Collq. C. N. R. S. 272*, pp. 279–287.

JAVOY M., PINEAU F. and DELORME H. (1986) Carbon and nitrogen isotopes in the mantle. *Chem. Geol.* **57**, 41–62.

KURODA Y., SUZUOKI T. and MATSUO S. (1977) Hydrogen isotope composition of deep seated water *Contrib. Mineral. Petrol.* **60**, 311–315.

KYSER T. K. (1986): Stable isotopes variations in the mantle. In *Stable Isotopes in High Temperature Geological Processes* (eds. J. W. VALLEY, H. P. TAYLOR and J. R. O'NEIL); *Rev. in Mineral.* **16**, pp. 141–164. Mineralogical Society of America.

KYSER T. K. and O'NEIL J. R. (1984) Hydrogen isotope systematics of submarine basalts. *Geochim. Cosmochim. Acta* **48**, 2123–2133.

KYSER T. K., O'NEIL J. R. and CARMICHAEL S. E. (1982) Genetic relations among basic lavas and ultramafic nodules: evidence from oxygen isotope compositions. *Contrib. Mineral. Petrol.* **81**, 88–102.

LALOU C., BRICHET E. and HEKINIAN R. (1985) Age dating of sulfide deposits from axial and off axial structures on the EPR near 12°50'N. *Earth Planet. Sci. Lett.* **75**, 59–71.

MACCREA J. M. (1950) On the isotopic chemistry of carbonates and a paleotemperature scale. *J. Chem. Phys.* **18**, 849–857.

MACCULLOCH M. T., GREGORY R. T., WASSERBURG G. J. and TAYLOR H. P. JR. (1981) Sm-Nd, Rb-Sr and $^{18}O/^{16}O$ isotopic systematics in an oceanic crustal section: evidence from the Samail ophiolite. *J. Geophys. Res.* **86**, 2721–2735.

MACDOUGALL J. D. and LUGMAIR G. W. (1986) Sr and Nd isotopes in basalts from the East Pacific Rise: significance for mantle heterogeneity. *Earth Planet. Sci. Lett.* **77**, 273–284.

MARTY B. and OZIMA M. (1986) Noble gas distribution in oceanic basalt glasses. *Geochim. Cosmochim. Acta* **50**, 1093–1097.

MATHEZ E. A. (1976) Sulfur solubility and magmatic sulfides in submarine basalt glass. *J. Geophys. Res.* **81**, 4269–4276.

MATTEY D. P. (1987) Carbon isotopes in the mantle. *Terra Cognita* **7**, 31–37.

MATTEY D. P., CARR R. H., WRIGHT I. P. and PILLINGER C. T. (1984) Carbon isotopes in submarine basalts. *Earth Planet. Sci. Lett.* **70**, 196–206.

MICHARD A., GURNET P., SOUDANT M. and ALBARÈDE F. (1985) Nd isotopes in French Phanerozoic shales: external versus internal aspects of crustal evolution. *Geochim. Cosmochim. Acta* **49**, 601–610.

O'NEIL J. R., CLAYTON R. N. and MAYEDA T. K. (1969) Oxygen isotope fractionation in divalent metal carbonates. *J. Chem. Phys.* **51**, 5547–5558.

PIEPGRAS D. S. and WASSERBURG G. J. (1982) Isotopic composition of neodymium in waters from the Drake Passage. *Science* **217**, 207–214.

PINEAU F. and JAVOY M. (1983) Carbon isotopes and concentrations in mid-oceanic ridge basalts. *Earth Planet. Sci. Lett.* **62**, 239–257.

PINEAU F., JAVOY M. and BOTTINGA Y. (1976) $^{13}C/^{12}C$ ratios of rocks and inclusions in popping rocks of the mid-Atlantic ridge and their bearing on the problem of the isotopic composition of deep-seated carbon. *Earth Planet. Sci. Lett.* **29**, 413–421.

POREDA R., SCHILLING J-G. and CRAIG H. (1986) Helium and hydrogen isotopes in ocean-ridge basalts north and south of Iceland. *Earth Planet. Sci. Lett.* **78**, 1–17.

PRINZHOFER A., LEWIN E. and ALLÈGRE C. J. (1989) Stochastic melting of the marble cake mantle: evidence from local study of the East Pacific Rise at 12°50'N. *Earth Planet. Sci. Lett.* **92**, 189–206.

SAKAI H., CASADEVALL T. J. and MOORE J. G. (1982) Chemistry and isotopic ratios of sulfur in basalts and volcanic gases at Kilauea volcano, Hawaii. *Geochim. Cosmochim. Acta* **46**, 729–738.

SAKAI H., DES MARAIS D. J., UEDA A. and MOORE J. G. (1984) Concentrations and isotope ratios of carbon, nitrogen and sulfur in ocean floor basalts. *Geochim. Cosmochim. Acta* **48**, 2433–2441.

SARDA P., STAUDACHER T. and ALLÈGRE C. J. (1985) $^{40}Ar/^{36}Ar$ in MORB glasses: constraints on atmosphere and mantle evolution. *Earth Planet. Sci. Lett.* **72,** 357–375.

SHEPPARD S. M. F. (1980) Isotopic evidence for the origins of water during metamorphic processes in oceanic crust and ophiolite complexes. In *Basic Ultramafic Association in Orogenic Belts; Intl. Collq. C. N. R. S. 272,* pp. 135–147.

SHEPPARD S. M. F. and DAWSON J. B. (1975) Hydrogen, carbon and oxygen isotope studies of megacryst and matrix minerals from Lesotho and South African kimberlites. In *Physics and Chemistry of the Earth* (eds. L. H. AHRENS *et al.*), Vol 9, pp. 743–763. Pergamon Press.

SHEPPARD S. M. F. and EPSTEIN S. (1970) D/H and $^{18}O/^{16}O$ ratios of minerals of possible mantle or lower crustal origin. *Earth Planet. Sci. Lett.* **9,** 232–239.

SHEPPARD S. M. F., BROWN P. E. and CHAMBERS A. D. (1977) The Lilloise intrusion, East Greenland: hydrogen isotope evidence for the efflux of magmatic water into the contact metamorphic aureole. *Contrib. Mineral. Petrol.* **63,** 129–147.

STAUDACHER T. and ALLÈGRE C. J. (1988) Recycling of oceanic crust and sediments: the noble gas subduction barrier. *Earth Planet. Sci. Lett.* **89,** 173–183.

SUZUOKI T. and EPSTEIN S. (1976) Hydrogen isotope fractionation between OH-bearing minerals and water. *Geochim. Cosmochim. Acta* **40,** 1229–1240.

TAYLOR B. E. (1986) Magmatic volatiles: isotopic variation of C, H, and S. In *Stable Isotopes in High Temperature Geological Processes* (eds. J. W. VALLEY, H. P. TAYLOR and J. R. O'NEIL); *Rev. in Mineral. 16,* pp. 185–225. Mineralogical Society of America.

TAYLOR H. P., JR. (1977) Water/rock interaction and the origin of $H_2O$ in granitic batholiths. *J. Geol. Soc. London* **133,** 509–558.

TAYLOR H. P., JR. (1980) Stable isotope studies of spreading centers and their bearing on the origin of granophyres and plagiogranites. In *Basic Ultramafic Associations in Orogenic Belts; Intl. Collq. C. N. R. S. 272,* pp. 149–165.

TAYLOR H. P., JR. and SHEPPARD S. M. F. (1986) Igneous rocks: I. Processes of isotopic fractionation and isotope systematics. In *Stable Isotopes in High Temperature Geological Processes* (eds. J. W. VALLEY, H. P. TAYLOR and J. R. O'NEIL); *Rev. in Mineral. 16,* pp. 227–271. Mineralogical Society of America.

THODE H. G., MONSTER J. and DUNFORD H. B. (1961) Sulfur isotope geochemistry. *Geochim. Cosmochim. Acta* **25,** 159–174.

UEDA A. and SAKAI H. (1983) Simultaneous determination of the concentration and isotope ratio of sulfate and sulfide sulfur and carbonate carbon in geological samples. *Geochem. J.* **17,** 185–196.

YANG J. and EPSTEIN S. (1983) Interstellar organic matter in meteorites. *Geochim. Cosmochim. Acta* **47,** 2199–2216.

ZINDLER A., STAUDIGEL H. and BATIZA R. (1984) Isotope and trace element geochemistry of young Pacific seamounts: implication for the scale of upper mantle heterogeneity. *Earth Planet. Sci. Lett.* **70,** 175–195.

Stable Isotope Geochemistry: A Tribute to Samuel Epstein
© The Geochemical Society, Special Publication No. 3, 1991
Editors: H. P. Taylor, Jr., J. R. O'Neil and I. R. Kaplan

# Degassing of Obsidian Dome rhyolite, Inyo volcanic chain, California

BRUCE E. TAYLOR

Geological Survey of Canada, 601 Booth Street, Ottawa, Ontario, Canada K1A 0E8

**Abstract**—Research drilling of Obsidian Dome and a nearby feeder dike in Inyo volcanic chain, California, has provided a set of samples that gives us an opportunity to characterize the isotopic signature of rhyolite magma degassing in several near-surface igneous environments. A positive correlation between $\delta D$ and wt.% $H_2O$ is observed for $H_2O$-rich obsidian clasts from tephra deposits and $H_2O$-poor samples of the flow erupted from Obsidian Dome; these samples record progressive degassing of the magma. The initial water content and $\delta D$ of the magma are estimated to be, respectively, 4.1 wt.% $H_2O$ (based on analyses of melt inclusions, HERVIG et al., 1989) and $-40$ (assuming closed-system degassing prior to the first eruption). Subsequent to the first eruption, variations in $\delta D$ and wt.% $H_2O$ indicate that degassing became effectively more open-system in character as multiple stages of dominantly closed-system degassing were periodically interrupted by removal of water and melt during successive tephra eruptions. Quantitative modelling of the isotopic effects of vapor loss, including fractionation of hydrogen involving the melt species OH and $H_2O$, according to a multi-step scheme, reproduces the observed $\delta D$ vs. wt.% $H_2O$ trend of the obsidian data. Final-stage, dominantly open-system degassing resulted in $\delta D$ values of the obsidian flow as low as $-120$.

Crystallization (devitrification) of the vitreous dome flow and conduit magma yielded no large differences in $\delta D$ and $\delta^{18}O$ relative to flow obsidian. Water-loss upon crystallization was virtually complete, except for that retained in biotite, and thus no degassing signature was recorded. Low-Ba and high-Ba varieties of rhyolite (VOGEL et al., 1989) have similar $\delta^{18}O$ values, but a larger variation in $\delta D$ is found for the low-Ba rhyolite. Crystalline rhyolite and, in particular, the glassy margin of the feeder dike record interaction with hydrothermal meteoric waters, as does the hydrogen isotopic composition of basement granitic rocks. Glassy pyroclasts from tephra-filled, sub-horizontal fractures suggest only minor interaction with meteoric water, and much of the hydrothermal alteration probably occurred after emplacement of the dike.

## INTRODUCTION

SEVERAL RECENT FIELD and experimental studies have demonstrated that exsolution of water from vapor-saturated rhyolite magma results in a change in the D/H ratio of the silicate liquid. Obsidian fragments in tephra units, and glassy zones in subsequent dome-building flows, represent quenched melt from which the degassing history of the magma may be surmised. Isotopic studies by TAYLOR et al. (1983) first suggested that obsidian flows from the Inyo volcanic chain and from Medicine Lake Highlands with $\delta D$ values as low as $-130$ were the products of open-system magmatic degassing of $H_2O$. NEWMAN et al. (1988) refined this model to include the effects of $H_2O$-OH speciation on bulk melt-$H_2O$ hydrogen isotope fractionation during degassing. Experimental determination of deuterium partitioning between $H_2O$ and hydrous rhyolite melts (TAYLOR and WESTRICH, 1985; DOBSON et al., 1989) permits us to construct quantitative models of the degassing of such rhyolite magmatic systems.

A Department of Energy–funded drilling program at Obsidian Dome in the Inyo volcanic chain, California (EICHELBERGER et al., 1984, 1985; Fig. 1) provides a unique opportunity to sample a young, 600–525 year-old (MILLER, 1985) rhyolitic flow, its

conduit and near-by feeder dike, and its wallrocks. I report here hydrogen and oxygen isotope data for glassy and crystalline samples collected from these drill holes, and for obsidian and pumice clasts from two sections through related tephra deposits. I use these data to constrain a degassing model for the Obsidian Dome magma which includes both first-boiling (i.e., depressurization-driven degassing) and second-boiling (i.e., crystallization-driven degassing) phenomena. The proposed degassing scenario for Obsidian Dome magma more accurately describes observed isotopic changes than do previous models. In this model, first-boiling is a multi-step degassing process that evolves from an essentially closed-system to an open-system during tephra eruption and doming.

## GEOLOGICAL AND PETROLOGICAL BACKGROUND

Obsidian Dome represents one of seven centers in the 11-km long Inyo volcanic chain from which rhyolite to rhyodacite tephra and lava flows erupted 650–550 years ago (MILLER, 1985; SAMPSON, 1987; Fig. 1). The eruptions are from a dike intrusion localized along one of several en echelon north-northeast-trending fractures (FINK, 1985) within a major north-south trending fracture zone (MILLER,

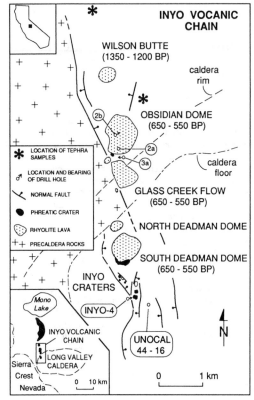

FIG. 1. Location map showing location of drill holes (RDO-) 2a, 2b, and 3a through and adjacent to Obsidian Dome in the Inyo volcanic chain (modified after EICHELBERGER et al., 1988; SUEMNICHT and VARGA, 1988; MILLER, 1985). Locations of two sampled sections of Obsidian Dome tephra are also indicated (C. D. MILLER, pers. comm.).

1985). FINK (1985) interprets the location of the vents and orientation of the local fracture geometry to reflect near-surface rotation of segments of the dike. SUEMNICHT and VARGA (1988) suggest that the vent locations were controlled by the intersection of regional fault trends, both within and northwest of Long Valley caldera. Numerous explosion craters, including Inyo Craters within the caldera (Fig. 1), formed in places along the N–S fracture zone above the dike. This occurred after explosive eruption of tephra from the vents, but prior to emplacement of the lava domes (MILLER, 1985; MASTIN and POLLARD, 1988; EICHELBERGER et al., 1988).

Petrologic and petrochemical studies, including those by BAILEY et al. (1976, 1983), SAMPSON (1987), SAMPSON and CAMERON (1987), and VOGEL et al. (1989) recognize two chemically distinct types of rhyolitic lava: (1) a finely-porphyritic variety (ca. 70–74 wt.% $SiO_2$), which comprises Obsidian

Dome, and (2) a coarsely porphyritic rhyolite found intermingled with the finely porphyritic rhyolite in the Glass Creek flow and at South Deadman Dome. The finely and coarsely porphyritic rhyolites appear to be derived from separate magma chambers (SAMPSON and CAMERON, 1987; HIGGINS, 1988; VOGEL et al., 1989). The finely porphyritic rhyolite of Obsidian Dome can be further classified as a high-$SiO_2$ (73.40 ± 0.22 wt.%), low-Ba (<475 ppm) variety and a low-$SiO_2$ (71.48 ± 0.90), high-Ba (>475 ppm) variety (VOGEL et al., 1989). The low-Ba variety occupies the lower portion of the dome and outer part of the conduit, whereas the high-Ba variety occurs in the center of the conduit and in the upper portion of the dome (VOGEL et al., 1989). The high-Ba rhyolite constituted was the last magma to be emplaced.

Various kinds of evidence suggest a complex thermal and degassing history for Obsidian Dome magma. Estimates of crystallization temperature based on Fe-Ti oxides in rhyolite from the conduit margin and center (hole RDO-2b; VOGEL et al., 1989) are similar (912 to 927°C), whether for quickly cooled conduit margins, or for the more slowly cooled conduit interior; these must therefore represent pre-eruption temperatures which were effectively quenched. Higher temperatures are estimated utilizing the phase equilibria for the observed mineral assemblages, and combined with the measured water contents of the glasses (SWANSON et al., 1989). SWANSON et al. (1989) suggest that the quenching of Fe-Ti oxide equilibria was the result of vapor loss from the magma (i.e., constitutional supercooling) rather than thermal undercooling. The Fe-Ti oxide temperatures are, however, higher than the 600°C formation temperature suggested by STOLPER (1989) for the conduit margins at Mono Craters (Fig. 1) based on IR-measured $H_2O/OH$ ratios in obsidian tephra clasts. NEWMAN et al. (1988) and STOLPER (1989) suggest that, in fact, the obsidian clasts found in tephra represent rapidly-cooled melt (to ca. 600°C) originating at glassy dike margins, but subsequently eroded during eruption.

The initial water content, initial δD value, and pressure of the Obsidian Dome magma are required to formulate a quantitative degassing model using hydrogen isotope and water contents of obsidian. HERVIG et al. (1989) found a mean value of 4.1 ± 1.2 wt.% $H_2O$ in glass inclusions in feldspar phenocrysts from tephra, in marked contrast to the 0.4 to 1.5 wt.% $H_2O$ in matrix glass. The higher water content is in general agreement with the presence of hornblende, which indicates >4.0 wt.% $H_2O$ at a vapor-saturated pressure of 200 MPa (NANEY, 1983); this compares with the minimum water content of 2.04 wt.% estimated for nearby Glass Creek rhyolite (TAYLOR *et al.,* 1983). Two inclusions in biotite analyzed by HERVIG *et al.* (1989) give lower values (1.0 and 1.3 wt.%), indicating lower pressure crystallization, and/or that interface kinetics may result in non-representative water contents in the glass inclusions.

The degassing of rhyolitic magma may be considered in terms of two end-member processes: single or multi-step closed-system (batch equilibrium) degassing on the one hand, and open-system (equilibrium or Rayleigh) degassing on the other. The complete degassing process may involve aspects of both processes. At magmatic temperatures, the magnitude and sign of the $H_2O$-melt hydrogen isotope factionation factor are sufficient to cause distinctly different $\delta D$ signatures for open-system and closed-system degassing. Thus, there should be a correlation between the style of volcanism and the nature of the degassing process, as indicated by its isotopic signature.

## SAMPLE SELECTION AND ANALYTICAL PROCEDURES

Samples were analyzed from both extrusive tephra and dome deposits, and from intrusive glass, partially vesicular glass, pumice, crystalline rhyolite, and wall rocks sampled by drill core. Comparison of results for rhyolite of varying texture and depths with those for tephra from both distal and proximal sections (Fig. 1) permits investigation of the effect of degassing during first- and second-boiling in three different magmatic environments. The extrusive tephra and dome flow and the intrusive rhyolite conduit and feeder dike are generally similar in chemical composition (except for distinction of the low- and high-Ba members; C. D. MILLER, pers. comm.; VOGEL *et al.,* 1989). All of these are believed to have originated from the same, or a closely related, magma system.

### Tephra

Obsidian and pumice clasts were analyzed from a proximal, *ca.* 1.5 m-thick, 7-layer section, and from a distal, 85 cm-thick, 5-layer section of tephra erupted from Obsidian Dome (C. D. MILLER, pers. comm.; see locations in Fig. 1). Obsidian clasts are generally dark gray, with frosted exteriors and slightly rounded edges, are typically <1 cm in diameter, and comprise less than about 25% of each sample. Pumice and lithic fragments make up the rest. The least vesicular obsidian clasts were selected for analysis. Several clasts of associated pumice >1 cm in diameter were also selected for analysis.

### Dome flow, intrusive rhyolite, and wall rocks

Three drill holes (RDO-2a, -2b, and -3a; Fig. 1) cored different portions of the dome and conduit complex. Hole RDO-2a (Fig. 2) cored the distal portion of the Obsidian Dome flow, hole RDO-2b the proximal portion of the flow, and hole RDO-3a, immediately south of the dome, cored a dike not exposed at the surface. This dike is in-

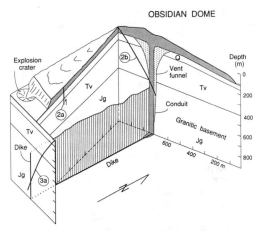

FIG. 2. Block diagram of Obsidian Dome showing location of the distal drill hole (RDO-) 2a, through the dome flow; proximal hole 2b, through the near-vent flow and flow conduit; and dike hole 3a, which intersects the feeder dike just south of the dome. Abbreviations are: Jg, Jurassic granitic rocks (basement); Tv, Tertiary basalt and rhyolite, and fluvial sediments; and Q, Quaternary gravels (modified after WESTRICH *et al.,* 1988).

terpreted to be part of the feeder dike which supplied magma to the Obsidian Dome conduit.

In the drill core samples RDO-2a and -2b, the uppermost part of the flow is characterized by finely vesicular pumice, underlain by coarsely vesicular glass, an obsidian zone (only in hole RDO-2a), a zone of devitrified, crystalline rhyolite, and (only in hole RDO-2a) a lower zone of obsidian. A breccia zone is intersected in each hole at the base of the flow. Hole RDO-2b also penetrated the crystalline rhyolite of the conduit beneath the dome; this material has a microporphyritic texture (SWANSON *et al.,* 1989).

To the south, the intrusive rhyolite dike of hole RDO-3a is generally similar to the conduit rhyolite, except for a water-rich glassy margin along one wall. Other distinctive samples of glass are from the drill core fragments of glass comprising "intrusive pyroclasts" (HEIKEN *et al.,* 1988). These samples, together with the water-rich glassy margin of the dike, are particularly important in interpreting the origin of the obsidian and in understanding the isotopic variations.

Several samples of flow basalt and pre-caldera basement (Jurassic quartz monzonite) were obtained from core of holes RDO-2b and -3a.

### Sample preparation and isotopic analysis

Samples from drill core were generally prepared in one of two ways: either by washing of ground material (to −100 mesh) with distilled $H_2O$ and "high purity" acetone, or ultrasonically rinsing alternately with distilled water and dilute HCl. Tephra clasts were ultrasonically washed in dilute HCl and acetic acid, followed by rinsing in distilled water and acetone. Obsidian selected from splits of tephra samples was washed in distilled $H_2O$. Fresh glass was hand-picked from individual, coarsely crushed clasts in order to exclude any exterior surfaces. Pumice was treated similarly, and interior portions of clasts were hand-picked for analysis. Obsidian and pumice were also analyzed from samples collected from the dome flow. Crystalline grano-diorite was coarsely crushed and a pulverized sample prepared from washed interior ("fresh"-sided) fragments.

Hydrogen isotope extraction procedures used were similar to those described in TAYLOR *et al.* (1983), except that all samples described in this paper were, upon conversion to $H_2$, Toepler-pumped into a 12″ length of 3/8″ O.D. pyrex tubing, and sealed with a torch for later mass spectrometric analysis. No leakage from the stored tubes was detected. Data are reported in the usual δ-notation relative to V-SMOW, and duplicate analyses indicate an uncertainty of the average δD values of replicate analyses in the same laboratory on the order of 1.0 per mil. Data were collected at the Geological Survey of Canada (Ottawa) and at the U.S. Geological Survey (Menlo Park, California).

Water contents determined by $H_2$ manometry are precise to better than 5% of the reported values. The total water contents determined by $H_2$ manometry reported here can be as much as 0.1 wt.% larger than water contents determined by Karl Fischer titration (WESTRICH, 1987; WESTRICH *et al.*, 1988), for samples containing less than 0.6 wt.% $H_2O$. Oxygen isotope extraction was accomplished using $ClF_3$, and followed procedures noted in TAYLOR *et al.* (1983). The average difference in $δ^{18}O$ of 12 replicate analyses of rhyolite was 0.17 per mil; a mean δ-value of +9.6 was measured for NBS-28.

## RESULTS

### Tephra

As shown in Fig. 6 virtually bubble-free obsidian clasts in tephra contain 0.51 to 1.27 wt.% $H_2O$ and δD = −82 to −57 in the distal section, and 0.42 to 1.21 wt.% $H_2O$ and δD = −61 to −88 in the proximal section. Pumice clasts vary from 0.30 to 1.88 wt.% $H_2O$ and in δD from −115 to −80 in the distal section, whereas pumice in the proximal section has from 0.54 to 1.16 (one clast has 2.22) wt.% $H_2O$ and δD values of −124 to −96. Although pumice can alter readily owing to its high surface area, the glass comprising most of these young pumice clasts is not extensively hydrated by secondary water, owing to the very recent age of eruption and to the relatively arid climate.

### Dome flow

Two outcrop samples of obsidian from the distal edge of the Obsidian Dome have water contents and δD values of 0.19 and 0.14, and −89 and −104, respectively. These are similar to other bubble-free glasses from the distal drill hole RDO-2a, which contain 0.07 to 0.23 wt.% $H_2O$, and δD values of −104 to −114. Except for one sample with 0.13 wt.% $H_2O$, obsidian from the proximal hole RDO-2b exhibits much higher water contents, 0.50 to 0.93, and a slightly lower range of δD values, −95 to −122. Coarsely vesicular glass and pumiceous samples in the proximal portion of the flow have

similar ranges of δD as the obsidian, but occasionally slightly higher water contents (to 0.93). In comparison to pumice from the tephra sections, pumiceous samples from the dome flow have the lowest water contents and most negative δD values of any of the tephra samples. The basal breccia zone contains welded glass with δD of −92 to −94 and 0.34 to 0.49 wt.% $H_2O$ (Fig. 3).

Crystalline rhyolite in the lower portion of the flow in both distal and proximal portions (Fig. 3) has 0.07 to 0.34 wt.% $H_2O$, similar to the associated flow obsidian which contains ≤0.6 wt.% $H_2O$ (most samples have ≤0.40 wt.%). The δD of the rhyolite (−113 to −119) is also broadly similar to that of the obsidian. Water in the crystalline rhyolites is primarily sequestered in biotite. The data for both the glassy and the crystalline rocks are plotted for comparison in Fig. 4.

The above-described data are plotted in Fig. 5 and indicate the following: (1) slightly lower δD values of obsidian occur higher in the flow; (2) the δD values of the two analyzed pumice samples span the entire range exhibited by all of the other samples; (3) crystalline rhyolite from the lower portion of the flow has a comparatively uniform δD, distinctly lower than the obsidian; (4) glassy samples exhibit a larger range and extend to much higher values of δD than the crystalline rhyolite; and (5) rhyolite samples have a lower mean δD value (−118) than do the samples of obsidian (−107; including two samples from the edge of the flow not plotted in

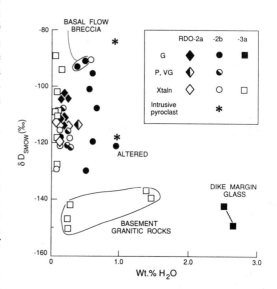

FIG. 3. Plot of δD vs. wt.% $H_2O$ for whole-rock samples of crystal-line (Xtaln) rhyolite, granitic basement rocks, vitreous rhyolite (G, obsidian; VG, coarsely vesicular glass; and P, pumice), and glass from tuff-breccia dikes (∗).

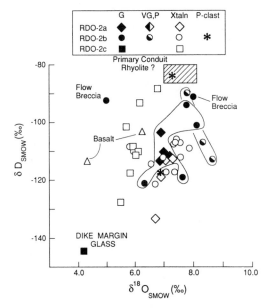

FIG. 4. Plot of δD vs. δ¹⁸O for whole-rock samples of obsidian (G), coarsely vesicular glass (VG), pumice (P), and crystalline rhyolite (Xtaln). The compositions of two glass fragments from tuff-breccia dikes (∗) are shown for comparison. The field of "primary rhyolite" represents the approximate composition of the Obsidian Dome rhyolite degassed to a pressure equivalent to about 400–600 m depth.

slightly lower than those measured for obsidian (see Fig. 4).

### Glassy dike margin and intrusive pyroclasts

Two samples of gray, finely porphyritic glass with a waxy luster were analyzed from "tuff breccia dikes" intersected by hole RDO-3a at vertical depths of approximately 329 and 413 m, giving, respectively, δD values of −85 and −119. The dikes and their tuffaceous contents are described by HEIKEN et al. (1988). The water contents of the obsidian (0.92 and 0.97 wt.% $H_2O$) are close to those expected for equilibrium (see also WESTRICH et al., 1988). The higher δD value in the shallower samples is consistent with open system degassing as discussed below, and is consistent with a near primary composition, whereas the lower δ-value clearly suggests interaction with meteoric water.

Analyses of glass from the margin of the dike intersected in RDO-3a at ca. 650 m vertical depth yielded variable water contents dependent upon the length of time of high-vacuum degassing in our laboratories at 150–200°C, prior to water extraction. For example, after ca. four hrs. degassing at 150°C the total water content was as high as 2.65 wt.% (O'NEIL and TAYLOR, 1985). Other experiments showed that up to 2.6 wt.% (B. TAYLOR, unpubl. data) of water can be released during such pretreat-

Fig. 5). In addition, obsidian from the distal part of the flow (hole RDO-2a) has a smaller range of δD than the near-vent obsidian (hole RDO-2b).

Oxygen isotope compositions of the proximal flow are similar to those reported previously for the Glass Creek flow (TAYLOR et al., 1983), with δ¹⁸O of 6.3 to 8.1 for obsidian and 7.9 to 8.7 for coarsely vesicular glass and pumice. Most crystallized rhyolite and glass from the basal breccia zone typically have δ¹⁸O values of 6.0 to 8.0, although rare samples are as low as 5.0.

### Intrusive rhyolite of the conduit and feeder dike

Microcrystalline rhyolite in the conduit, at an approximate vertical depth of 410 to 490 m, contains 0.08 to 0.39 wt.% $H_2O$, which is considerably less than the equilibrium values (of the order of 1.2 to 1.4 wt.% $H_2O$) expected for confining pressures on vapor-saturated rhyolite magma at this depth (cf. WESTRICH et al., 1988). The δD values of the conduit rhyolites vary from −128 to −89, similar to the dome flow, whereas the δ¹⁸O values of the rhyolite (6.5 to 7.9) and, especially, of the conduit-margin breccia (4.3 to 6.0; not plotted in Fig. 4) are

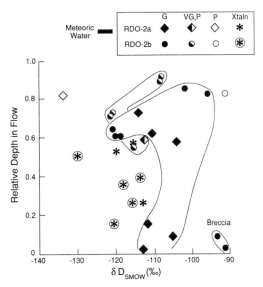

FIG. 5. Plot of δD vs. relative position in the dome flow for the principal textural varieties of rhyolite (G, obsidian; VG, coarsely vesicular glass; P, pumiceous; and Xtaln, crystalline). The composition of local meteoric water (from Glass Creek; TAYLOR et al., 1983) is plotted for comparison.

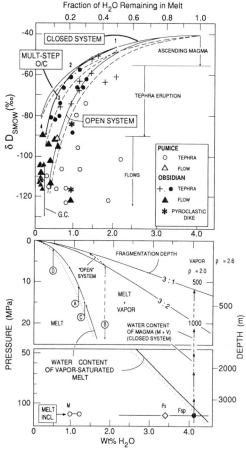

FIG. 6. Plot of δD (top) and pressure (bottom) versus water content of rhyolite melt, illustrating hydrogen isotope fractionations and variations in water content of melt during magma ascent, Plinian eruption of tephra, and emplacement of dome flows under open and closed systems. Data are plotted for obsidian and pumice from both tephra and dome flows. Hydrogen isotope fractionation models were calculated for: (1) an initial water content of 4.1 wt.%, based on analyses of glass (melt) inclusions in feldspar (HERVIG et al., 1989; mean values are plotted for inclusions in feldspar (Fsp), and individual analyses of glass inclusions in pyroxene (Px), and biotite (M)); (2) a $H_2O/OH$ distribution for dissolved water based on quick-quench experiments in SILVER et al. (1990); and (3) $H_2O$-melt fractionation factors from DOBSON et al. (1989; dashed lines) and as discussed in the text (solid lines). The initial δD of the magma is assumed to be −40 (see text). Solubility curves (solid curves, lower two portions of the diagram) are based on BURNHAM (1979), at 950°C, and on quick-quench experiments of SILVER et al. (1990) at 850°C, and equivalent depths are indicated for melt densities of 2.6 and 2.0. Point (A) represents the highest water content of tephra obsidian reported by WESTRICH et al. (1988), and point (C) the most water-rich tephra obsidian in this study. Point (B) is the water content of the melt upon eruption (fragmentation) of a closed-system magma (see text) with initial water content of 4.1 wt.%, and point (D) is the approximate low-water limit of melt erupted as tephra. Curves in the melt + vapor field are drawn for bubble:

ment at 150 to 200°C; this is more than usually retained by surface adsorption (cf. WESTRICH, 1987). Water contents of 1.48–1.58 wt.% were determined after extended (12–14 hrs.) high-vacuum pretreatment at 150–200°C, and these are interpreted to represent the primary water content of the glass. These values are close to a probable equilibrium value for the depth of sampling.

A low δD value of −148 and a $\delta^{18}O$ value of 4.2 were reported for the water-rich glass by O'NEIL and TAYLOR (1985). These data indicate high-temperature contamination of the glassy dike margin by meteoric water.

### Wall rocks and basement

A basalt flow and breccia, and granitic rocks, also brecciated where near the margin of the conduit have δD values of −104 to −151, presumably reflect some hydrothermal alteration. Whereas the $\delta^{18}O$ of the basalt (6.2) has not been greatly affected by any hydrothermal alteration, the granitic rocks have $\delta^{18}O$ values of 6.7–7.3, slightly lower than most other orogenic granites (TAYLOR and SHEPPARD, 1986), and also possibly indicative of minor isotopic exchange with meteoric waters.

### DISCUSSION

*First boiling: magmatic degassing during tephra eruption and dome emplacement*

The positive correlation found between δD and total water content for obsidian from Obsidian Dome's tephra and flow units (Fig. 6) is broadly similar to that found for the Glass Creek tephra and dome rhyolite by TAYLOR et al. (1983) and for the tephra and dome obsidian from Mono Craters (NEWMAN et al., 1988). A general characteristic of rhyolitic Plinian eruptions appears to be a general decrease in both the average value and the range of wt.% $H_2O$ in obsidian fragments with increasing stratigraphic height in tephra sequences (e.g., Medicine Lake Highlands: Fig. 2 in TAYLOR et al., 1983; Mono Craters: NEWMAN et al., 1988). The magnitude of the variation in water content of obsidian clasts is broadly similar in both the distal and prox-

melt ratios of 3:2 and 3:1 (fragmentation) based on EICHELBERGER et al. (1986) and SPARKS (1978). The "open" system curve illustrates the decrease in water content of vapor-saturated magma (i.e., bubbles + melt) upon diffusive loss of water from a magmatic foam. Date for tephra obsidians from the near-by eruption site of the Glass Creek flow (crosses (+); TAYLOR et al., 1983) are shown for comparison.

imal sections of Obsidian Dome tephra. A marked bottom-to-top variation in total water content is not apparent, but the sample population is probably too small at this stage to characterize any stratigraphic trend. As found in other studies, the tephra obsidian clasts contain up to ten times more water than the obsidian in the subsequently erupted Obsidian Dome flow. Inasmuch as equilibration of magma at successively lower pressures (*i.e.*, at shallower depths) can explain the decrease in water content of the obsidian with progress of eruption (EICHELBERGER and WESTRICH, 1981; EICHELBERGER *et al.*, 1986; WESTRICH *et al.*, 1988), I will presume that the variations in wt.% $H_2O$ (and also $\delta D$) reflect a common degassing process, and proceed by comparison of the measured $\delta D$ *vs.* wt.% $H_2O$ relationship for the Obsidian Dome tephra with calculated degassing trends.

Figure 6 compares $\delta D$ and water content data for obsidian from tephra clasts, dome flow, and tephra dikes to several calculated degassing trends, in conjunction with pressure-solubility relationships (calculated and experimental) for a rhyolite melt at 850°C. In addition, the water content of the melt is shown as a function of pressure for two bubble: melt volume ratios: 3:2 and 3:1. The 75% bubble volume represents the bubble content beyond which the melt would fragment and erupt, although SPARKS (1978) suggests that bubbles could comprise as much as 83 vol.% before eruption. In any case, three principal stages of magmatism can be described using with the water content and $\delta D$ data: ascent of a magma to the point of rupture, Plinian eruptions producing tephra, and quiescent dome emplacement. The boundaries for each are approximate and correspond to the $\delta D$ ranges of the samples analyzed.

A melt with initially 4.1 wt.% $H_2O$ may fragment and erupt from a depth as shallow as perhaps 400 m, when the equilibrium water content of the melt (silicate liquid) is 1.15 wt.% $H_2O$ (*i.e.*, melt with composition of point (A)). Removal of some of the $H_2O$-saturated magma (due to draw-down in the magma column) will result in residual melt with a water content higher than at point (A). Bubble growth in response to depressurization during eruption may lead to additional degassing of entrained melt (SPARKS, 1978). Point (B) represents the highest water content (1.8 wt.% $H_2O$) found to date for the Obsidian Dome tephra obsidian (WESTRICH *et al.*, 1988). Point (C) represents the water content of the most water-rich obsidian (1.21%; proximal section) analyzed in this study.

NEWMAN *et al.* (1988) demonstrated the marked effect of varying hydrogen speciation on the bulk

$H_2O$-melt hydrogen isotope fractionation factor. Accurate modelling of the isotopic effect of water loss from a rhyolitic melt requires the hydrogen isotope fractionation factors between the exsolved $H_2O$ and the hydrogen species dissolved in the melt (*i.e.*, OH and $H_2O$). DOBSON *et al.* (1989) determined the $H_2O$-($OH_{melt}$) fractionation factor ($\alpha = 1.0415$) by equilibration between water and rhyolite at low pressures, for which OH is virtually the sole species (STOLPER, 1982; SILVER *et al.*, 1990). The bulk fractionation between $H_2O$ gas and coexisting melt can be expressed as follows:

$$1000 \ln \alpha_{(H_2O\text{-melt})} = X_{H_2O}10^3 \ln \alpha_{H_2O\text{-}(H_2O_{melt})}$$
$$+ (1 - X)_{OH} \ln \alpha_{H_2O\text{-}(OH_{melt})} \quad (1)$$

where $X$ and $1 - X$ are, respectively, the atom fractions of hydrogen present in the melt as $H_2O$ and as OH.

In a manner analogous to that of DOBSON *et al.*, I estimate the fractionation factor for $H_2O$-($H_2O_{melt}$) using (1) DOBSON *et al.*'s $H_2O$-($OH_{melt}$) fractionation factor at 750°C ($\alpha = 1.0415$); (2) the relationship between total water content, dissolved $H_2O$, and dissolved OH determined spectroscopically for rapidly quenched rhyolite by SILVER *et al.* (1990); and (3) the preliminary bulk $H_2O$-melt fractionation at 950°C ($\alpha = 1.0239$) for rhyolite melt with 3.1 wt.% $H_2O$ (TAYLOR and WESTRICH, 1985; see TAYLOR, 1986). The estimated value of $\alpha_{H_2O\text{-}(H_2O_{melt})}$ is 0.9896, which is comparable to a value of 1.000 estimated by DOBSON *et al.* (1989). DOBSON *et al.*'s choice of 1.000 avoids the problematical cross-over in the fractionation factor implied by a value of less than 1.000.

The closed-system and open-system degassing trends were each calculated step-wise, for small increments of water loss, by recalculation of the effective vapor-melt fractionation at each step. In this way the continual variation in the bulk $H_2O$-melt fractionation factor was approximated. In terms of the bulk fractionation factor (derived from Eq. 1), the closed-system trend was calculated by

$$\delta D_{final} = \delta D_{initial} - (1 - F) 1000 \ln \alpha_{(H_2O\text{-melt})}. \quad (2)$$

Similarly, the open-system trend was calculated with the step-wise recalculated bulk fractionation using

$$\delta D_{final} = \delta D_{initial} - 1000 (1 - F^{(\alpha(H_2O\text{-melt})-1)}). \quad (3)$$

The mean value of 4.1 wt.% $H_2O$ determined by HERVIG *et al.* (1989) for glass inclusions in plagioclase and potassium feldspar phenocrysts in Obsidian Dome tephra provides the best estimate for the wt.% $H_2O_{initial}$, presuming that this was not elevated beyond the bulk water content of the melt due to rapid growth of the feldspar. The $\delta D_{initial}$ cannot be directly measured, but should be at least as high as the value of $-57$ measured in an obsidian clast with 1.09 wt.% $H_2O$ from the distal section. If the magma is presumed to have approximated a closed system prior to eruption of the first tephra deposit, then $\delta D_{initial}$ was $-40$ (derived from Eq. 2 for $H_2O_{initial}$ = 4.1 wt.%, and $\delta D = -57$ for a melt with 1.0 wt.% $H_2O$). This is a reasonable estimate, since for this same $\delta D_{initial}$ value, both open- and closed-system model $\delta D$ values at 1 wt.% $H_2O$ differ by only 3.1 per mil.

Complete degassing of magma with $\delta D_{initial} = -40$ and $H_2O_{initial}$ = 4.1 wt.% results in $\delta D$ values of ca. $-80$ (closed-system) and $-120$ (open-system; Fig. 6). A marked increase in the bulk $H_2O$-melt fractionation factor accentuates the depletion in deuterium during degassing, calculated for either open- or closed-systems in Fig. 6. The increase in the bulk fractionation factor is primarily due to the rising proportion of OH relative to $H_2O$ in the melt.

Neither the open-system nor the closed-system trend in Fig. 6 exactly mimics the $\delta D$ vs. wt.% $H_2O$ variation of the tephra and flow obsidian. The small difference in values estimated for $\alpha_{H_2O-(H_2O_{melt})}$ by DOBSON et al. (1989) and by the present author does not affect the calculation (as also noted by DOBSON et al., 1989). Thus, none of the open-system scenarios of TAYLOR et al. (1983) and NEWMAN et al. (1988), nor the two-stage, closed- followed by open-system degassing scenarios of NEWMAN et al. (1988) and DOBSON et al. (1989), completely describe the first-boiling process for Obsidian Dome. Rather, the present data seem to require a degassing process that becomes in effect progressively more open from initiation of the tephra eruptions to emplacement of the dome flow.

Open-system behavior via a magma-foam model has been called upon to explain the marked depletion of deuterium in the flow obsidian (TAYLOR et al., 1983; TAYLOR, 1986), as well as to explain the variation in water content of tephra obsidian and the non-explosive emplacement of co-magmatic flows (EICHELBERGER et al., 1986). The shortening of the diffusion path length due to a greater volume of bubbles facilitates gas flow through the melt, which is otherwise severely restricted by the slowness of water diffusion in the melt (SHAW, 1974; SPARKS, 1978; summary in TAYLOR, 1986). EICHELBERGER et al. (1986) measured a marked increase in apparent $N_2$ permeability of pumice with 60 vol.% of bubbles under a pressure differential of 1.2–50 bars, at Earth-surface temperatures. Although not directly applicable to the diffusion of $H_2O$ through rhyolite

melt at 850°C, the pumice measurements demonstrate an increasing permeability with bubble content, analogous to that envisioned to explain vapor loss from a saturated melt during ascent.

The distance $H_2O$ may migrate is limited, even with the foam-diffusion model. EICHELBERGER et al. (1986) show that an exponential increase in degassing time is required with a linear increase in width of the magma conduit (or magma body; cf. SPARKS, 1978). They suggest that significant water loss could have occurred through the Obsidian Dome feeder dike's walls, but that larger magma bodies would tend to behave as closed-systems and erupt more catastrophically. The diffusive loss of water from the magma (melt + vapor) with a total water content given by point (B) is indicated schematically in Fig. 6 by the dashed curve line labeled "Open System." As a consequence, magmas following such a path may more closely approach the surface before erupting than those characterized by large, catastrophic eruptions that follow strictly closed-system degassing. Indeed, a purely open-system magma would obviously not erupt explosively (i.e., would not fragment).

Two facts suggest that the Obsidian Dome magma did not behave as a purely open system: (1) the very existence of multiple tephra beds from the same source, and (2) a $\delta D$ vs. wt.% $H_2O$ trend for the data in Fig. 6 that lies between the end-member open- and closed-system cases. At some point, the magma must have been effectively closed (i.e., the rate of bubble growth exceeded the rate of vapor loss), although the progressively lower $\delta D$ values measured for tephra obsidian and for dome flow obsidian require some "open" character to the degassing process.

A quasi-open degassing process, which I term here "multi-step open/closed," may consist of several closed or nearly closed stages. Each "stage" represents bubble growth during ascent of vapor-saturated magma, and vapor loss at each successive eruption. This is described schematically in Fig. 7(I–IV). Consider a magma in Fig. 7(II) that is virtually closed to water loss up to the point of first eruption at (A'), at which point the lowest equilibrium water content is that of (A). Draw-down during eruption (which could be as much as 200–300 m: SPARKS, 1978; see Fig. 7(III)) may remove some, but not all of the vapor-saturated magma. The erupted magma might have a water content (at initiation of the eruption) as high as, say (A''). If the magma remains a closed system, it can erupt (at point (B'')) when the lowest equilibrium water content is that of (B), and extract magma with a range of wt.% $H_2O$. The range of water contents of glass which survives the

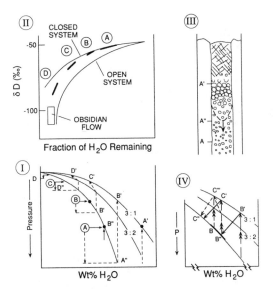

FIG. 7. Schematic diagrams illustrating the change in δD of rhyolitic melt by open-system and multi-step open/closed (eruption) degassing for a magma with initial water content equal to A': (I) Points A and A' are, respectively, the water contents of the melt and melt + vapor at the point of rupture. Draw-down to point A" during eruption marks the water content of the ascending magma which erupts at point B'; similarly for points C and C'. The saturation curve A"-B"-C" may not be reached (*i.e.*, probably not all vapor-saturated magma is erupted). Open-system degassing of a portion of the upper-most melt prior to eruption causes a decrease in the water content of the melt + vapor. (II) Points A-B-C record the continuous variation in water content and δD of the melt during magma ascent and $H_2O$ exsolution. Points A'-B'-C'-D' record the discontinuous variation in water content of the magma (melt + bubbles) during ascent and eruption: (III) Upward increase in bubble density and volume is shown in a dike (conduit) intrusion. The draw-down and extraction of melt with fewer bubbles during eruption is represented by the heavy dashed line. (IV) This illustrates lowering of the water content of the magma by episodic eruption following closed-system degassing. Upon eruption at B', pressure and water content might change along path B'-B" (or some similar path). Generally, B' is not reached, and only a portion of the vapor-saturated magma may be extracted. Continued ascent results in further bubble growth until eruption at C', and so on.

rapid unroofing of the magma column is likely to be more restricted than is consistent with the range of the depths from which magma is excavated, because much of the upper portion of the magma column will be lost as ash. Changes in water content upon eruption are schematically illustrated in Fig. 7(IV) by the paths (B')–(B") and (C')–(C"). Figure 7(III) implies the existence of gradients in δD and wt.% $H_2O$ in the melt column (*i.e.*, in the dike). The principal point is that the water content of the magma is reduced with each eruption, and this pro-

duces a quasi-open system isotopic shift which cannot be modelled as a single-step batch equilibrium.

This multi-step degassing scenario can be modelled to fit the isotopic relationships, and it is at the same time consistent with both the measured water contents of glass found at depth (*i.e.*, the pressure-dependent solubility constraint) and the multiple-layer tephra deposits (*i.e.*, evidence for some degree of closure to water loss). It also provides a mechanism (*i.e.*, sudden vapor loss) to produce the constitutional super cooling consistent with textural and phase relationships (*cf.* SWANSON *et al.*, 1989). An infinite number of similar closed-system degassing stages would approach the open-system end-member, Rayleigh fractionation.

With closer approach to the surface, the pressure difference between intervals of fragmentation and vapor undersaturation decreases, as does the water content of the magma. Although pressure is not likely to be a strictly linear function of depth (due to changing magma density), the foregoing implies that the volume of successively erupted tephra layers should generally decrease with time. This is broadly consistent with the relative order of layer thickness in the Obsidian Dome tephra (C. D. MILLER, pers. comm.).

The Obsidian Dome tephra comprise three thick layers in the 5-layer distal section and five thick layers in the proximal section of ten beds (C. D. MILLER, pers. comm.). Therefore, I chose a simple 4-step degassing model for the tephra series to illustrate the isotopic effects of major water loss during eruption. Each stage is presumed to extract 50% of the water contained in the vapor-saturated magma column at chemical and hydrogen isotope equilibrium. Closed-system degassing (Eq. 2) describes the isotopic variation of each stage. Two such degassing paths are shown in Fig. 6, the dashed curves for $\alpha_{H_2O-(H_2O_{melt})} = 0.9896$, and the solid curve for $\alpha_{H_2O-(H_2O_{melt})} = 1.000$ (see discussion above). Although only approximations, both curves more closely mimic the trend of the data than do either of the single-step closed- or continuously open-system trends. A more accurate model would require constraints for the number of stages and for the resultant change in water content of the magma. Nevertheless, the cumulative effect resembles an open system (*cf.* B. TAYLOR, 1986).

Some continuously open-system vapor loss probably also occurs through the magma foam, prior to eruption, and this is shown schematically by the shift in magma water content from point (C') to (C") in Fig. 7(IV). Quantitative evaluation of the isotopic effect is difficult, however, because the relative amount of water lost via diffusion through the bubble walls is unknown. EICHELBERGER *et al.* (1986) suggest that eruptions fed by thin dikes may be more open than eruptions fed by larger conduits. However, multi-step, *Rayleigh-dominated* degassing is precluded. Such a process would produce extreme deuterium depletions, and few samples of either tephra or flow obsidian indicate greater deuterium depletion than the simple open-system model path.

The markedly low $\delta D$ values attained by obsidian comprising the dome flow are consistent with the cumulative effect of multi-step open/closed-system degassing. Rayleigh degassing of magma in the shallow (<100 m) portions of the conduit with water contents on the order of 0.5 wt.% and $\delta D$ values of *ca.* −90 (similar to residual magma at step no. 4 in Fig. 6) is also consistent with the low $\delta D$ values and, in particular, large variation in both $\delta D$ of the dome obsidian and the water content of 0.1 to 0.2 wt.% (*e.g.*, WESTRICH *et al.*, 1988). Diffusion of exsolved water through a foam, perhaps aided by local rupture of bubble walls, provides a mechanism to decrease (1) internal pressure (approaching equilibrium at one bar), and (2) deuterium in the magma. This eventually ceases due to loss of permeability, collapse, and re-welding to form the obsidian zones (TAYLOR *et al.*, 1983; EICHELBERGER *et al.*, 1986; WESTRICH *et al.*, 1988). The effect of increasing deuterium fractionation between $H_2O$ and $OH_{melt}$ with decreasing temperature could be on the order of 10 per mil, or so (DOBSON *et al.*, 1989), but this is minor in comparison to Rayleigh effects. The softening point of the obsidian is in the vicinity of 650°C (WESTRICH *et al.*, 1988; STOLPER, 1989), which limits any large variations due to temperature.

## Pumice: the open system?

Despite the potential for hydrous alteration, owing to the high surface area of the frothy glass, a case can be made that most of the $H_2O$ in pumices from tephra units and dome flow tops is primary. If one excludes the two samples on Fig. 6 with more than 1.9 wt.% $H_2O$, there is a generally positive correlation between water content and $\delta D$ value; this correlation is broadly similar to that illustrated in Fig. 6 for obsidian, but the pumices show more scatter and are shifted toward high water contents and lower $\delta D$ values. This could indicate that *all* of the pumices are slightly contaminated by meteoric water. However, a number of pumice clasts have water contents greater than the one bar equilibrium value (*e.g.*, WESTRICH *et al.*, 1988) yet still display high $\delta D$ values. Also, hydration of pumice by local meteoric water ($\delta D \approx -122$; *e.g.*, TAYLOR

*et al.*, 1983) would cause a negative correlation between $\delta D$ and wt.% $H_2O$ on Fig. 6.

Although not apparent from Fig. 6, many pumice clasts have water contents only about 0.5 wt.% higher, and 20–40 per mil lower in $\delta D$, than obsidian clasts from the same layer. The $\delta^{18}O$ values of the pumice (6.3 to 7.9) are in the same range of $\delta^{18}O$ as the obsidian, and clearly do not display the type of $^{18}O$ enrichment that is indicative of low-temperature surface weathering (*e.g.*, H. P. TAYLOR, 1968). This is mainly due to the extremely young age of the pumice but in part may also be attributed to the relatively arid conditions and to the protective insulation of the outer pumiceous portions of the clasts (only the interiors were sampled; see above).

If any sample of quenched hydrous melt approaches Rayleigh-type degassing, it probably should be pumice, especially those pumices that formed or continued to degas during eruption. Interestingly, none of the pumice samples plots above the Rayleigh model path. The generally positive correlation of the pumice data on Fig. 6 is probably indicative of a degassing signature, despite the fact that some absorption of meteoric water has occurred. Four samples of flow pumice are either isotopically similar or slightly heavier to coexisting obsidian. This is consistent with both the suggested origin of flow obsidian (*i.e.*, from collapse of magmatic foam) and some additional degassing of tephra pumice relative to the obsidian. Flow pumice may have absorbed minor quantities of magmatic water.

## Interaction between magma and meteoric water

Some evidence for direct magma-water interaction is found in the physical characteristics of pyroclastic particles and bed forms of explosively erupted products (*e.g.*, WOHLETZ, 1986, 1987). Lowered $\delta^{18}O$ values of unaltered igneous rocks also provide evidence of incorporation of meteoric water by magmas (probably most commonly via assimilation of altered rocks; FRIEDMAN *et al.*, 1974; HILDRETH *et al.*, 1984; H. P. TAYLOR, 1986). The latter occurrences are not necessarily closely associated with an explosive eruption.

The low $\delta^{18}O$ (+4.2) of the glassy dike margin in hole RDO-3a suggests high-temperature contamination by, or isotopic exchange with, meteoric water, because low-temperature hydration is known to increase the $\delta^{18}O$ of silicic glasses (H. P. TAYLOR, 1968). The glass has a distinct reddish color, indicative of oxidation, consistent with post-quench meteoric-hydrothermal alteration. However, if water was present in the fractured wall rocks, why did the glass survive and not crystallize? Perhaps the rapid undercooling experienced by magma at the dike margins was sufficient to prevent crystallization.

One obsidian clast from a tephra dike (329 m depth; 0.92 wt.% $H_2O$; hole RDO-3a) with a $\delta D$ value of $-119$ further suggests isotopic exchange with meteoric water without loss of the sample's glassy character. The water content of the clast is appropriate for equilibrium at the depth of sampling, and, like the glassy dike margin, may have acquired its low $\delta D$ value via vapor-saturated exchange with local meteoric ground waters. This could have occurred prior to the quenching and collapse of vesicular melt to form obsidian (see below). Granitic rocks in and adjacent to the tuff-filled fractures have $\delta D = -147$, which further document alteration by heated meteoric waters.

The tephra-dike glass sampled in RDO-3a at 413 m vertical depth (0.92 wt.% $H_2O$; $\delta D = -85$; $\delta^{18}O = 7.3$) from thin (7 to 40 cm-thick) sub-horizontal pyroclast-filled fractures (see HEIKEN et al., 1988) is consistent with open-system degassing (see Fig. 6). The $\delta^{18}O$ values and water contents of the glassy tephra clasts permit only minor high-temperature absorption of meteoric water. HEIKEN et al. (1988) concluded that the glassy clasts were injected into subhorizontal fractures during phreatomagmatic hydrofracturing late in the eruptive sequence, prior to the emplacement of the dome. MILLER (1985) suggested a similar chronology for "phreatic vents" along the Inyo chain.

### Origin of obsidian

The difference between the measured water contents for flow, conduit, and dike glass with that expected for equilibrium in a silicic melt at the depths of emplacement (e.g., WESTRICH et al., 1988) suggests that obsidian is derived from an originally vapor-saturated melt. Two somewhat different quench histories have been suggested: (1) The obsidian may have originated by collapse of magmatic foam associated with loss of internal vapor pressure due to outward diffusion of water, followed by collapse and annealing of vesicles along conduit walls, probably assisted by ascending magma (TAYLOR et al., 1983; EICHELBERGER et al., 1986; DUNBAR and KYLE, 1989). (2) On the other hand, NEWMAN et al. (1988) and STOLPER (1989) suggest that the obsidian forms by thermal quenching of magma on the roof and walls of the conduit, and is subsequently eroded during eruption. Having cooled below its softening point (ca. 670°C; WESTRICH et al., 1988), the glass would not vesiculate upon eruption. The mean temperature for all obsidian with >0.8 wt.% $H_2O$

is ca. 600°C (STOLPER, 1989; compare NEWMAN et al., 1988). Inasmuch as apparent equilibration temperatures of $H_2O$/OH ratios in rhyolite glasses on the order of 600°C result from quenching 850°C melts at 3–4°C s$^{-1}$ (SILVER et al., 1990), a glassy margin on a conduit a few centimeters thick could form in minutes.

The above two hypotheses are not mutually exclusive, because thermal quenching could readily occur against the walls of ascending and degassing magma. Both hypotheses are consistent with the variation in water content with depth, according to the eruption scenario discussed above. Magma that was thermally quenched to form glass on the conduit margins must have at one time been vesicular (i.e., vapor-saturated) in order to explain the variation in water content with eruption (and degassing) progress.

For how long could the glassy walls of the conduits survive unaltered? Experiments at 400°C reported by STOLPER (1989) indicate that rhyolite glass can coexist with water at 400°C for at least 15½ days without crystallizing. Obsidian dome probably took much longer to cool, and thick obsidian zones survived. Chemical and isotopic equilibration between water and rhyolitic melts at 850–950°C can occur within four hours over a scale of 1–2 mm (TAYLOR and WESTRICH, 1985; STOLPER, 1989). Isotopic data for the 10 cm-thick glass conduit (dike) margin suggest that glass held in high temperature hydrothermal environments will either isotopically exchange or exhibit other alteration signatures. However, neither isotopic nor textural evidence for alteration are evident in the tephra obsidians analyzed in this study or those of TAYLOR et al. (1983) and NEWMAN et al. (1988). Therefore, the dike margins must have been relatively dry, or the time between glass formation and eruption was relatively short. Hydrothermal alteration of the still-glassy dike margin (hole RDO-3a) would have occurred after, rather than during, tephra eruptions.

### Second boiling, or subsolidus reactions?— Evidence from Ba, Cl, and S

Comparison of the texture of crystalline rhyolite in the dome (sampled by drill holes RDO-2a and RDO-2b) with that of the holocrystalline rhyolite in the conduit and feeder dike (penetrated by hole RDO-2b and 3a, respectively) provides evidence for distinct crystallization histories (SWANSON et al., 1989). These studies indicate (1) growth of phenocrysts prior to extrusion, (2) probable growth of microlites in response to degassing, and (3) devitrification of the slower cooling portion of the dome flow and crystallization of the conduit magma. The water contents of microcrystalline rhyolite sampled in the conduit and dike (average: 0.22 wt.% $H_2O$ in RDO-2b; 0.1 in RDO-3a) are considerably lower than expected for equilibrium (as much as 1.5 wt.%) and lower than the values measured in the intrusive glassy pyroclast from the tuff-breccia dikes (Fig. 6). Indeed, two samples from the glassy margin of the feeder dike have an average of 1.53 wt.% $H_2O$ and are within several centimeters of rhyolite with <0.25 wt.% $H_2O$.

Loss of water (degassing) upon cooling and crystallization (so-called second boiling) may be contrasted between the environments of the dome flow and the conduit. Comparison of the water contents of the glassy intrusive pyroclast and rhyolite (Fig. 3) indicates that crystallization of the conduit magma was accompanied by a loss of about 1.3 wt.% $H_2O$. The final water content of the rhyolite would be controlled by phase equilibria primarily involving biotite. Devitrification of the dome flow, on the other hand, did not result in a substantial loss of water, as the melt had already degassed to its present water content (i.e., that of equilibrium at ca. one bar; WESTRICH et al., 1988). However, based on deformed flow banding about spherulites, SWANSON et al. (1989) suggest that the devitrification proceeded at or above the softening point of the glass.

The fact that the $\delta D$ values of crystalline rhyolite and glassy samples (obsidian and coarse vesicular glass) from the flow are generally similar (Fig. 5) is, in part, because devitrification followed degassing. Figure 4 illustrates that crystalline rhyolite is typically characterized by $\delta^{18}O$ values 0.5 to 2.0 per mil lower than adjacent obsidian. The field of "primary conduit rhyolite" denotes the approximate compositional range expected for rhyolitic magma that had achieved internal equilibrium at approximately 400 to 600 m. In contrast, both the hydrogen and oxygen isotope compositions of the basalt and granitic basement indicate exchange with hydrothermal meteoric water, and samples of crystalline rhyolite from the thin dike (hole RDO-3a) are relatively more depleted in D and $^{18}O$ than the conduit rhyolite, also suggesting some exchange with local meteoric water. Nevertheless, it is puzzling that the dike margin glass, which bears evidence of the largest isotopic and chemical changes (see below) also remains today a glass and has not crystallized (because hydrothermal activity was very short-lived?).

The correspondence between state of crystallization and $\delta^{18}O$ is particularly well-shown for the high-Ba and low-Ba magmas (Fig. 8). None of the $\delta$-values of the rhyolite is so low (especially in view

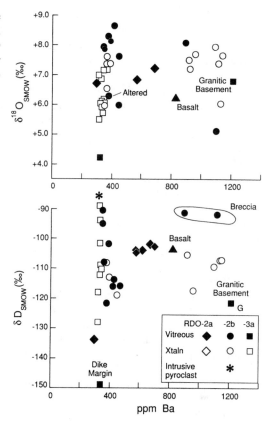

FIG. 8. Plot of $\delta^{18}O$ and $\delta D$ vs. Ba for vitreous and crystalline (Xtaln) rhyolite, and an obsidian clast from a tuff-breccia dike. The two "Breccia" samples represent the basal flow breccia beneath the dome flow. The high-Ba type rhyolite (see VOGEL et al., 1989) appears to have a more restricted range of $\delta^{18}O$ and $\delta D$ than the low-Ba rhyolite. Barium analyses are from WESTRICH et al. (1988) and H. STOCKMAN (pers. comm.).

of the degassing effect on $\delta D$) as to unequivocally indicate meteoric-hydrothermal alteration, although the $\delta^{18}O$ values <6.0 are strongly suggestive. Typically, variation in $\delta^{18}O$ (and $^{18}O$-depletion) of feldspar-bearing rocks due to meteoric-hydrothermal exchange will increase with increasing water/rock ratio (e.g., CRISS and TAYLOR, 1986). Presumably, the Ba resides with the feldspar or with the glass, yet there is no apparent variation with decreasing $\delta^{18}O$, such as might be due to leaching at a higher water/rock ratio. Barium has evidently remained largely immobile.

The variations of $\delta^{18}O$ and $\delta D$ with Cl and S are illustrated in Figs. 9 and 10. Second boiling is thought to generate a Cl-rich fluid (e.g., BURNHAM, 1979; WESTRICH et al., 1988), and, indeed, the vitreous rhyolite has a higher concentration of Cl than crystalline rhyolite with a similar range in $\delta^{18}O$ and

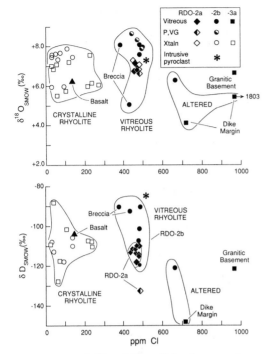

FIG. 9. Plot of $\delta^{18}O$ and $\delta D$ vs. Cl for vitreous and crystalline (Xtaln) rhyolite, an obsidian clast (∗) from a tuff-breccia dike, and for samples of basaltic and granitic wall rocks. Chlorine analyses are from WESTRICH et al. (1988) and H. STOCKMAN (pers. comm.).

of vesicular magma from Obsidian Dome vent became a progressively more open process with time because of the removal of magmatic water with melt after successive stages of essentially closed-system degassing (with each stage punctuated by eruption of a tephra layer). Completely open-system degassing would result in no eruption at all, and this may have been the fate of the magma in the feeder dike.

Devitrification of glassy rhyolite was not accompanied by any major shifts in either $\delta D$ or $\delta^{18}O$, probably because of virtually complete water loss from the hydrous melt. Only biotite remained behind as a hydrous component.

Isotopic evidence of magma-water interaction is recorded in the glassy margin of the feeder dike. Glassy pyroclasts in sub-horizontal, tuff-breccia–filled fractures related to emplacement of the dike record some (minor) hydrogen isotopic exchange with meteoric water.

The $\delta D$ value of water in the Obsidian Dome magma prior to degassing is estimated to have been

$\delta D$. Dike margin glass and one sample of apparently exchanged or "altered" flow obsidian have markedly higher Cl contents. The trend shown for Cl could be considered consistent with progressive degassing of Cl (the dike margin glass would then represent quenched higher, primary contents). However, the low $\delta^{18}O$ and $\delta D$ values of the dike margin glass most likely imply that Cl released by crystallization of the vitreous rhyolite may have been added to the dike margin during meteoric-hydrothermal alteration (via a brine?).

Slightly lower S contents are also apparent for the crystalline rhyolite (WESTRICH et al., 1988), although the distinction from vitreous rhyolite is less clear than for Cl. Either sulfur was not particularly mobile, or most samples have suffered approximately equal sulfur loss.

## CONCLUSIONS

The hydrogen isotopic compositions and water contents measured for tephra and dome obsidian (and, to some degree, pumice clasts) are consistent with calculated isotopic degassing trends which quantitatively account for D/H fractionation of $H_2O$ and OH in the melt. Degassing and eruption

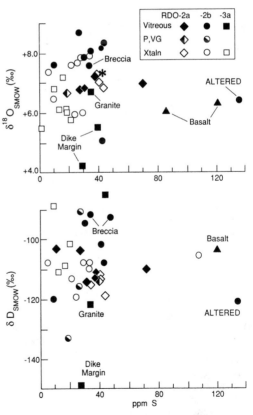

FIG. 10. Plot of $\delta^{18}O$ and $\delta D$ vs. S for vitreous and crystalline (Xtaln) rhyolite, an obsidian clast (∗) from a tuff-breccia dike and samples of basaltic and granitic wall rocks. Sulfur analyses are from WESTRICH et al. (1988) and H. STOCKMAN (pers. comm.).

approximately −40. This is in stark contrast to the δD of local meteoric water (*ca.* −122), and somewhat higher than usually considered for magmatic water (*cf.* B. TAYLOR, 1986; H. P. TAYLOR and SHEPPARD, 1986). The large variation in δD of the obsidian, to final values of −120, represents fractionation dominated by OH species in the melt as it progressively degassed. Exsolved magmatic water was not nearly so deuterium-depleted; the bulk of it had a δD value −50 or higher. Final-stage degassing during emplacement of the dome was dominantly open-system in nature, with distal portions of the flow more degassed than either the basal breccia or the later-extruded proximal portion.

*Acknowledgments*—J. R. O'Neil permitted use of the stable isotope laboratory in Menlo Park, California, for determination of a number of the data reported in this paper, and J. Sekerka assisted in collection of data in the stable isotope laboratory of the Geological Survey of Canada, in Ottawa. K. Nyugen drafted the illustrations. C. D. Miller (U.S. Geological Survey) provided samples of Obsidian Dome tephra. Detailed work on these and other samples will be the subject of a future paper on the Inyo volcanic chain. H. Stockman (Sandia National Laboratory) is thanked for use of the Ba, Cl, and S data reported in illustrations in an earlier paper. Finally, I am grateful to J. C. Eichelberger (Sandia National Laboratory) for the opportunity to participate in research on drill core from Obsidian Dome.

## REFERENCES

BAILEY R. A., DALRYMPLE G. B. and LANPHERE M. A. (1976) Volcanism, structure and geochronology of the Long Valley caldera, Mono County, California. *J. Geophys. Res.* **81**, 725–744.

BAILEY R. A., MACDONALD R. A. and THOMAS J. E. (1983) The Inyo-Mono craters: Products of an actively differentiation rhyolite magma chamber, eastern California (abstr.). *Eos* **64**, 336.

BURNHAM S. W. (1979) Magmas and hydrothermal fluids. In *Geochemistry of Hydrothermal Ore Deposits* (ed. H. L. BARNES), 2nd edn., pp. 71–136. J. Wiley & Sons.

CRISS R. E. and TAYLOR H. P. JR. (1986) Meteoric-hydrothermal systems. In *Reviews in Mineralogy, Vol. 16* (eds. J. W. VALLEY, H. P. TAYLOR JR., and J. R. O'NEIL), Chap. 11, pp. 373–424. Mineral. Soc. Amer., Washington, D.C.

DOBSON P. F., EPSTEIN S. and STOLPER E. M. (1989) Hydrogen isotope fractionation between coexisting vapor and silicate glasses and melts at low pressure. *Geochim. Cosmochim. Acta* **53**, 2723–2730.

DUNBAR N. W. and KYLE P. R. (1989) Volatile contents of obsidian from the Taupo Volcanic Zone, New Zealand, and implications for eruption processes (abstr.). *New Mexico Bureau Mines Mineral. Res., Bull.* **131**, 77.

EICHELBERGER J. C. and WESTRICH H. R. (1981) Magmatic volatiles in explosive rhyolitic eruptions. *Geophys. Res. Lett.* **8**, 757–760.

EICHELBERGER J. C., LYSNE and YOUNKER L. W. (1984)

Research drilling at Inyo Domes, Long Valley caldera, California: 1984 results (abstr.). *Eos* **65**, 723–725.

EICHELBERGER J. C., LYSNE P. C., MILLER C. D. and YOUNKER L. W. (1985) Research drilling at Inyo Domes, California: 1984 results (abstr.). *Eos* **66**, 186–187.

EICHELBERGER J. C., CARRIGAN C. R., WESTRICH H. R. and PRICE R. H. (1986) Non-explosive silicic volcanism. *Nature* **323**, 598–602.

EICHELBERGER J. C., VOGEL T. A., YOUNKER L. W., MILLER C. D., HEIKEN G. H. and WOHLETZ K. H. (1988) Structure and stratigraphy beneath a young phreatic vent: South Inyo crater, Long Valley caldera, California. *J. Geophys. Res.* **93**, 13,208–13,220.

FINK J. (1985) Geometry of silicic dikes beneath the Inyo Domes, California. *J. Geophys. Res.* **90**, 11,127–11,133.

FRIEDMAN I., LIPMAN P. W., OBRADOVICH J. D. and GLEASON J. D. (1974) Meteoric waters in magmas. *Science* **184**, 1069–1072.

HEIKEN G., WOHLETZ K. and EICHELBERGER J. C. (1988) Fracture fillings and intrusive pyroclasts, Inyo Domes, California. *J. Geophys. Res.* **93**, 4335–4350.

HERVIG R. L., DUNBAR N., WESTRICH H. R. and KYLE P. R. (1989) Pre-eruptive water content of rhyolitic magmas as determined by ion microprobe analyses of melt inclusions in phenocrysts. *J. Volcanol. Geotherm. Res.* **36**, 293–302.

HIGGINS M. D. (1988) Trace element geochemistry of the Inyo volcanic chain, California: Evidence for multiple magma sources, magma mixing and post-eruption loss of boron. *J. Volcanol. Geotherm. Res.* **35**, 97–110.

HILDRETH W., CHRISTIANSEN R. L. and O'NEIL J. R. (1984) Catastrophic modification of rhyolitic magma at times of caldera subsidence, Yellowstone Plateau volcanic field. *J. Geophys. Res.* **89**, 8339–8369.

MASTIN L. G. and POLLARD D. D. (1988) Surface deformation and shallow dike intrusion processes at Inyo Craters, Long Valley, California. *J. Geophys. Res.* **93**, 13,221–13,235.

MILLER C. D. (1985) Holocene eruptions at the Inyo volcanic chain, California: Implications for possible eruptions in Long Valley caldera. *Geology* **13**, 14–17.

NANEY M. T. (1983) Phase equilibria of rock-forming ferromagnesian silicates in granitic systems. *Amer. J. Sci.* **283**, 993–1033.

NEWMAN S., EPSTEIN S. and STOLPER E. (1988) Water, carbon dioxide, and hydrogen isotopes in glasses from the ca. 1340 A.D. eruption of the Mono Craters, California: Constraints on degassing phenomena and initial volatile content. *J. Volcanol. Geotherm. Res.* **35**, 75–96.

O'NEIL J. R. and TAYLOR B. E. (1985) Degassing of Obsidian Dome magma: Hydrogen and oxygen isotope studies in the Inyo Dome Chain, Long Valley area, California (abstr.). *Eos* **66**, 387.

SAMPSON D. E. (1987) Textural heterogeneities and vent area structures in the 600-year-old lavas of the Inyo volcanic chain, eastern California. *Geol. Soc. Amer. Spec. Pap.* **212**, 89–101.

SAMPSON D. E. and CAMERON K. L. (1987) The geochemistry of the Inyo volcanic chain: Multiple magma systems in the Long Valley region, eastern California. *J. Geophys. Res.* **92**, 10,403–10,421.

SHAW H. R. (1974) Diffusion of H₂O in granitic liquids: Part I. Experimental data; Part II: Mass transfer in magma chambers. In *Geochemical Transport and Ki-*

*netics* (ed. A. W. KOFFMAN), pp. 139–170. Carnegie Inst. Wash., Washington, D.C.

SILVER L. A., IHINGER P. D. and STOLPER E. (1990) The influence of bulk composition on the speciation of water in silicate glasses. *Contrib. Mineral. Petrol.* **104,** 142–162.

SPARKS R. S. J. (1978) The dynamics of bubble formation and growth in magmas: A review and analysis. *J. Volcanol. Geotherm. Res.* **3,** 1–37.

STOLPER E. (1982) The speciation of water in silicate melts. *Geochim. Cosmochim. Acta* **46,** 2609–2620.

STOLPER E. (1989) Temperature dependence of the speciation of water in rhyolitic melts and glasses. *Amer. Mineral.* **74,** 1247–1257.

SUEMNICHT G. A. and VARGA R. J. (1988) Basement structure and implications for hydrothermal circulation patterns in the western moat of Long Valley caldera, California. *J. Geophys. Res.* **93,** 13,191–13,207.

SWANSON S. E., NANEY M. T., WESTRICH H. R. and EICHELBERGER J. C. (1989) Crystallization history of Obsidian Dome, Inyo Domes, California. *Bull. Volcanol.* **51,** 161–176.

TAYLOR B. E. (1986) Magmatic volatiles: isotopic variation of C, H, and S. In *Reviews in Mineralogy, Vol. 16* (eds. J. W. VALLEY, H. P. TAYLOR JR. and J. R. O'NEIL), Chap. 7, pp. 185–225. Mineral. Soc. America, Washington, D.C.

TAYLOR B. E. and WESTRICH H. R. (1985) Hydrogen isotope exchange and water solubility in experiments using natural rhyolite obsidian. *Eos* **66,** p. 387.

TAYLOR B. E., EICHELBERGER J. C. and WESTRICH H. R. (1983) Hydrogen isotopic evidence for rhyolitic magma degassing during shallow intrusion and eruption. *Nature* **306,** 541–545.

TAYLOR H. P. JR. (1968) The oxygen isotope geochemistry of igneous rocks. *Contrib. Mineral. Petrol.* **19,** 1–71.

TAYLOR H. P. JR. (1986) Igneous rocks: II. Isotopic case studies of circumpacific magmatism. In *Reviews in Mineralogy, Vol. 16* (eds. J. W. VALLEY, H. P. TAYLOR JR. and J. R. O'NEIL), Chap. 9, pp. 271–319. Mineral. Soc. America, Washington, D.C.

TAYLOR H. P. JR. and SHEPPARD S. M. F. (1986) Igneous Rocks: I. Processes of isotopic fractionation and isotope systematics. In *Reviews in Mineralogy, Vol. 16* (eds. J. W. VALLEY, H. P. TAYLOR JR. and J. R. O'NEIL), Chap. 8, pp. 227–271. Mineral. Soc. America, Washington, D.C.

VOGEL T. A., EICHELBERGER J. C., YOUNKER L. W., SCHURAYTZ B. C., HORKOWITZ J. P., STOCKMAN H. R. and WESTRICH H. R. (1989) Petrology and emplacement dynamics of intrusive and extrusive rhyolites Obsidian Dome, Inyo craters volcanic chain, eastern California. *J. Geophys. Res.* **94,** 17,937–956.

WESTRICH H. R. (1987) Determination of water in volcanic glasses by Karl Fischer titration. *Chem. Geol.* **63,** 335–340.

WESTRICH H. R., STOCKMAN H. W. and EICHELBERGER J. C. (1988) Degassing of rhyolitic magma during ascent and emplacement. *J. Geophys. Res.* **93,** 6503–6511.

WOHLETZ K. H. (1986) Explosive magma-water interactions: Thermodynamics, explosive mechanisms, and field studies. *Bull. Volcanol.* **48,** 245–264.

WOHLETZ K. H. (1987) Chemical and textural surface features of pyroclasts from hydromagmatic eruption sequences. In *Characterization and Quantification of Surface Features on Clastic and Pyroclastic Particles* (ed. J. R. MARSHALL), Chap. 2-2, pp. 79–97. Hutchinson Press, San Francisco.

Stable Isotope Geochemistry: A Tribute to Samuel Epstein
© The Geochemical Society, Special Publication No. 3, 1991
Editors: H. P. Taylor, Jr., J. R. O'Neil and I. R. Kaplan

# Application of stable isotopes in identifying a major Hercynian synplutonic rift zone and its associated meteoric-hydrothermal activity, southern Schwarzwald, Germany*

HUGH P. TAYLOR, JR., MORDECKAI MAGARITZ, and STEPHEN M. WICKHAM

Division of Geological and Planetary Sciences, California Institute of Technology, 170-25 NM,
Pasadena, CA 91125, U.S.A.
Department of Environmental Sciences and Energy Research, The Weizmann Institute,
Rehovot, 76 100 Israel P.O.B. 26
Department of the Geophysical Sciences, University of Chicago, Chicago, IL 60637, U.S.A.

**Abstract**—Whole-rock and mineral $\delta^{18}O$ analyses were obtained on granites, gneisses, migmatites, and a variety of metamorphosed sedimentary and volcanic rocks from the Schwarzwald massif, focusing on Variscan-age (270–360 Ma) igneous, metamorphic, and hydrothermal events. The data display some remarkable geographical and temporal systematics; the extremely $^{18}O$-depleted samples ($\delta^{18}O < +3$) occur only in the southern Schwarzwald, confined to a 3–6 km wide, 50 km long, E–W zone of down-dropped Upper Devonian-Lower Carboniferous sediments and volcanics sandwiched between older, high-grade gneisses on the north and south. This belt of rocks, the Badenweiler-Lenzkirch (B-L) tectonic line, was intruded all along its length by the 1–2 km wide Rand Granite pluton, which also exhibits extremely low $\delta^{18}O$ values. The data imply that a very large meteoric-hydrothermal system was established here within a rift-zone setting, in Late Visean time ($\approx 340$ Ma). This date is fixed by paleontological evidence indicating that the B-L zone sediments changed from marine to terrestrial at this time, because the meteoric-hydrothermal event documented by the $^{18}O/^{16}O$ data obviously could not have occurred while marine sedimentation was taking place. The $\delta D$ values of biotite, hornblende, and chlorite in 31 migmatite, schist, and gneiss samples from the B-L zone range from $-60$ to $-111$, but the most $^{18}O$-depleted of these samples ($\delta^{18}O < +4$) all have $\delta D < -90$. Assuming that these rocks were altered by hydrothermal fluids that originally had $\delta^{18}O$ and $\delta D$ on the Meteoric Water Line, we calculate that the ground waters in this area had $\delta^{18}O \approx -6$ to $-9$ and $\delta D \approx -40$ to $-65$ at that time, compatible with geological data suggesting a low latitude and sub-tropical climate. Previous geological models of the B-L zone emphasize collisional tectonics and conclude that it is a thrust-zone; however, such models are not compatible with the $^{18}O/^{16}O$ data. Our preferred model invokes formation of a dilatant zone along a major strike-slip fault at about 340 Ma. This pull-apart was intruded by the Rand Granite, which acted as the main "heat engine" that drove this large convective system. As the hydrothermal activity weakened, the B-L zone continued to deform, and the solidified pluton was stretched out and strongly attenuated. The hydrothermal episode and the strike-slip deformation both terminated prior to intrusion of some large, post-tectonic, two-mica granite plutons (which truncated the B-L zone and Rand Granite at about 300–315 Ma); these late plutons are not hydrothermally altered or $^{18}O$ depleted. This work suggests that in complex geological terranes stable isotope data may be one of the best ways to identify fossil synplutonic rifts or pull-aparts associated with major strike-slip faults.

## INTRODUCTION

IN THIS PAPER we discuss $^{18}O/^{16}O$ and D/H relationships of the igneous and metamorphic rocks of the southern Schwarzwald (Black Forest), particularly focusing on the area from Badenweiler and Freiburg, eastward to Lenzkirch (Fig. 1). The study area is an uplifted block of Hercynian (=Variscan) and pre-Hercynian crystalline basement rocks on the eastern side of the Rhine Graben (Fig. 1). An analogous basement uplift occurs to the west of the Rhine, forming the Vosges Mountains in France.

Previous stable isotope studies of the Schwarz-

wald massif are those of MAGARITZ and TAYLOR (1981), HOEFS and EMMERMANN (1983), and SIMON and HOEFS (1987). The present study builds upon, and is an outgrowth of, these earlier studies. The original study by MAGARITZ and TAYLOR (1981) was undertaken specifically to examine the $^{18}O/^{16}O$ and D/H relationships in granite migmatites, in the hope that such studies might provide added information about the genesis of such rocks and about the general problem of anatexis of the continental crust. The localities chosen for that stable isotope study by MAGARITZ and TAYLOR (1981) were some of the classic migmatite outcrops described by MEHNERT (1968); the sampling was carried out specifically with the migmatite problem in mind, with the guidance and assistance of W. Wimmenauer. At each migmatite outcrop, samples were taken from coexisting leucosome-melanosome

* Contribution No. 5069. Division of Geological and Planetary Sciences, California Institute of Technology, Pasadena, CA 91125, U.S.A.

pairs (the leucosome being the medium- to coarse-grained, granitic portion of the migmatite and the melanosome being the biotite-rich, finer-grained, more mafic portion). Several of the most interesting of these migmatite exposures are found adjacent to, and within, an east-trending, elongate zone of strongly foliated granitic rocks and Upper Paleozoic sediments and volcanics that extends about 50 km eastward from Badenweiler. This zone (shown in black on Fig. 1) is referred to in the literature as the Badenweiler-Lenzkirch zone or tectonic line; in this paper, we commonly abbreviate it either as B-L zone or B-L line.

MAGARITZ and TAYLOR (1981) also carried out a variety of regional isotope studies of the Hercynian granites and older gneisses throughout the area of the southern Schwarzwald, extending these studies southward almost to Basel, Switzerland. Similar reconnaissance stable isotope studies were carried out by HOEFS and EMMERMANN (1983) and SIMON and HOEFS (1987), and these latter studies also extended much farther north, encompassing the entire Schwarzwald massif. Each of the above studies discovered some systematic relationships in the Hercynian igneous and metamorphic rocks of the Schwarzwald that were generally similar to relationships established elsewhere in the Hercynian of Western Europe, for example in the Pyrenees by MICHARD-VITRAC et al. (1980), in Brittany by AL-BARÈDE et al. (1980), in Cornwall by SHEPPARD (1977), and also to relationships established subsequently in the Pyrenees by WICKHAM and TAYLOR (1985, 1987). We will not review these previous studies here, as they have been discussed in some detail by SHEPPARD (1986a), who also reviewed data from the Massif Central. We simply note the following: (1) Many of the granitic plutons emplaced *during* these Pan-European Variscan orogenic and metamorphic events are cordierite-, biotite-, or muscovite-bearing, peraluminous, S-type granites with relatively high $\delta^{18}O$ values of +11 to +12. (2) Other Variscan granitic rocks, particularly those emplaced after the peak of metamorphism, are typically calcalkaline and have lower $\delta^{18}O$ values, usually about +9 to +10.

In striking contrast to the Hercynian localities mentioned above, a unique feature was discovered in the $^{18}O/^{16}O$ studies of the southern Schwarzwald that clearly implied the existence of a Hercynian meteoric-hydrothermal metamorphic event of some type. MARGARITZ and TAYLOR (1981) found a few isolated samples with unusually low $\delta^{18}O$ values, particularly in some of the granitic plutons, and similar effects were also observed by HOEFS and EMMERMANN (1983). More significantly, however, MAGARITZ and TAYLOR (1981) found that many

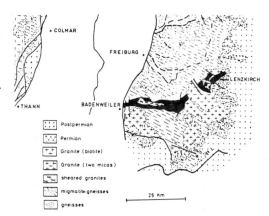

FIG. 1. Generalized geologic map of the southern Schwarzwald, Germany (on the right) and the easternmost Vosges, France (on the left); these two Hercynian (Variscan) terranes are separated by the Rhine graben. The elongate, east-trending, solid black area in the Schwarzwald is the Badenweiler-Lenzkirch (B-L) zone interpreted as a north-dipping thrust zone by FLUCK et al. (1980), but which we are interpreting as a rift zone or pull-apart, based upon characteristic $\delta^{18}O$ values lower than +4 (see text). The elongate granite body in the western part of the B-L rift zone is the Münsterhalden Granite. The later-stage Hercynian granites that truncate the low-$^{18}O$ B-L zone southwest of Lenzkirch are the Bärhalde and Schluchsee plutons discussed in the text. Modified after FLUCK et al. (1980).

of the samples that they had selected for their migmatite study had unusually low $\delta^{18}O$ values, in the range +1 to +5. This astonishing result was totally unexpected, as it seemed to imply that deep circulation of low-$^{18}O$ meteoric groundwaters might be occurring downward into the realm of anatexis and migmatite genesis. In fact, it was this suggestion of MAGARITZ and TAYLOR (1981) that triggered the original studies by WICKHAM and TAYLOR (1985), who searched for similar features in the Pyrenees. Although WICKHAM and TAYLOR (1985) did not find such low-$^{18}O$ meteoric-hydrothermal signatures in the Pyrenees, they did find abundant evidence showing that large quantities of analogous, higher-$^{18}O$, higher-D aqueous fluids were involved in Hercynian prograde metamorphism; they concluded that those metamorphic-hydrothermal fluids in the Pyrenees were also derived from surface waters, either sea water or marine formation water, based on their distinctive isotopic signatures.

Thus, it appeared that generally similar processes might be occurring in these two widely separated areas of Hercynian metamorphism, except that low-$^{18}O$ meteoric ground waters were clearly involved locally in the Schwarzwald, whereas higher-$^{18}O$ marine formation waters appeared to have been involved in the Pyrenees. Note that it is inherently easier to discern the metamorphic effects of low-¹⁸O meteoric-hydrothermal waters than the effects of higher-¹⁸O marine waters, because of the much greater isotopic contrast between the former and most crustal rocks. Thus, it seemed likely that a detailed stable isotope comparison between the Hercynian of the Schwarzwald and the Hercynian of the Pyrenees might prove to be very informative. To this end we collected more than 200 new samples during the summer of 1987, and most of these were subsequently analyzed at Caltech. In this interim report we integrate and compare these new isotopic data with the pre-existing data set of MAGARITZ and TAYLOR (1981) and HOEFS and EMMERMANN (1983).

During our field studies in 1987 it became even more apparent to us that it was going to be important to center our new sampling upon the elongate B-L zone that extends eastward from Badenweiler (Fig. 1), which through serendipity had been the focus of the migmatite sampling effort by MAGARITZ and TAYLOR (1981). In particular, we realized that this B-L zone had probably been misinterpreted as a compressional feature in earlier geologic studies, and that it was instead very likely some type of extensional feature, such as a rift-zone or a pull-apart. Thus we re-sampled the B-L zone in detail, and we also extended our new sampling well to the east, along the extension of this zone all the way to Lenzkirch. In addition, in order to provide comparisons with all the new isotopic data obtained along the B-L tectonic line, we also obtained considerable new isotopic data on the older gneisses and migmatites to the north and south, and on the younger Hercynian granite plutons that truncate the B-L zone.

## GENERAL GEOLOGICAL RELATIONSHIPS

### Regional overview

Variscan and pre-Variscan crystalline basement rocks appear on both sides of the Rhine Graben in two distinct massifs—the Vosges and Black Forest (Fig. 1). Although there are distinct differences between the individual histories of the two massifs, a number of similar sedimentary, volcanic, metamorphic and intrusive sequences can be established on both sides of the Rhine Graben. Below we review the geology in some detail because the main purpose of this paper is to use the evidence of stable isotope geochemistry to propose a new geological model for the evolution of part of the southern Schwarzwald.

### Crystalline basement

The basement rocks of the two massifs are mainly of Precambrian age, but could possibly include a range into early Paleozoic ages (HOFMANN, 1979; FLUCK et al., 1980; WIMMENAUER, 1980). They include leucocratic gneisses, amphibolites, kinzigitic gneisses and sillimanite-biotite gneisses with quartzites. These gneisses apparently underwent a widespread anatectic event at about 470 Ma (HOFMANN and KÖHLER, 1973).

In the southern Schwarzwald migmatites are abundant, as are metagreywacke paragneisses (plagioclase-biotite-quartz ± cordierite ± sillimanite) with abundant small amphibolite bodies. At the southern margin of the Schwarzwald massif, leucocratic gneisses and interstratified amphibolites may represent a metavolcanic sequence (silicic tuffs and/or subvolcanics with basaltic interlayers; WIMMENAUER, 1980). Gneisses and migmatites immediately to the north of the B-L zone have yielded ages of about 330–360 Ma (LEUTWEIN and SONET, 1974; KROHE and EISBACHER, 1988; BREWER and LIPPOLT, 1974), which is similar to the age of emplacement of the elongate Rand Granite pluton (see below).

As discussed by EISBACHER et al. (1989) and LUSCHEN et al. (1987) the Schwarzwald crust is about 25–26 km thick and the refraction Moho (Vp = 8.2 km s⁻¹) is remarkably flat. The lower crust is 10–12 km thick (Vp = 6.7 km s⁻¹). The upper crust down to a depth of 8 km exhibits an increase in Vp from 5 to 6 km s⁻¹ and it contains distinct groupings of dipping reflectors that extend all the way through the upper crust. These reflectors are correlated with the mylonitic shear zones of the Todtnau thrust complex, which crops out at the north edge of the B-L zone (see below).

### Low-grade Upper Devonian-Lower Carboniferous sediments and volcanics

Upper Devonian and Lower Carboniferous sedimentary and volcanic rocks of low metamorphic grade (e.g., chlorite, epidote) are found along several of the so-called Hercynian-age tectonic lines that cut the Vosges and Schwarzwald massifs. Although such rocks are fairly common in the southern Vosges, in the entire Schwarzwald massif they are found only along the Badenweiler-Lenzkirch (B-L) line, within a narrow, down-dropped block sandwiched between basement gneisses on the north and a complex gneiss-granite terrane on the south (Fig. 2). According to FLUCK et al. (1980), the metamorphism of these rocks occurs close to thrusts and has no stratigraphic significance. Intense mylonitization transforms the sediments as well as the adjacent basement gneisses, producing a prograde effect in the sediments and a retrograde effect in the gneisses (FLUCK et al., 1980).

The B-L zone sediments include greywackes, shales, slates, minor cherts, arkosic sandstones, and conglomerates, and they can be differentiated into two distinct belts that parallel the B-L line (SITTIG, 1981; ALTHERR and MAASS, 1977; MAASS, 1981). In the southern "Schonau" unit, sparsely distributed but stratigraphically distinctive fossils indicate an Upper Devonian to Visean age range (~380–330 Ma, HARLAND et al., 1990). The earliest rocks are marine shales and cherts that must have been deposited in deep water conditions, and these are overlain by more than 1000 m of Lower Carboniferous greywacke and shale, i.e. a facies very similar to the Upper Devonian. Some calcareous ooids are found among the greywackes, and subaquatic slides (with pebbles of gneiss) are common. Locally, there are abundant spilites, keratophyres and chert, and the upper parts of the Lower Carboniferous contain reworked ooliths and fossils. Marine sedimentation finally gave way to subaerial conditions, evidenced by the fact that the youngest rocks are terrestrial conglomerates, arkosic sandstones and siltstones, and carbonaceous shales that interfinger with hundreds of meters of lavas and py-

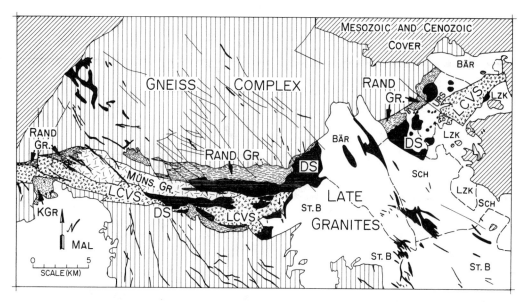

FIG. 2. Generalized geologic map of part of the southern Schwarzwald (modified after METZ and
REIN, 1958), showing the principal rock types in the vicinity of the Badenweiler-Lenzkirch (B-L)
tectonic line. From generally oldest to youngest, these rock types are: (1) Vertical lined pattern—
Basement Gneiss Complex. (2) DS—Upper Devonian-Lower Carboniferous shales and greywacke
siltstones and sandstones. (3) LCVS—Lower Carboniferous silicic volcanics, agglomerates, sandstones,
and conglomerates, with intercalated crinoidal limestone at one locality. (4) Sub-horizontal dashed
pattern—Rand Granite. (5) KGr—Klemmbach Granite. (6) Müns. Gr.—Münsterhalden Granite.
(7) Blank pattern—Late Hercynian Granites; this area shown in white contains several plutons of
varying ages. In the west, southeast and northeast this area comprises, respectively, the Malsburg
(Mal), St. Blasien (St.B), and Lenzkirch (Lzk) granites. In the east, in the vicinity of the gap between
the eastern and western parts of the B-L zone, we have the undeformed, very late-stage, post-tectonic
granite plutons (Bär—Bärhalde, Urs—Ursee, and Sch—Schluchsee) that definitely truncate the Rand
Granite and are clearly much younger than the rocks of the B-L zone. These three plutons are also
clearly younger than the aforementioned Late Hercynian granites. (8) The solid black patterns represent
latest Hercynian quartz porphyry dikes and hypabyssal plutons of Late Carboniferous to Permian
age intruded along a set of pre-existing NW-trending fractures; the age of this brittle deformation has
not yet been established, but these conceivably could represent *en echelon* fractures that began to
form during pre-Bärhalde strike-slip displacements within the B-L zone (see text). Only a few of these
NW-trending fractures are shown on Fig. 2, but they are extremely abundant and pervasive just north
of the central B-L zone. (9) Diagonal lined pattern—Mesozoic and Cenozoic cover rocks (*i.e.,* Triassic
and younger) that unconformably overlie the Hercynian and pre-Hercynian granites and metamorphic
rocks.

roclastic volcanic rocks; the sediments have yielded Late
Visean (340–330 Ma) terrestrial plant fossils (BURGATH
and MAASS, 1973). In the northern "Geschwend" unit
there are large volumes of unfossiliferous sediments that
probably span an age range similar to that of the southern
unit. The general succession of rock types is similar in
both the Vosges and the Schwarzwald, but the sequences
in the Badenweiler-Lenzkirch area are much more highly
tectonized.

*Badenweiler-Lenzkirch (B-L) tectonic line*

The Badenweiler-Lenzkirch (B-L) zone is a 3 to 6 km
wide, 50-km long, E–W belt of post-Silurian rocks juxtaposed between considerably older basement gneisses; it
is just one of a number of such tectonic lines mapped in
the Hercynian of Europe. Both the narrow B-L zone and
its package of included sediments are completely distinct
from the much larger and younger, Upper Carboniferous

to Permian, NE-trending, volcano-sedimentary clastic basins that truncate the Schwarzwald to the north and south.

The principal features of the B-L zone are: (1) a down-
dropped section of Upper Devonian-Lower Carboniferous
metasedimentary and metavolcanic rocks (described
above) which forms the southern half of the zone (units
DS and LCVS on Figs. 2 and 3); and (2) highly sheared,
elongate, syntectonic granite bodies (described below)
which were intruded along the contact between these low-
grade metamorphic rocks and the older gneisses that lie
to the north. The terrane to the south of the B-L line is
also made up of older gneisses, but those gneisses are intruded by a variety of Hercynian granites of different ages.
The continuation of the B-L tectonic line to the west could
lie between the migmatites of Kayserberg-Trois Épis and
the Lower Carboniferous of Marckstein (north of Treh),
or it could intersect the line of klippen in the southern
Vosges (MAASS, 1981; FLUCK *et al.,* 1980).

The oldest sediments in the B-L zone are deep water

shales, cherts, red siltstones and sporadic calcareous olistostromes (SITTIG, 1969; MAASS and STOPPEL, 1982). These must originally have been deposited over a wide area (as indicated by their much more widespread occurrence in the southern Vosges). The fact that in the entire Schwarzwald massif the only place that they are preserved (as effectively unmetamorphosed sediments) is within the B-L zone, requires that this zone was sharply downdropped with respect to the mid-crustal high-grade gneisses that comprise most of this region.

Sheared granites (dated at 360–330 Ma) in the Black Forest and the Vosges all seem to be tied to these major tectonic lines. The best example of such a sheared granite in the Schwarzwald is the Rand Granite pluton, which is only about 1–2 km wide, but which stretches almost the entire length of the B-L zone (Fig. 2). The later Hercynian magmatic activity at 330–280 Ma is obviously free of any such ties to the E–W structures that control the shapes and deformational features of these earlier Hercynian granites.

FLUCK et al. (1980) believe that these tectonic lines are genuine thrusts, described as follows: Immediately at the contact of the thrusts, the overridden, strongly mylonitized Paleozoic sedimentary rocks are metamorphosed, but away from the thrust the same units are essentially unmetamorphosed. The higher-grade gneisses in the opposed, overriding unit also display strong mylonitization, shearing, and drag folds. On the north boundary of the B-L zone EISBACHER et al. (1989) use seismic reflection profiles to trace this north-dipping structure (termed the Todtnau thrust zone) to a depth of 12 km into the continental crust. In contrast to the above interpretations, SITTIG (1981) has interpreted most of the features within the B-L zone in terms of wrench-fault tectonics.

## Hercynian granitic rocks

The Hercynian granites in the Schwarzwald have been studied by a large number of workers, including EMMERMANN (1977), who argued that as they evolved these magmas had a progressively deeper crustal origin through time. In the southern Schwarzwald, all of these granites are intruded either within the B-L zone (syntectonic), south of the B-L zone (late-tectonic), or adjacent to and truncating the B-L zone (post-tectonic).

At an early stage, relatively small leucogranite stocks were emplaced, uplifted, and rapidly eroded, as they are found as pebbles in the synorogenic Lower Carboniferous conglomerates. The various deformed granites in the B-L zone (Rand, Klemmbach, etc.) also probably belong to this early phase of activity. One interesting pluton in the B-L zone that was intruded adjacent to the Rand Granite but which is much less deformed than that body, is the Münsterhalden Granite (Fig. 2). This narrow, elongate pluton is probably the youngest pluton emplaced wholly within the B-L zone, based on its relative lack of internal deformation and shearing compared to the other B-L zone granites, and also because (as we demonstrate below) it is the only granite in the B-L zone that has not been appreciably hydrothermally altered. SITTIG (1981) has proposed that this pluton was tectonically emplaced, based on fault contacts and lack of contact metamorphic effects.

A number of larger, less deformed plutons to the south of the B-L zone (e.g., the Malsburg, Lenzkirch, and St. Blasien; see Fig. 2) were probably intruded next (METZ and REIN, 1958). EMMERMANN (1977) suggests that this episode of granitic magmatism commenced with melting of plagioclase- and biotite-rich paragneisses, producing

large volumes of biotite granite (e.g., St. Blasien). This was followed by a major change in tectonic style of magma emplacement during the period about 300–320 Ma, at which time melting at deeper crustal levels is thought to have formed K-rich, H₂O-undersaturated magmas that intruded to higher crustal levels. The large, undeformed, coarser-grained, two-mica granite plutons that truncate the east-central part of the B-L zone (Fig. 2) were emplaced at this time (e.g., Bärhalde, Schluchsee, and Ursee).

## Geochronology

Despite the large amount of geochronological work in the Schwarzwald, we do not yet know the exact emplacement ages of most of these plutons. However, the relative ages of emplacement can in many cases be constrained by the detailed geological mapping (e.g., METZ and REIN, 1958).

On the basis of geological relationships, a crude subdivision of the igneous activity into four stages can be made. In decreasing order of age these are: (1) syntectonic, highly deformed granites such as the Rand and Klemmbach granites, probably emplaced roughly synchronous with low pressure-moderate temperature metamorphism of the B-L zone rocks; (2) late-tectonic, less-deformed granites (e.g., St. Blasien, Malsburg, Münsterhalden); (3) post-tectonic, undeformed plutons such as the Bärhalde and Schluchsee granites; and (4) volcanic and subvolcanic igneous rocks intercalated with the Late Carboniferous and Permian clastic basin fills.

The inability to obtain accurate radiogenic ages of emplacement particularly applies to the early, highly deformed plutons in the B-L zone, as these have all undergone considerable post-emplacement deformation and recrystallization, thereby obscuring their primary magmatic ages. Perhaps the most reliable radiogenic ages are the Rb-Sr whole-rock ages of LEUTWEIN and SONET (1974), who have reported the following ages (in Ma) for some of the older granites of the study area: Rand (346 ± 15), Klemmbach (340), Münsterhalden (322 ± 15), and Malsburg (314 ± 15). The above isotope geochronology agrees quite well with the geological relationships described above.

The ages of the granitic rocks also are constrained by cooling ages on metamorphic minerals within the adjacent high-grade metamorphic rocks. Rb-Sr and K-Ar ages of hornblende, muscovite, and biotite have yielded ages of 330–325 Ma (biotite and muscovite) and 328–342 Ma (hornblende) (VENZLAFF, 1971; VON DRACH, 1978; LIPPOLT et al., 1986; KROHE and EISBACHER, 1988). Granitic dikes which appear to cut the regional gneissic foliation, but themselves have a distinct schistosity, have given muscovite K-Ar ages of 341–329 Ma (LIPPOLT et al., 1986). Although there is a crying need for more work (particularly U-Pb dating of zircon) the combined data are consistent with an age for the peak of low-pressure metamorphism at around 330–340 Ma, and this age range is probably contemporary with intrusion of the earliest syntectonic granites. Interestingly, this overlaps exactly with the age of the latest sedimentation documented in the B-L zone, the terrestrial, Late Visean (330–340 Ma) coarse clastic sediments. This means that metamorphism at depth was going on simultaneously with sedimentation at the surface.

This is extremely similar to the situation in the Hercynian of the Pyrenees where a similar style of low-pressure metamorphism at depth (~340–310 Ma, see summary in BICKLE et al., 1988) also accompanied sedimentation at the surface (see WICKHAM and OXBURGH, 1986). The difference between the two situations is that in the Pyrenees this sedimentation was marine, whereas in the Schwarz-wald it was subaerial.

There are slightly better age constraints on the late- and post-tectonic granites and high-level porphyry dikes which cut them. The best dated plutons are the post-tectonic plutons (Bärhalde and Schluchsee) and these of course, provide a minimum age boundary for emplacement of the demonstrably older, deformed plutons. MÜLLER-SOHNIUS et al. (1976) conclude that these two plutons were intruded virtually simultaneously at about 304 Ma, whereas WENDT et al. (1974) suggest that the Schluchsee was intruded first (≈315 Ma) and the Bärhalde much later (≈290 Ma). Rb-Sr, K-Ar and Ar-Ar ages on biotite and muscovite from these and other somewhat earlier-stage granites range from 327 to 320 Ma in the southern Schwarzwald (WENDT et al., 1970; BREWER and LIPPOLT, 1972; LIPPOLT et al., 1983; LIPPOLT and RITTMANN, 1984). The porphyry dikes have been dated at 323–317 Ma. The post-orogenic Permo-Carboniferous basin vol-canics give ages ranging from 307–286 Ma (Rb-Sr on bio-tite and apatite). This overlaps with the older end of the range of ages for the "late granodiorites" in the Pyrenees.

The combined evidence from the sediments and the ages on the granites and metamorphic minerals implies that metamorphism accompanied sedimentation at the surface. This rules out the possibility that the metamor-phism was accompanying regional uplift as in collision-type scenarios. The localized pockets of terrestrial sedi-ments of 330–340 Ma age in the B-L zone strongly suggest that local rifting occurred within a major belt of strike slip-extensional deformation. The oxygen isotope data to be discussed below fit this picture perfectly, and the contrast in the type of water involved in hydrothermal metamor-phism in the Pyrenees and the Schwarzwald is mirrored by the contrasts in syn-metamorphic sediment type.

## OXYGEN ISOTOPE DATA

Our detailed study of $^{18}O/^{16}O$ ratios in more than 200 samples of igneous and metamorphic rocks and their co-existing minerals from the southern Schwarzwald (Black Forest) covers an area of more than 3000 km² from Basel and Freiburg eastward to Lenzkirch (Fig. 1). The $^{18}O/^{16}O$ sample localities in the vicinity of the B-L zone are shown in Fig. 3; other localities lie off this figure to the north and to the south. All of the whole-rock $\delta^{18}O$ analyses are re-ported graphically in Fig. 4, together with available data from MAGARITZ and TAYLOR (1981), HOEFS and EM-MERMANN (1983), and SIMON and HOEFS (1987). The whole-rock $\delta^{18}O$ values were determined by conventional fluorination techniques (TAYLOR and EPSTEIN, 1962). Representative portions of hand-specimen-sized samples of the rocks were pulverized and ground to −200 mesh in a SiC mortar, and then reacted with fluorine gas. The re-sulting oxygen gas then was converted into $CO_2$ and an-alyzed in a mass spectrometer. The data are reported in per mil relative to SMOW (Standard Mean Ocean Water). In our laboratories, NBS-28 has a $\delta^{18}O = +9.60$ on this scale.

A condensed version of the present paper was published two years ago at the EPSTEIN 70th Birthday Symposium (TAYLOR et al., 1989). Subsequently, SIMON (1990) pre-sented new whole-rock $\delta^{18}O$ and biotite-chlorite $\delta D$ values in 31 samples from four Hercynian granite plutons as fol-lows: St. Blasien (+3.7 to +8.8, −65 to −108); Albtal (+8.9 to +10.4, −86 to −105); Bärhalde (+7.9 to +11.1, −66 to −91); and Schluchsee (+9.5 to +11.4, −60 to −90). These data provide additional evidence to that reported

by SIMON and HOEFS (1987) concerning the meteoric-hydrothermal $^{18}O$-depletions in these four granites, con-firming that such effects are virtually non-existent in the late-stage Bärhalde and Schluchsee plutons and minor in the two earlier plutons. SIMON (1990) does not report any dramatic $^{18}O$ depletions similar to those in the B-L zone samples discussed below in the present paper. Three of his samples from the St. Blasien granite are slightly depleted in $^{18}O$, but only one of these has $^{18}O < +4.9$. The other 28 samples studied by SIMON (1990) range from $\delta^{18}O = +6.8$ to $+11.4$, and would all plot as black dots on Fig. 3.

## DISCUSSION

### Low-$^{18}O$ rocks in the vicinity of the B-L zone

Because of the large number of sample localities shown on Fig. 3, for clarity we do not letter in the actual whole-rock $\delta^{18}O$ values. Instead, we show three categories of data-points, and if we assume that essentially all samples started out with $\delta^{18}O > +7$ (which is justified below), then: (1) samples with $-2.3 < \delta^{18}O < +3$ must have been depleted in $^{18}O$ by at least 4 to 13 per mil; (2) samples with $+3 < \delta^{18}O < +6$ have been lowered by at least 1 to 8 per mil; and (3) samples with $\delta^{18}O > +6$ are either unchanged in $\delta^{18}O$ or they have been depleted in $^{18}O$ by only a few per mil. We cannot be more pre-cise about these $^{18}O$ depletions because the original protoliths of the hydrothermally metamorphosed samples in the Schwarzwald are lithologically very diverse and undoubtedly had variable initial $\delta^{18}O$ values. However, based on a wealth of $^{18}O/^{16}O$ data from other Hercynian terranes all over Europe (e.g., see review by SHEPPARD, 1986a), it is reasonably certain that all of the rocks studied in this work started out with $\delta^{18}O > +7.5$. In the entire European Hercynian $\delta^{18}O$ values lower than this are typically found only in mafic igneous rocks, and such rocks were not analyzed in the present study. In particular, most of the granitic rocks probably had initial $\delta^{18}O > +8.5$, and many of the Upper Devonian-Lower Carboniferous detrital sediments in the B-L zone very likely started out with $\delta^{18}O$ values as high as $+13$ to $+17$ or higher, because similarly high $\delta^{18}O$ values are typical of such sedimentary rocks throughout the world. Note that a number of the lowest $\delta^{18}O$ values observed in the study area are from these sediments, indicating that some of these whole-rock samples may have been depleted in $^{18}O$ by as much as 15 to 20 per mil (Fig. 4). A single analyzed chert sample ($\delta^{18}O = +6.9$) has apparently been depleted in $^{18}O$ by more than 20 per mil (be-cause marine cherts typically are deposited with $\delta^{18}O > +30$).

In this study, we obtained 39 whole-rock analyses with $-2.3 < \delta^{18}O < +3$. Except for a single sample near the contact of a quartz porphyry that cuts the

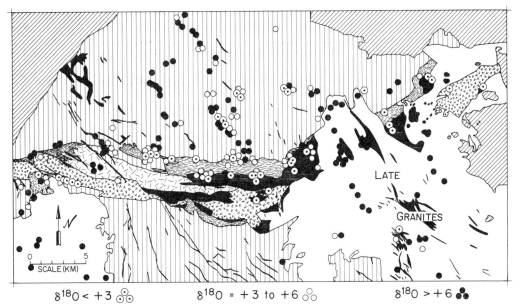

$\delta^{18}O < +3$ ⊛    $\delta^{18}O = +3$ to $+6$ ⊙⊙    $\delta^{18}O > +6$ ●●

FIG. 3. Same map as in Fig. 2, showing the oxygen isotope sample localities studied in this work, but with the lithologic symbols and the generalized NW-trending fracture set both deleted for clarity. The samples are divided into three groups: (1) Whole-rock $\delta^{18}O < +3$ is indicated by large white dots with black centers; (2) $+3 < \delta^{18}O < +6$ is shown by small white dots; and (3) whole-rock $\delta^{18}O > +6$ is indicated by small black dots. Note the concentration of low-¹⁸O rocks in the vicinity of the B-L zone and along the zone of northwest-trending fractures in the gneiss complex just north of the B-L zone (the major fractures are schematically shown in Fig. 2). Note also the concentration of high-¹⁸O values throughout the Late Hercynian granite plutons that truncate the B-L zone (28 additional black dots could have been added to that part of the map if we had utilized the new data of SIMON, 1990).

St. Blasien granite, every one of the other 38 samples is from a locality less than about 5 km from the contact of the Rand Granite of the B-L zone (Figs. 3 and 4). No other samples with $\delta^{18}O < +3$ have been found outside this narrow zone anywhere in the Schwarzwald, either by us or by HOEFS and EMMERMANN (1983) or SIMON (1990). We also obtained 59 whole-rock analyses with $+3 < \delta^{18}O < +6$ within the outcrop area delineated in Figs. 2 and 3. Of these 59 moderately ¹⁸O-depleted samples, only 9 (*i.e.* 15%) are from localities farther than 5 km from the contact of the Rand Granite. The geographic correlation with proximity to the Badenweiler-Lenzkirch tectonic line could not be more clear.

Even more compelling than the above correlations, however, is the fact that (if we exclude the less deformed, younger Münsterhalden Granite) of the 60 samples that were collected well within the boundaries of the B-L zone, only one has a $\delta^{18}O > +6$. Of the other 59 samples, 30 have $\delta^{18}O < +3$, and 29 have $\delta^{18}O$ between +3 and +6. In other-words, from the entire set of Schwarzwald samples, 77% (30/39) of the sub-set of extremely ¹⁸O-depleted samples were collected from within the confines of

the narrow B-L zone, and 97% of these very low-¹⁸O samples (38/39) lie within about 5 km of this zone.

The geographic distribution of ¹⁸O-depleted whole-rock samples shown in Figs. 3 and 4 implies intense focusing of meteoric-hydrothermal metamorphism along the B-L zone. Based on many earlier studies (*e.g.,* as reviewed by TAYLOR, 1988, 1990; CRISS and TAYLOR, 1986), it is clear that low-¹⁸O meteoric-hydrothermal fluids are the only materials on Earth that could have produced such dramatic oxygen isotope effects. The geological features and age-dating described above require this meteoric-hydrothermal activity to have taken place in the Lower Carboniferous at sometime within the interval 320–360 Ma, probably starting at the time of intrusion of the elongate Rand Granite pluton. This is proved by the striking ¹⁸O depletions (whole-rock $\delta^{18}O = -2$ to $+4$) that exist all along the B-L zone (Fig. 3) and which are also observed *throughout* the highly deformed, syntectonic Rand Granite, together with the fact that such ¹⁸O depletions are *not* observed in the post-tectonic granites. The Rand Granite and its associated migmatites are confined to the B-L zone, and although this elongate pluton

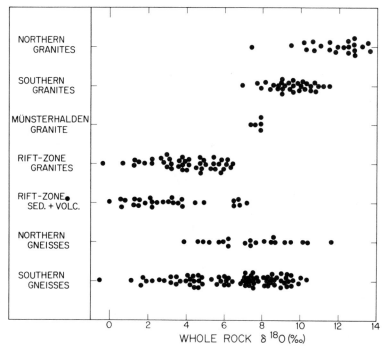

FIG. 4. Whole-rock $^{18}O/^{16}O$ ratios of various samples from the Schwarzwald, Germany, from this work, from MAGARITZ and TAYLOR (1981) and from HOEFS and EMMERMANN (1983). The samples labeled as Northern Gneisses and Northern Granites are from the northern half of the Schwarzwald massif, mostly well off the top of the map shown in Fig. 1. The lowest-$^{18}O$ samples of the Southern Gneisses all lie within a few km of the B-L rift zone, either in close proximity to the Rand Granite or in the vicinity of a major northwest-trending fracture system that locally offsets the Rand Granite. The rift-zone (= B-L zone) granite data-points in the figure are mainly from the Rand Granite, but they also include the Klemmbach Granite and a couple of other (sheared and foliated) granites analyzed from the B-L zone. The only granitic samples from the B-L zone that are plotted separately are those from the Münsterhalden Granite. The rift-zone sedimentary and volcanic data-points represent analyses of sedimentary and volcanic rocks from the DS and LCVS units of the B-L zone shown on Fig. 2. Note that one of these samples has an extremely low $\delta^{18}O$ (−2.3) and plots off the diagram to the left.

is split apart and truncated by the later-stage, un-deformed, high-$^{18}O$ Hercynian granites (Bärhalde, Schluchsee), the Rand Granite *and* its associated low-$^{18}O$ signature extend through virtually the entire length of the B-L zone from Lenzkirch almost all the way to Badenweiler (Figs. 1 and 2). Strong $^{18}O$ depletions are also very pronounced in the "classic" migmatites (MEHNERT, 1968) found along the contacts of the Rand Granite, both against the anatectic gneisses on the north and against the metasediments and metavolcanics to the south (Fig. 3).

*Low-$^{18}O$ values in gneisses cut by the NW-trending fracture systems*

Although the effects are much weaker than those observed in the B-L zone, measurable $^{18}O$ depletions also occur locally up to 10–15 km north and south from the B-L zone, associated either with the earliest Late Hercynian granites (*e.g.,* St. Blasien) or with

northwest-trending fractures in the basement gneisses. The general patterns of these NW-trending fractures are shown in Fig. 2.

These fractures were clearly conduits for the me-teoric-hydrothermal fluids, because: (1) in the field there is a clear-cut geographic association between areas of intense fracturing and the occurrence of low-$^{18}O$ rocks, both on a regional scale (Fig. 2) as well as on an outcrop scale (readily observed in road cuts); (2) the fractures that permeate the low-$^{18}O$ outcrops of gneiss are typically "healed" by meta-morphic-hydrothermal recrystallization; and (3) there is extensive replacement of the original gneiss mineralogy by new hydrothermal minerals such as epidote and chlorite.

These fracture systems clearly pre-date the Late Carboniferous to Permian quartz porphyries and granite porphyries shown in black on Fig. 2, because the fractures acted as conduits for these late Hercynian magmas. The orientation and age of formation of this fracture system are both compatible with our model for the origin of the B-L zone as a pull-apart associated with a major strike-slip fault (see below), because such *en echelon* fractures commonly are oriented about 45° to the trend of the wrench fault which produced them.

### $^{18}O/^{16}O$ ratios of coexisting minerals and juxtaposed rocks

In the course of our studies on the Schwarzwald we obtained a large number of $^{18}O/^{16}O$ analyses of coexisting minerals (mainly quartz and feldspar), as well as considerable data on directly adjacent whole-rock samples or samples from different lithologies in the same outcrop. These data will be presented in future publications by us, so in this brief summary we only mention the features of this data set that are pertinent to our interpretations of the geological history of the B-L zone.

A remarkable aspect of the oxygen isotope data on coexisting quartz-feldspar pairs from the gneisses, schists, migmatites, and granites in the B-L zone is its heterogeneity. The isotopic fractionations (reported as $\Delta$qtz-feld = $\delta$qtz − $\delta$feld) range widely, from near-equilibrium $\Delta$-values of one to two per mil to strikingly large $\Delta$-values of five to eight per mil, values which are typical of the (subsolidus) meteoric-hydrothermal alteration of most epizonal plutons on Earth. In several samples $\delta^{18}O$qtz is very low (+3 to +6) and $\Delta$qtz-feld less than three per mil, indicative of either (1) crystallization from pockets of low-$^{18}O$ magma (probably formed by partial melting of rocks previously hydrothermally altered); or (2) much higher-temperature and/or longer-lived hydrothermal exchange with low-$^{18}O$ fluids, based on the fact that quartz is so much more resistant to $^{18}O/^{16}O$ exchange than is feldspar (*e.g.*, see TAYLOR, 1988; GREGORY *et al.*, 1989).

The same level of heterogeneity is observed in whole-rock $\delta^{18}O$ values from the juxtaposed melanosome-leucosome pairs of B-L zone migmatites (MAGARITZ and TAYLOR, 1981). A few of these pairs tend to have similar $\delta^{18}O$ values, with the granitic part being less than one per mil higher than the more mafic part, typical of most other migmatites that have been studied isotopically, and which is to be expected if the mineral assemblages closely equilibrated at high temperatures. However, in several of the B-L zone samples the granitic portion of the migmatite is either two to five per mil higher in $\delta^{18}O$ than the coexisting more mafic portion or in an equal number of other cases the rock pairs display reversed fractionations of one to three

per mil; both situations are incompatible with isotopic equilibrium among the assemblages.

What are we to make of the above-described isotopic heterogeneities among such closely coexisting or adjacent materials? First, we must conclude that the metamorphic-hydrothermal-temperature history of the area either has been (1) very complex, or (2) rocks and granitic melts with widely divergent hydrothermal or temperature histories have somehow been assembled together and tectonically juxtaposed within the B-L zone. The actual situation probably involves a combination of these phenomena. In particular, we believe that these isotopic data are telling us that this rift zone had a complex origin and evolution, and that there probably have been major geologic modifications of the B-L zone that post-date the early stages of meteoric-hydrothermal activity (*e.g.*, post-rift deformation and continued water/rock interactions along strike-slip faults or thrust faults, or overlapping hydrothermal systems at different temperatures as a result of emplacement of new igneous bodies). This interpretation of these heterogeneous oxygen isotope fractionations coincides nicely with our preferred model for the B-L zone, described below.

### Münsterhalden Granite and westernmost outcrops of Rand Granite

The only part of the B-L zone where the kinds of $^{18}O$ depletions described above are not present is: (1) within the relatively undeformed Münsterhalden Granite body (Figs. 2 and 3); and (2) in the northern part of the extreme western extension of this tectonic line, where five samples have $\delta^{18}O$ = +6.2 to +8.9 and the other three have $\delta^{18}O$ = +5.4 to +5.8; in this area the outcrop width of Rand Granite narrows to less than a few hundred meters and then virtually vanishes.

The elongate Münsterhalden Granite body was apparently emplaced within the B-L zone after the main stage of hydrothermal activity ceased, because like the post-tectonic plutons it has undergone little or no $^{18}O$-depletion (*e.g.*, compare Figs. 2, 3, and 4). It is, however, *slightly* more $^{18}O$ depleted than these latest-stage Hercynian plutons (Fig. 4), and it may have been incipiently affected by the hydrothermal fluids. There is also the possibility that its relatively low $\delta^{18}O$ values of +7.3 to +7.9 are primary magmatic values (Could its protolith at depth have undergone a small amount of hydrothermal $^{18}O$ depletion prior to being partially melted?).

It thus appears that the strength of the meteoric-hydrothermal system was decreasing to the west as the volume of immediately adjacent Rand Granite became smaller and smaller. This is compatible with the geological relationships (Fig. 2) that indicate that the Rand Granite was the principal "heat engine" driving the B-L meteoric-hydrothermal circulation system. It is logical to assume that the strength of the hydrothermal system was also decreasing with time, perhaps coming to a halt as the Rand Granite underwent final crystallization and cooling. Both the geographical effect and the temporal effect probably worked together to diminish the intensity of the hydrothermal system in the westernmost B-L zone at the time of emplacement of the Münsterhalden Granite.

The $^{18}O/^{16}O$ data, taken together with the narrow, elongate aspect ratio of the outcrops of Münsterhalden Granite strongly suggest that E-W structural features in the B-L zone were still active in guiding granitic pluton emplacement in the upper crust, even though the episode of faulting was coming to a close. Certainly, soon after this the geologic situation changed dramatically as the large latest-stage Hercynian granitic bodies like the Bärhalde and Schluchsee were emplaced. These large masses of granite sharply truncate the east-trending faults that lie within and define the B-L zone, and there is no evidence whatsoever that any of these latest-stage Hercynian magmas infiltrated the B-L zone in the way that the Rand or Münsterhalden Granites did. Perhaps by Bärhalde-Schluchsee time the entire B-L zone at its present level of exposure either had evolved into a new stress regime less favorable for open fractures, or perhaps had subsided to greater depths, or both (in order to avoid the inevitable low-$^{18}O$ meteoric-hydrothermal interactions).

*Later Hercynian granites*

Meteoric-hydrothermal activity clearly must have largely terminated prior to truncation of the B-L rift zone by the latest-stage (*ca.* 290–315 Ma) Hercynian granites just southwest of Lenzkirch (Bärhalde, Ursee, Schluchsee), because these granites in general show only minor meteoric-hydrothermal effects and little or no subsolidus $^{18}O$ depletions. We analyzed 16 whole-rock samples from these plutons and SIMON (1990) reports another 17 analyses. This entire combined data set exhibits a $\delta^{18}O$ range only from +8 to +11.

*D/H ratios*

MAGARITZ and TAYLOR (1981) determined the $\delta D$ values of 31 samples collected all along the B-L zone; these range from −60 to −111 (Fig. 5), and are mainly biotite, but include some hornblende and rare chlorite (as well as some impure biotite and hornblende mineral separates that contain mi-

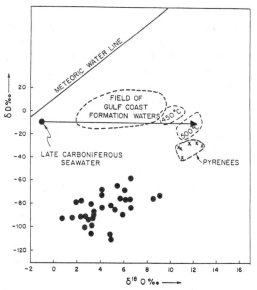

FIG. 5. The black dots represent analyses of whole-rock $\delta^{18}O$ and $\delta D$ of biotite, hornblende, or chlorite (rare) for samples of the older gneisses, migmatites, schists, and sheared granites within the Badenweiler-Lenzkirch zone in the southern Schwarzwald. The $\delta D$ values are from MAGARITZ and TAYLOR (1981). The uppermost four samples with highest $\delta D$ and highest $\delta^{18}O$ are from the extreme western end of the B-L zone (see text). Note that these B-L zone Schwarzwald samples are all much lower in $\delta^{18}O$ and $\delta D$ than the Hercynian igneous and metamorphic rocks from the Pyrenees (crosses) analyzed by WICKHAM and TAYLOR (1985); the Pyrenees samples appear to have formed from high-temperature marine waters (the calculated equilibrium fields are shown at 450° and 500°C), whereas the Schwarzwald samples clearly formed from exchanged meteoric-hydrothermal fluids that would have had $\delta D \approx -40$ to $-65$ and $\delta^{18}O \approx -2$ to $+6$, all derived from original ground waters that had $\delta^{18}O \approx -6$ to $-9$ (see text).

nor chlorite). Most of the analyzed rocks are only incipiently chloritized, so it is clear that much of the hydrothermal metamorphism occurred at moderately high temperatures, in the stability field of biotite. Many of these samples were collected either along the contacts of the Rand Granite or within 100 meters of its contact, both on the north against the gneiss complex, or along its contact against Upper Paleozoic metasediments on the south.

The Schwarzwald data-points on Fig. 5 display a crude trend subparallel to the Meteoric Water Line (extending toward the analogous data-points from the Pyrenees). The most logical interpretation of this trend is that it represents an isotopic shift in the OH-bearing minerals from their original igneous and/or metamorphic values downward and to the left toward values that indicate thorough exchange with large volumes of the aqueous fluids. The four samples that are highest in $\delta D$ and $\delta^{18}O$ on this diagram are in fact from the extreme western end of the B-L zone, where the hydrothermal metamorphism was apparently very weak (see above).

The pattern of data points shown on Fig. 5 is not typical of the simpler geological situations encountered in most meteoric-hydrothermal systems studied to date, for example where a single, undeformed epizonal pluton is emplaced into permeable country rocks. Ordinarily that kind of situation produces a characteristic "inverted-L" shaped trajectory, i.e., first a $\delta D$ shift directly downward and then a $\delta^{18}O$ shift horizontally to the left as the water/rock ratio increases (e.g., see TAYLOR, 1977). Thus the results on Fig. 5 seem to *demand* a much more complex geologic or hydrothermal history for the B-L zone.

One possible interpretation of the data on Fig. 5 is that the early stages of water/rock interaction in the B-L zone did indeed produce a simple "inverted-L" shaped pattern in the rocks, but that subsequently the area underwent other metamorphic events that evolved a series of "mixing lines" between high-$\delta D$, high-$\delta^{18}O$ samples and nearby low-$\delta^{18}O$, low-$\delta D$ samples, thereby smearing out the isotope pattern. Another interpretation is that the samples shown on Fig. 5 represent structural juxtaposition of rocks with widely different hydrothermal histories. Still another interpretation is that two or more water sources, with different isotopic compositions, were involved (e.g., sea water *and* meteoric water). Finally, it is possible that the hydrothermal activity occurred in multiple episodes over a long period of time, long enough for the climate to change and the $\delta D$ of the local meteoric ground water to shift by more than 20 per mil. The latter is probably the least likely explanation, based on what we know about the paleolatitude of this area in the Late Paleozoic (see below), and also because nearby granites intruded well after the Rand Granite show a range of $\delta D$ values practically identical to those of the B-L zone (MAGARITZ and TAYLOR, 1981; SIMON, 1990).

Any or all of the above explanations may apply to the B-L zone samples represented by the data points in Fig. 5. Inasmuch as we know from the paleontological evidence that the marine-to-freshwater transition in the sediments of the B-L zone did occur fairly close in time to the age of emplacement of the Rand Granite, the explanation involving two isotopically distinct kinds of water has a good deal of attraction (and it might also explain the crude trend on Fig. 5 toward the Pyrenees data points!). This concept is developed more fully below in a later section.

In spite of the above complications, and also in spite of some inherent problems of retrograde D/H exchange and of applying the D/H fractionations between OH-bearing minerals and $H_2O$ (because of differences in Fe/Mg and Fe/Al chemical compositions of the various OH-bearing minerals, e.g., see SUZUOKI and EPSTEIN, 1976), it is instructive to examine the $\delta D$ values of the most $^{18}O$-depleted group of samples in Fig. 5. This is the group that is probably most representative of exchange with the end-member meteoric waters of the B-L zone, regardless of which of the interpretations in the above list one favors (e.g., see TAYLOR, 1977). The 14 samples with whole-rock $\delta^{18}O < +4$ have $\delta D$ values of ranging from $-79$ to $-106$. However, most of these samples show a $\delta D$ variation only from $-90$ to $-100$. Applying a plausible range of hydrothermal temperatures (350–500°C) and using the calibration curves of SUZUOKI and EPSTEIN (1976), one obtains a range of $\delta D$ values of about $-40$ to $-65$ for the original meteoric ground waters of the region. Such values are typical of sub-tropical regions of the Earth today (i.e., southeastern U.S.A., Mediterranean Sea, Southeast Asia; see SHEPPARD, 1986b). If we use these values and then go horizontally over to the Meteoric Water Line, the initial $\delta^{18}O$ values of the groundwaters can be calculated to have been about $-6$ to $-9$.

There is little doubt that the paleolatitude of the Schwarzwald was close to or within the tropics during the Visean and most of the Carboniferous (SCOTESE and MCKERROW, 1990). The climate at the time was certainly hot, because evaporites and carbonate platform sediments were being deposited immediately to the north (ZIEGLER, 1982). The preservation of terrestrial plant fossils in the Visean of the B-L zone also provides evidence that the climate was wet, because it is only in humid climates that such fossils are commonly preserved (A. M. ZIEGLER, pers. comm., 1991). The combined evidence suggests that at the time that the B-L hydrothermal system developed, a humid sub-tropical climate prevailed, and in view of the low paleolatitudes, it is unlikely that local meteoric waters were ever extremely low (e.g., $\delta^{18}O$ of the local fresh waters could not possibly have been lower than $-10$, a conclusion in good agreement with our calculations using the data in Fig. 5).

Note that the $\delta D$ values of most of the B-L zone samples are not much different from the typical values of $-50$ to $-85$ observed in most igneous and metamorphic rocks on Earth (e.g., see TAYLOR and SHEPPARD, 1986). However, the *combination* of extremely $^{18}O$-depleted and moderately D-depleted rocks is nevertheless conclusive evidence for the strong involvement of meteoric-hydrothermal fluids in the metamorphism of the B-L zone.

## Northern Schwarzwald

Such $^{18}O$-depleted rocks as described above from the B-L zone have *not* been found anywhere in the northern Schwarzwald, either by us or by HOEFS and EMMERMANN (1983). Across the entire Schwarzwald massif, such extreme $^{18}O$ depletions are confined to the vicinity of this narrow tectonic line. Although weaker $^{18}O$ depletions are found locally over a much broader area, they also are basically confined to the southern Schwarzwald, either to the B-L zone or to the set of NW-trending fractures, although a few examples also are associated with certain early-stage Hercynian granites (*e.g.*, St. Blasien).

Note also that the primary magmatic $\delta^{18}O$ values of late-stage Hercynian granites from the northern Schwarzwald are higher than those of their post-rift equivalents in the south (Fig. 4). The sequence of increasing $^{18}O$ in these later granites thus correlates with their geographic proximity to the Badenweiler-Lenzkirch tectonic line. Some of these geographic effects are undoubtedly attributable to subsolidus hydrothermal alteration, but most of them seem to be primary magmatic effects. It is thus tempting to speculate that the reason why the younger Hercynian granites in the southern Black Forest tend to be lower in $^{18}O$ then those farther north is because they may have formed by melting of gneisses that had earlier become somewhat depleted in $^{18}O$ by the major meteoric-hydrothermal-metamorphic event that was confined to the south, and that increased in intensity toward the B-L tectonic line. This correlation becomes even more compelling if the Münsterhalden Granite is added to the picture (Fig. 4), because this pluton is even lower in $^{18}O$ than the other southern granites and it was emplaced totally within the B-L zone.

## A RIFT-ZONE MODEL FOR THE B-L ZONE

### Extensional tectonics in the Hercynian of Europe

Although traditional interpretations of late Hercynian (Variscan) orogenesis in Western Europe have invoked collisonal tectonic settings (*e.g.*, see MATTE and ZWART, 1989), recently several workers have suggested that instead, the characteristic low-pressure metamorphic sequences were generated within, or were associated with, zones of crustal extension (*e.g.*, WICKHAM and OXBURGH, 1985, 1987; WICKHAM and TAYLOR, 1990, 1985, 1987; BICKLE *et al.*, 1988; DESAINT BLANQUAT *et al.*, 1990; ECHTLER and MALAVIELLE, 1990). In the Pyrenees the evidence for deep circulation of marine waters, together with the evidence for contemporeneity of metamorphism at depth and marine sed-

imentation at the surface, are both incompatible with a model of regional uplift associated with continent-continent collision, as is the complete absence those rock types commonly found within collision zones, such as high-pressure metamorphic assemblages or ophiolite complexes.

Clearly, major regional crustal extension was occurring throughout Western Europe from latest Carboniferous time onward (MÉNARD and MOLNAR, 1988). These authors present an interesting map comparing the Permo-Carboniferous basins in central Europe with the sub-parallel grabens and half-grabens linked by normal and strike-slip faults in the Basin and Range Province of western North America. The outcrops and subcrops of these Permo-Carboniferous basins define linear belts that trend roughly E–W right across the Vosges and Schwarzwald massifs, before bending SW toward the Massif Central. The basins are hundreds of km in length and typically 5 to 25 km in width. Although they are clearly younger, there might be an evolutionary connection between these regional structural features and the down-dropped block of Lower Carboniferous sediments and volcanics in the B-L zone. MÉNARD and MOLNAR (1988) also point out that the normal faults that are found in some of the Hercynian basins have been re-activated as reverse faults; thus, even though the B-L zone exhibits some features attributable to thrusting (FLUCK *et al.*, 1980), compressional deformation need not have been dominant during the entire evolution of the B-L zone.

### Comparison with the Hercynian of the Pyrenees

Except for involvement of low-D, low-$^{18}O$ meteoric waters instead of high-D marine formation waters (Fig. 5), the Schwarzwald results are comparable with data from the Trois Seigneurs Massif, Pyrenees, where a rift-zone setting is also hypothesized and where analogous prograde hydrothermal metamorphism and somewhat analogous syn- and post-metamorphic granites are documented (WICKHAM and TAYLOR, 1985). The contemporeneity of metamorphism, anatexis, and granite emplacement with marine sedimentation at the surface (in the Pyrenees) and with terrestrial sedimentation at the surface (in the Schwarzwald) is a particularly striking parallel. Thus, rift-related, high thermal-gradient hydrothermal metamorphism involving marine or meteoric waters may be a common feature of Hercynian orogenic activity in Europe; in the southern Black Forest, the most likely tectonic setting for these effects would appear to be a narrow pull-apart associated with a major transform or strike-slip fault, perhaps analogous to what is going on at present along the Dead Sea rift zone in Israel or the Salton Sea trough in southern California. The enhanced fracture permeability, intrusive magmatic activity, and high heat flow associated with such pull-apart zones promotes hydrothermal metamorphism and deep convective circulation of surface-derived waters.

### Emplacement of granites in dilatant zones associated with faulting

Numerous cases have been described in the literature of granites emplaced into dilatant zones of extension during regional deformation of their country rocks, either by transcurrent shear or by thrust shear. The syntectonic character of these bodies is evidenced by the concordance of the contours of petrographic, metamorphic, and structural features, and by internal rock structures that are similar in both the granite and in the country rocks (GUINEBERTEAU et al., 1987; CASTRO, 1985; DAVIES, 1982; HUTTON, 1982). Typically such plutons are elongate in shape parallel to the regional vertical foliation.

### Evidence for a rift origin for the B-L zone

It is the premise of this paper that the B-L tectonic line was an early Hercynian rift-zone of some type, and that the combination of (1) emplacement of a "heat engine" (i.e., the Rand Granite) simultaneously with (2) the enhanced hydrologic fracture permeability attributable to the extensional tectonics, together produced a very large-sized (and long-lived?) meteoric-hydrothermal system somewhere in the time interval 320–360 Ma, based on radiogenic isotope geochronology. However, by combining the paleontological evidence for a Late Visean ($\approx 340$ Ma) change from marine to fresh-water sedimentation in the B-L zone, we believe we can restrict this time interval even more tightly. The meteoric-hydrothermal event documented by the $^{18}O/^{16}O$ data could not have begun before the Late Visean, because it certainly involved meteoric waters, not seawaters. This hydrothermal system was most intense within the Rand Granite pluton and within the adjacent down-dropped block of Devonian and Carboniferous sediments and volcanics, but its effects also spread out for a distance of at least 5-10 km away from the B-L zone. Thus, an area of about 1000 km², centered on the B-L zone, was affected by this giant Carboniferous-age ($\approx 330$–340 Ma) hydrothermal system.

Meteoric-hydrothermal effects on a small scale can be observed in a variety of tectonic environments where there has been intense deformation,

for example in the mylonite zones associated with detachment faults in the metamorphic core complexes of western North America (e.g., FRICKE et al., 1991; LEE et al., 1984) or associated with mylonites of major shear zones (e.g., McCAIG et al., 1990). However, the meteoric-hydrothermal $^{18}O/$ $^{16}O$ effects in these kinds of systems are even more tightly focused than they are in the B-L zone, occurring over distances of just a few tens of meters in the immediate vicinity of the shear zone (probably because most of them lack any good-sized magma body nearby, and thus have only limited thermal energy to drive the aqueous fluids through the rocks). These kinds of tectonic environments obviously cannot explain the data set from the B-L zone.

Our premise that the B-L zone was some type of rift is based mainly on the fact that all of the giant hydrothermal systems on Earth (both fossil and present-day) are known to be rift-related (e.g., mid-ocean ridges, Iceland, Salton Sea, etc.; see CRISS and TAYLOR, 1986). For example, in this volume SOLOMON and TAYLOR (1991) discuss somewhat analogous rift-related $^{18}O$-depletions associated with Jurassic igneous activity in California. Even where the individual intrusions or "heat engines" are cylindrical in shape rather than elongate, if they produced large-sized hydrothermal systems they are invariably associated with extensional tectonics (e.g., the Tertiary ring dikes of the Scottish Hebrides, the Skaergaard intrusion associated with the East Greenland dike swarm, the Yellowstone Park calderas that lie on the eastward extension of the Snake River rift zone, etc.). Thus we are virtually compelled by the $^{18}O/^{16}O$ evidence to conclude that the B-L zone also must have been an extensional environment at the time of the hydrothermal activity.

To the best of our knowledge, no one in the literature has proposed a rift-zone origin for the Badenweiler-Lenzkirch tectonic line. However, although we were driven to the rift-zone hypothesis by the $^{18}O/^{16}O$ evidence, we also believe that the structural and lithological features of the B-L zone are totally compatible with such an origin, particularly its shape and the fact that the sediments are typical rift-zone lithologies made up dominantly of greywackes, arkoses, siltstones, and conglomerates intercalated with silicic and intermediate volcanic rocks.

Other than the $^{18}O/^{16}O$ evidence, probably the best indication that the B-L zone is a rift is its geometry. It is clearly a down-dropped block bounded by faults of considerable displacement, because the fine-grained sediments of Upper Devonian and Lower Carboniferous age that are the basal Paleozoic sedimentary units in this area certainly must have originally been deposited over a much larger area. However, except for their occurrence in the very narrow B-L zone they are now completely absent from the rest of the Schwarzwald massif. Clearly the B-L crustal block went down relative to the older gneisses that bound it on the north and south. However, are these boundary faults normal faults or thrust faults? The present-day geometry of the north contact between the Rand Granite and the anatectic gneiss complex certainly appears to be that of a thrust (the north-dipping Todtnau thrust zone; e.g., EISBACHER et al., 1989). However, we believe that this geologic boundary perhaps could have started out as a normal fault, and only later was it perhaps tilted and deformed into a thrust-fault geometry. In point of fact, EISBACHER et al. (1990) themselves describe the south edge of the B-L zone as a normal fault.

Because the gneisses to the north appear to have been thrust over the Badenweiler-Lenzkirch sediments, the entire zone has commonly been interpreted as a compressional (subduction-related?) feature, as for example by FLUCK et al. (1980) and EISBACHER et al. (1989). In fact, EISBACHER et al. (1989) in the Schwarzwald and WICKERT and EISBACHER (1988) in the Vosges, have had to develop a rather unusual model of two-sided (bivergent) crustal-scale thrusting to explain the same kinds of features that we are explaining either as a rift-zone or as a pull-apart along a strike-slip fault. A compressional setting is, however, incompatible with the observed stable isotope signatures; of course, none of this stable isotope information was available to these earlier workers, as we only formulated this concept very recently (TAYLOR et al., 1989). Also, we do not deny that some of the observed structures along the B-L zone are thrust-related. It is virtually certain that this zone was at some stage the focus for such compressional deformation, but we believe that these structures have been superimposed upon earlier extensional events. However, much of the intense shearing and mylonitization observed along the B-L line may not even be thrust related; it could equally well be mainly attributable to strike-slip deformation along the B-L zone, as the "pull-aparts" that are common features of major strike-slip fault zones are themselves later closed up and sheared. SITTIG (1981) has in fact presented evidence for several kilometers of right-lateral displacement along the B-L zone, with a significant amount of slip occurring during the critical Visean time period.

We suggest that one of the reasons why a rift-zone origin for the B-L line has been overlooked is that it is extremely difficult to "look back" through all of the complex series of events (strike-slip, transpressional, transtensional, etc.) that probably

have affected the B-L zone. The earliest geologic events that are clearly associated with the genesis of the B-L zone and are also the least likely to be destroyed by subsequent geologic events, are the formation of an elongate, narrow, sedimentary-volcanic trough in the Lower Carboniferous, and the intrusion of the Rand Granite along the contact between these Upper Paleozoic rocks and the basement gneisses. Based on the geological evidence cited above, in combination with the low $\delta^{18}O$ values that provide such compelling evidence for rift-zone hydrothermal activity, we believe that our extensional model for the B-L zone (closely followed or accompanied by strike-slip deformation), is much more likely than the thrust zone models favored by FLUCK et al. (1980) or EISBACHER et al. (1989).

## SUMMARY AND CONCLUSIONS

Virtually all of the known areas on Earth where deep convective circulation of surface waters has produced giant hydrothermal systems and striking $^{18}O$ depletions on a regional scale can be shown to be associated with rift-zone magmatism and extensional tectonics (e.g., the mid-ocean ridges, the sheeted dikes and gabbros of ophiolite complexes such as Oman and Cyprus, Iceland, Yellowstone Park calderas, the Salton Sea rift, the Red Sea rift, the East Greenland dike swarm, the Jurassic rift of the Mojave Desert in California, the early Tertiary volcanic centers of the Hebrides in Scotland, etc. (e.g., see CRISS and TAYLOR, 1986; SOLOMON and TAYLOR, 1991). Therefore, based on our success in demonstrating that similar phenomena took place during Carboniferous time along the Badenweiler-Lenzkirch (B-L) tectonic line in the southern Schwarzwald, we suggest that in the future it may be possible to utilize $^{18}O/^{16}O$ and D/H systematics as a tool to "prospect" for rift-zones and pull-aparts, and thereby help to unravel the structure and stratigraphy of other geologically complex regions of the Earth's crust.

We believe that such an approach could turn out to be a very useful application of stable isotope geochemistry studies, because evidence of an early stage of extension can often be obscured as the stress regime changes. For example, terrane boundaries that began as a normal-fault-bounded rift-zone can evolve into a strike-slip regime, or the original faults can be re-activated as thrust faults. Plutons originally emplaced into pull-aparts along a transcurrent fault can later be sheared, stretched out, and attenuated as the local stress pattern evolves from extension to shear or transpression, etc. Therefore we can be very solicitous of the poor geologist who has the difficult task of looking back through a complex zone of deformation associated with a major, long-lived strike-slip fault zone or thrust zone, to try to identify an earlier episode of rifting and extension. Perhaps stable isotope geochemistry can help!

In spite of these complexities, if a major meteoric-hydrothermal system was established during an early period of rift-zone magmatism it will invariably produce widespread $^{18}O$ depletion in the rocks, and the pattern of $^{18}O$ depletion will reflect the location and intensity of the hydrothermal activity. More important, once large-scale $^{18}O/^{16}O$ changes have taken place in such large volumes of rocks, these $\delta^{18}O$ signatures can survive a long series of metamorphic and deformational events; the only way that such patterns can be destroyed or severely modified is for large amounts of some oxygen-bearing fluid to again move through the rocks and for them to again undergo massive and widespread $^{18}O/^{16}O$ exchange.

We believe that something like the above scenario is what happened along the Badenweiler-Lenzkirch line at about 330–340 Ma. In our view the $^{18}O/^{16}O$ systematics can only be explained by invoking some type of rift-zone magmatism, even though the geological and structural evidence for such an extensional event has escaped notice in earlier geological studies of the Schwarzwald. However, once we were driven to this particular conclusion by the $\delta^{18}O$ signatures in the rocks, we were then fortunate to find a number of pieces of evidence for this extensional event that support our hypothesis, based on the wealth of detailed studies carried out in this area by a large number of geologists over the past 100 years, many of which are put together in the magnificent geologic map compiled by METZ and REIN (1958) that we used as a base for our studies.

Using the paleontological evidence that the transition from marine to terrestrial conditions in the B-L zone occurred in the Late Visean, we also believe we can use our model to help unravel the complex and difficult geochronological relationships in this region. We can be absolutely certain from the stable isotope evidence that the B-L zone hydrothermal fluids (as well as all later-stage hydrothermal fluids that incipiently affected other Late Hercynian granites; e.g., SIMON, 1990) were derived from meteoric ground waters, not seawater. Although the B-L rift must have formed prior to the marine-freshwater transition, and thus could have been the site of some early marine-hydrothermal activity (for which the evidence has since been erased), it is very clear that the major hydrothermal episode associated with intrusion of the Rand Granite "heat engine" could not have begun until after this Late Visean transition (about 340 Ma). This is because the pore spaces and fractures within the sediments and volcanics obviously could not have been permeated by the required meteoric ground waters while marine sedimentation was taking place at the surface.

*Acknowledgements*—This paper is dedicated to Samuel Epstein, whom we honor in this volume for a lifetime of creative work. He has been a valued asset, friend, inspirational teacher and colleague to all of us over the years. His continued research creativity at a very high level even at the age of 72 is an inspiration to everyone lucky enough to be able to interact with him. We also wish to thank a number of others with whom we have had important discussions about these kinds of problems over the years, principally Ron Oxburgh, Al Hofmann, and particularly to Prof. Dr. W. Wimmenauer who provided some samples and who also aided us in collecting others. We also would like to recommend the southern Schwarzwald as an outstanding and interesting area in which to do field work. This research was supported by the National Science Foundation, Grants No. EAR-83-13106, EAR-88-16413, and EAR-90-19190.

## REFERENCES

ALBARÈDE F., DUPUIS C. and TAYLOR H. P., JR. (1980) $^{18}O/^{16}O$ evidence for non-cogenetic magmas associated in a 300 Ma old concentric pluton at Ploumanach'h (Brittany, France). *J. Geol. Soc. London* **137**, 641–647.

ALTHERR R. and MAASS R. (1977) Metamorphite am Südrand der zentralschwarzwälder Gneisanatexit masse zwischen Geschwand und Bernau. *Neues Jahrb. Geol. Paläontol. Abh.* **154**, 129–154.

BICKLE M. J., WICKHAM S. M., CHAPMAN H. J. and TAYLOR H. P., JR. (1988) A strontium, neodymium, and oxygen isotope study of hydrothermal circulation and crustal anatexis in the Trois Seigneurs Massif, Pyrenees, France. *Contrib. Mineral. Petrol.* **100**, 399–417.

BREWER M. S. and LIPPOLT H. J. (1972) Isotopische Altersbestimmungen an Schwarzwaldgesteinen, eine Übersicht. *Fortschr. Mineral.* **50**, 42–50.

BREWER M. S. and LIPPOLT H. J. (1974) Petrogenesis of basement rocks of the Upper Rhine region elucidated by Rb-Sr systematics. *Contrib. Mineral. Petrol.* **45**, 123–141.

BURGATH K. and MAASS R. (1973) Die variskische Entwicklung im sudlichen Schwarzwald. *Compte Rendu Septieme Congres International de Stratlgraphie et de Geologie du Carbonifere, Krefeld.* **2**, 195–209.

CASTRO A. (1985) The central Extremadura Batholith: Geotectonic implications (European Hercynian Belt). *Tectonophysics* **120**, 57–68.

CRISS R. E. and TAYLOR H. P., JR. (1986) Meteoric-hydrothermal systems. In *Stable Isotopes in High-Temperature Geological Processes* (eds. J. W. VALLEY, H. P. TAYLOR, JR. and J. R. O'NEIL); *Reviews in Mineralogy 16*, pp. 425–444. Mineralogical Society of America.

DAVIES F. B. (1982) Pan-African granite intrusions in response to tectonic volume changes in a ductile shear zone from northern Saudi Arabia. *J. Geol.* **90**, 467–483.

DE SAINT BLANQUAT M., LARDEAUX J. M. and BRUNEL M. (1990) Petrological arguments for high-temperature extensional deformation in the Pyrenean Variscan crust. *Tectonophysics* **177**, 245–262.

ECHTLER H. and MALAVIELLE J. (1990) Extensional tectonics, basement uplift and a Stephano-Permian collapse basin in a late Variscan metamorphic core complex (Montagne Noire, Southern Massif Central). *Tectonophysics* **177**, 125–138.

EISBACHER G. H., LÜSCHEN E. and WICKERT F. (1989) Crustal-scale thrusting and extension in the Hercynian Schwarzwald and Vosges, Central Europe. *Tectonics* **8**, 1–21.

EMMERMANN R. (1977) A petrogenetic model for the origin and evolution of the Hercynian granite series of the Schwarzwald. *Neues Jahrb. Mineral. Abh.* **128**, 219–253.

FLUCK P., MAASS R. and RAUMER J. F. (1980) The Variscan units east and west of the Rhine Graben. *Publ. Internat. Geol. Congr. Paris* **C.6**, 112–131.

FRICKE H. C., WICKHAM S. M. AND O'NEIL J. R. (1991) Oxygen and hydrogen isotope evidence for meteoric water infiltration during mylonitic deformation and uplift in the Ruby-East Humboldt Range core complex, Nevada. *Contrib. Mineral. Petrol.* (submitted).

GREGORY R. T., CRISS R. E. and TAYLOR H. P., JR. (1989) Oxygen isotope exchange kinetics of mineral pairs in closed and open systems: Applications to problems of hydrothermal alteration of igneous rocks and Precambrian iron formations. *Chem. Geol.* **72**, 1–42.

GUINNEBERTEAU B., BOUCHEZ J.-L. and VIGNERESSE J.-L. (1987) The Mortagne granite pluton (France) emplaced by pull-apart along a shear zone: Structural and gravimetric arguments and regional implication. *Geol. Soc. Amer. Bull.* **99**, 763–770.

HARLAND W. B., ARMSTRONG R. L., COX A. V., CRAIG L. E., SMITH A. G. and SMITH D. G. (1990) *A Geologic Time Scale. 1989.* Cambridge Univ. Press.

HOEFS J. and EMMERMANN R. (1983) The oxygen isotope composition of Hercynian granites and pre-Hercynian gneisses from the Schwarzwald, S. W. Germany. *Contrib. Mineral. Petrol.* **83**, 320–329.

HOFMANN A. W. (1979) Geochronology of the crystalline rocks of the Schwarzwald. In *Lectures in Isotope Geology* (eds. E. JÄGER and J. C. HUNZIKER), pp. 215–221. Springer, New York.

HOFMANN A. W. and KÖHLER H. (1973) Whole-rock Rb-Sr ages of anatectic gneisses from the Schwarzwald, S. W. Germany. *Neues Jahrb. Mineral. Abh.* **119**, 163–187.

HUTTON D. H. W. (1982) A tectonic model for the emplacement of the Main Donegal granite, NW Ireland. *J. Geol. Soc. London* **129**, 615–631.

KROHE A. and EISBACHER G. H. (1988) Oblique crustal detachment in the Variscan Schwarzwald, southwestern Germany. *Geol. Rundschau* **77**, 25–43.

LEE D. E., FRIEDMAN I. and GLEASON J. D. (1984) Modification of δD values in eastern Nevada granitoid rocks spatially related to thrust faults. *Contrib. Mineral. Petrol.* **88**, 288–298.

LEUTWEIN F. and SONET J. (1974) Geochronological studies in the southern Black Forest. *Neues Jahrb. Mineral. Abh.* **121**, 254–271.

LIPPOLT H. J. and RITTMANN K. L. (1984) Die Jungre variszische Geschichte der granite des SE Schwarzwalds; $^{40}Ar/^{39}Ar$ Untersuchungen an Glimmer. *Fortschr. Mineral.* **62**, 134.

LIPPOLT H. J., SCHLEICHER H. and RACZECK I. (1983) Rb-Sr systematics of Permian volcanites in the Schwarzwald (SW Germany). Part I: Space of time between plutonism and late orogenic volcanism. *Contrib. Mineral. Petrol.* **84**, 272–280.

LIPPOLT H. J., KOBER B., HRADETZKY H. and MERTZ

D. F. (1986) Schwarzwald Geochronologische Studien an Metamorphiten und Mineralisation. *2nd KTB Koll, Seeheim. Poster Prog. Abstr.* **41**.

LÜSCHEN E., WENZEL F., SANDMEIR K.-J., MENGES D., RÜHL T., STILLER M., JANOTH W., KELLER F., SÖLLNER W., THOMAS R., KROHE A., STENGER R., FUCHS K., WILHELM H. and EISBACHER G. (1987) Near-vertical and wide-angle seismic surveys in the Black Forest, SW Germany. *J. Geophys.* **62**, 1–30.

MAASS R. (1981) The Variscan Black Forest. *Geol. Mijnbouw* **70**, 137–143.

MAASS R. and STOPPEL D. (1982) Nachweis von Oberdevon bei Markstein (Bl. Munster, S. Vogesen). *Zeit. Deutsche Geol. Ges.* **133**, 403–408.

MAGARITZ M. and TAYLOR H. P., JR. (1981) Low $^{18}O$ migmatites and schists from the tectonic contact zone between Hercynian (= Variscan) granites and the older gneissic core complex of the Black Forest (Schwarzwald), West Germany. *Geol. Soc. Amer. Abstr. Prog.* **13**, 501.

MATTE P. (1986) Tectonics and plate tectonic model for the Variscan belt of Europe. *Tectonophysics* **126**, 329–372.

MATTE P. and ZWART H. J. (1989) Palaeozoic plate tectonics with emphasis on the European Caledonian and Variscan belts. *Tectonophysics* **169**, 221–352.

MCCAIG A. M., WICKHAM S. M. and TAYLOR H. P., JR. (1990) Deep fluid circulation in Alpine shear zones, Pyrenees, France: Field and oxygen isotope studies. *Contrib. Mineral. Petrol.* **106**, 41–60.

MEHNERT K. R. (1968) *Migmatites and the Origin of Granitic Rocks.* Elsevier, Amsterdam-London-New York.

MÉNARD G. and MOLNAR P. (1988) Collapse of a Hercynian Tibetan plateau into a late Paleozoic European Basin and Range Province. *Nature* **334**, 235–237.

METZ R. and REIN G. (1958) Erläuterungen zur Geologisch—petrographischen ÜbersichtsKarte des Südschwarzwaldes 1:50,000. Lahr/Schwarzwald: Moritz Schauenburg.

MICHARD-VITRAC A., ALBARÈDE F., DUPUIS C. and TAYLOR H. P., JR. (1980) The genesis of Variscan (Hercynian) plutonic rocks: inferences from Sr, Pb, and O isotope studies on the Maladeta igneous complex, central Pyrenees (Spain). *Contrib. Mineral. Petrol.* **72**, 57–72.

MÜLLER-SOHNIUS D., PROPACH G. and KÖHLER H. (1976) Gleichzeitige Intrusion von Bärhalde und Schluchseegranit. *Neues Jahrb. Mineral. Abh.* **127**, 174–186.

SCOTESE C. R. and MCKERROW W. S. (1990) Revised world maps and introduction. In *Palaeozoic Palaeogeography and Biogeography* (eds. W. S. MCKERROW and C. R. SCOTESE); *Geol. Soc. Amer. Mem.* **12**, pp. 1–21.

SHEPPARD S. M. F. (1977) The Cornubian batholith, SW England: D/H and $^{18}O/^{16}O$ studies of kaolinite and other alteration minerals. *J. Geol. Soc. London* **133**, 573–591.

SHEPPARD S. M. F. (1986a) Igneous Rocks: III. Isotopic case studies of magmatism in Africa, Eurasia and oceanic islands. In *Stable Isotopes in High Temperature Geological Processes* (eds. J. W. VALLEY, H. P. TAYLOR, JR. and J. R. O'NEIL); *Reviews in Mineralogy 16*, pp. 319–371. Mineralogical Society of America.

SHEPPARD S. M. F. (1986b) Characterization and isotopic variations in natural waters. In *Stable Isotopes in High Temperature Geological Processes* (eds. J. W. VALLEY, H. P. TAYLOR, JR. and J. R. O'NEIL); *Reviews in Min-*

*eralogy 16,* pp. 165–183. Mineralogical Society of America.

SIMON K. (1990) Hydrothermal alteration of Variscan granites, southern Schwarzwald, Federal Republic of Germany. *Contrib. Mineral. Petrol.* **105**, 177–196.

SIMON K. and HOEFS J. (1987) Effects of meteoric water interaction on Hercynian granites from the Südschwarzwald, S.W. Germany. *Chem. Geol.* **61**, 253–261.

SITTIG E. (1969) Zur geologischen Charakterisierung des Moldanubikums am Oberrhein (Schwarzwald). *Oberrhein. Geol. Abh.* **18**, 119–161; Karlsruhe.

SITTIG E. (1981) Evidence for wrench faulting within the Paleozoic Badenweiler-Lenzkirch Zone (Southern Schwarzwald Mountains, Germany). *Neues Jahrb. Geol. Paleontol. Mh.* **7**, 431–448.

SOLOMON G. C. and TAYLOR H. P., JR. (1991) Oxygen isotope studies of Jurassic fossil hydrothermal systems, Mojave Desert, southeastern California (this volume).

SUZUOKI T. and EPSTEIN S. (1976) Hydrogen isotope fractionation between OH-bearing minerals and water. *Geochim. Cosmochim. Acta* **40**, 1229–1240.

TAYLOR H. P., JR. (1977) Water/rock interactions and the origin of $H_2O$ in granitic batholiths (30th William Smith Lecture). *J. Geol. Soc. London* **133**, 509–558.

TAYLOR H. P., JR. (1988) Oxygen, hydrogen, and strontium isotope constraints on the origin of granites. *Trans. Roy. Soc. Edinburgh, Earth Sci.* **79**, 317–338.

TAYLOR H. P., JR. (1990) Oxygen and hydrogen isotope constraints on the deep circulation of surface waters into zones of hydrothermal metamorphism and melting. In *The Role of Fluids in Crustal Processes, Studies in Geophysics* (eds. D. L. NORTON and J. D. BREDEHOEFT), pp. 72–95. National Academy Press, Washington, D.C.

TAYLOR H. P., JR. and EPSTEIN S. (1962) Relationship between $O^{18}/O^{16}$ ratios in coexisting minerals of igneous and metamorphic rocks, Part 1: Principles and experimental results. *Geol. Soc. Amer. Bull.* **73**, 461–480.

TAYLOR H. P., JR. and SHEPPARD S. M. F. (1986) Igneous rocks: I. Processes of isotopic fractionation and isotope systematics. In *Stable Isotopes in High-Temperature Geological Processes* (eds. J. W. VALLEY, H. P. TAYLOR, JR. and J. R. O'NEIL); *Reviews in Mineralogy 16,* pp. 227–271. Mineralogical Society of America.

TAYLOR H. P., JR., MAGARITZ M. and WICKHAM, S. M. (1989) Application of stable isotopes in identifying a major Hercynian rift zone and its associated meteoric-hydrothermal activity, Southern Schwarzwald, West Germany. In *Epstein 70th Birthday Symposium Vol-*

*ume,* pp. 86–90. California Institute of Technology, Pasadena.

VENZLAFF V. (1971) Alterbestimungen nach der Rb/Sr Methode an Biotien aus Gesteinen des Schwarzwaldes. *Zeitschr. Naturforsch.* **26a**, 1372–1373.

VON DRACH V. (1978) *Mineralalter im Schwarzwald.* Inauguraldiss. Univ. Heidelburg, Germany.

WENDT L., LENZ H., HARRA W., and SCHOELL M. (1970) Total rock and mineral ages of granites from the southern Schwarzwald, Germany. *Eclogae Geol. Helv.* **63**, 365–370.

WENDT I., LENZ H. and HOHNDORF A. (1974) Das Alter des Bärhalde-Granites (Schwarzwald) und der Uranlagerstätte Menzenschwand. *Geol. Jahrb.* **E2**, 131–143.

WICKERT F. and EISBACHER G. H. (1988) Two-sided Variscan thrust tectonics in the Vosges Mountains, northeastern France. *Geodinamica Acta* **2**, 101–120.

WICKHAM S. M. and OXBURGH E. R. (1985) Continental rifts as a setting for regional metamorphism. *Nature* **318**, 330–333.

WICKHAM S. M. and OXBURGH E. R. (1986) Continental rifts and the tectonic setting for Hercynian high thermal gradient metamorphism in the Pyrenees. In *The evolution of the Pyrenees* (eds. E. BANDA and S. M. WICKHAM); *Tectonophysics 129,* pp. 53–69.

WICKHAM S. M. and OXBURGH E. R. (1987) Reply to P. Matte and M. Mattauer. *Nature* **325**, 739–740.

WICKHAM S. M. and TAYLOR H. P., JR. (1985) Stable isotopic evidence for large-scale seawater infiltration in a regional metamorphic terrane, the Trois Seigneurs massif, Pyrenees, France. *Contrib. Mineral. Petrol.* **91**, 122–137.

WICKHAM S. M. and TAYLOR H. P., JR. (1987) Stable isotope constraints on the origin and depth of penetration of hydrothermal fluids associated with Hercynian low-pressure regional metamorphism and crustal anatexis in the Pyrenees. *Contrib. Mineral. Petrol.* **95**, 255–268.

WICKHAM S. M. and TAYLOR H. P., JR. (1990) Hydrothermal systems associated with regional metamorphism and crustal anatexis: Example from the Pyrenees, France. In *The Role of Fluids in Crustal Processes, Studies in Geophysics* (eds. D. L. NORTON and J. D. BREDEHOEFT), pp. 96–112. National Academy Press, Washington, D.C.

WIMMENAUER W. (1980) Lithology of the Precambrian in the Schwarzwald. An interim report. *Neues Jahrb. Mineral. Mh.* **H8**, 364–371.

ZIEGLER P. A. (1982) *Geological Atlas of Western and Central Europe.* Shell International, B. V. Elsevier, Amsterdam.

Stable Isotope Geochemistry: A Tribute to Samuel Epstein
© The Geochemical Society, Special Publication No. 3, 1991
Editors: H. P. Taylor, Jr., J. R. O'Neil and I. R. Kaplan

# An oxygen and hydrogen isotope study of high-grade metamorphism and anatexis in the Ruby Mountains–East Humboldt Range core complex, Nevada

Stephen M. Wickham[1], Hugh P. Taylor Jr.[2], Arthur W. Snoke[3] and James R. O'Neil[4]

[1]Department of the Geophysical Sciences, University of Chicago,
5734 South Ellis Avenue, Chicago, IL 60637, U.S.A.
[2]Division of Geological and Planetary Sciences, California Institute of Technology, Pasadena, CA 91125, U.S.A.
[3]Department of Geology and Geophysics, University of Wyoming, Laramie, WY 82071, U.S.A.
[4]Department of Geological Sciences, University of Michigan, 1006 C.C. Little Building,
Ann Arbor, MI 48109-1063, U.S.A.

**Abstract**—Oxygen isotope analyses were made of 91 whole rock and mineral separate samples from the Ruby Mountains-East Humboldt Range metamorphic core complex and other nearby areas in eastern Nevada. In addition, ten hydrogen isotope analyses were made of the hydrous minerals muscovite, biotite, and hornblende. The samples include plutonic igneous rocks, high-grade metasedimentary rocks, and low-grade sediments that are thought to be their protoliths. The $\delta^{18}O$ values vary systematically in each of these categories. Most of the metasediments were shifted to lower $\delta^{18}O$ values than their protoliths, but the magnitude and pervasiveness of this $^{18}O$-depletion varies in different geographic areas, becoming most intense at Lizzies Basin in the East Humboldt Range where the deepest structural levels in the area are exposed. Within the area sampled at this locality, all silicate rock-types are isotopically homogenized over scales of at least tens of meters and shifted to $\delta^{18}O$ values close to +6. Quartz from contrasting igneous and metasedimentary rock-types has a uniform oxygen isotope composition implying that this mineral was very well equilibrated (see also Wickham and Peters, 1990). Elsewhere, exchange was less effective as illustrated by contrasts in the $\delta^{18}O$ values of adjacent marble, quartzite, and leucogranite layers. The $\delta^{18}O$ values of chemically similar leucogranites vary widely within the area studied. The most $^{18}O$-rich samples are from the northern Ruby Mountains ($\delta^{18}O > +12$), and these must have been derived by anatexis from sedimentary material. The lower-$^{18}O$ leucogranites were probably derived from similar material that had been isotopically altered at an earlier, metamorphic stage. $^{18}O$-depletion in the deep-seated metasediments and igneous rocks was probably the result of exchange with fluids derived from primitive mantle-derived intrusive rocks or with the rocks themselves. This conclusion is supported by the "normal" plutonic igneous $\delta D$ values shown by these same samples. At high structural levels, mylonites and associated rocks within the low-angle fault zone exposed at Secret Creek gorge were variably affected by meteoric water infiltration, which probably occurred during Tertiary extensional deformation, resulting in anomalously low D/H and $^{18}O/^{16}O$ ratios. Low-grade sedimentary rocks from other areas are also sporadically $^{18}O$-depleted, and this is similarly attributable to exchange with meteoric waters. These new isotopic data from Nevada add to, and complement, data from other terranes, such as the Pyrenees (Wickham and Taylor, 1985), that demonstrate that profound $^{18}O$-depletions and isotopic homogenization of metasedimentary rocks can take place during certain types of regional metamorphism. However, it is also becoming clear that these metamorphic $^{18}O$-depletions are probably produced by a variety of different mechanisms.

## INTRODUCTION

Oxygen is the most abundant element in most terrestrial rocks, fluids, and silicate melts. Because of this, and because systematic variations of $^{18}O/^{16}O$ ratios are observed in different terrestrial reservoirs such as the hydrosphere, mantle, and continental crust, oxygen is an exceedingly important tracer in investigations of petrological processes. These include, among others, several of the topics addressed in this study: magma formation by crustal anatexis, magma transport in the crust, and the interaction of aqueous fluids with subsolidus (metamorphic) and supersolidus (anatectic) rocks, during major tectonothermal events.

A characteristic feature of oxygen isotope variations in metamorphosed sedimentary rocks is a lowering of $\delta^{18}O$ values at higher metamorphic grades, and this also may be accompanied by a systematic change in D/H ratio (Wickham and Taylor, 1985). This $^{18}O$-depletion process is commonly between two and four per mil but may be in excess of ten per mil where the sedimentary rocks are $^{18}O$-rich carbonates and cherts. With the exception of $^{18}O$-depletions caused by decarbonation of impure limestones, these open-system effects are clearly attributable to isotopic exchange with an oxygen reservoir that undergoes a complementary $^{18}O$-enrichment. The most common large oxygen reservoirs available to bring about these isotopic shifts are (1) primitive igneous rocks (and associated volatiles) derived from the Earth's upper mantle, which have a relatively constant $\delta^{18}O$ value of $\sim +6$, and (2) meteoric waters or ocean waters with $\delta^{18}O \leq 0$. Previous studies of metamorphic sequences have identified both of these types of low-$^{18}O$ reservoirs as possible agents of metasediment $^{18}O$-depletion (e.g., GARLICK and EPSTEIN, 1967; SHIEH and SCHWARCZ, 1974; WICKHAM and TAYLOR, 1985), but it remains uncertain which is dominant during crustal metamorphism, whether in certain circumstances both may become involved, and whether either process may be contingent upon a particular type of tectonic setting.

In this paper we present data from a metamorphic core complex in northeastern Nevada, which provides a well-constrained opportunity to evaluate the cause of $^{18}O$-depletions in metamorphosed sedimentary rocks. Two factors make the area particularly attractive to study. First, although the $^{18}O$-depletions are variable, in certain areas they are particularly extreme, with metapelite and metacarbonate rocks attaining $\delta^{18}O$ values of $+7$ to $+9$ (representing downward shifts of 10 to 15 per mil from their protolith values). Second, the low-grade sedimentary equivalents of these same lithologies are exposed nearby in well-preserved, fossiliferous sedimentary sequences of the Cordilleran miogeocline, so that direct comparisons between low- and high-grade rocks and direct quantitative assessments of $^{18}O$-depletions can be made.

## GEOLOGY AND PETROLOGY OF THE RUBY MOUNTAINS-EAST HUMBOLDT RANGE

### Regional setting

The Ruby Mountains-East Humboldt Range is one of a series of north-northeast striking Late Cenozoic uplifts that characterize the Basin and Range Province of Nevada (Fig. 1). This area comprises one of the largest and best-exposed metamorphic core complexes in the western United States (ARMSTRONG, 1982), exposing high-grade metamorphic and igneous rocks of Mesozoic and Tertiary age. In this complex the metasedimentary rocks include pelite, quartzite, marble, and calc-silicate gneiss chiefly correlative with Late Precambrian and Paleozoic stratigraphic units (HOWARD, 1971; SNOKE and MILLER, 1988). These are intruded by numerous distinct bodies of leucogranite, monzogranite, diorite, and related igneous rocks.

In some areas (such as the southern Ruby Mountains) the metamorphic grade is very low, and the miogeoclinal strata are effectively unmetamorphosed, whereas in other areas (such as the northern Ruby Mountains and the East Humboldt Range) the rocks are pervasively recrystallized, plastically deformed, intruded, and partly melted (in appropriate lithologies). This important feature permits direct geochemical comparisons to be made between the high-grade rocks and their low-grade precursors,

making it possible to quantify the geochemical, mineralogical, and isotopic modifications that the miogeoclinal sediments have experienced during their metamorphism.

These rocks preserve a record of polyphase metamorphism and deformation. A complex and poorly understood Mesozoic history includes contractile deformation, polyphase folding, amphibolite-facies metamorphism, and mafic to silicic magmatism. During the Tertiary the area experienced strong and complex extensional deformation, leading to the tectonic emplacement of sheets of very low-grade supracrustal rocks over sections of mid-crustal rocks along low-angle normal fault systems. Mid-crustal extension was facilitated by kilometer-scale zones of plastic flow, represented by well-developed zones of mylonitic rocks, best exposed along the western flanks of the northern Ruby Mountains and East Humboldt Range. Tertiary extension was accompanied by plutonism, volcanism, and a strong low-pressure (sillimanite-grade) metamorphic overprint in the mid-crustal rocks.

Geochronological measurements on igneous and metamorphic rocks from the high-grade terranes have identified both Mesozoic and Tertiary thermal events (SNOKE et al., 1979; KISTLER et al., 1981; DALLMEYER et al., 1986; DOKKA et al., 1986; WRIGHT and SNOKE, 1986; LUSH et al., 1988), but the details of the thermal history, particularly the Mesozoic portion, are still very poorly known. Late Jurassic ($\sim 155$ Ma) and Late Cretaceous ($\sim 80$ Ma) igneous events have been documented by Rb-Sr (KISTLER et al., 1981) and U-Pb zircon and monazite (SNOKE et al., 1979; HUDEC and WRIGHT, 1990) techniques. Amphibolite-facies regional metamorphism and deformation accompanied the Jurassic magmatism (HUDEC and WRIGHT, 1990). The Cretaceous metamorphic history is as yet poorly constrained, the best data being U-Pb monazite ages (SNOKE et al., 1979; J. E. WRIGHT and A. W. SNOKE, unpubl. data), but was probably roughly synchronous with magmatism. The Tertiary thermal history has been better documented by U-Pb zircon, $^{40}Ar/^{39}Ar$, and fission track techniques. Tertiary igneous rocks comprise andesitic to rhyolitic volcanic rocks in the unmetamorphosed supracrustal sequence, the Harrison Pass granitoid pluton (36 Ma), and many meter-scale pods and sills of dioritic to granitic orthogneiss, including 29 Ma monzogranite and 32 and 39 Ma orthogneisses (WRIGHT and SNOKE, 1986).

### Lower plate igneous-metamorphic complex

Most of the isotopic data reported in this paper are from the polyphase amphibolite-facies rocks that comprise much of the study area. Rock-types include quartzite, marble, calc-silicate gneiss, metapelite, and metapsammite intruded by leucogranite, biotite monzogranite, biotite-hornblende quartz diorite, quartzo-feldspathic orthogneiss, and amphibolite. At deep structural levels, the igneous rocks occur mostly as small meter-scale pods and sills, although there are also some hundred-meter–thick sills of biotite-hornblende quartz diorite within the East Humboldt Range. The deep-seated metamorphic complex thus comprises a sequence of many hundreds of igneous and metasedimentary layers, intercalated on a relatively fine scale, and dipping at moderate angles throughout much of the area (Fig. 2).

Although quantitative geobarometry and thermometry is lacking for much of this terrane, HURLOW et al. (1991) reported P-T conditions of 3.1 to 3.7 kbar and 580–620°C

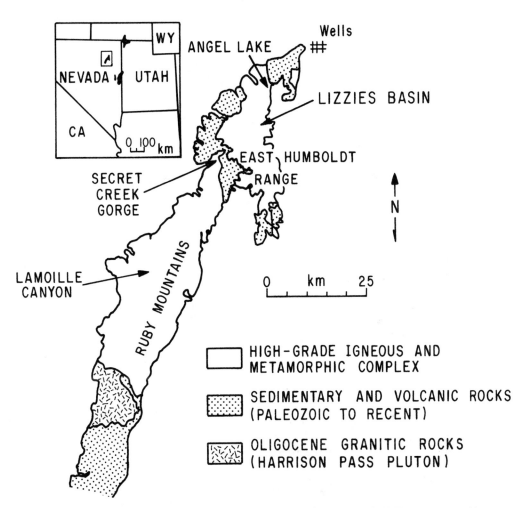

FIG. 1. Location and simplified geology of the Ruby Mountains-East Humboldt Range metamorphic core complex. High-grade metamorphic and plutonic igneous rocks are confined to the northern Ruby Mountains and the East Humboldt Range, while the southern Ruby Mountains comprise low-grade miogeoclinal sediments. The locations of the areas from which samples were taken for this study are indicated by arrows.

for a phase of the Tertiary mylonitization. The most recent metamorphic equilibration at Lizzies Basin (the deepest structural level exposed in the area) is estimated to have been at 5–6 kbar and 650–700°C (M. T. PETERS, pers. comm., 1991). Sillimanite is widespread in metapelitic rocks throughout the terrane and locally postdates kyanite (SNOKE and MILLER, 1988). Some of the sillimanite growth is probably due to Tertiary metamorphism (SNOKE et al., 1990), though some may be Late Cretaceous (SNOKE et al., 1979). The kyanite grew during an earlier high-pressure metamorphism probably in the Late Jurassic or Early Cretaceous (SNOKE and MILLER, 1988). This would suggest that these rocks resided at crustal depths in excess of 20 km during the Mesozoic and at shallower levels of perhaps 10–20 km during the Tertiary.

## ANALYTICAL PROCEDURES

Oxygen was extracted from silicates by reaction with fluorine gas at ~550°C (TAYLOR and EPSTEIN, 1962).

Oxygen was converted to $CO_2$ for mass spectrometric analysis by reaction with an electrically heated graphite rod. Silicate samples comprised whole-rock powders and mineral separates of quartz, biotite, and amphibole. Calcite from carbonate samples was analyzed using the $H_3PO_4$ technique (McCREA, 1950) corrected using the fractionation factor 1.01020 (modified after SHARMA and CLAYTON (1965) by FRIEDMAN and O'NEIL (1977)). Analytical error for oxygen and carbon isotope ratios is 0.1 to 0.2 per mil. The oxygen isotope data are reported in $\delta$-notation relative to Standard Mean Ocean Water (SMOW). NBS-28 has a $\delta^{18}O = +9.60$ on this scale. The $\delta^{13}C$ values are relative to PDB.

Hydrogen isotope analyses were made using the method of VENNEMAN and O'NEIL (1991). After initial degassing at 150°C, samples were dehydrated by heating to 1400°C and the water evolved converted to hydrogen by reaction with zinc. The precision of the $\delta D$ values is ±2 per mil. The $\delta D$ value of NBS-30 biotite is −65 per mil at the University of Michigan.

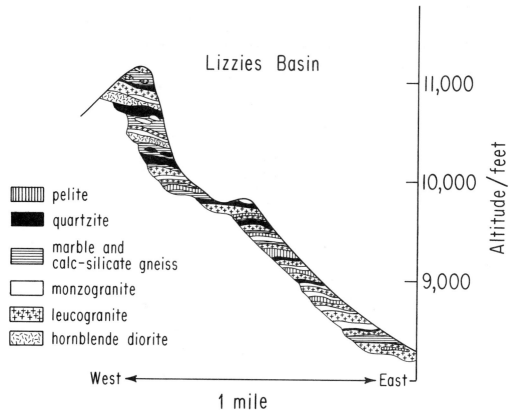

FIG. 2. Cross-section through the lower-plate igneous-metamorphic complex exposed at Lizzies Basin in the East Humboldt Range (after WICKHAM and PETERS, 1990). Strong plastic attenuation has resulted in subhorizontal layering, with many hundreds of individual rock units intercalated on meter to centimeter scales. The proportion of granitic rocks increases towards the bottom of the section, and the proportion of marble increases towards the top.

## STABLE ISOTOPE DATA

*Previous work*

The only previous oxygen isotope study of this area was that of KISTLER *et al.* (1981), who report data for minerals separated from 12 rocks collected from various localities throughout the northern Ruby Mountains. All of the four granitoids analyzed in that study were two-mica granites which had relatively high $\delta^{18}O$ values (*e.g.,* values for quartz are +14.0, +12.3, +11.6, and +14.9), indicating that these magmas were derived from a sedimentary protolith. According to KISTLER *et al.* (1981) these granites are Mesozoic or older, and they were probably in large part derived from shales and psammites of the McCoy Creek Group, which is the lowest stratigraphic unit within the miogeoclinal sequence, and one which can be readily inferred to have had an oxygen isotopic composition similar to that of the two-mica granites mentioned above (*e.g.,* compared with analogous sedimentary rocks of the Belt

Series further north studied by ESLINGER and SAVIN, 1973). The other rocks analyzed by KISTLER *et al.* (1981) included several metasediments—quartzite, marble, and mica schist, as well as one amphibolite. These tend to have slightly lower $\delta^{18}O$ than the granites (*e.g.,* $\delta^{18}O$ of quartz in mica schists is +10.2 and +10.1), which implies that those particular metasediments were probably not the immediate source for the granites, or, if they were, that they have since become selectively $^{18}O$-depleted.

*Northern Ruby Mountains (NRM)*

Our new oxygen isotope data from the northern Ruby Mountains (NRM) (for quartz, biotite, muscovite, and whole-rock samples) are given in Table 1. Samples were collected from two localities within Lamoille Canyon (shown in Fig. 1), and include various rock-types within the high-grade igneous-metamorphic complex forming the deepest exposed structural levels. The samples are from two traverses across intercalated metacarbonate, quartzite, and leucogranite, which are the predominant rock-types in this region.

The data for the leucogranites are similar to those reported by KISTLER *et al.* (1981), with quartz ranging between +14.9 and +12.2, confirming the $^{18}$O-rich nature of leucogranites in the NRM. However, the quartzites also display high $\delta^{18}$O values for quartz which are uniform within the samples studied (+12.2 to +12.8), similar to the values in quartz from the granites. The $\delta^{18}$O values of calcite in the metacarbonates vary more widely (+12.6 to +18.5), but all values are much lower than typical sedimentary carbonate values (+20 to +30). All of the analyzed samples are from amphibolite-facies assemblages, dominated by diopside, scapolite, plagioclase, and calcite; they have all clearly undergone decarbonation, and this process is accompanied by an $^{18}$O-depletion of the rocks because of loss of high-$^{18}$O $CO_2$ (*e.g.*, NABELEK *et al.*, 1984). The magnitude of the $^{18}$O-depletion, however, is generally much more than can be accounted for by simple decarbonation alone, and these metacarbonates therefore must also have exchanged with a low-$^{18}$O reservoir. In any case, there is no correlation between $\delta^{18}$O and extent of decarbonation in these samples. The variation in calcite $\delta^{18}$O contrasts with the relative homogeneity of quartz in the leucogranites and quartzites, and this indicates failure of *all* the carbonate lithologies to equilibrate with adjacent silicates at amphibolite-facies metamorphic temperatures. Locally, however, these lithologies may evidently approach equilibration on meter or 10-meter scales, as illustrated in Fig. 3, profile A. Those samples, collected over a 30-meter traverse, contain calcite and quartz which are relatively homogeneous in $^{18}$O/$^{16}$O and are almost equilibrated to plausible 700°C metamorphic temperatures. The $\delta D$ value of biotite from one of the quartzite samples is −58, a typical value for a sedimentary or metasedimentary rock.

A smaller three-meter section from near Lake Lamoille at the head of Lamoille Canyon (Fig. 3, profile B) is much more heterogeneous, with calcite and quartz samples less than a meter apart being well out of isotopic equilibrium. There has been some local approach toward isotopic equilibrium between metacarbonate and silicate lithologies but clearly no pervasive oxygen isotope homogenization. This may reflect the high proportion of relatively impermeable carbonate rocks within this region, (see below and WICKHAM and PETERS, 1990).

## Angel Lake, East Humboldt Range

Angel Lake is located at the northern end of the East Humboldt Range (Fig. 1), within the lower plate igneous-metamorphic complex that makes up most of the range. Detailed mapping at this locality (LUSH *et al.*, 1988; McGREW and SNOKE, 1988; A. J. McGREW, unpubl. data) has identified a number of different miogeoclinal stratigraphic units including Cambrian Prospect Mountain Quartzite and Ordovician to Devonian metacarbonates. These metamorphic rocks are interlayered with the full range of igneous lithologies described above, and also with a distinctive gneiss unit that forms a large fold-nappe structure comprising a mixture of orthogneiss, amphibolite, and paragneiss; these rocks may represent the Archaean to Early Proterozoic basement upon which the miogeoclinal metasediments were originally deposited (LUSH *et al.*, 1988).

All of these lithologies are represented in the suite of samples analyzed, many of which were taken from a single ~30-meter profile illustrated in Fig. 4, but also from several other localities in the same vicinity. The data are similar to the NRM data but there are some important distinctions. The carbonates are even more heterogeneous in $^{18}$O/$^{16}$O, with one sample preserving a $\delta^{18}$O value (+23.5) close to its sedimentary value. Other samples have undergone strong $^{18}$O-depletion, with the lowest value (+12.4) similar to the values observed in the NRM data. Granitic rocks at Angel Lake are in general lower in $\delta^{18}$O than those in the NRM. Whole-rock samples of two basement orthogneisses are +8.5 and +7.9, with quartz in one sample at +9.5. Quartz separates from two leucogranites have $\delta^{18}$O = +10.9 and +12.1, but are as low as +7.5 in a pelitic migmatite. All of the quartz $\delta^{18}$O values are lower than quartz from NRM lithologies, although the mean value is only about two per mil lower. Minerals from individual samples typically are near to isotopic equilibrium, with typical high-grade metamorphic fractionations (*e.g.*, $\Delta_{quartz\text{-}biotite}$ = 5.5). However, it is clear that, although there has been an approach to equilibrium in these diverse lithologies, the section has not fully equilibrated on a meter scale. Calcite $\delta^{18}$O-values from metacarbonates within the 30-meter profile are within three per mil of their expected equilibrium values with adjacent quartz from intercalated silicate lithologies. This compares with probable 10–15 per mil contrasts that would initially have existed at the pre-metamorphic stage.

Hydrogen isotope analyses of muscovite and biotite from these samples are variable. Muscovite

Table 1. Oxygen, carbon, and hydrogen isotope data for rocks and minerals from the Ruby-East Humboldt Range metamorphic core complex and other locations in north-eastern Nevada. All data are $\delta^{18}O$ values unless otherwise indicated

| Sample number | Rock-type | Whole rock | Quartz | Biotite | Muscovite | Calcite | $\delta^{13}C$ | % cc |
|---|---|---|---|---|---|---|---|---|
| **Northern Ruby Mountains** (* Stop 9 in Snoke and Howard, 1984; # Lake Lamoille) | | | | | | | | |
| RB30* | marble | | | | | +14.50 | −3.36 | 19 |
| RB31* | marble | | | | | +12.64 | +1.46 | <2 |
| RB32* | marble | | | | | +13.39 | −1.57 | 6 |
| RB33* | leucogranite | +11.14 | +12.22 | | | | | |
| RB34* | marble | | | | | +15.52 | −3.08 | 9 |
| RB35* | quartzite | | +12.43 | +7.86 | | | | |
| | | | | ($\delta D = -58$) | | | | |
| RB42# | leucogranite | +11.40 | +12.36 | | | | | |
| RB43# | calc-silicate gneiss | | | | | +15.16 | −2.61 | 2 |
| RB44# | marble | | | | | +18.50 | −1.28 | 45 |
| RB45# | leucogranite | +13.21 | +14.89 | | | | | |
| RB46# | marble | | | | | +18.35 | −2.25 | 40 |
| RB47# | quartzite | +12.42 | +12.25 | | | | | |
| RB48# | quartzite | +12.30 | +12.76 | | | | | |
| **Secret Creek Gorge** (Stop 12 in Snoke and Howard, 1984) | | | | | | | | |
| RB59 | leucogranite | +3.12 | +10.94 | | | | | |
| RB60 | amphibolite | +2.44 | | | | | | |
| RB61 | leucogranite | | +10.47 | | +8.52 | | | |
| RB62 | quartzite | | +11.10 | +5.03 | +8.96 | | | |
| | | | | ($\delta D = -128$) | ($\delta D = -115$) | | | |
| RB63 | quartz vein | | +10.74 | | | | | |
| RB65 | quartzite | +7.37 | | | | | | |
| RB66 | leucogranite | +8.43 | | | | | | |
| SP3 | marble | | | | | +13.47 | −3.72 | 55 |
| SP4 | quartzite | +14.93 | | | | | | |
| SP5 | limestone | | | | | +12.79 | +1.64 | 96 |
| SP5 | calcite vein | | | | | +1.49 | +1.93 | 97 |
| **Angel Lake** | | | | | | | | |
| AL14 | leucogranite | +12.14 | +12.26 | | | | | |
| AL15 | marble | | | | | +12.40 | +5.36 | 4 |
| AL16 | biotite gneiss | +8.64 | +10.85 | | | | | |
| AL17 | marble | | | | | +13.53 | +5.59 | 12 |
| AL18 | pelite | +8.92 | +7.49 | +6.70 | | | | |
| | | | | ($\delta D = -88$) | | | | |
| AL19 | quartzite | +10.52 | | | | | | |
| AL20 | leucogranite | +9.86 | +10.86 | | +8.66 | | | |
| | | | | | ($\delta D = -40$) | | | |
| AL21 | marble | | | | | +16.12 | −1.85 | 74 |
| AL22 | leucogranite | +11.99 | | | | | | |
| AL23 | marble | | | | | +15.74 | −2.59 | 47 |
| AL24 | marble | | | | | +23.51 | −0.51 | 13 |
| AL25 | quartzite | +12.67 | | | | | | |
| AL30 | orthogneiss | +7.93 | +9.42 | +4.17 | | | | |
| | | | | ($\delta D = -108$) | | | | |
| AL31 | amphibolite | +5.92 | | | | | | |
| AL33 | orthogneiss | +8.51 | | | | | | |
| **Lizzies Basin** | | | | | | | | |
| LB1 | biotitite | | | +5.28 | | | | |
| | | | | ($\delta D = -68$) | | | | |
| LB2 | leucogranite | +6.72 | +9.67 | +5.56 | | | | |
| LB4 | vein | | +9.57 | +5.43 | | | | |
| | | | | ($\delta D = -58$) | | | | |
| LB5 | leucogranite | | +9.03 | +4.37 | | | | |
| LB6 | amphibolite[1] | +6.60 | | | | | | |
| | | ($\delta D = -50$) | | | | | | |

Table 1. (Continued)

| Sample number | Rock-type | Whole rock | Quartz | Biotite | Muscovite | Calcite | $\delta^{13}C$ | % cc |
|---|---|---|---|---|---|---|---|---|
| **Lizzies Basin** | | | | | | | | |
| LB10 | calc-silicate gneiss | +7.87 | | | | | | |
| LB10V | vein | | +11.43 | | | | | |
| LB11 | leucogranite | | +9.23 | | | | | |
| LB12 | calc-silicate gneiss | +7.35 | +9.19 | | | | | |
| LB13 | marble | | | | | +12.11 | +2.80 | 93 |
| LB14 | calc-silicate gneiss | +8.21 | | | | | | |
| LB15 | marble | | | | | +9.42 | +0.02 | 90 |
| LB16 | pelite | +7.89 | +9.67 | +4.08 ($\delta D = -66$) | | | | |
| LB17 | leucogranite | +8.02 | +9.19 | | | | | |
| **Southern Ruby Mountains (Lindsay Creek)** | | | | | | | | |
| SR23[2] | limestone | | +20.01 (QV) | | | +14.45 | -1.41 | 83 |
| SR25[2] | limestone | | | | | +18.50 | +0.61 | 66 |
| SR29[2] | limestone | | | | | +17.51 | -4.92 | 66 |
| SR32[4] | quartzite | +12.35 | | | | | | |
| **Schell Creek Range** | | | | | | | | |
| SC7[3] | phyllite | +16.21 | | | | | | |
| SC8[3] | quartzite | +14.35 | +15.14 (QV) | | | | | |
| SC14[4] | quartzite | +11.66 | | | | | | |
| SC17[4] | quartz vein | | +13.51 | | | | | |
| **Egan Range (Lund Canyon)** | | | | | | | | |
| EG1[5] | limestone | | | | | +16.46 | -0.37 | 83 |
| EG3[5] | limestone | | | | | +15.63 | -18.96 | 98 |
| EG4[5] | chert | +19.69 | | | | | | |
| EG8[6] | quartzite | +13.32 | | | | | | |

In the Schell Creek Range column, SC7 and SC8 are bracketed as "Piermont Creek" and SC14 and SC17 are bracketed as "Pattersons Pass".

[1] 98% hornblende.
[2] Middle Cambrian limestone.
[3] McCoy Creek Group (Late Pre-Cambrian).
[4] Prospect Mountain quartzite (Lower Cambrian).
[5] Upper Cambrian limestone and chert.
[6] Ordovician quartzite.
(QV): cross-cutting quartz vein.

from a leucogranite ($\delta^{18}O = +9.9$) has a relatively normal plutonic $\delta D$ value of $-40$, but the two biotite samples are anomalously light ($\delta D = -88$ and $-108$ in a pelite and basement orthogneiss, respectively). This may represent late-stage infiltration of small amounts of meteoric water during uplift of these rocks into the near-surface environment. Alternatively, the infiltration could have occurred synchronous with the most recent phase of deformation as observed in the mylonitic rocks at Secret Creek gorge (see below and FRICKE et al., 1991). In any event, the quantities of water involved were probably tiny, because there was no significant $^{18}O$-depletion and only small changes in $\delta D$ (as compared with the much stronger effects at Secret Creek gorge).

## Lizzies Basin, East Humboldt Range

Oxygen isotope data for quartz, biotite, and amphibole separated from silicate lithologies, whole-rock silicates, and calcite from metacarbonates from Lizzies Basin are plotted in Fig. 5. This locality is in the central part of the East Humboldt Range (Fig. 1) and exposes the deepest structural levels seen in the entire terrane. The data are mostly from a two-meter section across various intercalated lithologies and from other sampling sites close by

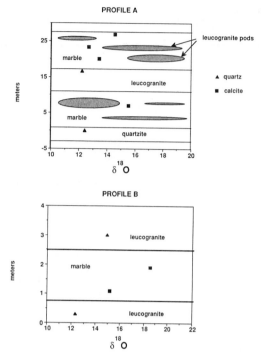

FIG. 3. Profile A: oxygen isotope variation in quartz and calcite from a 30-meter section through intercalated quartzite, leucogranite, and marble layers. All of the calcite $\delta^{18}O$ values are much lower than typical sedimentary carbonate values, and in the case of the upper marble layer are close to a composition that would be in equilibrium with the adjacent leucogranite quartz at amphibolite-facies metamorphic temperatures. Biotite from the quartzite layer has a $\delta^{18}O$ value of +7.86 and a $\delta D$ value of −58.

Profile B: $\delta^{18}O$ values of quartz and calcite from adjacent leucogranite and marble near Lake Lamoille at the head of Lamoille Canyon. The isotopic heterogeneity exhibited by samples less than a meter apart indicates limited exchange between these layers, but the carbonate samples have clearly experienced some $^{18}O$-depletion.

(<100 meters away). Two important features are immediately recognizable. One is the very low $\delta^{18}O$ of the entire suite of rocks. The second is the extreme oxygen isotope uniformity of quartz in all samples.

Despite the fact that these rocks include metasediments that elsewhere characteristically have $\delta^{18}O$ values well in excess of +10, all of the Lizzies Basin samples have $\delta^{18}O < +10$ (except for one carbonate). Most whole-rock silicate values, including a wide variety of both igneous and metasedimentary rocks, lie between +6 and +8, close to the range of primitive, mantle-derived igneous rocks. These values are in striking contrast to those of the mineralogically and compositionally identical leucogranites in the northern Ruby Mountains, which are much more $^{18}O$-rich. Note that even the migmatitic paragneiss from Lizzies Basin (which

contains leucogranite leucosomes and may represent a leucogranite source material) has a similarly low $\delta^{18}O$, implying that in the Lizzies Basin region, either the leucogranite source materials were strongly $^{18}O$-depleted before they were melted or that subsequent $^{18}O$-depletion affected *all* lithologies. Certainly, $^{18}O$-depletion here was much more profound than anywhere else within the Ruby-East Humboldt igneous-metamorphic complex and involved downward shifts in $\delta^{18}O$ of 5 to 10 per mil in silicate metasediments, and 10 to 15 per mil in metacarbonates, which is probably as extreme as has been observed in any other high-grade terrane worldwide.

In addition to extreme $^{18}O$-depletion, mineral pairs within the Lizzies Basin rocks are close to high-temperature isotopic equilibrium, both within and between samples. Quartz-biotite fractionations range from 3.6 to 5.5, indicating equilibration temperatures of 550–800°C (FRIEDMAN and O'NEIL, 1977). This compares favorably with metamorphic temperature estimates of 650–700°C (M. T. PETERS, pers. comm., 1991). Most of the variation in

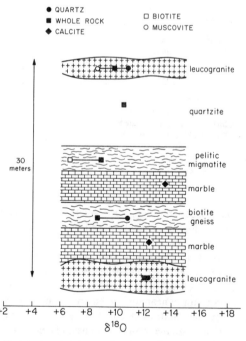

FIG. 4. Oxygen isotope variation across a 30-meter profile through intercalated leucogranite, quartzite, pelite, biotite gneiss, and marble layers at Angel Lake at the northern end of the East Humboldt Range (see Fig. 1). All the metasedimentary rocks (with the possible exception of the quartzite) have $\delta^{18}O$ values considerably lower than those of their inferred sedimentary protoliths.

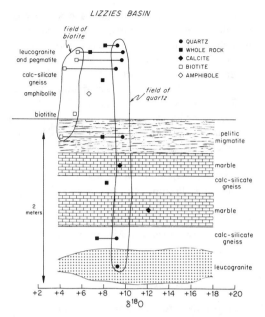

FIG. 5. Oxygen isotope whole-rock and mineral data from Lizzies Basin, including samples from a two-meter section through interlayered metasediments and granites. Other data for samples collected nearby (over an area of ~0.5 km²) are listed by rock-type and plotted in the upper part of the diagram. Note the extremely narrow range of $\delta^{18}O$ of quartz and biotite from contrasting rock-types; quartz-biotite fractionations of 4–5 per mil are typical of high-grade metamorphic rocks and indicate a close approach to equilibrium in these samples. The two calcite samples are slightly out of equilibrium with the quartz and biotite but are nevertheless very $^{18}O$-poor compared with normal limestones, indicating that they have undergone $\delta^{18}O$ shifts in excess of ten per mil.

the $\Delta_{quartz\text{-}biotite}$ values is due to variation in the $\delta^{18}O$ of biotite, which may be due to several factors: (1) the smaller modal abundance of biotite in most samples; (2) the fact that biotite continues to exchange oxygen down to lower temperatures than quartz; or (3) to small amounts of alteration minerals in biotite separates (e.g., interlayer chlorite), although this third possibility is unlikely because the samples are very fresh and do not have abnormally low $\delta D$ values (see below).

Quartz, on the other hand, is extremely homogeneous in all samples analyzed (with the exception of one quartz vein within calc-silicate gneiss which may be a late-stage phenomenon). Seven other samples all have $\delta^{18}O$ quartz between +9.0 and +9.7, a remarkably narrow grouping considering the diverse range of rock types. This shows that at Lizzies Basin, all lithologies were profoundly $^{18}O$-depleted, and also came close to high temperature equilibrium on much longer length scales (at least tens of meters) than is observed anywhere else in

the study area. The only rock types not equilibrated are calcite-rich marbles, which, if they were in equilibrium with the quartz at 700°C temperatures, should have attained $\delta^{18}O$ in the range +8.6 to +9.3 (CHIBA et al., 1989). Nevertheless, considering that they would have started out with sedimentary values in the range +20 to +30, their measured values of +9 to +12 represent a close (although not complete) approach to equilibrium. The $\delta D$ values of three of the biotite samples are relatively constant ($\delta D$ = −58 to −68) and have typical plutonic values (as does the amphibolite, LB6), which suggests that no late-stage meteoric-hydrothermal alteration has occurred.

### Secret Creek gorge

All data discussed so far have been from high-grade rocks located at deep structural levels within the lower plate of the Ruby-East Humboldt core complex. In the Secret Creek gorge area, a cross-section through the upper plate-lower plate boundary is well exposed (SNOKE and HOWARD, 1984). This consists of a several hundred meter–thick zone of strongly mylonitic lower-plate rocks (including all the main lithologies from the igneous-metamorphic complex) that passes up into an anastomosing system of low-angle normal faults separating the mylonites from a low-grade, brittley deformed sedimentary and volcanic cover (SNOKE, 1980). Movement on this fault zone has been responsible for exhuming the mid-crustal lower-plate rocks (SNOKE and LUSH, 1984).

Preliminary data from the northern Ruby Mountains (KISTLER et al., 1981; FRICKE and WICKHAM, 1990) suggested that certain fault-zone lithologies had been strongly $^{18}O$-depleted as a result of interaction with heated meteoric water. In order to investigate this phenomenon further, and to evaluate any connection with the deformational history in this area, we analyzed minerals and whole-rock samples from a variety of lithologies. Results are shown in Fig. 6 and include mostly mylonitic rock-types, variably affected by late-stage brittle deformation. Again, as seen at Lizzies Basin, quartz from leucogranite, quartzite, and a quartz vein (all mylonitized) is relatively uniform in $\delta^{18}O$ (+10.5 to +11.1), although the values are about one per mil higher than at the more deep-seated locality. However, whole-rock values in the various leucogranite lithologies are variable and include one very low value (+3.1 in RB59) that is clearly attributable to meteoric-hydrothermal alteration. Inasmuch as these samples comprise mostly quartz and feldspar, the $\delta^{18}O$ of the feldspars can be calculated by material balance to be even more $^{18}O$-

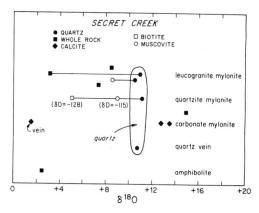

FIG. 6. Oxygen isotope data for whole-rock and mineral samples from Secret Creek gorge. Quartz from various rock-types is fairly homogeneous in isotopic composition and probably corresponds to metamorphic, pre-deformational values. However, some of the whole-rock values must have been affected by interaction with meteoric water because the $\delta^{18}O$ values are less than +6. Biotite and muscovite from a quartzite mylonite have very low $\delta D$ values that are also consistent with meteoric hydrothermal alteration.

depleted than the +3.1 whole-rock value, underscoring the strong isotopic disequilibrium observed in these samples. This type of disequilibrium is commonly observed in meteoric hydrothermal systems around cooling high-level plutons and the $^{18}O$-depletions at Secret Creek gorge may have been generated in a similar way, albeit with a different heat source, namely the rapidly uplifted mid-crustal rocks of the lower plate.

The $\delta D$ values of muscovite (−115) and biotite (−128) in the quartzite mylonite (RB62) also provide evidence for meteoric water infiltration, even though $^{18}O/^{16}O$ ratios of the minerals in this sample are virtually unaffected (there are no obvious disequilibrium $^{18}O/^{16}O$ fractionations, and $\Delta^{18}O_{quartz-biotite}$ is ~6, only slightly higher than quartz-biotite fractionations at much deeper structural levels). The biotite in this rock is very fresh and unchloritized, suggesting that mylonitization and water infiltration occurred at moderately high temperatures (>400°C?). HURLOW et al. (1991) estimated a temperature of 580–620°C for a stage of the mylonitization, but it is possible that isotopic exchange could have occurred at lower temperatures.

The only other sample in which a strong $^{18}O$-depletion is observed is in a calcite vein ($\delta^{18}O$ = +1.5) within low-grade limestone of the Devonian Guilmette Formation from a locality immediately above the detachment fault zone. This unit is heavily veined, brittley deformed, but contains

no mylonitic textures and cannot have been heated to high temperatures. Similar veins are common throughout the upper-plate rocks and probably indicate infiltration pathways of surface-derived fluids.

Very recently, FRICKE and WICKHAM (1990) and FRICKE et al. (1991) have detected strong $^{18}O$-depletions ($\delta^{18}O$ as low as −1) in quartzite mylonites from the same locality. Because these samples have high quartz contents >95%, it is certain that even the quartz was strongly $^{18}O$-depleted. This may be because fluid infiltration occurred locally at higher temperatures—or more likely that the strong dynamic recrystallization of quartz promoted isotopic exchange at temperatures of perhaps 400–500°C. In the absence of deformation, quartz would normally be very resistant to exchange with water in this temperature range.

*Low-grade Paleozoic rocks*

One of the great advantages in studying the metasedimentary rocks of the Northern Great Basin is that their low-grade protoliths are exposed nearby within the same region. Amphibolite-facies quartzites, schists, and marbles in the Ruby-East Humboldt Range have been identified as various elements of the miogeoclinal succession (HOWARD, 1971), including the Late Proterozoic McCoy Creek Group, Prospect Mountain Quartzite, and various Lower and Middle Paleozoic carbonate units. Unmetamorphosed fossiliferous sections through the Paleozoic rocks are exposed nearby in the southern Ruby Mountains and the Egan Range, and moderately metamorphosed (greenschist to locally garnet-grade, MISCH and HAZZARD, 1962) McCoy Creek Group rocks are exposed in the Schell Creek Range.

A few samples from these regions were analyzed in order to make direct comparisons between the various low- and high-grade stratigraphic units. The results are given in Table 1, plotted in Fig. 7 and discussed below. The quartzite samples were taken from Prospect Mountain Quartzite from both the southern Ruby Mountains and the Egan Range, and have typical sedimentary quartzite values of +12.3 and +13.3, respectively. Note that these values overlap only with the most $^{18}O$-rich of the high-grade silicate samples. The McCoy Creek samples are even heavier, ranging from +11.7 to +16.2 in three samples from the Schell Creek Range. The higher-$^{18}O$ samples are typical of low-grade shales, whereas the other is more typical of metapelites that have experienced some $^{18}O$-depletion (at this locality the McCoy Creek rocks have locally been recrystallized to garnet-biotite schists).

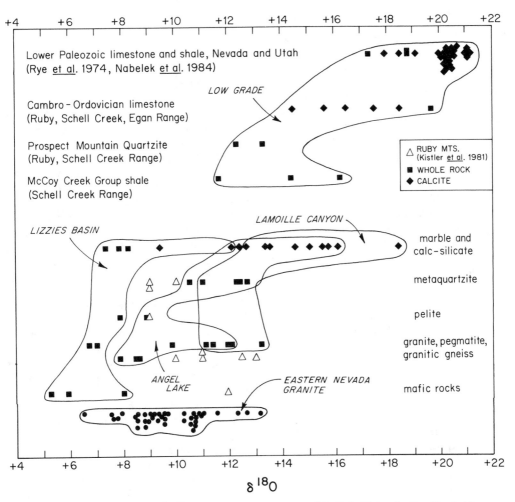

FIG. 7. A compilation of $^{18}O/^{16}O$ data from high-grade rocks of the Ruby Mountains-East Humboldt Range and from low-grade sediments elsewhere in the northern Great Basin, including some possible protoliths to the high-grade metasediments and granites. The high-grade lithologies are fairly homogeneous at a given locality, but vary considerably between localities, with Lizzies Basin being isotopically lightest and Lamoille Canyon being heaviest. Most of the high-grade lithologies have $\delta^{18}O$ values that are much lower than their present-day low-grade equivalent, and almost all the carbonates are much lower than typical sedimentary carbonate values of +20 to +30. These data imply that some of the metasediments have undergone shifts of 5–10 per mil to lighter values during their metamorphic history. Mesozoic and Tertiary granitic rocks span a range of values from +6.5 to +13.5, even though the granites at Lizzies Basin (+7) are mineralogically and compositionally almost identical to those from Lamoille Canyon (+11 to +13.5), implying that all these granites are derived from similar source material and suggesting that the metasedimentary source materials may have been variably depleted in $^{18}O$ prior to melting. The range is similar to that observed by SOLOMON and TAYLOR (1989) for many granite plutons from throughout eastern Nevada (solid circles at bottom of diagram).

The $\delta^{18}O$ values of limestones range from +14.4 to +18.5 (+19.7 in a chert from within one of the Egan Range limestones). Although these samples are all very low-grade, fossiliferous rocks, they all have $\delta^{18}O$ values considerably lower than those of typical sedimentary limestones (+20 to +30). $\delta^{13}C$ values in these samples are more normal (+0.6 to −4.9), with the exception of one sample (EG3) with a strongly negative $\delta^{13}C$ of −19.0, which probably indicates a strong influence of organic matter on the carbon isotope signature.

The relatively low $\delta^{18}O$ values of these fossiliferous limestones indicates that $^{18}O$-depletion processes have operated at quite low grades within certain parts of the miogeoclinal sedimentary sequences, even in seemingly unrecrystallized rocks, presumably either promoted by near-surface hydrothermal activity or occurring during diagenesis. Although none of the samples of limestone are close to any obvious intrusive igneous complexes, these kinds of $\delta^{18}O$ values are in fact typical of exposed carbonate rocks throughout much of the Basin and Range Province, which has had a complex Cenozoic history involving widespread volcanism and shallow plutonism accompanied by considerable low-temperature meteoric-hydrothermal alteration and formation of mineral deposits. Although we cannot as yet prove it with the available data set, it is possible that the $^{18}O$-depletions in the low-grade limestones are largely attributable to shallow Cenozoic activity, and this would mean that the deeper-seated carbonate protoliths in the Mesozoic core complexes were not in general subjected to these low-temperature meteoric effects. If true, this would imply that the *metamorphic* $^{18}O$-depletions discussed above are even larger than might be inferred from direct comparison of the $\delta^{18}O$ values of the metamorphic rocks with their "unmetamorphosed" protoliths.

## DISCUSSION

### Origin of $^{18}O$-depletions in high-grade metasedimentary rocks

There is a wide variation of $\delta^{18}O$ within low- and high-grade equivalents of the same rock type (*e.g.*, limestones and marbles, shales and pelites), as well as a wide variation in the oxygen isotope composition of the granites, many of which are metasediment-derived. For example, calcite from metacarbonate rocks spans 15 per mil in all samples (+9 to +24 in high-grade rocks, +14 to +19 in low-grade rocks), which covers virtually the entire range of metamorphic and sedimentary values that are commonly reported worldwide. For pelites the range in all samples is 8 per mil (+8 to +16), whereas for leucogranites it is 6.5 per mil (+6.7 to +13.2), covering almost the entire range of $\delta^{18}O$ values in fresh, unaltered igneous rocks.

In general, the higher-grade metamorphic rocks have lower $\delta^{18}O$ values than the lower-grade rocks, though there is also some geographic and geologic control on $^{18}O/^{16}O$. This $^{18}O$-depletion effect is particularly apparent in our data in the samples from the Lizzies Basin region of the East Humboldt Range, where the metasediments acquire extraordinarily low $\delta^{18}O$ in the range +7 to +9 (for silicates) and +9 to +12 (for carbonates). WICKHAM and PETERS (1990) analyzed a large selection of samples from the same area and documented similar low values over a considerably wider area, averaging

+7.6 in silicate rocks. They also noted that $\delta^{18}O$ increased to higher values at higher structural levels at this locality (average +10.4 in silicates), though these rocks were still markedly $^{18}O$-depleted compared with their low-grade sedimentary precursors.

Each of the three high-grade geographic regions sampled in this study exhibits different degrees of $^{18}O$-depletion (see Fig. 7), with the Lizzies Basin samples being most extreme, the northern Ruby Mountains samples being least extreme, and the Angel Lake samples being somewhat intermediate. The magnitude of the isotopic shift is different for different rock-types, with the quartzites least affected (a shift in the mean value of about 2 per mil between low- and high-grade samples), the pelites shifted about 5 per mil, and the carbonate rocks variably $^{18}O$-depleted from 0 to >10 per mil. The *geographical* variation in $^{18}O$-depletion is superimposed on this *lithological* variation.

The most extremely $^{18}O$-depleted region also is the most isotopically homogeneous and the one in which the mineral phases are closest to being in isotopic equilibrium (although the more detailed study by WICKHAM and PETERS (1990) has identified less well-equilibrated regions at structural levels above the Lizzies Basin rocks discussed in this work). This correlation between the degree of isotopic equilibration and the magnitude of $\delta^{18}O$ shift suggests a possible common cause. Clearly the isotopic effects require exchange with oxygen from a reservoir having a low $\delta^{18}O$ value—at Lizzies Basin lower than the average whole-rock value of $\sim +7.5$ that the metasedimentary rocks attain. The most likely oxygen reservoirs are

(1) mantle-derived igneous rocks or magmatic fluids derived therefrom, having $\delta^{18}O$ values of $\sim +6$;

(2) meteoric waters having a wide range of possible $\delta^{18}O$ values initially lower than or equal to 0;

(3) formation waters contained within the miogeoclinal sedimentary pile.

It seems unlikely that reservoir (2), pristine meteoric water, was responsible for the $^{18}O$-depletion effects, because: (a) very low $\delta^{18}O$ values ($\leq 0$) are not observed in these rocks (except in the special case of the Secret Creek mylonites; see below); (b) the most extreme $^{18}O$-depletions are observed in rocks from the deepest structural levels in the area (the "Lower Zone" at Lizzies Basin), and that are not near major fault zones; (c) hydrous silicates in these same rocks (with the exception of Secret Creek and two biotite samples from Angel Lake) do not have abnormally low $\delta D$ values that would be characteristic of the meteoric ground water of this region in the Mesozoic ($\delta D_{muscovite}$ is $-40$; $\delta D_{biotite}$ is $-58$ to $-68$). However, reservoir (3), composed of relatively $^{18}O$-rich formation waters derived originally from surface water, could potentially have played an important role in the $^{18}O$-depletion process, particularly if such fluids became mobilized within the miogeoclinal sedimentary pile during metamorphism. Typical formation waters would have isotopic compositions ($\delta^{18}O = 0$ to $+8$, CLAYTON et al., 1966) lower than any of the low-grade sediments in the area and could easily account for shifts in $\delta^{18}O$ of several per mil, as suggested for Hercynian metasedimentary terranes in the Pyrenees (WICKHAM and TAYLOR, 1985).

Although formation waters could account for some of the $^{18}O$-depletion, it is unlikely that the unusually low $\delta^{18}O$ values observed at Lizzies Basin were generated this way. Not only is this strongly $^{18}O$-depleted zone restricted to the deepest structural levels in the area, but the values appear to be limited by $+6$ as a lowermost limit to $\delta^{18}O$; also, $\delta D_{biotite}$ has typical plutonic values ($-58$ to $-68$). This suggests that the isotopic composition is being buffered, not by the isotopic composition of surface-derived pore fluids, but perhaps by mantle-derived igneous rocks and fluids derived therefrom. The average $\delta^{18}O$ of the homogeneous quartz at Lizzies Basin is $+9.4$, which would be in $^{18}O/^{16}O$ equilibrium with olivine of $+5.5$, diopside of $+6.5$, and anorthite of $+7.2$ at 700°C (CHIBA et al., 1989). In other words, these quartz values could very plausibly be buffered by isotopic equilibration with gabbro with a mantle-type $\delta^{18}O$ of about $+6$. In this respect, it is important to note that there is abundant geological and geophysical evidence for intrusion of mantle-derived magmas into the lower and middle crust of this area, particularly during Tertiary extension (GANS, 1987; VALASEK et al., 1989; SNOKE et al., 1990; GRUNDER and WICKHAM, 1991). These magmas are required to account for Tertiary mafic volcanism and would have provided a heat-source for the metamorphism and anatexis.

Small quantities of pore fluid circulating within the mantle-derived igneous rocks and adjacent metasediments could have promoted exchange between these two reservoirs (after the mafic igneous rocks had crystallized) while the total quantity of fluid in the system remained quite low. In this respect it is interesting to note that some of the Lizzies Basin mafic rocks analyzed by WICKHAM and PETERS (1990) show significant $^{18}O$-enrichment ($\delta^{18}O$ as high as $+8$) in line with this sort of process. Alternatively, magmatic aqueous fluids released from the crystallizing magmas could also have been instrumental in buffering metasediment oxygen down

to values of $+6$. Material-balance calculations based on a much larger Lizzies Basin dataset, as well as detailed mapping to estimate lithological proportions, will both be discussed in detail in a future publication (PETERS and WICKHAM, 1991).

*Isotopic systematics in marbles*

Metacarbonate rocks vary widely in isotopic composition, and part of this can be attributed to decarbonation, involving loss of high-$^{18}O$ and high-$^{13}C$ $CO_2$. However, these effects cannot amount to more than a few per mil (e.g., NABELEK et al., 1984) and are incapable of being the sole explanation of the observed variation. The data can be filtered to exclude low-calcite rocks that have been extensively decarbonated; considering only those samples containing $>45\%$ calcite, there is still a wide range of $\delta^{18}O$, and these values exhibit the same general pattern observed in the entire dataset, with the most extreme $^{18}O$-depletion at Lizzies Basin and the least in the northern Ruby Mountains.

Carbon and oxygen isotope systematics from many calcite-rich marbles at Lizzies Basin (WICKHAM and PETERS, 1991) define mixing trajectories between sedimentary values ($\delta^{18}O \sim +22$, $\delta^{13}C$ variable but constant within a single layer) and mantle-type values ($\delta^{18}O \sim +6$, $\delta^{13}C \sim -6$). Figure 8 is a plot of $\delta^{13}C$ vs. $\delta^{18}O$ in the most calcite-rich samples from this study, which shows that the Lizzies Basin, Angel Lake, Ruby Mountains, and Low-Grade samples all plot as distinct groups having positive correlations of $\delta^{13}C$ and $\delta^{18}O$. This suggests that these samples were shifted to lower $\delta^{13}C$ values as well as lower $\delta^{18}O$ values by the petrologic processes being considered, consistent with shifts towards mantle-type $^{13}C/^{12}C$ and $^{18}O/^{16}O$.

*Timing of $^{18}O$-depletion*

The high-grade rocks of the study area have experienced multiple intrusive, metamorphic, and deformational episodes. Without detailed geochronology it is very difficult to pin down the timing of the isotopic shifts with any certainty. Indeed, there is every likelihood that there have been multiple isotopic alteration events associated with the various heating episodes. Existing geochronometric data (WRIGHT and SNOKE, 1986; DALLMEYER et al., 1986; SNOKE et al., 1990) suggest that the most recent high-grade metamorphic event was early Tertiary and associated with anatexis and intrusion of various granitoids. This makes it likely that the most recent isotopic equilibration event (e.g., the uniform $\delta^{18}O$ of quartz and uniform $\Delta_{quartz-biotite}$ at Lizzies

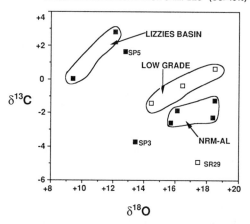

CALCITE FROM CALCITE-RICH SAMPLES (CC>40%)

FIG. 8. $\delta^{13}C$ and $\delta^{18}O$ values of calcite from calcite-rich marble samples. The $\delta^{18}O$ values of all samples are significantly lower than the values of typical limestones. $\delta^{13}C$ values are variable but are positively correlated with $\delta^{18}O$ in the three groups of samples from Lizzies Basin, northern Ruby Mountains and Angel Lake, and three of the low-grade samples (shown as open symbols). This is similar to the correlations observed by WICKHAM and PETERS (1990, 1991) at Lizzies Basin based on a much larger data set. They conclude that carbon and oxygen isotopic compositions are being shifted towards equilibrium with a water-rich C-O-H fluid buffered to mantle-type $\delta^{13}C$ and $\delta^{18}O$ of $-6$ and $+6$, respectively. The two samples from Secret Creek gorge are a low-grade limestone (SP5) and a marble (SP3). The marble lies on the trend of the Ruby Mountains–Angel Lake samples, and it does not appear to have been significantly affected by late-stage meteoric effects.

Basin) may be of this age. The Tertiary was also a favorable time for mantle-derived magmatism which seems necessary to explain the extreme $^{18}O$-shifts at Lizzies Basin. However, not all of the $^{18}O$-depletion need have taken place at this time. Interaction between the miogeoclinal metasediments and pore fluids could have occurred much earlier in their history, from low-grade diagenetic effects on through any of the Mesozoic or Tertiary high-grade events.

There are clear differences between the low- and high-grade metasediments, and therefore most of the $^{18}O$-depletion can be linked to metamorphism. Any heating event is likely to promote aqueous fluid movement within a metasedimentary pile, this fluid originating as either trapped formation water, original surface water, magmatic water, or metamorphic water liberated by dehydration reactions. Such movement of aqueous fluids will promote isotopic homogenization within and between different rock-types. If significant amounts of low-$^{18}O$ fluid are present or can flux through the rocks, exchange at elevated temperatures will cause $^{18}O$-depletion. Al-

ternatively, the same kinds of $^{18}O$-depletions could occur at relatively low water-rock ratios by fluid-mediated homogenization between primitive igneous rocks and metasediments. Perhaps interaction with pore fluids was more important during an early (Mesozoic) metamorphic cycle when the rocks were more hydrous and perhaps more permeable (as in the single metamorphic episode in the Hercynian of the Pyrenees, WICKHAM and TAYLOR, 1990). During a later stage (*e.g.,* the Tertiary) when the metamorphic pile had become more dehydrated, the metamorphism may have been dominated by isotopically primitive fluids from below (with these later effects only visible at the lowest part of the structurally deepest locality, Lizzies Basin). As indicated above, it is unlikely that any of the $\delta^{18}O$ signatures in the high-grade rocks (with the exception of those at Secret Creek gorge, see below) were significantly modified by any late-stage, low-temperature alteration event (although very local effects may be reflected in the anomalously low D/H ratio of the two Angel Lake biotites).

## $^{18}O/^{16}O$ systematics in granites

Like the metasediments, the granitic rocks span a wide range of $\delta^{18}O$ values from $+6.7$ to $+13.2$ (Fig. 7). Although there are different types of granite in the region, this range cannot be explained by compositional variation because the entire $\delta^{18}O$ range is observed within a single granite type, namely the leucogranites, which are the dominant igneous rock-type in the area. Leucogranites in the NRM are compositionally identical to those at Angel Lake or Lizzies Basin (S. M. WICKHAM and B. CHAPPELL, unpubl. data) yet vary in $\delta^{18}O$ by more than six per mil (see Fig. 7). The $\delta^{18}O$ variation cannot be ascribed to late-stage low-temperature hydrothermal alteration because, as noted above, the mineral pairs all have high-temperature equilibrium fractionations. It is thus likely that the $\delta^{18}O$ values of the leucogranites are magmatic values.

The leucogranites are compositionally uniform and identical in mineralogy to migmatite leucosomes in anatectic pelites; therefore, they could be derived from similar metasedimentary sources. Clearly the Ruby Mountains leucogranites must be almost exclusively metasediment-derived because they are so $^{18}O$-rich ($+11 < \delta^{18}O < +14$). Why then is there a range to much lower $\delta^{18}O$ values in the East Humboldt Range? A probable answer lies in the widely varying $\delta^{18}O$ of pelitic metasediments in this region. Given that shales or pelites are favorable protoliths for these leucogranites, Fig. 7 shows that these rocks occur with $^{18}O/^{16}O$ ratios spanning a wide range from +16 to +8. All are compositionally similar (the only important difference being a lower water content in the higher-grade rocks) and all would, on melting, produce leucogranitic silicate melt; however, these different melts would obviously have strongly contrasting isotopic compositions inherited from the variable $\delta^{18}O$ of the source rock.

It thus seems likely that leucogranite petrogenesis probably involved metasedimentary source material first being isotopically altered to take on a range of $\delta^{18}O$ values—low values close to +6 in some areas such as Lizzies Basin, higher, more typical metasedimentary values around +12 or higher in other areas such as the northern Ruby Mountains. This material was then melted to produce leucogranitic magmas which, although derived from similar source rocks, would thus vary widely in $^{18}O/^{16}O$ ratio.

This effect has broad implications for the interpretation of isotopic systematics in crustally derived granitic rocks. Isotopic compositions are frequently used to identify source regions or source materials, and in the case of $^{18}O/^{16}O$ systematics, low $\delta^{18}O$ values < +8 are often taken to indicate a primitive igneous source containing little or no sedimentary material. The data from this study show that this interpretation can be flawed. Pelitic rocks and granitic magmas derived therefrom have a wide range of $\delta^{18}O$ values, depending on the degree of $^{18}O$-depletion experienced at the diagenetic or metamorphic stage. This type of pre-anatectic isotopic alteration effect has been suggested to be important in a number of different terranes worldwide (WICKHAM, 1990) including the Hercynian of the Pyrenees (BICKLE et al., 1988) and of Brittany (WICKHAM, 1990) but it is particularly well illustrated in this study. All of the leucogranites analyzed have identical major and trace element compositions and thus appear to be derived from similar source materials, yet they span the entire range of normal igneous rock $\delta^{18}O$. We believe this is because they were derived from sedimentary material that was isotopically altered in variable degrees at the metamorphic stage.

In Fig. 7 we show oxygen isotope data from granites from a large part of eastern Nevada, as compiled by SOLOMON and TAYLOR (1989). Although their compilation includes granites of more diverse chemical compositions and emplacement ages than the granites studied in the present work, it is interesting that their dataset covers the same range of values observed in the granites of the Ruby Mountains-East Humboldt Range. Although SOLOMON and TAYLOR (1989) used these data to suggest a

model for the deep crustal structure of the northern Great Basin assuming that granites with different isotopic compositions were sampling different source regions, it remains possible that some of the variation is due to isotopic alteration of metasedimentary source material as demonstrated in this study, leading to a broadening of the range of $^{18}O/$ $^{16}O$ ratios of magmas derived from a single unique source-rock.

### Meteoric-hydrothermal effects (Secret Creek gorge)

Clear evidence for meteoric water infiltration is absent in most of the high-grade igneous and metamorphic rocks studied, with the exception of the samples from Secret Creek gorge. Here there is both mineralogical evidence for retrogression of higher grade rocks and strong deformational overprinting associated with the mylonite zone immediately underlying the detachment fault in this area. The oxygen and hydrogen isotope compositions of rocks from Secret Creek also show the effects of partial re-equilibration with low-$^{18}O$ aqueous fluids. Several samples of both vein calcite and whole rock have very low $\delta^{18}O$, less than +6, which clearly result from exchange with meteoric fluids (see Fig. 6). In the leucogranite mylonite sample RB59, the whole-rock value of +3.1 is much lower than the value for quartz (+11.1), implying a quartz-feldspar fractionation of more than eight per mil, which is indicative of strong $^{18}O/^{16}O$ disequilibrium in this sample. This is typical of quartz-feldspar systematics in rocks subjected to meteoric-hydrothermal alteration (e.g., CRISS and TAYLOR, 1986).

The quartzite mylonite (RB62) preserves high (amphibolite-facies) temperature fractionations between quartz, biotite, and muscovite, and the bulk $\delta^{18}O$ value for the sample is normal in the sense that it is similar to that of high-grade quartzites elsewhere in the region. However, the $\delta D$ values of muscovite and biotite in this sample are −115 and −128, respectively, indicating that it has also interacted with meteoric water, although not in sufficient quantity to have disturbed the $^{18}O/^{16}O$ ratios. These data are plotted in Fig. 9 together with the other samples for which both $^{18}O/^{16}O$ and D/H ratios were determined. This diagram illustrates the contrasting isotopic systematics at different structural levels in the study area. The deepest level rocks at Lizzies Basin have "normal" plutonic D/H ratios and preserve no evidence for interaction with meteoric fluids. Two Angel Lake biotites are significantly D-depleted in comparison with these samples, while the Secret Creek micas (from the shallowest struc-

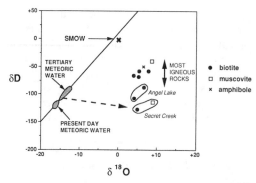

FIG. 9. The variation in $\delta^{18}O$ and $\delta D$ for biotite, muscovite, and amphibole samples analyzed in this study. With four exceptions, all samples (including the low $\delta^{18}O$ samples from Lizzies Basin) have normal $\delta D$ values that lie within the typical range observed in most igneous and metamorphic rocks. The anomalous samples all have unusually low $\delta D$ values that reflect interaction with low-D meteoric water. This is most clearly displayed by biotite and muscovite from the Secret Creek quartzite mylonite (RB62), but the two Angel Lake biotites are also significantly D-depleted. The meteoric water line and the range of compositions observed in both modern day and Tertiary local meteoric water are shown (SHEPPARD et al., 1969). The arrow indicates the likely evolution of such water towards a composition that could have equilibrated with the Secret Creek micas.

tural levels in the lower plate) have the lowest $\delta D$ values of all. These samples could very plausibly have attained these values by equilibration with local Tertiary meteoric waters that had become $^{18}O$-enriched by interaction with the local country rocks that they flowed through (as indicated by the arrow in the diagram). The more detailed study of FRICKE et al. (1991) has documented similarly D-depleted rocks throughout the Secret Creek region, coupled with strong $^{18}O$-depletion in some samples.

The variation in $^{18}O$-depletion observed at Secret Creek presumably reflects a very heterogeneous pattern of fluid infiltration. We find mylonitic high-grade rocks that have both preserved their high-grade mineral $^{18}O/^{16}O$ systematics and also those in which strong disequilibrium effects occur due to exchange with infiltrating meteoric water at moderate temperatures. Infiltration was probably fracture-controlled within the mylonitic rocks in the vicinity of the detachment fault. Fluid movement was probably promoted by the rapid uplift of rocks from mid-crustal levels. Uplift involved movement on the detachment fault, providing a favorable site for fluid infiltration due to the generation of abundant fractures, and the rapid uplift increased thermal gradients, promoting vigorous ground-water circulation within upper-plate rocks down to and including the level at which detachment faulting

and mylonitization were occurring. The more comprehensive study of FRICKE et al. (1991) documents and discusses these processes in greater detail.

The only other low-temperature effects which have affected these samples are discernible in the very low-grade samples. As described above, some of the low-grade carbonate rocks have rather low $\delta^{18}O$ values compared with typical sedimentary limestones (+15 to +20), though clearly they are not nearly as $^{18}O$-depleted as some of the carbonates in the high-grade areas. These low-grade rocks may have been affected by the same type of meteoric hydrothermal system as documented at Secret Creek, since these flow systems must have traversed extensive regions of the upper plate. More extensive studies of upper-plate sequences are now warranted in order to determine the extent of $^{18}O$-depletion both in terms of the volume of rocks affected and the magnitudes of the isotopic shifts. Such studies will be important for improving our understanding of the formation of ore deposits hosted in low-grade miogeoclinal sedimentary rocks in northern Nevada (e.g., HOFSTRA et al., 1991). These relatively low-temperature effects may be important precursors to the high-temperature $^{18}O$-depletion processes occurring at deeper structural levels and higher metamorphic grades, or conversely, it is possible that the deeper samples never were subjected to such effects. A great deal of further work will be required to sort out these problems.

## CONCLUSIONS

The generally observed $^{18}O$-depletions in high-grade metasedimentary rocks, first documented by GARLICK and EPSTEIN (1967), provide testimony to the importance of aqueous fluid-rock interaction in metamorphic environments. In a previous study of this phenomenon in the Hercynian rocks of the Pyrenees (WICKHAM and TAYLOR, 1985, 1990) widespread lowering of $\delta^{18}O$ values in metapelites was attributed to interaction with surface-derived marine pore fluids during the single episode of prograde regional metamorphism that affected that area. This conclusion was based on regionally high $\delta D$ values, and an absence of a local source of low-$^{18}O$ primitive igneous rocks with which the metasediments could have exchanged. Similarly, in Hercynian rocks of the Black Forest, D/H and $^{18}O/^{16}O$ systematics were again instrumental in identifying surface water (this time meteoric) as the probable cause of regionally low $\delta^{18}O$ values in the metasediments and anatectic granites (TAYLOR et al., this volume).

Although striking $^{18}$O-depletions are also observed in the Ruby Mountains-East Humboldt Range core complex, this area differs significantly from the above Hercynian terranes in that much more carbonate and much less pelite are present in the sedimentary section. Also, Nevada has experienced multiple Mesozoic and Cenozoic metamorphic events. The extreme $^{18}$O-depletion observed at Lizzies Basin, where the rocks approach mantle-like $^{18}$O/$^{16}$O ratios yet also have normal plutonic δD values, probably occurred during the most recent (Cenozoic) metamorphic event. These systematics suggest that the $^{18}$O/$^{16}$O and D/H ratios in these rocks may have been buffered by the isotopic compositions of mantle-derived magmas rather than by surface-derived pore fluids (although pore fluids certainly played an important role in the isotopic exchange process).

We do not rule out the possibility that aqueous fluids were an important low-$^{18}$O reservoir during the earlier (Mesozoic) metamorphic events experienced by this terrane. In particular, the first metamorphic event experienced by a thick sedimentary sequence is perhaps more likely to be dominated by the large scale movement of pore fluids, as evidently occurred in the European Hercynian terranes. In this way it is possible that both of these types of low-$^{18}$O reservoirs were involved in bringing about the variable degrees of $^{18}$O-depletion observed in the Ruby Mountains-East Humboldt Range rocks. However, the details of the Mesozoic history of this terrane will be virtually indecipherable without a great deal more geochronological work. On the other hand, because it has not been overprinted, the most recent (Cenozoic) metamorphic event and associated buffering of the rocks to mantle-like isotopic compositions is accessible to detailed geochemical and petrological studies. The results of these investigations will be discussed more fully in future publications (WICKHAM and PETERS, 1991).

*Acknowledgements*—It is a pleasure to acknowledge many constructive discussions with Samuel Epstein on the subject of oxygen isotope systematics in igneous and metamorphic rocks. Technical assistance from Jack Coulson and Joop Goris and typing by James Eason is gratefully appreciated. SMW acknowledges a Visiting Research Associateship at the California Institute of Technology, a NERC postdoctoral fellowship, and a research fellowship at Trinity Hall, Cambridge, during the completion of part of this work. Financial support was in part provided by NSF grants EAR 87-20097 and EAR 90-19256 to Wickham, EAR 83-13106 and EAR 88-16413 to Taylor, and EAR 90-05717 to O'Neil. Snokes' recent studies in the Ruby Mountains-East Humboldt metamorphic core complex were supported by NSF grant EAR 87-07435.

## REFERENCES

ARMSTRONG R. L. (1982) Cordilleran metamorphic core complexes—from Arizona to southern Canada. *Ann. Rev. Earth Planet. Sci.* **10**, 129–154.

BICKLE M. J., WICKHAM S. M., CHAPMAN H. J. and TAYLOR H. P., JR. (1988) A strontium, neodymium and oxygen isotope study of hydrothermal metamorphism and crustal anatexis in the Trois Seigneurs Massif, Pyrenees, France. *Contrib. Mineral. Petrol.* **100**, 399–417.

CHIBA H., CHACKO T., CLAYTON R. N. and GOLDSMITH J. R. (1989) Oxygen isotope fractionations involving diopside, forsterite, magnetite, and calcite: application to geothermometry. *Geochim. Cosmochim. Acta* **53**, 2985–2995.

CLAYTON R. N., FRIEDMAN I., GRAF D. C., MAYEDA T. K., MEERTS W. F. and SHIMP N. F. (1966) The origin of saline formation waters: I. Isotopic composition. *J. Geophys. Res.* **71**, 3869–3882.

CRISS R. E. and TAYLOR H. P., JR. (1986) Meteoric-hydrothermal systems. In *Stable Isotopes in High Temperature Geological Processes* (eds. J. W. VALLEY, H. P. TAYLOR, JR. and J. R. O'NEIL); *Rev. Mineral.* **16**, pp. 373–424. Mineralogical Society of America.

DALLMEYER R. D., SNOKE A. W. and MCKEE E. H. (1986) The Mesozoic-Cenozoic tectonothermal evolution of the Ruby Mountains-East Humboldt Range, Nevada: a Cordilleran metamorphic core complex. *Tectonics* **5**, 931–954.

DOKKA R. K., MAHAFFIE M. J. and SNOKE A. W. (1986) Thermochronologic evidence of major tectonic denudation associated with detachment faulting, northern Ruby Mountains-East Humboldt Range, Nevada. *Tectonics* **5**, 995–1006.

ESLINGER E. V. and SAVIN S. M. (1973) Oxygen isotope geothermometry of the burial metamorphic rocks of the PreCambrian Belt Supergroup, Glacier National Park, Montana. *Bull. Geol. Soc. Amer.* **84**, 2549–2560.

FRICKE H. C. and WICKHAM S. M. (1990) Meteoric water infiltration and oxygen isotope exchange during mylonitic deformation in the Ruby Mountains-East Humboldt Range, northeastern Nevada. *Geol. Soc. Amer. Abstr. Prog.* **22**, A118.

FRICKE H. C., WICKHAM S. M. and O'NEIL J. R. (1991) Oxygen and hydrogen isotope evidence for meteoric water infiltration during mylonitic deformation and uplift in the Ruby-East Humboldt Range core complex, Nevada. *Contrib. Mineral. Petrol.* (submitted).

FRIEDMAN I. and O'NEIL J. R. (1977) Compilation of stable isotope fractionation factors of geochemical interest. *U.S. Geol. Survey Prof. Pap.* 440-KK.

GANS P. B. (1987) An open-system, two-layer crustal stretching model for the eastern Great Basin. *Tectonics* **6**, 1–12.

GARLICK G. D. and EPSTEIN S. (1967) Oxygen isotope ratios in coexisting minerals of regionally metamorphosed rocks. *Geochim. Cosmochim. Acta* **31**, 181–214.

GRUNDER A. L. and WICKHAM S. M. (1991) Homogenization and lowering of $^{18}$O/$^{16}$O in mid-crustal rocks during extension-related magmatism in Eastern Nevada. *Earth Planet. Sci. Lett.* (in press).

HOFSTRA A. H., LEVENTHAL J. S., NORTHROP H. R., LANDIS G. P., RYE R. O., BIRAK D. J. and DAHL A. R. (1991) Genesis of sediment-hosted disseminated-gold deposits by fluid mixing and sulfidization: chemical-reaction-path modeling of ore depositional processes documented in the Jerritt Canyon district, Nevada. *Geology* **19**, 36–40.

HOWARD K. A. (1971) Paleozoic metasediments in the northern Ruby Mountains, Nevada. *Geol. Soc. Amer. Bull.* **82**, 259–264.

HUDEC M. R. and WRIGHT J. E. (1990) Mesozoic history of the central part of the Ruby-East Humboldt Range metamorphic core complex, Nevada. *Geol. Soc. Amer. Abstr. Prog.* **22**, 56.

HURLOW H. A., SNOKE A. W. and HODGES K. V. (1991) Temperature and pressure of mylonitization in a Tertiary extensional shear zone, Ruby Mountains-East Humboldt Range, Nevada: tectonic implications. *Geology* **19**, 82–86.

KISTLER R. W., GHENT E. D. and O'NEIL J. R. (1981) Petrogenesis of garnet two-mica granites in the Ruby Mountains, Nevada. *J. Geophys. Res.* **86**, 10,591–10,606.

LUSH A. P., MCGREW A. J., SNOKE A. W. and WRIGHT J. E. (1988) Allochthonous Archean basement in the northern East Humboldt Range, Nevada. *Geology* **16**, 349–353.

MCCREA J. M. (1950) On the isotopic chemistry of carbonate and a paleotemperature scale. *J. Chem. Phys.* **18**, 849–857.

MCGREW A. J. and SNOKE A. W. (1988) Cenozoic and Mesozoic folding and migmatization in the East Humboldt Range metamorphic core complex, Nevada. *Geol. Soc. Amer. Abstr. Prog.* **22**, 66.

MISCH P. and HAZZARD J. C. (1962) Stratigraphy and metamorphism of late PreCambrian rocks in central northeastern Nevada and adjacent Utah. *Amer. Assoc. Petrol. Geol. Bull.* **53**, 307–339.

NABELEK P. K., LABOTKA T. C., O'NEIL J. R. and PAPIKE J. J. (1984) Contrasting fluid/rock interaction between the Notch Peak granitic intrusion and argillites and limestones in western Utah: evidence from stable isotopes and phase assemblages. *Contrib. Mineral. Petrol.* **86**, 25–34.

PETERS M. T. and WICKHAM S. M. (1991) Stable isotope constraints on mid-crustal igneous and metamorphic processes in the East Humboldt Range core complex, Nevada (in prep.).

SHARMA T. and CLAYTON R. N. (1965) Measure of $^{18}O/^{16}O$ ratios of total oxygen from carbonates. *Geochim. Cosmochim. Acta* **29**, 1347–1353.

SHEPPARD S. M. F., NIELSEN R. L. and TAYLOR H. P., JR. (1969) Oxygen and hydrogen isotope ratios of clay minerals from porphyry copper deposits. *Econ. Geol.* **64**, 755–777.

SHIEH Y. and SCHWARCZ H. P. (1974) Oxygen isotope studies of granite and migmatite, Grenville Province of Ontario, Canada. *Geochim. Cosmochim. Acta* **38**, 21–45.

SNOKE A. W. (1980) Transition from infrastructure to suprastructure in the northern Ruby Mountains, Nevada. In *Cordilleran Metamorphic Core Complexes* (eds. M. D. CRITTENDEN P. J. CONEY and G. H. DAVIS); *Geol. Soc. Amer. Memoir 153*, pp. 287–333.

SNOKE A. W. and HOWARD K. A. (1984) Geology of the Ruby Mountains-East Humboldt Range Nevada—a Cordilleran metamorphic core complex. In *Western Geological Excursions, Vol. 4* (ed. J. LINTZ), pp. 260–303. Geological Society of America 1988 Annual Meeting, Reno, Nevada.

SNOKE A. W. and LUSH A. P. (1984) Polyphase Mesozoic-Cenozoic deformational history of the northern Ruby Mountains-East Humboldt Range, Nevada. In *Western Geological Excursions, Vol. 4* (ed. J. LINTZ), pp. 232–260. Geological Society of America 1988 Annual Meeting, Reno, Nevada.

SNOKE A. W. and MILLER D. M. (1988) Metamorphic and tectonic history of the northeastern Great Basin. In *Metamorphism and Crustal Evolution of the Western United States, Rubey Vol. VII* (ed. W. G. ERNST), pp. 606–648.

SNOKE A. W., MCKEE E. H. and STERN T. W. (1979) Plutonic, metamorphic and structural chronology in the northern Ruby Mountains, Nevada: a preliminary report. *Geol. Soc. Amer. Abstr. Prog.* **11**, 520–521.

SNOKE A. W., MCGREW A. J., VALASEK P. A. and SMITHSON S. B. (1990) A crustal cross-section for a terrain of superimposed shortening and extension: Ruby Mountains-East Humboldt Range metamorphic core complex, Nevada. In *Exposed Cross Sections of the Continental Crust* (eds. M. H. SALISBURY and D. M. FOUNTAIN), pp. 103–135. Kluwer Academic Publishers.

SOLOMON G. C. and TAYLOR H. P., JR. (1989) Isotopic evidence for the origin of Mesozoic and Cenozoic granitic plutons in the northern Great Basin. *Geology* **17**, 591–594.

TAYLOR H. P., JR. and EPSTEIN S. (1962) Relationships between $^{18}O/^{16}O$ ratios in coexisting minerals of igneous and metamorphic rocks. Part I: principles and experimental results. *Bull. Geol. Soc. Amer.* **73**, 461–480.

VALASEK P. A., SNOKE A. W., HURICH C. A. and SMITHSON S. B. (1989) Nature and origin of seismic reflection fabric, Ruby-East Humboldt Range metamorphic core complex, Nevada. *Tectonics* **8**, 391–415.

VENNEMAN T. W. and O'NEIL J. R. (1991) A new method of determination of D/H ratios and water contents of hydrous minerals (in prep.).

WICKHAM S. M. (1990) Isotopic modification of the continental crust; Implications for the use of isotope tracers in granite petrogenesis. In *High Temperature Metamorphism and Crustal Anatexis* (eds. J. R. ASHWORTH and M. BROWN), pp. 124–148. Unwin Hyman.

WICKHAM S. M. and PETERS M. T. (1990) An oxygen isotope discontinuity in high-grade rocks of the East Humboldt Range, Nevada. *Nature* **345**, 150–153.

WICKHAM S. M. and PETERS M. T. (1991) Oxygen and carbon isotope profiles in metasediments at Lizzies Basin, East Humboldt Range, Nevada: implications for mid-crustal volatile fluxes (in prep.).

WICKHAM S. M. and TAYLOR H. P., JR. (1985) Stable isotopic evidence for large-scale seawater infiltration in a regional metamorphic terrane: the Trois Seigneurs Massif, Pyrenees, France. *Contrib. Mineral. Petrol.* **91**, 122–137.

WICKHAM S. M. and TAYLOR H. P., JR. (1990) Hydrothermal systems associated with regional metamorphism and crustal anatexis: examples from the Pyrenees, France. In *The Role of Fluids in Crustal Processes* (eds. D. NORTON and J. D. BREDEHOEFT), pp. 96–112. National Research Council, Studies in Geophysics, National Academy Press.

WRIGHT J. E. and SNOKE A. W. (1986) Mid-Tertiary mylonitization in the Ruby Mountain-East Humboldt Range metamorphic core complex, Nevada. *Geol. Soc. Amer. Abstr. Prog.* **18**, 795.

Stable Isotope Geochemistry: A Tribute to Samuel Epstein
© The Geochemical Society, Special Publication No. 3, 1991
Editors: H. P. Taylor, Jr., J. R. O'Neil and I. R. Kaplan

# Daughter-parent isotope systematics in U-Th-bearing igneous accessory mineral assemblages as potential indices of metamorphic history: A discussion of the concept

LEON T. SILVER

Division of Geological and Planetary Sciences, California Institute of Technology, Pasadena, CA 91125, U.S.A.

**Abstract**—It is proposed that the patterns of isotopic disturbance in Pb-U-Th systems for the assemblage of radioactive minerals in any granite or equivalent orthogneiss may have value not only as geochronological tools for determining the time constants of metamorphic events but also may have significant potential as indices of the nature and intensity of metamorphism (including thermal, hydrothermal, deformational, weathering, and other environments of change). One of the special qualities of radiogenic Pb-U-Th geochemistry is the coexistence of three daughter-parent (D/P) systems: $^{206}Pb/^{238}U$, $^{207}Pb/^{235}U$, and $^{208}Pb/^{232}Th$. The uranogenic pair of D/P systems are coupled chemically so that they lead to rigorously linked isotope ratio variations during disturbance. The thorogenic D/P system, because of the contrasting Th and U chemistry, may behave quite independently, providing special insights into the mobility of Pb, U, and Th.

Accessory mineral assemblages in most rocks contain from three to eight or more radioactive minerals in which U and Th commonly are quite fractionated. Each mineral and its three contained D/P systems appear to have distinctive responses to metamorphism and show differential sensitivity to different metamorphic variables. The responses are conditioned by accumulated radiation damage at the time of metamorphism. Each mineral species has a unique structural response to $\alpha$-fluence, and commonly shows large inter- and intra-grain variations in accumulated disorder. The rate-competitive roles of structural annealing and metamorphic disturbance are believed to determine the net effect on the D/P systems.

Any individual sample may be treated as an isogradic collection of responses at a given position in a metamorphic gradient. The number of minerals $\times$ 3 D/P systems provides a large matrix of sensitive, precisely measured parameters for characterizing that position in the gradient. Several properly selected samples can characterize the entire gradient. This then offers a general basis for extracting quantitative indices of the nature and intensity of the metamorphism. Ultimately, this may permit calibration of metamorphic effects derived from several important variables neglected in some current thermochronological models. Hypothetical models representing possible assemblage D/P responses derived from different metamorphic disturbances are offered. Some examples from southern California of natural responses to metamorphism are provided: (1) The effects of mylonitization as a modifier of the radioactive mineral assemblages are clearly demonstrated in titanite, apatite, and allanite in a tonalite pluton cut by the Eastern Peninsular Ranges mylonite zone. (2) The correlation of radiation damage with isotopic disturbance in zircons is documented in a Cretaceous granodiorite that was hydrothermally altered during the Miocene.

## INTRODUCTION

EVIDENCE FOR DIFFERENTIAL migration of daughter and/or parent isotopes is observed commonly in the natural radioactive/radiogenic systems of minerals employed in geochronology. Open-system behavior appears to defeat basic assumptions for calculation of apparent ages, and generally is assiduously avoided in sampling and minimized in interpretation. For some isotopic systems (*e.g.*, Pb/U pairs in cogenetic zircons; $^{39}Ar/^{40}Ar$ plateaus) models have been devised for treating arrays of data for partially opened systems to permit inferences about the closed-system end points that can be taken as primary ages. Currently concordant U-Pb isotope ratios from a zircon, or the well-defined arrays of discordant U-Pb isotope ratios in cogenetic zircon fractions (SILVER and DEUTSCH, 1961) compared to the "Concordia" relationship for ideal closed U-

Pb systems (WETHERILL, 1956), are accepted as providing the most precise magmatic ages available. The origins of discordance (*e.g.*, the implications of lower discordia intercepts on "Concordia") usually are not pursued. The Th-Pb isotope ratios in zircons and other minerals are seldom measured, probably because they yield apparent ages that commonly disagree with and lack the independent power of the paired U-Pb ratios.

Developing an understanding of the *diverse* origins of open-system behavior in geochronological systems has been neglected. The comparative simplicity of substituting thermally activated diffusion models has been favored since the classic works of HANSON and GAST (1967), HART (1964), and HART *et al.* (1968). The more recent developments of fission track and $^{39}Ar/^{40}Ar$ methodologies have contributed elegant insights into cooling or thermal histories related to emplacement, tectonic uplift, and/or unroofing (*e.g.,* NAESER, 1979; DODSON, 1973; and many works cited in McDOUGALL and HARRISON, 1988). Thermochronology is an essential component of understanding metamorphism, but it does not provide a comprehensive description in time and in multi-parameter metamorphic space. Fluids, mineral and rock strains, tectonic loading and unloading, changes in bulk rock chemistry, and re-equilibration of minerals also enter into metamorphic processes. For example, many stable isotope investigations have demonstrated the importance of fluids.

In this work, a concept and possible models for extracting more extensive information from opened uranium and thorium daughter-parent (D/P) systems in metamorphosed intermediate to felsic granites are examined. A large number of demonstrably sensitive isotopic parameters in radiogenic systems can be measured with precision, and pragmatically, the three relevant radiogenic isotope systems can all be determined with a single set of chemical and instrumental analytical procedures.

Patterns of imprinted variations are well organized among the families of opened and closed (D/P) isotope systems in an assemblage of several cogenetic uranium and thorium accessory minerals in a meta-igneous rock. How well do the imprints individually or collectively represent responses to the many complex parameters of the metamorphic environments? Are there special correlations with other important metamorphic variables besides temperature, *e.g.,* activity of $H_2O$? Do they provide valuable characteristic signatures and quantitative measures of the nature as well as timing of the modifying episode? Can systematic radiogenic D/P isotopic investigations, with independent mineralogical and petrological calibrations, yield significantly more information about the rock history and the metamorphic processes than the primary age and a modeled secondary thermal history?

The U-Th-Pb assemblage approach appears particularly applicable to intermediate to felsic granites which have participated in a single important post-crystallization modification event (*e.g.,* deformation, regional or contact thermal metamorphism, hydrothermal circulation, ancient or modern weathering). Its prospects are most favorable where a well-defined metamorphic gradient has been established in a uniform granitic mass (or at least, in a single generation of granites) that can be sampled at more than one position. However, preliminary evaluation indicates the approach may be extended into less ideal situations.

The minerals that can be examined might include, in addition, the cogenetic hosts for $^{40}K$, $^{87}Rb$, $^{147}Sm$, etc. Pb-U-Th systematics should and can be compared profitably with other D/P isotopic systems in other cogenetic minerals when data for such systems are available (see below). This approach was undertaken in the collective works of Hart and his colleagues in their investigation of the contact metamorphic aureole around the Eldora stock in the Colorado Front Range (HART, 1964; DOE and HART, 1963; DAVIS *et al.,* 1968; HART *et al.,* 1968). These authors were primarily concerned with the stabilities of mineral ages and feldspar isotopic endowments in the contact metamorphic thermal gradients of a Paleocene intrusive into a Precambrian schist complex. They found large effects and recognized the potential correlations of modified ages with the metamorphic facies zonation, but they did not attempt to invert their observations to use isotopic systematics as metamorphic indicators.

HANSON *et al.* (1971) studied the effects of contact metamorphic gradients induced in zircons, titanites, hornblende, and biotites in the Giants Range granite as a result of intrusion of the Duluth gabbro. They found relative ages to be titanite $^{206}Pb/^{238}U$ > zircon $^{206}Pb/^{238}U$ > hornblende $^{40}K$-$^{40}Ar$ > biotite $^{40}K$-$^{40}Ar$. They inferred any discordance was induced by the thermal effects of contact metamorphism, but could not resolve whether earlier disturbances had influenced the zircons and titanites.

Neither investigation considered the role of fluids. In retrospect, their integration with stable isotope investigations of both accessory and major rock minerals would have been rewarding.

## RATIONALE FOR USING PB-U-TH SYSTEMATICS

In this discussion minerals that contain the Pb-U-Th chemical and isotope systems have been selected because of their peculiar properties and powers and the author's familiarity with a variety of case studies:

$$^{238}U \rightarrow {}^{206}Pb \quad \lambda = 1.5513 \times 10^{-10}/y$$

$$^{235}U \rightarrow {}^{207}Pb \quad \lambda = 9.848 \times 10^{-10}/y$$

$$^{232}Th \rightarrow {}^{208}Pb \quad \lambda = 0.4948 \times 10^{-10}/y$$

Both uranium and thorium commonly are found enriched relative to the bulk rock in a shared group of accessory minerals. Th/U ratios display a great range of fractionation of the actinides among these different primary minerals (Table 1). All of the stable end products of the actinide decay chains are isotopes of lead. Chemical losses or gains of parents

Table 1. A summary of Pb, U, Th concentrations and the ratios $^{238}U/^{204}Pb$ and $^{232}Th/^{204}Pb$ for a representative suite of calcic tonalites to monzogranites from the eastern Peninsular Ranges batholith. The two isotope ratios determine the magnitude of initial lead corrections for calculating radiogenic D/P ratios

|  | Data pts. | Initial Pb ppm | U ppm | Th ppm | $\dfrac{Th}{U}$ | $\dfrac{^{238}U}{^{204}Pb}$ | $\dfrac{^{232}Th}{^{204}Pb}$ |
|---|---|---|---|---|---|---|---|
| Zircon | (18) | ≤0.3 | 665 | 191 | 0.29 | $>2 \times 10^5$ | $>5 \times 10^4$ |
| Titanite | (17) | 2.1 | 175 | 285 | 1.63 | $6 \times 10^3$ | $10^4$ |
| Apatite | (18) | 3.2 | 37 | 31 | 0.84 | $10^3$ | $7 \times 10^2$ |
| Allanite | (13) | 64 | 189 | 10000 | 53 | $2 \times 10^2$ | $10^4$ |
| Monazite | (1) | 11.8 | 3960 | 14080 | 3.55 | $2.5 \times 10^4$ | $9 \times 10^4$ |

or daughters have very different relative effects on the radiogenic lead isotopic evolution in each host. Each mineral species tends to display a different sensitivity and a characteristic style of response (mobilization of lead, uranium, and/or thorium) to chemical disturbances. Experimental work (*e.g.,* PIDGEON *et al.,* 1966, 1973) and field observations indicate that fluids can play a major role in opening these systems in zircons. These variable response characteristics make the assemblage approach potentially very powerful.

Mobilization of lead affects all three D/P systems. U and Th mobility influences only two or one D/P system, respectively, permitting considerable discrimination. The paired Pb-U systems have the special property that chemical disturbances affect daughters and parents in both isotope systems equally. The radiogenic $^{207}Pb/^{206}Pb$ ratios resulting from the integrated history of the uranium-generated D/P pair can convey unique temporal information.

Typically, an intermediate to felsic granitic rock contains from three to five readily separated radioactive minerals. Less commonly, there may be eight or more such minerals (Fig. 1 and SILVER *et al.,* 1982). In a typical calcalkaline granodiorite or granite with four radioactive minerals (*e.g.,* zircon, titanite, apatite, allanite) a matrix of up to 12 responsive parameters (four minerals × three D/P isotope ratios) can be utilized to characterize and evaluate the chemical disturbances produced in the metamorphic episode.

To be effective the model assumes that each host mineral phase will

(a) retain its mineralogical identity;

(b) respond chemically to the modification event with consequences to its contained U, Th, and Pb peculiar to the phase and to the nature of the event;

(c) contain a sufficiently small initial lead endowment in each mineral relative to the U and Th concentrations (favorable $^{238}U/^{204}Pb$ and $^{232}Th/^{204}Pb$ ratios); and

(d) accumulate a radiogenic increment in the total Pb large enough for concentrations to be determined (after correction for initial lead and blank) to better than a few percent precision by isotope chemistry and mass spectrometry.

The initial lead composition is determined from analysis of cogenetic feldspars, preferably from unaltered granite protolith. It is desirable that the assemblage include minerals with a wide range of sensitivities; observation suggests it commonly does.

The decay constants of the several actinide parents are such that the geologic time constants for examining metamorphic effects appear generally favorable for rocks on the order of 100 Ma or older. With higher yet still reasonable actinide levels, even younger systems, 10–100 Ma, can be utilized. The intervals of post-crystallization cooling to closure of all of the U-Th phases in batholithic rocks emplaced at middle or upper crustal levels generally appear brief relative to a $10^8$ Ma primary age. The duration of the period of open-system behavior during an imposed metamorphic episode can be quite variable depending on the nature and setting of the metamorphic process. For optimal resolution, it should be brief relative to the primary age. When it may not be, the consequent observed dispersion of ages should reveal the extended history. Very young disturbances (*e.g.,* modern weathering, geothermal activity, active faulting, crustal xenoliths in active volcanoes) offer profitable opportunities for testing and calibrating disturbance models.

Inheritance effects from a pre-magmatic history may influence the ratios in some phases, notably zircon. For zircons, discordia projections to "Concordia" can provide proxy $^{206}Pb/^{238}U$ and $^{207}Pb/^{235}U$ values for a primary magmatic age when their radioactivity levels are low to moderate. Monazite has been reported to contain inherited lead in some situations. Few other common radioactive mineral species have inheritance documented. In the discussions below, inheritance phenomena will be provisionally accepted as treatable or minimal.

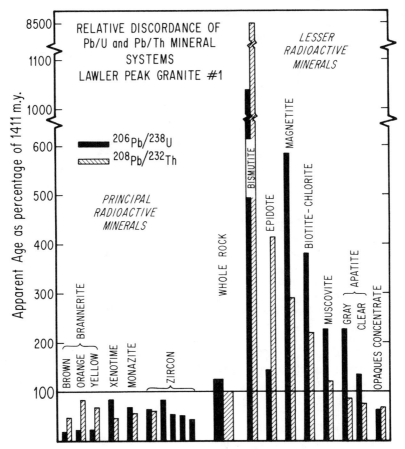

FIG. 1. Graph from SILVER *et al.* (1982), showing the relative discordance of a large assemblage of radioactive minerals in a sample from a highly evolved, radioactive, middle Proterozoic granite near Bagdad, Arizona. The sample is undeformed and not visibly altered, but it is located 2 km from a major Cretaceous mineralized intrusion. The age of the granite, established by zircon discordia, is 1411 ± 3 Ma. The daughter-parent ratios, $^{206}Pb/^{238}U$ and $^{208}Pb/^{232}Th$, for each mineral fraction have been calculated as ages. The bars indicate the ages as percentage of the accepted age. Ages deviating from 1411 Ma by more than a few percent reflect post-magmatic chemical and isotopic disturbance, and such disturbance is observed in almost all of the listed minerals. The assemblage of minerals and their diverse styles of open-system behavior indicate the extensive influence of a hydrothermal cell generated by the Cretaceous intrusion.

## ACCESSORY MINERAL SPECIES AND ASSEMBLAGES

In metaluminous quartz-rich calcic to calcalkaline plutonic rocks, an ubiquitous assemblage is zircon, titanite, apatite, allanite ± thorite. In peraluminous rocks zircon, monazite, apatite ± thorite ± xenotime are encountered. Highly differentiated rocks (leucocratic granites, pegmatites, aplites) may be significantly enriched in the actinides and other incompatible elements, and may also contain uraninite, thorianite, cerianite, coffinite, uranothorite, basnaesite-parisite, complex multiple oxides of Nb, Ta, Ti such as fergusonite, euxenite, brannerite, microlite-pyrochlore, and other exotic phases. Figure 1 illustrates a complex assemblage. The best age for the rock is $1.411 \pm 0.003 \times 10^9$ y, based on the multiple zircon fractions. D/P ratios have been converted to percentage of the zircon age. The great range of values reflects an extensive Mesozoic disturbance history. Alkaline plutonic rocks may contain, in addition, perovskite, baddeleyite, zirkelite, and various phosphates and carbonates containing significant uranium and thorium.

By far the most prevalent radioactive minerals in common plutonic rocks are, in approximate descending order of abundance: titanite, apatite, allanite, zircon, monazite, thorite, and xenotime. Average values of Pb, U, and Th and the ratios

$^{238}U/^{204}Pb$ and $^{232}Th/^{204}Pb$ for each of these species (xenotime is not present) from a number of plutonic rocks of the eastern Peninsular Ranges batholith are given in Table 1. Various combinations of this group represent the suites of cogenetic minerals which can be considered for general use in this approach. Any given assemblage will contain at least three and probably more phases. The suite zircon-titanite-apatite-allanite ± thorite ± an additional unspecified species will be employed in our hypothetical modeling.

## INTRASPECIES COMPOSITIONAL VARIATIONS

Comparison of individual grains of any of these mineral species in a given rock sample can show a significant range of uranium and thorium concentrations. These variations may range from factor of two or less in titanite to as great as ten or more in zircons. These grain to grain variations are accompanied by compositional zonation of the actinide elements within individual crystals. Variations among zones may cover a large part of the total grain-to-grain range. In several species, the spectrum of variations in a particular sample can be subdivided into aliquots with quite different actinide endowments. This is the fundamental basis for generating linear arrays of zircon U-Pb isotope ratios from a single granite population for interpretation of discordant ages (SILVER, 1963a,b; SILVER and DEUTSCH, 1961, 1963). Monazite, titanite, allanite, and thorite are other species where such discrimination is possible and profitable. These qualities extend the potential for detailing the isotopic responses of the radioactive assemblage to metamorphism.

## RADIATION DAMAGE

Each grain of a radioactive mineral species is exposed over its lifetime to a significant flux of energetic charged nuclear particles (alpha, beta, and spontaneous fission) and gamma radiation from the decay of a fraction of its contained radionuclides. The energy delivered to the crystal lattice, primarily via alpha recoil, introduces various degrees of structural disorder. This disorder is a function of the actinide concentrations, the elapsed time of exposure since crystallization (HOLLAND and GOTT-FRIED, 1955; WOODHEAD et al., 1991), and the self-annealing properties of the host structure under various geologic conditions. Thorite, allanite, and zircon show the most conspicuous accumulations of radiation damage. Some may become completely metamict in as little as $10^8$ years. An approximate

sequence for acquiring damage is thorite > allanite > zircon > titanite > monazite > xenotime > apatite. These accumulations reflect their typical relative actinide contents, and their capacity for self-annealing. The imposition of radiation damage modifies the physical properties and enhances the fundamental chemical susceptibility of each species to metamorphic effects. This, in turn, contributes to the distinctive chemical and isotopic responses recorded in each species.

## OBSERVATIONS ON MINERAL SUSCEPTIBILITIES TO DISTURBANCE

A very large body of observations exists on the open or closed nature of uranium- and thorium-enriched minerals used in geochronology.

### Zircon (Zr, Hf, Y, U, Th) SiO₄

The widespread use of populations of cogenetic zircons and their Pb-U isotope pairs (especially on the "Concordia" plot of WETHERILL, 1956) has shown that Precambrian zircons commonly have been opened (TILTON et al., 1957; SILVER and DEUTSCH, 1961, 1963; and by many other workers). SILVER (1963a,b) demonstrated a strong correlation between radioactivity and discordance for families of zircons from several Precambrian granites.

PIDGEON et al. (1966, 1973) reported experimental evidence for the extensive removal of radiogenic lead without disturbance of uranium from a metamict Sri Lanka zircon by high-temperature aqueous saline solutions under hydrothermal conditions equivalent to a depth of about 6 km. BANKS and SILVER (1966) observed that even Cretaceous granitic zircons may be discordant at high radioactivity levels, and that the degree of disturbance correlated with relative radioactivities.

SILVER (1966) suggested that three rate-competitive processes may produce the disturbed, yet orderly, D/P relations commonly observed in zircons:

(1) Accumulation of radiation damage in the zircon crystal structure, which is time and actinide-concentration dependent ($\alpha$-particle fluence), determines the threshold susceptibility and initial rate of response of the zircon to a given modifying geologic process.

(2) Lead removal from the crystal, perhaps initially by local short-term diffusion at elevated temperatures, and ultimately by solution leaching or volatilization, proceeds at rates determined by the nature of the disturbing geologic process and the residual disorder in the crystal structure.

(3) Crystal structure annealing, which may occur

continuously at low rates, can accelerate enormously in more intense (hotter? wetter?) hydrothermal or metamorphic episodes, thereby reducing vulnerability to lead loss.

Process (1) is accumulative. Processes (2) and (3) are dominantly episodic in response to the nature of specific geologic metamorphic episodes in the middle or upper crust. Uranium or thorium gain or loss appears to occur only during growth or re-action of zircon as a phase participating in an evolving metamorphic assemblage. The relative rates of processes (2) and (3) are critical in determining the degree of lead loss, for the typical zircon response is self-quenching of losses by progressive annealing.

The sensitivity of many zircons to disturbance initially surprised workers, especially geochemists less familiar with the details of local geologic history. Since some low-level geologic events are cryptic (*i.e.*, do not leave readily visible macroscopic evidence for their existence on igneous rock outcrops) several other explanations have been suggested, not all of which will be reviewed here (*viz.* STERN *et al.*, 1966; GOLDICH and MUDREY, 1972; GRAUERT *et al.*, 1974; SOMMERAUER, 1976). Some early workers (NICOLAYSEN, 1957; TILTON, 1960; WASSERBURG, 1963; SHESTAKOV, 1972) proposed models for continuous lead diffusion in zircons as possible disturbance mechanisms to explain the then widening evidence for disturbance in "unmetamorphosed" rocks. Any continuous disturbance mechanism is of concern here because it would tend to obscure the discrete effects of imposed metamorphic episodes. However, no well-documented examples of natural systems which fit uniquely to such diffusion models have been provided. In many case studies, geology-controlled interpretations involving specific disturbance episodes have been more successful. There still remain some suites and situations for which appropriate independent evidence for discrete geologic disturbances has not been obtained.

In the context of the present proposal, the susceptibility of zircon to disturbance is considered a valuable asset. It is important to note, however, that complete resetting of the isotope systems in zircon has been suggested rarely, and is not documented.

## Titanite (Ca, U, Th, Y) TiSiO₅

Since the early analyses of titanite in geochronological studies (TILTON *et al.*, 1955; TILTON and GRUNENFELDER, 1968; MATTINSON, 1978) it has been observed that cogenetic titanite (sphene) and zircon have dissimilar responses to disturbance.

Titanite appears to be more resistant to discordance from low-grade processes but has been found to be totally reset by certain high-grade metamorphic events. It appears to have a relatively high temperature of closure (~500°C) and in young undisturbed systems gives ages very close to those of zircons. Radiation damage in titanite is well-established (VANCE and MATSON, 1985), but visually much more subtle than in associated zircons, except in the very radioactive variety, keilhauite. Its isotopic responses to metamorphism have been examined principally by HANSON *et al.* (1971).

## Apatite (Ca, REE, U, Th)₅ (PO₄)₃ (OH, F, Cl)

Lead loss appears to be a principal effect of disturbance in apatite. However, evidence for parent migration and/or exchange has been observed in apatite in radioactive granites (*e.g.*, Fig. 1). Apatite is ubiquitous in granites and rarely displays any evidence of radiation damage. Its uranium and thorium levels and $^{238}U/^{204}Pb$ ratios are much less favorable than found in zircon or titanite (Table 1). Apatite was shown to have distinctly lower closure temperatures than zircon or titanite during initial cooling (MATTINSON, 1978; SILVER *et al.*, 1982). Its D/P ratios have been observed to be completely reset.

## Allanite (Ca, LREE, Th, U)₂ (Mn, Fe, Al)₂ AlO-OH (Si₂O₇) (SiO₄)

Allanite is relatively abundant in calcic and calcalkaline plutonic rocks. It is characteristically chemically zoned, and may have a corona of epidote. Very little was known about Pb-U-Th systematics of allanite until recently (SILVER, 1989, 1990; SILVER *et al.*, 1991). Radiation damage accumulates rapidly because of its high Th content and crystals usually are extensively metamict even in late Mesozoic plutons. Once metamict, extensive daughter and parent mobility appears characteristic of allanites disturbed by external processes. The threshold for mobility responsive to such disturbances is quite low for Pb and U, and apparently somewhat higher for Th. The author has observed complete or nearly complete resetting of allanite at the garnet-amphibolite grade of regional metamorphism.

## Thorite (Th, U) SiO₄

Thorite (and uranothorite) is an isostructural analogue to zircon and shows limited solid solution with it. When present it is similar in form to zircon and should be carefully discriminated in geochronological work. Its actinide contents are stoichiometric and may be as much as 70% of the bulk composition. This is up to 1000 times the actinide level in associated zircons. Hence, even 60 Ma crystals have been observed to be largely metamict. SILVER (1963a) and SILVER and DEUTSCH (1963) reported extremely disturbed isotopic systems (>90% apparent lead loss) in thorite in Precambrian granites with late Mesozoic tectonic disturbances. BANKS and SILVER (1966) measured a number of uranothorites from a 115 Ma zircon-age granite and found them to yield apparent U-Pb ages from 86 to 111 Ma. The age variations correlated inversely with the actinide concentrations. If any mineral might be nominated for lead loss by continuous diffusion, it is thorite. However, no demonstration of such loss has yet been made. Clearly, thorite is a very susceptible mineral for chemical and isotopic disturbance. When metamict, it is probably open during normal surface weathering.

## Monazite (Ce, LREE, Th, U) PO₄

Monazite is a common accessory in biotite, muscovite, or two-mica granites. Like other phosphates it does not appear to accumulate radiation damage characteristics of silicate minerals with comparable actinide concentrations. NIER (1939) and HOLMES (1954, 1955) utilized monazites to obtain the first isotopic ages in Precambrian nuclei of several continents. They encountered clearly discordant systematics in many of their samples. TILTON and NICOLAYSEN (1957) examined four additional Precambrian monazites. Many showed the property that the $^{206}$Pb/$^{238}$U apparent age significantly exceeded the $^{207}$Pb/$^{206}$Pb apparent age (reverse discordance). Others showed the opposite relation (normal discordance). Unfortunately, these workers did not report independent evidence for the effects of metamorphic processes. SILVER et al. (1984) found both types of relations in a single sample and in different samples from the same pluton. These observations illustrate the complex behavior of monazite isotope systems. Workers in central Europe (KÖPPEL and GRUNENFELDER 1971, 1975; GEBAUER and GRUNENFELDER, 1973; KÖPPEL, 1974) measured many concordant monazites in metamorphosed rocks. They suggested monazite can be a powerful tool for dating metamorphic events because of complete resetting in high-grade regional metamorphism (GEBAUER and GRUNENFELDER, 1979).

## Xenotime (Y HREE, U, Th) PO₄

Xenotime also is isostructural with zircon, but shows little evidence of radiation damage. Least common of the minerals considered available for this assemblage approach, xenotime is quite radioactive. Both U and Th are typically at the ½–1½% level and overwhelm by radiogenic increment modest initial lead contents. Xenotime isotopic analyses are few in number (SILVER et al., 1982, 1984; L. T. SILVER, unpubl. data). They show slight to moderate isotopic disturbance with D/P ratios suggesting apparent lead loss relative to uranium and thorium. Where cogenetic monazites have been analyzed, they show greater isotopic disturbance than xenotime. No instances of complete resetting of xenotime have been encountered.

Analyses of assemblages in 18 tonalites, granodiorites, and monzogranites from the eastern Peninsular Ranges batholith provide some insights into typical initial lead, uranium, and thorium endowments of various mineral species (Table 1). The columns on the right show average $^{238}$U/$^{204}$Pb and $^{232}$Th/$^{204}$Pb values for the different minerals. These values indicate the relative magnitudes of initial lead corrections in calculating the radiogenic D/P ratios for each mineral.

## ASSEMBLAGES IN "UNMETAMORPHOSED" AND METAMORPHOSED GRANITES

There have been comparatively few comprehensive isotopic studies of *assemblages* of cogenetic radioactive accessory minerals from either undeformed or metamorphosed granitic rocks. TILTON et al. (1955) established the importance of such studies in their pioneering work on the Essonville granite. That rock was, in fact, a foliated granite gneiss deformed in the later stages of the "Grenville" orogeny. The possible effects of its metamorphic history on the radioactive minerals' systems was not appreciated. BANKS (1963) and BANKS and SILVER (1966) completed a comparable study on two intrusive phases of the apparently undeformed early Cretaceous Rubidoux Mtn. leucogranite in the Peninsular Ranges batholith and found isotopically disturbed systems suggesting a younger episode. MATTINSON (1978) explored zircon-titanite-apatite assemblages in several essentially undeformed Cretaceous granites in the Salinian block of central California, and found differences within the apparent ages of the several species of up to 25%, which he attributed to cooling histories down to ~300°C. LUDWIG and STUCKLESS (1978) examined partial assemblages in some radioactive Precambrian granites in Wyoming and found widespread evidence for isotopic disturbance.

SILVER et al. (1980, 1982, 1984) examined assemblages from five "unmetamorphosed" radioactive granites from Arizona and California, including their responses to weathering and hydrothermal alteration. They inferred widespread evidence for Mesozoic and Cenozoic disturbances for which independent geological support could be cited. CHEN and MOORE (1982) reported on seven zircon-titanite pairs from the central Sierra Nevada batholith that were close to concordant. DEWITT *et al.* (1984) reported disturbed U-Th-Pb systematics in zircons and titanites in several samples of a metamorphosed Proterozoic granite complex in the eastern Mojave desert, California. The disturbance reflected more than one metamorphism in the late Mesozoic.

SILVER and JAMES (1988, 1991) have completed assemblage studies on a dozen tonalites to granites or gneissic equivalents from the Cajon Pass deep scientific drill hole in the southwestern Mojave desert. At least half of these rocks are protomylonitic and some are metamorphosed to upper-amphibolite facies. The evidence points persuasively to a profound late Cretaceous tectonic event which imprinted all of the rock column. The author also has examined nearly 50 complete or partial assemblages from other Cretaceous and Jurassic granites from different petrologic settings and tectonic environments in southwestern North America.

The accumulating evidence points to some generalizations:

(1) Different Pb-U-Th-bearing species have widely different sensitivities to low-grade events.

(2) Many apparently unmetamorphosed granites have seen unsuspected low-grade events.

(3) Many late Phanerozoic granites of the Cordilleran batholiths show only slight effects of secondary events on their assemblages.

(4) More intensely metamorphosed granites show quite different, yet systematic, responses among their mineral assemblages than do weakly modified or cryptically influenced "unmetamorphosed" granites.

(5) Older granites tend to carry more imprints of low-grade disturbances. Some can be correlated with local or regional tectonic or magmatic events.

In a geological sense the last observation is not surprising. Even the most stable craton has had an ongoing history of vertical tectonics including basin formation, marine transgression, and tectonic uplift, as well as intraplate volcanism and local strain and deformation. Older granite assemblages with greater accumulations of radiation damage in the participating species also have accumulated greater sensitivities. It is this general phenomenon that probably has stimulated continuous diffusion interpretations. In older granites, any new imprints of metamorphism necessarily must be read against any previously acquired background of minor disturbances.

## MODELS FOR D/P VARIATIONS IN PROGRADE METAMORPHISM OF RADIOACTIVE MINERAL ASSEMBLAGES

Some assumptions and simplifications must be made in order to present graphic models of conceptual D/P trajectories in metamorphic space for a granite mineral assemblage. Much of the background for these assumptions has already been discussed:

(1) A sample of modified granite represents a point on a metamorphic gradient. Several samples, properly spaced, can define the gradient.

(2) For each kind of prograde metamorphic process, the Pb-U-Th system in each mineral host responds with distinctive patterns reflecting daughter and/or parent mobility. The threshold for initiation of mobility and conditions for complete isotopic resetting are peculiar to that mineral species for the particular metamorphic process. The net effect is a distinctive trajectory in a D/P vs. metamorphic intensity field.

(3) Retrograde phenomena do not significantly modify and blur the prograde record.

(4) External petrology, isotopic and geochemical indicators, and experimental studies, each permit some independent calibration of characteristic D/P trajectories along various kinds of natural metamorphic gradients.

The simplifications applied to the graphic presentation involve additional assumptions:

(5) A single dimension can be used to represent any type of metamorphic gradient even though the metamorphism involves complex variables.

(6) Each granite and each mineral species constituted an initially homogeneous population before being subjected to the metamorphic gradient. The assumption of initial homogeneity will be reexamined below.

(7) The Pb-U-Th systems in the selected mineral species have favorable abundances, and sampling and analysis uncertainties are small relative to the natural D/P variations. In reality not all systems, especially younger ones, may be treated this way.

(8) The primary cooling time interval is negligible.

*Model I—Thermally driven diffusive loss*

In this case the mobility responses of Pb-U-Th bearing minerals are modeled as thermally driven diffusive phenomena governed by an Arrhenius relationship peculiar to each mineral. DODSON (1973, and in subsequent papers) developed a closure temperature model for slow cooling now widely applied for $^{40}$Ar-$^{40}$K and $^{39}$Ar-$^{40}$Ar geochronology (see discussions in MCDOUGALL and HARRISON, 1988).

In Fig. 2 a three-dimensional orthogonal rhombohedron is employed to represent the three major parameters: *mineral species, metamorphic gradient,* and *D/P ratios* for a particular daughter/parent system. The diagram is designed to illustrate a hypo-thetical two-stage history: (1) primary crystallization of U-Th mineral assemblages with a negligible cooling interval, whose closed-system age is $(D/P)_1$, and (2) a short-duration metamorphic episode that has created a well-defined metamorphic gradient. In the time elapsed since metamorphism new or completely reset systems produced $(D/P)_2$. The diagram is generalized and uncalibrated.

The front face is bounded by the parameters of D/P ratio and intensity of metamorphism along the gradient. In this case, it shows the D/P response in

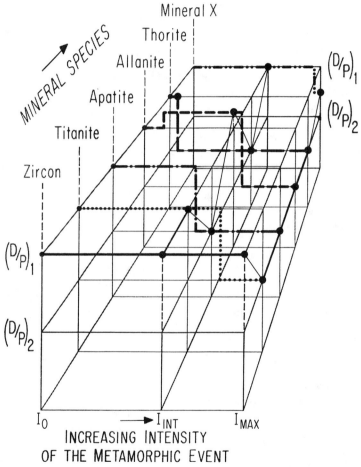

FIG. 2. A three-dimensional representation of three parameters: *Mineral Species, Metamorphic Gradient,* and *D/P ratios* for a model for thermally driven diffusive lead loss in the radioactive minerals. It is used to present hypothetical trajectories for the radiogenic D/P system for each of six minerals showing Arrhenius-relationship disturbance at some abrupt point along a thermal metamorphic gradient. The indicated responses are models assuming $(D/P)_1$ represents an undisturbed primary age system; $(D/P)_2$ represents a D/P system completely reset by metamorphism and since undisturbed. Planes perpendicular to the front face at $I_{int}$ and $I_{max}$ are isogradic planes displaying the accumulated D/P response for each mineral (the piercing points are indicated by heavy dots). An important point is that the form of the array in each isogradic plane represents the assemblage for only a limited interval along the gradient. However, three such trajectory diagrams are provided from the uranogenic and thorogenic systems, contributing to a greater degree of D/P pattern uniqueness. Each point along the gradient is characterized by measurements from a single granite assemblage.

zircon (none). Behind this face are parallel fields for related U-Th minerals in the assemblage. This includes an unspecified species, mineral $X$, to symbolize the variability possible in such systems. (Alternatively, mineral $X$ might represent a $^{40}K$, $^{87}Rb$, $^{147}Sm$, etc., geochronometer.)

Any plane perpendicular to the front face is an isogradic plane. It contains presently observed D/P values in phases of the assemblage collected at a particular point in the metamorphic gradient. The D/P values for each species in three isogradic (isothermal) planes, $I_0$, $I_{int}$, $I_{max}$, on the metamorphic gradient are represented as heavy dots. At $I_0$, the protolith condition, all values are $(D/P)_1$. Within the plane $I_{int}$, at some intermediate position, the D/P values for two of six species have been reset and show $(D/P)_2$, reflecting individual closure characteristics. In the plane at $I_{max}$, only zircon has $(D/P)_1$ memory; all others have been reset and have accumulated $(D/P)_2$. It can be seen that the array of D/P values encountered in any isogradic plane is duplicated only over limited intervals along the intensity gradient and could serve as an approximate index of metamorphic grade. Construction of additional diagrams for the other two D/P systems, however, creates a more unique specification of D/P systematics at any point on the metamorphic gradient.

In a temporal sense, the four mineral species in the isogradic plane at $I_{max}$ with D/P values equal to $(D/P)_2$ form a depressed plateau rather analogous to an $^{39}Ar/^{40}Ar$ plateau. Of course, the plane at $I_0$ displays the primary age $(D/P)_1$ plateau. Thus, the relative D/P values in any intermediate isogradic plane, which can be obtained from any single sample and compared with isogradic patterns from the other pair of D/P systems, can be rich in useful information.

The comparative D/P responses for representatives of each species at all points *along* the metamorphic gradient produce a locus (heavy patterned line). The locus (or D/P trajectory) reflects the integrated geochemical behavior of the daughter and parent elements in the species along the metamorphic gradient. The illustrated loci are hypothetical. They show sharply defined closure (resetting) temperatures, based upon tendencies observed for each mineral. They are poorly controlled and perhaps quite inappropriate.

Most D/P trajectories in this model show relative daughter loss as ultimately dominant. Daughter loss can be expected. The radiogenic daughters are not structurally ordered in the host phase, are in damaged domains, and may be susceptible to diffusive migration. However, some degree of parent loss or addition is not precluded, even where daughter loss has occurred. Where lower grade metamorphism affects high temperature assemblages, internal re-equilibration might occur. In allanite under certain metamorphic conditions it appears that uranium may be more mobile than lead; hence, the D/P ratio $> (D/P)_1$ is shown for part of the allanite trajectory.

For the relatively simple condition of thermally driven diffusive phenomena three different three-dimensional representations like Fig. 2, representing $^{206}Pb/^{238}U$, $^{207}Pb/^{235}U$, $^{208}Pb/^{232}Th$ can be used to analyze daughter versus parent migration. If lead loss alone is involved, the three D/P systems differ but are linked in a simple relation through the different decay constants. If parents are also mobile, more complex D/P trajectory lines for each mineral are generated along the metamorphic gradient. The added complexity adds uniqueness to the array of D/P values developed in the assemblage at a particular level of metamorphic intensity, thereby raising the potential use of D/P arrays as indices of metamorphism.

In summary, it may be possible to apply a Pb-U-Th assemblage approach to a purely thermally driven metamorphic event where such events exist, or if certain species were sensitive only to temperature. However, there is such extensive evidence of multiple variables affecting the Pb-U-Th systems that it seems necessary to consider a more general model. Perhaps it may be possible to assess the role of thermal diffusion when an increased number of case studies with favorable geologic conditions or careful laboratory studies permit isolation of the contributions of several important variables. Fortunately, argon systems are available for thermochronology.

### Model II—Complex disturbance mechanisms

The complex interplay of several imposed variables defines the character of the metamorphic event and its influence on Pb-U-Th minerals. Temperature, activities of $H_2O$ and other fluids, open chemical systems, and strain are particularly prominent. Indices of these parameters are major targets for investigation.

A generalized model for imposed metamorphic modification is provided in Fig. 3. The parameters of the diagram are the same as in Fig. 2. Again, the isogradic planes, $I_0$, $I_{int}$, and $I_{max}$, are emphasized by heavy dots where the D/P trajectories for each species penetrate the three planes. The D/P trajectories are distinctive curved lines with possible inflection points. Indicated trajectories are hypothetical, largely uncontrolled, except for the biases de-

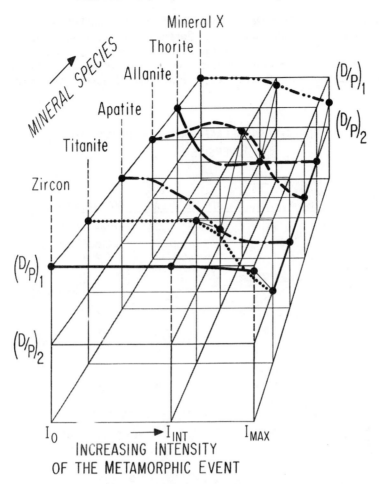

FIG. 3. A three-dimensional representation using the parameters: *Mineral Species, Metamorphic Gradient,* and *D/P ratios* for a model in which multiple variables provide a complex metamorphic gradient ($p$H$_2$O, strain, temperature, bulk rock chemical changes, etc.). The variables contribute competing influences to the hypothetical trajectory of a given D/P system in each mineral. (D/P)$_1$ represents the granite primary age; (D/P)$_2$ represents a completely reset D/P system at time of metamorphism. For such a collection of trajectories, the arrays of piercing points (heavy dots) in the isogradic planes, $I_{int}$, and $I_{max}$ are unique compared to any other position along the gradient. Each array can be derived from a single sample, and because three such diagrams may be derived from the three D/P systems an even greater degree of specificity of responses to the metamorphic process is possible. It is this capacity for unique characterization which forms the basis for suggesting the family of D/P ratios might provide metamorphic indices.

rived from the author's observations. In this illustration, only at the $I_{max}$ isograd has a well-supported plateau developed, with four species displaying (D/P)$_2$ ratios.

If a family of *real* D/P trajectories possesses comparably distinctive forms, then the assemblage D/P values contained in any isogradic plane between $I_0$ and $I_{max}$ will differ from the array of values in other planes. Using the trajectories of three D/P systems, the position of a sample in the metamorphic gradient should be uniquely defined, within analytical uncertainties.

Considerations of D/P responses in this model are again influenced by the chemical nature of each mineral species and its radiation damage. However, in this model the form of the trajectories may be equally determined by the nature of the metamorphic process. For example, the effects produced in a mylonite zone should, in principle, be distinguishable from those produced in a hydrothermal cell, or in a weathering profile. Certainly each process will have its own threshold intensity level for disturbing a particular mineral, and it may or may not achieve complete resetting.

The author currently is pursuing these questions in several types of metamorphic situations. An example from work in progress is given in Fig. 4, which shows mineral assemblage analyses in six different rocks from the San Jacinto Mtns., Riverside Co.,

California. Ages and D/P ratios vary nearly linearly at this age; only the ages are plotted in this diagram. Five samples are from a nest of three unmetamorphosed plutons described by HILL (1988) and HILL et al. (1988). These samples indicate emplacement

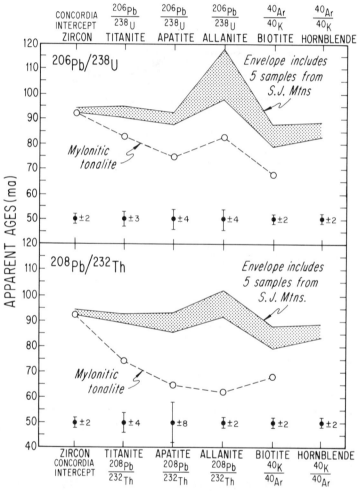

FIG. 4. Examples of D/P arrays from actual granite samples are shown for $^{206}Pb/^{238}U$ and $^{208}Pb/$ $^{232}Th$. Five closely related granitic samples from the San Jacinto Mtns., southern California, yielded D/P ratios (expressed as ages) for the array zircon-titanite-apatite-allanite. In addition, they can be assigned $^{40}Ar$-$^{40}K$ ages in biotite and hornblende, from previous work. The analytical uncertainties are shown by the error figures. The D/P arrays for the two systems in the five samples form rather tight envelopes (stippled) that are in good agreement (except for allanite), suggesting primary emplacement followed by rapid cooling. They each represent an isogradic plane close to $I_0$ in Fig. 3. The anomalous allanite ages indicate the sample may have experienced some form of younger overprint involving parent mobilization. A sixth sample is a protomylonitic tonalite gneiss of the same primary age (zircon) from a great mylonite zone 15 km to the east; its assemblage shows markedly lower D/ P ratios (ages) for both systems in all minerals except zircon. These displacements suggest that the mylonitic environment can have more pronounced disturbance effects on several of the radioactive minerals compared to zircon.

of the plutons between 92 and 95 Ma, based on well-defined microdiscordant zircon suites. The sixth sample is a protomylonite from a neighboring tonalite pluton 15 km to the east, from the margin of the great eastern Peninsular Ranges mylonite zone. In addition, titanite, apatite, and allanite have been analyzed in all samples. Previous studies (ARMSTRONG and SUPPE, 1973; MORTON and MILLER, 1987) provide $^{40}$Ar-$^{40}$K ages in biotite and hornblende from the same plutons in the vicinity of several of the Pb-U-Th samples. The D/P ratios, calculated as ages, are shown for $^{206}$Pb/$^{238}$U and $^{208}$Pb/$^{232}$Th. The $^{207}$Pb/$^{235}$U ages, within analytical error, track the $^{206}$Pb/$^{238}$U ages and are omitted. All of the ages of the five unmetamorphosed samples are contained within the stippled envelopes. The range for each mineral should be compared with the indicated analytical uncertainty bars.

For the five unmetamorphosed samples, the envelope for zircon-titanite-apatite shows progressively slightly younger ages for both D/P systems, suggesting at most, a five million year cooling interval to apatite closure. However, allanite in both systems displays D/P values greater than those for zircon, especially for $^{206}$Pb/$^{238}$U. This is strong evidence for mobility of U and Th and does not preclude some Pb loss. Because allanite is clearly disturbed and this disturbance by its magnitude *must* be post cooling, how much of the D/P differentials between zircon and titanite and apatite also might be post-cooling? Several hornblende and biotite ages are slightly lower (5–10 Ma) than the apatite ages and are part of a gentle local gradient that suggests a modest overprint. Thus the "unmetamorphosed" samples are not quite as pristine as was initially thought. What disturbed them?

In any interpretation the greater sensitivity to the disturbance of allanite, biotite, and hornblende compared to zircon-titanite-apatite seems apparent. Was this produced by thermal history alone? Thermal diffusion coefficients for U and Th in partly metamict allanite are not known. Several arguments suggest that the diffusion mechanisms operative in biotite and hornblende must differ from whatever mechanisms are responsible for the disturbance in allanite. More detailed discussion of this problem will be developed in a separate paper. Neglecting allanite, the D/P ratios in the other five minerals would be accepted generally as the product of a simple cooling and uplift history, and suitable for approximately characterizing the $I_0$ position in models I and II. They will be used in that way, provisionally, for comparison with the sixth sample from the edge of the great mylonite zone to the east. A geologic reconstruction of the east-dipping

eastern Peninsular Ranges mylonite zone (SHARP, 1979) projects some 10 ± 3 km above the other five samples. This zone has been called late Cretaceous or Paleogene, synplutonic or post-emplacement, by various workers, and its age has considerable significance in southern California tectonics. The grade of metamorphism where it is most profoundly mylonitized is amphibolite facies. The sample recorded in Fig. 4 was a tonalite and is now a penetratively foliated tonalite gneiss whose major mineral assemblage, hornblende-biotite-quartz-plagioclase, remains unchanged. Most of the major minerals remain macroscopic and a good yield of all accessory minerals was obtained. This sample represents an intermediate position in the strain gradient as indicated by its fabric modification. There is no evidence of low grade H$_2$O-supported alteration. The age of its protolith from nearly concordant zircons is indistinguishable from the other five samples. The D/P ratios (ages) for the other Pb-U-Th systems are lower by 10–35% than the D/P ratios for the emplacement age.

The allanite D/P ratios show the greatest differences and are among the lowest values in the mylonitic accessory mineral suite, indicating that apparent lead loss dominated over parent loss. Thus, the character of the D/P responses in the protomylonite allanite is in strong contrast with whatever factors influenced the D/P ratios in allanites in the western samples.

The patterns of ages for the two D/P systems in the protomylonite assemblages cannot yet be related to the post-tectonic cooling and uplift history. Until the gradient sampling is completed, the observed D/P ratios must be used cautiously in any interpretation of the age of mylonitization. If it reflects a thermal anomaly induced by the tectonics which produced the mylonite, one might expect the thermal anomaly and its cooling history to have imprinted the deeper underlying samples as well. Was the intense strain associated with the local fabric development a critical factor in developing the D/P patterns? Answers to the several questions above are not available at this point, but it is the questions are central to the arguments for continued testing and delineation of elements of models I and II.

*Model III—Intraspecies variations in actinide concentrations and associated D/P ratios*

In presenting models I and II, it was assumed, for purposes of simplification, that each mineral species was a homogeneous population of crystals in a homogeneous granitic protolith. Even though this is rarely the case, heterogeneity is no real barrier to the consideration of those models provided it is recognized, evaluated, and normalized effectively. If radiation damage is an important factor influencing species responses, then normalization to a common degree of radiation damage can be achieved by comparing actinide concentrations. Some other influential compositional variations may also require normalization. In model III, the intent is to indicate briefly how intraspecies variations can add additional definition to the metamorphic responses recorded in the D/P values of the mineral assemblages.

The correlation between actinide concentrations (dominated by uranium) and degree of discordance in zircon is well established (SILVER, 1963a,b). In model III we propose that this correlation in zircon also may provide a sensitive index of metamorphism, and that other intraspecies variations may be useful. In Fig. 5, another block model rather similar to Figs. 2 and 3 is presented. It differs only in that the Mineral Species coordinate has been replaced by Radiation Damage in zircon subsets. Various fractions of a single mineral species, zircon in this case, are separated on the basis of their actinide concentrations and associated radiation damage.

Present-day radiation damage is not the most significant parameter if some annealing has taken place; the accumulated damage at the time of metamorphic disturbance is the relevant value. That value cannot be uniquely determined at present, but one can reasonably assume a proportionality correlated to the present actinide concentration values.

In this model, since the correlation of magnitude of disturbance with magnitude of radiation damage is accepted, the family of zircon subsystems might respond to the metamorphic gradient along the trajectories shown by heavy lines in Fig. 5. The values on the isogradic planes are indicated at $I_{int}$ and $I_{max}$. The prograde changes are shown by the model as sufficiently large to be clearly established by isotope dilution mass spectrometry. The disturbance effects in some zircon systems are much larger.

An actual example of this type of response corresponding to an $I_{int}$ isogradic plane has been measured in a Cretaceous granodiorite near Randsburg, California. This intrusive has been intruded, in turn, by a small mid-Tertiary stock which generated a locally intense hydrothermal cell. The granodiorite sample was collected on the outer perimeter of the cell and shows only slight recrystallization affects. However, titanite-apatite-biotite-hornblende D/P ratios all yield Miocene ages. The zircons have been separated into several fractions. Each fraction appears concordant, within analytical error, when plotted on "Concordia."

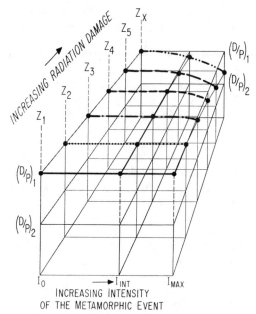

FIG. 5. A three-dimensional representation of the parameters *Radiation Damage, D/P ratios,* and *Metamorphic Gradient,* illustrating the influence of the degree of accumulated radiation damage on susceptibility to D/P disturbance in zircons with different actinide concentrations. The diagram is derived from many observations and, while generalized, can be matched from real systems. The arrays of points in the isogradic planes at $I_{int}$ and $I_{max}$ may also serve as indices of the nature and intensity of a metamorphic event. $(D/P)_2$ and $(D/P)_1$ as in Figs. 2 and 3.

In Fig. 6, the D/P ratios (as calculated ages) for all three D/P systems are plotted against uranium concentration in four zircon fractions. The Th/U ratio is close to a constant for these fractions and uranium has contributed more than 85% to the total alpha particle fluence. Therefore, uranium is a good indicator of the relative radiation damage at the time metamorphism was imposed. The most radioactive zircons show a 10% discrepancy between the ages for the Pb/U pair and the $^{208}Pb/^{232}Th$ ratio. As D/P trends are followed to lower radioactivity fractions, the three D/P systems converge and yield concordant ages well within indicated limits of analytical precision. In effect, for this sample, this graph represents the superimposed $I_{int}$ isogradic plane of Fig. 5 for each of the three D/P systems.

The radioactivity levels of these zircons are quite normal, even slightly low. The pre-metamorphism interval for radiation damage accumulation in the suite was only about 60 Ma. Yet the sensitivity of part of the suite to the particular metamorphic con-

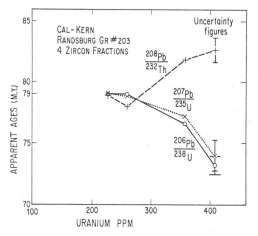

FIG. 6. A suite of zircons from a Cretaceous granite in the Mojave desert, California, has been analyzed for all Pb–U–Th D/P systems. The sample is from the edge of a hydrothermal cell generated around a Miocene porphyry stock intruded into the granite. All other radioactive minerals, plus biotite and hornblende, have been reset to Miocene ages. The zircon suite shows a systematic correlation of increasing discordance with increasing actinide (uranium) concentration. This is attributed to the effect of differential accumulations of radiation damage present at the time of hydrothermal activity. Arrays in this plot should be compared with the $I_{int}$ isogradic plane in Fig. 5. This graph presents all three D/P systems on the same plane.

ditions is manifest. What were the conditions that opened zircon D/P systems with more than 300 ppm of uranium but did not significantly affect those with less than 250 ppm? Does the threshold of susceptibility to disturbance shift downward in uranium concentration along the gradient toward the young intrusive center? How far from the center must samples have been located for all of their zircons to escape disturbance? For their titanite? Apatite, etc.?

Many examples are known of comparably sensitive zircon suites with D/P ratios converging toward concordance with decreasing actinide concentrations. Much less data is available on the D/P behavior of radiation-damaged species such as thorite, allanite, and titanite. Nevertheless, these data do support the possibility of using intraspecies actinide variations and D/P responses in several minerals to obtain more detailed information about the conditions of metamorphism affecting a suite of samples along a metamorphic gradient.

## SUMMARY

This paper is intended to present the concept that the patterns of isotopic disturbance in Pb–U–Th systems found in radioactive accessory minerals in metamorphosed granites are potentially as rich in information about the nature and intensity of post-magmatic processes as they are about the time constants. The radiogenic daughter–parent ratios can be measured with great precision. They offer a powerful matrix of data which has not been adequately investigated much less utilized. To properly assess their potential, they require careful investigation in selected natural situations where the important characteristics of a metamorphic process can be reasonably unraveled and the influence of key variables on the chemical response of each mineral in an assemblage can be determined. A variety of laboratory experiments involving experimental petrology, mineralogy and geochemistry also can be rewarding (*e.g.,* PIDGEON *et al.,* 1966, 1973). At one end of the metamorphic intensity scale, the behavior of assemblages in the most pristine of granites needs continuing analyses to provide understanding of the base-line isotopic signatures. At the other end of the intensity scale where new, radioactive metamorphic mineral species enter the assemblages, the petrological stability fields of most of the common igneous accessory minerals are, in large part, unknown. Given the diverse nature of the modifying processes here included in the term metamorphism (*e.g.,* production of granulites, mylonites, ore deposits, soils, etc.) there is a great number and variety of studies to be completed before the validity and the efficiency of the approach can be established. This author will report on a few of them in forthcoming papers.

There is one other significant product that can emerge from these generic studies. The geochemical cycles of uranium, thorium, and lead are well established as critical to understanding crustal and planetary evolution. Since the assemblages discussed in this paper represent the principal sites for radiogenic lead, uranium, and thorium in the continental crust, their behavior in various modifying environments must be understood. Completion of the types of studies suggested here will vastly improve our comprehension of those cycles.

*Acknowledgements*—The observations leading to the proposals in this paper have been collected with the assistance of many colleagues and students over a period of nearly 40 years. Their discussions and labors are deeply appreciated. Geraldine Silver has been an unflagging partner in this effort for most of that time. During all of that period I have enjoyed the powerful intellectual companionship of Samuel Epstein. I want to thank him for the rich flavors he has contributed to my working environment and for his warm friendship. Parts of the work represented in this paper have been supported at length by the Department of Energy and by a National Science Foundation grant #EAR-851927. Division of Geological and Planetary Sciences, California Institute of Technology, Contribution No. 5045.

## REFERENCES

ARMSTRONG R. L. and SUPPE J. (1973) Potassium-argon geochronometry of Mesozoic igneous rocks in Nevada, Utah, and southern California. *Bull. Geol. Soc. Amer.* **84**, 1375–1392.

BANKS P. O. (1963) Some systematics of uranium and lead distribution in relation to the petrology of the Mt. Rubidoux leucogranites, Riverside Co., California. Ph.D. thesis, California Institute of Technology.

BANKS P. O. and SILVER L. T. (1966) Evaluation of the decay constant of uranium 235 from lead isotope ratios. *J. Geophys. Res.* **71**, 4037–4046.

CHEN J. H. and MOORE J. G. (1982) Uranium-lead isotopic ages from the Sierra Nevada batholith, California. *J. Geophys. Res.* **87**, 4761–4784.

DAVIS G. L., HART S. R. and TILTON G. R. (1968) Some effects of contact metamorphism on zircon ages. *Earth Planet. Sci. Lett.* **5**, 27–34.

DEWITT E., ARMSTRONG R. L., SUTTER J. F. and ZARTMAN R. E. (1984) U-Th-Pb, Rb-Sr, and Ar-Ar whole-rock isotopic systematics in a metamorphosed granitic terrane, southeastern California. *Bull. Geol. Soc. Amer.* **95**, 723–739.

DODSON M. H. (1973) Closure temperatures in cooling geochronological and petrological systems. *Contrib. Mineral. Petrol.* **40**, 259–274.

DOE B. R. and HART S. R. (1963) The effect of contact metamorphism on lead in potassium feldspars near the Eldora Stock, Colorado. *J. Geophys. Res.* **68**, 3521–3530.

GEBAUER D. and GRUNENFELDER M. (1973) U-Pb zircon and Rb-Sr systems during progressive metamorphism. *Fortsch. Mineral.* **50**, 76–78.

GOLDICH S. S. and MUDREY J. R. (1972) Dilatancy model for discordant U-Pb zircon ages. In *Contributions to Recent Geochemistry and Analytical Chemistry* (Vinogradov volume), pp. 415–418. Nauka Publ. Office, Moscow.

GRAUERT B., SEITZ M. G. and SOPTRAJANOVE G. (1974) Uranium and lead gain of detrital zircon studied by isotopic analyses and fission track mapping. *Earth Planet. Sci. Lett.* **21**, 389–399.

HANSON G. N. (1971) Radiogenic argon loss from biotites in whole rock heating experiments. *Geochim. Cosmochim. Acta* **35**, 101–107.

HANSON G. N. and GAST P. (1967) Kinetic studies in contact metamorphic zones. *Geochim. Cosmochim. Acta* **31**, 119.

HANSON G. N., CATANZARO E. J. and ANDERSON D. H. (1971) U-Pb ages for sphene in a contact metamorphic zone. *Earth Planet. Sci. Lett.* **12**, 213–237.

HART S. R. (1964) The petrology and isotopic-mineral age relations of a contact zone in the Front Range, Colorado. *J. Geol.* **72**, 493–525.

HART S. R., DAVIS G. L., STEIGER R. H. and TILTON G. R. (1968) A comparison of the isotopic mineral age variations and petrologic changes induced by contact metamorphism. In *Radiometric Dating for Geologists* (eds. E. I. HAMILTON and R. M. FARQUHAR), pp. 73–110. Interscience, New York.

HILL R. I. (1988) San Jacinto Intrusive Complex I. Geology and mineral chemistry, and a model for intermittent recharge of tonalite magma chambers. *J. Geophys. Res.* **93**, B9, 10,325–10,348.

HILL R. I., CHAPPELL B. W. and SILVER L. T. (1988) San Jacinto Intrusive Complex 2. Geochemistry. *J. Geophys. Res.* **93**(B9), 10,344–10,372.

HOLLAND H. D. and GOTTFRIED D. (1955) The effect of nuclear radiation on the structure of zircon. *Acta Crystallogr.* **8**, 291–300.

HOLMES A. (1954) The oldest dated minerals of the Rhodesian Shield. *Nature* **173**, 612.

HOLMES A. (1955) Dating the Precambrian of peninsular India and Ceylon. *Proc. Geol. Assoc. Canada* **7**, 81–106.

KÖPPEL V. (1974) Isotopic U-Pb ages of monazites and zircons from the crust-mantle transition and adjacent units of the Ivrea and Ceneri zones (southern Alps, Italy). *Contrib. Mineral. Petrol.* **43**, 55–70.

KÖPPEL V. and GRUNENFELDER M. (1971) A study of inherited and newly formed zircon from paragneisses and granitised sediments of the Strona-Ceneri-zone (southern Alps). *Schweiz. Mineral. Petrogr. Mitt.* **51**, 385–409.

KÖPPEL V. and GRUNENFELDER M. (1975) Concordant U-Pb ages of monazites from the central Alps and the timing of the high temperature alpine metamorphism, preliminary report. *Schweiz. Mineral. Petrogr. Mitt.* **55**.

LUDWIG K. R. and STUCKLESS J. S. (1978) Uranium-lead isotope systematics and apparent ages of zircons and other minerals in Precambrian granitic rocks, Granite Mountains, Wyoming. *Contrib. Mineral. Petrol.* **65**, 2433–2454.

MATTINSON J. M. (1978) Age, origin, and thermal histories of some plutonic rocks from the Salinian block of California. *Contrib. Mineral. Petrol.* **67**, 233–245.

McDOUGALL I. and HARRISON T. M. (1988) *Geochronology and Thermochronology by the $^{40}Ar/^{39}Ar$ Method.* Oxford Univ. Press, New York.

MORTON D. M. and MILLER F. K. (1987) K-Ar apparent ages of plutonic rocks from the northern Peninsular Ranges batholith, southern California. *Geol. Soc. Amer. Abstr. Prog.* **19**, no. 6, p. 435.

NAESER C. W. (1979) Fission-track dating and geologic annealing of fission tracks. In *Lectures in Isotope Geology* (eds. E. JÄEGER and J. HUNZIKER), pp. 154–169. Springer-Verlag, Berlin.

NICOLAYSEN L. O. (1957) Solid diffusion in radioactive minerals and the measurement of absolute age. *Geochim. Cosmochim. Acta* **11**, 41.

NIER A. O. (1939) The isotopic composition of radiogenic leads and the measurement of geological time. *Phys. Rev.* **55**, 153–163.

PIDGEON R. T., O'NEIL J. R. and SILVER L. T. (1966) Uranium and lead isotopic stability in a metamict zircon under experimental hydrothermal conditions. *Science* **154**, 1538–1540.

PIDGEON R. T., O'NEIL J. R. and SILVER L. T. (1973) Observations on the crystallinity and the U-Pb system of a metamict Ceylon zircon under experimental hydrothermal conditions. *Fortschr. Mineral.* **50**, 118–119.

SHARP R. V. (1979) Some characteristics of the eastern Peninsular Ranges mylonite zone. In *Proceedings, Conference VII, Analysis of Actual Fault Zones in Bedrock; U.S. Geol. Surv. Open-File Rept., 79-1239*, pp. 258–267.

SHESTAKOV G. I. (1972) Diffusion of lead in monazite, zircon, sphene and apatite. *Trans. Geokhimiza* **10**, 1197–1202.

SILVER L. T. (1963a) The relation between radioactivity and discordance in zircons. *NAS-NRC Nuclear. Geophys.* **1075**, 34–39.

SILVER L. T. (1963b) The use of cogenetic uranium-lead isotope systems in zircons in geochronology. In *Radioactive Dating,* pp. 279–287. IAEA, Vienna.

SILVER L. T. (1989) Daughter-parent isotope systematics in U-Th-bearing accessory mineral assemblages as indices of metamorphism: I. the concept. *Geol. Soc. Amer. Abstr. Prog.* **21**(7), A142.

SILVER L. T. (1990) Initial U, Th and Pb concentrations and fractionations in radioactive accessory minerals in some calcic to calcalkaline plutonic rocks. *Geol. Soc. Amer. Abstr. Prog.* **22**(7), A26.

SILVER L. T. and DEUTSCH S. (1961) Uranium-lead method on zircons. *New York Acad. Sci. Ann.* **91**, 279–283.

SILVER L. T. and DEUTSCH S. (1963) Uranium-lead isotopic variations in zircons: a case study. *J. Geol.* **71**, 721–758.

SILVER L. T., WILLIAMS I. S. and WOODHEAD J. A. (1980) *Uranium in Granites from the Southwestern United States: Actinide Parent-Daughter Systems, Sites and Mobilization.* DOE-GJBX-45(81), Dept. of Energy, Grand Junction, CO.

SILVER L. T., WOODHEAD J. A. and WILLIAMS I. S. (1982) Primary mineral distribution and secondary mobilization of uranium and thorium in radioactive granites. *Uranium Exploration Methods Symp.* 355–366. Paris Proceedings NEA-IAEA.

SILVER L. T., WOODHEAD J. A., WILLIAMS I. S. and CHAPPELL B. W. (1984) *Uranium in Granites from the Southwestern United States: Actinide Parent-Daughter Systems, Sites, and Mobilization.* DOE-GJBX-7(84), Dept. of Energy, Grand Junction, CO.

SILVER L. T., JAMES E. W., COTKIN S. and CHAPPELL B. W. (1991) Petrology and geochemistry of crystalline basement rocks in the Cajon Pass Scientific Drillhole, San Bernardino Co., CA. (in prep.).

SOMMERAUER J. (1976) Die chemisch-physikalische stabilitat naturlicher zirkone und ihr U-(Th)-Pb system. Ph.D. thesis, ETH Zurich.

STERN T. W., GOLDICH S. S. and NEWELL M. F. (1966) Effects of weathering on the U-Pb ages of zircon from the Morton gneiss, Minnesota. *Earth Planet. Sci. Lett.* **1**, 369–371.

TILTON G. R. (1960) Volume diffusion as a mechanism for discordant lead ages. *J. Geophys. Res.* **65**, 2933–2945.

TILTON G. R. and GRUNENFELDER M. (1968) Sphene, uranium-lead ages. *Science* **159**, 1458–1461.

TILTON G. R. and NICOLAYSEN L. O. (1957) The use of monazites for age determination. *Geochim. Cosmochim. Acta* **11**, 28–40.

TILTON G. R., PATTERSON C., BROWN H., INGHRAM M., HAYDEN R., HESS D. and LARSEN E. (1955) Isotopic composition and distribution of lead, uranium, and thorium in a precambrian granite. *Bull. Geol. Soc. Amer.* **66**, 1131–1148.

TILTON G. R., DAVIS G. L., WETHERILL G. W. and ALDRICH L. T. (1957) Isotopic ages of zircon from granites and pegmatites. *Trans. Amer. Geophys. Union* **38**, 360–371.

VANCE E. R. and MATSON J. B. (1985) Radiation damage in natural titanites. *Phys. Chem. Mineral.* **12**, 255–260.

WASSERBURG G. J. (1963) Diffusion processes in lead-uranium systems. *J. Geophys. Res.* **68**, 4823–4846.

WETHERILL G. S. (1956) Discordant uranium-lead ages, I. *Trans. Amer. Geophys. Union* **37**, 320–326.

WOODHEAD J. A., ROSSMAN G. R. and SILVER L. T. (1991) The metamictization of zircon: radiation dose-dependent structural characteristics. *Amer. Mineral.* **76**, 74–82.

Stable Isotope Geochemistry: A Tribute to Samuel Epstein
© The Geochemical Society, Special Publication No. 3, 1991
Editors: H. P. Taylor, Jr., J. R. O'Neil and I. R. Kaplan

# Retrograde exchange of hydrogen isotopes between hydrous minerals and water at low temperatures

T. Kurtis Kyser and Robert Kerrich

Department of Geological Sciences, University of Saskatchewan, Saskatoon, Canada, S7N 0W0

**Abstract**—Fine-grained hydrous silicates may undergo retrograde H-isotope exchange with meteoric waters at low temperatures ($<100°C$) in near-surface environments and along faults, in the absence of significant concurrent O-isotope exchange, thereby generating characteristic vertical trends in $\delta D$ versus $\delta^{18}O$ plots. The mechanism involves exchange with OH-sites, and is distinct from the D/H changes that accompany recrystallization or neoformation, both of which are associated with changes in $\delta^{18}O$ values. Theoretical considerations and experimental data show that self-diffusion of hydrogen in clays is 100 times faster than for oxygen, and that a 2 $\mu m$ clay mineral would completely re-equilibrate H isotopes at 25°C in a few million years, whereas H-isotope exchange in a 200 $\mu m$ clay would be negligible. Selective $\delta D$ shifts are documented in several U-deposits, serpentinites, authigenic clays, regoliths, shear zones, and gold deposits. In the Proterozoic Athabasca basin, fine-grained illite, chlorite, kaolinite, and dravite originally formed at about 1500 Ma and 200°C from basinal or basement fluids having high $\delta D$ values. These minerals then subsequently exchanged intermittently with D-depleted ($\delta D = -180$), relatively modern meteoric fluids at low temperatures. Exchanged clays show no change of $\delta^{18}O$, chemical composition, or crystallinity, but in some illites the $\delta D$ values and K-Ar ages decrease in concert. Serpentinized ultramafic rocks in the Archean Abitibi Greenstone Belt have $\delta^{18}O$ values of +3.4 to +4.7, reflecting synvolcanic seawater alteration; however, the $\delta D$ values vary from $-54$ to $-114$, and the most D-depleted samples contain more of the fine-grained lizardite that preferentially exchanged H isotopes with modern meteoric waters especially in the environs of fault zones. Similarly, in the Cassiar serpentinized harzburgite, British Columbia, early coarse-grained antigorites are relatively D-enriched ($\delta D = -103$), whereas fine-grained lizardite has a uniform $\delta^{18}O$ but variable $\delta D \geq -196$. Mesothermal gold vein deposits of all ages are characterized by uniform $\delta^{18}O$ quartz values, and uniform $\delta^{18}O$ and $\delta D$ of medium- to coarse-grained mica, chlorite, and tourmaline. Fine-grained micas, however, may be D depleted due to H-isotope exchange with late meteoric waters infiltrating the veins. Bulk extracts of $H_2O$ from quartz are also variably D depleted, stemming from entrapment of the meteoric water in secondary fluid inclusions. If unrecognized, secondary H-isotope exchange may lead to invalid interpretations of the isotopic composition of fluids involved in primary formation of hydrous silicate minerals.

## INTRODUCTION

HYDROGEN ISOTOPES IN hydrous minerals can be the most definitive indicator of the origin of aqueous fluids that have affected rocks, because the original oxygen isotopic composition of the fluid is commonly altered by exchange with the large reservoir of oxygen in rocks. In most geologic processes, water/rock ratios are usually high enough, and the hydrogen contents of most rocks and minerals low enough, that the D/H ratios of hydrous minerals are solely determined by the isotopic composition and temperature of the ancient fluid (*e.g.*, TAYLOR, 1974). However, in applying this technique, an assumption that must be made is that the D/H ratio of the mineral has remained unchanged since the mineral originally formed.

The assumption that most hydrous minerals retain their original hydrogen isotopic compositions is based primarily on a few studies of natural samples and limited experimental data. YEH and EPSTEIN (1978) concluded that the D/H ratio of de-

trital clay minerals from deep-sea sediments were unaffected by exchange with seawater for at least 2–3 Ma. HASSANIPAK and ESLINGER (1985) suggested that Cretaceous and Tertiary kaolin minerals from Georgia retained their original hydrogen and oxygen isotopic compositions, as did SHEPPARD *et al.* (1969), in their studies of Mesozoic and Tertiary porphyry copper deposits. Exchange experiments between serpentine minerals and water (WENNER and TAYLOR, 1974) and clay minerals and water (O'NEIL and KHARAKA, 1976) for durations of less than two years also indicate that exchange of hydrogen isotopes between hydrous minerals and water is very slow at temperatures less than 100°C.

The apparently slow rates of exchange of hydrogen isotopes between hydrous minerals and water at low temperatures make it difficult to design meaningful laboratory experiments. An obvious alternative to experiments is to use well-characterized natural samples that have been subjected over several million years to the influence of meteoric waters having radically different D/H ratios than the waters that originally equilibrated with the hydrous mineral. This study reviews data from previous studies pertinent to post-formational exchange of hydrogen isotopes, and also presents additional evidence based on clay minerals in a Proterozoic sedimentary basin, serpentine deposits in Canada, hydrous minerals in fault zones in the Alps, and hydrous minerals and fluid inclusions in mesothermal gold deposits. The possible mechanisms by which hydrogen isotopes in some minerals exchange with low-temperature meteoric waters are discussed, as are the geological implications of retrograde D/H exchange for isotope studies in high latitudes.

## PREVIOUS STUDIES

Many hydrous minerals in terrestrial rocks have been, or currently are, residing in environments where they coexist with substantial quantities of meteoric waters. WENNER and TAYLOR (1974) were concerned with the extent to which serpentine minerals retain their original $\delta D$ values in these low-temperature environments.

They examined the exchange of hydrogen isotopes between natural serpentines and water in laboratory experiments at 100 and 185°C for six to eight weeks. Although exchange for antigorite was found to be minimal, chrysotile exchanged up to 18 percent of its hydrogen with water, particularly for smaller grain sizes. WENNER and TAYLOR (1974) concluded from these results that most serpentine minerals probably do not undergo significant amounts of post-formation exchange at Earth-surface temperatures, but some exchange would be expected under conditions of high water/rock ratios and temperatures in excess of 100°C.

Other laboratory experiments indicate that differential exchange of hydrogen and oxygen isotopes between water and hydrous minerals can occur at temperatures below 100°C. O'NEIL and KHARAKA (1976) reported that the hydrogen isotopes in montmorillonite and kaolinite were exchanged up to 26% and 6%, respectively, with water at 100°C over a period of 265 days, whereas concurrent oxygen isotope exchange was negligible. They concluded that the D/H ratios of clay minerals could be altered by later exchange, especially for those clay minerals that contain interlayer water. Because of the drastically different rates at which hydrogen and oxygen in clay minerals exchange with water, O'NEIL and KHARAKA (1976) proposed that hydrogen isotope exchange occurs via proton exchange which, unlike oxygen isotope exchange, does not involve the breaking of strong Si-O and Al-O bonds.

Studies of well-characterized natural samples subjected to the influence of meteoric waters with substantially different $\delta D$ values from those in the original hydrous mineral provide the most convincing evidence that some minerals can undergo differential isotope exchange. For example, biotites weathering at low temperatures in migmatites in Chad record shifts in $\delta D$ values of up to 30 per mil regardless of the relative degree of alteration of the biotites as deduced from other changes in chemical composition (CLAUER et al., 1982).

Preferential exchange of hydrogen isotopes between clay minerals and low-temperature meteoric waters has been proposed as a mechanism to explain the variable $\delta D$ values but relatively constant $\delta^{18}O$ values and chemical compositions of some clay minerals. LONGSTAFFE and AYALAN (1990) suggested that Cretaceous authigenic kaolinites in sandstones of the Western Canadian Basin have aberrantly low $\delta D$ values as a result of exchange with formation waters at <40°C, even though the $^{18}O/^{16}O$ ratios of the kaolinites are preserved. WILSON et al. (1987) and KOTZER and KYSER (1991) proposed that low $\delta D$ values of less than $-100$ in illite, kaolinite, and chlorite associated with structures hosting unconformity-type uranium deposits in the Proterozoic Athabasca Basin resulted from the preferential retrograde exchange between the hydroxyl groups of clay minerals having original $\delta D$ values of $ca. -60$ and late Cenozoic, low-D meteoric water at low temperatures (e.g. $T < 50°C$ and $\delta D$ values as low as $-180$). BIRD and CHIVAS (1988, 1989) concluded that post-formational exchange of oxygen isotopes is negligible in kaolinite from Permian and post-Paleozoic regolith profiles in Australia, whereas hydrogen isotope exchange with D-rich meteoric waters has shifted the original $\delta D$ values of about $-160$ to much higher values. In the first three studies, the D/H ratios of clay minerals were lowered as a result of differential isotope exchange, whereas in the latter study, the D/H ratios were increased, even though in all cases the $\delta^{18}O$ values remained relatively uniform.

## THEORETICAL CONSIDERATIONS

The kinetics of isotopic exchange between minerals and fluids have been reviewed by COLE and OHMOTO (1986). Data for exchange of hydrogen isotopes between water and hydrous minerals via self-diffusion are available down to temperatures as low as 100°C. This compilation indicates that at low temperatures, rates of exchange as a result of self-diffusion are several orders of magnitude slower than the rates from recrystallization. Using the activation energies and pre-exponential coefficients calculated by COLE and OHMOTO (1986) and assuming that the reaction rates follow an Arrhenius relation down to low temperatures, we obtain the results shown in Fig. 1. The diffusion rate of hydrogen appears to be similar for most hydrous minerals, and the self-diffusion reaction rate at $ca.$ 25°C for hydrogen in kaolinite is at least 100 times faster than for oxygen. The faster rate of exchange of $^{18}O/^{16}O$ for montmorillonite compared to kaolinite probably reflects a much faster rate of exchange of oxygen during recrystallization than during self-diffusion.

The self-diffusion rates at 25°C shown in Fig. 1 can be used to estimate the extent that a hydrous mineral such as kaolinite could, in theory, exchange with a meteoric water. The extent of isotopic exchange can be modelled using the relation $L = (Dt)^{1/2}$ where $L$ = distance that hydrogen or oxygen diffuses into the mineral, $D$ = diffusion coefficient, and $t$ = time (Fig. 2). A more precise model is unwarranted because of the large uncer-

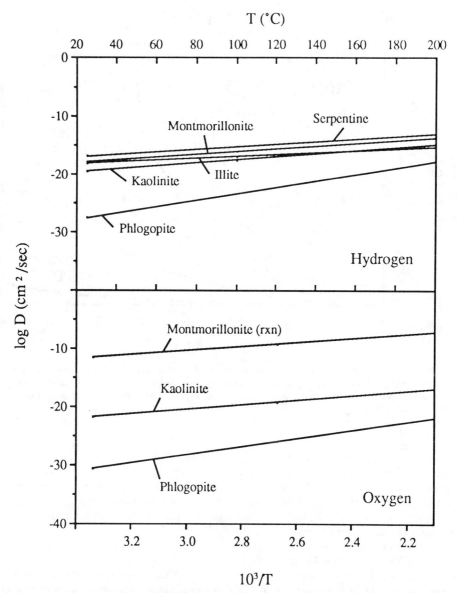

FIG. 1. Average self-diffusion rates of hydrogen and oxygen isotopes in various hydrous minerals, obtained from mineral-water exchange experiments as a function of temperature. With the exception of the values for phlogopite, which are extrapolated from 400°C, all rates are extrapolated from experimental results obtained between 100 and 200°C as compiled by COLE and OHMOTO (1986). The line for montmorillonite represents the rate of isotope exchange during recrystallization (rxn) in NaCl solution (O'NEIL and KHARAKA, 1976).

tainties associated with extrapolation of diffusion coefficients to low temperatures and the more general applicability of the results from the simple model to many different hydrous minerals. Given the self-diffusion rates from Fig. 1, the simple model predicts that a 2-micron kaolinite grain would completely exchange hydrogen isotopes with co-existing water in about 2 Ma, whereas only about

ten percent of the oxygen will have exchanged. Larger grains, such as medium- to coarse-grained serpentines in hydrothermally altered basalt, or hydrothermal muscovite in quartz veins, should undergo little exchange over a geologically reasonable period of time (Fig. 2).

The consequences of differential isotopic exchange in contrast to complete isotopic equilibrium

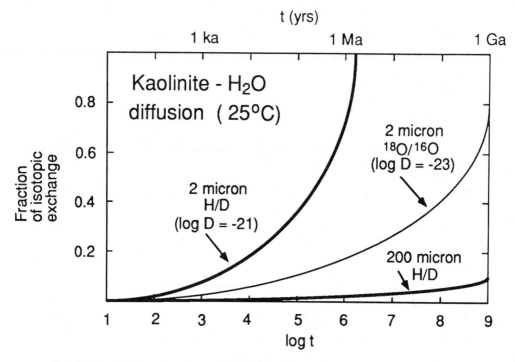

FIG. 2. Plot of fraction of exchange of hydrogen and oxygen isotopes vs. time (log scale) for a 2 micron diameter kaolinite grain and a large reservoir of water at 25°C, assuming self-diffusion coefficients of $D = 10^{-21}$ for hydrogen and $10^{-23}$ cm$^2$/sec for oxygen. Also shown is the extent of hydrogen isotope exchange in a kaolinite of 200 micron diameter.

with a later fluid can be evaluated by considering a kaolinite that originally formed at 200°C from a fluid having a $\delta D$ of $-40$ and a $\delta^{18}O$ of 0 (fluid A; Fig. 3). The isotopic composition of this fluid is typical of meteoric-hydrothermal fluids in near-coastal or low-latitude environments (*e.g.* see TAYLOR, 1974). The kaolinite formed would have a $\delta D$ of $-40$ and a $\delta^{18}O$ of $+10$ (kaol A; Fig. 3). If this hydrothermal kaolinite later underwent low-temperature exchange with local meteoric waters, it would shift toward kaol A' (Fig. 3). However, if the terrane were later tectonically transported into higher latitudes or uplifted, differential isotopic exchange with new kinds of meteoric waters, for example with $\delta D$ of $-180$ and $\delta^{18}O$ of $-24$ (fluid B), would result in the systematics shown in Fig. 3. Moreover, the apparent "temperature" of formation from anything other than a specific $^{18}O$-shifted hydrothermal fluid would be unreasonably low. In contrast, neoformation or recrystallization of kaolinite at 25°C from the high-latitude or high-altitude meteoric water would result in a kaolinite with very low $\delta D$ and $\delta^{18}O$ values (kaol B; Fig. 3); thus, most samples would have isotopic compositions between those of the new kaolinite and the original

kaolinite. The trends in Fig. 3 should apply to all hydrous minerals, indicating that, in general, preferential exchange of hydrogen isotopes in hydrous minerals should be distinct from the effects observed in neoformed or recrystallized hydrous minerals.

### ATHABASCA BASIN

One of the best studies showing that hydrogen isotopes in hydrous minerals exchange preferentially relative to oxygen isotopes at low temperature is that by WILSON *et al.* (1987) on the mid-Proterozoic Athabasca Basin. These basin sediments are dominantly quartz-sandstones deposited in a shallow shelf environment, and they are host to many unconformity-type uranium deposits and diagenetic clay minerals that display petrographic, chemical, and isotopic relationships indicative of several distinct fluid events (WILSON *et al.*, 1987; WILSON and KYSER, 1987; KOTZER and KYSER, 1991). The Athabasca Basin originally formed at about 1700 Ma in a near-coastal, low-latitude environment, but during the Cenozoic it has been inland at a latitude of 60°N where the meteoric waters have much lower $\delta D$ values. Illite, kaolinite, chlorite, and the Mg-

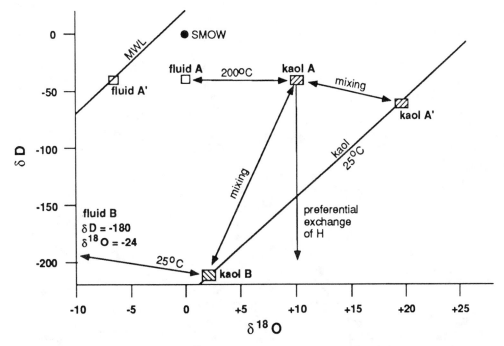

FIG. 3. Variations in the δD and δ$^{18}$O values of kaolinite formed from different fluids. A low latitude environment with meteoric water of fluid A' produces a hydrothermal fluid having the composition of fluid A, which at 200°C will form kaol A. Subsequent preferential exchange of hydrogen isotopes with meteoric water having the composition of fluid B at 25°C in a high latitude environment will result in a vertical trend that can extend below the kaolinite 25°C line as shown. Neoformed kaolinite from fluid B at 25°C will have the composition of kaol B. Kaol A' represents kaolinite in equilibrium at 25°C with the meteoric water of fluid A'. Also shown is the meteoric water line (MWL) and standard mean ocean water (SMOW). Fractionation factors for kaolinite-water are from LAMBERT and EPSTEIN (1980), LIU and EPSTEIN (1984), and LAND and DUTTON (1978).

tourmaline, dravite, are ubiquitous hydrous minerals in the basin. The earliest fluid event recorded by these minerals occurred *ca.* 1500 Ma, and involved basinal fluids or basement fluids having high δD values and temperatures of about 200°C. The mineral paragenesis and fluid history of the basin is discussed by KOTZER and KYSER (1991).

Unconformity-type uranium deposits, which form in fracture systems at the unconformity between crystalline basement rocks and the overlying sandstones, yield a spectrum of U-Pb ages from 900 to 1500 Ma. The variable ages are interpreted as resulting from retrograde interactions of uraninite with basinal fluids. Subsequent to the formation of the uranium deposits, the Athabasca Basin experienced episodic influxes of meteoric waters that had substantially lower D/H and $^{18}$O/$^{16}$O ratios than the original basinal fluids. Late-stage kaolinite and dravite were formed in fractures (Fig. 4). However, all of the clay minerals and dravite in the environs of fracture systems throughout the basin exhibit aberrantly low δD values without any apparent

changes in their δ$^{18}$O values or crystal structure (Fig. 4). In some minerals that formed early in the paragenesis the only changes observed are in the D/H ratios; these minerals are not altered even on the scale of XRD, SEM, and TEM analysis (KOTZER and KYSER, 1991). The trends towards low δD values are consistent with preferential retrograde exchange of hydrogen isotopes.

Other subtle changes occur in the chemical compositions of some of the changed hydrous minerals in the Athabasca Basin. The most notable change is a slight increase in the water content of the dravite and all of the clay minerals that correlates with decreasing δD value, despite the fact that there is no apparent change in the crystallinity of the minerals (WILSON *et al.*, 1987; WILSON and KYSER, 1987; KOTZER and KYSER, 1991). Fe/Mg ratios are slightly higher in the exchanged chlorites and dravites, and the K$_2$O contents and K-Ar ages of illites decrease with increasing water contents and decreasing δD values. These subtle changes in the hydrous minerals in the Athabasca Basin cannot be

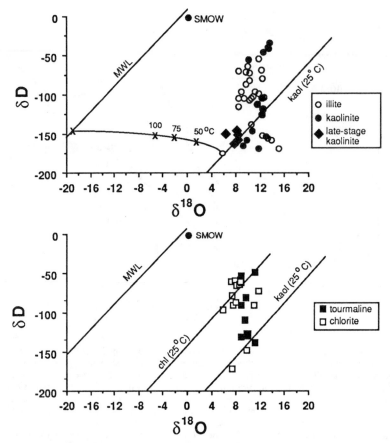

FIG. 4. δD and δ[18]O values of clay minerals and dravite (Mg-tourmaline) from fracture zones in the Athabasca Basin, Canada. The late-stage kaolinite formed along fractures from relatively modern low-D meteoric water. All other minerals have crystallinity and paragenesis compatible with formation from low-latitude basinal brines at 900–1500 Ma. Also shown are the meteoric water line (MWL), the isotopic "lines" for chlorite (chl) and kaolinite (kaol) in equilibrium with meteoric waters at 25°C, and the isotopic composition of kaolinite in equilibrium with modern meteoric water in the basin at 100, 75, 50, and 25°C using the fractionation factors listed in Fig. 3 for kaolinite and extrapolation of data in WENNER and TAYLOR (1971) and TAYLOR (1974) for chlorite.

attributed to increasing proportions of neoformed minerals, but represent retrograde alteration of the minerals by low-temperature meteoric waters in a high water/rock environment near fracture systems. The earliest and most clear-cut signature of this retrograde process is the record of preferential exchange of hydrogen isotopes in the minerals; the other geochemical effects become evident only as retrograde alteration continues. Because illite in the basin records in its K-Ar and Rb-Sr isotope systematics the timing of the chemical changes that occur during this retrograde process, KOTZER and KYSER (1991) proposed a series of steps wherein meteoric water enters the interlamellar sites, exchanges hydrogen isotopes with the hydroxyl groups, and eventually displaces $K^+$ ions, affecting the K-Ar ages of the illites. In the most advanced stages of retro-

grade alteration, oxygen isotopes in the hydroxyl groups are also affected, although even here the crystallinity is not affected. Eventually the illite is recrystallized, resulting in δ[18]O values compatible with formation from high-latitude, meteoric water at low temperatures. Similar processes are presumed to operate for all the micron-sized clay minerals and dravite in the basin.

## SERPENTINIZATION

### General statement

The interaction of hydrothermal fluids with mafic and ultramafic rocks often results in the formation of serpentine minerals and lesser quantities of chlorite, talc, tremolite, brucite, magnesite, and magnetite. Recorded in the isotopic compositions of these alteration products are the temperatures and isotopic compositions of the fluids involved in the formation of the serpentinite. The first systematic stable isotopic study of the serpentinites was by WENNER and TAYLOR (1971). They showed that the fractionation of oxygen isotopes between co-existing antigorite and magnetite is invariably smaller than between coexisting chrysotile-lizardite and magnetite. These relationships are observed in both continental and oceanic environments, and they imply that the antigorite formed at higher temperatures than lizardite or chrysotile. The distinct hydrogen and oxygen isotopic compositions and formation temperatures of the serpentine minerals led WENNER and TAYLOR (1973) to suggest that serpentines in oceanic environments form predominantly from heated seawater, under conditions of high water/rock ratios. Antigorites in most continental ophiolites have $\delta D$ and $\delta^{18}O$ values compatible with formation from metamorphic fluids (WENNER and TAYLOR, 1973; SHEPPARD, 1980), whereas chrysotiles and lizardites from ophiolites, which have $\delta D$ values that parallel those of modern meteoric waters at each locality, most likely form at relatively shallow levels in the crust in the presence of hydrothermal meteoric waters or formational brines (WENNER and TAYLOR, 1973, 1974). Most of the more recent studies on the isotopic systematics of serpentinites have confirmed the results of WENNER and TAYLOR (1971, 1973, 1974), although recent studies on some serpentinites where the paragenesis is known (*e.g.* IKIN and HARMON, 1983; BURKHARD and O'NEIL, 1988; YUI *et al.*, 1990) have revealed that some serpentine minerals in continental areas have hydrogen and oxygen isotope systematics that differ from those reported by WENNER and TAYLOR (1973, 1974).

## Abitibi serpentines (Archean)

The Late Archean Abitibi Greenstone Belt of Canada represents the largest and youngest volcano-plutonic terrane to be accreted to the vast Superior Province of Canada. Serpentinized komatiitic and tholeiitic flows and associated ultramafic sills are abundant in the Southern Volcanic Zone. The komatiitic flows, serpentinite sills, and other rock types in the Abitibi Belt are cut by Matachewan dikes, dated at 2450 Ma (HEAMAN, 1989), indicating that serpentinization probably occurred during the Late Archean.

The ultramafic flows are fractured and consist of variably serpentinized samples of up to 90% serpentine, predominantly antigorite pseudomorphic

after olivine. The restriction of antigorite only to certain flows and the pseudomorphic texture after olivine is compatible with the idea that serpentinization in part occurred shortly after eruption during alteration by heated seawater. The rims of some antigorite grains are partially replaced rims by finer-grained lizardite, and the earliest alteration event in the serpentinized sills is recorded by pseudomorphic lizardite, similar in texture and grain size to the lizardite in the serpentinized komatiitic flows. Chrysotile asbestos veins postdate the lizardite in some bodies and SCHANDL *et al.* (1990) measured homogenization temperatures of 290°C for fluid inclusions in diopside in rodingite that is contemporaneous with the formation of this chrysotile.

Serpentine minerals from variably serpentinized flows in the Abitibi Belt have a restricted range of $\delta^{18}O$, +3.4 to +4.7, but more variable $\delta D$ values of −114 to −54 (Fig. 5). Neither the hydrogen nor oxygen isotopic compositions vary systematically with the stage of serpentinization, except that those serpentinites having the lowest $\delta D$ values also have

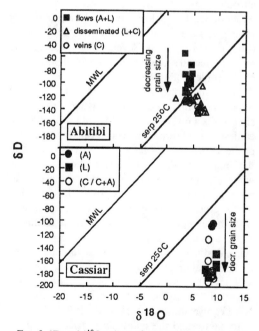

FIG. 5. $\delta D$ and $\delta^{18}O$ values of serpentine minerals from the Archean Abitibi Greenstone Belt, Canada, and the Cassiar serpentine, British Columbia. Abbreviations are A = antigorite, L = lizardite, C = chrysotile. The arrow depicts the change in isotopic composition with generally decreasing grain size of serpentines in both areas. Also shown is the meteoric water line (MWL) and the approximate line depicting serpentine in equilibrium with meteoric waters at 25°C (KYSER, 1987).

a higher proportion of fine-grained lizardite relative to more coarsely crystalline antigorite. One antigorite sample from the Abitibi komatiites falls within the field of oceanic antigorites as defined by WENNER and TAYLOR (1973), compatible with the δD value of Archean seawater being similar to that of modern seawater. However, most of the other antigorites and the lizardites have lower δD values, suggestive of preferential exchange of the hydrogen isotopes with relatively modern meteoric waters having low δD values. The late chrysotiles in asbestos veins in the serpentinite sills tend to be more ¹⁸O rich and D depleted relative to earlier formed lizardite.

## Cassiar serpentinite (Cretaceous)

The Cassiar serpentinite, located in north-central British Columbia at 59°40′N, is a low-grade alpine-type serpentinite that originally was a harzburgite tectonite prior to serpentinization. The age of serpentine formation at Cassiar is constrained from the age of undeformed lamprophyric dikes in the area, which were emplaced at ages > 67 Ma (O'HANLEY, 1990) along normal faults that offset all other types of faults and crosscut the Cassiar serpentinite. The paleolatitude of Cassiar during Middle to Late Cretaceous time was about 50°N (BUTLER et al., 1988). Several faults transect the serpentinite and some are associated with formation of chrysotile asbestos veins.

The mineralogy, composition, and texture of serpentine minerals from the Cassiar serpentinite are described by WICKS and O'HANLEY (1988). The earliest-formed serpentine is lizardite in the matrix of the serpentinite. A later antigorite is present in the matrix of the hangingwall alteration zone, whereas an interlocking texture of lizardite, chrysotile ± antigorite ± chlorite is present in the center of the serpentinite body. All of the above textures, with the exception of the hangingwall alteration zone, are cut by chrysotile asbestos ± magnetite veins. Rodingites throughout the deposit are related to the formation of the late chrysotile asbestos veins and have fluid inclusion homogenization temperatures of 250–300°C and salinities of 4–10 wt.% NaCl equivalent (SCHANDL et al., 1990).

In contrast to the relatively restricted range in their δ¹⁸O values, the δD values of the serpentines from Cassiar vary significantly from −196 to −103 (Fig. 5). Coarse-grained antigorites are the most D-rich serpentines whereas lizardites from the late carbonate-serpentine-magnetite veins have the lowest δD values. On a plot of δD versus δ¹⁸O, the

serpentines as a group form a trend similar to that observed in the Abitibi flows; namely, the δ¹⁸O values are relatively constant but the δD values are intermediate between those of the coarse-grained antigorite and the fine-grained serpentine minerals. Differences between the δ¹⁸O values of coexisting chrysotile and magnetite yield apparent equilibration temperatures of 300 ± 50°C using the empirical isotope geothermometer of WENNER and TAYLOR (1973). These temperatures are comparable to those obtained from homogenization temperatures of fluid inclusions in the rodingites. Lizardite-magnetite oxygen isotope fractionations yield an apparent equilibration temperature of 300°C for the late lizardite-carbonate-serpentine veins.

## Summary

There are several aspects of the isotope systematics of the serpentine minerals from the Abitibi and Cassiar that favour a mechanism of retrograde hydrogen isotope exchange rather than neoformation to explain the coexistence of variable δD but constant δ¹⁸O values. Serpentines from the Abitibi display δ¹⁸O values that correlate with textural changes, and hence with paragenesis, the δD values do not vary with texture. Most of the data from paragenetically different generations of serpentines from both localities display variable δD values at relatively constant δ¹⁸O values, with the finest-grained serpentines showing the most substantial shifts in δD. The coarse serpentines, which are early-formed antigorites in the Abitibi flows or the later-stage antigorites at Cassiar, generally have the highest δD values. In addition to the correlation with mineralogy and grain size, those serpentines most closely associated with fractures and faults along which meteoric waters can infiltrate also have the lowest δD values. There is no apparent relation between the δD values and δ¹⁸O values, and serpentine-magnetite isotopic temperatures are similar to those obtained from fluid inclusions in associated rodingites, implying that oxygen isotopes in the serpentines have probably not been altered. Finally, WENNER and TAYLOR (1974) noted that the δD values of serpentinites from North America vary directly with their present latitude and the δD values of local meteoric waters, whereas δ¹⁸O values in general do not (Fig. 6). In effect, δD values of serpentinites throughout North America vary directly with the δD value of modern meteoric water despite different apparent ages of the serpentinites (Fig. 6).

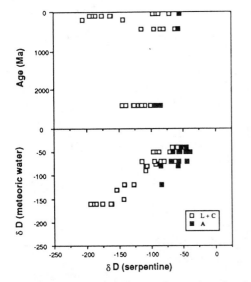

FIG. 6. Variation in the δD values of serpentine minerals from serpentines throughout North America with age of serpentinite (as determined from geologic relations) and the estimated δD value of meteoric water presently in the area of the serpentine using data from TAYLOR (1974). Data are from this study and WENNER and TAYLOR (1971, 1973, 1974). Abbreviations as in Fig. 5.

## ALPINE OVERPRINTING

This section addresses stable and radiogenic isotope resetting that accompanied the Alpine orogeny in Europe, with specific reference to retrograde shifting of δD values. Stable isotope and petrologic studies in the European Alpine belt have revealed pronounced differences between basement and cover tectonic units, in terms of metamorphic temperatures, effects of overprinting, scale of isotope exchange, and fluid regimes. In general the basement units (Penninic nappes and thrust sheets) are pre-Mesozoic in age and polymetamorphic, whereas the Mesozoic cover has experienced only Alpine tectonism and metamorphism.

Localized isotopic effects of Alpine overprinting on Hercynian basement gneisses have been identified. Maximum Alpine metamorphic temperatures in the Monte Rosa area derived from oxygen isotopic compositions of coexisting minerals were ca. 460°C (FREY et al., 1976). Some biotites retain oxygen isotopic temperatures indicative of Permian metamorphism, but have K-Ar systems reset to Alpine ages.

Biotite and muscovite in the pre-Alpine basement gneisses are characterized by a restricted range of δD values, independent of rock type. Biotite δD values cluster at −35 to −60 in the Otztal-Stubai

Alps, at −40 to −80 in the Monte Rosa area, and −60 to −65 in the Swiss Central Alps (although the total range here is −50 to −140). Pre-Alpine phengites in the Sesia Zone have δD between −30 and −45 (DESMONS and O'NEIL, 1978). HOERNES and FRIEDRICHSEN (1978, 1980) attributed the narrow range of δD values to pervasive exchange with magmatic fluids in a pre-Alpine metamorphic event. However, δD values of biotite in equilibrium with most "magmatic fluids" would be somewhat more D depleted (−60 to −80 per mil) than the observed values. An alternative explanation for δD values as enriched as −35 was proposed by FREY et al. (1976), who suggested that D-enriched connate fluids originally affected the rocks. A similar suggestion was advanced by WICKHAM and TAYLOR (1985) for the Hercynian metamorphic rocks of the Pyrenees. The presence of such fluids would also account for the widespread oxygen-isotope homogenization observed in the Austrian basement gneisses.

In Mesozoic metasedimentary cover rocks, δD values of biotites are inherently more variable, and extend to lower values, than those in the basement gneisses. For example, the δD values of biotite are −40 to −95 in the Otztal-Stubai Alps, −60 to −130 in the Swiss Central Alps, and −134 to −157 at Monte Rosa (Fig. 7). The two processes proposed to explain the populations of most D-depleted biotites (δD = −80 to −157) involve either infiltration of an external, D-depleted aqueous fluid during Alpine metamorphism (FREY et al., 1976; HOERNES and FRIEDRICHSEN, 1978, 1980) or loss of water enriched in D accompanying metamorphic recrystallization (HOERNES and FRIEDRICHSEN, 1978). There are difficulties in accounting for the most depleted biotites (δD = −140) by the second mechanism, given that most mineral-water fractionations are less than 60 per mil at all temperatures (e.g. SUZUOKI and EPSTEIN, 1976). The contrast between uniform biotite δD values throughout the Penninic basement gneisses (δD = −57 ± 3), and larger dispersions in the Mesozoic cover (δD = −60 to −90), rules out extensive fluid exchange between basement and cover during Alpine tectonism.

Hydrogen and oxygen isotopic compositions of biotites and muscovites are not correlated in the population of low-δD micas (Fig. 7), compatible with the micas having preferentially undergone H-isotope exchange with meteoric water at relatively low temperatures, while at the same time remaining far from isotopic equilibrium with oxygen in the water. This interpretation is consistent with evidence from calcite-filled fractures for infiltration of low $\delta^{18}O$ fluids during buoyant rise of the Alpine

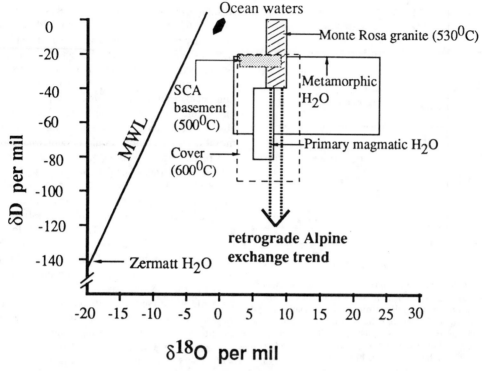

FIG. 7. Calculated hydrogen and oxygen isotope compositions of waters in equilibrium with basement (stippled) and cover (dashed field) tectonic units of the Alpine orogenic belt. Also shown is the trend of δD values of biotites in the Mesozoic metasedimentary cover rocks, as well as the values for modern meteoric waters at Zermatt. Sources of data: Monte Rosa, FREY *et al.* (1976); Swiss central Alps (SCA), HOERNES and FRIEDRICHSEN (1978). Ocean water, meteoric water line (MWL), metamorphic and primary magmatic fields after TAYLOR (1974).

mountain belt (BURKHARD and KERRICH, 1988). Micas in the Alpine cover units are finer grained than their basement counterparts, which may in part explain the observed preferential D depletion in the Mesozoic cover.

## GOLD-QUARTZ VEINS

The origin of Mother Lode–type mesothermal gold-quartz vein systems is enigmatic. These veins may have vertical and lateral extents of several kilometers, are generally restricted to greenschist- or amphibolite-facies metamorphic rocks, and occur near regional structures that have been interpreted as major terrane boundaries. Examples include the Kirkland Lake–Cadillac fault zone in the Archean Abitibi Belt of Ontario, the Jurassic Melones fault in the Foothills Metamorphic Belt in California, and the Cretaceous-Tertiary Coast Range Megalineament near Juneau, Alaska.

Irrespective of age, or the relative proportions of supracrustal lithologies, the vein systems and as-

sociated mesothermal precious metal deposits share a number of common features at a variety of scales including: association with the brittle-ductile transition; uniformly low fluid inclusion salinities ($\leq 3$ wt.% NaCl equivalent) with $CO_2$ contents of 5–30 mole %; a paragenesis dominated by quartz, carbonate, mica, chlorite, pyrite, scheelite, and tourmaline; vertical extents of up to 2 km and a lack of zoning; restricted ranges of O, C, Sr, and Pb isotopic compositions within vein systems, albeit with a geographic provinciality; and late-kinematic timing (WYMAN and KERRICH, 1988; KERRICH and WYMAN, 1990). These common features support the view that all such vein systems formed by similar genetic processes, whatever their age. The origin of the ore-forming fluids is controversial. Here, we critically consider the H-isotope evidence on which a meteoric water model is based.

The majority of Archean and Proterozoic mesothermal gold deposits are characterized by relatively uniform $\delta^{18}O$ values of vein quartz and temperature (280–340°C). Ore-forming fluids have estimated $\delta^{18}O$ ($H_2O$) = +5 to +11, and $\delta D$ ($H_2O$) = −20 to −80, where $\delta D$ was determined on medium- to coarse-grained (0.1–2 mm) micas or chlorite (Fig. 8). Based on this and other lines of evidence, the ore-forming fluids have been interpreted as being metamorphic in origin by KERRICH (1989). Phanerozoic mesothermal deposits similarly feature uniform $\delta^{18}O$ values of quartz and temperature (280–360°C), albeit with somewhat larger inter-deposit variations of $\delta^{18}O$ (quartz); and the calculated $\delta^{18}O$ values of the ore-forming fluids range from +5 to +14 (Fig. 8D), whereas the calculated $\delta D$ values of the hydrothermal fluids range from −15 to −70, based on analyses of coarse-grained hydroxy-silicates (Fig. 8).

NESBITT et al. (1986) proposed that the Mother Lode–type mesothermal quartz vein systems and precious metal deposits in the Cordillera formed in response to deep circulation of meteoric water along transcurrent faults under conditions of low water/rock ratios. They have extended this model to Archean mesothermal veins (NESBITT, 1988; NESBITT and MUEHLENBACHS, 1989). The meteoric water model stems from the observation that the $\delta D$ values of $H_2O$, obtained by decrepitating fluid inclusions from some vein quartz, become lighter at higher latitudes. Uniform $\delta^{18}O$ quartz values at each deposit, but a spread of $\delta D$ values, define a vertical band in $\delta D_{H_2O}$ versus $\delta^{18}O_{H_2O}$ coordinates (Fig. 8D). On the other hand, for Cordilleran mesothermal deposits in Alaska, PICKTHORN et al. (1987) and GOLDFARB et al. (1991) measured $\delta D$ values of −75 to −53 on hydrothermal micas, giving calculated $\delta D$ values for the hydrothermal fluids of −35 to −20; these are interpreted to be metamorphic in origin. Data for the Proterozoic Homestake and Jurassic Mother Lode deposits also plot as vertical bands in $\delta D_{H_2O}$ versus $\delta^{18}O_{H_2O}$ coordinates, defined

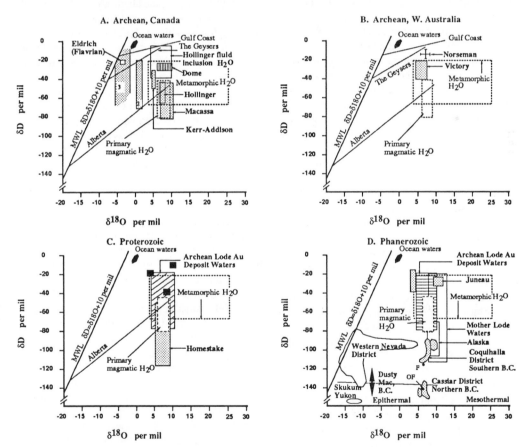

FIG. 8. Calculated isotopic compositions of ore-forming fluids associated with Archean (A, B), Proterozoic (C), and Phanerozoic (D) mesothermal gold deposits. Note that the D-depleted trend from Homestake (C) and the Cordilleran mesothermal deposits (D) are exclusively based on bulk extraction of fluid inclusion waters (modified after KERRICH, 1989). F and OF (D) are the adjacent Fairview and Oro Fino deposits in southern British Columbia (after ZHANG et al., 1989).

by uniform $\delta^{18}O_{quartz}$ values, but a spread of $\delta D_{H_2O}$ values from bulk extraction of fluid inclusions (Fig. 8C,D). There is clearly a discrepancy between D-depleted values obtained from bulk extraction of fluid inclusions and the D-enriched values obtained from co-existing medium- to coarse-grained (0.1 to 2 mm) micas.

As suggested by PICKTHORN et al. (1987), the $\delta D$ results from bulk extraction of fluid inclusions may not reflect the primary ore-forming hydrothermal solutions, but rather secondary inclusions formed in the presence of surface meteoric waters infiltrating down the vein. In a detailed study, GOLDFARB et al. (1991) showed that bulk extracted fluid inclusion waters from vein quartz of the Juneau mesothermal deposits exhibit a wide range of $\delta D$ values from −48 in relatively undeformed quartz to −110 in deformed counterparts. This span reflects decrepitation of variable proportions of two endmember fluid inclusion populations: a D-enriched ore-forming fluid in primary inclusions and a D-depleted meteoric water trapped in secondary inclusions along fractures. Significant spreads of $\delta D$ values from bulk extraction of fluid inclusion waters are also evident in the data of ZHANG et al. (1989) and NESBITT and MUEHLENBACHS (1989). For example, it is not clear why the Fairview ($\delta D = -121$) and Oro Fino ($\delta D = -148$) mesothermal gold deposits, which share a common geographic and altitudinal position in southern British Columbia, should have such disparate bulk fluid inclusion $\delta D$ values, if these are indeed all primary.

Numerous lines of evidence indicate that late infiltration of meteoric water does indeed occur along such vein-hosting structures. WEIR and KERRICK (1987) showed that late vuggy vein quartz was precipitated from such meteoric waters in the Mother lode, and O'HANLEY et al. (1989) reported that serpentine was shifted to low $\delta D$ values along faults in the Cassiar district, British Columbia. In the Canadian Shield, the $\delta^{18}O$ values of calcite and ferroan dolomite paragenetically associated with vein quartz were isotopically reset by exchange with later meteoric water (KERRICH, 1989), even though the quartz was not affected. A problem also arises with the NESBITT et al. (1986) meteoric-water model, because of the magnitude of the $^{18}O$-shifts required in the most northerly deposits. Under the conditions of low fluid/rock ratio and moderate temperatures (300–500°C) required for the pronounced $^{18}O$-shifts in the fluids, the $\delta D$ values of meteoric waters might also be expected to evolve off the meteoric water line with significant positive $\delta D$ shifts (TAYLOR, 1974; OHMOTO, 1986). Finally, the meteoric water

model does not account for the observation that mesothermal vein systems are restricted to terrane boundary structures and their splays. The model would predict mesothermal veins in any large transcurrent fault with the appropriate attributes of fluid infiltration, thermal structure, and permeability; this does not seem to be the case (KERRICH, 1989).

In summary, we interpret the $\delta D$ values determined by NESBITT et al. (1986) and NESBITT and MUEHLENBACHS (1989) on bulk extracted fluid inclusion waters from quartz as consonant with other examples of late meteoric water infiltration, such as in the Alps (Fig. 7). Such terranes are characterized by pronounced shifts in $\delta D$ values but minor changes in $\delta^{18}O$ values, and the hydrogen isotopic overprinting is indicative of a secondary process superimposed upon the primary hydrothermal regime. Primary fluid inclusion waters from undeformed quartz and coarse-grained hydrothermal micas yield mutually consistent D-enriched values for the ore-forming fluids. This interpretation implies that a major re-setting of the secondary fluid inclusions in such quartz veins is common, and that this occurs without any significant re-setting of the $\delta D$ values of the coarse-grained hydrous minerals. If this interpretation is valid, it shows clearly that the medium- to coarse-grained hydrous minerals can preserve their D/H ratios, whereas an earlier discussion has demonstrated that micron-sized hydrous minerals under similar conditions do not preserve their original $\delta D$ values.

## CONCLUSIONS

Preferential exchange of hydrogen isotopes relative to oxygen isotopes during hydrous mineral-water exchange at low temperatures is supported by theoretical considerations of experimental results and, most importantly, by detailed studies of natural samples. Environments in which preferential alteration of $\delta D$ values in micron-sized hydrous minerals are enhanced include reactivated fracture systems that permit the influx of meteoric waters having substantially different D/H ratios than the minerals. These environments may also enhance entrapment of the meteoric waters as secondary fluid inclusions along microfractures, and under these conditions some medium- to coarse-grained hydrous minerals seem to almost perfectly preserve their D/H ratios. These effects of grain-size and mineralogy on D/H exchange require a great deal more study.

## REFERENCES

BIRD M. I. and CHIVAS A. R. (1988) Stable-isotope evidence for low-temperature weathering and post-formational hydrogen-isotope exchange in Permian kaolinites. *Chem. Geol.* **72**, 249–265.

BIRD M. I. and CHIVAS A. R. (1989) Stable-isotope geochronology of the Australian regolith. *Geochim. Cosmochim. Acta* **53**, 3239–3256.

BURKHARD D. J. M. and O'NEIL J. R. (1988) Contrasting serpentinization processes in the eastern Central Alps. *Contrib. Mineral. Petrol.* **99**, 498–506.

BURKHARD M. and KERRICH R. (1988) Fluid regimes in the deformation of the helvetic nappes, Switzerland, as inferred from stable isotope data. *Contrib. Mineral. Petrol.* **99**, 416–429.

BUTLER R. F., HARMS T. A. and GABRIELSE H. (1988) Cretaceous remagnetization in the Sylvester Allochthon: limits to post-105 Ma northward displacement of north-central British Columbia. *Canadian J. Earth Sci.* **25**, 1316–1322.

CLAUER N., O'NEIL J. R. and BONNOT-COURTOIS C. (1982) The effect of natural weathering on the chemical and isotopic compositions of biotites. *Geochim. Cosmochim. Acta* **46**, 1755–1762.

COLE D. R. and OHMOTO H. (1986) Kinetics of isotopic exchange at elevated temperatures and pressures. *In Stable Isotopes in High Temperature Geological Processes* (eds. J. W. VALLEY, H. P. TAYLOR, JR., and J. R. O'NEIL; *Rev. Mineral. 16*, pp. 41–90. Mineralogical Society of America.

DESMONS J. and O'NEIL J. R. (1978) Oxygen and hydrogen isotope compositions of eclogites and associated rocks from the E. Sesia Zone (W. Alps, Italy). *Contrib. Mineral. Petrol.* **67**, 79–85.

FREY M., HUNZIKER J. C., O'NEIL J. R. and SCHWANDER H. W. (1976) Equilibrium-disequilibrium relations in the Monte Rosa Granite, W. Alps: petrological, Rb-Sr and stable isotope data. *Contrib. Mineral. Petrol.* **55**, 147–179.

GOLDFARB R. J., NEWBERRY R. J., PICKTHORN W. J. and GHERT C. A. (1991) Oxygen, hydrogen, and sulfur isotope studies in the Juneau gold belt, SE, Alaska: constraints on the origin of hydrothermal fluids. *Econ. Geol.* **86**, 66–80.

HASSANIPAK A. A. and ELSINGER E. (1985) Mineralogy, crystallography, $O^{18}/O^{16}$, and D/H of Georgia kaolins. *Clays Clay Mineral.* **33**, 99–106.

HEAMAN L. M. (1989) U-Pb dating of mafic dyke swarms: what are the options? *New Mexico Bur. Mines Min. Res. Bull.* **131**, 125.

HOERNES S. and FRIEDRICHSEN H. (1978) Oxygen and hydrogen isotope study of the polymetamorphic area of the Northern Otztal-Stubai Alps. *Contrib. Mineral. Petrol.* **67**, 305–315.

HOERNES S. and FRIEDRICHSEN H. (1980) Oxygen and hydrogen isotopic composition of Alpine and Pre-Alpine minerals of the Swiss Central Alps. *Contrib. Mineral. Petrol.* **72**, 19–32.

IKEN N. P. and HARMON R. S. (1983) A stable isotope study of serpentinization and metamorphism in the Highland Border Suite, Scotland, U.K., *Geochim. Cosmochim. Acta* **47**, 153–167.

KERRICH R. (1989) Shear zone hosted mesothermal gold deposits; a review of geochemical evidence on the sources of fluids and solutes, *In Mineralization and Shear Zones* (ed. J. T. BURSNALL); *Geol. Assoc. Canada Short Course Notes 6*, pp. 129–197.

KERRICH R. and WYMAN D. A. (1990) Geodynamic set-

ting of mesothermal gold deposits: an association with accretionary tectonic regimes. *Geology* **18**, 882–885.

KOTZER T. G. and KYSER T. K. (1991) Retrograde alteration of clay minerals in uranium deposits: radiation catalyzed or simply low temperature exchange? *Chem. Geol.* **86**, 307–321.

KYSER T. K. (1987) Equilibrium fractionation factors for stable isotopes. In *Mineralogical Association of Canada Short Course in Stable Isotope Geochemistry,* (ed. T. K. KYSER), 13, 1–84.

LAMBERT S. J. and EPSTEIN S. (1980) Stable isotope investigations of an active geothermal system in Valles Caldera, Jemez Mountains, New Mexico. *J. Volcanol. Geotherm. Res.* **8**, 111–129.

LAND L. S. and DUTTON S. P. (1978) Cementation of a Pennsylvanian deltaic sandstone: isotopic data. *J. Sediment. Petrol.* **48**, 1167–1176.

LIU K. and EPSTEIN S. (1984) The hydrogen isotope fractionation between kaolinite and water. *Isotope Geosci.* **2**, 335–350.

LONGSTAFFE F. J. and AYALON A. (1990) Hydrogen-isotope geochemistry of diagenetic clay minerals from Cretaceous sandstones, Alberta, Canada: evidence for exchange. *Appl. Geochem.* **5**, 657–668.

NESBITT B. E. (1988) Gold deposit continuum: A genetic model for lode Au mineralization in the continental crust. *Geology* **16**, 1044–1048.

NESBITT B. E. and MUEHLENBACHS K. (1989) Origins and movement of fluids during deformation and metamorphism in the Canadian Cordillera. *Science* **245**, 733–736.

NESBITT B. E., MUROWCHICK J. B. and MUEHLENBACHS K. (1986) Dual origin of lode deposits in the Canadian Cordillera. *Geology* **14**, 506–509.

O'HANLEY D. S. (1990) The structural geology of the Mont McDame area, north-central British Columbia. *British Columbia Geol. Surv. Branch Geological Fieldwork 1889, Paper 1990-1,* 223–228.

O'HANLEY D. S., KYSER T. K. and WICKS F. J. (1989) Evidence from lizardite/chrysotile serpentinites for proton exchange without recrystallization. *Geol. Soc. Amer. Abstr. Prog.* **21**, A13.

OHMOTO H. (1986) Stable isotope geochemistry of ore deposits. In *Stable Isotopes in High Temperature Geological Processes* (eds. J. W. VALLEY, H. P. TAYLOR JR. and J. R. O'NEIL); *Rev. Mineral. 16*, pp. 491–559. Mineralogical Society of America.

O'NEIL J. R. and KHARAKA Y. K. (1976) Hydrogen and oxygen isotope exchange reactions between clay minerals and water. *Geochim. Cosmochim. Acta* **40**, 241–246.

PICKTHORN W. J., GOLDFARB R. J. and LEACH D. L. (1987) Comment on "Dual origins of lode gold deposits in the Canadian Cordillera." *Geology* **15**, 471–472.

SCHANDL E. S., O'HANLEY D. S., WICKS F. J. and KYSER T. K. (1990) Fluid inclusions in rodingite: a geothermometer for serpentinization. *Econ. Geol.* **85**, 1273–1276.

SHEPPARD S. M. F. (1980) Isotopic evidence for the origins of water during metamorphic processes in oceanic crust and ophiolite complexes. *Colloques Internationaux du C.N.R.S.* **272**, 135–147. Assoc. Mafiques Ultra-mafiques Dan Les Orogenes.

SHEPPARD S. M. F., NIELSON R. L. and TAYLOR H. P. JR. (1969) Oxygen and hydrogen isotope ratios of clay minerals from porphyry copper deposits. *Econ. Geol.* **64,** 755–777.

SUZUOKI T. and EPSTEIN S. (1976) Hydrogen isotope fractionation between OH-bearing minerals and water. *Geochim. Cosmochim. Acta* **40,** 1229–1240.

TAYLOR H. P., JR. (1974) The application of oxygen and hydrogen isotope studies to problems of hydrothermal alteration and ore deposition. *Econ. Geol.* **69,** 843–883.

WEIR R. H. and KERRICK D. M. (1987) Mineralogical, fluid inclusion, and stable isotope relations of several gold mines in the Mother Lode, Tuolumne and Mariposa Counties, California. *Econ. Geol.* **82,** 328–344.

WENNER D. B. and TAYLOR H. P., JR. (1971) Temperatures of serpentinization of ultramafic rocks based on $O^{18}/O^{16}$ fractionation between coexisting serpentine and magnetite. *Contrib. Mineral. Petrol.* **32,** 165–185.

WENNER D. B. and TAYLOR H. P., JR. (1973) Oxygen and hydrogen isotope studies of the serpentinization of ultramafic rocks in oceanic environments and continental ophiolite complexes. *Amer. J. Sci.* **273,** 207–239.

WENNER D. B. and TAYLOR H. P., JR. (1974) D/H and $O^{18}/O^{16}$ studies of serpentinization of ultramafic rocks. *Geochim. Cosmochim. Acta* **38,** 1255–1286.

WICKHAM S. M. and TAYLOR H. P., JR. (1985) Stable isotopic evidence for large-scale seawater infiltration in a regional metamorphic terrane: the Trois Seigneurs Massif, Pyrenees, France. *Contrib. Mineral. Petrol.* **91,** 122–137.

WICKS F. J. and O'HANLEY D. S. (1988) Serpentine minerals: structure and petrology. In *Hydrous Phyllosilicates other than Micas* (ed. S. W. BAILEY), *Rev. Mineral. 19,* pp. 91–168. Mineralogical Society of America.

WILSON M. R. and KYSER T. K. (1987) The stable isotope geochemistry of alteration associated with the Key Lake uranium deposits, Canada. *Econ. Geol.* **82,** 1540–1557.

WILSON M. R., KYSER T. K., MEHNERT H. H. and HOEVE J. (1987) Changes in the H-O-Ar isotope composition of clay during retrograde alteration. *Geochim. Cosmochim. Acta* **51,** 869–878.

WYMAN D. A. and KERRICH R. (1988) Archean lamprophyres, gold deposits and transcrustal structures: implications for greenstone belt gold metallogeny. *Econ. Geol.* **83,** 454–459.

YEH H.-W. and EPSTEIN S. (1978) Hydrogen isotope exchange between clay minerals and seawater. *Geochim. Cosmochim. Acta* **42,** 140–143.

YUI T.-F., YEH H.-W. and LEE C. W. (1990) A stable isotope study of serpentinization in the Fengtien ophiolite, Taiwan. *Geochim. Cosmochim. Acta* **54,** 1417–1426.

ZHANG X., NESBITT B. E. and MUEHLENBACHS K. (1989) Gold mineralization in the Okanagan Valley, Southern British Colombia: fluid inclusion and stable isotope studies. *Econ. Geol.* **84,** 410–424.

# Part F.
# Ore Deposits and Hydrothermal Alteration

Sam Epstein measuring isotope ratios on the D/H mass spectrometer in 1963.

Stable Isotope Geochemistry: A Tribute to Samuel Epstein
© The Geochemical Society, Special Publication No. 3, 1991
Editors: H. P. Taylor, Jr., J. R. O'Neil and I. R. Kaplan

# Stable isotope studies of quartz-vein type tungsten deposits in Dajishan Mine, Jiangxi Province, Southeast China

Yuch-Ning Shieh

Department of Earth and Atmospheric Sciences, Purdue University, West Lafayette, IN 47907, U.S.A.

and

Guo-Xin Zhang

Institute of Geochemistry (Guangzhou Branch), Academia Sinica,
Guangzhou, Guangdong 510640, People's Republic of China

**Abstract**—The Dajishan tungsten deposits belong to the wolframite-quartz vein type. These occur as fissure-fillings in the contact zone between the Jurassic Yenshanian granites and Cambrian metasandstones and slates. Quartz, beryl, muscovite, wolframite, scheelite, and sulfides are the major minerals formed in the main stage of mineralization. Late-stage minerals include calcite, dolomite, quartz, fluorite, and scheelite (replacing wolframite). No granitic rocks are exposed at the surface, but drilling has revealed hidden granitic bodies ranging in composition from biotite granite and two-mica granite to muscovite granite and pegmatite. These may represent a differentiation series from a common magma. Exceedingly uniform $\delta^{18}O$ values are found in the minerals from the main-stage veins: quartz = 11.1–12.7 ($n = 27$), muscovite = 8.4–10.0 ($n = 22$), wolframite = 4.1–5.3 ($n = 15$), scheelite = 4.2–5.5 ($n = 4$), suggesting that isotopic equilibrium apparently has attained and that relatively constant physico-chemical conditions prevailed throughout the main-stage of mineralization. Oxygen isotope fractionations for quartz-wolframite, quartz-scheelite, and quartz-muscovite pairs give concordant isotopic temperatures of 320–390°C, consistent with results from fluid inclusion studies. $\delta^{18}O$ values for the mineralizing solution were calculated to be 6.1 to 9.0; $\delta D$ values of $H_2O$ as determined from fluid inclusions in quartz and calculated from $\delta D$ of muscovite range from −51 to −85. Both are typical values for magmatic waters. The $\delta^{18}O$ values for minerals in the late stage are: quartz = 6.4 and 6.9 ($n = 2$), scheelite = −7.6, calcite = 4.3–12.1 ($\delta^{13}C = -7.6$ to −11.9, $n = 8$). Quartz-scheelite oxygen isotope fractionation yields 140°C for the temperature of mineralization. The isotopic compositions of the fluid in the late stage were calculated to be −9.8 for $\delta^{18}O$ and −43 for $\delta D$, within the range displayed by local meteoric waters. The granitoid rocks have uniform $\delta^{18}O$ values in quartz (11.1–12.8, $n = 13$) and muscovite (7.9–9.3, $n = 6$), but more variable $\delta^{18}O$ values in the feldspars (5.2–10.5, $n = 14$) and biotite (3.9–6.5, $n = 3$). The $\delta^{18}O$ values of quartz and muscovite in the granitoids are practically identical to those in the wolframite-quartz veins, suggesting that the hydrothermal fluid from which the ore veins precipitated was derived from the granitoids. The large variation of $\Delta_{q-f}$ (1.8–5.9) suggests that oxygen isotope exchange has occurred between the feldspars and the meteoric water-dominant hydrothermal fluid in the late stage. The primary $\delta^{18}O$ values of the granitic magmas are estimated to be 10.1–11.8, similar to the values observed in many S-type granitoids in S.E. China.

## INTRODUCTION

The Dajishan Tungsten Mine, located in southern Jiangxi Province, belongs to the wolframite-quartz vein type deposits which are the most widespread and economically the most important type of tungsten deposits in southeast China. The wolframite-quartz veins occur as fissure-fillings in the contact zones between the Jurassic Yenshanian granite and the Cambrian metasandstones and slates.

Because of their economic importance and relatively simple geologic occurrences, many wolframite-quartz vein deposits in the world have been subjected to detailed geologic and geochemical studies. These include the Pasto Bueno deposit, Peru (Landis and Rye, 1974), Carrock Fells deposit,

Cumbria (Shepherd et al., 1976), Panasquiera deposit, Portugal (Kelly and Rye, 1979), Tungsten Queen deposit, North Carolina, U.S.A. (Casadevall and Rye, 1980), Grey River deposit, Newfoundland, Canada (Higgins and Kerrich, 1982), San Cristobal deposit, Peru (Campbell et al., 1984), Dae Hwa and Weolag deposits, Korea (So et al., 1983; Shelton et al., 1987), and a number of deposits in southeast China (e.g., Xu and Hu, 1981; Gu, 1981; Liu, 1981; Mu et al., 1981; Zhang et al., 1982; Rye et al., 1986; Giuliani et al., 1988). These studies have given rise to a generalized genetic model that involves an early stage magmatic fluid followed by influx of meteoric water during the late stage of mineralization.

425

In this paper, we present the results of detailed oxygen, carbon, and hydrogen isotope studies on the Dajishan tungsten deposits. The concealed granitoid bodies, identified and sampled through drilling, have also been studied. Emphasis is placed on elucidating the origin and evolution of the hydrothermal fluid and the genetic relationships between the ore deposits and the granitoids.

## GEOLOGIC SETTING

A simplified geologic map of the Dajishan Mine is shown in Fig. 1. A N–S cross section is shown in Fig. 2. More than 90 wolframite-quartz veins have been discovered in the mining district. They range from a few cm to tens of cm in thickness and extend some 600–800 m in both horizontal and vertical directions. The veins occur in fracture zones that trend approximately NW–SE between two major faults in low-grade metasandstones and slates of Cambrian age. No granitic rocks are exposed in the vicinity of the ore veins, but numerous drill holes in the mine area reveal hidden granitic bodies ranging in composition from biotite granite and two mica granite to muscovite granite and pegmatite. The muscovite granite is genetically related to tungsten mineralization in that it contains disseminated wolframites and is commonly crosscut by quartz veins.

K-Ar age for the biotite granite was determined to be *ca.* 180 Ma and that for the muscovite in the wolframite quartz veins *ca.* 167 Ma (WU and MEI, 1982).

The mineralization can be subdivided into two stages:

1) main stage—beryl, muscovite, quartz, wolframite, scheelite, molybdenite, chalcopyrite, pyrrhotite, sphalerite, pyrite;
2) late stage—calcite, dolomite, quartz, fluorite, scheelite.

Note that scheelite occurs in the main as well as the late stages. In the latter case, it usually replaces wolframite.

## EXPERIMENTAL PROCEDURES

To determine the isotopic variation of vein minerals in the area, samples were systematically collected from the ore veins in the north, central, and south groups (Fig. 1) at levels 467, 517, 567, and 601 (Fig. 2). The sampling of the granitoids is less regular; representative samples were collected from four rock types: biotite granite, two-mica granite, muscovite granite, and pegmatite.

Mineral separations were performed by hand-picking and by standard heavy liquid and Frantz magnetic separa-

rator techniques. Quartz was purified from the quartz-calcite and quartz-feldspar mixtures by dissolution of calcite or feldspar with HCl or HF acid, respectively. Isotopic analyses were performed using standard techniques and expressed in the $\delta$-notation in per mil relative to SMOW for O and H and PDB for C. The silicate reference sample NBS-28 was routinely included in the analysis and an average $\delta^{18}O$ value of +9.6 was obtained.

## RESULTS AND DISCUSSION

### The granitoids

From major and trace element studies (FONTEILLES *et al.,* 1987), all the granitoids in the Dajishan mine are comagmatic; they represent a continuous differentiation sequence emplaced at successively higher levels (Fig. 2). The oxygen isotope data are consistent with this view. As can be seen from Table 1 and Fig. 3, the $\delta^{18}O$ values of quartz and muscovite in the granitoids show a very restricted range (quartz = 11.1–12.8; muscovite = 7.9–9.1), regardless of rock types. These values are probably close to the original magmatic values. On the other hand, the $\delta^{18}O$ values of the feldspar and biotite are more variable (feldspar = 5.2–10.5; biotite = 3.9–6.5). They most likely reflect the effects of hydrothermal alteration at moderate temperatures (>300°C). Both from experimental studies and from natural samples, it has been shown that among the common rock-forming minerals quartz is the most resistant and feldspar is the least resistant to oxygen isotope exchange with aqueous fluids. The alteration effects are readily seen in the abnormally large quartz-feldspar oxygen isotope fractionations ($\Delta_{Q\text{-}F}$), which range from 1.8 to 5.9 per mil. At magmatic temperatures, $\Delta_{Q\text{-}F}$ values normally range from 1–2 per mil. The measured whole-rock $\delta^{18}O$-values of the granitoids, which range from 8.6 to 10.9, therefore cannot be used as a petrogenetic indicator of granitic magma genesis in this study. The original $\delta^{18}O$ value of the granitoid, however, can be estimated from the $\delta^{18}O$ value of quartz and from its modal abundance, assuming $\Delta_{Q\text{-}F} = 1.5$. The calculated $\delta^{18}O$ values range from 10.1 to 11.8; these are typical values for most "S" type granitoids in southeast China (ZHANG *et al.,* 1982). These granitoids also possess many geochemical features such as peraluminous character and high alkali element concentrations (see Table 2), suggesting their derivation from pelitic metasedimentary rocks.

### Country rocks and mafic dikes

The main rock types into which the ore veins were emplaced include the Cambrian metasand-

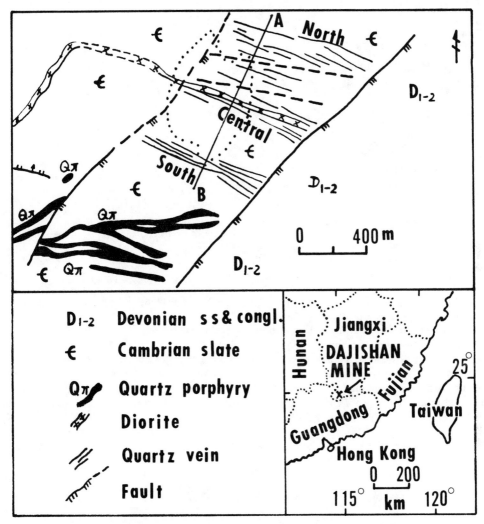

FIG. 1. Simplified geologic map of the Dajishan mining district, Jiangxi province, southeast China. Dotted line indicates concealed granitic intrusions. Cross-section along AB is shown in Fig. 2.

stones and silty slate. In addition, many dikes (diorite and quartz porphyry) can also be seen to crosscut the country rocks and the granitoids. Table 2 lists some representative chemical and isotopic analyses. The country rocks have $SiO_2$-contents (wt.%) that range from 65.5% for slate to 81.2% for metasandstone and to 85.0% for silicified sandstone. A corresponding increase of $\delta^{18}O$ is observed, from 8.1 to 10.8 to 11.3, respectively, for the above rock types.

Southeast China is an area of W geochemical anomaly. The average W contents in the strata are: Pre-Sinian 14.0 ppm, Sinian 6.7 ppm, Cambrian 6.1 ppm, Devonian 3.5 ppm, Carboniferous 6.0 ppm (YEN, 1981). These are potential source rocks

for the granitoids and the oxygen isotope data are in support of this view.

*Tungsten-bearing quartz veins (main-stage mineralization)*

Quartz, muscovite, wolframite, and scheelite are the predominant gangue and ore minerals that occur in the main stage of mineralization. As can be seen in Table 3, each mineral shows exceedingly uniform $\delta^{18}O$: quartz = 11.1–12.7 ($n = 27$); muscovite = 8.4–10.0 ($n = 22$); wolframite = 4.1–5.3 ($n = 15$); scheelite = 4.2–5.5 ($n = 4$). To determine if there is any isotopic compositional variation within a single quartz vein, we have plotted the $\delta^{18}O$

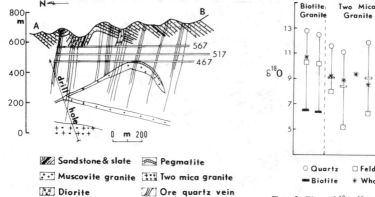

FIG. 2. Geologic cross-section of the Dajishan mining district, showing spatial relationship between the wolframite-quartz veins and the granitic intrusions. Also shown are three horizontal adits at levels 567, 517, and 467 m (above sea-level).

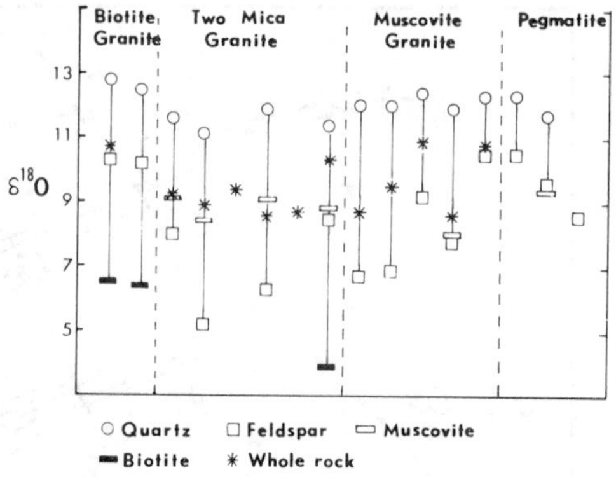

FIG. 3. Plot of $^{18}O/^{16}O$ ratios of whole rock and coexisting minerals in the granitic rocks. The feldspars are a mixture of microcline and Na-plagioclase separated by hand-picking.

of the minerals in four quartz veins as a function of depth (Fig. 4). No significant isotopic variation was detected. The isotopic uniformity is observed in all 12 quartz veins we analyzed as shown in the histograms (Fig. 5). This implies that there is little change in either the temperature or the oxygen isotope composition of the hydrothermal fluid during the main stage of formation of the tungsten-bearing quartz veins.

To determine if there is any regional variation,

we have also arranged the $\delta^{18}O$ of the minerals into north, central, and south groups (Fig. 6). There is a slight increase of $\delta^{18}O$ from north to south, e.g., quartz from 11.7 to 12.2 and muscovite from 8.8 to 9.3. The $\delta^{18}O$ values of quartz and muscovite of the granitoids are also shown for comparison. The $\delta^{18}O$ values of the minerals in the ore veins and the granitoids are the same, suggesting that the hydrothermal fluids that precipitated the quartz veins were either derived from or were in isotopic equilibrium with the granitoids. This inference is sup-

Table 1. Oxygen isotope compositions of whole rock and mineral phases in granitic rocks from Dajishan Mine

| Rock type | Sample No. | Locality | $\delta^{18}O$ | | | | | $\Delta^{18}O$ | | |
|---|---|---|---|---|---|---|---|---|---|---|
| | | | WR | Q | F | B | M | Q-F | Q-B | Q-M |
| Biotite granite | D-23-1 | North outcrop | 10.7 | 12.8 | 10.3 | 6.5 | | 2.5 | 6.3 | |
| | D-23-2 | North outcrop | | 12.5 | 9.9 | 6.4 | | 2.6 | 6.1 | |
| Two-mica granite | 84-D-82 | CK307, 350 m | 10.3 | 11.4 | 8.5 | 3.9 | 8.8 | 2.9 | 7.5 | 2.6 |
| | 84-D-85 | CK307, 360 m | 8.7 | | | | | | | |
| | 84-D-73 | CK307, 472 m | 8.6 | 11.9 | 6.3 | | 9.1 | 5.6 | | 2.8 |
| | 84-D-74 | CK307, 474 m | 9.4 | | | | | | | |
| | 84-D-75 | CK307, 475 m | 8.9 | 11.1 | 5.2 | | 8.4 | 5.9 | | 2.7 |
| | 84-D-76 | CK307, 478 m | 9.2 | 11.6 | 8.0 | | 9.1 | 3.6 | | 2.5 |
| Muscovite granite | D-12-1 | C, L517, No. 6 | 10.7 | 12.3 | 10.5 | | | 2.2 | | |
| | D-31 | C, Body 69, 11W | 8.6 | 11.9 | 7.8 | | 7.9 | 4.1 | | 4.0 |
| | D-32-1 | C, L467, W6H | 8.7 | 12.0 | 6.7 | | | 5.3 | | |
| | D-32-2 | C, L467, W6H | 9.5 | 12.0 | 6.9 | | | 5.1 | | |
| | D-32-6 | C, L467, W6H | 10.9 | 12.4 | 9.2 | | | 3.2 | | |
| Pegmatite | D-12 | C, L517, No. 6 | | 12.3 | 10.5 | | | 1.8 | | |
| | D-10-1 | C, L517, No. 6 | | 11.7 | 9.6 | | 9.3 | 2.1 | | 2.4 |
| | D-48 | C, L467 | | | 8.6 | | | | | |

WR = Whole rock, Q = Quartz, F = Feldspar, B = Biotite, M = Muscovite.
Locality codes: CK307 = Shaft No., 350 m = 350 m below surface, C = Central group, L = Level, No. 6 = Vein No. 6.

Table 2. Representative chemical and oxygen isotope compositions of igneous intrusions and country rocks

| | D-23 Biotite granite | 84-D-82 Two-mica granite | D-31-1 Muscovite granite | D-5-1 Diorite dike | D-9-2 Diorite porphyry | D-34-2 Siliceous sandstone | D-26-1 Meta-sandstone | D-19-1 Slate |
|---|---|---|---|---|---|---|---|---|
| $SiO_2$ | 66.30 | 76.81 | 74.10 | 47.53 | 44.72 | 85.03 | 81.21 | 65.55 |
| $TiO_2$ | 0.60 | 0.02 | 0.04 | 2.72 | 1.38 | 0.30 | 0.31 | 0.76 |
| $Al_2O_3$ | 14.05 | 12.14 | 14.74 | 13.42 | 11.17 | 6.42 | 8.11 | 15.53 |
| $Fe_2O_3$ | 1.13 | 0.33 | 0.32 | 2.68 | 3.62 | 0.69 | 0.57 | 0.95 |
| FeO | 2.61 | 0.75 | 0.32 | 10.83 | 5.33 | 2.28 | 3.04 | 5.61 |
| MnO | 0.05 | 0.19 | 0.06 | 0.15 | 0.10 | 0.03 | 0.06 | 0.05 |
| MgO | 1.85 | 0.11 | 0.13 | 5.77 | 9.60 | 0.90 | 1.59 | 0.37 |
| CaO | 3.45 | 0.36 | 0.34 | 10.50 | 11.86 | 0.80 | 0.25 | 2.71 |
| $Na_2O$ | 2.77 | 3.64 | 4.88 | 2.92 | 1.40 | 1.07 | 0.53 | 0.51 |
| $K_2O$ | 4.43 | 4.17 | 3.60 | 1.04 | 2.51 | 2.00 | 2.28 | 4.44 |
| $H_2O^+$ | 0.59 | 1.03 | 0.64 | 0.94 | 3.46 | 0.43 | 1.42 | 2.39 |
| $H_2O^-$ | 0.13 | 0.16 | 0.42 | 0.23 | 1.22 | 0.09 | 0.13 | 0.41 |
| $P_2O_5$ | 0.25 | n.d. | n.d. | 0.19 | 1.01 | 0.08 | 0.15 | 0.14 |
| $CO_2$ | — | — | — | — | 3.46 | — | — | — |
| S | 0.06 | — | — | 0.18 | — | — | — | 0.06 |
| Total | 98.27 | 99.70 | 99.59 | 99.10 | 100.84 | 100.12 | 99.65 | 99.48 |
| $\delta^{18}O$ | 10.7 | 10.3 | 8.6 | 6.9 | 6.8 | 11.3 | 10.8 | 8.1 |

Chemical analyses by D. H. Chen and T. S. Ye, Institute of Geochemistry, Academia Sinica, Guiyang.

Table 3. Oxygen isotope compositions of mineral phases in the main-stage ore veins and the calculated isotopic temperatures

| Sample No. | Locality | $\delta^{18}O$ Q | M | Wf | Sch | Q-M Δ | $T\,°C$ | Q-Wf Δ | $T\,°C$ | Q-Sch Δ | $T\,°C$ |
|---|---|---|---|---|---|---|---|---|---|---|---|
| 84-D-34 | C, L517, No. 6 | | | 4.0 | | | | | | | |
| 84-D-35 | C, L517, No. 6 | | | 4.8 | | | | | | | |
| 84-D-23 | C, L467, No. 12 | | | 4.4 | | | | | | | |
| D-38 | S, L567, No. 20 | 11.4 | 8.4 | 4.5 | | 3.0 | 358 | 6.9 | 382 | | |
| D-40 | S, L567, No. 13 | 11.7 | 9.0 | | | 2.7 | 400 | | | | |
| D-7-2 | S, L517, No. 20 | 12.0 | 8.9 | 4.7 | | 3.1 | 346 | 7.3 | 367 | | |
| D-8-1 | S, L517, No. 19 | 11.3 | | 4.2 | | | | 7.1 | 373 | | |
| D-9-4 | S, L517, No. 13 | 12.5 | 9.2 | | | 3.3 | 324 | | | | |
| D-24 | S, L467, No. 20 | 11.1 | 8.7 | | | 2.4 | 451 | | | | |
| D-25-1 | S, L467, No. 20 | 11.4 | 8.5 | | | 2.9 | 371 | | | | |
| D-29-1 | S, L467, No. 13 | 12.2 | 8.6 | | | 3.6 | 294 | | | | |
| D-30 | S, L467, No. 13 | 11.9 | | | | | | | | | |
| D-1 | C, L601, No. 7 | 11.1 | 8.8 | | | 2.3 | 470 | | | | |
| D-2-1 | C, L601, No. 7 | 12.3 | 9.1 | 5.3 | 4.8 | 3.2 | 334 | 7.0 | 378 | 7.5 | 356 |
| D-4-2 | C, L601, No. 10 | 12.0 | 9.1 | 5.2 | | 2.9 | 371 | 6.8 | 386 | | |
| D-6 | C, L601, No. 11 | 11.2 | 8.8 | 4.5 | | 2.4 | 451 | 6.7 | 391 | | |
| D-41 | C, L567, No. 11 | 11.9 | 8.9 | 4.4 | | 3.0 | 358 | 7.5 | 336 | | |
| D-44-1 | C, L567, No. 6 | 12.4 | 9.3 | 4.1 | | 3.1 | 346 | 8.3 | 317 | | |
| D-13-2 | C, L517, No. 6 | 11.3 | 9.0 | 4.2 | | 2.3 | 470 | 7.1 | 373 | | |
| D-14 | C, L517, No. 8 | 11.4 | | | | | | | | | |
| D-20 | C, L517, No. 1 | 12.2 | | | 4.2 | | | | | 8.0 | 327 |
| D-35 | C, L467, No. 6 | 11.8 | 9.8 | 4.2 | | 2.0 | 541 | 7.6 | 351 | | |
| D-3-1 | N, L601, No. 27 | 12.4 | 8.7 | | | 3.7 | 285 | | | | |
| D-45-1 | N, L567, No. 23 | 12.3 | 9.3 | 4.6 | | 3.0 | 358 | 7.7 | 346 | | |
| D-46-1 | N, L567, No. 23 | 12.1 | | | 4.8 | | | | | 7.3 | 369 |
| D-47 | N, L567, No. 23 | 12.6 | 10.0 | | 5.5 | 2.6 | 415 | | | 7.1 | 383 |
| D-16-1 | N, L517, No. 23 | 12.7 | | | | | | | | | |
| D-18-2 | N, L517, No. 23 | 11.3 | 9.3 | 4.5 | | 2.0 | 541 | 6.8 | 386 | | |
| D-36 | N, L467, No. 23 | 12.0 | 9.6 | | | 2.4 | 451 | | | | |
| D-37 | N, L467, No. 23 | 12.1 | 9.1 | | | 3.0 | 358 | | | | |

Q = Quartz, M = Muscovite, Wf = Wolframite, Sch = Scheelite.
Locality codes: N = North, C = Central, S = South, L = Level, No. = Vein number.

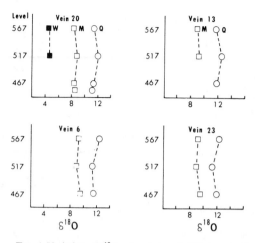

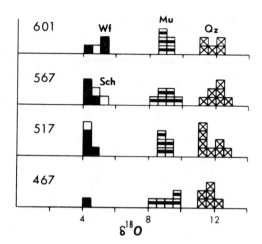

FIG. 4. Variation of $\delta^{18}O$ values in quartz (Q), muscovite (M), and wolframite (W) in individual ore veins as a function of depth at levels 567, 517, and 467.

FIG. 5. Histogram showing the frequency distribution of $\delta^{18}O$ values in quartz (Qz), muscovite (Mu), wolframite (Wf), and scheelite (Sch) at levels 601, 567, 517, and 467.

ported by the uniform oxygen isotope fractionations among the co-existing minerals, as discussed below.

*Oxygen isotope geothermometry*

Table 3 lists the oxygen isotope fractionations among quartz, muscovite, wolframite, and scheelite from the main stage of mineralization. The rather constant isotopic fractionations for quartz-muscovite ($\Delta = 2.0$–$3.7$) and quartz-wolframite ($\Delta = 6.7$–$8.3$) over the entire mining district suggest that isotopic equilibrium was probably attained. Quartz-$H_2O$ and muscovite-$H_2O$ oxygen isotope fractionation curves have been calibrated as a function of temperature in the laboratory (CLAYTON *et al.*, 1972; MATSUHISA *et al.*, 1979; O'NEIL and TAYLOR, 1969). However, because of the small isotopic fractionation between quartz and muscovite, uncertainty in temperatures resulting from experimental errors will be large. On the other hand, oxygen isotope fractionations in quartz-wolframite and quartz-scheelite pairs are large and would offer much more sensitive geothermometers. Recently, L. G. ZHANG (1990, pers. comm.) experimentally determined the following wolframite-$H_2O$ equilibrium isotopic fractionation curves:

$250$–$370°C$   $1000 \ln \alpha_{wf-H_2O}$

$$= 1.03 \times 10^6 T^{-2} - 4.96 \quad (1)$$

$370$–$420°C$   $1000 \ln \alpha_{wf-H_2O}$

$$= 0.21 \times 10^6 T^{-2} - 2.91 \quad (2)$$

When combined with the quartz-water fractionation

equation of CLAYTON *et al.* (1972), the following equations are obtained:

$250$–$370°C$   $1000 \ln \alpha_{q-wf}$

$$= 2.35 \times 10^6 T^{-2} + 1.56 \quad (3)$$

$370$–$420°C$   $1000 \ln \alpha_{q-wf}$

$$= 3.17 \times 10^6 T^{-2} - 0.49. \quad (4)$$

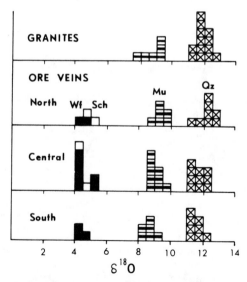

FIG. 6. Histogram showing the regional variation (north, central, south) of $\delta^{18}O$ values of quartz (Qz), muscovite (Mu), wolframite (Wf), and scheelite (Sch) in the ore veins as compared with those in the granitoids.

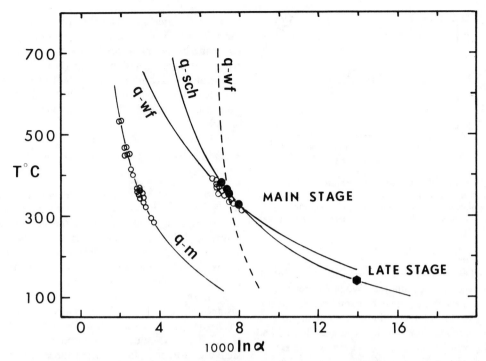

FIG. 7. Oxygen isotopic temperatures obtained from quartz-muscovite, quartz-wolframite, and quartz-scheelite fractionation curves for samples from the main- and late-stage ore veins. Fractionation equations used: quartz-$H_2O$ (CLAYTON et al., 1972); muscovite-$H_2O$ (O'NEIL and TAYLOR, 1969); wolframite-$H_2O$ (L. G. ZHANG, 1990, pers. comm.); scheelite-$H_2O$ (WESOLOWSKI and OHMOTO, 1986). The dashed quartz-wolframite curve is from LANDIS and RYE (1974).

The quartz-wolframite oxygen isotope fractionations of 6.7 to 8.3 observed in Dajishan would yield temperatures of 391–317°C according to Eqns. (3) and (4). When the empirical wolframite-$H_2O$ fractionation curve of LANDIS and RYE (1974) is used, unrealistic high temperatures (>1000°C) are obtained. WESOLOWSKI and OHMOTO (1986), using an analogy based on that between $CaSO_4$ and $CaWO_4$, derived the following scheelite-$H_2O$ fractionation equation:

$$1000 \ln \alpha_{sch-H_2O} = 1.39 \times 10^6 T^{-2} - 5.87. \quad (5)$$

When this is combined with the quartz-$H_2O$ fractionation equation of CLAYTON et al. (1972), the following quartz-scheelite fractionation equation is obtained:

$$1000 \ln \alpha_{q-sch} = 1.99 \times 10^6 T^{-2} + 2.47. \quad (6)$$

In Dajishan, $\Delta_{q-sch} = 7.1–8.0$ would yield $T = 383–327°C$, similar to the quartz-wolframite temperatures obtained from Eqns. (3) and (4).

The quartz-muscovite oxygen isotope fractionations correspond to temperatures of 541–285°C. However, the majority of samples fall between 400

and 300°C, consistent with temperatures obtained from quartz-wolframite and quartz-scheelite pairs (see Fig. 7).

LU et al. (1974) measured the fluid inclusion homogenization temperatures in quartz which range from 287–260°C, slightly lower than the oxygen isotope temperatures discussed above.

### Scheelite in the late (carbonate) stage mineralization

Characteristic of many quartz-vein type tungsten deposits (as cited in the Introduction) is the occurrence of carbonate minerals in the late stage of mineralization. In the Dajishan deposit, large euhedral crystals of wolframite occur in the carbonate veins. Under the microscope, aggregates of scheelite replacing wolframite, mostly along grain boundaries and cleavage planes, can usually be seen. Did the wolframite and scheelite form in the main stage or in the late stage? Oxygen isotope determination of the minerals has given a definite answer to this question (ZHANG and SHIEH, 1989). Because of the intimate intergrowth of scheelite and wolframite, it

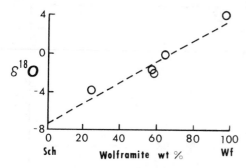

FIG. 8. Plot of $\delta^{18}O$ values of wolframite-scheelite intergrowth samples in the carbonate veins as a function of wt. % of wolframite. Extrapolation to 0% wolframite gives the $\delta^{18}O$ value for the late-stage scheelite, which equals $-7.6$

is not feasible to physically separate the two minerals for oxygen isotope analyses. We have obtained the $\delta^{18}O$ values of the pure end-members by analyzing the $\delta^{18}O$ of several scheelite-wolframite mixtures of various proportions and by extrapolating to 0 and 100% wolframite, as shown in Fig. 8. The extrapolation gives $\delta^{18}O_{wf} = +3.6$ and $\delta^{18}O_{sch} = -7.6$. The isotopic data clearly suggest that the wolframite was formed in the main stage and the scheelite was formed in the late stage by replacement of the wolframite:

$$FeWO_4 + Ca^{2+} \rightarrow CaWO_4 + Fe^{2+}.$$

wolframite            scheelite

This reaction would be favored under the alkaline conditions suggested by the presence of calcite in the late stage. In addition, some fine-grained quartz crystals are associated with the calcite and scheelite

in the carbonate veins. The $\delta^{18}O$ values of quartz range from 6.4 to 6.9, distinctly different from those occurring in the main stage. The quartz-scheelite oxygen isotope geothermometer (Eqn. 6) gives temperatures of equilibration at 134–142°C, comparable to the calcite fluid inclusion homogenization temperature of 129°C as determined by LU *et al.* (1974).

*Oxygen and carbon isotope compositions of carbonates*

Calcite occurs as fine-granular aggregates and as fine-laminations in the carbonate veins. Oxygen and carbon isotope compositions in the calcite are shown in Table 4. The variations of $\delta^{18}O$ (4.3 to 12.1) and $\delta^{13}C$ ($-7.6$ to $-11.9$) are large, particularly for oxygen, reflecting large changes in temperature and in isotopic composition of the hydrothermal fluid during precipitation of the calcite. Within a distance of 1 cm, the laminated calcite can vary in $\delta^{18}O$ from 4.3 to 5.3 and in $\delta^{13}C$ from $-11.4$ to $-10.7$. The $\delta^{13}C$ values of the carbonates in Dajishan are distinctly different from those occurring in the nearby Xihuashan mine, which range from $+4.4$ to $-9.0$ (MU *et al.*, 1981). The carbon isotope compositions in the carbonates are probably controlled by the dissolved carbonate and bicarbonate ions in groundwaters.

*Evolution of the hydrothermal fluids*

The $\delta^{18}O$ and $\delta D$ values of the hydrothermal fluid that would have been in equilibration with the granites and the wolframite-quartz veins are shown in Table 5. The $\delta^{18}O$ values of $H_2O$ were calculated

Table 4. Oxygen and carbon isotope compositions of minerals in the late-stage carbonate veins

| Sample No. | Locality | Mineral | $\delta^{18}O$ | $\delta^{13}C$ |
|---|---|---|---|---|
| D-16-1A | N, L517, No. 23 | Calcite | 4.3 | $-11.4$ |
| D-16-1B | Same | Calcite | 5.4 | $-10.7$ |
| D-29-1 | S, L467, No. 20 | Calcite | 8.1 | $-11.9$ |
|  |  | Quartz | 6.9 |  |
|  |  | Wolframite[a] | 3.1 |  |
| D-39-1 | S, L567, No. 13 | Calcite | 5.5 | $-7.6$ |
|  |  | Quartz | 6.4 |  |
|  |  | Wolframite[a] | 4.1 |  |
|  |  | Scheelite | $-7.6$[b] |  |
| II-4 | S, L567, No. 13 | Calcite | 4.9 | $-8.1$ |
| II-6 | S, L467, No. 13 | Calcite | 7.2 | $-9.9$ |
| II-7-1 | S, L467, No. 12 | Calcite | 8.2 | $-10.4$ |
| II-7-2 | Same | Calcite | 12.1 | $-9.5$ |

[a] Formed in the main stage.
[b] Estimated from Fig. 8.

Table 5. Oxygen and hydrogen isotope compositions of waters coexisting with the granites and wolframite-quartz veins

| Sample No. | Mineral | $T \,°C^a$ | $\delta D^b$ | $\delta^{18}O$ | $\delta D_{H_2O}$ Calculated | $\delta D_{H_2O}$ Measured[b] | $\delta^{18}O_{H_2O}$ (calculated) |
|---|---|---|---|---|---|---|---|
| **Granites** | | | | | | | |
| D-31 | Feldspar | 526 | | 7.8 | | −70 | 6.7 |
| | Quartz | 526 | | 11.9 | | −70 | 9.9 |
| | Muscovite | 526 | −82 | 7.9 | −66 | | 8.1 |
| D-32-4 | Microcline | 503 | | 9.2 | | −70 | 7.8 |
| **Ore veins** | | | | | | | |
| D-36-1 | Quartz | 451 | | 12.0 | | −59 | 9.0 |
| D-9-4 | Quartz | 324 | | 12.5 | | −59 | 6.4 |
| D-1-2 | Quartz | 470 | | 11.1 | | −22 | 8.4 |
| D-2-1 | Muscovite | 378 | −70 | 9.1 | −57 | | 7.4 |
| D-6 | Quartz | 391 | | 11.2 | | −70 | 6.9 |
| D-40-2 | Muscovite | 400 | −81 | 9.0 | −68 | | 7.6 |
| D-41-2 | Muscovite | 336 | −80 | 8.9 | −67 | | 6.4 |
| D-44-2 | Quartz | 317 | | 12.4 | | −51 | 6.1 |
| D-35-1 | Quartz | 351 | | 11.8 | | −60 | 6.5 |
| | Muscovite | 351 | −98 | 9.8 | −85 | | 7.6 |

[a] Temperatures in the granites are the fluid inclusion homogenization temperatures (from LU *et al.*, 1974). Temperatures in the wolframite-quartz veins are oxygen isotope temperatures (from Table 3).
[b] Hydrogen isotope analyses by Fuji Yu, Institute of Geochemistry, Academia Sinica, Guiyang.

from the $\delta^{18}O$ of minerals and fluid inclusion homogenization temperatures (for granites) or oxygen isotope temperatures (for ore veins). The $\delta D$ values of $H_2O$ were obtained from analysis of fluid inclusions in quartz or feldspar and by calculation from $\delta D$ in muscovite.

Thus, the $\delta^{18}O$ values of the hydrothermal fluid in the main ore-forming stage range from 6.1 to 9.0

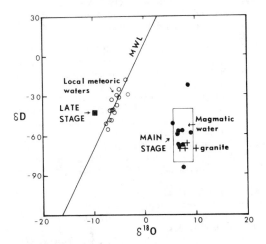

FIG. 9. Plot of $\delta^{18}O$ and $\delta D$ values of aqueous fluids associated with the granitoids (crosses) and the ore-veins in the main-stage (dots) and late-stage (large square). Also shown are isotopic compositions of local meteoric waters (open circles) and the world meteoric water line (MWL).

and $\delta D$ from −51 to −85 (except for sample D-1-2 which shows abnormally high $\delta D = −22$). The late-stage hydrothermal fluid has $\delta^{18}O = −9.8$ to −10.1 (calculated from quartz-scheelite oxygen isotope fractionation) and $\delta D = −43$ (from analysis of fluid inclusions in calcite), distinctly different from those in the early stage.

The evolution of the hydrothermal fluid during the formation of tungsten deposit in Dajishan is illustrated in Fig. 9. In the main stage, the hydrothermal fluids have isotopic compositions that fall within or very close to the "magmatic-water box." The hydrothermal fluids, regardless of their ultimate origins, have been isotopically equilibrated with the granitic magmas at very low water/rock ratio, *i.e.*, the isotopic compositions of the fluids were buffered by the granites. In the late stage, the system was subjected to a sudden influx of large amount of meteoric water so that the isotopic compositions lie very close to the cluster displayed by the local meteoric waters (Fig. 9).

## CONCLUSIONS

1. The Dajishan tungsten deposits possess several geologic and geochemical characteristics that are similar to most wolframite-quartz vein type deposits around the world. The ore deposits appear to be genetically related to the underlying granitoids.

2. The granitoid rocks, consisting of biotite granite, two-mica granite, muscovite granite, and

pegmatite, possess many petrological and geochemical features of "S" type granitoids. The Dajishan granitoids are most likely the product of anatexis of Precambrian and Paleozoic sedimentary rocks that are widespread in the region; most of these show W geochemical anomalies ranging from 4 to 14 ppm.

3. The $\delta^{18}O$ value of quartz in the granitoids is exceedingly uniform (11.1–12.8); this probably represents the primary magmatic oxygen isotopic value. In contrast, the feldspars show more variable $\delta^{18}O$ values (5.2–10.5), reflecting the effects of hydrothermal alteration at subsolidus temperatures (300–400°C).

4. The oxygen isotope compositions of quartz, muscovite, wolframite, and scheelite formed in the main stage of mineralization show very restricted range; these minerals most likely formed in isotopic equilibrium with a hydrothermal fluid that had a relatively constant isotopic composition and temperature. The oxygen isotope temperatures for quartz-wolframite and quartz-scheelite pairs are concordant at 320–390°C, and the coexisting aqueous fluids have calculated $\delta^{18}O$ of 6.1 to 9.1 and calculated $\delta D$ of −51 to −85, clearly within the range shown by the magmatic waters in isotopic equilibrium with the granitoids.

5. The minerals formed in the late stage of mineralization, including calcite, quartz, and scheelite, all have lower $\delta^{18}O$ values, reflecting the influx of large amounts of meteoric waters into the hydrothermal system.

6. Scheelite can form in the late as well as in the main stage of mineralization. In the late stage, small crystals of scheelite are commonly found replacing wolframite along grain boundaries and cleavage planes. The late-stage scheelite has a very low $\delta^{18}O$ value (−7.6) and formed at low temperature (140°C) from a meteoric water-dominant hydrothermal fluid ($\delta^{18}O \approx −10$). In contrast, all of the wolframite crystals, including those found in association with calcite, were formed in the main stage.

*Acknowledgments*—GXZ wishes to thank the personnel of the Dajishan Tungsten Mining Geology Division for their hospitality and assistance during sample collection in the mine. Thanks are also due to Prof. Yimao Liu for supplying some of the samples used in this study, to Mr. Fuji Yu of the Institute of Geochemistry, Academia Sinica, who kindly performed the hydrogen isotope analyses, to Prof. Guangzhi Tu and Prof. Jinsheng Yu for helpful discussions and suggestions during the course of this study. Prof. Ligang Zhang of the Yichang Institute of Geology and Mineral Resources kindly allowed us to quote his unpublished wolframite-water oxygen isotope fractionation curve which he recently calibrated in his laboratory. Review by Prof. H. P. Taylor Jr. greatly improved the clarity of the manuscript. Most of the experimental work was conducted while GXZ was a visiting scholar at the Department of Earth and Atmospheric Sciences, Purdue University and was supported by Academia Sinica and U.S. National Science Foundation Grant No. EAR85-17203.

## REFERENCES

CAMPBELL A., RYE D. and PETERSEN U. (1984) A hydrogen and oxygen isotope study of the San Cristobal Mine, Peru: implications of the role of water to rock ratio for the genesis of wolframite deposits. *Econ. Geol.* **79**, 1818–1832.

CASADEVALL T. and RYE R. O. (1980) The Tungsten Queen deposit, Hamme District, Vance County, North Carolina: a stable isotope study of a metamorphosed quartz-huebnerite vein. *Econ. Geol.* **75**, 523–537.

CLAYTON R. N., O'NEIL J. R. and MAYEDA T. (1972) Oxygen isotope exchange between quartz and water. *J. Geophys. Res.* **77**, 3057–3067.

FONTEILLES M., RAIMBAULT L. and FOUILLAC A. (1987) Magmatic history and geochemical characteristics of granites associated with Dajishan tungsten deposit (abstr.). *Int. Symp. Petrogenesis and Mineralization of Granitoids. Guangzhou, China*, 78–79.

GIULIANI G., LI Y. D. and SHENG T. F. (1988) Fluid inclusion study of Xihuashan tungsten deposit in the southern Jiangxi province, China. *Mineral. Deposita* **23**, 24–33.

GU G. Y. (1981) The occurrence of vein-type tungsten deposits in southeast China. *Proc. Symp. Tungsten Geology, Jiangxi, China* 35–45 (in Chinese).

HIGGINS N. C. and KERRICH R. (1982) Progressive $^{18}O$ depletion during $CO_2$ separation from a carbon dioxide-rich hydrothermal fluid: evidence from the Grey River tungsten deposit, Newfoundland. *Canadian J. Earth Sci.* **19**, 2247–2257.

KELLY W. C. and RYE R. O. (1979) Geologic, fluid inclusion, and stable isotope studies of the tin-tungsten deposits of Panasqueira, Portugal. *Econ. Geol.* **74**, 1721–1822.

LANDIS G. P. and RYE R. O. (1974) Geologic fluid inclusion and stable isotope studies of the Pasto Bueno tungsten-base-metal ore deposit, northern Peru. *Econ. Geol.* **69**, 1025–1059.

LIU C. G. (1981) Characteristics and genetic models of mineralization of vein-type tungsten deposits in south China. *Proc. Symp. Tungsten Geology, Jiangxi, China*, 93–104 (in Chinese).

LU H. C., SHIH C. H. and YU T. M. (1974) Determination of the temperature of ore formation and genesis of a deposit from southern China. *Geochimica* **3**, 145–156.

MATSUHISA Y., GOLDSMITH J. R. and CLAYTON R. N. (1979) Oxygen isotope fractionation in the system quartz-albite-anorthite-water. *Geochim. Cosmochim. Acta* **43**, 1131–1140.

MU Z. G., HUANG F. S., CHEN C. Y. and CHENG S. H. (1981) Oxygen, hydrogen, and carbon isotope studies of quartz vein-type tungsten deposits, Piaotang and Xihuashan. *Proc. Symp. Tungsten Geology, Jiangxi, China*, 153–169 (in Chinese).

O'NEIL J. R. and TAYLOR H. P. (1969) Oxygen isotope

equilibrium between muscovite and water. *J. Geophy. Res.* **74,** 6012–6022.

RYE R. O., DING T. P., WHELAN J. F. and LANDIS G. P. (1986) Preliminary hydrogen, oxygen and sulfur isotopic study of the Xihuashan quartz-wolframite deposit, China. *U.S. Geol. Surv. Bull.* **1622,** 157–169.

SHELTON K. L., TAYLOR R. P. and SO C. S. (1987) Stable isotope studies of the Dae Hwa tungsten-molybdenum mine, Republic of Korea: evidence of progressive meteoric water interaction in a tungsten-bearing hydrothermal system. *Econ. Geol.* **82,** 471–481.

SHEPHERD T. J., BECKINSALE R. D., RUNDLE C. C. and DURHAM J. (1976) Genesis of Carrock Fells tungsten deposits Cumbria: fluid inclusion and isotopic study. *Inst. Mining Metallurgy Trans.* **85,** B63–B73.

SO C. S., RYE D. M. and SHELTON K. L. (1983) Carbon, hydrogen, oxygen, and sulfur isotope and fluid inclusion study of the Weolag tungsten-molybdenum deposit, Republic of Korea: fluid histories of metamorphic and ore-forming events. *Econ. Geol.* **78,** 1551–1573.

WESOLOWSKI D. and OHMOTO H. (1986) Calculated oxygen isotope fractionation factors between water and the minerals scheelite and powellite. *Econ. Geol.* **81,** 471–477.

WU Y. L. and MEI Y. W. (1982) Multi-phase intrusion and multi-phase mineralization and their evolution in Xihuashan tungsten ore field. *Tungsten Geology Symp., Jiangxi, China.* ESCAP-RMRDC, Bandung, Indonesia, 437–449.

XU K. Q. and HU S. X. (1981) Regional factors controlling the formation of tungsten deposits in south China. *Proc. Symp. Tungsten Geology, Jiangxi, China,* 243–258 (in Chinese).

YEN M. Z. (1981) Prospecting for tungsten deposits in Jiangxi province: basic principles and methods. *Proc. Symp. Tungsten Geology, Jiangxi, China,* 259–270 (in Chinese).

ZHANG G. X. and SHIEH Y. N. (1989) The oxygen isotopic composition of scheelite in the carbonate-stage mineralization of the Dajishan tungsten deposit, Jiangxi province. *Geochimica* **1,** 77–83 (in Chinese).

ZHANG L. G., ZHUANG L. C., QIAN Y. Q., GUO Y. S. and QU P. (1982) Stable isotope geochemistry of granites and tungsten-tin deposits in Xihuashan-Piaotang area, Jiangxi province. *Tungsten Geology Symp., Jiangxi, China.* ESCAP-RMRDC, Bandung, Indonesia, 553–566.

Stable Isotope Geochemistry: A Tribute to Samuel Epstein
© The Geochemical Society, Special Publication No. 3, 1991
Editors: H. P. Taylor, Jr., J. R. O'Neil and I. R. Kaplan

# Oxygen isotope study of the fossil hydrothermal system in the Comstock Lode mining district, Nevada

ROBERT E. CRISS

Department of Geology, University of California, Davis, CA 95616, U.S.A.

and

DUANE E. CHAMPION

U.S. Geological Survey, M.S. 937, Menlo Park, CA 94025, U.S.A.

**Abstract**—$\delta^{18}O$ analyses of >250 samples of volcanic and intrusive rocks from outcrops, mine workings, and drill cores are used to deduce numerous characteristics of the important hydrothermal system that was active in the Comstock Lode mining district in Miocene time. A bimodal distribution of whole-rock $\delta^{18}O$ values is observed: a group with $\delta^{18}O \approx +5$ to $+9$ made up of fresh to weakly altered samples, and a group with $\delta^{18}O \approx -4$ to $+3$ made up of samples that have been intensely altered by heated, low-$^{18}O$ fluids derived from meteoric waters. The spatial variations of the $\delta^{18}O$ values are extremely regular on a regional scale, and the variations are small on the outcrop scale, even when samples having marked differences in appearance are compared. These observations provide strong confirmation of the pervasive nature of fluid-rock interactions in fracture-controlled meteoric-hydrothermal systems. A contour map of whole-rock $\delta^{18}O$ values reveals a 75 km$^2$ isotopic anomaly that was produced by this fluid-rock exchange event. The 2 km$^2$ Davidson Granodiorite occupies the central part of the anomaly, suggesting that the hydrothermal system was principally driven by this intrusion. The discrepancy in size between the altered zone and its central intrusion is significant, but can be explained if the region represents the remains of a major stratovolcano, a feature of appropriate areal size in which successive pulses of magma utilize the same central vent. Analogous relations at Bohemia, OR, Yankee Fork, ID, and Pilot Mountain, NC, suggest that these mining districts likewise represent ancient stratovolcanic centers, and imply that this geologic environment may be conducive to the formation of precious metal deposits.

The original configuration of the Comstock isotopic anomaly has been disturbed by displacements on large normal faults. The anomaly appears to have been extended in a southeastern direction by normal slip, and significant right-lateral distortion of the anomaly also may have occurred. A pronounced NNE-trending discontinuity in the $\delta^{18}O$ contours coincides with the trace of the mineralized Comstock fault. An intricate relation between faulting and hydrothermal activity is indicated, whereby fault displacement occurred both during and after the period of intense fluid circulation. An isotopic cross-section of the Comstock Lode, primarily based on analyses of outcrops and on samples collected by BECKER (1882) along the six-km-long Sutro tunnel and the one-km-deep Combination Shaft, displays: (1) a steep vertical $\delta^{18}O$ gradient in the hanging wall rocks directly beneath Virginia City, (2) a sharp, sloping, eastern margin for the hydrothermal system, (3) a pronounced, plume-like deflection of the $\delta^{18}O$ contours near the Comstock fault, and (4) an apparent one-km vertical offset of the $\delta^{18}O$ contours by the Comstock fault. We interpret these features as indicating that hot, buoyant groundwaters were strongly focussed upward along the Comstock fault, and that during subsequent rapid cooling and decompression these fluids deposited the most spectacular epithermal bonanzas ever discovered in the United States.

## INTRODUCTION

ECONOMICALLY IMPORTANT concentrations of ore minerals commonly result from the migration of moderate- to high-temperature aqueous fluids in the Earth's crust. Oxygen isotope studies have unparalleled potential in deciphering the nature of hydrothermal processes, in part because (1) oxygen is *the* major constituent of water and crustal rocks; (2) oxygen isotope data can be used to estimate both the temperature of fluid-rock interactions and the isotopic composition of the fluid, which is, in many instances, indicative of the fluid source (*e.g.* UREY, 1947; CLAYTON and EPSTEIN, 1958; TAYLOR,

1974); (3) the $\delta^{18}O$ values of unaltered rocks fall within rather narrow and well-understood ranges, so that deviations produced by alteration are readily apparent (*e.g.* TAYLOR, 1968, 1971); (4) contour maps of $\delta^{18}O$ values provide remarkably regular images of the integrated intensity of fluid circulation in fossil hydrothermal systems (TAYLOR, 1971, 1977; TAYLOR and FORESTER, 1971, 1979; GREGORY and TAYLOR, 1981; CRISS and TAYLOR, 1983, 1986; LARSON and TAYLOR, 1986); and (5) many different types of ore deposits are hosted in rocks with anomalous $\delta^{18}O$ values, with mineralization being particularly concentrated in zones where $^{18}O$

gradients are steepest (see BEATY and TAYLOR, 1982; ENGEL et al., 1958; TAYLOR, 1973, 1977; O'NEIL et al., 1973; RYE, 1986; SHEPPARD et al., 1971; SHEPPARD and TAYLOR, 1974; CRISS and TAYLOR, 1983, 1986; CRISS et al., 1983, 1985).

Previous $\delta^{18}O$ and $\delta D$ studies of the Comstock Lode mining district by SUGISAKI and JENSEN (1971), TAYLOR (1973), O'NEIL and SILBERMAN (1974), and VIKRE (1989) disclosed the relation of the main-stage mineralization to fluids of meteoric origin. An indication of the size and shape of the fossil hydrothermal system in this region was provided by the preliminary oxygen isotope map discussed by CHAMPION and CRISS (1987) and CRISS et al. (1988).

This paper provides the first detailed discussion of the oxygen isotope contour map in the Comstock Lode mining district. In addition, these surface data are combined with data on samples from mine workings to provide a detailed vertical section of the $\delta^{18}O$ relations in the district. This three-dimensional isotopic image provides significant new and independent insights into the nature of this fossil hydrothermal system, including the geologic controls on the fluid circulation, the amount of post-alteration displacement on the principal faults, and the paleoenvironment of the district during Miocene time.

## GEOLOGIC SETTING

The Virginia City area of western Nevada is famous for the Comstock Lode mining district, which produced more than 8 million ounces of gold and nearly 200 million ounces of silver, mostly during the period of 1863 to 1880 (BECKER, 1882; SMITH, 1943; WHITEBREAD, 1976; HUDSON, 1987). The district is principally comprised of a gently dipping sequence of volcanic flow deposits, mostly Miocene andesites of the Alta and the Kate Peak Formations, which overlie Mesozoic metasedimentary and metavolcanic rocks that have been intruded by Cretaceous granitic plutons (Fig. 1; THOMPSON, 1956). The Alta Formation, the main host of the ore deposits, is intruded by the ca. 2 km² Davidson Granodiorite, and the Alta and Kate Peak Formations are intruded by small bodies of andesite porphyry (THOMPSON, 1956).

This important mining district attracted the attention of many early geologists, all of whom commented on the widespread occurrence of gray-green andesites, termed "propylites" by von Richtofen in 1868 (see COATES, 1940). BECKER (1882) probably first recognized that this aspect of the rock was the result of some type of secondary alteration process, and these early studies therefore give the Comstock district the distinction of being the "type locality" for "propylitization" (COATES, 1940). Much discussion of this phenomenon followed, and geologists now recognize that propylitic assemblages, generally defined by the presence of epidote and/or chlorite plus other secondary minerals, are the product of moderate-temperature

hydrothermal processes (e.g. COATES, 1940; ROSE and BURT, 1979). WHITEBREAD (1976) made a detailed chemical and mineralogical study of alteration in the Virginia City area, subdivided the propylitic assemblages into several subtypes, recognized the existence of alunitic and argillic alteration types, and noted a zonal arrangement of these assemblages around the main channelways of fluid transport.

The principal ore bodies in the Comstock district occur as wide, high-grade stockworks that are closely associated with major normal faults, principally the Comstock, Silver City, and Occidental faults (see Fig. 1; BECKER, 1882; HUDSON, 1987). Some of the displacement on these faults predates, or is synchronous with, the mineralization, whereas some displacement is also known to postdate the mineralization (COATES, 1940; HUDSON, 1987). The economically important main-stage mineralization occurred at 13 Ma, approximately synchronous with deposition of the Kate Peak Formation (WHITEBREAD, 1976). However, VIKRE et al. (1988) found that most of the alunite assemblages formed between 17 and 14 Ma, significantly before the formation of the principal lodes.

## METHODS

Standard fluorination techniques were used to extract oxygen from igneous rocks and vein materials (CLAYTON and MAYEDA, 1963; BORTHWICK and HARMON, 1982). The oxygen isotope ratios were determined on $CO_2$ gas in a mass spectrometer and are reported as per mil deviations from SMOW; precision is ±0.2 per mil. NBS-28 has $\delta^{18}O$ = +9.6 on the scale we are using. All analyses reported here represent crushed but otherwise untreated whole-rock materials.

## $\delta^{18}O$ VARIATIONS IN THE COMSTOCK LODE MINING DISTRICT

### Subsurface vs. outcrop samples

The whole-rock $\delta^{18}O$ values of igneous rocks (mostly andesites) from the Comstock Lode mining district vary from +11.7 to −4.3. Two histograms (Fig. 2), one for outcrops and one for subsurface samples, were made to investigate this range and to determine whether weathered surface rocks provide an appropriate representation of the rock volume. Each of the two histograms exhibits two populations: a group with $\delta^{18}O$ values of about +5 to +9, and a group that has anomalously low $\delta^{18}O$ values (< +2). Questions arise as to the origin of these groups and of the sparsely populated range between them.

It is clear that the high-$\delta^{18}O$ group (+5 to +9) represents fresh or weakly altered igneous rocks in the region. Such values are typical of essentially unaltered, isotopically "normal" igneous rocks throughout the world (e.g., TAYLOR, 1968). Also, most such rocks in the Virginia City area occur several kilometers from the zones of intense alteration and mineralization, although important exceptions

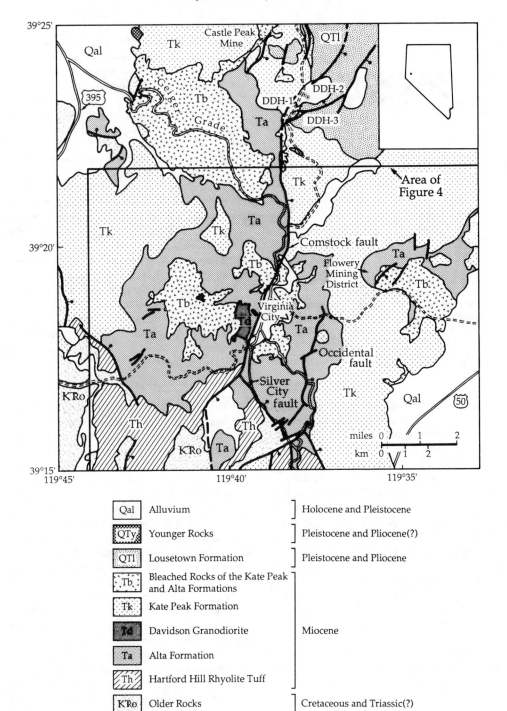

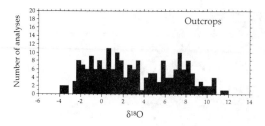

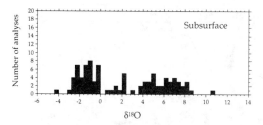

FIG. 2. Histograms of whole-rock $\delta^{18}O$ determinations for outcrop and subsurface samples from the Comstock Lode mining district. Both histograms display a population of isotopically "normal" rocks ($\delta^{18}O > +6$), a population of "strongly altered" rocks ($\delta^{18}O < +2$) affected by exchange with significant volumes of low-$^{18}O$ fluid, and an intervening "gap" representing values typical of the perimeter of the hydrothermal system.

occur, as discussed below. The tails of this "normal" population on the high and low-$^{18}O$ sides probably represent rocks that were hydrothermally altered at low and moderate temperatures, respectively.

It is equally clear that the low-$\delta^{18}O$ population represents "strongly altered" rocks that have undergone significant degrees of interaction and exchange with large volumes of heated, low-$^{18}O$ fluids derived from meteoric waters. TAYLOR (1971, 1973, 1974, 1977) demonstrated that such hydrothermally altered rocks occur worldwide and are common in the western United States, as has been borne out by many subsequent studies (see CRISS and TAYLOR, 1986). All previous stable isotope studies of the Comstock Lode mining district have demonstrated that the rocks and vein materials bear the distinctive signature imparted by meteoric-hydrothermal fluids (SUGISAKI and JENSEN, 1971; TAYLOR, 1973; O'NEIL and SILBERMAN, 1974; CHAMPION and CRISS, 1987; CRISS et al., 1988; VIKRE, 1989).

The sparsely populated "gap" between these "normal" and "strongly altered" populations mostly represents "peripheral zone" rocks collected near the edge of the fossil hydrothermal system. Such zones are typically characterized by very steep lateral or vertical $\delta^{18}O$ gradients (TAYLOR and FORESTER, 1979; CRISS and TAYLOR, 1983, 1986).

Accordingly, the volume of rock exhibiting $\delta^{18}O$ values in this intermediate range is small relative to the volumes of essentially unaltered or highly altered rocks, and this translates into their low abundance, as seen in the histograms.

A difference between the outcrop and subsurface samples is that the latter seem to be systematically lower in $^{18}O$ (Fig. 2), exemplified by the fact that the altered population has a higher average $\delta^{18}O$ value in outcrop than in the subsurface. Also, the "peripheral zone" samples have $\delta^{18}O$ values that range from approximately +2 to +5.5 in outcrop, but from 0 to +4 in the subsurface. Last, rocks having very high $\delta^{18}O$ values of $> +9$ almost exclusively occur in outcrop; these probably represent alteration very close to the paleosurface. In total, the differences between the surface and subsurface samples probably do not represent some recent weathering effect, but rather the fact that the subsurface samples were altered at systematically higher temperatures than those of the outcropping rocks, a direct consequence of their lower average structural and stratigraphic positions.

*Pervasive character of the alteration*

Some reports in the current literature emphasize the importance of "channelized flow" in hydrothermal systems, wherein the fluid flux is presumed to be largely confined to a few large, identifiable structures. Although permeabilities will typically be enhanced along major faults, for example, along caldera ring faults (CRISS and TAYLOR, 1983; LARSON and TAYLOR, 1986) and along large normal faults such as the Comstock fault (see below), we have concluded from studies of this and numerous other fossil hydrothermal systems that, in general, pervasive flow typically dominates the fluid flux and the oxygen isotopic relations.

The most direct and straightforward way to determine whether the fluid flow in a fossil hydrothermal system was channelized or pervasive is to examine lateral $\delta^{18}O$ variations on different scales. If the subsurface flow was dominantly channelized on a regional scale, then extremely sharp gradients in the $\delta^{18}O$ values should occur near the major structures, and rocks further away should all have normal values. If the flow was dominantly channelized but on a smaller scale, then different samples from individual outcrops should have highly variable $\delta^{18}O$ values, depending on the proximity to controlling minor structures such as small faults and joints. If, on the other hand, the flow was dominantly pervasive, the $\delta^{18}O$ values should exhibit smooth lateral variations on a large scale, and different samples from single outcrops would have similar $\delta^{18}O$ values.

Figure 3 compares the $\delta^{18}O$ values of multiple (in most cases, two) samples collected from individual outcrops. These samples were generally collected within 2 and 30 meters of each other. This comparison is an extreme one, because in all cases the multiple samples were collected because the rocks at the outcrop exhibited notable differences in appearance; some of the plotted pairs even compare dikes, and in one case vein matter, with wall rocks. The order of assignment of the data pairs to the cartesian coordinates of the graph is random.

Figure 3, like the histograms discussed above, demonstrates the dominance of the "normal" and "strongly altered" rock populations, as well as the intermediate "gap" where the "peripheral zone" samples would plot. In none of our investigated outcrops do isotopically normal rocks occur with strongly $^{18}O$-shifted ones. Thus, visibly different samples from single outcrops exhibit, within a few per mil, similar $\delta^{18}O$ values. This result, together with the smooth and regular $\delta^{18}O$ variations on larger scales (see Figs. 4, 5, and 6, below), confirms the pervasive character of the alteration in the Comstock Lode mining district.

## GEOGRAPHIC $\delta^{18}O$ VARIATIONS IN THE VIRGINIA CITY REGION

### $\delta^{18}O$ contour map

A contour map of $\delta^{18}O$ values in the Virginia City region (Fig. 4) reveals two separate zones of anomalously low ($< +6$) values. The most important of these comprises a regular, equant, 75 km² zone that encompasses Virginia City. The very lowest ($<0$) $\delta^{18}O$ values occur along and west of the famous, NNE-trending Comstock lode and its southern extension, the Silver City lode, and along the subparallel Occidental lode. In addition, a few kilometers to the east of Flowery Peak is a separate, somewhat smaller (*ca.* 20 to 40 km²) low-$^{18}O$ zone that includes the Flowery Mining district. These two anomalous areas represent the former locations of important meteoric-hydrothermal systems.

Most of the anomalous areas are directly underlain by andesites of the Alta Formation (*cf.* Fig. 1; THOMPSON, 1956; WHITEBREAD, 1976). As already mentioned, the term "propylite" was coined by von Richtofen to describe these rocks, although many years passed before their indurated character was attributed to alteration by heated meteoric groundwaters (TAYLOR, 1973; this study).

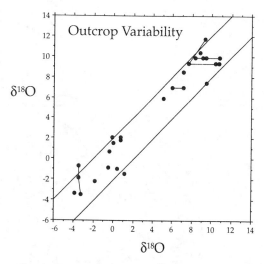

FIG. 3. Graph comparing the $\delta^{18}O$ values of multiple rock samples collected at single outcrops. In most cases each point represents two rock samples from a single site, but in cases where more than two samples were analyzed, the points representing that outcrop are connected by line segments. Even though the samples at each site exhibit notable differences in appearance, their $\delta^{18}O$ values are similar, demonstrating the pervasive character of the alteration. See text.

The geographic variations of the $\delta^{18}O$ values in the 75 km² system are very smooth, comprising a coherent pattern that is approximately centered on the small (2 km²) composite granodiorite stock at Mt. Davidson (Fig. 4). This variation would conform to a simple concentric, or "bullseye," pattern were it not for later distortion and a few rather abrupt discontinuities caused by faulting. The most important discontinuity coincides with the trace of the NNE-trending Comstock fault, which dips approximately 45°E. The first-order consequence of the displacement on this fault is that a "high-$^{18}O$ tongue" of rocks, representing downdropped rocks of the hanging wall directly underlying Virginia City, divides the most altered rocks, *i.e.* those with $\delta^{18}O < 0$, into two separate zones. Because the vertical displacement on the Comstock fault is considerable—approximately one km, as discussed below—relative motion along it has extended the isotopic anomaly to the southeast. The $\delta^{18}O$ pattern additionally suggests that perhaps as much as two kilometers of right-lateral distortion has occurred, perhaps also representing fault displacement.

### $\delta^{18}O$ variations along the Sutro Tunnel

Because of the economic importance of the Virginia City area, more than 1000 km of workings

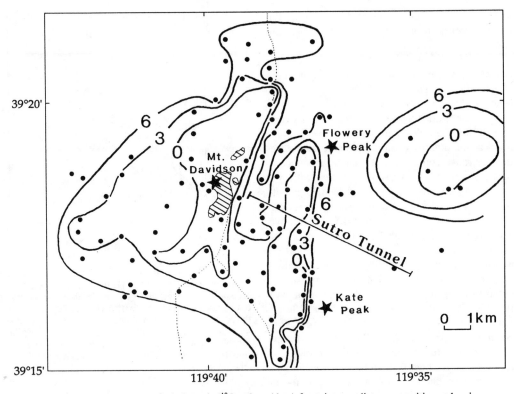

FIG. 4. Contour map of whole-rock $\delta^{18}O$ values (dots) from intermediate composition volcanic rocks of the Comstock Lode mining district. A 75 km² zone of low ¹⁸O rocks ($-4 < \delta^{18}O < +6$), produced by interactions of the rocks with low-¹⁸O fluids, is centered on a small, 2 km² stock at Mt. Davidson (ruled pattern) that represents an ancient volcanic center. The famous Comstock Lode ore deposits occur near and along the prominent, NNE-trending Comstock and Silver City faults (dotted lines). See Fig. 1 for geologic and geographic features. Modified after CRISS *et al.* (1988).

were excavated for exploration and production. One of the most famous ventures was the six-km-long Sutro Tunnel, dug between 1869 and 1878 for drainage, exploration, and haulage (SMITH, 1943; see Fig. 4 for location). Although this and most other old workings in the district are now either caved, flooded, or otherwise inaccessible, nearly 1500 sub-surface samples were collected more than 100 years ago by George Becker and his associates; these collections have been carefully curated by the Smithsonian Institution. Becker collected samples every 100 feet along the Sutro Tunnel, and sometimes at shorter intervals, so that more than 270 samples are available in the Smithsonian Institution collection along this transect. A separate collection of Sutro Tunnel samples is curated by the U.S. Geological Survey.

Figure 5 is a graph of $\delta^{18}O$ variations vs. distance along the Sutro Tunnel. Because distances along the tunnel were very accurately known, we have experienced no difficulty in combining the results

for the Smithsonian Institution collection with those obtained on the samples curated by the U.S.G.S. We originally were unaware of the extensive Smithsonian Institution collection and were delighted to learn of it, in part because the U.S.G.S. collection does not include any samples in the particularly interesting interval between 8,000 and 13,000 feet.

Figure 5 clearly illustrates the pronounced isotopic contrast between the "normal" ($> +6$) rocks outside the hydrothermal system and the "strongly altered" ($-4.3$ to $+1.5$) rocks within it. It is interesting that many of these low-¹⁸O rocks occur about 500 meters directly beneath surface rocks, with $\delta^{18}O$ values as high as $+7.4$ (*cf.* Fig. 4), indicating that a steep vertical ¹⁸O gradient existed in the hydrothermal system. Also obvious is the sharp but continuous character of the $\delta^{18}O$ variations in the peripheral zone, again demonstrating the relative rarity of rocks with $\delta^{18}O$ values that lie between those of the "normal" and "strongly altered" populations. CRISS and TAYLOR (1983, 1986) emphasize the im-

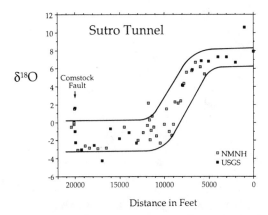

FIG. 5. Variations in the whole-rock $\delta^{18}O$ values of samples along the Sutro Tunnel. Solid squares represent samples curated by the U.S. Geological Survey, and open symbols represent samples from the extensive Becker collection of the National Museum of Natural History. Note that the isotopically normal samples near the tunnel portal are separated from the strongly altered samples by a zone of high-$^{18}O$ gradients between approximately 6,500 and 9,000 feet.

portance of such peripheral "high-$^{18}O$ gradient" zones in fossil hydrothermal systems, but these new results provide the best documented example.

The uniform $\delta^{18}O$ values of rocks in the strongly altered zone provide probably the best confirmation to date that the alteration in meteoric-hydrothermal systems is generally of a pervasive character even in systems whose permeability is dominantly controlled by faults and fractures. This is because the rocks along the Sutro Tunnel (a) represent 100% exposure, so the data are not influenced by any effects such as differential preservation of altered and unaltered rocks, and samples could be collected at uniform intervals; (b) have not been exposed, and so cannot be affected by any surface effects such as weathering; and (c) were not collected by us or by any person involved with this type of study whose sampling techniques might be biased. In virtually all other fossil hydrothermal systems that have been studied, the notion of pervasive fluid infiltration has been derived from $\delta^{18}O$ analyses of surface samples (*e.g.*, TAYLOR, 1971; TAYLOR and FORESTER, 1979; CRISS *et al.*, 1985; CRISS and TAYLOR, 1983, 1986). All previous surface studies except for the Skaergaard intrusion, which is almost continuously exposed as fresh, glacially polished outcrop (TAYLOR and FORESTER, 1979), have suffered from this problem. It follows that none of the above-mentioned potential problems have previously arisen in any serious way, and that the concept of

$\delta^{18}O$ mapping as originally practiced by H. P. Taylor and his coworkers is valid.

*Isotopic cross-section of the Comstock Lode hydrothermal system*

The $\delta^{18}O$ results for outcrops can be combined with the above described results along the Sutro Tunnel to construct the most detailed isotopic cross-section yet available of a hydrothermal system in an important mining district. This effort is enhanced because BECKER (1882) also collected numerous samples along the one-km-deep Combination Shaft, the Savage Shaft, the North Potosi Tunnel, and the Lightning Drift, all of which can be projected laterally for short distances into the vertical plane of the Sutro Tunnel. In addition, we have recently made a much more extensive collection of surface samples directly above the Sutro Tunnel than is indicated on Fig. 4.

The contours of Fig. 6 represent the available $\delta^{18}O$ results, superimposed on the vertical geologic cross-section along the line of the Sutro Tunnel drawn by BECKER (1882). The apparent large-scale features, from east to west, are (a) the isotopically normal rocks from the portal (0 feet, not shown) to a distance of about 6500 feet at tunnel level; (b) the sharp, east-sloping zone of high-$^{18}O$ gradients, between about 6,500 and 9,000 feet at tunnel level, representing the effective eastern perimeter of the hydrothermal system; (c) the strongly altered zone that extends from this high-gradient zone to and beyond the tunnel terminus near the Comstock fault; and (d) the significant deflections of the isotopic contours along and above the Comstock fault.

It is interesting to examine in more detail the geometry of several noteworthy isotopic features that occur within the strongly altered zone. For example, a steep vertical $^{18}O$ gradient is present everywhere; analogous effects have been observed in several other fossil hydrothermal systems (*e.g.* TAYLOR and FORESTER, 1979; GREGORY and TAYLOR, 1981; CRISS *et al.*, 1984; LARSON and TAYLOR, 1986). In general, these vertical $^{18}O$ gradients probably reflect steep vertical temperature gradients in the fossil hydrothermal systems and possibly in some cases indicate the position of the water table. It is interesting to note that the hanging wall rocks near Virginia City, a short distance east of the Comstock fault, contain the most pronounced $^{18}O$ gradient in the region, ranging upward into rocks with essentially normal $\delta^{18}O$ values. Apparently, this part of the hanging wall was originally located very near the paleosurface directly above

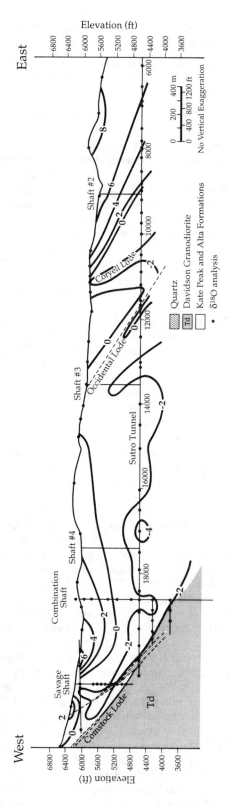

the central part of the fossil hydrothermal system; these rocks were probably preserved by significant downdropping (see below).

In addition, the $\delta^{18}O$ contours on either side of the Comstock fault seem to exhibit a very substantial vertical offset. Simply stated, the $\delta^{18}O$ values of the footwall at the summit of Mt. Davidson (elev. 7864 feet ASL; see Fig. 4) are quite similar to those of the hanging wall at the Sutro Tunnel Level (*ca.* 4600 feet ASL)! The straightforward interpretation is that the original, hydrothermally produced $\delta^{18}O$ contours have been vertically offset by approximately 3200 feet (one km). Additional improvements in this isotopic cross-section and the construction of others may serve to refine this estimate, but our result is in reasonable agreement with geologic estimates of displacement (see summary in VIKRE *et al.*, 1988).

The Comstock fault did not merely displace the $\delta^{18}O$ anomaly, however. The vein material and associated mineralization clearly indicate that this major fault was in existence, and probably repeatedly active, while the hydrothermal system was active. This relation is also indicated by the pronounced, "plume-like" upward deflection of the $\delta^{18}O$ contours in a broad zone of enhanced permeability along the fault (Fig. 6). Because this zone is several hundred meters wide, however, the fluid flow is seen even in this case to have had an extremely pervasive character. An important effect of this buoyant plume is that it brought high-temperature fluids very close to the paleosurface, further steepening the already steep $^{18}O$ gradients referred to above. It is no accident that the rocks in this zone hosted several of the most spectacular epithermal bonanzas ever exploited. Again, this zone is characterized by several very important features, including: (1) the spatial association of a major fault near the central intrusion of a hydrothermal system; (2) the repeated activity of this fault during (and after) mineralization; (3) the preservation of hanging wall rocks that were originally located very close to the paleosurface; and (4) the existence of one of the steepest $^{18}O$ gradients ever observed in a meteoric-hydrothermal system. A close association between

FIG. 6. $\delta^{18}O$ cross-section of the Comstock Lode along the line of the Sutro Tunnel. The contours define a meteoric-hydrothermal system with a vertical extent of several km that featured focussed, buoyant uprise of deep, hot, fluid along the highly mineralized Comstock fault. See text.

steep $^{18}O$ gradients and economic mineralization has also been found in several other mining districts (CRISS et al., 1983, 1985; CRISS and TAYLOR, 1983, 1986).

Other areas of interesting isotopic structures occur in the altered zone. A plume-like structure is associated with the "Coryell Lode" mapped by BECKER (1882), about 10,500 feet from the portal of the Sutro Tunnel. It is not known whether this zone represents a fault zone or perhaps a small intrusion. Another example is near the Occidental fault, where an upward, plume-like deflection of the contours occurs in the footwall, yet an oppositely directed isotopic structure (an "antiplume") occurs in the hanging wall. It is interesting to speculate that this coupled isotopic structure could represent a convective gyre *centered on* the fault, and driven by a temperature difference between the hanging-wall and footwall rocks. Very different types of fluid flow might then be associated with faults, depending on conditions.

## THE COMSTOCK LODE PALEOENVIRONMENT

The $\delta^{18}O$ map (Fig. 4) indicates that the 75 km$^2$ altered zone is much too large to be accounted for by the associated igneous intrusions (primarily the 2 km$^2$ Davidson Granodiorite) if the aggregate size of the latter is judged by their outcrop extents. For example, an intrusive mass of such size simply would not contain sufficient heat energy, by a factor of perhaps 100, to heat up the large volumes of fluid and rock involved in the fossil hydrothermal system. CRISS et al. (1988) suggest that this size discrepancy can be explained if the hydrothermal system was related to a repetitively active Miocene stratovolcanic center correlative to the Kate Peak Formation. Stratovolcanoes are of appropriate areal size, and could produce the andesitic and grano-dioritic rocks at Comstock. Also, they are generally subaerial and so would typically be associated with meteoric groundwaters, and would logically be associated with symmetrical geologic features such as "bullseye" isotopic anomalies. Even more importantly, the heat-balance problem mentioned above could be explained because successive pulses of magma could utilize the same central vent.

In following up on the stratovolcano concept of CRISS et al. (1988), VIKRE (1989) concluded from his fluid inclusion data that the important mineralization in the Comstock lode district was related to a Miocene stratovolcano at Cedar Hill, approximately one mile north of Virginia City. He also argued that the bonanzas are located "somewhat distal to thermal centers." The feature that VIKRE (1989) is describing is much too small and in the wrong area to produce either the isotopic patterns evident in Figs. 4 and 6 or the ore deposits that are clearly related to them.

If stratovolcanic environments indeed are associated with the types of oxygen isotope effects documented in the Comstock district, then one would expect that similar anomalies would be relatively common elsewhere. As pointed out by CRISS et al. (1988), available data suggests that this is indeed the case. "Bullseye" type meteoric-hydrothermal anomalies that are approximately 50 to 75 km$^2$ in areal extent have been found and extensively studied in: (1) the Miocene volcanic rocks of the Western Cascades, particularly in the Bohemia mining district, Oregon (TAYLOR, 1971); (2) Eocene rocks of the Challis volcanic field, Yankee Fork mining district, Idaho (CRISS et al., 1985); and (3) late Precambrian metavolcanic rocks of the Carolina slate belt at Pilot Mountain, North Carolina (KLEIN and CRISS, 1988). All three of these areas are characterized by large piles of andesitic rocks that include zones of propylitic or sericitic alteration associated with major zones of $^{18}O$ depletion. Associated with these altered areas in every case are anomalous concentrations of precious and base metals. Significant orebodies were discovered at Yankee Fork and Bohemia. Last, in all three cases the area of the central intrusion appears to be *much* smaller than that of the low-$^{18}O$ country rocks.

## CONCLUSIONS

$\delta^{18}O$ determinations of volcanic and intrusive rocks from the Comstock Lode mining district have been used to obtain an image of the important meteoric-hydrothermal system that operated there in Miocene time. Extreme $^{18}O$ depletions occur in a 75 km$^2$ zone where pervasive fluid-rock interactions resulted in regional propylitization. The pervasive character of these interactions is proved by the extremely regular variations of the $\delta^{18}O$ values on a regional scale, together with the small $\delta^{18}O$ variations among visibly different rocks at the outcrop scale. The low-$^{18}O$ zone may to first order be described as a set of concentric $\delta^{18}O$ contours centered on the rather small granodiorite stock at Mount Davidson. Several geologic and isotopic features are explained if a stratovolcanic center formerly existed in the region.

The significant relief and numerous historical samples from mine workings have been exploited to define the $^{18}O$ variations in the vertical dimension. The results confirm the sharp lateral boundary of the fossil hydrothermal system and show that a sharp vertical $^{18}O$ gradient is present throughout the altered area. Several plume-like areas of fluid upwelling are identified; the most important of these is associated with the Comstock fault and appears to be largely responsible for the deposition of the epithermal bonanzas for which the district is famous.

Post-alteration displacement along major faults in the region has distorted the original shape of the $\delta^{18}O$ anomaly. Significant vertical displacement along NNE-trending normal faults has extended the altered zone in a NW-SE direction. It also appears that significant right-lateral distortion of the isotopic anomaly has occurred. Detailed examination of the $\delta^{18}O$ contours indicates as much as one km of post-alteration vertical displacement along the Comstock fault. One consequence of this latter displacement is that rocks originally located near the paleosurface and directly above the central part of the hydrothermal system are preserved directly beneath Virginia City. Many of the most valuable orebodies were deposited in these rocks, including the famous Con Virginia bonanza. Additional isotopic data should help clarify the ancient geological and geochemical environment at the Comstock Lode, the relationship of fluid circulation to faulting, and the relationship of $\delta^{18}O$ contours to zones of economic mineralization.

*Acknowledgements*—We thank H. P. Taylor, D. H. Whitebread, P. B. Larson, J. R. O'Neil, D. M. Hudson, and G. A. Thompson for valuable discussions. Most of the $\delta^{18}O$ analyses were made by L. Adami and M. F. Horan. S. Sorenson helped us locate many critical samples in the valuable Becker Collection curated by the National Museum of Natural History of the Smithsonian Institution. Janice Fong did an outstanding drafting job. This research was supported by the U.S. Geological Survey and by National Science Foundation Grant EAR 89-15788.

## REFERENCES

BEATY D. W. and TAYLOR H. P., JR. (1982) Some petrologic and oxygen isotopic relationships in the Amulet Mine, Noranda, Quebec, and their bearing on the origin of Archean massive sulfide deposits. *Econ. Geol.* **77**, 95–108.

BECKER G. F. (1882) Geology of the Comstock lode and Washoe district. *U.S. Geol. Surv. Mon.* **3**.

BORTHWICK J. and HARMON R. S. (1982) A note regarding ClF$_3$ as an alternative to BrF$_5$ for oxygen isotope analyses. *Geochim. Cosmochim. Acta* **46**, 1665–1668.

CHAMPION D. E. and CRISS R. E. (1987) Oxygen isotope and physical property studies of the Comstock Lode mining district, Nevada. *Geol. Soc. Amer. Abstr. Prog.* **19**, 616–617.

CLAYTON R. N. and EPSTEIN S. (1958) The relationship between O$^{18}$/O$^{16}$ ratios in coexisting quartz, carbonate, and iron oxides from various geological deposits. *J. Geol.* **66**, 352–373.

CLAYTON R. N. and MAYEDA T. K. (1963) The use of bromine pentafluoride in the extraction of oxygen from oxides and silicates for isotopic analysis. *Geochim. Cosmochim. Acta* **27**, 43–52.

COATES R. (1940) Propylitization and related types of alteration on the Comstock lode. *Econ. Geol.* **35**, 1–17.

CRISS R. E. and TAYLOR H. P., JR. (1983) An $^{18}O/^{16}O$ and D/H study of Tertiary hydrothermal systems in the southern half of the Idaho batholith. *Geol. Soc. Amer. Bull.* **94**, 640–663.

CRISS R. E. and TAYLOR H. P., JR. (1986) Meteoric-hydrothermal systems. In *Stable Isotopes in High-Temperature Geological Processes* (eds. J. W. VALLEY, H. P. TAYLOR, JR., and J. R. O'NEIL); *Rev. Mineral.* **16**, pp. 373–424. Mineralogical Society of America.

CRISS R. E., SOLOMON G. C. and TAYLOR H. P., JR. (1983) Application of $\delta^{18}O$ and $\delta D$ contour maps to exploration for epithermal and porphyry mineral deposits formed in subaerial environments. *Geol. Soc. Amer. Abstr. Prog.* **15**, 278.

CRISS R. E., EKREN E. B. and HARDYMAN R. F. (1984) Casto ring zone: A 4,500-km$^2$ fossil hydrothermal system in the Challis volcanic field, central Idaho. *Geology* **12**, 331–334.

CRISS R. E., CHAMPION D. E. and McINTYRE D. H. (1985) $\delta^{18}O$, aeromagnetic and gravity anomalies associated with hydrothermally-altered zones in the Yankee Fork Mining District, Custer County, Idaho. *Econ. Geol.* **80**, 1277–1296.

CRISS R. E., CHAMPION D. E. and HORAN M. F. (1988) Oxygen isotope map of the fossil hydrothermal system in the Comstock Lode Mining District, Nevada. *U.S. Geol. Surv. Circ.* **1035**, 11–13.

ENGEL A. E. J., CLAYTON R. N. and EPSTEIN S. (1958) Variations in isotopic composition of oxygen and carbon in Leadville limestone (Mississippian, Colorado) and its hydrothermal and metamorphic phases. *J. Geol.* **66**, 374–393.

GREGORY R. T. and TAYLOR H. P., JR. (1981) An oxygen isotope profile in a section of Cretaceous oceanic crust, Samail ophiolite, Oman: Evidence for $\delta^{18}O$-buffering of the oceans by deep (>5 km) seawater-hydrothermal circulation at mid-ocean ridges. *J. Geophys. Res.* **86**, 2737–2755.

HUDSON D. M. (1987) Summary of the geology of the Comstock district, Nevada. In *Bulk Mineable Precious Metal Deposits of the Western United States; Geol. Soc. Nevada, Guidebook for Field Trips*, pp. 413–418.

KLEIN T. L. and CRISS R. E. (1988) An oxygen isotope and geochemical study of meteroic-hydrothermal systems at Pilot Mountain and selected other localities, Carolina slate belt. *Econ. Geol.* **83**, 801–821.

LARSON P. B. and TAYLOR H. P., JR. (1986) $^{18}O/^{16}O$ relationships in hydrothermally altered rocks from the Lake City caldera, San Juan Mountains, Colorado. *J. Volcanol. Geotherm. Res.* **30**, 47–82.

O'NEIL J. R. and SILBERMAN M. L. (1974) Stable isotope relations in epithermal Au-Ag deposits. *Econ. Geol.* **69**, 902–909.

O'NEIL J. R., SILBERMAN M. L., FABBI B. P. and CHESTERMAN C. W. (1973) Stable isotope and chemical relations during mineralization in the Bodie mining district, Mono County, California. *Econ. Geol.* **68**, 765–784.

ROSE A. W. and BURT D. M. (1979) Hydrothermal alteration. In *Geochemistry of Hydrothermal Ore Deposits* (ed. H. L. BARNES), Vol. 2, pp. 173–235. John Wiley, N.Y.

RYE R. O. (1986) A model for the formation of carbonate-hosted disseminated gold deposits based on geologic, fluid inclusion, geochemical, and stable isotope studies of the Carlin and Cortez deposits, Nevada. *U.S. Geol. Surv. Bull.* **1646**, 35–42.

SHEPPARD S. M. F. and TAYLOR H. P., JR. (1974) Hydrogen and oxygen isotope evidence for the origins of water in the Boulder batholith and the Butte ore deposits, Montana. *Econ. Geol.* **69**, 926–946.

SHEPPARD S. M. F., NIELSON R. L. and TAYLOR H. P., JR. (1971) Hydrogen and oxygen isotope ratios in minerals from porphyry copper deposits. *Econ. Geol.* **66**, 515–542.

SMITH G. H. (1943) The History of the Comstock Lode, 1850–1920. *University of Nevada Bull.* **3**.

SUGISAKI R. and JENSEN M. L. (1971) Oxygen isotopic studies of silicate minerals with special reference to hydrothermal mineral deposits. *Geochim. J.* **5**, 7–12.

TAYLOR H. P., JR. (1968) The oxygen isotope geochemistry of igneous rocks. *Contrib. Mineral. Petrol.* **19**, 1–71.

TAYLOR H. P., JR. (1971) Oxygen isotope evidence for large-scale interaction between meteoric ground waters and Tertiary granodiorite intrusions, western Cascade Range, Oregon. *J. Geophys. Res.* **76**, 7855–7874.

TAYLOR H. P., JR. (1973) $O^{18}/O^{16}$ evidence for meteoric-hydrothermal alteration and ore deposition in the Tonopah, Comstock lode, and Goldfield mining districts, Nevada. *Econ. Geol.* **68**, 747–764.

TAYLOR H. P., JR. (1974) The application of oxygen and hydrogen isotope studies to problems of hydrothermal alteration and ore deposition. *Econ. Geol.* **69**, 843–883.

TAYLOR H. P., JR. (1977) Water/rock interactions and the origin of $H_2O$ in granitic batholiths. *J. Geol. Soc. London* **133**, 509–558.

TAYLOR H. P., JR. and FORESTER R. W. (1971) Low-$^{18}O$ igneous rocks from the intrusive complexes of Skye, Mull, and Ardnamurchan, western Scotland. *J. Petrol.* **12**, 465–497.

TAYLOR H. P., JR. and FORESTER R. W. (1979) An oxygen and hydrogen isotope study of the Skaergaard intrusion and its country rocks: a description of a 55-m.y. old fossil hydrothermal system. *J. Petrol.* **20**, 355–419.

THOMPSON G. A. (1956) Geology of the Virginia City quadrangle, Nevada. *U.S. Geol. Surv. Bull.* **1042-C**, 45–77.

UREY H. C. (1947) The thermodynamic properties of isotopic substances. *J. Chem. Soc.*, 562–581.

VIKRE P. G. (1989) Fluid-mineral relations in the Comstock Lode. *Econ. Geol.* **84**, 1574–1613.

VIKRE P. G., MCKEE E. H. and SILBERMAN M. L. (1988) Chronology of Miocene hydrothermal and igneous events in the Western Virginia Range, Washoe, Storey, and Lyon Counties, Nevada. *Econ. Geol.* **83**, 864–874.

WHITEBREAD D. H. (1976) Alteration and geochemistry of Tertiary volcanic rocks in parts of the Virginia City quadrangle, Nevada. *U.S. Geol. Surv. Prof. Pap.* **936**.

Stable Isotope Geochemistry: A Tribute to Samuel Epstein
© The Geochemical Society, Special Publication No. 3, 1991
Editors: H. P. Taylor, Jr., J. R. O'Neil and I. R. Kaplan

# Oxygen isotope studies of Jurassic fossil hydrothermal systems, Mojave Desert, southeastern California*

G. Cleve Solomon† and Hugh P. Taylor, Jr.

Division of Geological and Planetary Sciences, California Institute of Technology, Pasadena, CA 91125, U.S.A.

**Abstract**—Whole-rock oxygen isotope analyses of 66 Jurassic plutonic and subvolcanic granodiorites and monzogranites from the Rodman-Ord Mountains (ROM) area in the Mojave Desert range from $\delta^{18}O = -3.2$ to $+9.4$. These data define an elongate WNW–ESE zone of $^{18}O$ depletion, where intrusive igneous rocks with original $\delta^{18}O$ values of $+7.5$ to $+9$ have been partially altered and veined by epidote, chlorite, and sericite, and depleted in $^{18}O$ by two to ten per mil over an area of more than 1000 km$^2$. These effects were produced by exchange with heated low-$^{18}O$ meteoric ground waters in association with a series of volcanic centers. These centers are identified by ovoid-shaped areas of extreme $^{18}O$ depletion where $\delta^{18}O < +2$. Earlier Triassic plutons (4 samples) and later Cretaceous plutons (10 samples) from the ROM area do not display any analogous $^{18}O$ depletions, indicating that the identifiable hydrothermal events are confined to the Jurassic igneous episode, which clearly had to be epizonal in nature. Reconnaissance $^{18}O/^{16}O$ analyses of another 20 early Mesozoic grano-diorites and monzogranites elsewhere in Southern California demonstrate that the ROM-type low-$^{18}O$ effects extend well to the southeast along the major Jurassic rift zone and associated calderas proposed by BUSBY-SPERA (1988). This graben depression extends from Yerington, Nevada (where the associated Jurassic hydrothermal waters were higher in $^{18}O$ and probably marine in origin) south-eastward across a Jurassic coastline and through the subaerial ROM area (where the hydrothermal fluids were continental meteoric in origin); the low-$^{18}O$ rift-zone continues across southeastern California and then into southern Arizona where only scattered oxygen isotope data are available. In the ROM area the low-$^{18}O$ patterns are truncated by the Cretaceous plutons and they are also offset by displacements along NW-trending late Cenozoic strike-slip faults. The $\delta^{18}O$ systematics can be used to map offsets on these faults, confirming that they are relatively small. For example, the right-lateral offset on the Camp Rock Fault is constrained by the $^{18}O/^{16}O$ patterns to be only $5 \pm 2$ km.

## INTRODUCTION

THIS PAPER IS part of a series of studies by us of the oxygen isotope geochemistry of plutonic igneous rocks of the Transverse Ranges and Mojave Desert regions of Southern California. These studies were undertaken mainly to map the primary $\delta^{18}O$ values of Mesozoic plutons in this region, in order to expand on and supplement the data of TAYLOR and SILVER (1978) and MASI *et al.* (1981) on the Peninsular Ranges and Sierra Nevada batholiths. However, it soon became apparent that in contrast to the Cretaceous-age plutons, many of the Jurassic-age plutons of this broad region constituted a special case, in that their original $^{18}O/^{16}O$ ratios had been shifted down to lower values as a result of meteoric-hydrothermal alteration. We learned that we would have to "look through" and understand this low-$^{18}O$ overprint if we were going to be able to map the primary $\delta^{18}O$ values of the original magmas.

This paper reports on reconnaissance isotope studies throughout the Mojave Desert region, but it particularly focuses on detailed studies of what appears to be the largest and most accessible of these Jurassic hydrothermal centers, namely the Rod-man-Ord Mountains (ROM) area in the vicinity of Stoddard Valley and Lucerne Valley, north of the San Bernardino Mountains, east of the town of Victorville, and south of the town of Barstow (Fig. 1). This area exhibits the sorts of $^{18}O/^{16}O$ relationships that are characteristic of most fossil meteoric-hydrothermal systems throughout the world, such as are found in Tertiary volcanic centers like the Comstock Lode described in this volume (CRISS and CHAMPION, 1991) or the Eocene parts of the Idaho Batholith (TAYLOR and MAGARITZ, 1978; CRISS and TAYLOR, 1983).

A detailed sampling program involving analyses of whole-rock $\delta^{18}O$ in 80 intrusive igneous rocks was undertaken in the ROM study area for the reasons listed above, but also: (1) to define the size and characteristics of this area of altered rocks, inasmuch as no major $^{18}O/^{16}O$ study of such a large fossil meteoric-hydrothermal system has yet been carried out in Southern California; and (2) to test the possible usefulness of $^{18}O/^{16}O$ studies in determining offset along late Cenozoic faults in the area, by defining the limits of hydrothermal exchange and then

---

\* Contribution No. 5062, Division of Geological and Planetary Sciences, California Institute of Technology.

† *Present address:* J. M. Montgomery, Consulting Engineers, Inc. PAS-4, 301 N. Lake Ave., Suite 600, Pasadena, CA 91101, U.S.A.

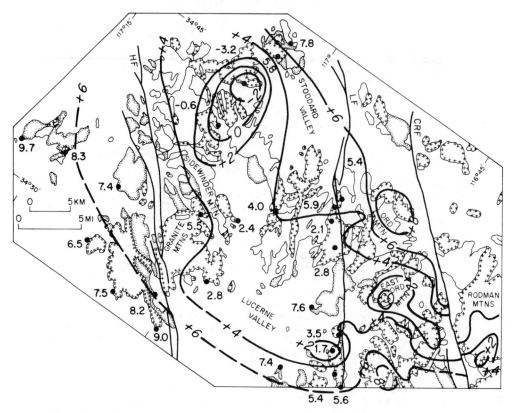

FIG. 1. Geologic map of the ROM area, showing Mesozoic batholithic rocks, pre-batholithic country rocks, late Cenozoic strike-slip faults, and whole-rock $\delta^{18}O$ contours on Jurassic intrusive rocks (geology after BISHOP, 1963; and BORTUGNO and SPITTLER, 1986). The $\delta^{18}O$ contours are based on the whole-rock $\delta^{18}O$ values given in Table 1 and plotted on this figure and on Fig. 2 (sample locations indicated by solid circles). The $\delta^{18}O$ values southwest of the Lenwood Fault (LF) are shown on this figure, but for rocks northeast of LF they are shown on Fig. 2. Mesozoic batholithic rocks are indicated according to age of emplacement by different symbols along inside margins of map units: (1) Triassic plutons are shown by small circle patterns; (2) Jurassic plutons are shown by cross patterns; and (3) late Cretaceous plutons are indicated by stippled patterns. Unlabeled outcrops on the map are the pre-batholithic country rocks, and include early Mesozoic silicic pyroclastic units and volcanic flows, Mesozoic sedimentary rocks, and Precambrian crystalline basement. HF = Helendale Fault; CRF = Camp Rock Fault.

mapping any fault displacements of the regional $\delta^{18}O$ contours.

## GEOLOGICAL RELATIONSHIPS

Mesozoic plutonism in the Mojave Desert is characterized by at least three separate magmatic episodes: (1) sparsely outcropping Permo-Triassic monzonite and granodiorite; (2) relatively abundant epizonal Jurassic granodiorite and monzogranite; and (3) very widespread late Cretaceous granodiorite and monzogranite (BURCHFIEL and DAVIS, 1981; MILLER, 1978; JOHN, 1981). The Jurassic plutons commonly show intense hydrothermal alteration, and in places are mineralized. They are typically emplaced into volcanic rocks, and many probably represent exhumed volcanic centers. Late Cretaceous plutonism in the Mojave Desert was locally accompanied by emplacement of muscovite-bearing granites, and in places

developed pegmatitic facies. No volcanic carapace has been mapped for the Cretaceous episode of magmatism, and in general that plutonic episode appears to have been relatively deep-seated.

The tectonic processes responsible for the immense mobility of upper plate rocks in latest Cretaceous time eventually culminated in the formation of mid-Tertiary metamorphic core complexes throughout the Cordillera, including parts of the Mojave Desert (CONEY, 1980). Miocene volcanism and related hypabyssal plutonism are known to occur within the study area, as part of a northwest-trending belt that extends throughout the Mojave region. However, these features post-date the igneous and hydrothermal events of concern in this paper, and they are not discussed further. The late Cenozoic strike-slip faulting, which resulted in displacements of the Jurassic crystalline basement within the study area, is of interest and is discussed in more detail below.

Figure 1 is a generalized geologic map of the Rodman-

Ord Mountains (ROM) area. Figure 2 shows the geology of the eastern portion of this area at a larger scale. This eastern region between the Lenwood Fault and Camp Rock Fault was studied in more detail because an initial reconnaissance revealed that this was a principal area of "disturbed" $^{18}O/^{16}O$ ratios.

The ROM area was geologically mapped by DIBBLEE (1960a,b,c; 1964a,b,c; 1967), MILLER (1978), MILLER and CARR (1978), and MILLER and CAMERON (1982). The area is underlain by Mesozoic plutonic rocks intrusive into Precambrian crystalline basement, PermoTriassic(?) volcanic rocks, and Paleozoic and Mesozoic metasediments and volcanics. The Mesozoic plutonism began in Triassic time with the intrusion of alkalic plutons, but it is dominated by hydrothermally altered Jurassic granodiorites that appear to be associated with a number of propylitized ring zones that are aligned along a major northwest-trending lineament. A prominent late-Jurassic(?) latite dike swarm is oriented sub-parallel to this lineament, and cuts the Jurassic plutons and their associated volcanic country rocks. Late Cretaceous plutons cross-cut the area, but are not affected by either hydrothermal alteration or by the main group of latite dikes, although several large felsic dike-like bodies may be late Cretaceous in age.

Crystalline rocks of probable Precambrian age crop out between Stoddard Ridge and Ord Mountain, and consist of quartz dioritic gneiss, granitic gneiss, and hornblende-biotite schist. DIBBLEE (1964c) describes these units as being generally similar to, and presumably correlative with, Precambrian(?) gneissic rocks of the San Bernardino Mountains (Baldwin Gneiss).

The ROM area was the site of late Precambrian to Paleozoic miogeoclinal sedimentation. STEWART and POOLE (1975) proposed that the Paleozoic section at Quartzite Mountain near Victorville is correlative with strata elsewhere in the southern Great Basin. MILLER and CAMERON (1982) review the Paleozoic geology, and suggest that the lack of Ordovician through lower Devonian strata in the Sidewinder Mountains probably indicates a transition from miogeoclinal to cratonal sedimentation.

During early Mesozoic plutonism, the Paleozoic rocks were multiply deformed and metamorphosed. The Triassic(?) alkalic pluton on the east side of Apple Valley in the Granite Mountains appears to have been intruded at this time. Mesozoic sedimentary and volcanic rocks were unconformably deposited on the Paleozoic section. These consist of shallow marine quartzites interbedded with latite prophyry flows and tuffs. The quartzitic rocks are lithologically correlative with the early Jurassic Aztec Sandstone in the eastern part of the Rodman Mountains area. The volcanic rocks are known locally as the Sidewinder Volcanics, and consist mainly of latite porphyry and latite porphyry breccia ranging in composition from quartz latite to andesite. Hydrothermal alteration is conspicuous throughout the volcanic country rocks, with chlorite and sericite replacing groundmass minerals, and epidote filling fractures and vesicles.

The main episode of Mesozoic plutonism in the ROM area involved the intrusion of Jurassic hypabyssal biotite-and hornblende-bearing granodiorites and less abundant quartz monzonites (=monzogranite) and granitic stocks. These plutons are typically medium-grained, and most are affected by hydrothermal alteration to varying degrees. Chlorite, epidote, and sericite are the common alteration minerals; in places these impart a greenish cast to the rock where feldspar has been pervasively altered. Epidote-filled fractures are common.

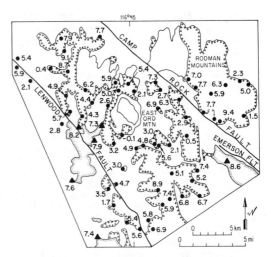

FIG. 2. Geologic map of the northeastern portion of the ROM area, showing Jurassic and Cretaceous granitic plutons, early Mesozoic volcanic units, and $^{18}O/^{16}O$ sample localities with whole-rock $\delta^{18}O$ values lettered in (geology after DIBBLEE, 1964a,b). The geologic map units and $^{18}O/^{16}O$ sample symbols are the same as those listed above for Fig. 1, except that the late Cretaceous sampling localities are shown on this figure by solid triangles.

On the west flank of Ord Mountain, molybdenum veinlets are locally abundant in intensely altered rocks. Surrounding the flanks of East Ord Mountain is a fine-grained, buff-colored, aplitic quartz monzonite whose outcrop pattern distinctly resembles a "ring structure" about four to five km in diameter (see Fig. 2). This pluton has abundant miarolitic cavities and a myrmekitic texture in thin section, clearly indicating a shallow depth of emplacement.

The final pulse of Mesozoic batholithic activity was the intrusion of late Cretaceous plutons. Throughout the ROM area, isolated late Cretaceous plutons intrude the hydrothermally altered Jurassic rocks, but are not themselves hydrothermally altered except in areas of silicification associated with aplitic-facies rocks. The late Cretaceous quartz monzonites (monzogranites) are medium-grained, mostly equigranular rocks whose main accessory mineral is biotite. These rocks weather in a friable manner by breaking down to separate grains around mounds of outcrop, serving to readily distinguish them from the Jurassic plutons, which are generally made up of much tougher rocks (mainly because of the effects of hydrothermal alteration).

The ages of the Jurassic plutons in the ROM area are not well known. For the northern and western portions of the area, minimum K-Ar ages obtained by MILLER and MORTON (1980) on hornblende are 163 to 186 Ma, and for biotite the ages are between 68 and 134 Ma. Where hornblende and biotite from the same sample are dated, the hornblende shows older ages than the biotite, with most biotites clustering between 70 and 80 Ma. Clearly, the late Cretaceous thermal event was important in imprinting biotite K-Ar ages on the Jurassic rocks.

The cluster of biotite ages probably gives a minimum age for the late Cretaceous plutonism, and with dates between 70 and 80 Ma, this event appears to be essentially synchronous with the late Cretaceous plutonism in the San Bernardino Mountains just to the south. Because the latitic dikes cut the Jurassic granodiorites, the age of dike emplacement must be younger than 163 Ma but earlier than 70 to 80 Ma. The dike swarm may correlate in age with the Independence Dike Swarm of the Owens Valley, which has been dated at around 142 Ma (L. T. SILVER, pers. comm.; CHEN and MOORE, 1982).

The major late Cenozoic strike-slip faults are, from west to east, the Helendale, Lenwood, Johnson Valley, and Camp Rock. The Emerson Fault forms the southeastern extension of the Camp Rock Fault, which dies out near Iron Ridge. These faults are part of the major group of strike-slip faults that have absorbed most of the late Cenozoic deformation in the Mojave Block (DOKKA, 1983). DOKKA (1983) places the timing of movement along the faults as mainly between the early Miocene and Pleistocene.

Figure 2 shows the locations of the Camp Rock and Lenwood faults relative to the detailed $^{18}O/^{16}O$ sampling grid. Previous estimates of offset for the Camp Rock Fault range anywhere from 1.5 to 10 km, and estimates for the Lenwood Fault range from 1.5 to 20 km (HAWKINS, 1975; GARFUNKEL, 1974; DOKKA, 1983). There is a wide disparity between these various estimates, because of the uncertain nature of geologic contacts in the post-Mesozoic volcanic terranes in the region, and because no tightly constrained piercing points have been found in the pre-Tertiary crystalline basement. Knowledge of the actual displacements would be extremely useful in reconstructing the late Cenozoic deformation of the Mojave Region.

## ISOTOPIC RELATIONSHIPS

### Rodman-Ord Mountains area

Figure 1 shows the sample locations and $^{18}O/^{16}O$ data for the western part of the ROM area, and Fig. 2 shows similar data for the more densely sampled eastern part of the area, at a somewhat larger scale. These isotopic analyses and exact locations of all Triassic, Jurassic, and Cretaceous samples studied from the ROM area are given in Table 1.

Triassic rocks crop out in the Granite Mountains and at Pitzer Butte; three of these samples have whole-rock $\delta^{18}O$ values of +6.5 to +8.0, and one sample from the southern edge of a dike-like extension of the major Granite Mountains pluton has a $\delta^{18}O = +9.0$. None of these rocks show obvious mineralogic signs of hydrothermal alteration, and it is assumed that these $\delta^{18}O$ values are primary, magmatic values. We simply note the general similarity of the $\delta^{18}O$ of these Triassic rocks to the values obtained for the Lowe Granodiorite complex (+6.8 to +7.8), a composite pluton of similar age in the San Gabriel Mountains (SOLOMON, 1989).

Late Cretaceous plutons occur as scattered outcrops across the area but are overshadowed volumetrically by the Jurassic rocks. The Cretaceous rocks do not show any signs of widespread $^{18}O$ depletion attributable to hydrothermal alteration; ex-

cept for the most westerly sample near Victorville, which has an anomalously high $\delta^{18}O = +9.7$, they have whole-rock $\delta^{18}O$ values between +7.3 and +8.6. Generalized contours of the primary whole-rock $\delta^{18}O$ values of these Cretaceous plutons are not shown on any of the figures in this paper, but they in fact fit in well with the regional patterns established by SOLOMON (1989) for the San Gabriel and San Bernardino Mountains; the pattern of primary magmatic Cretaceous $\delta^{18}O$ contours in the ROM area is characterized in a general way by an eastwardly decreasing $\delta^{18}O$, from +9.7 in the west to values as low as +7.3 and +7.4 in the east. In addition, as was found for all the other areas in Southern California, the higher-$^{18}O$ plutons are generally located adjacent to outcrops of Paleozoic miogeoclinal sediments, while the lower-$^{18}O$ plutons occur near Precambrian cratonal basement. The eastward decrease in $\delta^{18}O$ correlates with the appearance of a predominantly cratonic basement around West Ord Mountain.

The Jurassic plutons in the ROM area are associated with volcanic rocks that grade downward into hypabyssal stocks (DIBBLEE, 1964a,b). Figures 1 and 3 show contours of whole-rock $\delta^{18}O$ for these plutons. The zone of $^{18}O$-depletion is approximately 60 km in the east-west dimension, and 15 to 30 km in the north-south dimension. The low-$^{18}O$ zone is broadest in the north and west, and becomes narrower to the south and east. In detail, the contours define several oval-shaped, "ring-like" patterns within a broad, west-northwest trending zone in which the $\delta^{18}O$ values are all less than +4.0. Within the elliptical ring zones defined by the +2.0 per mil contours, the rocks are extremely variable in $\delta^{18}O$, as low as 0.0 or lower. The lowest value, −3.2, was observed just north of Stoddard Ridge in a sericitized dike-like body that intrudes the Sidewinder Volcanics.

Whole-rock $\delta^{18}O$ values of +7.7 to +9.4 are observed in some of the least altered Jurassic-age samples in the study area (see Figs. 1 and 2); these values are similar to those observed in other Jurassic-age plutons from analogous geologic settings elsewhere in the North American Cordillera, and we conclude that this range very likely represents the original $\delta^{18}O$ values of these plutons prior to hydrothermal alteration. Thus, an area more than 1000 km$^2$ in size has undergone an $^{18}O$ depletion of between two and ten per mil. The individual volcanic centers scattered along this zone correspond to the ovoid-shaped areas with $\delta^{18}O < +2$; the latter represent whole-rock $^{18}O$ depletions of at least five per mil, and together in the ROM area they aggregate about 100 km$^2$.

The overall size of the ROM $^{18}O$-depleted zone and the magnitude of the $^{18}O$-depletions are both nearly as large as those discovered by TAYLOR and MAGARITZ (1978) and CRISS and TAYLOR (1983) surrounding Eocene batholiths emplaced into the Cretaceous Idaho Batholith. The $^{18}O/^{16}O$ effects in the ROM area are spread over a much larger area than those reported for similar systems by TAYLOR (1974), LARSON and TAYLOR (1986), or FORESTER and TAYLOR (1976, 1977). The $\delta^{18}O$ contour patterns in these other areas have all been proven to be the result of sub-solidus interaction between the plutons and low-$\delta^{18}O$ heated meteoric waters within a hydrothermal circulation system. Therefore, a similar model undoubtedly also applies to the ROM area.

All of these meteoric-hydrothermal systems characteristically require that extremely large quantities of water must flow through highly fractured, permeable rocks, fed from surface recharge in a convection pattern around the plutonic heat source (e.g., see CRISS and TAYLOR, 1986). The low-$^{18}O$ fluids exchange oxygen isotopes with the rocks, producing higher-$^{18}O$ fluid and, by material-balance, an $^{18}O$-depleted rock. The actual magnitude of the effect depends on the initial $\delta^{18}O$ of the water, the $^{18}O/^{16}O$ fractionation factors between minerals and the fluids (which are a function of temperature), and on the overall mass of water that flowed through the system at temperatures where reaction kinetics promote exchange. The grain size of the rocks can also play a role in the exchange kinetics, but this is not a factor in the present study because we are comparing data on similar samples that are all relatively uniform, medium-grained plutonic rocks. All of the $\delta^{18}O$ contours on Figs. 1, 2, and 3 are based on intrusive samples; none of the isotope analyses are from fine-grained or aphanitic volcanic country rocks.

Cretaceous plutons in the area cross-cut the altered Jurassic plutons, but the Cretaceous rocks do not exhibit any $^{18}O$-depletions; therefore, it is clear that the hydrothermal systems responsible for $^{18}O$-depletion in the ROM area must have been older than the late Cretaceous plutonism, but either younger or synchronous with the Jurassic plutonism. These rocks thus represent some of the oldest and largest low-$^{18}O$ hydrothermal systems yet documented in the Cordillera of North America. This hydrothermal activity in the ROM area was sandwiched in time between the emplacement of the unaltered Triassic plutons and the emplacement of unaltered Cretaceous plutons. Clearly, there must have been a dramatic shift in the tectonic style of igneous activity in this area between the Triassic and Jurassic and also between the Jurassic and the Cretaceous.

The ROM low-$^{18}O$ zone is coincident with, and subparallel to, a major late-Jurassic dike swarm. This low-$^{18}O$ zone very likely continues to the northwest of the map area shown in Fig. 1, because there is no indication that the zone is narrowing in that direction. Indeed, BUSBY-SPERA (1988) has recently suggested that the ROM area is just one of a series of mid-Jurassic volcanic centers and calderas that occupied a continuous graben depression, more than 1000 km long, that extended from the central Sierra Nevada batholith at least as far as the Baboquivari Mountains in southern Arizona (see below).

It is therefore tempting to speculate that we may be looking at a very large rift-zone feature that may have been responsible for a whole series of overlapping meteoric-hydrothermal systems, and one which might conceivably be traced much farther to the northwest, as well as to the southeast. We know that the most important deep-seated hydrothermal systems on Earth today are all associated with such rift systems, notably Iceland, Yellowstone, and the mid-ocean ridge spreading centers (e.g., see TAYLOR, 1988, 1990). Extensional tectonics provide the open fractures and permeability necessary for deep circulation of surface waters, as well as providing the necessary heat energy by allowing upward access for magmas from depth. It would be most interesting to extend our $^{18}O/^{16}O$ studies, and try to follow the ROM low-$^{18}O$ zone in detail along strike to the northwest or to the southeast; in particular, it is important to see whether or not these $^{18}O/^{16}O$ effects correlate with the emplacement of the ~142 Ma Independence Dike Swarm in the Sierra Nevada region (CHEN and MOORE, 1982). The regional implications of these oxygen isotopic results are discussed more thoroughly below.

The existence of such low-$^{18}O$ fossil hydrothermal systems in Jurassic rocks of the Mojave Desert region has interesting paleogeographic implications. Meteoric waters derived from rainfall or snowfall become increasingly $^{18}O$-depleted with decreases in the atmospheric temperature, either as a result of increasing elevation or latitude, or both. Thus, in North America there is a general correlation with distance from the Pacific Coast, because oceanic water vapor, which is the ultimate source of the atmospheric meteoric water, becomes steadily depleted in $^{18}O$ as the air mass moves to the east and north (e.g., see SHEPPARD, 1986). Because of this fractionation process, inland regions have relatively lower-$^{18}O$ surface waters (e.g., $\delta^{18}O < -10.0$), particularly the high, mountainous regions that have

Table 1. Locations and oxygen isotope analyses of plutonic and subvolcanic igneous rocks from the Rodman-Ord Mountains Area, Southern California

| Samp. no. | Rock type | $\delta^{18}O*$ | Remarks | 34°N latitude | 116°W longitude |
|---|---|---|---|---|---|
| *Jurassic-Age Plutons* | | | | | |
| 158 | BGrd | +2.8 | Granite Mtns. Pluton, powerline Rd. | 31.89' | 58.27' |
| 159 | BHGrd[e,c] | +5.5 | Sidewinder Mtn. Pluton | 35.34' | 01.65' † |
| 160 | BHMzG[e,c] | +2.4 | Sidewinder Mtn. Pluton, Barstow Rd. | 36.21' | 58.76' |
| 161 | BMzG[e,c] | +4.0 | Barstow Rd. Pluton, Barstow Rd. | 38.27' | 56.75' |
| 163 | BHGrd[e,c] | +5.8 | Stoddard Valley Pluton, Stoddard Wells Rd. | 46.62' | 03.49' † |
| 164 | GPorph[e,s] | −3.2 | Stoddard Wells Pluton, Stoddard Wells Rd. | 43.96' | 04.53' † |
| 165 | GPorph[e,s] | −0.6 | Stoddard Wells Pluton, Stoddard Wells Rd. | 40.69' | 04.40' † |
| 167 | MiarG | +2.7 | East Ord Mtn. Pluton | 40.17' | 33.06' |
| 168 | BHGrd[e,c] | +4.9 | Fry Mtns. Pluton, Camp Rock Rd. | 36.14' | 44.83' |
| 268 | BHGrd[e,c] | +5.4 | Eastern Lucerne Valley Pluton | 32.02' | 45.89' |
| 272 | BHGrd | +5.6 | Eastern Lucerne Valley Pluton, powerline rd. | 31.39' | 44.69' |
| 274 | BHGrd[e,c] | +5.8 | Fry Mtns. Pluton, powerline rd. | 31.55' | 43.99' |
| 275 | BHGrd[e,c] | +5.9 | Fry Mtns. Pluton, powerline rd. | 32.59' | 42.59' |
| 276 | BHGrd | +7.4 | Fry Mtns. Pluton, powerline rd. | 32.89' | 41.86' |
| 277 | BHGrd[e,a] | +6.8 | Fry Mtns. Pluton, powerline rd. | 33.34' | 41.24' |
| 278 | BHGrd[e,a] | +5.2 | Fry Mtns. Pluton, powerline rd. | 33.98' | 40.43' |
| 280 | BMzG[e,s] | +0.5 | Fry Mtns. Pluton, powerline rd. | 36.88' | 40.72' |
| 281 | BMzG[e,s] | +2.1 | Fry Mtns. Pluton, powerline rd. | 36.39' | 42.47' |
| 282 | BHGrd[e,c] | +5.6 | Fry Mtns. Pluton, powerline rd. | 36.43' | 43.21' |
| 283 | BMzG[e,s] | +3.0 | Fry Mtns. Pluton, powerline rd. | 36.43' | 43.33' |
| 284 | BHGrd[e,c] | +4.8 | Fry Mtns. Pluton, powerline rd. | 36.32' | 44.26' |
| 285 | BHGrd[e,c] | +3.0 | Fry Mtns. Pluton, Camp Rock Rd. | 35.09' | 45.83' |
| 287 | BHGrd[e,c] | +1.7 | Eastern Lucerne Valley Pluton | 33.15' | 47.68' |
| 288 | BHGrd[e,c] | +3.5 | Eastern Lucerne Valley Pluton | 34.17' | 47.14' |
| 289 | BHGrd[e,c] | +4.7 | Fry Mtns. Pluton, Camp Rock Rd. | 34.06' | 46.62' |
| 292 | BHGrd[e,c] | +5.7 | Ord Mtn. Pluton, Tyler Valley Rd. | 38.65' | 50.08' |
| 293 | BHGrd[e,c] | +4.9 | Ord Mtn. Pluton, Tyler Valley Rd. | 39.74' | 50.27' |
| 294 | BHGrd[e,c] | +4.3 | Ord Mtn. Pluton, base of Ord Mtn. | 38.77' | 49.28' |
| 296 | BGorph[e,c] | +5.9 | Ord Mtn. Pluton, Ord Valley Rd. | 40.25' | 46.50' |
| 325 | BHGrd[e,c] | +3.2 | East Ord Mtn. Pluton | 36.58' | 46.51' |
| 328 | GPorph[e,c] | −0.1 | East Ord Mtn. Pluton, near mine | 37.24' | 45.66' |
| 329 | BMzG[b,ac,e] | +6.9 | Fry Mtns. Pluton, Camp Rock Rd. | 38.58' | 43.03' |
| 331 | BMzG[b,c] | +6.3 | Fry Mtns. Pluton, dirt road | 39.29' | 41.21' |
| 332 | BMzG[b,k,Cu] | +2.9 | Fry Mtns. Pluton, dirt road | 37.97' | 40.76' |
| 333 | MiarG[s] | +7.3 | East Ord Mtn. Pluton, Daggett Rd. | 40.43' | 43.04' |
| 334 | BGrd[e,c] | +2.1 | East Ord Mtn. Pluton, dirt road | 39.76' | 44.76' |
| 335 | BHGrd[e,c] | +5.4 | East Ord Mtn. Pluton, dirt road | 40.36' | 45.25' |
| 336 | BHGrd[e,c] | +5.0 | East Ord Mtn. Pluton, dirt road | 39.95' | 46.16' |
| 337 | GPorph[e,s] | +2.6 | East Ord Mtn. Pluton, dirt road | 38.92' | 45.66' |
| 338 | BHGrd[e,b,mo] | +6.2 | Ord Mtn. Pluton | 40.21' | 49.14' |
| 340 | BHGrd[e,c] | +4.4 | Ord Mtn. Pluton | 39.01' | 48.72' |
| 342 | BHGrd[e,c] | +6.9 | Fry Mtns. Pluton, dirt road | 31.04' | 43.94' |
| 347 | BHGrd | +7.4 | Fry Mtns. Pluton, powerline rd. | 34.62' | 40.08' |
| 348 | BMzG[a] | +6.7 | Fry Mtns. Pluton, powerline rd. | 33.16' | 40.23' |
| 349 | BHGrd | +8.9 | Fry Mtns. Pluton, powerline rd. | 33.46' | 43.33' |
| 350 | G[e,c,s] | +2.8 | Ord Mtn. Pluton, dirt road | 38.52' | 51.26' |
| 351 | BHGrd[e,c] | +2.1 | Ord Mtn. Pluton, dirt road | 39.65' | 52.52' |
| 352 | BHGrd[e,c] | +5.9 | Ord Mtn. Pluton, dirt road | 40.56' | 53.04' |
| 353 | BHGrd[e,c] | +5.4 | Ord Mtn. Pluton, dirt road | 41.07' | 52.87' |
| 354 | BHGrd[e,c] | +0.4 | Ord Mtn. Pluton, dirt road | 41.47' | 51.26' |
| 355 | BHGrd | +8.7 | Ord Mtn. Pluton, W side of Ord Mtn. | 41.12' | 39.89' |
| 356 | BHGrd | +9.1 | Ord Mtn. Pluton, Tyler Valley Rd. | 42.58' | 50.30' |
| 357 | BHGrd | +7.9 | Ord Mtn. Pluton | 43.62' | 50.57' |
| 359 | BHGrd[e,c] | +7.7 | Ord Mtn. Pluton | 43.39' | 47.58' |
| 506 | BHGrd[e,c] | +5.1 | Fry Mtns. Pluton | 34.89' | 42.01' |
| 507 | BHGrd | +7.7 | Rodman Mtns. Pluton | 37.79' | 38.51' |
| 508 | BHGrd | +9.4 | Rodman Mtns. Pluton | 37.69' | 38.12' |
| 509 | BHGrd[e,c] | +1.5 | Rodman Mtns. Pluton | 38.06' | 36.04' |
| 510 | BHGrd[e,c] | +5.0 | Rodman Mtns. Pluton, dirt road | 40.00' | 35.71' |

Table 1. (Continued)

| Samp. no. | Rock type | $\delta^{18}O^*$ | Remarks | 34°N latitude | 116°W longitude |
|-----------|-----------|------------------|---------|---------------|-----------------|
| *Jurassic-Age Plutons* | | | | | |
| 511 | BMzG[e,c] | +2.3 | Rodman Mtns. Pluton, dirt road | 40.38' | 36.43' |
| 512 | BMzG[e,c] | +6.3 | Rodman Mtns. Pluton, dirt road | 39.84' | 37.53' |
| 513 | BHGrd[e,c] | +5.9 | Rodman Mtns. Pluton, dirt road | 39.57' | 38.70' |
| 514 | BMzG | +7.7 | Rodman Mtns. Pluton, near Camp Rock Mine | 40.00' | 40.00' |
| 515 | BMzG[e] | +7.0 | Rodman Mtns. Pluton, near Camp Rock Mine | 40.64' | 40.29' |
| 516 | BMzG | +7.7 | Rodman Mtns. Pluton | 38.33' | 39.28' |
| 152 | HT | +8.3 | Bell Mtn. Pluton, road cut | 33.24' | 13.56' † |
| *Triassic-Age Plutons* | | | | | |
| 112 | LSy | +9.0 | Granite Mtns. Pluton, Rabbit Dry Lake | 27.24' | 59.59' |
| 154 | HMz | +6.5 | Granite Mtns. Pluton, Hwy 18 | 29.31' | 08.25' † |
| 155 | HMz | +7.5 | Granite Mtns. Pluton, Hwy 18 | 27.48' | 04.03' † |
| 156 | HMz | +8.0 | Pitzer Butte Pluton | 25.34' | 57.94' |
| *Cretaceous-Age Plutons* | | | | | |
| 111 | BMzG | +9.7 | Granite of Mojave River Wash, Hwy 18 | 32.34' | 17.18' † |
| 153 | BMzG | +7.4 | Fairview Valley Pluton | 33.55' | 08.62' † |
| 157 | BMzG | +8.2 | Granite Mtns. Pluton | 29.24' | 01.11' † |
| 162 | BMzG | +7.8 | Stoddard Valley Pluton, Stoddard Wells Rd. | 48.07' | 03.33' † |
| 166 | BMzG | +7.6 | Ord Mtns. Pluton, powerline rd. | 34.62' | 50.06' |
| 269 | BMzG | +7.4 | Eastern Lucerne Valley Pluton, powerline rd. | 30.01' | 49.48' |
| 279 | BMzG | +8.6 | Fry Mtns. Pluton, powerline rd. | 35.11' | 37.02' |
| 290 | BMzG | +7.9 | Ord Mtns. Pluton, Ord Valley Rd. | 36.39' | 48.33' |
| 295 | BMzG | +8.2 | Ord Mtns. Pluton | 37.85' | 49.37' |
| 326 | BMzG | +7.3 | Ord Mtns. Pluton | 37.69' | 47.25' |

Abbreviations: BGrd = Biotite Granodiorite; BHGrd = Biotite-Hornblende Granodiorite; BMzG = Biotite Monzogranite; BHMzG = Biotite-Hornblende Monzogranite; GPorph = Granite Porphyry; MiarG = Miarolitic Granite; G = Granite; LSy = Leucocratic Syenite; HMz = Hornblende Monzonite; HT = Hornblende Tonalite.

Brackets indicate that the sample is hydrothermally altered, and contains the hydrothermal minerals e = epidote; c = chlorite; a = albite; s = sericite; mo = molybenite; b = biotite; k = k feldspar; ac = actinolite; Cu = copper minerals.

* The $\delta^{18}O$ analyses were obtained by conventional fluorination techniques (TAYLOR and EPSTEIN, 1962) and are reported relative to SMOW (Standard Mean Ocean Water). In our laboratories, NBS-28 has a $\delta^{18}O = +9.60$ on this scale.

† 117° West Longitude.

low atmospheric temperatures (*e.g.,* Sierra Nevada region, Rocky Mountains).

The feldspar-$H_2O$ $^{18}O/^{16}O$ fractionation data of O'NEIL and TAYLOR (1967) allow some simple comparative calculations to be made. Between 300 and 400°C, which are likely hydrothermal temperatures, the equilibrium fractionation factors between An30 plagioclase and water are estimated at +4.8 (300°C), +3.5 (350°C), and +2.55 (400°C). Even if we conservatively assume an infinite water/ rock ratio, the observed $\delta^{18}O$ value of −3.2 in the most $^{18}O$-depleted sample would *require* an initial $\delta^{18}O$ at least as low as −8.0 to −5.8 for the hydrothermal fluid. Also, assuming a temperature of about 350°C, a plausible closed-system material-balance water-rock ratio of about unity (see CRISS and TAYLOR, 1986) for the ovoid areas with $\delta^{18}O$

< +2, and using an initial $\delta^{18}O$ rock = +8, these data *require* that the initial $\delta^{18}O$ of the water must have been lower than −7.5. The actual $\delta^{18}O$ values of the surface waters in this region during Jurassic time therefore must be at least this low, and were probably as low as −10 or lower. However, studies of the Mesozoic sedimentary rocks near Fairview Valley suggest that the environment was coastal in nature during the Jurassic (BURCHFIEL and DAVIS, 1981; MILLER, 1978; MILLER and CARR, 1978), as does the map shown in Fig. 5 (BUSBY-SPERA, 1988). If true, the Jurassic edge of the continent must have been a rather high mountainous region somewhat similar to the present-day geographic environment, in order to produce meteoric waters having $\delta^{18}O$ values as low as −10. To give a more specific comparison, this area could not possibly have had a

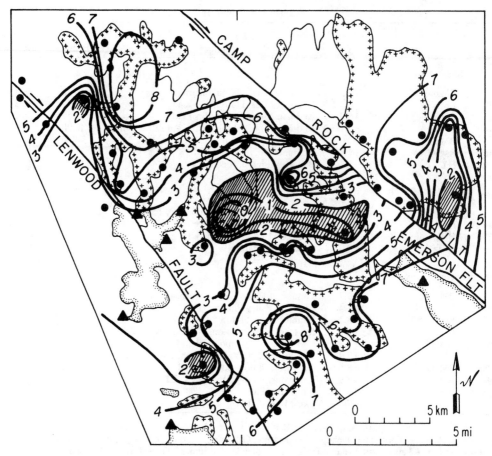

FIG. 3. Generalized geologic map of the northeastern portion of the ROM area (geology after DIBBLEE, 1964a,b), showing Jurassic whole-rock $\delta^{18}O$ contours based on $^{18}O/^{16}O$ data in Fig. 2. The Jurassic sample localities are shown with solid circles; late Cretaceous sample localities are shown with solid triangles. Symbolism for geologic map units is the same as in Fig. 2. The diagonal line pattern indicates areas where whole-rock $\delta^{18}O$ values are less than +2. Right-lateral offset of $\delta^{18}O$ contours (< +3) along the Camp Rock Fault is approximately four km (see discussion in text).

climate or a topography similar to that in the Gulf Coastal Region of the U.S.A. today. The fossil hydrothermal systems in this area clearly deserve more detailed study than was possible in this reconnaissance whole-rock investigation.

*Late Cenozoic fault offsets*

Late Cenozoic faults cut through and offset the plutons that were affected by the Jurassic hydrothermal circulation systems. DOKKA (1983) comments upon the disparate estimates for the magnitudes of offset along these faults (*e.g.,* GARFUNKEL, 1974; HAWKINS, 1975). In order to see if $\delta^{18}O$ contours could be of use in unraveling fault offsets, the area around East Ord Mountain and the Rodman Mountains was studied in somewhat more detail than the rest of the area. It is clear that the primary igneous $\delta^{18}O$ values in the late Cretaceous plutonic rocks do not have a large enough variation to be used for detailed local contouring. However, it was hoped that more closely spaced sampling of the Jurassic rocks would give sufficient contour resolution to detect any offsets of these fossil hydrothermal circulation centers along the Lenwood and Camp Rock faults.

Figure 3 is a map showing a more detailed set of $\delta^{18}O$ contours for the Jurassic plutons in the vicinity of these faults, which are known to exhibit right-lateral offsets (DOKKA, 1983). From the contours in Fig. 3 it is not possible to accurately determine offset along the Lenwood Fault, but it is probably very small (<5 km), as there is no obvious offset of the major trend of the regional low-$^{18}O$ zone shown in Fig. 1. As one crosses over to the east side of the Lenwood Fault, this broad zone of low-$^{18}O$ rocks (Fig. 1) narrows abruptly, but there are simply not enough outcrops of altered Jurassic plutons to establish detailed contouring. The low-$^{18}O$ zone continues to narrow eastward, however, and on Fig. 3 it can be seen that the Camp Rock Fault truncates a much narrower, better defined, more prominent set of low-$^{18}O$ contours. Surrounding East Ord Mountain, and extending with its long axis in an easterly direction, is an ovoid contour pattern defined by rocks with $\delta^{18}O < +3.0$. The low-$^{18}O$ ovoid zone abruptly terminates on its eastern end, against the Camp Rock Fault, and these low-$^{18}O$ rocks are juxtaposed against a Jurassic pluton whose $\delta^{18}O$ values are all higher than +7.7 (Figs. 2 and 3).

Contouring of $\delta^{18}O$ values in the Rodman Mountains to the east of the fault reveals another zone where $\delta^{18}O$ values are less than +3.0. If the $\delta^{18}O$ contours that define these two zones are extended to intersect the Camp Rock Fault (as shown in Fig. 3), then the magnitude of apparent right-lateral offset on the combined Emerson and Camp Rock faults is seen to be approximately $5 \pm 2$ km. Considering the errors involved, this compares well with the estimate of 1.6 to 4.0 km by DOKKA (1983) which is based upon offset of an early Miocene structural horizon, but it compares less well with the estimate of HAWKINS (1975). We note, however, that our minimum suggested displacement of about 3.0 km seems to be very tightly constrained by three closely spaced samples with $\delta^{18}O = +7.7$ to $+9.4$ collected just northeast of the Camp Rock Fault. The $^{18}O/^{16}O$ data thus corroborate, at least on the Camp Rock Fault, Dokka's hypothesis that offsets along these strike-slip faults in the ROM area are relatively small, and therefore that no large Cenozoic displacements have occurred in this portion of the Mojave Block.

*Pre-Cretaceous igneous rocks elsewhere in Southern California*

Figure 4 shows contours of whole-rock $\delta^{18}O$ values and a few initial $^{87}Sr/^{86}Sr$ values for Triassic and Jurassic plutons studied elsewhere in southeastern California (termed the SECA area). Most of these plutons have emplacement ages older than 160 Ma. The $\delta^{18}O$ contours on Fig. 4 are compiled from the more detailed $\delta^{18}O$ maps shown in SOLOMON (1989), but they are mainly based on the data shown in Table 2. This map for the early Mesozoic plutons (Fig. 4) does not have anywhere near the resolution of the $^{18}O/^{16}O$ maps we have made for the Cretaceous plutons (SOLOMON and TAYLOR,

1989; SOLOMON, 1989), both because the extent of outcrop is less for the older plutons, and also because there is less areal geochemical coverage for the older plutons. In addition, many of these older rocks exhibit "disturbed" $\delta^{18}O$ values (and $^{87}Sr/^{86}Sr$ ratios?) as a result of hydrothermal alteration. Nonetheless, several observations may be made regarding the older set of plutons.

In the northwestern part of the SECA area, the plutons have presumably "primary" $\delta^{18}O$ values > +8.0, with some indication of a slight decrease to the west to values lower than +7.0. There is a very clear indication of a broad decrease to characteristic regional values of about +6.5 to +7.5 in the eastern Mojave Desert. FOX (1988) analyzed K feldspars from the Jurassic plutons in the Bristol Mountains (BM-HC on Fig. 4) and found that primary $\delta^{18}O$ values were between +6.5 and +7.4; this indicates that primary whole-rock $\delta^{18}O$ for these rocks is likely to be near +7.8, after one takes into account the fact that $\delta^{18}O$ quartz will add about +0.4 per mil to the whole-rock mixture. The $\delta^{18}O$ contours have a northwesterly strike that roughly parallels the regional strike exhibited by the Jurassic magmatic arc as a whole. However, as was shown above, in the large Rodman-Ord Mountains (ROM) hydrothermal center the primary $\delta^{18}O$ patterns are almost totally obliterated. This is also true to a lesser extent in the other areas of hydrothermal alteration shown by the hatchured patterns on Fig. 4.

When we view the $^{18}O/^{16}O$ ratios in Jurassic hydrothermal centers on a regional basis within a zone extending from western Nevada southeast to southern Arizona and Sonora, some remarkable patterns emerge. The Jurassic hydrothermal centers in SECA make up the central portion of the northwest-trending, 1000 km-long graben depression proposed by BUSBY-SPERA (1988) for the early Mesozoic continental arc (Fig. 5). Whole-rock $\delta^{18}O$ values are available, at least in reconnaissance fashion, for several of the major Jurassic hydrothermal centers along the strike of this proposed graben (Fig. 4; Table 2). These centers are from northwest to southeast: (1) the Yerington District, western Nevada (YN; +5.7 to +7.8; 0.7039 to 0.7045; DILLES *et al.,* 1991; SOLOMON *et al.,* 1983); (2) the Rodman-Ord Mountains (ROM; −3.2 to +9.0; this work); (3) Devil's Playground (DP; +4.2; this work); (4) Bristol Mountains (BM; ∼ +1.7 to ∼ +7.8; FOX, 1988); (5) Copper Mountain and Dale Mining District (CM and DMD; +5.7 to +7.1; this work); (6) Palen Mountains (PM; +2.6; this work); (7) Big Maria Mountains (BMM; +6.7; this work); and (8) Brownell and Comobabi Mountains, south-central

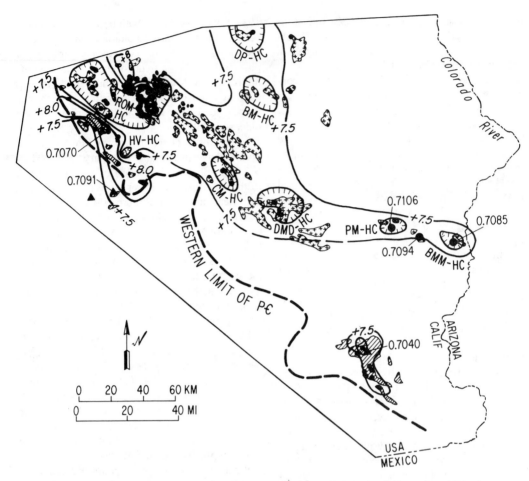

FIG. 4. Reconstructed geologic map of southeastern California (SECA), showing Jurassic and Triassic plutons and the locations of Jurassic hydrothermal centers defined by whole-rock $\delta^{18}O$ contours (based on data given in Table 2, and in Figs. 1 and 2). The hatchured contours enclose samples with $\delta^{18}O < +7$. Also shown are the sample localities where initial $^{87}Sr/^{86}Sr$ data are available (from sources reported in SOLOMON, 1989). Restoration of strike-slip displacements along late Cenozoic faults is discussed in SOLOMON (1989). Jurassic plutons have crosses along the inside margins of map unit, and Triassic plutons are indicated by diagonal lines inside map unit. Heavy dashed line indicates the western limit of mapped Precambrian crystalline basement rocks. The San Gabriel Mountains (SGM) terrane has been restored to its position prior to late-Cenozoic displacement along the San Andreas Fault using the reconstruction of POWELL (1982). Jurassic hydrothermal centers (HC) are: (1) ROM—Rodman-Ord Mountains; (2) DP—Devil's Playground; (3) BM—Bristol Mountains; (4) HV—Holcomb Valley; (5) CM—Copper Mountain; (6) DMD—Dale Mining District; (7) PM—Palen Mountains; (8) BMM—Big Maria Mountains.

Arizona (BM and CM; +6.7 to +9.2; SOLOMON, 1989).

BUSBY-SPERA (1988) proposes that this major graben structure was occupied by calderas, which in places were flooded by lakes or marine embayments, as evidenced by thick sequences of ignimbrites intercalated with fluvial, lake, or marine sedimentary deposits. Our $^{18}O/^{16}O$ data coincide nicely with Busby-Spera's boundary separating marine-type sedimentary sequences on the northwest from

predominantly continental-type strata on the southeast (see Fig. 5). The centers to the southeast, or continental side of the boundary, such as ROM, contain Jurassic plutons that were clearly hydrothermally altered by heated, low-$\delta^{18}O$ meteoric waters. In the case of the ROM area, these waters must have initially had $\delta^{18}O$ values as low as −10, indicating a relatively high, cool, mountainous terrane capable of fractionating coastal precipitation sufficiently to produce low-$^{18}O$ rain and snow (e.g., see

Table 2. Locations and oxygen isotope analyses of probable Jurassic-age samples from elsewhere in Southern California.

| Samp. no. | Rock type | $\delta^{18}O$ | Remarks | Latitude | Longitude |
|---|---|---|---|---|---|
| *San Bernardino Mountains* | | | | | |
| 51 | BHGrd | +7.7 | Cushenberry Grade Pluton, Hwy 18 | 34°19.93′ | 116°49.68′ |
| 52 | BHGrd | +7.8 | Cushenberry Grade Pluton, Hwy 18 | 34°20.05 | 116°49.82′ |
| 106 | BGrd | +7.8 | Johnson Valley Pluton, Johnson Valley Rd. | 34°20.24′ | 116°30.12′ |
| 107 | BGrd | +7.9 | SE part of Big Horn Mtns. | 34°16.38′ | 116°29.92′ |
| 127 | M (Triassic?) | +8.4 | Mill Creek Pluton, Mill Creek | 34°05.31′ | 116°56.58′ |
| 130 | BHGrd | +8.4 | Cienaga Seca Pluton, Hwy 38 | 34°10.24′ | 116°47.06′ |
| *Little San Bernardino Mountains* | | | | | |
| 98 | BGrd | +6.7 | Older Granite, Joshua Tree Monument | 33°59.89′ | 116°03.70′ |
| 194 | BMzG | +7.2 | Older Granite, Joshua Tree Monument | 34°06.83′ | 116°03.29′ |
| 198 | BMzG | +6.1 | Older Granite, Joshua Tree Monument | 34°04.07′ | 116°00.62′ |
| 199 | HBGd[e,c] | +6.5 | Copper Mtn. Pluton | 34°13.03′ | 116°15.00′ |
| 201 | HBGrd[e,c] | +6.4 | Copper Mtn. Pluton | 34°08.76′ | 116°11.13′ |
| 202 | HBGrd[e,c] | +7.1 | Dale Mining District H. C. | 34°04.07′ | 115°45.25′ |
| 205 | HBGrd[e,c] | +5.7 | Dale Mining District H. C. | 34°01.83′ | 115°44.59′ |
| 206 | HBGrd[e,c] | +7.1 | Dale Mining District H. C. | 34°00.07′ | 115°42.20′ |
| *Southeastern Mojave Region* | | | | | |
| 391 | BHMd | +6.7 | Big Maria Mtns. H.C. H808M372b K. Howard | 34°48.95′ | 114°52.07′ |
| 394 | BHGrd | +7.5 | Little Maria Pluton H80LM374 K. Howard | 33°51.03′ | 114°52.07′ |
| 402 | BMzG[e,c] | +4.2 | Palen Mtns. H.C. H80Pa189 K. Howard | 33°55.17′ | 115°02.25′ |
| 409 | BHGrd | +7.6 | Providence Mtns. KH78-1 K. Howard | 34°55.65′ | 115°36.13′ |
| 395 | BMzG | +7.6 | Marble Mtns. Pluton H80MM232 K. Howard | 34°58.90′ | 115°36.88′ |
| 403 | BMzG[e,c] | +4.2 | Devil's Playground H.C. Providence Mtns. H80DP220 K. Howard | 34°58.57′ | 115°51.17′ |

Abbreviations: Same as in Table 1, except M = Monzonite; BHMd = Biotite Hornblende Monzodiorite; H. C. = Hydrothermal Center.

TAYLOR, 1974). Farther southeast, in Arizona, there is no indication of such strongly $^{18}O$-depleted meteoric waters, but $^{18}O/^{16}O$ studies in that region are very sparse, and more work is required.

The only center for which we have $^{18}O/^{16}O$ data northwest of Busby-Spera's proposed marine/continental boundary is at Yerington, Nevada, where $\delta^{18}O$ values are relatively high (+5.7 to +7.8). One point worth mentioning is that granitic rocks at the Yerington center with $\delta^{18}O = +5.7$ are as intensely hydrothermally altered mineralogically as those with $\delta^{18}O$ between $-3.2$ and $+2.0$ at the ROM center. Both areas contain granodiorites and quartz monzonites with intense propylitic epidote-chlorite veining, and albitic replacement of K-feldspars. In some cases, hand specimens from both areas look identical to one another, but, as indicated by whole-rock $\delta^{18}O$ values, the type of water involved in the alteration is clearly different between the two areas. At Yerington, DILLES *et al.* (1991) and SOLOMON *et al.* (1983) demonstrated that waters with initial $\delta^{18}O$ of around 0.0 were responsible for propylitic

alteration, as compared with much lighter water ($-10$ per mil) in the ROM area. Thus, the waters at Yerington were either sea water or some type of connate or formation water; either of these types of waters would fit nicely with the inferences made by BUSBY-SPERA (1988) about the distribution of marine and terrestrial environments surrounding the graben depression shown on Fig. 5.

Another interesting point to make is that the initial $^{87}Sr/^{86}Sr$ values also show the transition from a marine, island arc–type environment on the northwest to a continentally rooted arc to the southeast. Where the arc sat in an oceanic environment, initial $^{87}Sr/^{86}Sr$ values were $\sim 0.7040$ (as at Yerington); and along the strike of the arc, to the southeast, much higher ratios are encountered (0.7085 to 0.7106 in SECA; and 0.7070 in southern Arizona; see Fig. 4). This type of effect is very reminiscent of the East Japan–Marianas arc discussed by TAYLOR (1986), where ITO and STERN (1985) showed that $\delta^{18}O$ and initial $^{87}Sr/^{86}Sr$ were elevated at the point where the northern portion of that arc cuts

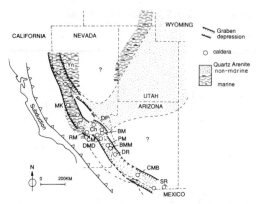

FIG. 5. Map of the southwestern United States showing Jurassic tectonic features, modified after a figure by BUSBY-SPERA (1988). The 1000 km graben depression is indicated by lines with perpendicular hash marks along the inside margins of the graben. The depositional environment for quartz arenitic sandstones associated with Jurassic volcanic centers is mapped by dashed lines, and differentiated according to either marine (horizontal lines within map unit) or non-marine deposition (stippled pattern within map unit). Jurassic hydrothermal centers are indicated by open circles and annotated with the following abbreviations: (1) Yn—Yerington District, NV; (2) MK—Mineral King, CA; (3) RM—Rodman Mountains, CA; (4) Ch—Cowhole Mountains, CA; (5) CM—Copper Mountain, CA; (6) DMD—Dale Mining District, CA; (7) DP—Devil's Playground, CA; (8) BM—Bristol Mountains, CA; (9) PM—Palen Mountains, CA; (10) BMM—Big Maria Mountains, CA; (11) DR—Dome Rock Mountains, AZ; (12) CMB—Comobabi Mountains, AZ; (13) CR—Cobre Ridge, AZ; and (14) SR—Santa Rita Mountains, AZ. Line with thrust-fault symbols indicates approximate location of the axis of a Jurassic subduction zone.

across continental terrane. Clearly, further $^{18}O/^{16}O$ and $^{87}Sr/^{86}Sr$ studies of unsampled portions of the Jurassic plutonic centers within Busby-Spera's regional graben would help refine and elaborate upon our initial reconnaissance observations and better map out these kinds of paleogeographic boundaries.

## CONCLUSIONS

In striking contrast to the other Mesozoic plutonic episodes (Triassic and Cretaceous), the Jurassic plutons in Southern California commonly developed extensive meteoric-hydrothermal convection systems which produced characteristic low-$^{18}O$ patterns in the altered intrusive rocks. This is particularly well shown in the Rodman-Ord Mountains area. This requires that the Jurassic plutonic event must have been epizonal and probably associated with extensional tectonics in order to provide the open fractures and necessary hydrologic permeability required. The $^{18}O/^{16}O$ data fit in well

with the rift-zone, caldera-emplacement model proposed by BUSBY-SPERA (1988).

We suggest that $^{18}O/^{16}O$ analyses may be a good way to search for such fossil rift zones in areas where the geological relationships are complex. An analogous example of this is given in the paper by TAYLOR et al. (1991) in this volume. It would be interesting to carry out $^{18}O/^{16}O$ analyses of the Independence Dike Swarm to see if this can be shown to be an extension of the Rodman-Ord Mountains hydrothermal activity.

We have also shown that the regional $\delta^{18}O$ patterns produced during Jurassic hydrothermal activity have been offset and truncated by the later-stage, deeper-seated Cretaceous plutons. In addition, in more recent geological times, late Cenozoic faulting has also offset these Jurassic-age $^{18}O/^{16}O$ patterns, and we have been able to use our $^{18}O/^{16}O$ data to measure these offsets, confirming the conclusions of DOKKA (1983) that the displacements along these faults in the Mojave Block are all relatively small (<5 km).

*Acknowledgements*—We wish to take this opportunity to salute Samuel Epstein as he continues to build upon and expand his life-long contributions to the field of stable isotope geochemistry. He has taught us both a great deal over the years. We also wish to thank Keith A. Howard, Leon T. Silver, Robert E. Powell, John H. Dilles, and Robert E. Criss for helpful discussions and for their aid in obtaining some of the samples studied in this work. Financial support for this research was provided by the National Science Foundation, Grants No. EAR-83-13106, EAR-88-16413, and EAR-90-19190.

## REFERENCES

BISHOP C. C. (1963) Needles Sheet. *Calif. Div. Mines Geol., Geological Atlas of California.*

BORTUGNO E. J. and SPITTLER T. E. (1986) Geologic map of the San Bernardino Quadrangle. *Calif. Div. Mines Geol., Regional Map Ser., Map* **3-A.**

BURCHFIEL B. C. and DAVIS G. A. (1981) Mojave Desert and environs. In *The Geotectonic Development of California* (ed. W. G. ERNST, RUBEY Vol.,), pp. 50–70. Prentice-Hall.

BUSBY-SPERA C. J. (1988) Speculative tectonic model for the early Mesozoic arc of the southwest Cordilleran United States. *Geology* **16,** 1121–1125.

CHEN J. H. and MOORE J. G. (1982) Uranium-lead isotopic ages from the Sierra Nevada batholith, California. *J. Geophys. Res.* **87,** 4761–4784.

CONEY P. J. (1980) Cordilleran metamorphic core complexes: An overview. In *Cordilleran Metamorphic Core Complexes* (eds. M. D. CRITTENDEN, JR., P. J. CONEY and G. H. DAVIS); *Geol. Soc. Amer. Mem.* **153,** pp. 7–34.

CRISS R. E. and CHAMPION D. E. (1991) Oxygen isotope study of the fossil hydrothermal system in the Comstock Lode mining district, Nevada (this volume).

CRISS R. E. and TAYLOR H. P., JR. (1983). An $^{18}O/^{16}O$ and D/H study of Tertiary hydrothermal systems in the northern half of the Idaho batholith. *Geol. Soc. Amer. Bull.* **94,** 640–663.

CRISS R. E. and TAYLOR H. P., JR. (1986) Meteoric-hydrothermal systems. In *Stable Isotopes in High Temperature Geological Processes* (eds. J. W. VALLEY, H. P. TAYLOR, JR. and J. R. O'NEIL); *Reviews in Mineralogy 16,* pp. 425–444. Mineralogical Society of America.

DIBBLEE T. W., JR. (1960a) Preliminary geologic map of the Apple Valley quadrangle, California. *U.S. Geol. Survey Misc. Field Studies Map* **MF-232.**

DIBBLEE T. W., JR. (1960b) Preliminary geologic map of the Shadow Mountain quadrangle, California. *U.S. Geol. Survey Misc. Field Studies Map* **MF-227.**

DIBBLEE T. W., JR. (1960c) Preliminary geologic map of the Victorville quadrangle, California. *U.S. Geol. Survey Misc. Field Studies Map* **MF-229.**

DIBBLEE T. W., JR. (1964a) Geologic map of the Rodman Mountains quadrangle, San Bernardino County, California. *U.S. Geol. Survey Misc. Geol. Inv. Map* **I-430.**

DIBBLEE T. W., JR. (1964b) Geologic map of the Ord Mountains quadrangle, San Bernardino County, California. *U.S. Geol. Survey Misc. Geol. Inv. Map* **I-427.**

DIBBLEE T. W., JR. (1964c) Geologic map of the Lucerne Valley quadrangle, San Bernardino County, California. *U.S. Geol. Survey Misc. Geol. Inv. Map* **I-426.**

DIBBLEE T. W., JR. (1967) Areal geology of the western Mojave Desert, California. *U.S. Geol. Survey. Prof. Paper* **522,** 1–153.

DILLES J. H., SOLOMON G. C., TAYLOR H. P., JR. and EINAUDI M. T. (1991) Oxygen and hydrogen isotope characteristics of hydrothermal alteration at the Ann-Mason porphyry copper deposit, Yerington, Nevada. *Econ. Geol.* (in press).

DOKKA R. K. (1983) Displacements on late Cenozoic strike-slip faults of the central Mojave Desert, California. *Geology* **11,** 305–308.

FORESTER R. W. and TAYLOR H. P., JR. (1976) $^{18}O$-depleted igneous rocks from the Tertiary complex of the Isle of Mull, Scotland. *Earth Planet. Sci. Lett.* **32,** 11–17.

FORESTER R. W. and TAYLOR H. P., JR. (1977) $^{18}O/^{16}O$, D/H, and $^{13}C/^{12}C$ studies of the Tertiary igneous complex of Skye, Scotland. *Amer. J. Sci.* **277,** 136–177.

FOX L. K. (1988) Albitization of K-feldspar during Jurassic hydrothermal sodium metasomatism, Bristol Mountains, east-central Mojave Desert, California. *Geol. Soc. Amer. Abstr. Prog.* **20,** A-255.

GARFUNKEL Z. (1974) Model for the late Cenozoic tectonic history of the Mojave desert, California. *Geol. Soc. Amer. Bull.* **85,** 1931–1944.

HAWKINS H. G. (1975) Strike-slip displacement along the Camp Rock-Emerson Fault, central Mojave Desert, San Bernardino County, California. *Geol. Soc. Amer. Abstr. Prog.* **7,** 324.

ITO E. and STERN R. J. (1985) Oxygen and stontium-isotopic investigations of subduction zone volcanism; the case of the Volcano Arc and the Marianas Island arc. *Earth Planet. Sci. Lett.* **76,** 312–320.

JOHN B. E. (1981) Reconnaissance study of Mesozoic plutonic rocks in the Mojave Desert region. In *Tectonic Framework of the Mojave and Sonoran Deserts, California and Arizona* (eds. K. A. HOWARD, M. D. CARR and D. M. MILLER); *U.S. Geol. Survey Open-File Rept.* **81-503,** pp. 48–50.

LARSON P. B. and TAYLOR H. P., JR. (1986) An oxygen isotope study of hydrothermal alteration in the Lake City Caldera, San Juan Mountains, Colorado. *J. Volcanol. Geotherm. Res.* **30,** 47–82.

MASI U., O'NEIL J. R. and KISTLER R. W. (1981) Stable isotope systematics in Mesozoic granites of central and northern California and southwestern Oregon. *Contrib. Mineral. Petrol.* **76,** 116–126.

MILLER E. L. (1978) The Fairview Formation: A Mesozoic intraorogenic deposit in the southwestern Mojave desert. In *Mesozoic Paleogeography of the Western United States* (eds. D. G. HOWELL and K. A. MCDOUGALL); *Pacific Coast Paleogeography Symposium 2,* pp. 277–282. Society of Economic Paleontologists and Mineralogists, Pacific Section.

MILLER E. L. and CAMERON C. S. (1982) Late Precambrian to late Cretaceous evolution of the southwestern Mojave Desert, California. In *Geology of Selected Areas in the San Bernardino Mountains, Western Mojave Desert and Southern Great Basin, California* (ed. J. D. COOPER), pp. 21–34. Death Valley Publishing Company, Shoshone, CA.

MILLER E. L. and CARR M. P. (1978) Recognition of possible Aztec-equivalent sandstones and associated Mesozoic metasedimentary deposits within the Mesozoic magmatic arc in the southwestern Mojave Desert, California In *Mesozoic Paleogeography of the Western United States* (eds. D. G. HOWELL and K. A. MCDOUGALL); *Pacific Coast Paleogeography Symposium 2,* pp. 283–290. Society of Economic Paleontologists and Mineralogists, Pacific Section.

MILLER F. K. and MORTON D. M. (1980) Potassium-argon geochronology of the Eastern Transverse Ranges and southern Mojave Desert, southern California. *U.S. Geol. Survey Prof. Pap.* **1152,** 1–30.

O'NEIL J. R. and TAYLOR H. P., JR. (1967) The oxygen isotope and cation exchange chemistry of feldspars. *Amer. Mineral.* **52,** 1414–1437.

POWELL R. E. (1982) Crystalline basement terranes in the southern Eastern Transverse Ranges, California. In *Geologic Excursion in the Transverse Ranges, Southern California, Field Trip* (ed. J. D. COOPER), pp. 109–136. Geological Society of America, 78th Annual Meeting, Cordilleran Section, Anaheim, CA.

SHEPPARD S. M. F. (1986) Characterization and isotopic variations in natural waters. In *Stable Isotopes in High Temperature Geological Processes* (eds. J. W. VALLEY, H. P. TAYLOR, JR. and J. R. O'NEIL); *Reviews in Mineralogy 16,* pp. 165–183. Mineralogical Society of America.

SOLOMON G. C. (1989) An $^{18}O/^{16}O$ study of Mesozoic and early Tertiary granitic batholiths of the southwestern North American Cordillera. Ph.D. thesis, California Institute of Technology.

SOLOMON G. C. and TAYLOR H. P., JR. (1989) Isotopic evidence for the origin of granitic plutons in the northern Great Basin. *Geology* **17,** 591–594.

SOLOMON G. C., DILLES J. H., CRISS R. E. and TAYLOR H. P., JR. (1983) $^{18}O/^{16}O$ and D/H characteristics of the Ann-Mason porphyry copper deposit, Yerington, Nevada. *Geol. Soc. Amer. Abstr. Prog.* **15,** 277.

STEWART J. H. and POOLE F. G. (1975) Extension of the Cordilleran miogeosynclinal belt to the San Andreas fault, southern California. *Geol. Soc. Amer. Bull.* **86,** 205–212.

TAYLOR H. P., JR. (1974) The application of oxygen and hydrogen isotope studies to problems of hydrothermal alteration and ore deposition. *Econ. Geol.* **69,** 843–883.

TAYLOR H. P., JR. (1986) Igneous rocks: II. Isotopic case

studies of circumpacific magmatism. In *Stable Isotopes in High Temperature Geological Processes* (eds. J. W. VALLEY, H. P. TAYLOR, JR. and J. R. O'NEIL); *Reviews in Mineralogy 16*, pp. 273–317. Mineralogical Society of America.

TAYLOR H. P., JR. (1988) Oxygen, hydrogen, and strontium constraints on the origin of granites. *Trans. Roy. Soc. Edinburgh, Earth Sci.* **79**, 317–338.

TAYLOR H. P., JR. (1990) Oxygen and hydrogen isotope constraints on the deep circulation of surface waters into zones of hydrothermal metamorphism and melting. In *The Role of Fluids in Crustal Processes; Studies in Geophysics*, pp. 72–95. National Research Council, National Academy Press, Washington, D.C.

TAYLOR H. P., JR. and EPSTEIN S. (1962) Relationship between $^{18}O/^{16}O$ ratios in coexisting minerals of igneous and metamorphic rocks. Part 1. Principles and experimental results. *Geol. Soc. Amer. Bull.* **73**, 461–480.

TAYLOR H. P., JR. and MAGARITZ M. (1978) Oxygen and hydrogen isotope studies of the Cordilleran batholiths of western North America. In *Stable Isotopes in the Earth Sciences* (ed. B. W. ROBINSON); *New Zealand Dept. Sci. Industry Res. Bull. 220*, pp. 151–173.

TAYLOR H. P., JR. and SILVER L. T. (1978) Oxygen isotope relationships in plutonic igneous rocks of the Peninsular Ranges Batholith, southern and Baja California. In *Short Papers of the 4th International Conference on Geochronology, Cosmochronology, and Isotope Geology* (ed. R. E. ZARTMAN); *U.S. Geol. Survey Open-File Rept. 78-701*, pp. 423–426.

TAYLOR H. P., JR., MAGARITZ M. and WICKHAM S. M. (1991) Application of stable isotopes in identifying a major Hercynian synplutonic rift zone and its associated meteoric-hydrothermal activity, southern Schwarzwald, Germany (this volume).

Stable Isotope Geochemistry: A Tribute to Samuel Epstein
© The Geochemical Society, Special Publication No. 3, 1991
Editors: H. P. Taylor, Jr., J. R. O'Neil and I. R. Kaplan

# Variations in $\delta^{18}O$ values, water/rock ratios, and water flux in the Rico paleothermal anomaly, Colorado

Peter B. Larson and Brian S. Zimmerman

Department of Geology, Washington State University, Pullman, WA 99164-2812, U.S.A.

**Abstract**—The Rico paleothermal anomaly, southwestern Colorado, records the effects of a large, ore-forming, hydrothermal system which was active at 4 Ma. A porphyry molybdenum deposit lies 1.5 km deep in the center of the system and marks the location of the system's heat source. Effects of the hydrothermal system vary symmetrically around the heat source, including mineral alteration patterns, paleotemperatures, and the degree of partial annealing of fission tracks. Whole-rock oxygen isotope ratios of altered rocks also follow this pattern: $\delta^{18}O$ values of the widespread, 65 Ma hornblende latite porphyry range from −4.0 to 9.9 per mil. The values decrease smoothly from nearly unaltered values of about +9 in distal areas of the hydrothermal system, to values as low as −4.0 in the deeper central part of the system. The $^{18}O$-depleted values suggest that meteoric groundwater was the dominant reservoir for the hydrothermal fluid which altered the latite. Open-system water/rock ratios are highest (0.54 to 1.10) in the central part of the system overlying the porphyry deposit, where the high ratios mark the location of a convecting hydrothermal plume that was 3 km wide. The water/rock ratios are lower (<0.01 to 0.41) in distal parts of the system. The water/rock ratios can be used to calculate the mass of water which has interacted with the latite: 20 to 45 mol $H_2O$ per Representative Equivalent Volume (REV = 10 cm-diameter sphere) have exchanged oxygen with the latite in the plume, whereas <10 mol $H_2O$/REV have exchanged with the distal latite. Water flux through the latite ranged from $0.5 \times 10^{-9}$ to $5.3 \times 10^{-9}$ mol/cm$^2 \cdot$ sec for hydrothermal durations of 100,000 to 500,000 years. Hydrothermal changes in the mass of major elements in the latite can be balanced with the mass of fluid to determine maximum changes in fluid concentrations due to water-rock interaction. $Na^+$ is added to the fluid by the latite throughout the hydrothermal system, whereas the latite nearly always removes $Mg^{++}$ and $K^+$ from the fluid. $Ca^{++}$ is added to the fluid unless the fugacity of carbon dioxide is high enough to produce calcite.

## INTRODUCTION

OXYGEN ISOTOPE RATIOS of hydrothermally altered rocks are very useful measures of the mass of water which has interacted with the rocks (*e.g.*, TAYLOR, 1971, 1979; GREGORY and TAYLOR, 1981; CRISS and TAYLOR, 1983; LARSON and TAYLOR, 1986). Mass balance of oxygen between a hydrothermal fluid and an altered rock can be used to calculate water/rock ratios if the temperature of interaction, the initial $\delta^{18}O$ value of the rock, and the initial $\delta^{18}O$ value of the fluid are known (TAYLOR, 1979). These techniques have been applied to continental hydrothermal systems, where they have revealed that $\delta^{18}O$ values of altered igneous rocks are lowered, vary regularly around thermal centers, and can be contoured (TAYLOR, 1971; CRISS and TAYLOR, 1983; LARSON and TAYLOR, 1986). The depleted $\delta^{18}O$ values of the altered rocks reflect the effects of high-temperature interaction between the rocks and meteoric-hydrothermal fluids integrated over the life of the hydrothermal system.

A young, 4 Ma, ore-forming hydrothermal system has altered rocks in a broad area in the Rico dome, Colorado (NAESER *et al.*, 1980; LARSON, 1987; LARSON *et al.*, 1991b). The system's thermal effects include partial annealing of fission tracks in older, 65 Ma intermediate intrusive rocks: fission

tracks in zircon and apatite exhibit greater degrees of partial annealing nearer the center of the system (NAESER *et al.*, 1980). These data show that temperatures near the center were higher for longer periods of time than in peripheral regions. Therefore, the Rico paleothermal anomaly (PTA) (CUNNINGHAM *et al.*, 1987) is an ideal location in which to apply oxygen isotope analyses to measure the magnitude of water/rock interaction, and to use these data to monitor the changes in fluid composition which result from this interaction.

This paper presents the results of whole-rock oxygen isotope measurements of the 65 Ma hornblende latite porphyry, an intrusive igneous rock that occurs as dikes and thick sills throughout the Rico dome (PRATT *et al.*, 1969; MCKNIGHT, 1974; PRATT, 1976). The results define a typical concentric pattern of depleted $^{18}O/^{16}O$ ratios which center on the deep, 4 Ma Silver Creek porphyry molybdenum deposit. Intrusive rocks associated with this deposit were the heat source which drove convective meteoric-hydrothermal circulation in the PTA. Other hydrothermal effects have been measured in the latite, and their variations are also distributed zonally about this heat source, including mineral alteration assemblages, alteration mineral structures and compositions, bulk rock density changes, and major element exchange between the latite and the hydrothermal fluid (LARSON *et al.*, 1991a,b). Here, we use the oxygen isotope ratios in the altered latite to calculate water/rock ratios, from which we constrain the minimum mass of fluid that has interacted with each of the samples. These data are combined with fluid/rock element exchange to calculate the change in the fluid concentrations of major dissolved cations during the alteration event. Both the fluid flux and change in fluid composition vary gradationally with respect to the central heat source in patterns that are similar to those of the other hydrothermal alteration effects.

## GEOLOGIC SETTING

The 12 by 12 km Rico dome (Fig. 1) comprises a thick sequence of Paleozoic and Mesozoic sedimentary rocks that have been uplifted more than 1 km (PRATT *et al.*, 1969; McKNIGHT, 1974; PRATT, 1976). The dome has been eroded to a group of high peaks just off the western

edge of the San Juan Volcanic Province, Colorado. The Dolores River flows from north to south and dissects the central part of the dome. This erosion provides more than a kilometer of vertical relief and access to deep structural levels. Deep diamond drill core from the central part of the dome provides an additional 1.5 km of vertical exposure. East-west and northwest-southeast trending fault zones are prevalent and intersect in the east-central part of the dome. These structures bound a central horst of Precambrian greenstone and quartzite.

Igneous rocks have been emplaced during two episodes. (1) Two contemporaneous and cogenetic intrusive rocks, the hornblende latite porphyry and an augite monzonite, were intruded about 65 Ma (McKNIGHT, 1974; NAESER *et al.*, 1980). The latite is found as dikes and thick sills throughout the district, whereas the monzonite forms a circular 2.5 km-diameter stock in the west central part of the dome. (2) A series of basalts, andesites, rhyolites, and lamprophyres is found as dikes throughout the district. One small rhyolitic stock is exposed at Calico Peak near the western end of the dome. Radiometric dating of several of these rocks yields ages between 3.4 and 4.5 Ma, contemporaneous with hydrothermal activity in the district (NAESER *et al.*, 1980).

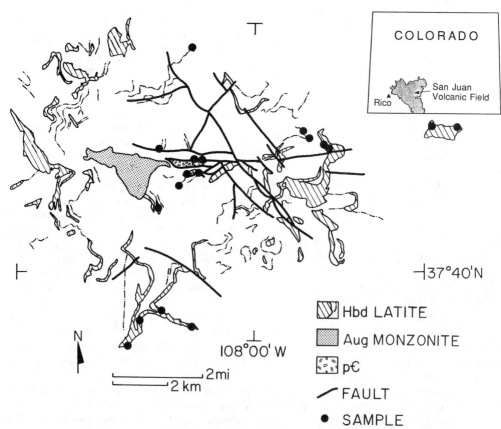

FIG. 1. Map showing the distribution of the 65 Ma hornblende latite porphyry and augite monzonite in the Rico dome, Colorado (modified from PRATT *et al.*, 1969 and PRATT, 1976). The horst of Precambrian greenstone and quartzite is also shown. The annular distributions of thick exposures of latite represent sills dipping outward and away from the center of the dome. The Silver Creek porphyry molybdenum deposit lies 1.5 km below the prominent zone of intersecting faults in the east-central part of the dome. Locations of samples used in this study are shown by heavy dots. Detailed sample locations are given in LARSON *et al.* (1991b).

Hydrothermal mineralization occurs in a diverse array of deposits (RANSOME, 1901; MCKNIGHT, 1974; BARRETT et al., 1985; LARSON, 1987). A 1.5 km-deep porphyry molybdenum deposite has been recently discovered in the central part of the dome (Fig. 1), and radiometric dating of alteration minerals has shown that intrusive activity associated with the molybdenum deposit is contemporaneous with alteration and mineralization throughout the district (NAESER et al., 1980). Shallower replacement deposits in calcareous sedimentary rocks and vein mineralization were exposed at the surface and were the source of historic metal production in the district (more than 80,000 tons each of Pb and Zn, more than 5000 tons of Cu, 14,513,288 ounces of Ag, and 83,045 ounces of Au from 1879 through 1968; MCKNIGHT, 1974).

The latite initially contained about 35 volume percent plagioclase phenocrysts and 5 to 10 volume percent hornblende phenocrysts set in a fine grained matrix of orthoclase, quartz, and plagioclase. Apatite and zircon are ubiquitous accessories. Now, all exposures of the latite exhibit some effects of interaction with a hydrothermal fluid. Hydrothermal alteration in the latite comprises a distal propylitic facies and a proximal facies which contains a quartz-illite-calcite assemblage and a chlorite-epidote assemblage. Detailed descriptions of the latite and its alteration products are given in LARSON et al. (1991b). The propylitic assemblage is defined by two reactions: (1) reaction of primary plagioclase phenocrysts ($An_{30-40}$) to illite and nearly pure albite ($An_{<2}$), and (2) reaction of hornblende to chlorite and hematite with or without calcite, illite, and epidote. The quartz-illite-calcite assemblage also exhibits the first propylitic reaction, but the hornblende has reacted to quartz and illite. The chlorite-epidote assemblage consists of pervasive replacement of primary phases by chlorite, epidote, and quartz.

## METHODS

Oxygen was extracted from latite whole-rock samples and converted to $CO_2$ at Washington State University using standard fluorination techniques (CLAYTON and MAYEDA, 1963; BORTHWICK and HARMON, 1982). The samples used for the extractions were aliquots of 7 to 10 grams of finely powdered and chemically untreated sample. $ClF_3$ was used as an oxidizing agent. Precision in the laboratory is better than 0.2 per mil, and NBS-28 has a $\delta^{18}O$ value of +9.6 on the laboratory's scale.

Major-element chemical gains and losses in the latite samples were calculated using whole-rock X-ray fluorescence measurements of major-element concentrations and assuming immobility of $TiO_2$ and $P_2O_5$ during the alteration process. Petrographic examination of the samples and major-element trends from unaltered to highly altered samples validate this assumption. Sample locations, the methods of calculating gains and losses, and the major-element data are presented in LARSON et al. (1991b). It is convenient to present the chemical concentrations normalized to a representative equivalent volume (REV) of rock (NORTON, 1984), which is chosen to be a 10 cm-diameter sphere (523.60 cm³). Bulk density measurements of the samples used for this normalization are tabulated in LARSON et al. (1991b).

### $\delta^{18}O$ VARIATIONS IN THE RICO PALEOTHERMAL ANOMALY

#### $\delta^{18}O$ variations and water/rock ratios

Whole-rock oxygen isotope ratios of the hornblende latite prophyry range from −4.0 to 9.9 per

Table 1. Oxygen isotope ratios, water/rock ratios, and the mass of fluid which has exchanged oxygen per Representative Equivalent Volume (REV) of rock

| Sample | $\delta^{18}O$ | $(W/R)_{OPEN}$ | M |
|---|---|---|---|
| RI-40 | −0.7 | 0.66 | 26.59 |
| RI-41 | 9.9 | — | — |
| RI-42 | 9.8 | — | — |
| RI-43 | −3.6 | 1.10 | 43.97 |
| RI-45 | −1.8 | 0.87 | 34.78 |
| RI-46 | 2.6 | 0.41 | 16.35 |
| RI-51 | 0.8 | 0.54 | 21.80 |
| RI-52 | −0.2 | 0.63 | 25.12 |
| RI-53 | −4.0 | 1.09 | 43.64 |
| RI-54 | 8.9 | 0.01 | 0.41 |
| RI-55 | −1.7 | 0.85 | 34.22 |
| RI-56 | −0.6 | 0.72 | 28.75 |
| RI-60 | 8.7 | 0.02 | 0.70 |
| RI-61 | 9.0 | 0.00 | 0.05 |
| RI-62 | 8.9 | 0.01 | 0.27 |
| HP-1 | 4.0 | 0.39 | 15.68 |
| HP-2 | 9.6 | — | — |
| HP-6 | 7.0 | 0.13 | 5.39 |
| HP-7 | 6.1 | 0.20 | 8.07 |
| HP-8 | 6.3 | 0.17 | 7.01 |
| HP-9 | 6.9 | 0.24 | 9.53 |
| HP-10 | 7.6 | 0.13 | 5.34 |

Isotope ratios are per mil relative to S.M.O.W.
Water/rock ratios are from Eq. (1).
M is the moles of water/REV.
REV = 523.60 cubic centimeters.

mil (Table 1). The $\delta^{18}O$ values vary gradationally both vertically and horizontally, with lower values deeper and closer to the system's center (Fig. 2). It is difficult to determine the initial value for the latite because the phenocryst assemblage typically does not contain quartz, which could be measured to

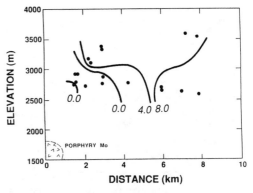

FIG. 2. Radial cross section of contours of latite oxygen isotope ratios in the Rico dome. The sample locations are plotted as a function of elevation and distance from a vertical pole through the center of the porphyry molybdenum deposit, which marks the location of the heat source for the Rico hydrothermal system. The latite grades to lower $\delta^{18}O$ values deeper and closer to the center of the system.

estimate the initial $\delta^{18}O$ value (CRISS and TAYLOR, 1983), and all of the samples exhibit some effects of interaction with the hydrothermal fluid. The least altered samples yield $\delta^{18}O$ values near +9.0 and this is probably near the igneous value. The depleted $\delta^{18}O$ values suggest that meteoric water was the dominant reservoir for the hydrothermal fluids which altered the latite. Note, however, that a magmatic water component has been identified in the fluid which produced the deep, central prophyry molybdenum deposit (LARSON, 1987). This component was not detected in the fluids from which quartz precipitated in the shallower veins, even though some of these veins are 1.5 km directly above the porphyry deposit (LARSON, 1987).

Water/rock ratios also vary gradationally and were highest in the central part of the dome (Fig. 3). Open-system material-balance water/rock ratios (W/R$_{OPEN}$) have been calculated on the basis of molar oxygen for the latite using the equation of TAYLOR (1979):

$$W/R_{OPEN} = \ln \left[ (^i\delta^{18}O_W + \Delta + {}^i\delta^{18}O_R) / \right.$$
$$\left. (^i\delta^{18}O_W - (^f\delta^{18}O_R - \Delta)) \right] \quad (1)$$

where the superscripts i and f refer to the initial and final isotope ratios, respectively, of the water (subscript W) and rock (subscript R), and $\Delta$ is the water-rock oxygen isotope fractionation. W/R$_{OPEN}$ curves have been calculated for the latite for temperatures of 100, 200, 300, and 400°C using an initial rock $\delta^{18}O$ value of +9.0 and an initial meteoric water value of −16.0 (Fig. 4). Fluids from which quartz precipitated in the Rico epithermal veins define a typical $^{18}O$-shifted trajectory (LARSON, 1987) which is characteristic of meteoric-hydrothermal fluids

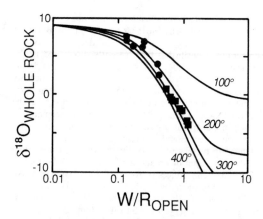

FIG. 4. Open-system water/rock ratio curves (log scale) for the hornblende latite porphyry. $\delta^{18}O$ values are per mil relative to S.M.O.W. Open-system water-rock behavior is demonstrated by the ability of the fluid to transport a significant mass of components into and out of the latite. The initial water $\delta^{18}O$ value was −16.0. The feldspar (An$_{30}$)-water fractionation of O'NEIL and TAYLOR (1967) was used to approximate the rock-water fractionation. The positions of the latite samples are also shown. These data are coded as distal (circles) or proximal (squares) to the porphyry molybdenum deposit, and this designation is based on the sample's alteration assemblage and position within the paleothermal anomaly (see LARSON et al., 1991b).

(CRAIG, 1963). The water-rock isotope fractionation is assumed to be approximately equal to that of plagioclase (An$_{30}$)-water. This assumption is valid because the latite contained about 40 volume percent oligoclase-andesine prior to alteration (LARSON et al., 1991b). The feldspar-water fractionation factors of O'NEIL and TAYLOR (1967) were used in these calculations.

W/R$_{OPEN}$ ratios have been calculated for the individual samples (Table 1) and are plotted in Fig. 4. The ratios are calculated for the samples using Eqn. (1), where initial rock and water $\delta^{18}O$ values are identical to those used to construct the theoretical curves, final rock $\delta^{18}O$ values are the measured values tabulated in Table 1, and water-rock oxygen isotope fractionation is again assumed to be approximately that of plagioclase (An$_{30}$)-water. The temperature of interaction for each sample was calculated using the empirical chlorite tetrahedral Al (Al$^{IV,CHL}$) geothermometer developed by CATHELINEAU (1988) (chlorite compositions and structural formulae are presented in LARSON et al., 1991b). Al$^{IV,CHL}$ has been found to be a useful parameter at Rico because it varies gradationally with respect to vertical and horizontal distance from the PTA's heat source, and chlorite is nearly ubiquitous in the samples (LARSON et al., 1991b). The water/rock data show that water-rock oxygen isotope in-

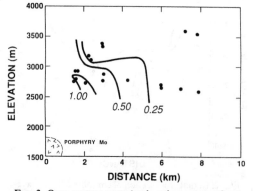

FIG. 3. Open-system water/rock ratio contours for the latite in the Rico dome. See caption for Fig. 2 for explanation of the composite cross section. The high values of W/R above the location of the system's heat source, the porphyry molybdenum deposit, mark the location of a convective hydrothermal plume.

teraction in the latite can be satisfactorily estimated by open-system exchange between a meteoric-hydrothermal fluid and the latite at about 300°C for proximal alteration samples and at 100 to 300°C for the distal alteration samples. Proximal samples also exhibit higher water/rock ratios (0.54 to 1.10) than the distal samples (<0.01 to 0.41).

Thus, the latite oxygen isotope data from Rico exhibit characteristics that are similar to other meteoric-hydrothermal systems. The latite becomes progressively depleted in $^{18}O$ both vertically and horizontally closer to the PTA's heat source (e.g., similar depletion patterns have been found in the Miocene Lake City caldera, Colorado, hydrothermal system; LARSON and TAYLOR, 1986). Water/rock ratios at Rico are variable and range up to between 1 and 2. These data represent water-rock isotope exchange integrated over the life of the hydrothermal system. The highest ratios are found in the central part of the PTA, where temperatures were also higher. Water/rock ratios of this magnitude appear to be typical of other meteoric-hydrothermal systems (TAYLOR, 1979).

### Water flux

The water/rock ratios calculated from the oxygen isotope data provide a minimum estimate of the mass of fluid which has flowed through and interacted with the rocks. It is therefore convenient to normalize the latite samples' water/rock ratios to the mass of water that has exchanged oxygen with an REV of rock. Oxygen isotope water/rock ratios (W/R$_{OPEN}$) calculated using Eqn. (1) are molar ratios of oxygen in the water to that in the rock. These are converted to moles of water which have exchanged oxygen with an REV ($M$, in units of mole $H_2O$/REV) by multiplying W/R$_{OPEN}$ by the inverse of the number of moles of water oxygen per mole of $H_2O$ ($m_{O,WATER}$), and by the moles of rock oxygen per REV ($m_{O,ROCK}$). Thus,

$$M = (W/R_{OPEN})(m_{O,WATER})^{-1}(m_{O,ROCK}) \quad (2)$$

where $m_{O,WATER}$ is 1 and $m_{O,ROCK}$ is calculated by summing the contribution of oxygen from each major oxide in the least-altered latite samples. The average $m_{O,ROCK}$ for the six freshest latite samples is 39.77 moles per REV, and this was used for all the calculations of mole $H_2O$/REV (Table 1).

Water/rock ratios in units of moles of $H_2O$ which have exchanged oxygen with an REV of rock vary from 0 to 44.0. The highest ratio of the volume of water to the volume of rock is 1.5, assuming that the fluid had a density of 1 gram per cubic centimeter. Distal propylitized latite has interacted with relatively low masses of fluid, usually less than 10

moles of $H_2O$ per REV. W/R$_{OPEN}$ values for these samples are also low and are generally less than 0.2. In contrast, proximal altered latite has exchanged oxygen with large masses of water, typically more than 20 moles of $H_2O$ per REV, and W/R$_{OPEN}$ values for these samples are all greater than 0.4. The area of proximal alteration in the Rico dome lies directly over the PTA's heat source, the porphyry molybdenum deposit, and exhibits water/rock ratios which are an order of magnitude greater than in the distal areas. Thus, these data support the conclusion of LARSON et al. (1991b) that the proximal area marks the location of an upwelling convectively driven hydrothermal plume which was 3 km wide and whose path is now exposed for over 2 km vertically.

The upward flux of water through each REV cube (8.06 cm on a side) in the proximal part of this 2 km long plume is:

$$f_{WATER} = 24,814(M)(a_{REV})^{-1}(t)^{-1} \quad (3)$$

where $M$ is from Eqn. (2) (in mole $H_2O$/REV), $a_{REV}$ is the cross-sectional area of the REV (64.96 cm$^2$), and $t$ is the duration of the water/rock interaction (seconds). The duration of the Rico PTA is not known, but theoretical models of continental convective hydrothermal systems suggest that they typically endure for several hundreds of thousands of years (NORTON and KNIGHT, 1977; NORTON, 1982). Water fluxes through the REVs range from $2.4 \times 10^{-9}$ to $5.3 \times 10^{-9}$ mol/cm$^2 \cdot$ sec for a duration of 100,000 years, and $0.5 \times 10^{-9}$ to $1.1 \times 10^{-9}$ mol/cm$^2 \cdot$ sec for a duration of 500,000 years. Minimum integrated fluid fluxes within the proximal upwelling plume range from 7,600 mol/cm$^2$ to 16,700 mol/cm$^2$.

### Changes in fluid composition

Once the mass of fluid which has interacted with the latite has been determined, the molar changes in the concentrations of major elements in the latite can be used to derive the changes in fluid concentrations. Gains and losses in the latite must be balanced by respective losses and gains in the fluid. The change in fluid composition integrated over the life of the hydrothermal system is then the change in mass of a component in the latite divided by the mass of fluid which has interacted with the latite. It is most convenient to measure these changes relative to a specific volume of rock, the REV. Table 2 shows the changes in molality of the major elements in the fluid during water/rock interaction for several of the samples. The masses of fluid used to calculate the changes in Table 2 are from Table 1, and the changes in major element

Table 2. Changes in the concentration of components in the hydrothermal fluid due to water-rock interaction with the hornblende latite porphyry

|           | RI-52  | RI-55  | HP-1   | HP-10  |
|-----------|--------|--------|--------|--------|
| $SiO_2$   | 3.35   | 0.82   | −0.58  | −0.30  |
| $Fe^{++}$ | −1.76  | −0.05  | 0.22   | −0.10  |
| $Mg^{++}$ | −0.69  | −0.19  | −0.05  | −0.22  |
| $Ca^{++}$ | −4.51  | −0.73  | 0.55   | −1.00  |
| $Na^+$    | 6.02   | 2.75   | 0.59   | 0.33   |
| $K^+$     | 1.98   | −0.37  | −0.15  | −0.27  |

All data are moles per 1000 grams of water.

concentrations for each sample are from LARSON *et al.* (1991b). The data in Table 2 are maximum changes in fluid composition because the water/rock ratios derived from the isotope data are minimum values.

Several components are consistently added to or removed from the fluid during reaction with the latite. Nearly all samples release $Na^+$ to the fluid, and nearly all remove $Mg^{++}$ and $K^+$ from the fluid. The $Na^+$ and $K^+$ changes result from reaction of part of the plagioclase albite component and the reaction of some plagioclase and hornblende to illite, respectively. $K^+$ is also fixed in hydrothermal potassium feldspar in several of the proximal samples. These data show that the reactions tend to increase the $Na^+/K^+$ ratio in the hydrothermal fluid. $Mg^{++}$ is typically removed from the fluid because it is concentrated in chlorite, which is a nearly ubiquitous alteration product in the latite.

$Ca^{++}$ exhibits variable changes and is added to the fluid for some samples and removed for others. $Ca^{++}$ is a product of both the plagioclase and hornblende reactions in the latite and is fixed in calcite, which is present in only about half of the samples. It appears, therefore, that the $Ca^{++}$ flux is determined by the fugacity of $CO_2$ in the hydrothermal fluid, which apparently varies, even though the major calcium-bearing minerals consistently react. The change in fluid concentration for $SiO_2$ is variable in the proximal area, where it has been removed from the fluid by samples which contain abundant hydrothermal quartz. Distal samples all remove small amounts of silica from the fluid.

$Fe^{++}$ exhibits either gains or losses in the fluid which are usually small when compared to those for the other components. Two samples of the proximal chlorite/epidote facies (RI-51 and RI-52, Table 2), however, have removed large quantities of iron from the fluid. These samples have also added significant $Al^{+++}$ to the fluid (2.5 molar change per 1000 grams of water for RI-52) and removed significant manganese (−0.4 molar change

per 1000 grams of water, RI-52). Aluminum and manganese changes for nearly all the other samples are small. It is interesting to note that these two samples have produced large changes in fluid concentrations for iron and manganese, which can be trivalent cations under conditions of increased oxygen fugacity, and aluminum, which is also trivalent.

Comparison of the compositional changes in the Rico fluid to typical geothermal fluids from active geothermal areas (*e.g.,* ELLIS, 1979) shows that water-rock interaction in the latite produces fluid compositions which trend toward typical geothermal fluids. However, it is not possible to use these techniques to estimate the total fluid concentrations in the Rico system because the initial, pre-interaction, fluid compositions are not known.

## SUMMARY AND CONCLUSIONS

The results of this investigation are summarized here:

1) Whole-rock $\delta^{18}O$ values of the latite range from −4.0 to +9.9. It had an initial $\delta^{18}O$ value of about +9. The $^{18}O$ depletions result from water-rock interaction between the latite and a meteoric-hydrothermal fluid. The values decrease gradationally, both laterally and vertically, toward the center of the Rico dome. Here, the young Silver Creek porphyry molybdenum deposit, which marks the location of the hydrothermal system's heat source, lies 1.5 km beneath the surface. The gradational variation in oxygen isotope ratios is parallel to other effects of the hydrothermal system, including mineral alteration patterns and paleotemperatures, which become higher toward the center of the system.

2) Open-system water/rock ratios in the latite are highest in the central part of the system, where they range from 0.54 to 1.10. The ratios range from <0.01 to 0.41 in the distal parts of the system. LARSON *et al.* (1991b) have suggested that a rising, convective, hydrothermal plume was emplaced above the porphyry deposit as part of the Rico hydrothermal system. The plume is the locus of the proximal alteration facies. The water/rock ratios suggest that, indeed, the area of the plume experienced elevated fluid flow relative to the distal part of the system.

3) The minimum mass of water which has exchanged oxygen with the latite ranges from 0 to 44.0 mol $H_2O$/REV. Distal samples have typically exchanged with low masses of water (<10 mol $H_2O$/REV), whereas proximal samples from within the plume have exchanged with 20 to 45 mol $H_2O$/REV. Water flux through the latite

ranges from $0.5 \times 10^{-9}$ to $5.3 \times 10^{-9}$ mol/ $cm^2 \cdot sec$ for durations of 100,000 to 500,000 years.

4) Maximum changes in the concentrations of major elements in the hydrothermal fluid can be determined using mass balance between the fluid and the latite. $Na^+$ is released to the fluid from the latite throughout the hydrothermal system, whereas $Mg^{++}$ and $K^+$ are nearly everywhere removed from the fluid and fixed in the latite. $Ca^{++}$ is typically removed from the latite by the fluid unless it can be precipitated in calcite, and calcium's mobility is therefore determined by the fugacity of carbon dioxide in the fluid. Silica and $Fe^{++}$ exhibit variable behavior.

*Acknowledgements*—The first author would like to thank Dr. Samuel Epstein, from whom I learned, and continue to learn, a great deal about isotope geochemistry. Don Cameron, John Wilson, and Larry Barrett helped during the early phases of this research. We thank Clive Rice, Chris Wareham, Tom Steven, Dave Beaty, Andy James, Charles Naeser, Bob Criss, and Hugh Taylor for valuable discussions. Hugh Taylor provided a useful critical review. This research was supported by National Science Foundation Grant EAR-8903492.

## REFERENCES

BARRETT L. F., CAMERON D. E. and WILSON J. C. (1985) Discovery of the Silver Creek molybdenum deposit, Rico, Colorado. *A.I.M.E. Preprint* 85-118.

BORTHWICK J. and HARMON R. S. (1982) A note regarding $CIF_3$ as an alternative to $BrF_5$ for oxygen isotope analyses. *Geochim. Cosmochim. Acta* **46**, 1665–1668.

CATHELINEAU M. (1988) Cation site occupancy in chlorites and illites as a function of temperature. *Clay Minerals* **23**, 471–485.

CLAYTON R. N. and MAYEDA T. K. (1963) The use of bromine pentafluoride in the extraction of oxygen from oxides and silicates for isotopic analysis. *Geochim. Cosmochim. Acta* **27**, 43–52.

CRAIG H. (1963) The isotopic geochemistry of water and carbon in geothermal areas. In *Nuclear Geology on Geothermal Areas* (ed. E. TONGIORGI), pp. 17–53. Spoleto: Pisa, Consiglio Nazionale della Richerche, Laboratorio de Geologia Nucleare.

CRISS R. E. and TAYLOR H. P., JR. (1983) An $^{18}O/^{16}O$ and D/H study of Tertiary hydrothermal systems in the southern half of the Idaho batholith. *Geol. Soc. Amer. Bull.* **94**, 640–663.

CUNNINGHAM C. G., NAESER C. W., CAMERON D. E., BARRETT L. F., WILSON J. C. and LARSON P. B. (1987) The Pliocene paleothermal anomaly at Rico, Colorado, as related to a major molybdenum deposit. *Geol. Soc. Amer. Abstr. Prog.* **19**, 268–269.

ELLIS A. J. (1979) Explored geothermal systems. In *Geochemistry of Hydrothermal Ore Deposits* (ed. H. L. BARNES), Vol. 2, pp. 632–683. John Wiley.

GREGORY R. T. and TAYLOR H. P., JR. (1981) An oxygen isotope profile in a section of Cretaceous oceanic crust, Samail ophiolite, Oman: evidence for $\delta^{18}O$-buffering of the oceans by deep (>5 km) seawater-hydrothermal circulation at mid-ocean ridges. *J. Geophys. Res.* **86**, 2737–2755.

LARSON P. B. (1987) Stable isotope and fluid inclusion investigations of epithermal vein and porphyry molybdenum mineralization in the Rico mining district, Colorado. *Econ. Geol.* **82**, 2141–2157.

LARSON P. B. and TAYLOR H. P., JR. (1986) $^{18}O/^{16}O$ relationships in hydrothermally altered rocks from the Lake City caldera, San Juan Mountains, Colorado. *J. Volcanol. Geotherm. Res.* **30**, 47–82.

LARSON P. B., ZIMMERMAN B. S., CUNNINGHAM C. G. and NAESER C. W. (1991a) Large-scale alteration effects in the Rico paelothermal anomaly, Colorado. *Geol. Soc. Amer. Abstr. Prog.* **23**, 40.

LARSON P. B., CUNNINGHAM C. G. and NAESER C. W. (1991b) Hydrothermal alteration and mass flux in the Rico paleothermal anomaly, Colorado. *Econ. Geol.* (submitted).

McKNIGHT E. T. (1974) Geology and ore deposits of the Rico district, Colorado. *U.S. Geol. Surv. Prof. Paper* **723**.

NAESER C. W., CUNNINGHAM C. G., JR., MARVIN R. F. and OBRADOVICH J. D. (1980) Pliocene intrusive rocks and mineralization near Rico, Colorado. *Econ. Geol.* **75**, 122–127.

NORTON D. L. (1982) Fluid and heat transport phenomena typical of copper-bearing pluton environments. In *Advances in Geology of the Porphyry Copper Deposits, Southwestern North America* (ed. S. R. TITLEY), pp. 59–72. University of Arizona Press, Tucson.

NORTON D. L. (1984) Theory of hydrothermal systems. *Ann. Rev. Earth Planet. Sci.* **12**, 155–177.

NORTON D. L. and KNIGHT J. E. (1977) Transport phenomena in hydrothermal systems. *Amer. J. Sci.* **277**, 937–981.

O'NEIL J. R. and TAYLOR H. P., JR. (1967) The oxygen isotope and cation exchange chemistry of feldspars. *Amer. Mineral.* **52**, 1414–1437.

PRATT W. P. (1976) Preliminary geologic map of the Hermosa Peak Quadrangle, Dolores, San Juan, La Plata, and Montezuma Counties, Colorado. *U.S. Geol. Surv. Open File Report* 76–314.

PRATT W. P., McKNIGHT E. T. and DEHON R. A. (1969) Geologic map of the Rico Quadrangle, Dolores and Montezuma Counties, Colorado. *U.S. Geol. Surv. Geol. Quad. Map* GQ-797.

RANSOME F. L. (1901) The ore deposits of the Rico Mountains, Colorado. *U.S. Geol. Surv. Ann. Rept.* **22**(2), 229–398.

TAYLOR H. P., JR. (1971) Oxygen isotope evidence for large-scale interaction between meteoric ground waters and Tertiary granodiorite intrusions, western Cascade Range, Oregon. *J. Geophys. Res.* **76**, 7855–7874.

TAYLOR H. P., JR. (1979) Oxygen and hydrogen isotope relationships in hydrothermal mineral deposits. In *Geochemistry of Hydrothermal Ore Deposits* (ed. H. L. BARNES), Vol. 2, pp. 236–277. John Wiley.

# Part G.
# Extraterrestrial Geochemistry

Sam Epstein working at his high-vacuum extraction lines at Caltech in the late 1950's (left) and the early 1980's (right).

Stable Isotope Geochemistry: A Tribute to Samuel Epstein
© The Geochemical Society, Special Publication No. 3, 1991
Editors: H. P. Taylor, Jr., J. R. O'Neil and I. R. Kaplan

# Initial Pb isotopic compositions of lunar granites as determined by ion microprobe

W. COMPSTON,[1] I. S. WILLIAMS[1] and C. MEYER[2]

[1]Research School of Earth Sciences, The Australian National University, Canberra, Australia
[2]NASA, Johnson Space Center, Houston, TX, U.S.A.

**Abstract**—The Pb isotopic compositions of selected areas within lunar feldspars were measured *in situ* on the SHRIMP ion microprobe at sensitivity up to 140 cps/ppm Pb. Usable data were obtained at the 1 ppm level, with analytical Pb blank ≤0.2 femtograms. The highest Pb content, 30 ppm, was found in Ba-rich feldspar in a felsite fragment from breccia 14163. There was no detectable U or Th and the Pb isotopic composition was uniform and highly radiogenic: very high $^{207}Pb/^{206}Pb$ at 1.50 ± 0.02 (2σ) with very low $^{204}Pb/^{206}Pb$ at 0.0029 ± 0.0002. It represents the true initial Pb ratios of the felsite magma, which must have been generated from a long-lived source having very high $^{238}U/^{204}Pb$ (μ) ≈ 1500. Multiple analyses of plagioclase and K-feldspar from a ≥4.32 Ga granite clast 14303, 1027 show high $^{207}Pb/^{206}Pb$ averaging 1.56, but with a distinct internal $^{207}Pb/^{206}Pb$ vs. $^{208}Pb/^{206}Pb$ trend. The latter suggests addition of radiogenic Pb formed in U-rich minerals outside the analysed areas, presumably as a result of thermally induced Pb isotope exchange during a metamorphism at 3.5–4.0 Ga. Consequently, the true initial $^{207}Pb/^{206}Pb$ for the granite would be at least 1.65, with an upper limit of 1.78, corresponding to single-stage U-Pb evolution from 4.55 Ga to 4.32 Ga in a high-μ (*ca.* 1500) source.

K-feldspars from a clast of VHK basalt from breccia 14305 also contain highly radiogenic Pb and have a single-stage model age of 3.81 ± 0.07 Ga, within error of the Rb-Sr crystallization age of 3.75 Ga. The radiogenic initial Pb requires high μ at 1120 for a single-stage source, or greater for a variety of two-stage source models. If the Pb is truly indigenous, and not hybridized by assimilation of lunar granite, then the VHK basalt source must have high μ, in contrast to other mare basalts which have comparatively low μ. Plagioclase from the quartz monzodiorite clast in 15405 records radiogenic initial Pb but extremely low contents of U and Th, which contrasts with thermal ionization results for mineral grains from the same rock.

High $^{207}Pb/^{206}Pb$ Pb values in many feldspar-rich fragments have been attributed to internal equilibration between U-rich and Pb-rich minerals that formed originally at 4.42 Ga, during a late lunar cataclysm at *ca.* 3.9 Ga. Radiogenic initial Pb at 4.4 Ga is not allowed in this model. Our data imply, on the contrary, that there must be some lunar initial Pb with $^{207}Pb/^{206}Pb$ > 1.65 that evolved earlier than 4.3 Ga in an extremely high μ environment. No metamorphism is needed for the 3.9 Ga granites, and a younger metamorphism would suffice for one of the 4.3 Ga granites. The implication for lunar history is that there was very early Pb loss from large volumes of the Moon, and later igneous production of lunar granite labelled by high $^{207}Pb/^{206}Pb$ from this long-lived Pb-depleted material.

## INTRODUCTION

THE INITIAL Pb isotopic compositions of lunar highland rocks remain poorly defined, making it difficult to trace the early evolution of lunar $^{238}U/^{204}Pb$ ("μ"). It is known that at some time close to 4.5 Ga, much or all of the assembled Moon lost Pb relative to U, thereby acquiring a high μ relative to the Earth (SILVER, 1970; TATSUMOTO, 1970). In addition, Pb loss from the Moon was evidently not uniform; the deep source rocks for mare basalts have comparatively low μ (~30, TATSUMOTO *et al.*, 1987) whereas some of the anorthositic remnants of the oldest lunar crust have high measured μ (TERA *et al.*, 1984).

Direct measurement of lunar initial Pb is especially difficult because of the very low Pb contents of lunar highland rocks, and, in addition, interpretation is complicated by their complex thermal histories due to meteoritic bombardment. Highly ra-

diogenic Pb was present in feldspars at ~3.9 Ga (TERA *et al.*, 1974). Was it wholly metamorphic in origin due to isotopic resetting during a "terminal cataclysm," or was there radiogenic initial Pb at, say, 4.4 Ga generated in still older high-μ rocks?

We applied the ion probe to this question primarily in the course of U-Pb age determinations on lunar zircons. In principle, the precision for U-Pb ages by ion probe for old zircons can be as high as a few million years, but this cannot be realized without reliable knowledge of the initial Pb isotopic composition. There were internal indications of a high-μ initial Pb at 4.35 Ga from our first lunar zircon measurements (COMPSTON *et al.*, 1984), but the particular zircons, being rounded grains in breccia, were not relatable texturally to adjacent minerals that might have enough initial Pb to measure. The later discovery, in several lunar granites, of euhedral zircons associated with Pb-rich K-feld-

spars (MEYER *et al.,* 1985) provided the necessary
cogenetic link. Such feldspars should contain original magmatic Pb appropriate to the adjacent zircons, and, moreover, their age will be accurately
and independently known through the zircon dating
itself. The combination of magmatic Pb compositions and known ages is exactly what is necessary
to explore and possibly define growth-curves for lunar Pb, making *in situ* Pb isotope analyses of dated
feldspars an important isotopic database.

## METHODS

Our first priority for feldspar Pb analysis was maximum
sensitivity, to have enough Pb counts N per mass during
an analysis period of *ca.* 20 minutes to obtain usable statistical precision ($1/\sqrt{N}$). At the same time, we elected to
operate at the usual zircon mass-resolution of 5500 (2%
definition) to reduce the possibility of low level isobaric
interferences that might become appreciable at sub-ppm
Pb and U levels. Sensitivity was enhanced first by matching
the large acceptance of the SHRIMP mass-analyser (CLEM-
ENT and COMPSTON, 1989) with the largest probe size
allowed by the fractured nature of the feldspar crystals, a
$25 \times 35$ μm ellipse (Fig. 1) and secondly by use of the
highest sputtering rate available for this probe size, *ca.* 20
μm/h for 12 nA of total negative oxygen in the primary
beam. Under these conditions, the sensitivity was *ca.* 10
cps/ppm Pb/nA based on the count-rate obtained for a K-
feldspar standard of known Pb content that was mounted
with the lunar polished thin-sections. The precision of the
measured isotope ratios is controlled almost entirely by
the total number of ions counted during the analysis, which
depends in turn on the Pb contents of the particular target.
For $^{207}Pb/^{206}Pb$, it ranged from a best of 0.6% (σ) in feldspar
having the greatest Pb content, to as poor as 10% for a
few areas below 0.1 ppm. For many feldspars it was around
3% which, although high, is nevertheless adequate to address the problem because of the Moon's uniquely high
average μ.

Data collection was similar to that described for zircon
U-Pb dating (COMPSTON *et al.,* 1984). The mass stations
in the peak switching cycle were confirmed using a reference zircon and Pb-rich feldspar. U and Th in the feldspars were monitored at $UO^+$ and $ThO^+$, automatic peak-
centering was used for $^{206}Pb$ only, and $^{204}Pb$ was counted
for 40 seconds per scan because of its extreme depletion
on the Moon. Each analysis took about 17 minutes for
seven scans.

Between our first analyses of lunar feldspars (COMPSTON
*et al.,* 1989) and the present, the SHRIMP primary column
was modified to operate in Köhler illumination mode
(LIEBL, 1984). This changed the ion-density profile of the
probe from "Gaussian," which produced at best a conical
pit often with a wide diffuse ion halo, to a very even profile
giving a flat-bottomed pit with sharply defined edges and
no halo (Fig. 1). The important consequence is rapid removal of surface-related Pb; the polished but contaminated
sample surface is quickly and uniformly removed by sputtering before the start of data collection. We are confident
that (almost) all common Pb remaining is located within
the body of the target and therefore properly belongs to
the analysis. In addition, the probe initially is rastered automatically about the selected area which cleans the surface
immediately outside the (future) pit-edges.

FIG. 1. Photomicrographs of thin section 14303, 205
showing a closely fractured plagioclase crystal in crossed
polarised, plane polarised, and reflected light, respectively.
Pits left after ion probe analysis of the least fractured regions
are clearly visible. Each pit is surrounded by a rectangular
etch mark produced by raster pre-cleaning of the sample's
surface. Field of view *ca.* 550 × 750 μm.

A "processing blank" for the analysis method can be
estimated from the results for plagioclase in 14305, 393,
which has an apparent Pb content of *ca.* 0.025 ppm (Table
1). In striking contrast to the associated K-feldspar, its
measured $^{207}Pb/^{206}Pb$ and $^{208}Pb/^{206}Pb$ are equal to modern
terrestrial Pb, indicating that all of the plagioclase Pb is
probably contamination (Fig. 11). (This is not so for $^{204}Pb/$
$^{206}Pb$, but the latter should be disregarded as only two
$^{204}Pb$ ions were detected during the whole analysis.) The
amount of Pb determined in the plagioclase can be estimated at $2 \times 10^{-16}$ g from its apparent Pb concentration
and the weight of feldspar consumed during analysis (*ca.*
8 ng). This extremely small amount, equivalent to about

half a million Pb atoms, is the blank. Its origin might be terrestrial Pb atoms on the surface of the polished section that are "knocked on" during sputtering, or residual surface Pb that continues to be slowly sputtered from the pit edges. In either case, the blank would be reduced by chemical cleaning of the surface prior to ion probe analysis.

For the present work, we expect that the blank varied according to the contamination of individual sample surfaces. For example, the measured $^{208}\text{Pb}/^{206}\text{Pb}$ for the low-Pb area 33.2 in granite 14303 (Table 1) indicates that *ca.* 90% of the measured Pb is initial feldspar Pb and therefore that the analytical blank is $\times 10$ lower than for 14305, 393. We also expect to see variation in Pb isotope ratios caused by the irregular presence of injected meteoritic material, which is known to occur in all but the most "pristine" lunar samples.

## PB ISOTOPE MODELLING

Measurements of $^{204}\text{Pb}$ by ion probe are imprecise compared with thermal ionisation owing to the much smaller amount of Pb used for the analysis (typically $\times 10^{-3}$). Consequently, we have not employed the traditional $^{207}\text{Pb}/^{204}\text{Pb}$ *vs.* $^{206}\text{Pb}/^{204}\text{Pb}$ diagram for modelling Pb isotope evolution in order to avoid the strong $y, x$ correlation generated in this plot by errors in $^{204}\text{Pb}$. Instead, we use $^{207}\text{Pb}/^{206}\text{Pb}$ *vs.* $^{204}\text{Pb}/^{206}\text{Pb}$ and $^{207}\text{Pb}/^{206}\text{Pb}$ *vs.* $^{208}\text{Pb}/^{206}\text{Pb}$.

### Secondary isochrons

For the above diagrams the starting point for Pb isotope modelling, the Canyon Diablo troilite, plots on the right-hand side (Fig. 2a,b). (Regardless of the exact age of the Moon, its starting Pb or that of its antecedents before assembly would derive ultimately from this primordial source.) Purely radiogenic Pb accumulated between times $T_0$ and $T_1$ (single-stage evolution with infinite $\mu$) is located on the $^{207}\text{Pb}/^{206}\text{Pb}$ axis in Fig. 2a at zero $^{204}\text{Pb}/^{206}\text{Pb}$. Its value is determined solely by $T_0$ and $T_1$:

$$^{207}\text{Pb}_*/^{206}\text{Pb}_*$$
$$= (e^{\lambda_5 T_0} - e^{\lambda_5 T_1})/(e^{\lambda_8 T_0} + e^{\lambda_8 T_1})/R \quad (1)$$

where $*$ denotes radiogenic Pb, $\lambda_5$, $\lambda_8$ the $^{238}\text{U}$, $^{235}\text{U}$ decay constants, and $R$ the present-day $^{238}\text{U}/^{235}\text{U}$. It constitutes the slope for secondary isochrons on the traditional plot.

In Fig. 2b, the $x$-value for purely radiogenic Pb will be

$$^{208}\text{Pb}_*/^{206}\text{Pb}_* = (^{232}\text{Th}/^{238}\text{U})(e^{\lambda_2 T_0} + e^{\lambda_2 T_1})/$$
$$(e^{\lambda_8 T_0} + e^{\lambda_8 T_1}) \quad (2)$$

so that a value for present-day $^{232}\text{Th}/^{238}\text{U}$ must be assumed.

In Fig. 2a, secondary isochrons are the straight lines joining the $T_1$ radiogenic end-member on the

$^{207}\text{Pb}/^{206}\text{Pb}$ axis with the Canyon Diablo point. In Fig. 2b, they join the $T_1$ radiogenic $^{207}\text{Pb}_*/^{206}\text{Pb}_*$, $^{208}\text{Pb}_*/^{206}\text{Pb}_*$ point with Canyon Diablo. When $T_1$ is the known age of the feldspar, its Pb isotope ratios must lie on the $T_0$ to $T_1$ secondary isochron for single-stage evolution. If it does not, two-stage evolution of the magma source is possible but only within defined limits (see below). If it falls beyond the two-stage limits, a post-magmatic metamorphic change in isotopic composition must be inferred.

Reference isochrons for 3.9 Ga and 4.35 Ga, appropriate for the lunar granites, are drawn on Fig. 2a and b.

### Growth curves

Pb isotope ratios at times $T_1$, evolved in single-stages of constant $\mu$ from common Pb at $T_0$ having isotope ratios relative to $^{204}\text{Pb}$ of $X_0$, $Y_0$, $Z_0$, are given by

$$(^{206}\text{Pb}/^{204}\text{Pb})_1 = X_1 = X_0 + \mu(e^{\lambda_8 T_0} + e^{\lambda_8 T_1}) \quad (3)$$

$$(^{207}\text{Pb}/^{204}\text{Pb})_1 = Y_1 = Y_0 + \mu/R(e^{\lambda_5 T_0} + e^{\lambda_5 T_1}) \quad (4)$$

$$(^{208}\text{Pb}/^{204}\text{Pb})_1 = Z_1 = Z_0 + \mu(^{232}\text{Th}/^{238}\text{U})$$
$$\times (e^{\lambda_2 T_0} + e^{\lambda_2 T_1}) \quad (5)$$

which are transformed to the Fig. 2 coordinates as
$$(^{204}\text{Pb}/^{206}\text{Pb})_1 = 1/X_1$$
$$(^{207}\text{Pb}/^{206}\text{Pb})_1 = Y_1/X_1$$
$$(^{208}\text{Pb}/^{206}\text{Pb})_1 = Z_1/X_1.$$

Single-stage growth curves from Canyon Diablo Pb have been plotted in Fig. 2 at various $\mu$ values from a low of 9.0 as for terrestrial Pb, to a high of 2000, which approximates the lunar granites.

### Two-stage Pb evolution

A more complex history of the magma source (and/or the metamorphic history of the feldspar) must be considered if the feldspar isotopic ratios do not lie on a single-stage isochron equivalent to its known age. Equation (3) above may be generalised to represent Pb isotope evolution in two successive U/Pb regimes for the magma source, specified as $\mu_0$ and $\mu_1$ for the time-periods $T_0$ to $T_1$ and $T_1$ to $T_2$:

$$(^{206}\text{Pb}/^{204}\text{Pb})_2$$
$$= X_0 + \mu_0(e^{\lambda_8 T_0} + e^{\lambda_8 T_1}) + \mu_1(e^{\lambda_8 T_1} - e^{\lambda_8 T_2}). \quad (6)$$

The term $(^{206}\text{Pb}/^{204}\text{Pb})_2$ is the initial ratio in the feldspar on crystallisation at $T_2$, when the production of the granite magma terminated the $\mu_1$ regime.

Table 1. U-Th-Pb analyses of lunar feldspars using the SHRIMP ion microprobe; "cts" refers to total ions counted during the analysis.

| Sample | 204/206 | ± | 207/206 | ± | 208/206 | ± | 206 cts | UO cts | ThO cts | Pb ppm | U ppb | Th ppb |
|---|---|---|---|---|---|---|---|---|---|---|---|---|
| 12033, 567 | | | | | | | | | | | | |
| K3 | 0.001 | 0.000 | 1.329 | 0.015 | 0.878 | 0.006 | 12826 | 16 | 56 | 4.2 | 5.0 | 17.5 |
| K4 | 0.001 | 0.000 | 1.304 | 0.015 | 0.841 | 0.005 | 13524 | 0 | 0 | 4.3 | 0.0 | 0.0 |
| K5 | 0.001 | 0.000 | 1.297 | 0.016 | 0.895 | 0.015 | 12107 | 208 | 877 | 3.8 | 68.7 | 289.8 |
| K6 | 0.002 | 0.000 | 1.174 | 0.014 | 0.897 | 0.017 | 12912 | 0 | 1 | 3.9 | 0.0 | 0.3 |
| PL3 | 0.002 | 0.001 | 1.194 | 0.036 | 0.938 | 0.024 | 2000 | 5 | 75 | 0.6 | 10.0 | 150.0 |
| PL4 | 0.005 | 0.001 | 1.174 | 0.038 | 0.921 | 0.033 | 1706 | 19 | 59 | 0.5 | 44.5 | 138.3 |
| PL5 | 0.004 | 0.001 | 1.219 | 0.037 | 1.012 | 0.044 | 1892 | 107 | 265 | 0.6 | 226.2 | 560.3 |
| K1, 1988 | 0.003 | 0.002 | 1.306 | 0.025 | 0.933 | 0.012 | 2072 | 10 | 26 | | | |
| K2, 1988 | 0.000 | 0.000 | 1.238 | 0.013 | 0.959 | 0.017 | 2192 | 1 | 14 | | | |
| K3, 1988 | 0.000 | 0.000 | 1.319 | 0.021 | 0.846 | 0.010 | 14398 | 1 | 3 | | | |
| K4, 1988 | 0.000 | 0.000 | 1.355 | 0.009 | 0.864 | 0.011 | 16531 | 0 | 0 | | | |
| 14321, 1047 | | | | | | | | | | | | |
| K4 | 0.001 | 0.000 | 1.471 | 0.019 | 0.771 | 0.015 | 10176 | 0 | 13 | 3.2 | 0.0 | 5.1 |
| K5 | 0.001 | 0.000 | 1.422 | 0.011 | 0.734 | 0.005 | 29080 | 2 | 3 | 9.1 | 0.3 | 0.4 |
| K6 | 0.001 | 0.000 | 1.415 | 0.011 | 0.720 | 0.006 | 30077 | 1 | 3 | 9.3 | 0.1 | 0.4 |
| K7 | 0.001 | 0.000 | 1.432 | 0.011 | 0.724 | 0.005 | 29410 | 0 | 10 | 9.2 | 0.0 | 1.4 |
| K8 | 0.001 | 0.000 | 1.463 | 0.011 | 0.727 | 0.005 | 27247 | 6 | 5 | 8.7 | 0.9 | 0.7 |
| K9 | 0.001 | 0.000 | 1.414 | 0.012 | 0.731 | 0.006 | 24569 | 0 | 5 | 7.8 | 0.0 | 0.8 |
| K1, 1988 | 0.002 | 0.000 | 1.398 | 0.009 | 0.759 | 0.005 | 41077 | 0 | 0 | | | |
| K2, 1988 | 0.002 | 0.000 | 1.403 | 0.009 | 0.756 | 0.005 | 46305 | 0 | 0 | | | |
| K3, 1988 | 0.003 | 0.000 | 1.434 | 0.011 | 0.791 | 0.005 | 33358 | 0 | 0 | | | |
| 14305, 393 | | | | | | | | | | | | |
| K1 | 0.003 | 0.000 | 1.485 | 0.028 | 0.833 | 0.010 | 4676 | 1 | 0 | 1.6 | 0.9 | 0.0 |
| K2 | 0.002 | 0.000 | 1.543 | 0.033 | 0.861 | 0.022 | 3560 | 0 | 0 | 1.3 | 0.0 | 0.0 |
| K3 | 0.004 | 0.000 | 1.472 | 0.029 | 0.850 | 0.012 | 4234 | 5 | 1 | 1.5 | 4.7 | 0.9 |
| K4 | 0.005 | 0.001 | 1.481 | 0.031 | 0.870 | 0.015 | 3692 | 4 | 0 | 1.3 | 4.3 | 0.0 |
| PLAG | 0.018 | 0.007 | 0.852 | 0.128 | 2.210 | 0.290 | 158 | 0 | 0 | 0.0 | 0.0 | 0.0 |
| 73215, 352 | | | | | | | | | | | | |
| K1 | 0.003 | 0.000 | 1.407 | 0.016 | 0.815 | 0.011 | 12389 | 1708 | 2824 | 4.0 | 551.5 | 911.8 |
| K2 | 0.002 | 0.000 | 1.500 | 0.022 | 0.865 | 0.014 | 7418 | 19 | 52 | 2.5 | 10.2 | 28.0 |
| K3 | 0.003 | 0.000 | 1.478 | 0.023 | 0.846 | 0.016 | 7013 | 157 | 190 | 2.4 | 89.5 | 108.4 |
| PL1 | 0.002 | 0.000 | 1.501 | 0.021 | 0.856 | 0.015 | 8065 | 8 | 55 | 2.7 | 4.0 | 27.3 |
| PL2 | 0.002 | 0.000 | 1.481 | 0.021 | 0.882 | 0.012 | 8404 | 10 | 111 | 2.9 | 4.8 | 52.8 |
| 14163, A | | | | | | | | | | | | |
| 1 | 0.013 | 0.006 | 1.453 | 0.070 | 1.117 | 0.081 | 672 | 1 | 0 | 0.5 | 6.0 | 0.0 |
| 2 | 0.006 | 0.002 | 1.320 | 0.071 | 1.057 | 0.066 | 573 | 0 | 2 | 0.4 | 0.0 | 14.0 |
| 3 | 0.011 | 0.003 | 1.283 | 0.077 | 0.998 | 0.068 | 446 | 0 | 0 | 0.3 | 0.0 | 0.0 |
| 4 | 0.007 | 0.001 | 1.372 | 0.055 | 0.922 | 0.069 | 1077 | 0 | 0 | 0.7 | 0.0 | 0.0 |

| Sample | | | | | | | | | | | | |
|---|---|---|---|---|---|---|---|---|---|---|---|---|
| **14163, B2** | | | | | | | | | | | | |
| 1 | 0.003 | 0.000 | 1.489 | 0.010 | 0.905 | 0.003 | 36727 | 0 | 0 | 24.5 | 0.0 | 0.0 |
| 2 | 0.003 | 0.000 | 1.477 | 0.009 | 0.912 | 0.002 | 45398 | 124 | 322 | 30.3 | 10.9 | 28.4 |
| 3 | 0.003 | 0.000 | 1.525 | 0.012 | 0.919 | 0.007 | 28764 | 2 | 2 | 19.5 | 0.3 | 0.3 |
| 4 | 0.003 | 0.000 | 1.497 | 0.009 | 0.910 | 0.005 | 42353 | 0 | 0 | 28.4 | 0.0 | 0.0 |
| **14163, B1** | | | | | | | | | | | | |
| 1 | 0.001 | 0.001 | 1.525 | 0.057 | 0.786 | 0.044 | 1186 | 1 | 0 | 0.8 | 3.4 | 0.0 |
| 2 | 0.009 | 0.002 | 1.318 | 0.054 | 1.005 | 0.054 | 1017 | 1 | 0 | 0.7 | 3.9 | 0.0 |
| 3 | 0.001 | 0.003 | 1.518 | 0.073 | 0.794 | 0.031 | 688 | 1 | 0 | 0.4 | 5.8 | 0.0 |
| **72275, 20** | | | | | | | | | | | | |
| K1 | 0.004 | 0.001 | 1.463 | 0.031 | 0.902 | 0.028 | 3688 | 0 | 16 | 1.6 | 0.0 | 17.4 |
| K2 | 0.003 | 0.000 | 1.457 | 0.025 | 0.901 | 0.024 | 5895 | 3 | 5 | 2.6 | 2.0 | 3.4 |
| K3 | 0.003 | 0.000 | 1.455 | 0.030 | 0.869 | 0.028 | 3880 | 0 | 52 | 1.7 | 0.0 | 53.6 |
| PL1 | 0.000 | 0.000 | 1.293 | 0.024 | 0.891 | 0.033 | 5023 | 3 | 170 | 2.1 | 2.4 | 135.4 |
| PL2 | 0.001 | 0.000 | 1.507 | 0.031 | 0.955 | 0.033 | 3844 | 0 | 1 | 1.7 | 0.0 | 1.0 |
| PL3 | 0.001 | 0.000 | 1.452 | 0.033 | 0.944 | 0.021 | 3283 | 0 | 0 | 1.5 | 0.0 | 0.0 |
| **14303, 205** | | | | | | | | | | | | |
| 2 | 0.003 | 0.000 | 1.055 | 0.027 | 0.735 | 0.014 | 10195 | 503 | 1107 | 3.2 | 197.4 | 434.3 |
| 3 | 0.004 | 0.001 | 1.667 | 0.066 | 0.911 | 0.045 | 2109 | 0 | 3 | 0.9 | 0.0 | 5.7 |
| 4 | 0.003 | 0.001 | 1.561 | 0.049 | 0.943 | 0.013 | 2340 | 0 | 1 | 1.1 | 0.0 | 1.7 |
| 5 | 0.005 | 0.001 | 1.539 | 0.090 | 1.592 | 0.209 | 2019 | 16 | 705 | 1.1 | 31.7 | 1396.7 |
| 6 | 0.005 | 0.002 | 1.499 | 0.046 | 0.888 | 0.040 | 2043 | 0 | 0 | 0.9 | 0.0 | 0.0 |
| 7 | 0.005 | 0.002 | 1.594 | 0.046 | 0.914 | 0.027 | 1971 | 0 | 0 | 0.9 | 0.0 | 0.0 |
| 8 | 0.004 | 0.001 | 1.575 | 0.057 | 0.935 | 0.040 | 1916 | 0 | 3 | 0.8 | 0.0 | 6.3 |
| 9 | 0.004 | 0.001 | 1.553 | 0.056 | 0.894 | 0.032 | 3558 | 0 | 1 | 1.5 | 0.0 | 1.1 |
| 10.1 | 0.003 | 0.001 | 1.626 | 0.052 | 0.880 | 0.034 | 3660 | 0 | 0 | 1.6 | 0.0 | 0.0 |
| 10.2 | 0.005 | 0.001 | 1.531 | 0.049 | 0.879 | 0.026 | 3508 | 0 | 0 | 1.4 | 0.0 | 0.0 |
| 11 | 0.005 | 0.001 | 1.603 | 0.070 | 1.000 | 0.049 | 3265 | 0 | 0 | 1.5 | 0.0 | 0.0 |
| 12 | 0.004 | 0.001 | 1.517 | 0.050 | 0.876 | 0.038 | 2277 | 2 | 15 | 1.0 | 2.5 | 18.4 |
| 13 | 0.004 | 0.001 | 1.525 | 0.091 | 0.883 | 0.023 | 2016 | 0 | 1 | 0.9 | 0.0 | 1.8 |
| 14 | 0.006 | 0.002 | 1.724 | 0.054 | 0.961 | 0.036 | 1682 | 0 | 0 | 0.8 | 0.0 | 2.0 |
| 15 | 0.004 | 0.001 | 1.892 | 0.131 | 1.012 | 0.044 | 1616 | 0 | 0 | 0.9 | 0.0 | 0.0 |
| 16 | 0.006 | 0.002 | 1.613 | 0.063 | 1.002 | 0.060 | 1418 | 0 | 7 | 0.7 | 0.0 | 19.7 |
| 17 | 0.005 | 0.002 | 1.733 | 0.079 | 0.979 | 0.040 | 1633 | 0 | 1 | 0.8 | 0.0 | 2.4 |
| 18 | 0.007 | 0.002 | 1.620 | 0.050 | 0.901 | 0.073 | 1736 | 1 | 2 | 0.9 | 2.3 | 4.6 |
| **14303, 209** | | | | | | | | | | | | |
| 2.2 | 0.005 | 0.000 | 1.437 | 0.018 | 0.905 | 0.009 | 16139 | 47 | 441 | 5.9 | 11.6 | 109.3 |
| 2.3 | 0.005 | 0.000 | 1.316 | 0.014 | 0.893 | 0.013 | 30435 | 153 | 1180 | 10.6 | 20.1 | 155.1 |
| 2.4 | 0.007 | 0.001 | 1.339 | 0.036 | 0.959 | 0.022 | 10697 | 274 | 629 | 3.8 | 102.5 | 235.2 |
| 2.5 | 0.005 | 0.000 | 1.518 | 0.018 | 0.911 | 0.013 | 12501 | 0 | 0 | 4.9 | 0.0 | 0.0 |
| 3.2 | 0.004 | 0.000 | 1.509 | 0.043 | 0.848 | 0.022 | 9128 | 0 | 4 | 3.8 | 0.0 | 1.8 |
| 3.3 | 0.005 | 0.001 | 1.528 | 0.035 | 0.879 | 0.028 | 7878 | 2 | 0 | 3.6 | 1.0 | 0.0 |
| 3.4 | 0.004 | 0.001 | 1.363 | 0.070 | 1.248 | 0.076 | 10586 | 268 | 3689 | 5.1 | 101.3 | 1393.9 |

Table 1. (Continued)

| Sample | 204/206 | ± | 207/206 | ± | 208/206 | ± | 206 cts | UO cts | ThO cts | Pb ppm | U ppb | Th ppb |
|---|---|---|---|---|---|---|---|---|---|---|---|---|
| 14303, 330 | | | | | | | | | | | | |
| 2 | 0.005 | 0.003 | 1.236 | 0.124 | 1.021 | 0.116 | 164 | 0 | 0 | 0.1 | 0.0 | 0.0 |
| 3 | 0.003 | 0.000 | 1.348 | 0.037 | 0.856 | 0.017 | 6531 | 33 | 335 | 2.6 | 20.2 | 205.2 |
| 4 | 0.005 | 0.001 | 1.528 | 0.040 | 0.903 | 0.029 | 4180 | 0 | 0 | 1.8 | 0.0 | 0.0 |
| 5 | 0.003 | 0.001 | 1.484 | 0.035 | 0.872 | 0.019 | 3168 | 0 | 7 | 1.3 | 0.0 | 8.8 |
| 15405, 57 | | | | | | | | | | | | |
| 1 | 0.004 | 0.002 | 1.403 | 0.097 | 1.016 | 0.090 | 596 | 4 | 5 | 0.2 | 26.8 | 33.6 |
| 2 | 0.002 | 0.002 | 1.346 | 0.096 | 1.038 | 0.054 | 484 | 0 | 0 | 0.2 | 0.0 | 0.0 |
| 3 | 0.002 | 0.001 | 0.961 | 0.040 | 1.057 | 0.027 | 3959 | 6 | 43 | 1.3 | 6.1 | 43.4 |
| 4 | 0.003 | 0.001 | 1.124 | 0.030 | 0.983 | 0.021 | 2686 | 2 | 1 | 0.9 | 3.0 | 1.5 |
| 5 | 0.002 | 0.000 | 0.902 | 0.028 | 0.979 | 0.010 | 5157 | 0 | 4 | 1.7 | 0.0 | 3.1 |
| 15405, 145 | | | | | | | | | | | | |
| 1 | 0.004 | 0.001 | 1.290 | 0.028 | 0.984 | 0.033 | 4154 | 0 | 3 | 1.4 | 0.0 | 2.9 |
| 2 | 0.002 | 0.000 | 1.462 | 0.031 | 0.984 | 0.025 | 4035 | 1 | 0 | 1.4 | 1.0 | 0.0 |
| 3 | 0.001 | 0.000 | 1.225 | 0.025 | 0.942 | 0.014 | 4321 | 0 | 0 | 1.4 | 0.0 | 0.0 |
| 4 | 0.003 | 0.001 | 1.111 | 0.021 | 1.016 | 0.018 | 5226 | 0 | 2 | 1.7 | 0.0 | 1.5 |
| 15405, 166 | | | | | | | | | | | | |
| 1 | 0.011 | 0.001 | 0.983 | 0.024 | 1.085 | 0.028 | 3674 | 0 | 0 | 1.2 | 0.0 | 0.0 |
| 2 | 0.004 | 0.001 | 0.751 | 0.013 | 0.982 | 0.019 | 7647 | 66 | 1498 | 2.2 | 34.5 | 783.6 |
| 3 | 0.006 | 0.001 | 1.009 | 0.033 | 1.000 | 0.035 | 3754 | 0 | 23 | 1.2 | 0.0 | 24.5 |
| 4 | 0.012 | 0.004 | 0.950 | 0.076 | 1.121 | 0.084 | 783 | 41 | 56 | 0.3 | 209.5 | 286.1 |
| 5 | 0.008 | 0.005 | 1.059 | 0.057 | 1.170 | 0.074 | 662 | 1 | 3 | 0.3 | 6.0 | 18.1 |
| 6 | 0.002 | 0.004 | 1.181 | 0.088 | 0.980 | 0.039 | 497 | 9 | 49 | 0.2 | 72.4 | 394.4 |
| 8 | 0.004 | 0.002 | 1.038 | 0.054 | 1.007 | 0.059 | 710 | 12 | 25 | 0.3 | 67.6 | 140.8 |
| 9 | 0.005 | 0.002 | 1.318 | 0.068 | 1.148 | 0.068 | 634 | 0 | 9 | 0.3 | 0.0 | 56.8 |
| 10 | 0.003 | 0.002 | 1.397 | 0.102 | 0.989 | 0.062 | 513 | 0 | 0 | 0.2 | 0.0 | 0.0 |

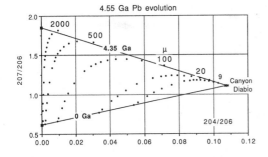

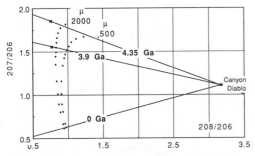

FIG. 2. Evolution of Pb composition with time in reservoirs of different $\mu$ ($^{238}U/^{204}Pb$), starting at 4.55 Ga with a Pb composition the same as that in Canyon Diablo. The straight lines are reference isochrons and the dotted curves represent different $\mu$ values ranging from 9 to 2000 (see text).

$T_1$, $\mu_1$, and $\mu_0$ are unknowns, but $\mu_0$ might represent the original Moon and $\mu_1$ the (local) lunar crust produced by differentiation at $T_1$ from which the granite will be formed later at $T_2$. Equation (6) combined with the generalised Eqn. (4) may permit an exact solution for $\mu_1$ and $\mu_0$ at a nominated $T_1$. Not all values of $T_1$ between $T_0$ and $T_2$ produce solutions, and sometimes no solutions are possible, which probably means that the feldspar has not preserved the initial isotopic ratios.

The $y$-intercept of the secondary isochron for the $T_0$ to $T_1$ stage is given by Eq. (1), which as $T_1$ approaches $T_0$ has the limiting value

$$^{207}Pb_* / ^{206}Pb_* = \lambda_5 e^{(\lambda_5 - \lambda_8)T_0}/R\lambda_8 \qquad (7)$$

which becomes 2.008 at 4.55 Ga. Two-stage solutions are possible if the measured feldspar $^{207}Pb/^{206}Pb$, $^{204}Pb/^{206}Pb$ point lies *below* the isochron corresponding to the above limit (joining 2.008 at zero $^{204}Pb/^{206}Pb$ with the Canyon Diablo Pb point in Fig. 2). Similarly, as $T_1$ approaches $T_2$, Eqn. (7) gives the minimum value for $^{207}Pb_*/^{206}Pb_*$ (corresponding to the instantaneous production of radiogenic Pb at $T_2$) in a second-stage isochron. The measured feldspar point must lie *above* the line

joining this minimum to Canyon Diablo to obtain a possible two-stage solution.

## RESULTS AND INTERPRETATION

### Granite clasts younger than 4.0 Ga

The samples can be subdivided into groups: those whose ages are ≥4.3 Ga, which would certainly have experienced the late basin-forming major impacts, and those ≤4.0 Ga, some of which may have escaped.

*Sawdust fragments, breccia 14163.* The highest Pb content, 30 ppm, was found in Ba-rich feldspar in the granite clast B from breccia 14163, which shows well-preserved magmatic texture and mineralogy. There was detectable U and Th in only one of four areas analysed (B2.2, Table 1). Although the relative sensitivity factor for $Pb^+$ and $UO^+$ in feldspar is not known, the $UO^+$ counts are so low in comparison to $Pb^+$ that a significant contribution of *in situ* radiogenic Pb to the B2.2 analysis seems unlikely, nor is there any visible reduction in its isotopic ratios relative to the U-free areas. The Pb isotopic compositions of the four B2 areas are nearly equal within counting statistics and very radiogenic: high $^{207}Pb/^{206}Pb$ averaging 1.50 ± 0.02 ($2\sigma$) with low $^{204}Pb/^{206}Pb$ at 0.0029 ± 0.0002 (Fig. 3). Because of the high Pb concentration, its constant isotope ratios, and the excellent crystal preservation, we interpret the Pb as original magmatic Pb, and because of its highly radiogenic nature, as signifying magma generation from a long-lived source having very high $\mu$ (*ca.* 1500). The crystallization age of this particular granite is not known, but its single-stage model Pb age is 3.81 Ga. The source Th/U can be estimated from the measured $^{208}Pb/^{206}Pb$ of the feldspar and the inferred source $\mu$, it is 4.15, consistent with direct measurements on other lunar rocks.

Two of the three areas analysed in the B1 clast have significantly lower $^{204}Pb/^{206}Pb$ and $^{208}Pb/^{206}Pb$ than B2, despite the much smaller Pb concentrations of these feldspars (Fig. 3). This is in the opposite direction to the greater blank effect expected in these samples; the differences would be enhanced if a blank correction were applied. The third area of B1 has isotope ratios much higher than B2, consistent with an added terrestrial contamination of *ca.* $2.5 \times 10^{-16}$ g relative to the others, which is well within the range of possible blank variation. It follows that the initial Pb ratios for granite B1 were even more radiogenic than B2, so that the two cannot have crystallised from the same magma. All four analyses of the A1 granite clast are consistent with admixture of B2 type initial Pb with small

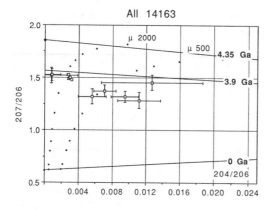

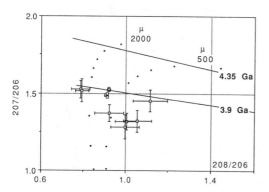

FIG. 3. Pb compositions measured on feldspar from sawdust fragments from breccia 14163 plotted on Pb evolution diagrams. Reference single stage isochrons for 4.35, 3.9 and zero Ga are shown, as are evolution curves for $\mu$ values of 500 and 2000.

amounts of contamination, but their Pb contents are too small for detailed interpretation.

*14321, 1027.* The petrology and chemistry of this clast has been described by WARREN *et al.* (1983). It is brecciated and contains 30% shock-melted glass, but undamaged areas showing igneous texture remain. Its crystallisation age has been determined at $3.96 \pm 0.02$ Ga by ion probe using cogenetic zircons (MEYER *et al.*, 1991).

Previous ion probe data on K-feldspars from this granite are well-fitted to a $^{204}Pb/^{206}Pb$ *vs.* $^{208}Pb/^{206}Pb$ mixing line between terrestrial Pb contamination and the mean of new data collected as described above (Fig. 4). We attribute that to surface-related Pb that remained in the former, and only the new data will be described here.

Five of the six new $^{208}Pb/^{206}Pb$ analyses agree to within error; the sixth is high in the direction of contamination and comes from an area having one-third of the Pb contents of the rest (Table 1). However, the ranges in $^{204}Pb/^{206}Pb$ and $^{207}Pb/^{206}Pb$ be-

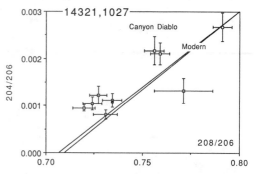

FIG. 4. Analyses of K-feldspar from granite clast 14321, 1027, plotted to show compositional variation consistent with mixing between a radiogenic end-member and common contaminant Pb.

tween different areas slightly exceed counting errors. Because of the high Pb contents and pristine nature of these samples, we consider that the mean values $1.429 \pm 0.018$ and $0.00102 \pm 0.00014$ for $^{207}Pb/^{206}Pb$, $^{204}Pb/^{206}Pb$ are at least *dominated* by the initial magmatic Pb, but the internal variation within

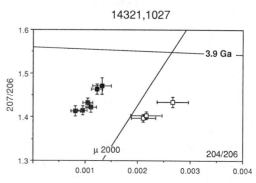

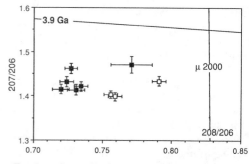

FIG. 5. Analyses of K-feldspars from granite clast 14321, 1027, showing the extremely uniform and highly radiogenic nature of their magmatic initial Pb. The single-stage isochron for 3.9 Ga and evolution curve for a $\mu$ value of 2000 are shown for reference. Open symbols indicate early analyses contaminated by surface Pb. Note greatly expanded scale on abscissa.

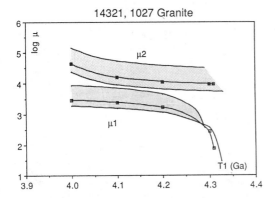

FIG. 6. Plot of log $\mu$ vs. time (Ga), showing solutions to two-stage modelling of the inferred initial Pb composition measured on K-feldspar from granite clast 14321, 1027. Possible values of first and second stage $\mu$ ($\mu_1$ and $\mu_2$, respectively) for different possible values of $T_1$ (the time of extreme Pb loss from the granite's source) are shown as shaded bands.

the feldspar might be real and if so, it signifies later alteration in the ratios (Fig. 5). All the ratios differ significantly from those of the 14163 granite fragments, and they lie within the allowed space between the single-stage 3.96 Ga isochron to 1.5937 for $^{207}Pb_*/^{206}Pb_*$ and the minimum $\mu_1$ isochron to 1.171, thus two-stage solutions are possible.

The results of two-stage modelling based on $^{207}Pb/^{206}Pb$ and $^{204}Pb/^{206}Pb$ are shown in Fig. 6. The maximum value allowable for $T_1$ cuts off sharply at 4.32 Ga. During the preceding $T_1$ to $T_0$ period, $\mu_0$ must be low but a definite value cannot be given because multiple solutions are allowed. For all $T_1$, values for $\mu_2$ are very high, at least 5000.

Does the sharp cut-off at 4.32 Ga correspond to a real lunar event? Pb isotopes will not answer that question conclusively, but only the lower values for $\mu_1$, which require the older choice for $T_1$, are realistic in view of direct measurements on lunar highland rocks (TERA et al., 1974). In addition, there is direct evidence for lunar magmatism between 4.32 Ga and 4.37 Ga in the form of widespread zircon crystallisation (MEYER et al., 1991), besides still older isotopic ages by other methods (CARLSON and LUGMAIR, 1988). In terms of source history for the 14321, 1027 granite, we visualize a low $\mu$ part of the lunar crust or mantle as old as 4.55 Ga that was transformed at 4.31 Ga to a high $\mu$ source by extreme loss of Pb (crystal fractionation and/or degassing). The high $\mu$ source then accumulated radiogenic Pb from 4.31 Ga until 3.96 Ga, when it melted to form the granite as an extreme crystal fractionate and incorporated most of the source U and Pb.

If the feldspar Pb ratios have been appreciably altered, the above modelling is invalid. Suppose that the apparent $^{207}Pb/^{206}Pb$ was too low due to thermally induced isotope exchange with young radiogenic Pb. Choose a higher value, 1.56, which permits effectively a single-stage evolution from 4.55 Ga, for which $\mu$ will be ca. 5600 for any choice of $T_1$. Even with this arbitrary adjustment of the data, a high $\mu$ is indicated for the granite source.

*73215, 352.* The petrology, genesis and history of this small clast of glass and relict crystalline rock was discussed by JAMES (1977). The age of either igneous crystallisation or glass formation is 3.91 ± 0.04 Ga by Ar-Ar and an internal Rb-Sr isochron; its maximum age is 4.0 Ga (COMPSTON et al., 1977; JESSBERGER et al., 1977).

Two areas of K-feldspar contained some U and Th (Table 1) and their $^{207}Pb/^{206}Pb$ and $^{208}Pb/^{206}Pb$ have been lowered by *in situ* radiogenic Pb (Fig. 7). The remaining three areas agree in all ratios to within counting statistics, giving means of 1.494 ± 0.023 for $^{207}Pb/^{206}Pb$ and 0.0020 ± 0.0003 for $^{204}Pb/^{206}Pb$. The conditions for two-stage modelling are met, and results show a cut-off of possible values

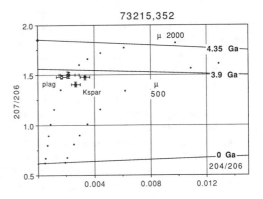

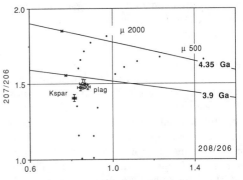

FIG. 7. Plot showing the similar Pb isotopic analyses of K-feldspar and plagioclase from felsite clast 73215, 352. Reference lines and curves as in Fig. 3.

for $T_1$ at 4.46 Ga, with low but non-specific $\mu_0$ and high $\mu_1$ at $\leq 3000$. As $T_1$ is reduced, $\mu_0$ increases rapidly and $\mu_1$ slowly. Thus, evolution of $\mu$ for the 73215, 352 felsite source follows that described for the 14321, 1027 granite: a long-lived penultimate source having very high $\mu$ preceded by one having permissably low $\mu$, with the difference that the high $\mu$ source for the 73215 felsite may have formed 0.1 Ga earlier. However, the timing for maximum $T_1$ depends sensitively upon the age $T_2$ of the felsite; if the latter is taken as 4.0 Ga, the maximum $T_1$ is reduced to 4.38 Ga. It is therefore important to obtain a zircon U-Pb age for the felsite.

*72275, 20.* STOESER *et al.* (1974) describe the chemistry and petrography of alkali-rich micro-granite clasts from this and other Apollo 17 Boulder 1 samples. Their age has been determined as 4.03 ± 0.03 Ga, on the basis of Rb-Sr analyses of breccia matrix rich in the microgranite (COMPSTON *et al.,* 1975).

The Pb contents of the feldspars are fairly uniform regardless of type and lower than K-feldspars described here so far, and free of detectable U, Th except for a small $ThO^+$ count in area P1 (Table 1). As in the other granites, the isotope ratios are highly radiogenic, so a high $\mu$ source is again indicated.

In detail, the relative ratios do not detect any variable surface contamination. The mean plagio-clase and K-feldspar ratios per area occur as separate groups in $^{208}Pb/^{206}Pb$ *vs.* $^{204}Pb/^{206}Pb$ coordinates, mainly because of the lower $^{204}Pb/^{206}Pb$ of the pla-gioclases; but the two do not lie on a mixing-line with terrestrial (or Canyon Diablo) Pb. They are uniform within error in $^{207}Pb/^{206}Pb$ except for one area which is low, and detectably spread in $^{204}Pb/^{206}Pb$ (Fig. 8). This might indicate early exchange with (external) radiogenic Pb having $^{207}Pb/^{206}Pb$ of *ca.* 1.2, but it cannot be due to Pb contamination. In view of the occurrence of the granite clasts as tiny fragments immersed in an impact melt, some Pb isotope exchange might be expected.

Some areas show apparent positive correlations between $^{207}Pb/^{206}Pb$ and $^{208}Pb/^{206}Pb$ within the se-rially measured seven ratios per analysis. This is maintained by the combined plot of all individual ratios, including $^{204}Pb/^{206}Pb$, supporting the possi-bility of early metamorphic Pb exchange but making it difficult to identify the magmatic Pb with confi-dence. On the grounds that the K-feldspar Pb ap-pears to be the least or even not exchanged, we have chosen its mean ratios, 1.458 for $^{204}Pb/^{206}Pb$ and 0.0036 for $^{204}Pb/^{206}Pb$, as the best estimate for initial Pb.

Two-stage modelling again shows a sharp cut-off

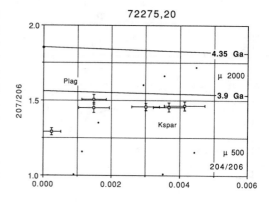

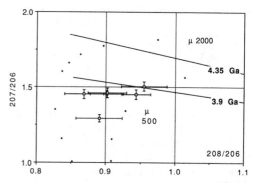

FIG. 8. Analyses of K-feldspar and plagioclase from mi-crogranite clast 72275, 20. Reference single-stage isochrons for 4.35 and 3.9 Ga are shown, as are growth curves for $\mu$ values of 500 and 2000. Note the change in scale of the abscissa compared to the previous graphs.

for possible values of $T_1$ at 4.31 Ga. An unspecified but low $\mu_0$ is allowed between 4.55 and 4.31 Ga, followed by $\mu_1$ of at least 3200 until magma gen-eration at 4.0 Ga.

*12033, 567.* This granite is mainly a fine-grained intergrowth of K-feldspar and silica, partly veined by brown glass and found as a small glass-coated fragment in the lunar soil (WARREN *et al.,* 1987). Its magmatic age has been measured by zircon U-Pb as 3.90 ± 0.01 Ga (MEYER *et al.,* 1991), with evidence in the zircons for variable and late decrease in $^{206}Pb/^{238}U$. The Ar-Ar age of the glass was mea-sured by EBERHARDT *et al.* (1973) at 800 ± 40 Ma, which we take to be the Pb loss event.

The K-feldspars contain more than a factor of five greater Pb concentrations than the plagioclases (Table 1), and because the measured ratios show variable Pb contamination in the latter (Fig. 9), we do not consider the plagioclase data further. Early K-feldspar analyses made at lower sensitivity show very low $^{204}Pb/^{206}Pb$ which are technically suspect, but the other ratios are consistent with

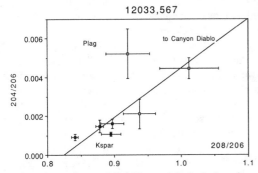

FIG. 9. Analyses of K-feldspar and plagioclase from granite clast 12033, 567, showing the effects of Pb contamination on the composition of the Pb in the plagioclase.

the new results. The first-order result is again the highly radiogenic Pb found, demanding a long-lived high $\mu$ source. In detail, there is a distinct range in the collective $^{207}Pb/^{206}Pb$, which has a weak negative correlation with $^{208}Pb/^{206}Pb$ for which there is no known *single* mixing end-member (Fig. 10). This is not due to *in situ* radiogenic Pb as two of the analysed areas are devoid of U, Th and there is no correlation with the amounts shown in the others. It probably signifies a combination of Pb contamination, possibly meteoritic, and isotope exchange with radiogenic Pb displaced from U-rich minerals, as such Pb is known to have been lost from the associated zircons. This makes it difficult to estimate the original magmatic Pb composition, but we have taken the highest measured $^{207}Pb/^{206}Pb$, $1.355 \pm 0.018$, as a minimum value, and combined it with the mean of the new $^{204}Pb/^{206}Pb$ analyses, $0.0013 \pm 0.0003$, for two-stage modelling.

With these parameters, the limiting value allowed for the maximum $T_1$ is lower than in previous granites; it is $\leq 4.25$ Ga, at which a low $\mu$ from 4.55 Ga must be increased to 7600. A greater value for the initial $^{207}Pb/^{206}Pb$ would increase the maximum $T_1$, and greater initial $^{204}Pb/^{206}Pb$ would permit lower $\mu_1$.

The mean apparent Th/U as calculated from the K-feldspar analyses is 4.2.

*14305, 393.* This is a clast of VHK basalt (Very High K) from breccia 14305, rather than lunar granite. It was selected for analysis for its abundant K-feldspar, which contains enough Pb for reliable ratio measurements (1.5 ppm) although the plagioclase does not, having the lowest (apparent) Pb contents that we have encountered so far, 0.025 ppm. $^{207}Pb/^{206}Pb$ and $^{208}Pb/^{206}Pb$ in four areas of K-feldspar agree to within counting statistics at $1.496 \pm 0.032$ and $0.845 \pm 0.016$, respectively, and

$^{204}Pb/^{206}Pb$ nearly to within error at $0.0039 \pm 0.0007$ (Fig. 11). The single-stage model age for this Pb is $3.81 \pm 0.07$ Ga, within error of the crystallisation age as determined by a Rb-Sr internal isochron at 3.75 Ga (SHIH *et al.*, 1986).

The radiogenic initial Pb requires high $\mu$ at 1130 for a single-stage source, but the data also permit a complete range of two-stage source models between $\geq 3.81$ Ga for $T_1$ up to $\leq 4.55$ Ga. These differ from other samples analysed so far first, in having no discontinuity in $T_1$ that might signify a major Pb loss event in the lunar source, and secondly, in requiring that the first stage $\mu$ must be the greater, for example $\mu_0$ 1260 and $\mu_1$ 940 for the latter beginning at 4.3 Ga. Regardless of the details, the K-feldspar Pb was produced in a high-$\mu$ long-lived source. If the Pb were truly indigenous, then the VHK basalt source must have high $\mu$, in contrast to mare basalts which have comparatively low $\mu$. SHIH *et al.* (1986) propose that VHK basalt magmas

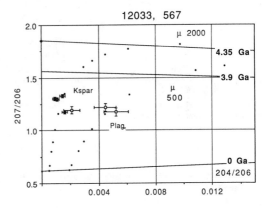

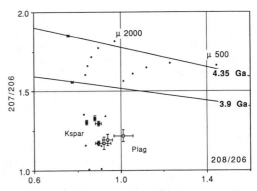

FIG. 10. Analyses of K-feldspar and plagioclase from granite clast 12033, 567. The K-feldspar Pb isotope compositions are less radiogenic than in other samples, probably because of exchange with younger radiogenic Pb displaced from U-rich minerals. Reference lines and curves as for Fig. 3.

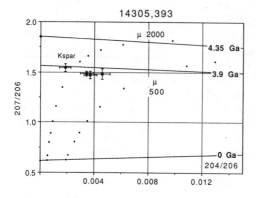

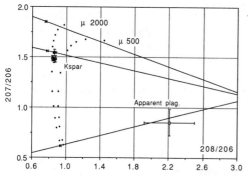

FIG. 11. Analyses of K-feldspar from clast 14305, 393, a very high K basalt, showing the extremely radiogenic initial Pb in the rock, much different from that of the apparent plagioclase (see text). Reference lines and curves as in Fig. 3. Note the change in scale of the abscissa compared to previous diagrams.

have been hybridised by assimilation of lunar granite, in which case their Pb isotope signatures would be dominated by the latter and the basalt source masked.

*Granite clasts older than 4.0 Ga*

*14303, 1027.* WARREN *et al.* (1983) have described and analysed this shock-melted granite clast. Some areas retain a coarse-grained graphic texture, and a few grains of diaplectic K-feldspar remain unmelted. The original age of crystallisation is reliably known as $\geq 4.32$ Ga (MEYER *et al.*, 1991), through ion probe U-Pb dating of euhedral, presumably comagmatic zircon grains within the clast. Multiple analyses have been made of K-feldspar and, mainly, plagioclase in three polished thin sections of the clast (Fig. 1). Altered zones within the feldspars contain U and Th, especially in the PTS 14303, 205, but other areas are devoid of those elements and free of fractures. The Pb concentrations vary considerably, but most were on the order of 1

ppm. Despite the comparatively low Pb level, we are not aware of any effects due to surface contamination in the U- and Th-free areas except for one extremely low-Pb area (33.2, Table 1).

All Pb isotope data from the 14303 feldspars share two features: high $^{207}\text{Pb}/^{206}\text{Pb}$ that averages 1.56 and a distinct internal trend when displayed in $^{207}\text{Pb}/^{206}\text{Pb}$ *vs.* $^{208}\text{Pb}/^{206}\text{Pb}$ coordinates (Fig. 12). This trend is wrong for admixture with meteoritic or terrestrial contamination, but it is consistent with contamination by external Pb characterised by $^{207}\text{Pb}/^{206}\text{Pb}$ at *ca.* 1.45 and $^{208}\text{Pb}/^{206}\text{Pb}$ *ca.* 0.85 (Fig. 12), which could form in U-rich mineral phases outside the analysed areas. Presumably the mechanism for contamination was thermally induced Pb isotope exchange which accompanied the high temperatures to which the clast was plainly exposed. On this interpretation, the true initial $^{207}\text{Pb}/^{206}\text{Pb}$ for the granite will be at the higher end of the measured range, say 1.65, or beyond. Its upper limit will be 1.78, corresponding to single-stage U/Pb evolution from 4.55 to 4.32 Ga in a source having high $\mu$ (*ca.* 1500). (We can think of no process that would disperse the magmatic ratios towards higher $^{207}\text{Pb}/^{206}\text{Pb}$.)

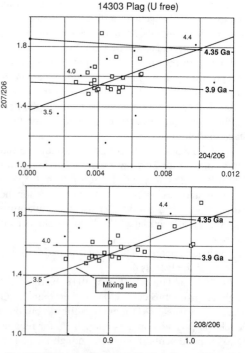

FIG. 12. Analyses of U-free plagioclase from granite clast 14303, 1027, showing a dispersion in composition consistent with mixing between initial Pb and radiogenic Pb. Scale of coordinates, reference lines, and curves as in Fig. 8.

It has not been possible to make a convincing independent estimate of the initial Pb ratios owing to the above internal trend. Suppose that the true ratios correspond to the highest U-free $^{207}Pb/^{206}Pb$ that can agree with each other to within error. The weighted mean for this group of 12 values is $1.62 \pm 0.02$ ($\sigma$), and the corresponding $^{204}Pb/^{206}Pb$ from the (poorly controlled) two-error regression of the observed $^{204}Pb/^{206}Pb$ $vs.$ $^{207}Pb/^{206}Pb$ is 0.0043. There are no possible two-stage paths from Canyon Diablo Pb to this point at the known age of the granite. A better estimate for the $^{204}Pb/^{206}Pb$ can be obtained via the assumed radiogenic Pb contaminant and the centroid of the $^{204}Pb/^{206}Pb$, $^{207}Pb/^{206}Pb$ regression, which gives 0.0060. However, there are no two-stage solutions for this also, which means that some higher point along the $^{207}Pb/^{206}Pb$, $^{204}Pb/^{206}Pb$ trend must be assumed. Various two-stage evolution models are possible above 1.65 for $^{207}Pb/^{206}Pb$ but results are sensitive to the numerical details. Nevertheless, it is clear that the 14303 granite source must have had high $\mu$ for most of the time between 4.55 and 4.32 Ga; it would be 1500 for a single-stage history (implying Pb depletion from the start of lunar existence) or higher during the second of any two-stage evolution.

$15405$. As already reported (COMPSTON $et$ $al.,$ 1989), plagioclase from the quartz monzodiorite clast in breccia 15405 (RYDER, 1976) records radiogenic initial Pb but low U and Th counts in the areas selected for analysis. This contrasts with thermal ionisation results for mineral grains from the same rock (TATSUMOTO and UNRUH, 1976), which gave much lower $^{207}Pb/^{206}Pb$ ratios (Fig. 13). The latter are evidently due to the high contents of U and Th present in the mineral separates and their resulting high contents of $in$ $situ$ radiogenic Pb. Very small U, Th-rich inclusions and/or fracture-fillings might occur in the hand-picked minerals, which can be avoided at the 30 $\mu$m sampling scale of ion-probe analysis. Combined, the two types of data indicate the mixing of leads of different origins: an initial Pb having $^{207}Pb/^{206}Pb \geq 1.33$; two $in$ $situ$ radiogenic leads corresponding to crystallization at 4.3 Ga and possible recrystallisation at $ca.$ 1.2 Ga, which is the time of Pb loss seen in some areas of zircon (MEYER $et$ $al.,$ 1991) as well as the Pb-Pb age given by whitlockites (TATSUMOTO and UNRUH, 1976); and either a low-$\mu$ meteoritic Pb in the rock or in the quartz monzodiorite magma or else a surface terrestrial contamination which would displace data points to the right in Fig. 13. The apparent initial $^{207}Pb/^{206}Pb$ of 1.33 is too low to permit two-stage evolution from 4.55 Ga, and we infer that younger radiogenic Pb must have been added to the plagioclase during later metamorphism.

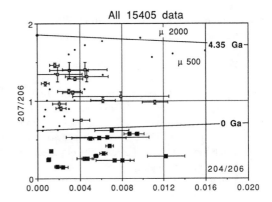

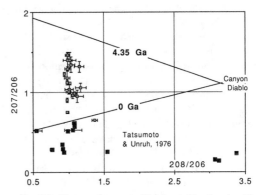

FIG. 13. Plots analogous to Fig. 2a and b, showing Pb analyses of minerals from the quartz monzodiorite clast in breccia 15405. Ion probe analyses of plagioclase (open symbols) show considerably higher $^{207}Pb/^{206}Pb$, and less dispersion in $^{204}Pb/^{206}Pb$ and $^{208}Pb/^{206}Pb$ than the thermal ionisation analyses of mineral separates by TATSUMOTO and UNRUH (1976).

## SUMMARY AND CONCLUSIONS

1. In each of the eight clasts or fragments of lunar granite and in one VHK basalt examined, Pb is concentrated in well-preserved feldspars at up to $ca.$ 30 ppm in certain Ba-rich feldspars. Also, nearly all of the inclusion-free areas of feldspar are devoid of U and Th at the sub-ppb level. This distribution is consistent with normal crystal-chemical controls in magmas. We therefore consider that this Pb is an original component of the granite magma, rather than introduced to the crystallised feldspars from an external source during later thermal events.

2. This Pb is very radiogenic, high in $^{207}Pb/^{206}Pb$ and very low in $^{204}Pb/^{206}Pb$. Such an isotopic composition labels the magma source as having had a very high $\mu$, up to 2000, for several hundred Ma prior to magma generation.

3. The crystallisation ages of all samples except the three fragments from breccia 72275, 20 are

known by independent isotopic dating. This places a strong constraint on Pb isotope modelling of the magma sources.

4. Using (numerical) modelling based on the initial Pb isotopic composition of the individual granites, their exact ages, and the Canyon Diablo Pb starting-point, none of the magma sources for the ≤4.0 Ga granites had a single-stage $\mu$ evolution (except possibly the 72275, 20 granites). Two-stage evolution is mandatory, and at least one of the stages must have had very high $\mu$. Nearly all sources are permitted a low-$\mu$ first stage, but the specific values cannot be determined.

5. The maximum time for the start of the second, high $\mu$ stage for several granites is *ca.* 4.3 Ga, which might signify a real lunar U-Pb fractionation event.

6. We have not succeeded in conclusively measuring the initial Pb isotope ratios in the two ≥4.3 Ga granites. Both are highly radiogenic, but their original ratios have been disturbed by addition of an external, younger radiogenic Pb. One, 14303, 205, has the highest lunar $^{207}Pb/^{206}Pb$ known at ≥1.65, which is the mean of ratios at the high end of a mixing line in $^{207}Pb/^{206}Pb$, $^{208}Pb/^{206}Pb$ coordinates defined by the collective data from all analysed samples.

7. Even 1.65 is too low to allow a two-stage (or single-stage) $\mu$ evolution to 4.32 Ga. The true initial $^{207}Pb/^{206}Pb$ must be higher still, and we have no way of correcting for the external Pb. Feldspars from the other 4.3 Ga granite likewise fail to allow two-stage solutions.

8. For 14303, the approximate age of the external radiogenic Pb is 3.5–4.0 Ga, but much younger radiogenic Pb is indicated for 15405. The former might correspond with high temperatures associated with a basin-forming impact, but the latter does not and is evidently associated with a comparatively minor impact.

9. The ion probe SHRIMP is very suitable for Pb isotope studies on existing lunar thin-sections. The effective terrestrial blank is less than 1 femtogram and often <0.1 fg. Useful results can be obtained at the level of 1 ppm (total) Pb at sensitivity 10 cps/ppm/ primary nA. The Moon itself is favourable for the purpose owing to the very high $\mu$ in substantial volumes of its crust and mantle, which generates large changes in Pb isotopic composition with time.

## REFERENCES

CARLSON R. W. and LUGMAIR G. W. (1988) The age of ferroan anorthosite 60025 oldest crust on a young Moon? *Earth Planet. Sci. Lett.* **90**, 119–130.

CLEMENT S. W. J. and COMPSTON W. (1989) SIMS at high sensitivity and high mass resolution. *Proc. 7th. Intl. Conf. Secondary Ion Mass Spectrometry.* J. Wiley & Sons.

COMPSTON W., FOSTER J. J. and GRAY C. M. (1975) Rb-Sr ages of clasts from within Boulder 1 Station 2 Apollo 17. *The Moon* **14**, 445–462.

COMPSTON W., FOSTER J. J. and GRAY C. M. (1977) Rb-Sr systematics in clasts and aphanites from consortium breccia 73215. *Proc. Lunar Sci. Conf. 8th,* 2525–2549.

COMPSTON W., WILLIAMS I. S. and MEYER C. (1984) U-Pb geochronology of zircons from lunar breccia 73217 using a sensitive high mass-resolution ion microprobe. *Proc. Lunar Sci. Conf. 14th; J. Geophys. Res.* **89**, B525–B534.

COMPSTON W., WILLIAMS I. S. and MEYER C. (1989) The Problem of Lunar initial Pb (abstr.). *Lunar Planet. Sci. Conf. 20th,* 179.

EBERHARDT P., GEISS J., GROGLER N. and STETTER A. (1973) How old is the crater Copernicus? *The Moon* **8**, 104–114.

JAMES O. B. (1977) Petrology of four clasts from consortium breccia 73215 (abstr.). *Lunar Planet. Sci. Conf. 8th,* 502–504.

JASSBERGER E. K., KIRSTEN T. and STAUDACHER TH. (1977) One rock and many ages—Further K-Ar data on consortium breccia 73215. *Proc. Lunar Sci. Conf. 8th,* 2567–2580.

MEYER C., COMPSTON W. and WILLIAMS I. S. (1985) Lunar zircon and the closure age of the lunar crust (abstr.). *Lunar Planet. Sci. Conf. 16th,* 557–558.

MEYER C., WILLIAMS I. S. and COMPSTON W. (1991) Direct evidence for ancient lunar granite (in prep.).

RYDER G. (1976) Lunar sample 15405 Remnant of a KREEP basalt-granite differentiated pluton. *Earth Planet. Sci. Lett.* **29**, 255–268.

SHIH C.-Y., NYQUIST L. E., BOGARD D. D., BANSAL B. M., WIESMANN H., JOHNSON P., SHERVAIS J. W. and TAYLOR L. A. (1986) Geochronology and petrogenesis of Apollo 14 very high potassium mare basalts. *Proc. Lunar Sci. Conf. 16th,* D214–D228.

SILVER L. T. (1970) Uranium-thorium-lead isotopes in some Tranquillity Base samples and their implications for lunar history. *Proc. Apollo 11 Lunar Sci. Conf.; Geochim. Cosmochim. Acta Suppl.* **1**, 533–1574.

STOESER D. B., MARVIN U. B. and BOWER J. F. (1974) Petrology and petrogenesis of Boulder 1. In *Interdisciplinary Studies of Samples from Boulder 1 Station 2 Apollo 17.* (ed. J. A. WOOD) Vol 2; *LSI Contrib. 211D,* III1–III51. Smithsonian Astrophysical Observatory, Cambridge, MA.

TATSUMOTO M. (1970) Age of the Moon: An isotopic study of U-Th-Pb systematics of Apollo 11 lunar samples—II. *Proc. Apollo 11 Lunar Sci. Conf.; Geochim. Cosmochim. Acta Suppl.* **1**, 1595–1612.

TATSUMOTO M. and UNRUH D. M. (1976) KREEP basalt age grain by grain U-Th-Pb systematics study of the quartz monzodiorite clast 15405 88. *Proc. Lunar Sci. Conf. 7th,* 2107–2129.

TATSUMOTO M., PREMO W. R., UNRUH D. M. (1987) Origin of lead from green glass of Apollo 15426 A search for primitive lunar lead. *Proc. Lunar Sci. Conf. 17th; J. Geophys. Res.* **92**, E361–E371.

TERA F., PAPANASTASSIOU D. A. and WASSERBURG G. J. (1974) Isotopic evidence for a terminal lunar cataclysm. *Earth Planet. Sci. Lett.* **22**, 1–21.

WARREN P. H., TAYLOR G. J., KEIL K., SHIRLEY D. N. and WASSON J. T. (1983) Petrology and chemistry of two "large" granite clasts from the Moon. *Earth Planet. Sci. Lett.* **64**, 175–185.

WARREN P. H., JERDE E. A. and KALLEMEYN G. W. (1987) Pristine Moon rocks: A large felsite and a metal-rich ferroan anorthosite. *Proc. Lunar Sci. Conf. 17th; J. Geophys. Res.* **92**, E303–E313.

Stable Isotope Geochemistry: A Tribute to Samuel Epstein
© The Geochemical Society, Special Publication No. 3, 1991
Editors: H. P. Taylor, Jr., J. R. O'Neil and I. R. Kaplan

# Silicon, carbon, and nitrogen isotopic studies of silicon carbide in carbonaceous and enstatite chondrites

J. STONE,* I. D. HUTCHEON,† S. EPSTEIN and G. J. WASSERBURG†

Division of Geological and Planetary Sciences, California Institute of Technology, Pasadena, CA 91125, U.S.A.

**Abstract**—Both carbonaceous and enstatite chondrites contain complex populations of silicon carbide (SiC) grains. SiC in carbonaceous chondrites contains highly anomalous Si, C, and N. Individual SiC grains and aggregates of sub-micron SiC analysed in this study show variations in $\delta^{29}Si$ and $\delta^{30}Si$ exceeding 120 per mil, $\delta^{13}C$ values ranging from $-300$ to $+24,500$, and $\delta^{15}N$ values between $-390$ and $-960$. This range of isotopic compositions suggests that the total SiC population consists of families of grains formed in a variety of stellar sites (ZINNER et al., 1989; TANG et al., 1989). One such family, common to Orgueil and Murchison, and distinguished by a platy surface morphology, contains consistently anomalous Si defining a binary mixing array in the Si three-isotope diagram. On formation, these grains incorporated varying proportions of two exotic Si components, one enriched in $^{28}Si$, the other in $^{29}Si$ and $^{30}Si$ relative to normal Si. Grains belonging to this family are consistently enriched in $^{13}C$ and $^{14}N$ relative to the solar isotopic compositions of these elements. The most plausible source for these grains is the circumstellar envelope of a low-mass red giant star on the Asymptotic Giant Branch (AGB) (GALLINO et al., 1990). In this case, the $^{28}Si$-rich component represents the seed composition preserved in the stellar envelope, to which was added $^{29}Si$ and $^{30}Si$ produced by neutron capture during He-burning. Enrichments in $^{13}C$ and $^{14}N$ are attributable to proton capture following convective dredge-down of H into the top of the He layer. The poor correlation of C and N with Si isotopes in the platy SiC grains suggests condensation over a number of convective mixing episodes, which enriched the stellar envelope in $^{13}C$ and $^{14}N$ to differing degrees.

Silicon carbide grains in Indarch differ in size and surface texture from those found in the carbonaceous chondrites. None of the Indarch grains analysed in this study contains isotopically anomalous Si or C, an observation difficult to reconcile with high concentration of the $^{22}Ne$-rich component, Ne-E(H), found in Indarch acid residues (HUSS, 1990). The grains analysed in this study either belong to a SiC family distinct from that presumed to host Ne-E(H), or formed in a region characterised by isotopically normal Si and C but anomalous Ne. In the former case, a solar-system origin for the grains analysed in this work cannot be ruled out.

## INTRODUCTION

EARLY CARBON ISOTOPIC studies revealed that the C2 chondrite Murchison contained an oxidation-resistant phase highly enriched in $^{13}C$ (SWART et al., 1982; YANG and EPSTEIN, 1984). This phase was found to persist in acid-dissolution residues of the meteorite, allowing it to be concentrated relative to isotopically normal material for more detailed study. Its acid resistance and breakdown temperature in stepwise-heating experiments led SWART et al. (1982) to suggest that this phase might also be the carrier of the anomalous noble gas components Ne-E(H) (rich in $^{22}Ne$) and Xe-S (dominated by isotopes made in s-process nucleosynthesis) found previously in Murchison residues (SRINIVASAN and ANDERS, 1978). Ion microprobe studies confirmed

---

\* *Present address:* Research School of Earth Sciences, Australian National University, G.P.O. Box 4, Canberra, A.C.T. 2601, Australia.

† *Also at:* Lunatic Asylum of the Charles Arms Laboratory, Division of Geological and Planetary Sciences, California Institute of Technology, Pasadena, CA 91125, U.S.A.

that $^{13}C$ enrichments in Murchison were concentrated in micron-sized grains, some with $\delta^{13}C$ values as high as $+7000$ (NIEDERER et al., 1985; ZINNER and EPSTEIN, 1987). Ion microscopy carried out by ZINNER and EPSTEIN (1987) showed $Si^+$ ion emission spatially associated with the $^{13}C$-rich carbon, suggesting silicon carbide as a possible carrier phase. The search culminated with identification of SiC by transmission electron microscopy (TEM) in several Ne-E- and Xe-S-rich residues of the Murray (C2) meteorite (BERNATOWICZ et al., 1987), and ion probe measurements which showed that this phase contained not only anomalous C, but Si and N with unusual isotopic compositions as well (ZINNER et al., 1987).

Silicon carbide grains in the C2 meteorites show features characteristic of material formed outside, and presumably prior to, the solar system. They are required to have condensed from a gas with C/O $> 1$ (LARIMER and BARTHOLOMAY, 1978), in contrast to the refractory oxide and silicate phases in their host meteorites. The isotopic compositions of their constituent atoms, Si and C, differ strongly from solar values (ZINNER et al., 1987, 1989; TANG *et al.*, 1989; STONE *et al.*, 1990, 1991). The same is true of trace N, Ne, Kr, Xe, Ca, Ti, Sr, Ba, and Nd incorporated in the grains (TANG and ANDERS, 1988; OTT *et al.*, 1988; ZINNER *et al.*, 1989, 1991a; OTT and BEGEMANN, 1990; LEWIS *et al.*, 1990; IRELAND *et al.*, 1991). At least some fraction of the SiC contains excess spallation $^{21}$Ne relative to bulk Murchison, suggesting a period of pre-solar irradiation (ZINNER *et al.*, 1989; LEWIS *et al.*, 1990).

Now that the existence of these exotic grains has been established, particular goals in further isotopic studies are to identify the environments in which they formed and to investigate the nucleosynthetic processes acting in those environments. Silicon, carbon, and nitrogen isotopic compositions, and the abundances of Ne-E and Xe-S, vary widely among SiC grain size fractions (*e.g.,* TANG *et al.*, 1988; TANG and ANDERS, 1988; ZINNER *et al.*, 1989). Large variations are also observed in Si, C, and N isotopic compositions amongst the coarsest SiC grains analysed individually in the ion microprobe (TANG *et al.*, 1989; ZINNER *et al.*, 1989; ALEXANDER *et al.*, 1990). It was believed until recently that the isotopic variability of Si must have originated through explosive nucleosynthesis in novae or supernovae; however, the combined presence of H-burning, He-burning, and s-process nucleosynthesic signatures in the C, N, and noble gas isotopic compositions of SiC pointed to an origin in red giant stars. The incompatibility between isotopic variations in Si and those in C, N, and the noble gases led to the interpretation that populations of grains with distinct Si isotopic compositions must have originated in (as many as six) separate red giant stars (TANG *et al.*, 1989; ZINNER *et al.*, 1989; ALEXANDER *et al.*, 1990). Clearly, a starting point for understanding the astrophysical phenomena through which these grains formed and evolved must be separation of the complex SiC population into its constituent families of related grains.

We undertook this work in an attempt to look for and understand the isotopic covariation of Si, C, and N in meteoritic SiC. In producing and characterising our acid residues, it became apparent that the goal of separating SiC into genetically related families of grains could best be achieved, at least for coarse grain sizes, by (1) using textural criteria observable by scanning electron microscopy (SEM) and (2) by confining our attention to grains large enough to be analysed individually. We attempted to enhance the efficiency of our search for families of related grains by producing residues from meteorites of different classes, since it seemed conceivable that the processes responsible for the distinctive features (*e.g.,* oxidation state, abundance

of refractory material) of these classes might also have selected amongst various types of pre-solar material (HUSS, 1990).

## EXPERIMENTAL METHODS

### Acid residues

Four meteorites were chosen for examination: Orgueil (CI), Murchison (CM2), Leoville (C3V), and Indarch (E4). These differ principally in their bulk compositions, contents of refractory phases, overall "matrix" abundance, oxidation state, and degree of hydrothermal alteration, all dictated by $P$, $T$ and $fO_2$ conditions which might have governed the preservation of SiC (HUSS, 1990). It was hoped that the comparative SiC contents of these meteorites would indicate the solar system processes crucial to SiC survival or destruction, potentially pointing to other samples rich in this and other exotic phases. Previous attempts to isolate SiC used the isotopically anomalous noble gas tracers Ne-E and Xe-S to indicate the abundance of SiC (TANG *et al.*, 1988; TANG and ANDERS, 1988; ANDERS, 1988). Early noble gas studies of the Leoville (MATSUDA *et al.*, 1980) and Indarch (CRABB and ANDERS, 1982) meteorites showed little evidence of Ne-E or Xe-S (though optimal methods for revealing these components, involving stepwise extraction of Ne and Xe from strongly oxidised acid residues, were not employed in either study). Accordingly, we included these meteorites in our set of samples to search for SiC components *not* associated with anomalous noble gases. Since commencing this work, HUSS (1990) has reported moderately high Ne-E concentrations in both Qingzhen (EH3) and Indarch, and SiC has been observed in Qingzhen (ALEXANDER *et al.*, 1991). The SiC abundance determined for Indarch in the course of this work, and that inferred by HUSS (1990) from Ne-E measurements, is discussed below.

Acid residues were prepared from whole meteorite samples (*i.e.,* without preliminary separation of chondrules and refractory inclusions from matrix material). As detailed below, comparison between SiC abundances found in these residues and those produced from matrix separates (TANG *et al.*, 1988; TANG and ANDERS, 1988; SWAN *et al.*, 1989; ZINNER *et al.*, 1989) provides information about the siting of the SiC. The dissolution procedures adopted follow those developed by the Chicago group for isolation of SiC (ALAERTS *et al.*, 1980; TANG *et al.*, 1988; TANG and ANDERS, 1988); the processing scheme is summarised in Fig. 1. Centimetre-sized pieces of each sample (some including fusion crust) were rinsed with distilled $H_2O$, methanol and benzene, then dissolved in 9 M HF/1 M HCl at approximately 50°C. For Indarch, rich in Fe-Ni metal, the HF treatment was preceeded by treatment with 3 M HCl. Fresh reagents were added as required to sustain reaction, typically at 6–12 hourly intervals, and sample tubes were sonicated for 30–60 minutes after each change. Each HF/HCl step was followed by treatment first with 6 M HCl and then with 1 M $AlCl_3$, successfully preventing formation of insoluble fluorides. After 4–6 of these cycles, the samples were again treated with organic solvents, followed by two further HF/HCl steps, leaving "CF" residues.

At this stage, the standard procedure was modified to allow recovery of coarse refractory material (such as hibonite and spinel) for Mg and Ti isotopic studies. The residues were suspended in methanol, to which $CS_2$ was added, forming a denser, immiscible phase. After vigorous

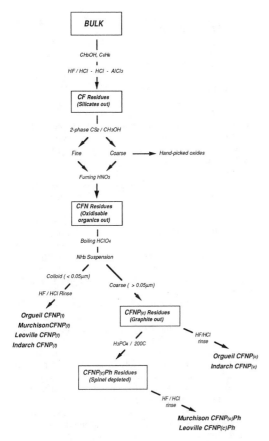

FIG. 1. Flowchart indicating methods used to concentrate SiC, as discussed in text. Procedures (reaction times, number of cycles per step) varied somewhat between samples according to amounts of metal/silicates/organics, etc. to be removed.

shaking, fine-grained material, especially black carbonaceous matter, separated into the methanol phase, whereas coarse, dense grains sank freely into the $CS_2$. After decanting the fine-grained suspension, centrifuging and drying, coarse grains could be hand-picked from the Orgueil and Murchison $CS_2$ fractions. (No attempt was made to recover equivalent material from Leoville; treatment of the Indarch residue in the above manner failed to yield any coarse material in the $CS_2$ phase.)

After recombining the coarse and fine fractions, the CF residues were oxidised, first in fuming $HNO_3$ (two changes, each 6–8 hours at 50–80°C) and then in boiling $HClO_4$ (two changes, each 1–2 hours). Reaction with $HClO_4$ was terminated on (sudden) bleaching of the formerly black suspensions, leaving small quantities of pale grey material. This was reacted briefly with HF/HCl, to dissolve any silica formed in the previous steps (cf. ZINNER et al., 1987) and to remove a gelatinous orange precipitate formed on cooling of the $HClO_4$.

The oxidised "CFNP" residues were taken up in 5 ml of $NH_3$ solution, sonicated to suspend fine material (principally Cδ diamond, which was found to form a colourless colloid in basic solution by TANG and ANDERS, 1988 then

separated into supernatant "CFNP$_{(f)}$" and residual "CFNP$_{(c)}$" fractions. This procedure was repeated 5–6 times, transferring the bulk of each residue into the fine-grained (<.05 μm) fraction. These fine-grained samples were given a final wash in HF/HCl to ensure removal of silica, rinsed, and stored under distilled methanol. The procedure was terminated at this stage for the Indarch and Orgueil residues, whose microgram-sized coarse fractions had become invisible in the base of their sample tubes.

The comparatively abundant coarse material remaining in the Murchison and Leoville residues was heated in 5 ml of 100% $H_3PO_4$ to ~200°C for three hours. The samples were observed to decrease in volume and darken (cf. TANG et al., 1988); however, the treatment appears to have been terminated prematurely, as the final residues of both samples retain substantial quantities of spinel. In preference to risking contamination in weighing of the microgram residues, weights were estimated from optical microscope and SEM grain counts of aliquotted material. These values (presented in Table 1) are estimated to be accurate to within a factor of about two, adequate for comparative purposes.

### Grain identifications

Aliquots of the residues were mounted on Au foils for SEM, electron probe, and ion probe analyses, using techniques similar to those described by MCKEEGAN et al. (1985). The 0.13 mm 99.99% Au foils were anchored by cold pressing (using a clean, stainless steel tool guided to form a flat Au surface) onto slotted upper surfaces of brass ion probe stubs. After briefly re-annealing the Au (hardened by pressing), the foils were washed in methanol and sputter-cleaned in an ion mill with 10 kV $Ar^+$ ions.

Acid residue grains were dispersed over the foils from a drop of distilled methanol and embedded by gentle pressing, using a second, work-hardened Au foil mount. The press was changed for each sample, to prevent carry-over of the few grains which inevitably lodged in its surface. Embedding with a second clean foil was found preferrable to pressing with a quartz disc (MCKEEGAN et al., 1985); the latter method failed to embed grains uniformly over the slightly undulating surfaces of the mounts and appeared also to result in Si contamination of the foil surfaces. Grains up to 10 μm, pressed deeply into the Au foils, showed little tendency to charge under ion probe primary beam currents of up to 2 nA, though some charging occurred under electron beams of ~10 nA.

After mounting, grains were examined in the SEM. SiC could be tentatively distinguished from other possible Si-bearing phases (such as silica precipitated during the chemical processing), by its high yield of Si X-rays (SWAN et al., 1989). Identifications made with the SEM were confirmed by semi-quantitative wavelength-dispersive X-ray analyses for C, N, and O in the electron probe. In addition to those SiC grains located and characterised in the SEM, a number of SiC grains were found as $C^-$ "hot spots" in ion images. The sizes and surface textures of these grains are unknown. Judging from the intensity of their $Si^-$ and $C^-$ emission (and the fact that several sputtered away during analysis) most are (or were) on the order of ~1 μm.

### Ion probe isotopic analyses

(1) Silicon. The isotopic compositions of Si, C, and N in selected grains and aggregates were determined using the Panurge IMS-3f ion microprobe (HUTCHEON et al.,

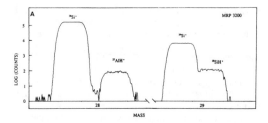

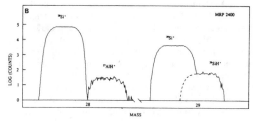

FIG. 2. Mass spectra showing resolution of isobars $^{28}Si^+$-$(^{27}AlH)^+$ and $^{29}Si^+$-$(^{28}SiH)^+$ at high mass resolving power (a), and partial overlap between $(^{28}SiH)^+$ and $^{29}Si^+$ at MRP = 2400 (b). The extent to which $Si^+$ ion yields can be maximised by degrading mass resolving power is dictated by overlap of intense $(^{27}AlH)^+$ beams (arising from Al-oxide grains in the residues) on $^{28}Si^+$ at resolving powers <2400.

1987). For the majority of the analyses, silicon was analysed as positive secondary ions, produced by a 0.2–0.5 nA $^{16}O^-$ primary beam rastered over a 20 $\mu$m square region surrounding each grain. The low sputter rate, <0.5 $\mu$m hr$^{-1}$, ensured preservation of material for C and N isotope studies. An 8 $\mu$m field aperture in the sample image plane transmitted only those ions originating at the centre of the rastered field, suppressing background $Si^+$ emission (from adjacent grains and impurities in and on the Au foil). In those cases in which the field aperture did not fully mask the sample grain, ion images were checked for other sources of $Si^+$ emission. Hibonite grains (containing a few percent $SiO_2$) were found to be the predominant source of spurious Si signals in the residues; these could be identified in ion images by their strong $Al^+$ and $Ca^+$ emission and, if necessary, avoided.

A mass resolving power (MRP) of greater than 3000 is required to separate fully hydride interferences $(^{28}SiH)^+$ and $(^{29}SiH)^+$ from isobaric $Si^+$ peaks, as shown in Fig. 2a. The high $(^{28}SiH)^+/^{29}Si^+$ ratios encountered when sputtering fine-grained material from the CFNP$_{(f)}$ series of residues required isotopic data to be taken at full resolving power. However, in order to maximise secondary ion transmission when analysing individual SiC grains, which yielded lower $(^{28}SiH)^+/^{29}Si^+$ ratios, resolving power was reduced to ~2400. This choice ensured separation of $^{28}Si^+$ from $(^{27}AlH)^+$ (arising from adjacent Al-bearing oxide grains), whilst limiting hydride tail contributions due to $(^{28}SiH)^+$ to <2 per mil of $^{29}Si^+$ signals (Fig. 2b), and yielding an ~2-fold gain in sensitivity. The overlap between $(^{28}SiH)^+$ and $^{29}Si^+$ was estimated at less than 2 per mil of the $^{29}Si^+$ signal both by peak stripping (Fig. 2b), and comparison of $^{29}Si/^{28}Si$ ratios measured at high and low MRP in synthetic SiC. The data reported here have not been corrected for this interference, as it proves negligible in comparison to isotopic effects intrinsic to the samples, and smaller

than the typical statistical uncertainties due to ion counting in the $^{29}Si^+$ measurements.

Additional Si isotopic measurements were made in conjunction with subsequent C isotopic analyses. In these runs, Si was analysed as $Si^-$ ions, sputtered by a ~0.1 nA $Cs^+$ primary ion beam defocussed over a 20 $\mu$m diameter area around the sample grain. The higher MRP of ~3500 required for concurrent C isotopic measurements (see below) ensured that the $Si^-$ peaks were free of isobaric interferences. As for positive ion analyses, a field aperture was employed to minimise $Si^-$ background contributions.

Nine of the negative ion analyses of Si isotopes were made on grains previously analysed using positive secondary ions, in order to check that sample grains could be relocated for C and N analyses, and to confirm the positive ion results. The comparison between measurements made with positive and negative secondary ions is shown in Fig. 3. The precision of the negative ion analyses is somewhat lower than that of the original data, due to the reduced transmission of the spectrometer at higher MRP. Nonetheless, the two sets of measurements are in full agreement, validating the positive ion results and confirming that the micron-sized SiC grains could be reliably relocated.

Sample Si isotopic compositions are expressed as $\delta^{29}Si$ and $\delta^{30}Si$, per mil deviations of $^{29}Si/^{28}Si$ and $^{30}Si/^{28}Si$ ratios, respectively, from values measured in synthetic SiC grains (5–10 $\mu$m grinding abrasive), mounted in an identical fashion to sample material. Sample to standard comparisons were made separately for the positive and negative secondary ion data, and in the former case relate data taken at the same mass resolving power. As an indication of the reproducibility of the data, the total scatter of Si isotope measurements on the synthetic SiC grains is shown in Fig. 4. For positive ion data this amounted to < ±2 per mil over the course of the study and was better than ±1.5 per mil on any given day, whilst the negative ion results scattered over a larger range of ±4 per mil, with a daily variability of ~ ±3 per mil. Instrumental mass fractionation for positive ion analysis of SiC, calculated by comparison of standard runs (made at high MRP) to the ref-

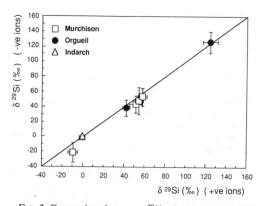

FIG. 3. Comparison between $\delta^{29}Si$ values measured with positive and negative secondary ions on the same sample grains. The data intersect a line of slope 1, indicating (1) good agreement between the $Si^+$ and $Si^-$ measurements, (2) homogeneity of the grains over the depth sputtered in successive analyses, and (3) reliable relocation of grains on the sample mounts.

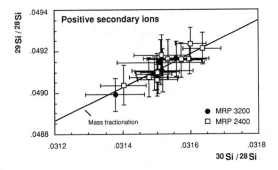

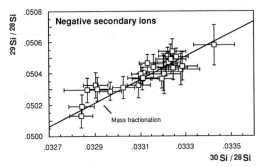

FIG. 4. SiC standard grain analyses made in the course of this work. Analyses of Si⁺ secondary ions are shown in the top panel, analyses of Si⁻ secondary ions in the lower panel. Note that mass fractionation is much less for Si⁻ than Si⁺ analyses. A power law mass-fractionation line drawn through the mean of the high MRP Si⁺ data (dark symbols, top panel) intersects the normal $^{29}Si/^{28}Si$ value of 0.0506331 (BARNES *et al.*, 1975) at $^{30}Si/^{28}Si = 0.033464$ ± 0.000040, in agreement with the value of 0.033450 ± 0.000066 calculated from the Si⁻ data. Note that standard data taken at low MRP (open symbols, top panel) are not substantially displaced from the fractionation line, indicating <2% interference of $(^{28}SiH)^+$ at $^{29}Si^+$. Indicated uncertainties are ±2σ.

erence $^{29}Si/^{28}Si$ value of 0.0506331 (BARNES *et al.*, 1975) is −30.3 per mil per amu, and that for negative ion analysis is −5.2 per mil per amu. This enrichment of the lighter Si isotopes is characteristic of ion probe Si isotope measurements. It is noteworthy that the $^{30}Si/^{28}Si$ ratios of the same SiC runs, corrected individually for fractionation using a power law fractionation function, indicate reference $^{30}Si/^{28}Si$ ratios of 0.033464 ± 0.000040 (positive secondary ions) and 0.033450 ± 0.000066 (negative secondary ions), in agreement with the value 0.033474 suggested by ZINNER *et al.* (1989), but differing significantly from the accepted value of 0.0336214 (BARNES *et al.*, 1975).

*(2) Carbon.* Carbon isotopic compositions were measured in a second series of runs, after heating the sample mounts to ~450°C in air for periods of 8–12 hours to remove carbonaceous material which might have survived the SiC separation procedure, and contaminants residing on the sample surfaces. Isotopic measurements were made on C⁻ secondary ions sputtered by a ~0.1 nA Cs⁺ primary beam, as described above for Si⁻ analyses. A MRP of ~3500 was used to resolve the $^{13}C^-$ signal from interfer-

ence by $(^{12}CH)^-$ ions. In order to check for spurious C contributions, the Si⁻/C⁻ ion yield was measured for each sample grain and compared to the mean value measured for synthetic SiC standard grains. In all but two cases the Si⁻/C⁻ ratios of sample grains agreed with that of the standard (1.28 ± .15). The low Si⁻/C⁻ ratios shown by two grains (Orgueil G3 and Murchison G7; see Table 2) indicate extraneous carbon contributions and suggest that the $\delta^{13}C$ values measured on these grains may underestimate their true values. No corrections have been applied to these data, however, as the $\delta^{13}C$ value of the contaminant is unknown. Neither of these grains was analysed subsequently for N isotopes.

Carbon isotopic data are expressed as $\delta^{13}C$ values (analogous to $\delta^{29}Si$ and $\delta^{30}Si$ values) relative to the conventional PDB standard, for which $^{13}C/^{12}C = 0.011235$ (CRAIG, 1957). Delta values were first calculated relative to the mean $^{13}C/^{12}C$ ratio measured on synthetic SiC standard grains and these results adjusted to the PDB scale using a $\delta^{13}C_{PDB}$ value of −30.0‰ for the standard SiC (analysed in bulk by conventional mass spectrometry). The mean $^{13}C/^{12}C$ ratio for synthetic SiC grains measured by ion probe was 0.010488 ± 0.000034 (2σ, $n = 25$ analyses) representing an instrumental fractionation of −37.6 per mil. Deviation of individual standard analyses from this mean value amounted to < ±6.5 per mil over the course of the study, and < ±3 per mil on any given day.

*(3) Nitrogen.* In their initial work on meteoritic SiC, ZINNER *et al.* (1987) showed that isotopic measurements could be made on trace amounts of N contained in SiC. Sputtering does not produce monatomic N secondary ions, but generates intense CN⁻ emission from C-rich samples. This allowed N isotopes to be measured on a subset of the grains analysed for Si and C, in a third series of runs, using procedures similar to those described by ZINNER *et al.* (1989). A defocussed ~0.2 nA Cs⁺ primary beam was used and the secondary beam masked by an 8 μm field aperture. The analyses were made at a MRP of ~6500. Under these conditions overlap between $(^{13}C_2)^-$ and $(^{12}C^{14}N)^-$ was eliminated, and well-resolved $(^{12}C^{15}N)^-$ and $(^{13}C^{14}N)^-$ signals could be collected at the mass 27 position, allowing C and N isotopic ratios to be determined simultaneously. The C isotopic data measured in this way (Fig. 5) showed satisfactory agreement with the results of $^{13}C^-/^{12}C^-$ analyses and confirmed that previously analysed grains had been relocated. A single exception (Orgueil G4; Table 2) gave $\delta^{13}C$ values of +907 and +609 in two successive analyses, compared to its original value of +1240, and these runs gave distinct Cn⁻/C⁻ ratios of 0.05 and 0.46, respectively. This may represent a case of mistaken identity, or the original grain may have been a composite.

Cn⁻/C⁻ ratios were measured during each analysis but cannot be used to calculate absolute N concentrations due to lack of a suitable N-bearing SiC standard. Nitrogen data are presented as $\delta^{15}N$ values, relative to the conventional air N standard ($^{15}N/^{14}N = 0.003676$; JUNK and SVEC, 1958). In order that data produced in this study be directly comparable to those of the Washington University group (ZINNER *et al.*, 1987, 1989, 1991b), we chose the same compound used previously, 1-hydroxybenzotriazole hydrate ($C_6H_5N_3O \cdot H_2O$) with $\delta^{15}N_{AIR} = -12$, as a working standard. The fact that N isotopic fractionation accompanying CN⁻ emission from this compound (−11 per mil) may differ from that accompanying emission from SiC adds some uncertainty to $\delta^{15}N$ measurements made in this way, though as discussed by ZINNER *et al.* (1989), this

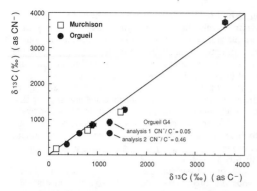

FIG. 5. Comparison between $\delta^{13}C$ values measured on the same sample grains using $C^-$ and $(CN)^-$ secondary ions. The data show reasonable agreement with the 1:1 line. The tendency of the $(CN)^-$ analyses to yield values lower than those originally measured using $C^-$ secondary ions may reflect build-up of carbonaceous contaminants (with normal $\delta^{13}C$ values) during and after the $C^-$ analyses. Orgueil G4 (indicated) is either heterogeneous, or was mislocated in repeat analyses (though these analyses gave similar $\delta^{15}N$ values of $-706 \pm 106$ and $-748 \pm 43$).

source of systematic error is likely to be small and will not affect the conclusions drawn below.

## RESULTS

### Acid residues

Details of the coarse-grained acid residues examined in this study are summarised in Table 1 (the weights and mineral contents of the fine-grained samples have not been determined). In all of the residues, silicon carbide is a minor phase relative to oxides, ranging in fractional abundance from ~1% in Leoville $CFNP_{(c)}Ph$ to ~20% in Indarch $CFNP_{(c)}$. The Orgueil and Indarch residues, not processed through $H_3PO_4$, are dominated by spinel. In addition, a few grains of chromite and hibonite occur in the Orgueil sample. Both Orgueil and In-

darch contain small grains (<2 $\mu m$) showing only a Ti X-ray line, possibly $TiO_2$ as suggested by ALEXANDER et al. (1989), a Ti-fluoride, or in the case of Indarch, perhaps osbornite, TiN. Titanium carbide, as observed by BERNATOWICZ et al. (1991), is a further possibility, though it is unlikely that coarse grains of this phase would have survived the acid dissolution procedures. Several grains showing only a Sn X-ray line (possibly cassiterite, $SnO_2$) occur in the Indarch residue. The final $H_3PO_4$ treatment applied to the Murchison and Leoville residues substantially reduced their spinel contents. However, spinel persists as coarse (mostly >1 $\mu m$) rounded grains at the 10–20% level in both these residues, in which hibonite and corundum are the major phases. Both residues also contain grains showing only a Ti X-ray line. The high corundum and hibonite contents of Murchison $CFNP_{(c)}Ph$ and Leoville $CFNP_{(c)}Ph$ most likely reflect the abundance of refractory aggregates and inclusions in the parental samples of these residues. Murchison residues described by ZINNER et al. (1989) contain SiC amounting to ~6 ppm of initial *matrix* material (*i.e.,* ~3 ppm of total meteorite, assuming ~50% matrix in Murchison), accompanied by only ~1 ppm of oxide grains. In comparison, the Murchison residue prepared in this study is equivalent to 3.4 ppm SiC accompanied by ~70 ppm insoluble oxides, indicating a much lower ratio of SiC to oxides in the refractory component of Murchison than in its matrix.

These observations highlight an interesting feature of the variability in SiC/refractory oxide ratios of the three carbonaceous chondrites examined— differences in this ratio are governed by differences in oxide abundance, with SiC concentrations remaining comparatively uniform. This conclusion is similar to that reached by HUSS (1990), who inferred the abundance of SiC in a large number of chondrites from their Ne-E(H) concentrations.

Table 1. Coarse-grained acid residues (>0.1 $\mu m$ fractions)

| Sample | Initial weight | Acid treatment[1] | Residue fraction (ppm)[2] | SiC fraction (ppm)[2] | | Other phases[3] |
|---|---|---|---|---|---|---|
| | | | | <1 $\mu m$ | >1 $\mu m$ | |
| Orgueil | 2.10 g | CF, N, P | 30 | 3 | 0.6 | Sp, Chr, (Co), (Hib) |
| Murchison | 9.89 g | CF, N, P, Ph | 95 | 3 | 0.4 | Sp, Chr, Cr-Sp, Hib, Co |
| Leoville | 2.76 g | CF, N, P, Ph | 400 | 4 | <0.2 | Sp, Chr, Cr-Sp, Hib, Co |
| Indarch | 10.85 g | C, CF, N, P | 2 | 0.3 | 0.1 | Sp, Chr, (Co) |

[1] C: 3M HCl, CF: 1M HCl/10M HF, N: fuming $HNO_3$, P: boiling $HClO_4$, Ph: $H_3PO_4/200°C$.

[2] Expressed as fractions of bulk meteorite. Residue weights estimated from SEM grain counts, considered accurate to a factor of ~2.

[3] Sp: spinel, Chr: chromite, Cr-Sp: Cr-spinel, Hib: hibonite, Co: corundum. Phases noted in brackets present at <2%.

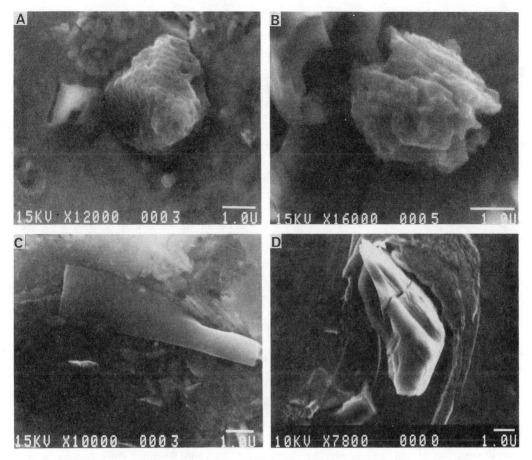

FIG. 6. SEM micrographs showing SiC grains from acid residues. Note the "platy" surface texture of SiC from Orgueil (a) and Murchison (b), in contrast to the conchoidally fractured and smooth surfaces of SiC grains in Indarch (c and d). The scale bar is 1 $\mu$m in all images.

There are discrepancies between the absolute SiC concentrations estimated by HUSS (1990) and those determined in this work, however, especially in the case of Leoville. It is difficult to compare the two sets of abundance estimates, since both may have been affected by losses during chemical processing and the abundances reported in this work do not include SiC in the CFNP$_{(f)}$ series of residues. Perhaps the tendency for the abundance of coarse-grained ($>1$ $\mu$m) SiC relative to fine SiC ($<1$ $\mu$m) to diminish from Orgueil to Murchison to Leoville reflects the same metamorphic process responsible for the variation in Ne-E(H) concentrations observed by HUSS (1990).

Silicon carbide in the Indarch CFNP$_{(c)}$ residue appears to occur at an abundance approximately one-tenth that in the carbonaceous chondrites (Table 1). This relative abundance is roughly in agreement with the Ne-E(H) data reported by HUSS (1990), though as in the case of the carbonaceous

chondrites, the absolute SiC abundance inferred from the Ne data is 2–3 times higher than that estimated in this work.

The contrasting abundances and grain sizes of SiC between carbonaceous and enstatite chondrites are also reflected in the physical characteristics of the grains. The coarse SiC grains encountered in the carbonaceous chondrite residues occur in (at least) two forms (Fig. 6, cf. TANG et al., 1989). Of the 22 coarse grains (from $2 \times 2$ $\mu$m to $9 \times 10$ $\mu$m) found in Orgueil (8), Murchison (11) and Leoville (3), 18 are approximately equant and characterised by a "platy" surface texture. Where grain shapes were evident, the "plates" appeared stacked normal to a 6-fold symmetry axis. This morphology suggests a $\langle 0001 \rangle$ cleavage or parting in hexagonal SiC (Fig. 6a), though some grains of this type may in fact possess cubic symmetry (WOPENKA et al., 1989). The remaining grains from Murchison and Leoville are rounded and smooth-surfaced. TANG et al.

(1989), ZINNER *et al.* (1989), and WOPENKA *et al.* (1989) report a somewhat higher relative abundance of what are described as "smooth-surfaced" grains (as opposed to "fluffy," "fuzzy," or "weathered" types) in their Murchison residues, and in addition they distinguish two types of smooth-surfaced grains—those with crystal faces and those with conchoidally fractured surfaces. However, it is uncertain whether differences between the coarse SiC population described by WOPENKA *et al.* (1989) and that reported here reflect heterogeneity in Murchison or differences in the starting materials (*i.e.,* presence or absence of coarse material) from which the two residues were prepared. The low abundance of smooth grains in our Murchison residue, and the apparent absence of these grains in our Orgueil sample, are unlikely to reflect differences between our extraction procedures and those employed by the Chicago group. The platy surface textures of some grains may have been enhanced by acid etching but are not artifacts of the procedure. Processing as far as the $HClO_4$ step failed to produce any platy grains in the Indarch residue. Nor can the platy textures have been etched by treatment with $H_3PO_4$, because platy grains are the sole type encountered in the Orgueil residue (which was never exposed to $H_3PO_4$). The $H_3PO_4$ treatment applied to Murchison and Leoville in this work was apparently milder than that employed by TANG *et al.* (1988), as it failed to dissolve spinel completely. In comparing our observations of acid residues with the observations of other workers, it should also be borne in mind that our method of locating SiC, by SEM searches, may have introduced a bias towards finding the distinctive "platy" variety of SiC.

In the Indarch residue, SiC occurs exclusively as smooth-surfaced grains, and the proportion of coarse grains is higher than in the carbonaceous chondrite residues. The largest grain observed in the Indarch $CFNP_{(c)}$ residue, $20 \times 23$ $\mu$m, is much larger than any of the grains found in Orgueil, Murchison, or Leoville. Both equant and bladed forms are present, the latter showing conchoidal fracture surfaces in several cases (Fig. 6c and d). Bladed SiC grains in the Indarch residue resemble the smooth-surfaced Murchison grains described and illustrated by TANG *et al.* (1989; Fig. 1, upper photos) and ZINNER *et al.* (1989; Fig. 4, upper right and lower left photos). In addition to SiC, the coarse Indarch residue contains grains (up to 10 $\mu$m) of an unidentified Si- and N-bearing phase. The most likely candidate for this phase is $Si_3N_4$, rather than sinoite ($Si_2N_2O$), as electron probe analyses show no indication of O (note that sinoite is also reported to be soluble in HF/HCl; CRABB and ANDERS, 1982).

$Si_3N_4$ is a plausible companion to the reduced phases found in E-chondrites, and has been observed both *in situ* in, and in acid residues prepared from, the EH3 chondrite Qingzhen (ALEXANDER *et al.,* 1991).

*Isotopic results*

The Si, C, and N isotopic compositions of SiC aggregates and individual coarse grains from the various acid residues are presented in Tables 2–4 and illustrated in Figs. 7–12. The dimensions and surface textures of those individually analysed grains characterised with the SEM are also tabulated. Note that the mineralogy and SiC contents of the finer-grained $CFNP_{(f)}$ samples are unknown. Isotopic analyses of these samples were made by rastering the primary beam over clumps of uncharacterised material, and it is presumed, but not certain, that the bulk of Si and C ion emission originated from fine-grained SiC. For clarity, the following discussion of the isotopic data deals separately with (1) the platy SiC grains in the coarse Orgueil and Murchison residues, (2) aggregates and uncharacterised SiC grains from Orgueil and Murchison, and (3) SiC from Indarch.

*(1) Coarse SiC in Orgueil and Murchison—* $CFNP_{(c)}$ *residues.* Silicon isotopic measurements were made on grains belonging to the class of coarse, platy SiC grains described above. Results are listed in Table 2 and illustrated in Fig. 7. All of the platy grains found in Orgueil (8 out of 8 SiC grains $>2$ $\mu$m) and Murchison (9 of 11) were analysed. Unfortunately, the sole coarse ($\sim 1.5$ $\mu$m) platy SiC grain observed in Leoville could not be relocated in the ion probe for isotopic analyses. Though the Si data have been discussed previously (STONE *et al.,* 1990, 1991) several points may be stressed again here.

Silicon in grains belonging to this group is consistently isotopically anomalous. In contrast to the fine-grained SiC in Orgueil, Murray and Murchison (see below, and ZINNER *et al.,* 1987, 1989), these grains show a simple, linear distribution of Si isotopic compositions in the Si three-isotope plot of Fig. 7. The slope of this array, $\delta^{29}Si/\delta^{30}Si \sim 1.4$, precludes mass-dependent fractionation or addition of any one isotope as possible causes of isotopic variability. The array does not intersect the normal Si isotopic value ("N" in these and subsequent figures), suggesting that the grains are formed from mixtures of two exotic Si components, neither related to solar Si. The $^{29}Si/^{30}Si$ ratio of the component enriched in $^{29}Si$ and $^{30}Si$ is given by the slope of the

Table 2. Platy SiC from Orgueil and Murchison

| $\delta^{29}Si$ (per mil) $\pm 2\sigma^{(1)}$ | $\delta^{30}Si$ (per mil) $\pm 2\sigma^{(1)}$ | $\delta^{13}C$ (per mil) $\pm 2\sigma^{(2)}$ | $(Si^-/C^-)^{(4)}$ | $\delta^{15}N$ (per mil) $\pm 2\sigma$ | $CN^-/C^-$ | Notes |
|---|---|---|---|---|---|---|
| Orgueil CFNP$_{(c)}$. Coarse grains (>2 $\mu$m) | | | | | | |
| 42.2 ± 3.8 | 46.9 ± 4.4 | 1548 ± 57 | 1.16 | −394 ± 76 | 1.6 | 10 × 11 $\mu$m |
| 67.5 ± 9.4 | 75.4 ± 9.6 | 518 ± 17 | 1.08 | — | — | 3 × 3 $\mu$m |
| 15.7 ± 7.7 | 35.9 ± 8.0 | 741 ± 55$^{(3)}$ | 0.86$^{(3)}$ | — | — | (Photo Fig. 6a) 3 × 3 $\mu$m |
| 43.0 ± 6.5 | 51.5 ± 9.9 | 1240 ± 17 | 1.10 | −706 ± 106$^{(5)}$ | 0.05$^{(5)}$ | 8 × 7 $\mu$m |
| 75.4 ± 7.0 | 70.7 ± 7.7 | 620 ± 11 | 1.19 | −817 ± 38 | 0.11 | 6 × 4 $\mu$m |
| 23.8 ± 6.4 | 41.2 ± 4.7 | 366 ± 26 | 1.13 | −864 ± 53 | 0.11 | 4 × 5 $\mu$m |
| 69.6 ± 6.4 | 68.6 ± 9.8 | 3603 ± 53 | 1.25 | −962 ± 26 | 1.0 | 3 × 2 $\mu$m |
| 124.2 ± 7.0 | 110.7 ± 7.2 | 903 ± 65 | 1.16 | −902 ± 50 | 0.09 | 4 × 5 $\mu$m |
| Murchison CFNP $_{(c)}$Ph. Coarse grains (>2 $\mu$m) | | | | | | |
| 26.1 ± 8.0 | 40.8 ± 8.3 | — | — | — | — | 3 × 3 $\mu$m |
| 51.2 ± 6.0 | 55.7 ± 6.0 | 1468 ± 43 | 1.19 | −461 ± 48 | 0.17 | 4 × 5 $\mu$m |
| 33.5 ± 26.3 | 42.7 ± 29.9 | — | — | — | — | 2 × 2 $\mu$m |
| −9.6 ± 4.5 | 24.6 ± 6.3 | 794 ± 30 | 1.19 | −890 ± 41 | 0.06 | 4 × 4 $\mu$m |
| 45.0 ± 10.5 | 66.9 ± 12.4 | 432 ± 50 | 1.08 | — | — | (Photo Fig. 6b) 2 × 2 $\mu$m |
| 58.1 ± 4.2 | 68.2 ± 4.3 | 155 ± 27 | 1.35 | −855 ± 40 | 0.15 | 6 × 4 $\mu$m |
| 49.5 ± 11.3 | 54.6 ± 9.6 | 353 ± 41$^{(3)}$ | 0.76$^{(3)}$ | — | — | 2 × 3 $\mu$m |
| 75.3 ± 9.3 | 71.9 ± 12.6 | 5188 ± 64 | 1.35 | — | — | 2 × 3 $\mu$m |
| 54.6 ± 4.1 | 54.2 ± 4.7 | 515 ± 42 | 1.24 | — | — | 4 × 4 $\mu$m |

[1] Data tabulated are $Si^+$ secondary ion data. [2] Data tabulated are $C^-$ secondary ion data. [3] $(Si^-/C^-)$ indicates extraneous carbon. [4] Individual data ± ~0.05. SiC standard gives 1.28 ± 0.15. [5] Possibly extraneous N. Repeat analysis gave $CN^-/C^- = 0.46$.

array in co-ordinates of $^{29}Si/^{28}Si$ *vs.* $^{30}Si/^{28}Si$, and equals ~2.1. In the same co-ordinates, the array intersects the $(^{30}Si/^{28}Si)$ axis at 0.013, indicating a minimum ~1.3% abundance of $^{30}Si$ (at $^{29}Si = 0$) in the $^{28}Si$-rich component.

The data shown in Fig. 7 are in good agreement

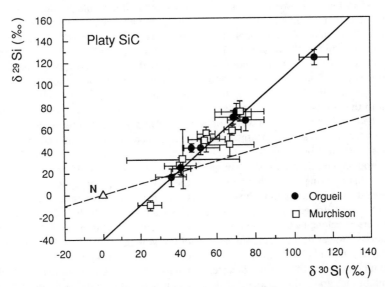

FIG. 7. Si isotope analyses of coarse platy SiC from Orgueil (dark circles) and Murchison (open squares) CFNP$_{(c)}$ residues. Note that the weighted, least-squares fit to the data (solid line) bypasses the point (N) corresponding to normal Si. Its slope of ~1.4 is distinct from that produced by mass fractionation, shown as a dashed line of slope 0.5. Uncertainties indicated are ±2σ.

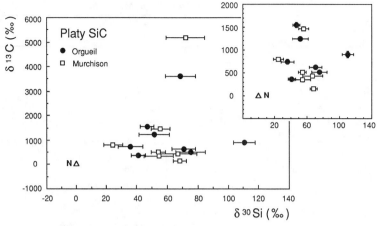

FIG. 8. Carbon isotopic compositions (shown as $\delta^{13}C$ values) plotted against silicon isotopic compositions for platy SiC from Orgueil (dark circles) and Murchison (open squares). Detail in the range $0 < \delta^{13}C < 1600$ is shown in the inset. Note that C isotopic measurements could only be made on 15 of the 17 grains originally analysed for Si isotopes. The point "N" represents the solar Si and C isotopic compositions. Indicated uncertainties are $\pm 2\sigma$.

with other analyses of coarse Murchison SiC (TANG *et al.*, 1988; ZINNER *et al.*, 1989; AMARI *et al.*, 1991). Nine grains (those described as equidimensional) from the Murchison acid residue HO (TANG *et al.*, 1989; ZINNER *et al.*, 1989) conform to the array in Fig. 7, and appear to belong to the same SiC population as the platy grains. A further ~70 grains (in the size range from 1.6–6 μm) from another Murchison residue KJG (AMARI *et al.*, 1991) have Si isotopic compositions distributed about the same correlation line as in Fig. 7. However, the spread of these data is greater than observed in the 17 analyses reported here; $\delta^{30}Si$ values for a number of the KJG grains extend out to the $^{30}$Si-poor side of the array by as much as ~40 per mil. Mixing of two isotopically invariant components cannot account for the outliers amongst the KJG grains. If these outliers belong to the family of "platy" grains described above, then a mixing process in which one or both end-members varied somewhat in their Si isotopic compositions must be invoked.

There are several physical scenarios which might account for the binary mixing trend shown by the Si isotopic measurements. One is that the coarse grains are composites—formed by aggregation of fine-grained precursors belonging to two isotopically distinct populations. However, the grains appear in SEM images (*e.g.*, Fig. 6a and b) to be single crystals, and Si isotopic inhomogeneities were not detected while sputtering through grains during analysis. Alternatively, mixing may have involved gas-phase heterogeneity in the region in which the grains formed or gas-grain isotopic exchange post-dating

their formation. In the former case, the platy grains may have formed in an environment characterised by isotopic heterogeneity over the length-scales sampled during condensation of grains or by temporal variations during the period in which the grains formed. In the latter, differing degrees of Si isotope exchange between a family of grains and an isotopically distinct gas phase could account for the Fig. 7 array.

Further constraints on the mixing process are provided by the C and N isotopic compositions of the platy SiC grains. As shown in Fig. 8, the grains are consistently enriched in $^{13}$C, with $\delta^{13}C$ values ranging from +155 to ~5190. Importantly, there is no evidence of a correlation between Si and C isotopic compositions; those grains representing extreme degrees of $^{13}$C enrichment, with $\delta^{13}C$ values of +155 and ~5190, have very similar $\delta^{30}Si$ values, of +68 and +75, respectively. Nitrogen in the platy grains is consistently enriched in $^{14}$N. Delta N-15 values range from −394 to −962 (Fig. 9), the latter representing a ~25-fold enhancement in $^{14}$N over the solar N isotopic composition. The Orgueil grain, G14, in which this extreme value occurs is also characterised by a high $\delta^{13}C$ value of ~3600, and it is noteworthy that the $^{13}C/^{12}C$ and $^{14}N/^{15}N$ ratios of this grain are ~0.2× and ~0.3× the ratios produced by equilibrium proton capture in CNO-cycle nucleosynthesis. Unfortunately, only seven of the grains originally analysed for Si isotopes survived in sufficient quantities for N analysis; in particular it was not possible to measure N in Murchison grain G8, with an even more extreme $^{13}$C enrichment.

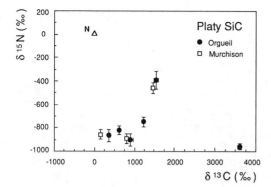

FIG. 9. Variation of nitrogen isotopic compositions (plotted as $\delta^{15}N$ values) with carbon isotopic compositions (as $\delta^{13}C$) in the platy SiC grains from Orgueil (dark circles) and Murchison (open squares). The absence of a correlation between these isotopic ratios applies also to variation between N and Si isotopes. Only nine of the platy SiC grains survived, or produced sufficiently intense (CN)⁻ beams, for N analyses. The point "N" denotes the solar N and C isotopic compositions. Indicated uncertainties are $\pm 2\sigma$.

Other than in the case of Orgueil G14 noted above, there is little evidence of a correlation between excess $^{13}C$ and $^{14}N$ in the platy grains, nor between their N and Si isotopic compositions.

The C and N data rule out simple binary mixing models for the platy SiC grains. In order to account for the spread of C and N isotopic compositions, more than two components must have participated in the formation of the grains, or the components involved must have varied in their C/Si and C/N ratios during condensation of SiC. The well-correlated isotopic variation of Si presumably arises through the involvement of several "components" sharing a common Si isotopic composition, disguising the multi-component nature of the array in Fig. 7. For example, products of nucleosynthetic processes such as H-burning, which do not affect the Si isotopes, could be highly enriched in $^{13}C$ and $^{14}N$ and varied in their C/N ratios, whilst retaining the Si isotopic composition of their seed material.

*(2) Fine-grained SiC in Orgueil and Murchison.* Silicon and carbon analyses were made on several otherwise uncharacterised grains from the Murchison and Orgueil CFNP$_{(c)}$ mounts. A number of analyses were also made of aggregates of sub-micron SiC from the Orgueil CFNP$_{(c)}$ and CFNP$_{(f)}$ samples. The results of these analyses are grouped in Table 3 and illustrated in Figs. 10 and 11. This fine-grained material contains anomalous Si ranging in isotopic composition over a much broader area of the Si three-isotope diagram than does Si in the coarse,

platy SiC grains (Fig. 10). The isotopic compositions of the fine-grained SiC scatter to both sides of the correlation line (Fig. 7) defined by the platy grains. In addition to grains with isotopic compositions like those of coarse Orgueil and Murchison SiC, this material must therefore contain (at least) two additional grain populations, with compositions in the ($\delta^{29}Si > 0$, $\delta^{30}Si < 0$) and ($\delta^{29}Si < 0$, $\delta^{30}Si > 0$) quadrants of Fig. 10. Similar conclusions apply to the fine-grained SiC in Murchison and Murray analysed by ZINNER *et al.* (1987, 1989) and to SiC in a number of the ordinary chondrites studied by ALEXANDER *et al.* (1990).

The C isotopic compositions of aggregates and uncharacterised grains in Orgueil and Murchison range even more widely than those of the platy SiC grains. For clarity in Fig. 11, the extreme range of isotopic compositions is plotted logarithmically, showing $^{12}C/^{13}C$ ratios rather than delta values. Delta C-13 values for these grains vary from $-303$

Table 3. Fine-grained SiC from Orgueil and Murchison.

| $\delta^{29}Si$ (per mil) $\pm 2\sigma$ | $\delta^{30}Si$ (per mil) $\pm 2\sigma$ | $\delta^{13}C$ (per mil) $\pm 2\sigma$ |
|---|---|---|
| Orgueil CFNP$_{(c)}$. Uncharacterised individual grains ($\sim 1\ \mu m$) | | |
| 54 ± 65 | 46 ± 35 | 2750 ± 80 |
| 31.9 ± 8.9 | 29.1 ± 10.4 | 4260 ± 990 |
| 47.0 ± 10.4 | 46.9 ± 10.9 | 1100 ± 50 |
| Murchison CFNP$_{(c)}$Ph. Uncharacterised individual grains ($\sim 1\ \mu m$) | | |
| 25 ± 18 | −19 ± 20 | 17,710 ± 580 |
| 8 ± 17 | 51 ± 20 | −304 ± 24 |
| Orgueil CFNP$_{(c)}$. Aggregates of fine grains ($<1\ \mu m$) | | |
| 49.1 ± 11.5 | 62.2 ± 11.2 | — |
| 30.8 ± 10.1 | 40.0 ± 10.4 | — |
| Orgueil CFNP$_{(f)}$. Aggregates of fine grains ($<0.1\ \mu m$) | | |
| −5 ± 21 | 59 ± 34 | — |
| 40 ± 17 | 51 ± 25 | — |
| 40 ± 17 | 42 ± 20 | — |
| 24.2 ± 8.0 | 22.1 ± 8.8 | — |
| 42 ± 16 | −23 ± 21 | — |
| −1.3 ± 4.7 | 17.9 ± 5.9 | — |
| 15 ± 18 | 19 ± 20 | 24,500 ± 850 |
| 27 ± 15 | 10 ± 15 | 9250 ± 1200 |
| 29 ± 10 | 45 ± 12 | 2070 ± 150 |
| 45 ± 12 | −5 ± 15 | 1770 ± 180 |
| −20 ± 8 | 22 ± 11 | 1322 ± 200 |
| 31 ± 10 | 27 ± 11 | 920 ± 180 |

Note: Analyses listing C isotopic data made using negative secondary ions. All others analysed as Si⁺.

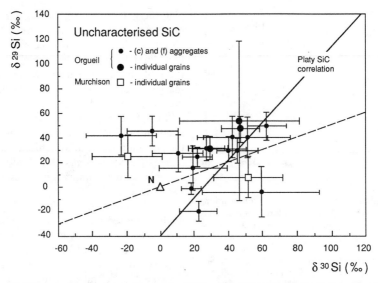

FIG. 10. Silicon isotope analyses of fine-grained SiC measured as individual ~1 μm grains (Orgueil, large dark circles; Murchison, open squares) and as aggregates of grains ~0.1 μm or smaller from Orgueil (small dark circles). Silicon isotope compositions of these grains scatter widely about the trend shown by coarse platy SiC in Orgueil and Murchison, denoting the presence of further exotic Si components in the fine-grained material. The point labelled "N" denotes normal Si, and the dashed line indicates compositions related to normal Si by mass fractionation. Uncertainties are ±2σ.

to 24,500, thus covering a range of $^{12}C/^{13}C$ ratios from greater than the solar value (89) through to values predicted for proton capture in the CNO cycle (~4). The negative $\delta^{13}C$ value found in one of the Murchison grains is particularly significant, as it implies the involvement of a $^{12}C$-rich component (in addition to any material with a near-solar $^{12}C/^{13}C$ ratio) in formation of the grains.

*(3) Indarch residues.* Silicon analyses of the Indarch CFNP$_{(c)}$ and CFNP$_{(f)}$ residues are presented in Table 4 and illustrated in Figs. 12a (individual grains) and 12b (aggregates). The isotopic compositions of coarse grains from Indarch CFNP$_{(c)}$ cluster around the point corresponding to normal Si, and define a trend roughly parallel to a mass-dependent fractionation trajectory of slope 0.5. It should be noted that the heaviest isotopic composition measured in an individual grain ($\delta^{30}Si = +12$) occurs in one of the N-rich grains, not in SiC. It is possible that the instrumental fractionation for the Si,N phase is different to that for SiC, in which case normalisation of this analysis to SiC standard measurements may have resulted in an incorrect estimate of the fractionation intrinsic to the grain. Two data points suggest small deficits in $^{29}Si$, but additional analyses are required to confirm this effect, as both fall within ~3σ of the mass-fractionation line. Note that these measurements and the standard

analyses to which they are normalised were made at high MRP. The effects are not due to normalisation of the sample data to standard runs at low resolving power, which could result in apparent $^{29}Si$ deficits due to hydride interferences in the standard measurements.

Silicon in fine-grained material from the Indarch CFNP$_{(c)}$ and CFNP$_{(f)}$ residues also clusters around the normal isotopic composition. Several analyses show enrichment in heavy Si isotopes. One of these falls slightly off the mass-fractionation line, suggesting enrichment in $^{29}Si$, or depletion in $^{28}Si$ or $^{30}Si$ in some fraction of the aggregated grains sputtered during this analysis. This is potentially an important observation; because most of the SiC grains in the Indarch residues appear to contain normal Si (as indicated by the coarse grain data shown in Fig. 12a) the net anomaly recorded in this run may signify the presence of a highly anomalous Si component contained in a small fraction of the CFNP$_{(f)}$ grains. A further separation of the Indarch CFNP$_{(f)}$ residue in the hope of enriching this component, and future measurements at higher precision will be required to clarify the possible presence of anomalous Si in Indarch SiC.

In keeping with these results, ALEXANDER *et al.* (1991) found isotopically normal Si in a number of Si,N-bearing grains (presumed to be Si$_3$N$_4$) from the EH3 chondrite Qingzhen. In contrast to the

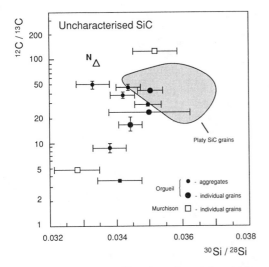

FIG. 11. Carbon and silicon isotopic variations in fine-grained SiC from Orgueil and Murchison. For clarity, the data are shown as isotopic ratios ($^{12}C/^{13}C$ and $^{30}Si/^{28}Si$) rather than delta values, and the C data have been plotted logarithmically to illustrate their extreme variability. For comparative purposes, note that $^{12}C/^{13}C$ ratios found in the platy SiC grains range from $\sim 14$ to $\sim 77$. The point labelled "N" indicates the solar C and Si isotopic ratios. Uncertainties are $\pm 2\sigma$.

scant evidence of isotopically anomalous SiC in Indarch, however, the sole SiC grain encountered by ALEXANDER *et al.* (1991) was found to have $\delta^{29}Si$ and $\delta^{30}Si$ values of +50 and +58, respectively.

Negative $\delta^{13}C$ values were measured in three Indarch SiC grains. The range of values, $-37 < \delta^{13}C < -4$, is comparable to that of trace carbon released at high temperatures in stepwise combustion of Indarch (GRADY *et al.,* 1986) and is typical of solar-system reservoirs.

## ISOTOPIC VARIABILITY OF METEORITIC SILICON CARBIDE

The search for SiC in CM meteorites was originally motivated by the suggestion of a common carrier for excess $^{13}C$ and the exotic noble gas components Ne-E and Xe-S (SWART *et al.,* 1982). It was not anticipated that, once isolated, SiC would be found to exhibit an extensive *range* of Si, C, and N isotopic compositions, complicating models for the origin of these grains. Major questions posed by the data relate to (1) the nuclear processes and stellar sites responsible for isotopic variation in the total SiC population, (2) distinctions between fine-grained SiC and the family of platy grains common to Orgueil and Murchison, (3) the origin of well-correlated Si isotopic variations in the platy SiC

and why these variations are decoupled from those in C and N isotopes, and (4) the source of isotopically normal SiC in Indarch.

It should be stressed at the outset that the isotopic variability observed in SiC from the carbonaceous chondrites cannot arise from physical or nuclear processing (after formation) of an initially uniform population of grains. The wide range of Si three-isotope data (Figs. 7 and 10) relative to any mass-dependent fractionation line (of slope 0.5) rules out kinetic processes such as evaporation, sputtering, or diffusive isotopic separation in accounting for gross Si isotopic differences amongst the grains. Because the fraction of "anomalous" atoms in the grains is so large (>10% in SiC with $\delta^{13}C \sim 25,000$), nuclear processes such as spallation or neutron capture *in situ* can also be discounted. Isotopic variation in these grains must be ascribed to stellar nucleosynthesis.

*Nucleosynthetic components and stellar origins for SiC in carbonaceous chondrites*

Clues to the stellar origins of SiC in the carbonaceous chondrites may be found by comparing the isotopic compositions of this material with nucleosynthetic model calculations. In general, production of $^{28}Si$ is dominated by oxygen-burning in supernovae and their precursor stars, whereas production of the neutron-rich Si isotopes is divided between contributions from He-, C-, and Ne-burning (WOOSLEY, 1986; CLAYTON, 1988). The latter two processes are associated with supernovae, while He-burning occurs in a variety of stellar environments including red giants, supernovae, and Wolf-Rayet stars. Silicon produced by O-burning ranges from pure $^{28}Si$ to compositions containing small amounts of $^{30}Si$ (THIELEMANN and ARNETT, 1985; WOOSLEY, 1986). Relative yields of $^{29}Si$ and $^{30}Si$ in He-, C-, and Ne-burning vary with the nucleosynthetic conditions (WOOSLEY, 1986), such that mixtures of these components with O-burning products encompass the Si isotopic variations observed in SiC. Condensation of SiC from undiluted C-, Ne-, or O-burning components (*e.g.,* in supernova outflows) is unlikely due to the low C/O ratios resulting from these processes. The isotopic signatures of these processes could be inherited by SiC grains formed in late-generation stars, however. Also, small amounts of C-, Ne-, or O-burning products with high $^{29,30}Si$/O ratios, added to C-rich regions of supernovae, could impart their Si isotopic signatures without lowering C/O ratios below the threshold for SiC condensation. Carbon-13 and nitrogen-14 enrichments found in the majority of SiC grains

Table 4. Indarch SiC.

| $\delta^{29}$Si (per mil) $\pm 2\sigma$ | $\delta^{30}$Si (per mil) $\pm 2\sigma$ | $\delta^{13}$C (per mil) $\pm 2\sigma$ | Notes |
|---|---|---|---|
| **Indarch CFNP$_{(c)}$ Coarse grains (>2 $\mu$m)** | | | |
| $-1.1 \pm 2.8$ | $-3.7 \pm 4.7$ | $-36.8 \pm 5.5$ | — |
| $-3.0 \pm 3.5$ | $-3.0 \pm 4.5$ | $-3.8 \pm 9.8$ | — |
| $1.4 \pm 2.3$ | $5.3 \pm 3.5$ | $-23.4 \pm 7.7$ | — |
| $-0.6 \pm 2.9$ | $2.3 \pm 2.9$ | — | $20 \times 23\ \mu$m |
| $-6.5 \pm 7.3$ | $-3.0 \pm 8.0$ | — | — |
| $-1.1 \pm 5.2$ | $-5.2 \pm 5.6$ | — | $4 \times 4\ \mu$m |
| $-10.5 \pm 5.9$ | $-6.5 \pm 8.0$ | — | (Photo Fig. 6d) $8 \times 2\ \mu$m |
| $2.8 \pm 1.9$ | $11.9 \pm 2.3$ | — | Si$_3$N$_4$ (?) $10 \times 10\ \mu$m |
| $-19.8 \pm 17.4$ | $-0.5 \pm 18.1$ | — | $2 \times 3\ \mu$m |
| $-2.4 \pm 5.3$ | $-4.4 \pm 7.1$ | — | $3 \times 3\ \mu$m |
| $1.6 \pm 2.5$ | $6.7 \pm 3.0$ | — | $10 \times 1\ \mu$m |
| **Indarch CFNP$_{(c)}$. Aggregates of fine grains (<1 $\mu$m)** | | | |
| $4.0 \pm 11.0$ | $4.6 \pm 12.5$ | — | — |
| $-0.6 \pm 7.3$ | $-5.6 \pm 9.6$ | — | — |
| $1.6 \pm 3.0$ | $3.3 \pm 4.2$ | — | — |
| $0.7 \pm 2.7$ | $5.0 \pm 3.3$ | — | — |
| **Indarch CFNP$_{(f)}$. Aggregates of fine grains (<0.1 $\mu$m)** | | | |
| $12.7 \pm 6.4$ | $18.1 \pm 9.0$ | — | — |
| $10.0 \pm 12.7$ | $-2.3 \pm 6.2$ | — | — |
| $5.6 \pm 10.4$ | $6.5 \pm 8.9$ | — | — |
| $15.7 \pm 7.5$ | $12.3 \pm 7.5$ | — | — |

Note: Analyses listing C isotopic data made using negative secondary ions. All others analysed as Si$^+$.

point to H-burning contributions, while excess $^{12}$C (found in one grain in the course of this work, and in several others by AMARI et al., 1991) requires a He-burning source.

The isotopically varied SiC population could be derived from a large number of separate stars, marked by distinct isotopic compositions (TANG et al., 1989; ZINNER et al., 1989; ALEXANDER et al., 1990). A smaller number of stars could account for the population if these stars contained active Si-, C-, and N-producing regions. Possible sources combining sites for Si, C, and N isotope production with regions in which C/O > 1 (allowing SiC to condense; LARIMER and BARTHOLOMAY, 1978) include He-burning layers of progenitors to Type II supernovae, red giant stars on the Asymptotic Giant Branch (AGB), and C-rich Wolf-Rayet (WC) stars. Theoretical studies indicate that all are capable of producing $^{29}$Si and $^{30}$Si in appropriate abundances, as well as s-process isotopes and excess $^{22}$Ne characteristic of meteoritic SiC (ARNETT, 1987; HASHIMOTO et al., 1989; PRANTZOS et al., 1988; GALLINO et al., 1990; CASSÉ and PAUL, 1982; CASSÉ, 1983). He-burning in Type II supernovae and WC stars is a more likely source of $^{12}$C-rich SiC, while AGB stars can produce abundant $^{13}$C through episodic

H-burning (see below). Observational evidence that red giant stars are the major source of C-rich interstellar dust (BODE, 1988; GEHRZ, 1988), combined with the similarity between $^{12}$C/$^{13}$C ratios in SiC and carbon-rich red giant stars (TANG et al., 1989), favours red giants as the major SiC sources.

Clearly, a large number of possible stellar sources may be represented amongst the total SiC population of carbonaceous and ordinary chondrites. Discrimination between these sources is difficult in the case of fine-grained SiC analysed as aggregates, and where isolated, unrelated grains have been studied. More specific conclusions can be drawn regarding families of related grains, such as those separated by grain size (LEWIS et al., 1990; AMARI et al., 1991), which show coherent Ne, Kr, and Xe isotopic systematics, and the family of platy SiC identified in this work.

### Platy SiC in Orgueil and Murchison

The distinctive morphology and well-correlated Si isotopic compositions (Fig. 7) of the platy SiC found in Orgueil and Murchison set these grains apart from other types of SiC (Fig. 10) in their host meteorites. It should be noted that these grains were

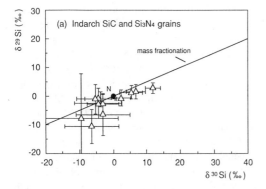

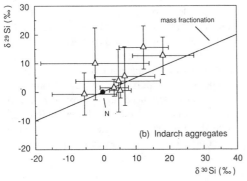

FIG. 12. (a) Si isotope analyses of coarse-grained SiC and Si₃N₄ (?) from the Indarch CFNP$_{(c)}$ residue. Analyses tend to cluster about the normal point (N) and the mass-fractionation trajectory passing through normal Si (solid line). Note the reduced scale compared to Figs. 7 and 10. Uncertainties are ±2σ.

(b) Analyses of aggregates of fine-grained SiC in the Indarch CFNP$_{(c)}$ and CFNP$_{(f)}$ residues. Again note the reduced scale relative to Figs. 7 and 10. Uncertainties are ±2σ.

first selected for analysis on the basis of their similar surface textures, and that the coherent Si isotopic systematics revealed by ion probe analyses reinforced the impression that they constitute a single family with a common origin. The issue of whether these grains formed around a single, isotopically heterogeneous star containing ²⁸Si-rich and ²⁹,³⁰Si-rich components, or a number of related stars, remains unresolved. The poor correlations among Si, C, and N isotopes are more easily reconciled with a number of parental stars, which differed in their H- and He-burning yields. If the grains originated in separate stars, however, these must have shared the same, non-solar, ²⁸Si-rich seed composition, and produced ²⁹Si and ³⁰Si under similar conditions in order to yield the isotopic array shown in Fig. 7. Red giant stars of similar age, formed in close association with one another, might satisfy these criteria.

Constraints available from analyses of SiC have provided an impetus for nucleosynthetic modelling, and attention has focussed on low-mass AGB stars as a source for SiC. Helium-burning and neutron capture proceeding from the reaction ¹³C($\alpha$, $n$)¹⁶O in intershell regions of AGB stars may account for characteristics of SiC such as excess ²²Ne and s-process effects in both light and heavy elements (IBEN and RENZINI, 1982; GALLINO et al., 1990; CLAYTON et al., 1991). An important feature which makes these stars likely sources of SiC is the evolution of cool, carbon-rich envelopes enriched in He-burning products by convective exchange with the stellar interior. Silicon carbide has been observed in the envelopes of several red giants, and C isotopic compositions measured in these stars compare well with the range found in the platy SiC grains (LEAHY et al., 1987; MARTIN and ROGERS, 1987; LAMBERT, 1989).

Theoretical models predict that, in thermally pulsing AGB stars, dredge-down of H from the stellar envelope into the He layer produces an intershell region enriched in ¹³C (and ¹⁴N). Subsequent He-burning (producing ¹²C and ²²Ne) engulfs the intershell region and supplies neutrons for s-process synthesis via the reaction ¹³C($\alpha$, $n$)¹⁶O. Convection initiated by the He-burning pulse then mixes ¹²C, ¹³C, ¹⁴N, ²²Ne, and s-process isotopes up to the stellar envelope (IBEN and RENZINI, 1982; GALLINO et al., 1990; CLAYTON et al., 1991). Within this framework, the Si isotopic trend of Fig. 7 could be interpreted as the product of mixing between a ²⁸Si-enriched precursor component preserved in the stellar envelope and freshly synthesized Si from the He layer of such a star. The following discussion examines the models in the light of isotopic effects preserved in the platy SiC grains.

First, the poor correlations between Si, C, and N isotopes suggest that the grains sampled the products of several dredge-up cycles marked by different isotopic compositions and relative abundances of C, N, and Si. Alternatively, prompt condensation of SiC after a single dredge-up event, on a timescale shorter than that required to mix the stellar envelope, could account for the isotopic variability. If the grains formed over a number of thermal pulses, then changes in parameters, such as initial H fraction, temperature, and neutron exposure, responsible for C and N isotopic shifts from pulse to pulse, had little effect on the ²⁹Si/³⁰Si production ratio, preserving the Si isotope correlation. Though the production ratio appears insensitive to burning conditions in successive pulses, the value of ~2.1 estimated from the slope of Fig. 7 is at variance with theoretical predictions of ~0.94 (GALLINO et *al.,* 1990) and ∼0.6–1.1 (CLAYTON *et al.,* 1991). Agreement between AGB model predictions and measured s-process effects in heavy elements such as Kr and Xe (LEWIS *et al.,* 1990) and Ba (ZINNER *et al.,* 1991) is somewhat better than for Si (this work) and Ti (IRELAND *et al.,* 1991). This suggests that current models are limited by uncertainties in cross-section data for competing $(n, \gamma)$, $(n, \alpha)$ and $\alpha$-particle reactions amongst the light elements. A further point of comparison between AGB models and the platy-grain data concerns the prevalence of anomalies in the proton-capture isotopes $^{13}C$ and $^{14}N$ in the SiC grains. Evolutionary models imply that dredge-up of $^{12}C$ from the He shell drives the C/O ratio of the stellar envelope past the threshold value of ∼1 required for SiC condensation. The isotopic data suggest, however, that H-burning also contributes C to the envelope and that the threshold for SiC formation is reached well before the $^{12}C/^{13}C$ ratio exceeds the solar value.

*Local and exotic SiC*

The presence of large isotopic anomalies in SiC from the carbonaceous chondrites identifies these grains as extra-solar in origin. It appears that this exotic SiC resides in the matrix, not in refractory material (HUSS, 1990), because residues produced from the matrix of carbonaceous chondrites (*e.g.,* ZINNER *et al.,* 1989) contain similar quantities of SiC to those produced from meteorites in bulk (this study). The same conclusion has been reached *via* SiC abundance measurements made by X-ray mapping (SWAN *et al.,* 1989; ALEXANDER *et al.,* 1989). Like other material of pre-solar origin present in the matrix of carbonaceous chondrites (such as D-rich organic compounds, YANG and EPSTEIN, 1984; EPSTEIN *et al.,* 1987), SiC must have experienced a low-temperature history in the solar nebula. Exposure to the hot, oxidising conditions responsible for formation of chondrules and refractory inclusions should have resulted in SiC breakdown (LARIMER and BARTHOLOMAY, 1978).

In contrast to SiC in the carbonaceous chondrites, the isotopic data for Indarch SiC (and $Si_3N_4$) suggest formation in isotopic equilibrium with a gas of solar Si and C isotopic composition. It is therefore important to establish whether Indarch SiC grains of the type analysed in this work host the Ne-E(H) found in Indarch residues (HUSS, 1990). If not, Indarch might be inferred to contain other pre-solar phases, or pre-solar SiC grains so rare (and therefore also $^{22}Ne$-rich) that none were encountered in this study.

The low abundance of SiC preserved in Indarch

(∼0.4–1.3 ppm; this study and HUSS, 1990) contrasts with the large fraction of Si expected to condense as SiC during cooling of a C-rich gas of solar composition. For example, in a cooling solar gas with a C/O ratio of ∼1.1, 50% of the Si destined to form silicates condenses as SiC before undergoing reactions with $Mg_{(g)}$ and CO to produce Mg silicates (LARIMER and BARTHOLOMAY, 1978). The fact that less than ∼$10^{-5}$ of the bulk Si in Indarch survives in SiC indicates that retrograde equilibration between gas and solid phases continued down to temperatures below the stability limit of SiC. If this process destroyed exotic SiC with the same efficiency as it destroyed SiC predicted to have formed in the solar system, then exotic SiC should not be found in the E-chondrites. Either the Ne-E(H) in these meteorites is hosted by another phase, or like the SiC of carbonaceous chondrites, the exotic SiC of E-chondrites is part of a "matrix" component which never experienced high temperatures in the solar nebula (HUSS, 1990). If the latter is true, it follows that the oxidation state of the high-temperature component of meteorites is a poor guide to likely SiC concentrations.

## CONCLUSIONS

Carbonaceous and enstatite chondrites contain distinct types of SiC. Silicon carbide grains in carbonaceous chondrites contain large Si, C, and N isotopic anomalies, indicating an extra-solar origin. The SiC analysed (thus far) from the enstatite chondrite Indarch contain Si and C of near-normal isotopic composition, and the possibility that these formed in the solar system cannot be ruled out on the basis of the available data.

The total SiC population of carbonaceous chondrites is a complex mixture of families of grains marked by distinct morphologies and Si isotopic characteristics. Isotopic differences amongst the total population of SiC may reflect a variety of nucleosynthetic processes, operating in a number of separate stars (TANG *et al.,* 1989; ZINNER *et al.,* 1989).

One family of texturally distinctive, platy SiC grains, common to Orgueil and Murchison, appears to have formed by mixing of two exotic Si components. Four criteria may be inferred for the source of this family of grains: (1) C/O > 1; (2) a density high enough to permit condensation; (3) the presence of two Si components, enriched in $^{28}Si$ and $^{29,30}Si$, respectively; and (4) variable degrees of enrichment in $^{13}C$ and $^{14}N$, decoupled from Si isotope effects. In combination with measurements of s-process isotope effects (*e.g.,* ZINNER *et al.,* 1991a) and astronomical evidence for dust production by red giant stars (BODE, 1988; GEHRZ, 1988), these constraints suggest an origin in the circumstellar envelope of an AGB star. There is good qualitative agreement between isotopic measurements of platy SiC and model predictions for grains formed episodically in an AGB envelope. Further insight into the stellar source may follow more detailed modelling aimed at reproducing the $^{29}Si/^{30}Si$ production ratio and the C isotopic compositions recorded by the platy SiC grains.

*Acknowledgments*—We thank L. Hedges for assistance with sample preparation, J. Armstrong for help with light element analyses on the electron probe, and J. Cali for assistance with C and N isotopic analyses of our standards. This work was supported by NASA grants NAG 9-46 (S.E.) and NAG 9-43 (G.J.W.). Division Contribution No. 4924 (715).

## REFERENCES

ALAERTS L., LEWIS R. S., MATSUDA J. and ANDERS E. (1980) Isotopic anomalies of noble gases in meteorites and their origins. VI. Presolar components in the Murchison C2 chondrite. *Geochim. Cosmochim. Acta* **44**, 189–209.

ALEXANDER C. M. O'D., HOHENBERG C., PIER J. G., SWAN P. D., VIRAG A., WALKER R. M., ARDEN J. W. and PILLINGER C. T. (1989) SiC in the ordinary chondrites (abstr.). *Meteoritics* **24**, 247.

ALEXANDER C. M. O'D., ARDEN J. W., PIER J., WALKER R. M. and PILLINGER C. T. (1990) Ion probe studies of interstellar SiC in ordinary chondrites (abstr.). *Lunar Planet. Sci.* **XXI**, 9–10.

ALEXANDER C. M. O'D., PROMBO C. A., SWAN P. D. and WALKER R. M. (1991) SiC and Si3N4 in Qingzhen (EH3) (abstr.). *Lunar Planet. Sci.* **XXII**, 5–6.

AMARI S., ZINNER E. and LEWIS R. S. (1991) The C, N and Si isotopic compositions of SiC grain size separates from Murchison: Indirect evidence for highly anomalous grains (abstr.). *Lunar Planet. Sci.* **XXII**, 19–20.

ANDERS E. (1988) Circumstellar material in meteorites: Noble gases, carbon and nitrogen. In *Meteorites and the Early Solar System* (eds. J. KERRIDGE and M. S. MATTHEWS), pp. 927–955. Univ. Arizona Press, Tucson.

ARNETT W. D. (1987) Supernova theory and Supernova 1987A. *Astrophys. J.* **319**, 136–142.

BARNES I. L., MOORE L. J., MACHLAN L. A., MURPHY T. J. and SHIELDS W. R. (1975) Absolute isotopic abundance ratios and the atomic weight of a reference sample of silicon. *J. Res. Natl. Bureau Standards* **79A**, 727–735.

BERNATOWICZ T., FRAUNDORF G., TANG M., ANDERS E., WOPENKA B., ZINNER E. and FRAUNDORF P. (1987) Evidence for interstellar SiC in the Murray carbonaceous meteorite. *Nature* **330**, 728–730.

BERNATOWICZ T., AMARI S., ZINNER E. K. and LEWIS R. S. (1991) Interstellar grains within interstellar grains (abstr.). *Lunar Planet. Sci.* **XXII**, 89–90.

BODE M. F. (1988) Observations and modelling of circumstellar dust. In *Dust in the Universe* (eds. M. E. BAILEY and D. A. WILLIAMS), pp. 73–102. Cambridge Univ. Press.

CASSÉ M. (1983) Cosmic ray sources. In *Composition and Origin of Cosmic Rays* (ed. M. M. SHAPIRO), pp. 193–230. Reidel.

CASSÉ M. and PAUL J. A. (1982) On the stellar origin of the $^{22}Ne$ excess in cosmic rays. *Astrophys. J.* **258**, 860–863.

CLAYTON D. D. (1988) Stellar nucleosynthesis and chemical evolution of the solar neighbourhood. In *Meteorites and the Early Solar System* (eds. J. KERRIDGE and M. S. MATTHEWS), pp. 1021–1062. Univ. Arizona Press, Tucson.

CLAYTON D. D., OBRADOVICH M., GUHA M. and BROWN L. E. (1991) Silicon and titanium isotopes in SiC from AGB stars (abstr.). *Lunar Planet. Sci.* **XXII**, 221–222.

CRABB J. and ANDERS E. (1982) On the siting of noble gases in E-chondrites. *Geochim. Cosmochim. Acta* **46**, 2351–2361.

CRAIG H. (1957) Isotopic standards for carbon and oxygen and correction factors for mass-spectrometric analysis of carbon dioxide. *Geochim. Cosmochim. Acta* **12**, 133–149.

EPSTEIN S., KRISHNAMURTHY R. V., CRONIN J. R., PIZZARELLO S. and YUEN G. U. (1987) Unusual stable isotope ratios in amino acid and carboxylic acid extracts from the Murchison meteorite. *Nature* **326**, 477–479.

GALLINO R., BUSSO M., PICCHIO G. and RAITERI C. M. (1990) On the astrophysical interpretation of isotope anomalies in meteoritic SiC grains. *Nature* **348**, 298–302.

GEHRZ R. D. (1988) Sources of stardust in the galaxy. In *Interstellar Dust* (eds. L. J. ALLAMANDOLA and A. G. G. M. TIELENS), pp. 445–453. Kluwer Academic Press, Dordrecht.

GRADY M. M., WRIGHT I. P., CARR L. P. and PILLINGER C. T. (1986) Compositional differences in enstatite chondrites based on carbon and nitrogen stable isotope measurements. *Geochim. Cosmochim. Acta* **50**, 2799–2813.

HASHIMOTO M., NOMOTO K. and SHIGEYAMA T. (1989) Explosive nucleosynthesis in supernova 1987A. *Astron. Astrophys.* **210**, L5–L8.

HUSS G. R. (1990) Ubiquitous interstellar diamond and SiC in primitive chondrites: abundances reflect metamorphism. *Nature* **347**, 159–162.

HUTCHEON I. D., ARMSTRONG J. T. and WASSERBURG G. J. (1987) Isotopic studies of Mg, Fe, Mo, Ru and W in Fremdlinge from Allende refractory inclusions. *Geochim. Cosmochim. Acta* **51**, 3175–3192.

IRELAND T. R., ZINNER E. K. and AMARI S. (1991) Isotopically anomalous Ti in presolar SiC from the Murchison meteorite. *Astrophys. J.* **376**, L53–L56.

JUNK G. and SVEC H. J. (1958) The absolute abundance of the nitrogen isotopes in the atmosphere and compressed gas from various sources. *Geochim. Cosmochim. Acta* **14**, 234–243.

LAMBERT D. L. (1989) The chemical composition of asymptotic giant branch stars. In *Evolution of Peculiar Red Giant Stars* (eds. H. R. JOHNSON and B. ZUCKERMAN), pp. 101–130. Cambridge Univ. Press.

LARIMER J. W. and BARTHOLOMAY M. (1978) The role of carbon and oxygen in cosmic gases: some applications to the chemistry and mineralogy of enstatite chondrites. *Geochim. Cosmochim. Acta* **43**, 1455–1466.

LEAHY D. A., KWOK S. and ARQUILLA R. A. (1987) CO

observations of IRAS sources with 11.3 micron silicon carbide dust features. *Astrophys. J.* **320,** 825–841.

LEWIS R. S., AMARI S. and ANDERS E. (1990) Meteoritic silicon carbide: pristine material from carbon stars. *Nature* **348,** 293–298.

MARTIN P. G. and ROGERS C. (1987) Carbon grains in the envelope of IRC + 10216. *Astrophys. J.* **322,** 374–392.

MATSUDA J., LEWIS R. S., TAKAHASHI H. and ANDERS E. (1980) Isotopic anomalies of noble gases in meteorites and their origins—VII. C3V carbonaceous chondrites. *Geochim. Cosmochim. Acta* **44,** 1861–1874.

MCKEEGAN K. D., WALKER R. M. and ZINNER E. (1985) Ion microprobe isotopic measurements of individual interplanetary dust particles. *Geochim. Cosmochim. Acta* **49,** 1971–1987.

NIEDERER F. R., EBERHARDT P., GEISS J. and LEWIS R. S. (1985) Carbon isotope abundances in Murchison residue 2C10c (abstr.). *Meteoritics* **20,** 716–717.

OTT U. and BEGEMANN F. (1990) S-process material in Murchison: Sr and more on Ba. *Lunar Planet. Sci.* **XXI,** 920–921.

OTT U., BEGEMANN F., YANG J. and EPSTEIN S. (1988) S-process krypton of variable isotopic composition in the Murchison meteorite. *Nature* **332,** 700–702.

PRANTZOS N., ARNOULD M. and CASSÉ M. (1988) Slow neutron capture nucleosynthesis in the progenitor of SN 1987A. *Astrophys. J.* **331,** L15–L19.

SRINIVASAN B. and ANDERS E. (1978) Noble gases in the Murchison meteorite: Possible relics of s-process nucleosynthesis. *Science* **201,** 51–56.

STONE J., HUTCHEON I. D., EPSTEIN S. and WASSERBURG G. J. (1990) Si isotopes in SiC from carbonaceous and enstatite chondrites (abstr.). *Lunar Planet. Sci.* **XXI,** 1212–1213.

STONE J., HUTCHEON I. D., EPSTEIN S. and WASSERBURG G. J. (1991) Correlated $^{29}$Si and $^{30}$Si enrichments in a family of SiC grains from the Orgueil and Murchison meteorites. *Earth Planet. Sci. Lett.* (in press).

SWAN P. S., WALKER R. M. and YUAN J. (1989) Location of small SiC crystals in meteorites using a low-voltage X-ray mapping technique (abstr.). *Lunar Planet. Sci.* **XX,** 1093–1094.

SWART P. K., GRADY M. M., PILLINGER C. T., LEWIS R. S. and ANDERS E. (1982) Interstellar carbon in meteorites. *Science* **220,** 406–410.

TANG M. and ANDERS E. (1988) Isotopic anomalies of Ne, Xe and C in meteorites. II. Interstellar diamond and SiC: Carriers of exotic noble gases. *Geochim. Cosmochim. Acta* **52,** 1235–1244.

TANG M., LEWIS R. S., ANDERS E., GRADY M. M., WRIGHT I. P. and PILLINGER C. T. (1988) Isotopic anomalies of Ne, Xe and C in meteorites. I. Separation of carriers by density and chemical resistance. *Geochim. Cosmochim. Acta* **52,** 1221–1234.

TANG M., ANDERS E., HOPPE P. and ZINNER E. (1989) Meteoritic silicon carbide and its stellar sources; implications for galactic chemical evolution. *Nature* **339,** 351–354.

THIELEMANN F.-K. and ARNETT W. D. (1985) Hydrostatic nucleosynthesis. II. Core neon to silicon burning and presupernova abundance yields of massive stars. *Astrophys. J.* **295,** 604–619.

WOOSLEY S. E. (1986) Nuclear astrophysics. In *Nucleosynthesis and Chemical Evolution; 16th SAAS-FEE Course Notes* (eds. B. HAUCK, A. MAEDER and G. MEYNET), pp. 3–195. Geneva Observatory.

WOPENKA B., VIRAG A., ZINNER E., AMARI S., LEWIS R. S. and ANDERS E. (1989) Isotopic and optical properties of large individual SiC crystals from the Murchison chondrite (abstr.). *Meteoritics* **24,** 342.

YANG J. and EPSTEIN S. (1984) Relic interstellar grains in Murchison meteorite. *Nature* **311,** 544–547.

ZINNER E. and EPSTEIN S. (1987) Heavy carbon in individual oxide grains from the Murchison meteorite. *Earth Planet. Sci. Lett.* **84,** 359–368.

ZINNER E., TANG M. and ANDERS E. (1987) Large isotopic anomalies of Si, C, N and noble gases in interstellar silicon carbide from the Murray meteorite. *Nature* **330,** 730–732.

ZINNER E., TANG M. and ANDERS E. (1989) Interstellar SiC in the Murchison and Murray meteorites: Isotopic composition of Ne, Xe, Si, C and N. *Geochim. Cosmochim. Acta* **53,** 3273–3290.

ZINNER E., AMARI S. and LEWIS R. S. (1991a) S-process Ba and Nd in presolar Murchison SiC. *Lunar Planet. Sci.* **XXII,** 1553–1554.

ZINNER E., AMARI S., ANDERS E. and LEWIS R. S. (1991b) Large amounts of extinct $^{26}$Al in interstellar grains from the Murchison meteorite. *Nature* **349,** 51–54.

# Subject Index

508